Integrals

$$\int \cot^2 ax \, dx = -\frac{\cot ax}{a} - x$$

$$\int \sec ax \, dx = \frac{1}{a}\ln(\sec ax + \tan ax)$$

$$\int \csc ax \, dx = \frac{1}{a}\ln(\csc ax - \cot ax)$$

$$\int x\cos ax \, dx = \frac{1}{a^2}\cos ax + \frac{x}{a}\sin ax$$

$$\int x\sin ax \, dx = \frac{\sin ax}{a^2} - \frac{x\cos ax}{a}$$

$$\int e^{bx}\sin ax \, dx = \frac{1}{a^2 + b^2}e^{bx}(b\sin ax - a\cos ax)$$

$$\int e^{bx}\cos ax \, dx = \frac{1}{a^2 + b^2}e^{bx}(a\sin ax + b\cos ax)$$

$$\int \cosh ax \, dx = \frac{1}{a}\sinh ax$$

$$\int \sinh ax \, dx = \frac{1}{a}\cosh ax$$

$$\int \tanh ax \, dx = \frac{1}{a}\ln \cosh ax$$

Derivatives

$$(uv)' = u'v + v'u$$

$$\left(\frac{u}{v}\right)' = \frac{u'v - v'u}{v^2}$$

$$\frac{dy}{dx} = \frac{dy}{du}\frac{du}{dx}$$

$$\frac{dy}{dx} = \frac{1}{dx/dy}$$

$$(x^n)' = nx^{n-1}$$

$$(e^{ax})' = ae^{ax}$$

$$(a^u)' = (a^u \ln a)\frac{du}{dx}$$

$$(\ln x)' = \frac{1}{x}$$

$$(\log_a u)' = \frac{\log_a e}{u}\frac{du}{dx}$$

$$(\sin x)' = \cos x$$

$$(\cos x)' = -\sin x$$

$$(\tan x)' = \sec^2 x$$

$$(\cot x)' = -\csc^2 x$$

$$(\sinh x)' = \cosh x$$

$$(\cosh x)' = \sinh x$$

$$(\sin^{-1}x)' = \frac{1}{\sqrt{1 - x^2}}$$

$$(\cos^{-1}x)' = -\frac{1}{\sqrt{1 - x^2}}$$

$$(\tan^{-1}x)' = \frac{1}{1 + x^2}$$

$$(\cot^{-1}x)' = \frac{1}{1 + x^2}$$

Differential Equations for ENGINEERS AND SCIENTISTS

Y. A. CENGEL
University of Nevada, Reno

W. J. PALM III
University of Rhode Island

McGraw Hill

Connect Learn Succeed™

DIFFERENTIAL EQUATIONS FOR ENGINEERS AND SCIENTISTS

Published by McGraw-Hill, a business unit of The McGraw-Hill Companies, Inc., 1221 Avenue of the Americas, New York, NY 10020. Copyright © 2013 by The McGraw-Hill Companies, Inc. All rights reserved. Printed in the United States of America. No part of this publication may be reproduced or distributed in any form or by any means, or stored in a database or retrieval system, without the prior written consent of The McGraw-Hill Companies, Inc., including, but not limited to, in any network or other electronic storage or transmission, or broadcast for distance learning.

Some ancillaries, including electronic and print components, may not be available to customers outside the United States.

MATLAB® is a registered trademark of The MathWorks, Inc., 3 Apple Hill Drive, Natick, MA 01760-2098 USA. Tel: 508-647-7000; Fax: 508-647-7000; e-mail: info@mathworks.com: web: mathworks.com.

This book is printed on acid-free paper.

1 2 3 4 5 6 7 8 9 0 RJE/RJE 0 9 8 7 6 5 4 3 2

ISBN 978-0-07-338590-7
MHID 0-07-338590-5

Publisher: Raghothaman Srinivasan
Executive Editor: Bill Stenquist
Marketing Manager: Curt Reynolds
Developmental Editor: Lorraine Buczek
Project Manager: Melissa M. Leick
Media Project Manager: Balaji Sundararaman
Buyer: Sherry L. Kane
Cover Design: Studio Montage, St. Louis, Missouri
Cover Image: © Ingram Publishing RF
Compositor: RPK Editorial Services
Typeface: 10.5/12 Times Roman
Printer: R. R. Donnelley Crawfordsville, IN

Library of Congress Cataloging-in-Publication Data

Çengel, Yunus A.
  Differential equations for engineers and scientists/Y.A. Cengel and W.J. Palm III.—1st ed.
     p. cm.
  ISBN 978-0-07-338590-7
1. Differential equations. 2. Engineering mathematics. I. Palm, William J. (William John), 1944- II. Title.
  TA347.D45C46 2013
  515'.35—dc23
                          2011047194

www.mhhe.com

CHAPTER FOUR

HIGHER-ORDER LINEAR DIFFERENTIAL EQUATIONS 197

*MuPAD® is a registered trademark of Sciface Software GmbH & Co.

CHAPTER EIGHT
LAPLACE TRANSFORMS 463

CHAPTER NINE
NUMERICAL SOLUTION OF DIFFERENTIAL EQUATIONS 531

---

*MATLAB® is a registered trademark of The MathWorks, Inc.

**Maple® is a registered trademark of Waterloo Maple, Inc.

†Mathematica® is a registered trademark of Wolfram Research, Inc.

Differential equations have long been an essential part of core curricula in most branches of physical sciences and engineering all over the world. Scientists and engineers often study systems that undergo changes, and differential equations enable the scientists and engineers to study the changes in key variables in a system and to gain a deeper understanding of the underlying physical phenomena. This book is intended to serve as a textbook for a first course on differential equations taken primarily by science and engineering students. It is the outcome of the lecture notes developed by the first author over the years in teaching differential equations to engineering students at the University of Nevada, Reno, and by computer assignments and engineering examples developed by the second author while teaching at the University of Rhode Island. The text covers the standard topics on ordinary differential equations with a wealth of applications drawn from engineering and sciences.

Pedagogical Approach This book intended as a friendly introduction to differential equations within the context of science and engineering. It dwells more on *intuition* rather than rigor. The emphasis is kept on the conceptual arguments in order to develop an intuitive understanding of the subject matter. The text strives to be *simple* and *understandable*, and encourages creative thinking. The authors believe that legal documents such as a rental lease agreements intended for plain people should be written in plain English instead of being written in a precise legal language that is beyond most people's grasp and requires a lawyer to translate. Likewise, a differential equations textbook should be written for the *student* to read and understand. Instructors do not need textbooks, students do. It is common experience that students flip through the pages of a mathematics textbook only when they are trying to find an example similar to the problem assigned. It is often stated that mathematical concepts must be explained in plain language to have a lasting impression. We should be able to tell our students that solving a differential equation is basically integration, and integration is basically summation, instead of using some abstract language for the sake of precision and rigor.

The material in the text is introduced at a level that an average student can follow comfortably. It speaks to the students, not over them. In fact, it is self-instructive. This frees the instructor to use class time more productively. The topics are ordered such that they flow well in a logical order, and each topic provides motivation for the subsequent topic. Every attempt is made to make this a "readable" mathematics text and to enhance learning and understanding. The goal throughout this project has been to offer an introductory differential equations textbook that is read by the students with interest and enthusiasm instead of one which is used as a reference guide to solve problems.

ORGANIZATION

CHAPTER OUTLINES

- Chapter 1 begins with an introduction to differential equations and their classification. We then demonstrate how the differential equations arise in sciences, and how the problems in science and engineering are modeled. We conclude this chapter by discussing how to solve differential equations by direct integration.

- In Chapter 2 we discuss first-order differential equations, and the associated solution techniques. At the end of this chapter we present a step-by-step approach on how to solve a given first-order differential equation.

- Chapter 3 deals primarily with second-order linear differential equations with constant coefficients, which are the types of equations most frequently encountered in sciences and engineering. We also discuss the Euler equation in this chapter since it can be transformed into a differential equation with constant coefficients. The method of undetermined coefficients to solve nonhomogeneous equations is developed in an intuitive manner.

- The discussions are extended to higher-order linear equations in Chapter 4.

- In Chapter 5 we consider second order linear differential equations with variable coefficients and their solution by power series. In this chapter we develop the Legendre polynomials and Bessel functions as solutions to certain differential equations, and discuss their features.

- In Chapter 6 we discuss the solution of systems of linear differential equations using a scalar approach.

- Chapter 7 introduces matrix methods for solving sets of equations.

- In Chapter 8 we introduce Laplace transforms to solve differential equations and systems of differential equations.

- Finally, in Chapter 9, we present the numerical solutions of differential equations using various techniques.

FEATURES

Use of Computers   The major software packages used today for solving ordinary differential equations are MATLAB® (with The Symbolic Math Toolbox™*, which contains MuPAD®), Maple™, and Mathematica®.** Using one of these packages, students can solve differential equations with specified initial or boundary conditions in symbolic form (provided they are of a standard form) and numerically to obtain the solution in tabular and graphical form. Students can experiment and ask "what if" questions in an interactive manner, often with no or minimal programming. At the end of each chapter is a section showing how to use these packages to solve problems of the type treated in the chapter.

Illustrations   Figures are important learning tools that help the students to "get the picture." The text makes effective use of graphics throughout. Most of the illustrations in this text are not figures in the traditional sense. They serve as a means of emphasizing key concepts which would otherwise go unnoticed, or as summaries of key ideas.

---

*The Symbolic Math Toolbox is a trademark of The MathWorks, Inc.
**The software examples in this text are compatible with the following software versions: MATLAB (ver 7.13), Symbolic Math Toolbox (ver 5.7), MuPAD (ver 5.7), Maple (ver 15), and Mathematica (ver 8).

Science and Engineering Examples Each chapter contains numerous worked out examples that clarify the material and illustrate the use of principles. A consistent and systematic approach is used in the solution of all example problems, with particular attention to limitations and generalizations.

There are a number of examples drawn from various applications in science, but a *unique* feature of the text is the number of *engineering* examples. The examples illustrate applications in various engineering fields such as Newtonian dynamics, heat transfer, electrical circuits and electric motors, mechanical vibrations, vehicle suspensions, and hydraulics.

Chapter Summaries A detailed and itemized summary is included at the end of each chapter for a quick overview of basic concepts and important relations.

Section Review At the end of each section, there is a *Section Review* that consists of relatively simple problems covering topics in that section. Problem answers are given with the problem so that the students can immediately check their work.

End-Of-Chapter Problems The end-of-chapter problems are grouped under by section in the order they are covered to make problem selection easier for both instructors and students. The problems within each group start with concept questions, indicated by "C", to check the students' level of understanding of basic concepts. The problems under *Review Problems* are more comprehensive in nature, and are not directly tied to any specific section of a chapter. The *Solutions Manual* is available to instructors only and provides complete and detailed solutions to all end-of-chapter problems.

ONLINE RESOURCES

Visit www.mhhe.com/cengel for all texts in the Cengel series and for the valuable resources available to students and instructors using this text. Visit www.mhhe.com/palm for all texts in the Palm series, including two texts devoted to MATLAB.

ACKNOWLEDGMENTS

Special thanks are due to Tahsin Engin of the University of Sakarya for his valuable contributions at all stages of the production of this book and the preparation of the Solutions Manual.

The authors would especially like to thank Bill Stenquist of McGraw-Hill for all of his help and encouragement as our editor for many years.

The authors wish to thank the following reviewers for their helpful comments and suggestions:

Antonio Campo
University of Texas at San Antonio

Dr. Harry Hardee
New Mexico State University

Eleanor Jenkins
Clemson University

Allen Plotkin
San Diego State University

David Rubenstein
Oklahoma State University

Scott Strong
Colorado School of Mines

Aleksandra Vinogradov
Montana State University

Ridvan Oz
Fatih University

Y. A. Cengel
W. J. Palm III

McGRAW-HILL CREATE™

Craft your teaching resources to match the way you teach! With McGraw-Hill Create™, you can easily rearrange chapters, combine material from other content sources, and quickly upload content you have written like your course syllabus or teaching notes. Find the content you need in Create by searching through thousands of leading McGraw-Hill textbooks. Arrange your book to fit your teaching style. Create even allows you to personalize your book's appearance by selecting the cover and adding your name, school, and course information. Order a Create book and you'll receive a complimentary print review copy in 3–5 business days or a complimentary electronic review copy (eComp) via email in minutes. Go to www.mcgrawhillcreate.com today and register to experience how McGraw-Hill Create™ empowers you to *teach your* students *your* way.

ELECTRONIC TEXTBOOK OPTIONS

This text is offered through CourseSmart for both instructors and students. CourseSmart is an online resource where students can purchase the complete text online at almost half the cost of a traditional text. Purchasing the eTextbook allows students to take advantage of CourseSmart's web tools for learning, which include full text search, notes and highlighting, and email tools for sharing notes between classmates. To learn more about CourseSmart options, contact your sales representative or visit www.CourseSmart.com.

INTRODUCTION TO DIFFERENTIAL EQUATIONS

Differential equations differ from algebraic equations in that they involve derivatives of functions. The study of differential equations requires a good understanding of calculus, and thus, we ask the student to review some important relevant topics (such as dependent and independent variables, continuous and discontinuous functions, ordinary and partial derivatives, differentials and increments, and integration). We begin this chapter with a discussion on the importance of differential equations in sciences and engineering and the value of mathematical modeling in solving real-world problems. We then continue with examples of how differential equations arise in practical problems, and discuss their solutions. After a brief review of some concepts from calculus, we give a classification of differential equations and discuss linear and nonlinear equations, as well as equations with constant and variable coefficients. We then demonstrate how to solve some simple differential equations by direct integration. Finally, we show how to use popular computer packages to solve simple differential equations and to plot their solutions.

Objectives

When you have finished this chapter, you should be able to:

1. appreciate the value of differential equations and understand how they arise in sciences and engineering,

2. identify continuous and discontinuous functions,

3. perform the basic operations of calculus, such as differentiation and integration,

4. classify differential equations according to: order, linear versus nonlinear, variable versus constant coefficient, and homogeneous versus nonhomogeneous,

5. classify solutions of differential equations as general, particular, singular, explicit, or implicit,

6. solve simple differential equations by direct integration, and

7. use a computer package to solve simple first-order differential equations and plot their solutions.

1–1 ▪ DIFFERENTIAL EQUATIONS IN SCIENCES AND ENGINEERING

A mathematical expression with an equal sign in it is called an **equation**. An equation that involves the derivatives of one or more functions is called a **differential equation**. In other words, a differential equation expresses a relationship between functions and their derivatives. The term "differential equation" has been around since 1676 when Leibniz first used it, and differential equations have long been used extensively by scientists and engineers to model and solve a wide range of practical problems.

You are probably wondering why we are studying differential equations. After all, it seemed like we could solve just about any problem using algebraic equations. Well, it will suffice to say that up to this point you were mostly exposed to problems that resulted in algebraic equations only. Now you are about to be exposed to a new world of problems that are encountered in various fields of science and engineering whose formulations result in differential equations and whose solutions depend on solving these differential equations.

The description of most scientific problems involves relations that relate the *changes* in some key variables to each other. Usually, the smaller the increment chosen in changing variables, the more general and accurate the description. In the limiting case of *infinitesimal* or *differential changes* in variables, we obtain differential equations that provide precise mathematical formulations for the physical principles and laws by representing the rates of changes as derivatives. Therefore, differential equations are used to investigate a wide variety of problems in sciences and engineering, and the study of differential equations have long been an integral part of science and engineering education.

The study of physical phenomena involves two important steps. In the first step, all the variables that affect the phenomena are identified, reasonable assumptions and approximations are made, and the interdependence of these variables is studied. The relevant physical laws and principles are invoked, and the problem is formulated mathematically, usually in the form of a differential equation. The equation itself is very instructive as it shows the degree of dependence of some variables on others, and the relative importance of various terms. In the second step, the differential equation is solved using an appropriate method, and relation is obtained for the unknown function in terms of the independent variables. (Figure 1–1)

Many processes that seem to occur in nature randomly and without any order are, in fact, being governed by some visible or not so visible physical laws. Whether we notice them or not, these laws are there, governing consistently and predictably what seem to be ordinary events. Most of these laws are well defined and well understood by scientists. This makes it possible to predict the course of an event before it actually occurs or to study various aspects of an event mathematically without actually running expensive and time-consuming experiments.

Consider, for example, the free fall of a rock off a cliff, as shown in Figure 1–2. Let us say that we would like to know the time it takes for the rock to reach the ground. One way of finding it out is, of course, to record the times of release and impact of the rock and to take the difference.

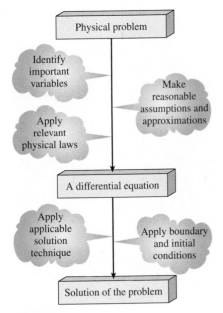

FIGURE 1–1

Mathematical modeling of physical problems.

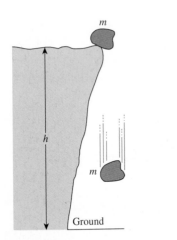

FIGURE 1–2

The free fall of a rock off a cliff.

Another way is to prepare a mathematical model of this process using all of the relevant physical laws, to formulate the problem, and to solve the problem for the quantity of interest, which is the falling time in this case. The more realistic the mathematical model, the more accurate the result obtained will be. As you will remember from physics, the free fall of a body is governed by the law of gravity, and the falling time is easily determined from $\Delta t = \sqrt{2h/g}$, where h is the vertical distance and g is the local gravitational acceleration.

Very accurate results can be obtained for meaningful practical problems by using a suitable and realistic mathematical model, for example, analyzing the temperature response of a potato in an oven by treating it as if it had the thermal properties of water (Figure 1–3). The preparation of such models requires an adequate knowledge of the natural phenomena involved, the relevant laws, as well as having a sound judgment. An unrealistic model will obviously give inaccurate and thus unacceptable results.

An analyst often finds himself or herself in a position to make a choice between a very accurate (but complex) model and a simple (but not so accurate) model. The right choice depends on the situation at hand. The right choice is usually the simplest model that yields adequate results. Preparing very accurate but complex models often is not so difficult. But such models are not much use to an analyst if they are very difficult to solve. At the minimum, the mathematical model should reflect the essential feature of the physical problem it represents.

The free-falling process discussed here is formulated considering the effect of gravity only, neglecting the air resistance and the variation of gravitational acceleration g with height. These simplifications are very reasonable for most falling objects, and they enable us to obtain a very simple solution to the problem. But these simplifications are obviously unacceptable for falling objects that experience a large air resistance (such as a parachute).

There are many significant real-world problems that can be analyzed with a simple mathematical model. But it should always be kept in mind that the results obtained from a mathematical analysis are no more accurate than the assumptions made in simplifying the problem. Therefore, the solution obtained should not be applied to situations for which the original assumptions do not hold.

A solution that is not quite consistent with the observed nature of the problem indicates that the mathematical model used is too crude. In that case, a more realistic model should be prepared by eliminating one or more of the questionable assumptions. This will result in a more complex equation that of course, is more difficult to solve. Thus, any solution to a differential equation should be interpreted within the context where the equation arose.

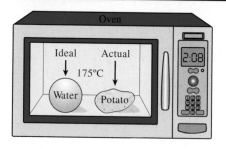

FIGURE 1–3

Modeling is a powerful tool that provides great insight and simplicity at the expense of some loss in accuracy.

Section Review

Problems Denoted with a C are Conceptual Problems for Discussion

1–1C Why do we often use differential equations instead of algebraic equations to model significant real-world problems?

1–2C Describe what is involved in preparing practical mathematical models for real-world problems.

1–2 ▪ HOW DO DIFFERENTIAL EQUATIONS ARISE?

As mentioned earlier, differential equations arise when relevant physical laws and principles are applied to a problem by considering infinitesimal changes in the variables of interest. Therefore, obtaining the governing differential equation for a specific problem requires an adequate knowledge about the nature of the problem, the variables involved, appropriate simplifying assumptions, and the applicable physical laws and principles involved, as well as a careful analysis. The procedure for obtaining differential equations in some areas is illustrated here with examples.

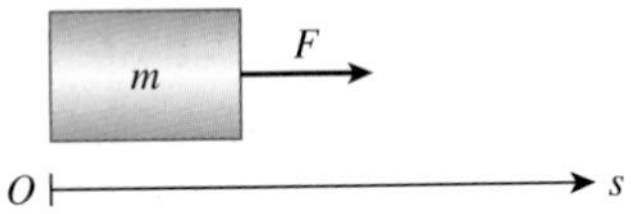

FIGURE 1–4

Schematic for Example 1–1.

EXAMPLE 1–1   Newton's Second Law of Motion

Using Newton's second law of motion, obtain the differential equation that describes the position s of a mass m along a straight line under the influence of a force F acting in the direction of motion.

SOLUTION   Newton's second law is a relation between quantities that have both *magnitude* and *direction*, and thus, it is correctly expressed in *vector* form. However, when dealing with motion on a straight line in the direction of the force, as shown in Figure 1–4, we can express it in *scalar* form by using magnitudes only since the direction is already specified. In this case, the quantities in opposing directions are indicated by opposite signs.
   We recall that velocity V and the acceleration a are defined as

$$V = \frac{ds}{dt}$$

and

$$a = \frac{dV}{dt} = \frac{d}{dt}\left(\frac{ds}{dt}\right) = \frac{d^2s}{dt^2}$$

Then the differential equation for the distance s traveled is obtained from Newton's second law, which is force = mass × acceleration or

$$F(t) = ma(t) = m\frac{d^2s}{dt^2} \tag{1–1}$$

Rearranging gives

$$\frac{d^2s}{dt^2} = \frac{F(t)}{m} \tag{1–2}$$

which is the desired differential equation. Note that we often drop the notation that explicitly indicates the dependence of the unknown function on the independent variable for simplicity and write F instead of $F(t)$.
   Here $F(t)$ is a given function that describes the variation of the force with time.
   As a special case, consider the free fall of a body under the influence of gravity. Disregarding air resistance, the only force acting on the body is the gravitational force. Taking the upward vertical direction as the positive z direction, the gravitational force can be expressed as $F = -mg$, where g is the local gravitational acceleration that is acting downwards (in the negative

z direction). Then replacing s with z and $F(t)$ with $-mg$ in Equation 1–2 and simplifying, we obtain

$$\frac{d^2z}{dt^2} = -g \qquad (1\text{–}3)$$

where z is the vertical distance from a reference level such as the ground. The free fall of a body with air resistance is considered in Chapter 2.

EXAMPLE 1–2 Newton's Law of Cooling

Consider a small, solid copper ball of mass m and radius R, which is initially at a temperature of $T_i = 20°C$. The ball is dropped into a large container filled with hot water at $T_0 = 70°C$, as shown in Figure 1–5.

As expected, heat is transferred to the ball from the water, and the temperature of the ball starts to rise. It is known that the *specific heat* of copper near room temperature is $c = 0.39\,kJ/kg°C$. That is, it takes $0.39\,kJ$ of energy to raise the temperature of 1 kg of copper by 1°C. It is also given that the *heat transfer coefficient* during this process is $h = 0.02\,kW/°C \cdot m^2$. That is, $0.02\,kJ$ of heat is transferred to copper per unit time per unit surface area of the ball and per unit temperature difference between the water and the ball. Obtain the differential equation that governs the variation of the temperature of the ball with time t.

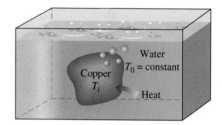

FIGURE 1–5

Schematic for Example 1–2.

SOLUTION The temperature of a body, in general, varies with location within the body as well as time. But for small metal objects such as this one, the variation of temperature with location is very small and can be disregarded. In other words, the temperature of the object can be assumed to be the same at every point at a given time. Thus, the temperature of the ball under consideration can be considered to be a function of time only. Note that this assumption is not a realistic one for large objects, especially when they are made of materials that are poor conductors of heat.

We know from experience that a cool object left in a warmer environment gradually warms up and eventually reaches the temperature of the environment. Therefore, at any time t, the temperature of the ball will be somewhere between 20 and 70°C, but we do not know exactly at what value. The accurate prediction of ball temperature at, say $t = 30$ seconds, requires a precise formulation of the problem, which is obtained by applying Newton's law of cooling and the conservation of energy principle.

Newton's law of cooling is expressed as

$$Q = hA(T_0 - T) \qquad (1\text{–}4)$$

where

$\qquad Q$ = rate of heat transfer to the ball at time t
$\qquad A$ = surface area of the ball, $A = 4\pi R^2$
$\qquad h$ = heat transfer coefficient between the ball and the environment
$\qquad T$ = temperature of the ball at time t
$\qquad T_0$ = temperature of the environment

The **conservation of energy principle** states that energy cannot be created or destroyed. Therefore, the increase in the energy content of the ball must be equal to the total amount of heat transferred to the ball. During a time interval Δt, the temperature of the ball will rise by an amount ΔT, where m is the mass of the ball and c is its specific heat. The total heat transferred to the ball during Δt is simply $Q\Delta t$, since Q is the rate of heat transfer (i.e., heat transfer per unit time). Thus,

$$\begin{pmatrix} \text{Increase in energy} \\ \text{content of the ball} \\ \text{during } \Delta t \end{pmatrix} = \begin{pmatrix} \text{Total heat transfer} \\ \text{into the ball} \\ \text{during } \Delta t \end{pmatrix}$$

or $mc\Delta T = hA(T_0 - T)\Delta t$. Dividing by Δt, we have

$$\frac{\Delta T}{\Delta t} = \frac{hA}{mc}(T_0 - T)$$

Taking the limit as $\Delta t \to 0$ yields

$$\frac{dT}{dt} = \frac{hA}{mc}(T_0 - T) \tag{1-5}$$

This is the desired differential equation, since it describes the variation of temperature with time. Solution of this differential equation will yield a function for ball temperature in terms of time. This will be done in Chapter 2.

It is important to note that differential equations describe physical phenomena in a specified interval of the independent variables. Thus the solution of a differential equation is applicable in that interval only. For example, Equation 1–5 describes the variation of temperature with time within the copper ball only. Therefore, the solution obtained for $T(t)$ is limited to the region within the copper ball and cannot be used to determine the temperature at a point outside the ball. Also, the differential equation describes the process starting with the moment the ball is dropped into the water ($t = 0$), and thus, the solution is applicable in the interval $0 \leq t < \infty$. The solution cannot be used to predict the temperature at times before the ball is dropped into the water.

EXAMPLE 1–3   Instantaneously Compounded Interest

A person deposits his money in the amount of A in a bank at an annual interest rate of r. Assuming instantaneous compounding, obtain the differential equation that governs the variation of the amount of money A in the bank with time t.

SOLUTION   To lay the ground work for the derivation of the equation, consider a person depositing $A_0 = \$100$ at a bank at an annual 4% interest rate, so that $r = 0.04$. Assuming yearly compounding, the money will increase by $4 during this time period. If he or she deposited $200 instead, the money would increase by $8. If he or she deposited this money for two years compounded once every two years, the increase in the money again would be twice as much.

Thus, we conclude that the increase in the money at the bank at the end of the compounding period is proportional to the amount of money A and the compounding period in years. The constant of proportionality is the annual interest rate r. Therefore, $\Delta A = rA\Delta t$

or

$$\frac{\Delta A}{\Delta t} = rA$$

Taking the limit as $\Delta t \to 0$, we obtain the differential equation that describes the change in the amount of money at the bank with time as a result of instantaneously compounded interest:

$$\frac{dA}{dt} = rA \qquad (1\text{--}6)$$

Here r is the annual interest rate expressed as a decimal number, and t is the time in years. As you will see in Chapter 2, the solution of this differential equation is

$$A = A_0 e^{rt} \qquad (1\text{--}7)$$

where A_0 is the money deposited at time $t = 0$.

EXAMPLE 1–4   Lambert's Law of Absorption

It is well known that when light or any other radiation passes through a medium, part of it is absorbed by the medium. The farther the light travels in the medium, the more of it is absorbed. Denoting the radiant energy of a light beam by E, obtain the differential equation that describes the weakening of the light with distance s.

SOLUTION   When light or any other radiation passes through a homogeneous medium, it is observed that a constant fraction of the radiation is absorbed per unit length in the direction of propagation, as illustrated in Figure 1–6 for light penetrating into a lake. This is another way of saying that the absorption of radiation per unit length is proportional to the magnitude of the radiation. Thus, following the reasoning in Example 1–3, the differential equation governing the absorption process can be expressed as

$$\frac{dE}{ds} = -\alpha E \qquad (1\text{--}8)$$

where α is the fraction of radiation absorbed per unit length and is called the **absorption coefficient**. It has the unit meter^{-1}. The independent variable s is the distance in the direction of propagation, and E is the radiant energy of the beam under consideration. By analogy to Example 1–3, the solution of this differential equation is

$$E = E_0 e^{-\alpha s} \qquad (1\text{--}9)$$

where E_0 is the radiant energy of the beam at $s = 0$. The details of the solution will be presented in Chapter 2.

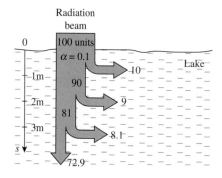

FIGURE 1–6

The absorption of light radiation as it propagates through a lake.

EXAMPLE 1–5   A Chemical Reaction

Chemists and engineers must be able to predict the changes in chemical concentration in a reaction. A model used for many single-reactant processes is

$$\text{Rate of change of chemical concentration} = \frac{dC}{dt} = -kC^n$$

where C is the chemical concentration and k is the rate constant. The order of the reaction is the value of the exponent n. The following data describe the first-order reaction that combines tert-butyl bromide and water to produce tert-butyl alcohol and hydrogen bromide.

$$(CH_3)_3CBr + H_2O \rightarrow (CH_3)_3COH + HB_r$$

From experimental data, the value of k was estimated to be $k = 0.0537$ per hour. Determine the concentration after 2 hours if $C(0) = 0.1$ mol/L.

SOLUTION   Using $n = 1$ and $k = 0.0537$ in the differential equation, we have

$$\frac{dC}{dt} = -0.0537C$$

This equation has the same form as Equation (1–8), and by analogy, we can see that the solution is $C(t) = C(0)e^{-kt}$ or $C(t) = 0.1e^{-0.0537t}$.
   Substituting $t = 2$ hours into this equation gives $C(2) = 0.1e^{-(0.0537)2} = 0.0892$ mol/L.

EXAMPLE 1–6   An *RC* Circuit

Figure 1–7 shows a circuit with a resistor and a capacitor. The battery voltage V is constant, and the capacitor is initially uncharged. The switch is initially closed at point B. At $t = 0$, the switch is suddenly moved from point B to point A. Obtain the differential equation model for the capacitor voltage v_1 as a function of time.

SOLUTION   The voltage–current relation for a capacitor states that the voltage $v_1(t)$ is the time integral of the current $i(t)$ divided by the capacitance C, plus the initial voltage, which is zero here. Thus,

$$v_1(t) = \frac{1}{C}\int_0^t i(t)\,dt$$

Taking the derivative of both sides yields

$$\frac{dv_1}{dt} = \frac{1}{C}i$$

From the voltage–current relation for a resistor, we obtain

$$i = \frac{V - v_1}{R}$$

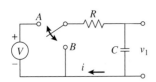

FIGURE 1–7

An *RC* circuit with a battery voltage.

Substituting this into the first equation and rearranging gives

$$RC\frac{dv_1}{dt} + v_1 = V \qquad (1\text{--}10)$$

This is a first-order linear, ordinary differential equation whose solution can be found using the methods of Chapter 2.

EXAMPLE 1–7   Flow Through an Orifice

Figure 1–8 shows a liquid container with vertical sides and a bottom area A. Liquid is pumped into the top at a volume flow rate q_{vi}. A hole is accidentally punched in the side of the tank, and liquid spills through it. Obtain the differential equation model of the liquid height h.

SOLUTION Around 1640, Torricelli discovered that the flow rate through an orifice is proportional to the square root of the pressure difference. Using the conservation of mass principle with a liquid mass density ρ, we see that the rate of change of liquid mass in the tank, ρAh_1, must equal the difference between the mass inflow rate q_{mi} and the mass outflow rate q_{mo}. Thus,

$$\frac{d(\rho Ah_1)}{dt} = q_{mi} - q_{mo}$$

Note that $q_{mi} = \rho q_{vi}$ and $h_1 = h + L$ so that $dh_1/dt = dh/dt$. Thus,

$$\rho A\frac{dh}{dt} = \rho q_{vi} - q_{mo}$$

Because atmospheric pressure p_a surrounds the tank, the pressure drop across the orifice is ρgh, and so from Torricelli's principle, we have

$$q_{mo} = k\sqrt{\rho gh}$$

where k is a proportionality constant. Thus, the model is

$$\rho A\frac{dh}{dt} = \rho q_{vi} - k\sqrt{\rho gh} \qquad (1\text{--}11)$$

As you will see later in this chapter, this is called a nonlinear equation because the dependent variable h appears within the square root. Its solution is discussed in Section 1–6.

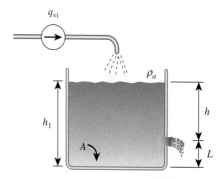

FIGURE 1–8

A liquid container with an orifice.

Section Review

1–3C What do we need to know in order to obtain an accurate differential equation for a given problem?

1–4C Why do we often utilize simplifying assumptions when we derive differential equations?

1–5 Consider a parachute dropping in the air at a constant velocity of V_0. Using Newton's second law of motion, obtain the differential equation that describes the position z of the parachute relative to the ground level as a function of time. Take the upward direction to be positive.

(*Answer:* $\frac{d^2Z}{dt^2} = z'' = 0$ with an initial condition of $z'(0) = V(0) = -V_0$)

1–6 A person deposits his money in the amount of A in a bank at an annual rate of r compounded continuously and, at the same time, withdraws money from the account at a constant rate of a. Obtain the differential equation that describes the amount of money in the bank as a function of time, $A(t)$.

(*Answer:* $\frac{dA}{dt} = iA - a$)

1–3 ▪ A BRIEF REVIEW OF BASIC CONCEPTS*

The study of differential equations requires a good understanding of the fundamental concepts of calculus, and in this section, we will review some of those concepts to the extent necessary. The reader may consult any calculus book for more in-depth discussions.

Dependent and Independent Variables

An equation in general may involve one or more variables. As the name implies, a **variable** is a quantity that may assume various values during a study. A quantity whose value is fixed during a study is called a **constant**. Constants are usually denoted by the earlier letters of the alphabet such as $a, b, c,$ and d; whereas, variables are usually denoted by the later ones such as $t, x, y,$ and z. A variable whose value can be changed arbitrarily is called an **independent variable** or **argument**. A variable whose value depends on the value of other variables and thus cannot be varied independently is called a **dependent variable** or a **function** (Figure 1–9).

A dependent variable y that depends on a variable x is usually denoted as $y(x)$ for clarity. However, this notation becomes very inconvenient and cumbersome when y is repeated several times in an expression. In such cases it is desirable to denote $y(x)$ simply as y when it is clear that y is a function of x. This shortcut in notation improves the appearance and the readability of the equations. The value of y at a fixed number a is denoted by $y(a)$.

During a study, we usually restrict a variable to take on only values that lie between two specified numbers. The range of values a variable can assume between the two specified numbers constitutes the **interval** of that variable. An interval consists of a set of numbers that are greater than one specified number and less than another. An interval is said to be closed if it includes the end number; otherwise, it is said to be open. For example, if we limit the radius r in the equation $P = 2\pi r$ to take on values between $r_1 = 3$ and $r_2 = 7.5$, including the end numbers, we say the interval of r is from 3 to 7.5 and express it as $3 \leq r \leq 7.5$. This is a closed interval, since it includes the end numbers.

Function $y(x) = x^2 + 1$	
Independent variable x	Dependent variable y
1	2
2	5
2.5	6.25
8	65

FIGURE 1–9

The value of a dependent variable depends on the value of the independent variable.

---

*This section is included to refresh students' memories. It can be skipped without a loss in continuity.

Continuous and Discontinuous Functions

In the study and characterization of functions, a concept of utmost importance is continuity. A function y is said to be **continuous** at a number a if (1) the function is defined at that number (that is, $y(a)$ has a finite value), (2) the limit $\lim_{x \to a} y(x)$ exists and (3) this limit is equal to the value of the function at a. That is, a function y is continuous at a if

$$\lim_{x \to a} y(x) = y(a) \qquad (1\text{–}12)$$

If a function is not continuous at a, then it is said to be **discontinuous** at a or to have a **discontinuity** at a. A function is said to be continuous on a closed interval if it is continuous at every number in that interval. A function is said to be discontinuous on a closed interval even if it is discontinuous at one number in that interval.

Continuous functions can be viewed as functions that can be plotted without lifting the pencil from the paper. Discontinuous functions typically involve sudden jumps, or they tend to infinity at some number in the interval. The graph of a function that is discontinuous at three numbers a, b, and c is given in Figure 1–10. Note that this function is continuous on any interval that does not contain any of these three numbers.

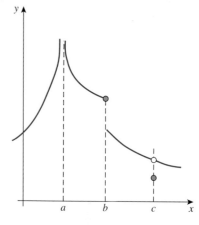

FIGURE 1–10

A function that has discontinuities at a, b, and c.

Derivatives and Differentials

We will briefly discuss derivatives and differentials since they are the building blocks of differential equations. The **derivative** of a function $y(x)$ at a point is equivalent to the slope of the tangent line to the graph of the function at that point and is defined as (Figure 1–11).

$$y'(x) = \lim_{\Delta x \to 0} \frac{y(x + \Delta x) - y(x)}{\Delta x} \qquad (1\text{–}13)$$

A function is said to be **differentiable** at x if this limit exists. A function is said to be differentiable on a closed interval if it is differentiable at every number in that interval. Being continuous is no guarantee for differentiability. A function is not differentiable at a point at which it experiences a sudden change in its slope (a corner). For example, the function plotted in Figure 1–12 is not differentiable at a, since its slope at a as we approach it from the left is different than its slope at a when we approach it from the right.

In the given definition, Δx represents a (small) change in the independent variable x and is called an **increment** of x. The corresponding change in the function y is called an **increment** of y and is denoted by Δy. It is expressed as

$$\Delta y = y(x + \Delta x) - y(x) \qquad (1\text{–}14)$$

Using the increment notation, the derivative of a function also can be expressed as

$$y'(x) = \lim_{\Delta x \to 0} \frac{y(x + \Delta x) - y(x)}{\Delta x} = \lim_{\Delta x \to 0} \frac{\Delta y}{\Delta x} \qquad (1\text{–}15)$$

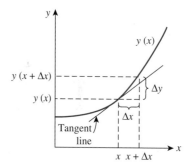

FIGURE 1–11

The derivative of function at a specified point represents the slope of the function at that point.

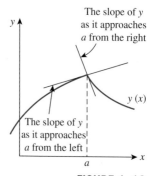

FIGURE 1–12

A function that has two slopes at a point is not differentiable (does not have a derivative) at that point.

Therefore, the derivative of a function can be viewed as the ratio of the increment Δy of the function to the increment Δx of the independent variable for very small Δx. Note that Δy (and thus $y'(x)$) will be zero if the function y does not change with x.

The increment Δx of the independent variable x is also represented by dx, which is called the **differential** of the independent variable. Then the **differential** dy of the dependent variable y is defined as

$$dy = y'(x)\,\Delta x = y'(x)\,dx \qquad (1\text{–}16)$$

Note that the increment Δx and the differential dx of the independent variable x are identical. But this is not the case for the dependent variable y unless it is a linear function of x (i.e., a straight line). The increment Δy represents the actual change in the function y corresponding to a change Δx in x; whereas, the differential dy represents the amount the tangent line rises (or falls if dy is negative) when x changes from x to $x + \Delta x$, as illustrated in Figure 1–13. Also note that when Δx is small, then $\Delta y \approx dy$, and dy can be used as an approximation to exact change Δy. This observation is the basis of the popular numerical method for solving differential equations called *the finite difference method*. Experience has shown that, with some care, very accurate results can be obtained in this manner.

For $dx \neq 0$, Equation 1–16 can be rewritten as

$$y'(x) = \frac{dy}{dx} \qquad (1\text{–}17)$$

which is another commonly used notation for derivative in terms of differentials. This notation is due to Leibniz who used it in his work in the late 17th century.

When differentiating a complicated function such as

$$y(x) = (2x^2 - 3x)^3 + 5 \qquad (1\text{–}18)$$

it is very convenient to define a new variable as $u = 2x^2 - 3x$ so that $y = y(u)$ or $y = y[u(x)]$. The derivative of a nested function like this is easily determined by applying the **chain rule**, which is expressed as follows: If $y = y(u)$ and $u = u(x)$ and both dy/du and du/dx exist, then the derivative of the nested function y with respect to x is given by

$$\frac{dy}{dx} = \frac{dy}{du}\frac{du}{dx} \qquad (1\text{–}19)$$

In our case, $y = u^3 + 5$ and $u = 2x^2 - 3x$, and the application of the chain rule gives (Figure 1–14)

$$\frac{dy}{dx} = \frac{dy}{du}\frac{du}{dx} = (3u^2)(4x - 3) = 3(2x^2 - 3x)^2(4x - 3) \qquad (1\text{–}20)$$

Most problems encountered in practice involve quantities that change with time t and their first derivatives with respect to time represent the **rate of change** of those quantities. For example, if $N(t)$ denotes the population of a bacteria colony at a specific time, then the first derivative $N' = dN/dt$ represents

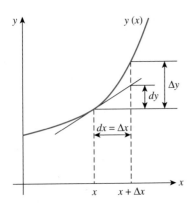

FIGURE 1–13

The graphical representation of the increment Δy and the differential dy of a function $y(x)$.

Given:

$\quad y = u^3 + 5$ and $u = 2x^2 - 3x$

Find:

$$\frac{dy}{dx} = ?$$

Solution:

$$\frac{dy}{dx} = \frac{dy}{du}\frac{du}{dx}$$

$$= (3u^2)(4x - 3)$$

$$= 3(2x^2 - 3x)^2(4x - 3)$$

FIGURE 1–14

Finding the derivative of a function y that depends on u, which depends on x by applying the chain rule.

the rate of change of the population, which is the amount the population increases or decreases per unit time.

The derivative of the first derivative of a function y, assuming it exists, is called the **second derivative** of y, and it is denoted by y''. Likewise, the derivative of the second derivative of y is called the **third derivative** of y, and it is denoted by y'''. In general, the derivative of the $(n-1)$th derivative of y is called the nth **derivative** of y and is denoted by $y^{(n)}$. Higher-order derivatives also are denoted using the differential notation as

$$y'' = \ = \frac{d^2y}{dx^2}, y''' = \ = \frac{d^3y}{dx^3}, \cdots, y^{(n)} = \frac{d^ny}{dx^n} \qquad (1\text{--}21)$$

Here n is a positive integer and is called the **order** of the derivative. The order n should not be confused with the **degree** of a derivative. For example, y''' is the third-order derivative of y, but $(y')^3$ is the third degree of the first derivative of y. The order of a derivative will be indicated by roman numerals, such as y^{IV}, or by a superscript enclosed in parentheses, such as $y', y'', y^{(n-2)}$, and $y^{(n)}$. Note that the first derivative of a function represents the *slope* or the *rate of change* of the function with the independent variable, and the second derivative represents the *rate of change of the slope* of the function with the independent variable.

When a function y depends on two or more independent variables (such as x and t), it is sometimes of interest to examine the dependence of the function on one of the variables only. This is done by taking the derivative of the function with respect to that variable while holding the other variables constant. Such derivatives are called **partial derivatives**. The first partial derivatives of the function $y(x, t)$ with respect to x and t are denoted by y_x and y_t, respectively, and are defined as

$$y_x(x, t) = \lim_{\Delta x \to 0} \frac{y(x + \Delta x, t) - y(x, t)}{\Delta x} = \frac{\partial y}{\partial x} \qquad (1\text{--}22)$$

and

$$y_t(x, t) = \lim_{\Delta t \to 0} \frac{y(x, t + \Delta t) - y(x, t)}{\Delta t} = \frac{\partial y}{\partial t} \qquad (1\text{--}23)$$

provided that the limits exist. Note that, when finding y_x, we treat t as a constant and differentiate y with respect to x. Likewise, when finding y_t, we treat x as a constant and differentiate y with respect to t. The differential dy of the dependent variable $y(x, t)$ in this case is defined as

$$dy = y_x dx + y_t dt = \frac{\partial y}{\partial x} dx + \frac{\partial y}{\partial t} dt \qquad (1\text{--}24)$$

where dx and dt are the differentials of the independent variables x and t, respectively (Figure 1–15). In this text, we will usually consider functions that depend on one variable only, and thus, we will primarily deal with ordinary derivatives.

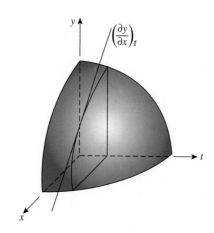

FIGURE 1–15

Graphical representation of the partial derivative $(\partial y / \partial x)$.

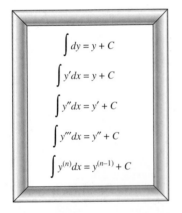

Given function:

$$y = 6x + 2$$

Integral of the function:

$$I = \int y\,dx = 3x^2 + 2x + C$$

Derivative of the integral:

$$\frac{dI}{dx} = 6x + 2 = y$$

FIGURE 1–16

Differentiation and integration are inverse processes, and integration can be checked by differentiating the integral.

$$\int dy = y + C$$

$$\int y'\,dx = y + C$$

$$\int y''\,dx = y' + C$$

$$\int y'''\,dx = y'' + C$$

$$\int y^{(n)}\,dx = y^{(n-1)} + C$$

FIGURE 1–17

Some indefinite integrals that involve differentials and derivatives.

Integration

Integration can be viewed as the inverse process of differentiation (Figure 1–16). Integration is commonly used in solving differential equations, since solving a differential equation is essentially a process of finding $\int y'(x)\,dx$ when the derivative $y'(x)$ is given. The integral of this derivative is expressed as

$$\int y'(x)\,dx = \int dy = y(x) + C \qquad (1\text{–}25)$$

since $y'(x)\,dx = dy$ (Equation 1–16) and the integral of the differential of a function is simply the function itself (plus a constant, of course). In Equation 1–25, x is the **integration variable**, and C is an arbitrary constant called the **integration constant**.

The derivative of $y(x) + C$ is $y'(x)$ no matter what the value of the constant C. Therefore, two functions that differ by a constant have the same derivative, and we always add a constant C during integration to recover this constant which is lost during differentiation. The integral in Equation 1–25 is called an **indefinite integral**, since the value of the arbitrary constant C is indefinite.

The integral in Equation 1–25 can be extended to higher derivatives (Figure 1–17). For example,

$$\int y''(x)\,dx = y'(x) + C \qquad (1\text{–}26)$$

This can be proved by defining a new variable $u(x) = y'(x)$, differentiating it to obtain $u'(x) = y''(x)$, and then applying Equation 1–25. Generalizing,

$$\int y^{(n)}(x)\,dx = y^{(n-1)}(x) + C \qquad (1\text{–}27)$$

Therefore, the order of a derivative decreases by one each time it is integrated.

In this section, we briefly reviewed some important concepts of calculus to lay the groundwork for differential equations. The reader is urged to do further reading on his or her own to gain a very good understanding of these concepts and to develop a mastery to manipulate them. It is the authors' experience that most difficulties students have in the study of differential equations are due to poor backgrounds in calculus. For example, the equation

$$\int x\,dx = \frac{x^2}{2} + C \qquad (1\text{–}28)$$

is correct, as is the following equation for a function $y(x)$:

$$\int y\,dy = \frac{y^2}{2} + C \qquad (1\text{–}29)$$

But the equation

$$\int y\,dx = \frac{y^2}{2} + C \qquad (1\text{--}30)$$

is NOT correct. If it were, we would not need any integral tables. We would simply take the square of the given function, divide it by 2, and add an arbitrary constant to obtain its integral. Yet many students do not realize this before making some costly mistakes.

Section Review

1–7C What is a variable? How do you distinguish a dependent variable from an independent one in a problem?

1–8C How do you identify discontinuous functions?

1–9C What is the difference between partial derivatives and ordinary derivatives?

1–10C What is the difference between the degree and the order of a derivative?

1–11C Consider a function $f(x)$ and its derivative df/dx. Can this derivative be determined by evaluating dx/df and taking its inverse?

1–12 Determine the intervals in which the following functions are continuous.

    (a) $x + 2$ (b) $(x - 1)\ln x$

    (c) $\dfrac{1}{x}$ (d) $\dfrac{e^x}{x^2 - 1}$

(*Answers:* (a) Continuous for all x. (b) Continuous for all positive x. (c) Continuous for all x except $x = 0$. (d) Continuous for all x except $x = \pm 1$.)

1–13 Determine the derivative of the following functions:

    (a) $x\ln 2x$ (b) $e^{-3x}\sin x$

    (c) $(x^2 - 1)^3 e^{\ln x}$ (d) $\sin^2(x\sqrt{x})$

(*Answers:* (a) $\ln(2x) + 1$ (b) $-e^{-3x}(3\sin x - \cos x)$ (c) $(x^2 - 1)^2(7x^2 - 1)$ (d) $\dfrac{3\sqrt{x}}{2}\sin(2x\sqrt{x})$)

1–14 Perform the following integrations:

    (a) $\displaystyle\int [x^2 + e^{-3x} + \sin 5x]\,dx$

    (b) $\displaystyle\int_1^5 \left[\ln 3x + \frac{5}{x}\right] dx$

(*Answers:* (a) $\dfrac{x^3}{3} - \dfrac{e^{-3x}}{3} - \dfrac{\cos 5x}{5} + C$ (b) $4\ln 3 - 4 + \ln 5$)

1–4 ▪ CLASSIFICATION OF DIFFERENTIAL EQUATIONS

A differential equation that involves only ordinary derivatives of one or more dependent variables with respect to a single independent variable is called an **ordinary differential equation**, and a differential equation that

(a) An ordinary differential equation:

$$\frac{d^2u}{dx^2} - 2\frac{du}{dx} = 2x^2 + 6$$

(b) A partial differential equation:

$$\frac{\partial^2 v}{\partial x^2} - 2\frac{\partial v}{\partial t} = 2x^2 + e^t$$

FIGURE 1–18

An ordinary and a partial differential equation.

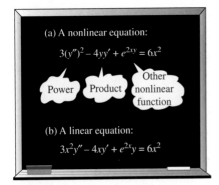

FIGURE 1–19

A differential equation that is (a) nonlinear and (b) linear. When deciding linearity, we check the dependent variable only.

involves partial derivatives with respect to two or more independent variables is called a **partial differential equation** (Figure 1–18). Then it follows that problems that involve a single independent variable result in ordinary differential equations, and problems that involve two are more independent variables result in partial differential equations. Since in this text we limit our discussions to ordinary differential equations, the problems we will attempt to solve are automatically limited equations like

$$y''' + 3x^2y' - 4y = xe^x + 2 \tag{1-31}$$

which involve a single independent variable. Here y is the dependent variable (the unknown function), and x is the independent variable.

A differential equation may involve several derivatives of various orders of an unknown function. The order of the highest derivative in a differential equation is the **order of the equation**. For example, the order of $y''' + (y'')^6 = 4x^5$ is 3, since it contains no fourth- or higher-order derivatives.

A differential equation is said to be in the **standard form** if the coefficient of its highest derivative is one. For example, the differential equation in Equation 1–31 is in standard form since the coefficient of y''' (which is the highest-order derivative in that equation) is 1. A differential equation can be put into the standard form by dividing the equation by the coefficient of the highest-order derivative.

You will remember from algebra that the equation $3x - 5 = 0$ is much easier to solve than the equation $x^4 + 3x - 5 = 0$, because the first equation is linear whereas the second one is nonlinear. This is also true for differential equations. Therefore, before we start solving a differential equation, we usually check for linearity. A differential equation is said to be **linear** if the dependent variable and all of its derivatives are of the first degree, and their coefficients depend on the independent variable only. In other words, a differential equation is linear if it can be written in a form that does not involve the following.

(1) Any powers of the dependent variable or its derivatives (such as y^3 or $(y'')^2$).
(2) Any products of the dependent variable or its derivatives (such as yy' or $y'y'''$).
(3) Any other nonlinear functions of the dependent variable (such as $\sin y$ or e^y).

Otherwise, it is **nonlinear**.

A linear differential equation may contain the following.

(1) Powers or nonlinear functions of the independent variable (such as x^2 and $\cos x$).
(2) Products of a dependent variable (or its derivatives) and functions of an independent variable (such as x^3y', x^4y, or $e^{-2x}y''$) (see Figure 1–19).

Thus, we see that the model of an RC circuit, as in Equation (1–10), is linear.

$$RC\frac{dv_1}{dt} + v_1 = V \tag{1-10}$$

The model of the draining coffee pot, Equation (1–11), is nonlinear because the dependent variable h is raised to the 1/2 power because it is within the square root.

$$\rho A \frac{dh}{dt} = \rho q_{vi} - k\sqrt{\rho g h} \tag{1-11}$$

A linear differential equation of order n can be expressed in the most general form as

$$y^{(n)} + f_1(x)y^{(n-1)} + \cdots + f_{n-1}(x)y' + f_n(x)y = R(x) \tag{1-32}$$

A differential equation that cannot be put into this form is nonlinear.

A linear differential equation in y is said to be **homogeneous** as well if $R(x) = 0$ for all x under consideration. Otherwise, it is **nonhomogeneous** (Figure 1–20). That is, each term in a linear homogeneous equation contains the dependent variable or one of its derivatives after the equation is cleared of any common factors. The term $R(x)$ is called the **nonhomogeneous term**.

A linear homogeneous equation of order n can be expressed in the general form as

$$y^{(n)} + f_1(x)y^{(n-1)} + \cdots + f_{n-1}(x)y' + f_n(x)y = 0 \tag{1-33}$$

The term homogeneous is also used in another meaning to describe a special kind of first-order differential equation, which is discussed in Chapter 2.

(a) A linear nonhomogeneous equation:

$$y'' + 3y' - 8x^2y = \underbrace{6e^{-2x} - 5}_{\text{Nonzero}}$$

(b) Its related homogeneous equation:

$$y'' + 3y' - 8x^2y = \underset{\uparrow}{0}$$
$$\text{Zero}$$

FIGURE 1–20

A nonhomogeneous differential equation and its related homogeneous equation.

EXAMPLE 1–8   Classification of Differential Equations

Determine the order of the seven differential equations given here and indicate whether they are linear or nonlinear. Also indicate which linear equations are homogeneous.

1. $y'' + 3y = 0$
2. $y'' + 3y = 2x + 5$
3. $y'' + 3yy' = 0$
4. $y''' + 2(y')^2 + 3y = 5$
5. $y'' + 3x^4y = 0$
6. $y'' + 3xy^4 = e^{-2x}$
7. $y''' + y' + \sin y = 0.2$

SOLUTION   By closely examining the equations above, we conclude the following:

1. second order, linear, homogeneous
2. second order, linear, nonhomogeneous
3. second order, nonlinear
4. third order, nonlinear
5. second order, linear, homogeneous
6. second order, nonlinear
7. third order, nonlinear

Differential equations are also classified by the nature of the coefficients of the dependent variable and its derivatives. A differential equation is said to have **constant coefficients** if the coefficients of all the terms that involve the dependent variable or its derivatives are constants. If, after cleared of any common factors, any of the terms with the dependent variable or its derivatives involve the independent variable as a coefficient, that equation is said to have **variable coefficients** (Figure 1–21). All of the differential equations in Example 1–8—except (5) and (6)—have constant coefficients.

Ordinary differential equations are characterized by having a single independent variable. Most of the differential equations we are going to study will also have a single dependent variable or unknown function. However, sometimes we encounter two or more unknown functions in two or more coupled differential equations. Such equations are called **systems of differential equations** and are usually solved using linear algebra. For example,

$$y'' + 3y' - 5z = 0$$
$$z'' - 2y - 2z - \sin x = 0$$

is a system of two differential equations in two unknown functions, z and y, with x as the independent variable.

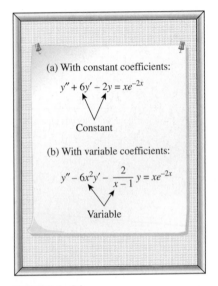

FIGURE 1–21

A differential equation with
(a) constant coefficients and
(b) variable coefficients.

Section Review

1–15C What is the difference between an algebraic equation and a differential equation?

1–16C What is the difference between an ordinary differential equation and a partial differential equation?

1–17C How is the order of a differential equation determined?

1–18C How do you distinguish a linear differential equation from a nonlinear one?

1–19 Determine the order of each of the differential equations given, whether they are linear or nonlinear, and whether they have constant or variable coefficients.

(a) $y''' + 3y = 8x$ (b) $y'' + 3xyy' = 0$

(c) $y'' + x^4 y' + y = 0$ (d) $y'' + 2e^x y = 0$

(e) $xy''' + 2xyy'' + 3xy = 5x^3$

(*Answers:* (a) Third order, linear, constant coefficient; (b) Second order, non-linear, variable coefficient; (c) Second order, linear, variable coefficient; (d) Second order, linear, variable coefficient; (e) Third order, nonlinear, constant coefficient.)

1–5 · SOLUTIONS OF DIFFERENTIAL EQUATIONS

Solving a differential equation can be as easy as taking one or more integrations, but such simple differential equations are the exception rather than the rule. There is no single general solution method that is applicable to all differential equations. There are different solution techniques where each is applicable to different classes of differential equations. Sometimes, solving a differential equation requires the use of two or more techniques as well as ingenuity and mastery of the solution methods. Some differential equations can be solved only by using some very clever tricks. Some cannot be solved analytically at all.

In algebra, we usually seek discrete *values* that satisfy an algebraic equation (such as $x^2 - 7x + 10 = 0$). When dealing with differential equations, however, we seek *functions* that satisfy the equation in a specified interval. For example, the algebraic equation $x^2 - 7x + 10 = 0$ is satisfied by two numbers only: 2 and 5. But the differential equation $y' - 7y = 0$ is satisfied by the function e^{7x} for any value of x (Figure 1–22).

Consider the algebraic equation $x^3 - 6x^2 + 11x - 6 = 0$. Obviously, $x = 1$ satisfies this equation, and thus, it is a solution. However, it is not the only solution of this equation. We can easily show by direct substitution that $x = 2$ and $x = 3$ also satisfy this equation: thus, they are solutions as well. But there are no other solutions to this equation. Therefore, we say that the set 1, 2, and 3 form the complete solution to this algebraic equation.

The same line of reasoning also applies to differential equations. Typically, differential equations have multiple solutions that contain at least one arbitrary constant. Any function that satisfies the differential equation on an interval is called **a solution** of that differential equation. A solution that involves one or more arbitrary constants represents a family of functions that satisfy the differential equation and is called **a general solution** of that equation. Not surprisingly, a differential equation may have more than one general solution. A general solution is referred to as **the general solution** or the **complete solution** if *every* solution of the equation can be obtained from it as a special case. A solution that can be obtained from a general solution by assigning particular values to the arbitrary constants is called a **particular solution** or a **specific solution**. A solution that cannot be obtained from the general solution by assigning particular values to the arbitrary constants is called **a singular solution**.

You will recall from algebra that a number is a solution of an algebraic equation if it satisfies the equation. For example, $x_1 = 2$ is a solution of the equation $x^3 - 8 = 0$, because the substitution of 2 for x yields identically zero. Likewise, a function is a solution of a differential equation if that function satisfies the differential equation. In other words, a solution function yields an identity when substituted into the differential equation.

(a) An algebraic equation:

$$y^2 - 7y + 10 = 0$$

Solution: $y = 2$ and $y = 5$

(b) A differential equation:

$$y' - 7y = 0$$

Solution: $y = e^{7x}$

FIGURE 1–22

Unlike algebraic equations, the solutions of differential equations are typically functions instead of discrete values.

EXAMPLE 1–9 **Solution of a Differential Equation**

Show that $y_1 = 3e^{-2x}$ is a solution of the differential equation $y'' - 4y = 0$.

SOLUTION The given function is a solution of the differential equation above if subtracting 4 times the function itself from its second derivative yields zero. The first and the second derivatives of $y_1 = 3e^{-2x}$ are $y'_1 = -6e^{-2x}$ and $y''_1 = 12e^{-2x}$:

Then we have $y'' - 4y = 12e^{-2x} - 4(3e^{-2x}) = 0$. Therefore, y_1 is a solution of the differential equation.

EXAMPLE 1–10   **General Solution of a Differential Equation**

Show that $y_1 = Cxe^{2x} + 2x - 3$ is a solution of the differential equation $y'' - 4y' + 4y = 8x - 20$ no matter what the value of the arbitrary constant C.

SOLUTION   The first and the second derivatives of $y_1 = Cxe^{2x} + 2x - 3$ are

$$y_1' = C(e^{2x} + 2xe^{2x}) + 2 = Ce^{2x} + 2Cxe^{2x} + 2$$

and

$$y_1'' = 2Ce^{2x} + 2C(e^{2x} + 2xe^{2x}) = 4Ce^{2x} + 4Cxe^{2x}$$

Then we have

$$
\begin{aligned}
y'' - 4y' + 4y &= (4Ce^{2x} + 4Cxe^{2x}) - 4(Ce^{2x} + 2Cxe^{2x} + 2) + 4(Cxe^{2x} + 2x - 3) \\
&= 4Ce^{2x} + 4Cxe^{2x} - 4Ce^{2x} - 8Cxe^{2x} - 8 + 4Cxe^{2x} + 8x - 12 \\
&= 8x - 20
\end{aligned}
$$

Therefore, y_1 is a solution of the differential equation regardless of the value of the constant C. This is a general solution since it involves an arbitrary constant.

Reconsider the differential equation that describes the temperature rise of a copper ball with time when dropped into hot water at temperature T_0 (Equation 1–5). As you will see in Chapter 2, the general solution of this differential equation is

$$T(t) = T_0 - (T_0 - C)e^{-hAt/mc} \tag{1–34}$$

where C is an arbitrary constant. We can easily show by direct substitution that this solution satisfies Equation 1–5 for any value of the constant C. In other words, Equation 1–5, like any other differential equation, has an infinite number of solutions, since the arbitrary constant C can have an infinite number of different values. This is not surprising, however, since the differential equation and its general solution do not involve the initial temperature T_i, and as you would expect, the temperature of the ball at a specified time t will certainly depend on T_i. For $t = 0$, Equation 1–34 yields $C = T(0) = T_i$, since $T(0)$ indicates the temperature of the ball at $t = 0$, which is the initial temperature. Substituting, the solution becomes

$$T(t) = T_0 - (T_0 - T_i)e^{-hAt/mc} \tag{1–35}$$

The solution curves are plotted in Figure 1–23 for a constant value of hA/mc and for different values of T_i, forming a family of non-intersecting curves. Notice that each curve corresponds to a specific value of T_i, which is

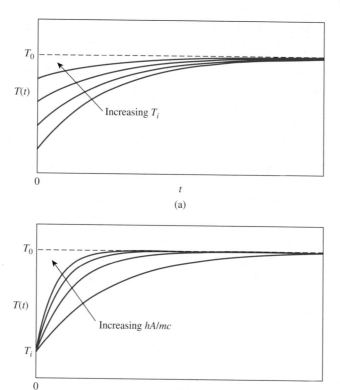

FIGURE 1–23

Solution curves for temperature as a function of time based on Equation 1–35. (a) Solution behavior for hA/mc fixed with four different values of the initial temperature T_i. (b) Solution behavior for a fixed initial temperature T_i with four different values of hA/mc.

the temperature axis (or $t = 0$ line). Therefore, once the initial temperature T_i is specified, the solution to the differential equation becomes specified. The solution we are interested in is the one that intersects the T axis at the specified T_i value.

This example demonstrates that although a well-posed problem usually has a unique solution, the differential equation that describes that problem may have an infinite number of solutions. This is because a differential equation is a relation between the *changes* in the dependent and independent variables, and it does not incorporate information dealing with the *values* of a function or its derivatives at some fixed values of the independent variable.

Consequently, many different problems related to the same physical phenomena have the same differential equation. For example, Equation 1–35 is the differential equation for the heating (or even cooling) of a solid ball in an environment at T_0, regardless of the initial temperature of the solid ball.

Then it follows that to obtain a unique solution to a problem, we need to specify more than just the governing differential equation. We need to specify some conditions (such as the value of the function or its derivatives at some value of the independent variable) so that forcing the solution to satisfy these conditions at specified points will result in a unique solution.

(a) An initial-value problem:

$$y'' - 3y' + y = 2xe^{-4x}$$
$$y(2) = 5$$
$$y'(2) = -3$$

(b) A boundary-value problem:

$$y'' - 3y' + y = 2xe^{-4x}$$
$$y(2) = 5$$
$$y'(8) = -3$$

FIGURE 1–24

Initial- and boundary-value problems.

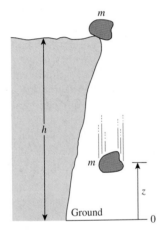

FIGURE 1–25

Illustration for Example 1–11.

But since the differential equation has no place for the needed additional information or conditions, we need to supply them separately. These conditions are called **initial conditions** if all of them are specified at the same value of the independent variable, and **boundary conditions** if they are specified at two or more values of the independent variable. A differential equation accompanied by a set of initial conditions is called an **initial-value problem**; whereas, a differential equation accompanied by a set of boundary conditions is called a **boundary-value problem** (Figure 1–24).

EXAMPLE 1–11 **Free Fall of a Body**

When the air resistance is negligible, the free fall of a body is governed by the law of gravity. Consider an object that is initially at elevation $z = h$ and is allowed to fall freely at time zero, as shown in Figure 1–25. Write the mathematical formulation of this problem, and determine whether it is an initial-value or a boundary-value problem.

SOLUTION The mathematical formulation of a problem involves writing the governing differential equation and the appropriate boundary or initial conditions. The differential equation for this problem was determined in Example 1–1 to be (Equation 1–3)

$$\frac{d^2z}{dt^2} = -g$$

where z is the vertical distance from a reference level such as the ground, and g is the gravitational acceleration. At time $t = 0$, the object is specified to be stationary (velocity $V(0) = 0$) at elevation h. Thus, the initial conditions for this problem can be expressed as

$$V(0) = \frac{dz}{dt}\bigg|_{t=0} = 0 \qquad \text{(1–36)}$$

$$z(0) = h$$

This is the complete formulation of the problem, and as you will see in the next section, it results in a unique solution for the unknown function z.

This problem is easily recognized as an initial-value problem, since both conditions are specified at the same value of the independent variable $t = 0$.

But if the velocity (or the position) was specified at a different time (such as $t = 15$ s) while the position was specified at $t = 0$, it would be a boundary-value problem.

When solving a differential equation, it is very desirable to obtain a closed-form solution that is an analytical expression for the unknown function in terms of the independent variable (such as $y = y(x)$). Numerous differential equations of practical interest have easily obtainable closed-form solutions, as you will see in later chapters. But most differential equations cannot be solved using any of the available methods, and thus, an approximate treatment becomes necessary. Such problems can be solved with reasonable accuracy using an appropriate numerical method discussed in Chapter 9. When a numerical method is used, the solution is obtained at discrete points rather than as a continuous function over the entire domain.

Note that any relation that satisfies the differential equation and involves the unknown function and the independent variables only (no derivatives) is a solution of the equation. If the unknown function can be expressed in terms of the independent variable only, then the solution is said to be **explicit**; otherwise, the solution is said to be **implicit**. The relation $g(x, y) = 0$ defines y implicitly as a function of x. For example, a solution such as $y = 3x^2 + \cos x + 5$ is an explicit solution, but a solution $y = e^{2xy} + 3xy^2 + 5$ is an implicit solution, since in this case, we cannot express y explicitly in terms of x only.

Section Review

1–20C What are boundary conditions? What is their value in the solution of differential equations?

1–21C When is a problem an initial-value problem, and when is it a boundary-value problem?

Show that the given functions are solutions of the given differential equation in each of the following problems.

1–22 $y'' = 0$, $y_1 = 5x$, and $y_2 = 2x + 1$

1–23 $y' + 3y = 0$, $y_1 = e^{-3x}$, and $y_2 = 5e^{-3x}$

1–24 $y'' - 4y = 0$, $y_1 = e^{2x}$, and $y_2 = -3e^{-2x}$

1–25 $x^2y'' + 5xy' + 3y = 0$, $y_1 = 1/x^3$, and $y_2 = 2/x$

1–6 ▪ SOLVING DIFFERENTIAL EQUATIONS BY DIRECT INTEGRATION

Since differential equations involve derivatives and each integration reduces the order of a derivative by one, it is natural to look at direct integration as a prospective method for solving differential equations. Solving differential equations by direct integration is more the exception than the rule, however, since most differential equations encountered in practice cannot be solved this way.

Some important differential equations are linear, have a single term that involves derivatives, and have no terms that involve the unknown function as a factor. Such differential equations can be solved by direct integration, assuming (of course) the integrations can be performed. Some others, including some nonlinear ones, can be put into that form, and those too can be solved by direct integration. For example, the differential equation

$$y''' - x^2e^{-6x} = 0 \qquad\qquad \text{(1–37)}$$

can be solved by direct integration, since it involves a single term with a derivative of y and no terms with y. But the differential equation

$$y''' + 3xy - x^2 e^{-6x} = 0 \qquad (1\text{--}38)$$

cannot be solved by direct integration, since it involves a term with the unknown function y.

When solving a differential equation by direct integration, all of the terms in the equation are integrated one by one using the rules of integration, and an integration constant is added. Each time the equation is integrated, the order of the derivative reduces by one, and a new integration constant is introduced. Thus, an nth-order differential equation (in this case) is solved by n successive integrations, and the solution involves n integration constants.

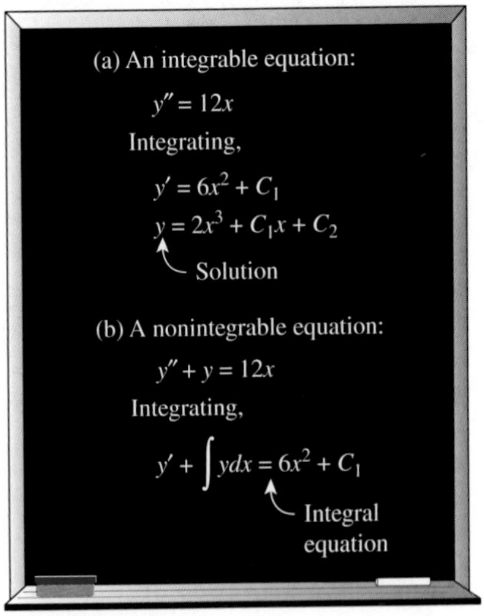

FIGURE 1–26

Some differential equations can be solved by integrating each term repeatedly until the equation involves no derivatives.

EXAMPLE 1–12   **Solution by Direct Integration**

Determine if the following differential equations can be solved by direct integration, and obtain the solution of those that can.

(a) $y' - 5y + 3 = 0$

(b) $y'' - 6x^2 = 0$

(c) $2yy' - 4 = 0$

SOLUTION   (a) This differential equation cannot be solved by direct integration, since the second term involves the unknown function y. If we attempted to solve this differential equation by direct integration, we would obtain

$$y - 5\int y\,dx + 3x = C_1$$

which does not involve any derivatives. Thus it has the appearance of a solution, but involves the integral of the unknown function instead, which is also not known. Therefore, this is not a solution in the real sense. By integrating, we simply converted the differential equation into an integral equation (Figure 1–26).

(b) This equation is linear and involves a single term with derivatives and no terms with the unknown function y as a factor. Therefore, it can be solved by direct integration. Integrating once yields $y' - 2x^3 = C_1$. Integrating one more time yields $y - 0.5x^4 = C_1 x + C_2$ or $y = 0.5x^4 + C_1 x + C_2$, which is the desired solution of the differential equation.

(c) This differential equation is nonlinear and does not look like it can be solved by direct integration. But a careful inspection of the equation reveals that the term $2yy'$ is nothing more than the derivative of y^2. Therefore, the integral of the first term is y^2, since integration is simply the inverse of differentiation. Thus, each term in this equation can be integrated, yielding $y^2 - 4x = C_1$ or $y = \pm\sqrt{4x + C_1}$, which is the desired solution.

EXAMPLE 1–13   **Free Fall of a Body**

A daredevil jumper equipped with a parachute jumps from the top of a 100-m high building at a location where the gravitational acceleration is $g = 9.8$ m/s². The parachute opens 3 seconds after the jump. Neglecting the air resistance, determine the height of the jumper when the parachute opens.

SOLUTION This is a free-falling process under the influence of gravity, and the problem can be solved easily using the relevant formulas from physics. But we are going to solve this simple problem using differential equations to demonstrate the solution of a differential equation and the application of the boundary or initial conditions. This will also help us gain a deeper understanding of those physical relations.

The function we want to find in this problem is the vertical distance z as a function of the independent variable t (time). We take the ground as the reference level and measure z from the ground level, as shown in Figure 1–27. The governing differential equation for this problem was determined in Example 1–1 to be (Equation 1–3)

$$\frac{d^2z}{dt^2} = -g$$

which is a linear, second-order, nonhomogeneous differential equation. A quick inspection of this differential equation reveals that it has a single term that involves derivatives and no terms that involve the unknown function z as a factor. Thus, it can be solved by direct integration. Since the differential equation is of second order, the solution will be obtained by two successive integrations, which will introduce two integration constants.

Integrating each term of the differential equation once yields

$$\frac{dz}{dt} = -gt + C_1 \qquad (1\text{–}39)$$

where C_1 is the first integration constant. Notice that the order of a derivative goes down by one with each integration. As a check, if we take the derivative of this equation, we will obtain the original differential equation. This equation is not the solution yet, since it involves a derivative.

Integrating one more time, we obtain

$$z(t) = -\frac{1}{2}gt^2 + C_1 t + C_2 \qquad (1\text{–}40)$$

which is the general solution of the differential equation (Figure 1–28).

We can show that it contains all of the solutions to the differential equation. Notice that the solution of a differential equation is a relation between the unknown function and the independent variable, and it contains no derivatives.

The general solution for z contains two arbitrary constants, and thus, we cannot determine the distance of the jumper from the ground when the parachute opens using this relation. This is not surprising, however, since that distance will depend on the height of the building as well as the initial velocity of the jumper, and the general solution contains no such information. A differential equation is a relation between the changes in the dependent and the independent variables and is not affected by the constraints or conditions imposed on the dependent variable at some values of the independent variable. If the building were 200 m high instead of 100 m high, for example, the differential equation and the general solution would still be the same. But the distance of the jumper from the ground at a specified time would obviously be different. Thus, the two arbitrary constants in the general solution provide the flexibility for it to adjust to different situations.

The general solution contains two unknown constants, and thus, we need two equations to determine them uniquely and to obtain the specific solution of our problem. These equations are obtained by forcing the general solution

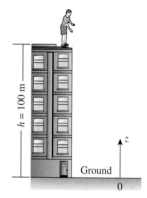

FIGURE 1–27

Illustration for Example 1–13.

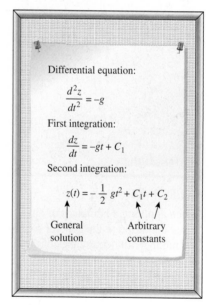

FIGURE 1–28

Obtaining the general solution of a simple second-order differential equation by integration.

to satisfy the specified initial or boundary conditions. The applications of each condition yields one equation, and thus, we need two conditions to determine the constants C_1 and C_2. In our case, it is specified that initially (at $t = 0$) the height of the jumper is 100 m, and his velocity is zero. Then as discussed in Example 1–8, these two conditions can be expressed mathematically as

$$V(0) = \frac{dz}{dt}\bigg|_{t=0} = 0$$

$$z(0) = 100$$

When applying an initial or a boundary condition to an equation, all occurrences of the dependent and independent variables and any derivatives are replaced by the specified values. Thus, the only unknowns the equations will contain are the arbitrary constants.

The first condition can be interpreted as *take the derivative of the general solution, and then replace all the t's and dz/dt's by zero.* That is,

$$\frac{dz}{dt} = -gt + C_1$$

$$\frac{dz}{dt}\bigg|_{t=0} = -g \times 0 + C_1$$

$$0 = 0 + C_1 \rightarrow C_1 = 0$$

The second condition can be interpreted as *in the general solution, replace all the t's by zero and z(t) by 100.* That is (Figure 1–29),

$$z(t) = -\frac{1}{2}gt^2 + C_1 t + C_2$$

$$z(0) = -\frac{1}{2}g \times 0^2 + C_1 \times 0 + C_2$$

$$100 = 0 + 0 + C_2 \rightarrow C_2 = 100$$

Substituting the calculated values of C_1 and C_2 into the general solution, we obtain

$$z(t) = -\frac{1}{2}gt^2 + 100$$

which is the desired specific solution since it satisfies not only the differential equation but also the two specified conditions at time zero. Then the distance of the jumper from the ground when the parachute opens is determined by substituting $g = 9.8$ m/s^2 and $t = 3$ s into this solution,

$$z(3 \text{ s}) = -(1/2)(9.8 \text{ m/s}^2)(3 \text{ s})^2 + 100 \text{ m} = 55.9 \text{ m}$$

That is, the jumper will be 55.9 m above the ground level when the parachute opens.

Even when a differential equation cannot be solved by direct integration, it may still be possible to reduce its order by successive integrations. Reduction of order is recognized as an important tool in solving differential equations, since solving lower-order equations is usually much easier solving than higher-order ones. When a linear differential equation involves various

Initial Condition: $z(0) = 100$

General Solution:

$$z(t) = -\frac{1}{2}gt^2 + C_1 t + C_2$$

$$100 = -\frac{1}{2}g \times 0^2 + C_1 \times 0 + C_2$$

Cannot involve the dependent or the independent variable after initial condition is applied.

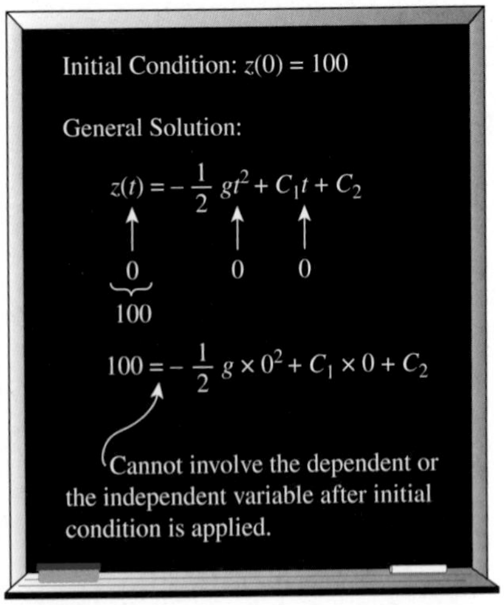

FIGURE 1–29

When applying a boundary or an initial condition to the general solution at a number, all occurrences of the dependent and the independent variables should be replaced by their specified values at that number.

derivatives of the unknown function but not the unknown function itself, its order can be reduced by m, where m is the order of the lowest-order derivative in the equation. For example, the third-order differential equation

$$y''' - 3y'' - 12x = 0 \qquad (1\text{-}42)$$

can be reduced to a first-order differential equation by integrating it, successively twice, yielding

$$y'' - 3y' - 6x^2 = C_1$$

and

$$y' - 3y - 2x^3 = C_1 x + C_2 \qquad (1\text{-}43)$$

This equation cannot be solved by direct integration, however, since the second term now involves the unknown function y.

EXAMPLE 1–14 Liquid Height in a Draining Tank

Consider the model of liquid height h when the tank has an opening in the side (Equation 1–11 and Figure 1–8).

$$\rho A \frac{dh}{dt} = \rho q_{vi} - k\sqrt{\rho g h}$$

Solve this equation for $h(t)$ for the case where the inflow rate q_{vi} is zero.

SOLUTION With $q_{vi} = 0$, the model is

$$\rho A \frac{dh}{dt} = -k\sqrt{\rho g h}$$

This can be simplified by combining the constants as

$$\frac{dh}{dt} = -b\sqrt{h}, \; b = \frac{k}{A}\sqrt{\frac{g}{\rho}}, \quad \text{or} \quad \frac{1}{\sqrt{h}}\frac{dh}{dt} = -b \qquad (1\text{-}44)$$

Recognizing that

$$\frac{1}{\sqrt{h}}\frac{dh}{dt} = 2\frac{d(\sqrt{h})}{dt} = -b$$

we can integrate the equation as

$$\sqrt{h} = C - \frac{b}{2}t = \sqrt{h(0)} - \frac{b}{2}t$$

So the solution is

$$h(t) = \left(\sqrt{h(0)} - \frac{b}{2}t\right)^2 \qquad (1\text{-}45)$$

FIGURE 1–30

A coffee pot.

EXAMPLE 1–15   Design of a Coffee Pot

A 15-cup coffee pot was placed under a faucet and filled to the 15-cup line (see Figure 1–30). With the outlet valve open, the faucet's flow rate was adjusted until the water level remained constant at 15 cups, and the time for one cup to flow out of the pot was measured. This experiment was repeated with the pot filled to 12, 9, and 6 cups. The data is shown in the first two columns of the following table. The flow rate is computed in the third column.

Liquid volume V (cups)	Time to fill one cup (sec)	Outflow rate $f = dV/dt$ (cups/sec)	$c = f/\sqrt{V}$
15	6	1/6	0.043
12	7	1/7	0.041
9	8	1/8	0.042
6	9	1/9	0.045

(a) From the table you can see that the time to fill decreases with the volume. The manufacturer wants to offer a pot that holds 36 cups but is concerned that a cup will fill too quickly and spill. Estimate the time to fill one cup if there are 36 cups in the pot.

(b) If the faucet is opened, how long will it take for the pot to empty if the pot holds 36 cups initially?

SOLUTION   (a) From Equation (1–44) in Example 1–14,

$$\frac{1}{\sqrt{h}}\frac{dh}{dt} = -b$$

Note that the volume V of liquid in the pot is $V = \rho A h$. Thus, the previous equation can be expressed in terms of V as

$$\frac{1}{\sqrt{V}}\frac{dV}{dt} = -b\sqrt{\rho A} = -c \qquad (1\text{–}46)$$

Using the first and third columns in the table, we can compute c for each data point. These are shown in the fourth column, and the average value is $c = 0.043$. Substituting $V = 36$ cups into Equation 1–46 and solving for the flow rate dV/dt, we obtain

$$\frac{dV}{dt} = -0.043\,(6) = -0.258$$

Thus, the time to fill one cup is $1/0.258 = 3.88$ sec. In fact, the manufacturer did build a 36-cup pot, and the measured time to fill was 4 sec!

(b) Following the same procedure as in Example 1–14, we can obtain the following solution of Equation 1–46.

$$V(t) = (\sqrt{V(0)} - 0.0215t)^2$$

The time for the pot to empty is found by setting $V(t) = 0$ to obtain
$t = \sqrt{V(0)}/0.0215 = \sqrt{36}/0.0215 = 279$ sec.

Section Review

1–26C What kind of differential equations can be solved by direct integration?

1–27C Consider a third-order linear and homogeneous differential equation that can be solved by direct integration. How many arbitrary constants will the solution involve?

1–28 Determine which of the following differential equations can be solved by direct integration. Obtain the general solution of those that can.

(a) $y' = 0$
(b) $y' + x = 0$
(c) $y' + y = 0$
(d) $e^x y'' + x e^{3x} = 0$
(e) $2yy'' + \sin 3x = 0$

(*Answers: Note:* C is an arbitrary constant. (a) $y = C$, (b) $y = \frac{x^2}{2} + C$, (c) $y(t) = e^{C-t}$ (d) $y = \frac{e^{2x}}{4}(2x - 1) + C$, (e) $y = \pm\sqrt{C - (\cos 3x)/3}$.)

1–7 · INTRODUCTION TO COMPUTER METHODS

The most popular programs used for engineering applications are Maple, Mathematica, MATLAB, the MATLAB Symbolic Math toolbox, and MuPAD, which is a notebook interface supplied with the MATLAB Symbolic Math toolbox using the same "engine" as the toolbox. In this section, we illustrate how to use these programs to solve problems of the following type encountered in this chapter.

- Plotting solutions
- Performing symbolic evaluation of the integrals required to solve equations using the direct integration method
- Interpreting solutions in terms of the special functions of mathematics
- Numerical evaluation of integrals

We assume that you are familiar with the basic operations of the program of your choice. When using these programs, be sure to first clear all relevant variables. We do not show this operation. Note that Maple formats your entries into mathematical notation as you type. Our Maple programs show the entries as you would type them before formatting takes place. Note also that Mathematica requires you to press **Shift-Enter** to evaluate a command, rather than just **Enter**, as required by the other programs. These actions are not explicitly shown in the programs in this text.

Plotting Solutions

In engineering applications, once you have the solution of a differential equation in closed form, you often need to analyze it. This often means you will need to plot the solution. Here we show how to use the major programs to do this.

Consider Equation 1–35, which is the solution for the temperature $T(t)$ of a copper ball after being dropped into hot water. It is

$$T(t) = T_0 - (T_0 - T_i)e^{-rt} \qquad (1\text{–}47)$$

TABLE 1–1

Computer Generated Plot of Equation 1–47

MATLAB

```
t = linspace(0, 2, 300);
T1 = 50 -(50 - 10)*exp(-2*t);
T2 = 50 -(50 - 30)*exp(-2*t);
plot(t,T1,t,T2,'--'),xlabel('Time (s)'),...
    ylabel('Temperature (^oC)'),legend('T1','T2')
```

MuPAD

```
T1 := 50 - (50 - 10)*exp(-2*t):
T2 := 50 - (50 - 30)*exp(-2*t):
F1 := plot::Function2d(T1, t = 0 .. 2):F2 := plot::Function2d
    (T2, t = 0 .. 2):
plot(F1,F2, AxesTitles = ["Time (s)", "Temperature (C)"]):
```

Maple

```
T1 := t->50 - (50-10)*exp(-2*t):
T2 := t->50 - (50-30)*exp(-2*t):
plot({T1,T2},0..2)
```

Mathematica

```
T1 := 50 -(50-10)*Exp[-2*t]
T2 := 50-(50-30)*Exp[-2*t]
Plot[{T1,T2},{t,0,2}]
```

where $r = hA/mc$. Choosing the values $r = 2$, $T_0 = 50°C$, and $T_i = 10$ and $30°C$, we can use the programs shown in Table 1–1 to obtain the plot shown in Figure 1–31, which was created with MATLAB.

A plot similar to this can be produced with the other programs as shown in Table 1–1.

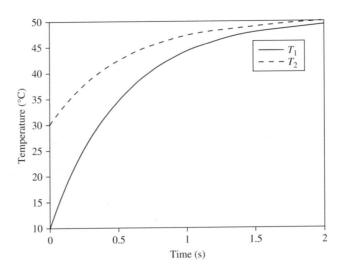

FIGURE 1–31

Plot of the temperature of a copper ball dropped into hot water.

Symbolic Integration

Symbolic processing describes how a computer program produces a solution to a problem in symbolic or closed form; that is, as a mathematical formula. Such programs can perform algebraic and trigonometric manipulations, solve algebraic and differential equations, and evaluate integrals, for example. The most popular symbolic processing programs are Maple, Mathematica, the MATLAB Symbolic Math toolbox, and MuPAD.

Symbolic processing software can be used to assist in obtaining solutions by direct integration. For example, consider the equation

$$\frac{dy}{dx} = x^2 e^{-2x} \tag{1-48}$$

Its solution by direct integration is

$$y(x) = \int_0^x u^2 e^{-2u} du + y(0) = \frac{1}{4} - \frac{1}{4} e^{-2x}(1 + 2x + 2x^2) + y(0) \tag{1-49}$$

Table 1–2 shows how this integral can be obtained with several programs.

TABLE 1–2
Computer Evaluation of the Definite Integral of $x^2 e^{-2x}$
MATLAB Symbolic Math Toolbox
`syms x` `int('x^2*exp(-2*x)',x, 0, x)`
MuPAD
`int(x^2*exp(-2*x),x=0..x)`
Maple
`int(x^2*exp(-2*x),x=0..x)`
Mathematica
`Integrate[x^2*Exp[-2*x],{x, 0, x}]`

The Special Functions of Mathematics

Some simple-looking integrals cannot be evaluated in closed form but they occur so often in applications that they were computed numerically and the results tabulated in mathematical handbooks. By approximating these integrals with infinite series, their values are now available in the popular computer programs. These functions are called the *special functions of mathematics* to distinguish them from the elementary functions (such as the exponential, logarithmic, and trigonometric functions). We introduce the topic of special functions now because you may encounter them when using a computer package.

An example of a special function is Fresnel's cosine integral, which appears in optics applications.

$$C(z) = \int_0^z \cos\frac{\pi x^2}{2} \, dx \tag{1-50}$$

This integral must be computed to solve the differential equation $dy/dx = \cos x^2$ with direct integration. If $y(0) = 0$, the solution in terms of $C(z)$ is

$$y(t) = \frac{1}{2}\sqrt{2\pi}\, C\left(\frac{\sqrt{2}x}{\sqrt{\pi}}\right) \qquad (1\text{--}51)$$

To obtain the indefinite integral in Equation 1–51, see Table 1–3.

The function fresnelC(x) is the MATLAB and Maple function for the Fresnel cosine integral. The functions $C(x)$ and FresnelC(x) are the corresponding MuPAD and Mathematica functions.

Computer packages use series representations of the special functions to evaluate them numerically. To compute the definite integral $y(\sqrt{2\pi})$, see Table 1–4. The result obtained to six decimal places from all programs is $y(\sqrt{2\pi}) = 0.611935$.

TABLE 1–3

Computer Evaluation of the Indefinite Fresnel Cosine Integral

MATLAB

```
syms x
int(cos(x^2),x)
```

Result

$$\frac{1}{2}\sqrt{2\pi}\ \text{fresnelC}\left(\frac{\sqrt{2}x}{\sqrt{\pi}}\right)$$

MuPAD

```
int(cos(x^2), x)
```

Result

$$\frac{1}{2}\sqrt{2\pi}\,C\left(\frac{\sqrt{2}x}{\sqrt{\pi}}\right)$$

Maple

```
int(cos(x^2), x)
```

Result

$$\frac{1}{2}\sqrt{2\pi}\ \text{fresnelC}\left(\frac{\sqrt{2}x}{\sqrt{\pi}}\right)$$

Mathematica

```
Integrate[Cos[x^2],x]
```

Result

$$\sqrt{\frac{\pi}{2}}\ \text{FresnelC}\left(\sqrt{\frac{2}{\pi}}x\right)$$

TABLE 1–4

Computer Evaluation of the Definite Fresnel Cosine Integral at $x = \sqrt{2\pi}$

MATLAB

```
int(cos(x^2),x, 0, sqrt(2*pi));
double(ans)
```

MuPAD

```
int(cos(x^2), x):
subs(%, x = sqrt(2*PI)):
float(%)
```

Maple

```
evalf(int(cos(x^2),t=0..sqrt(2*pi))
```

Mathematica

```
Integrate[Cos[x^2],{x,0,Sqrt[2*Pi]}]//N
```

Numerical Integration

We have seen several examples of the application of direct integration to solve a differential equation of the form $dy/dx = f(x)$. The solution can be expressed formally as

$$y(x) = \int_{x_0}^{x} f(u)\,du + y(x_0) \tag{1–52}$$

There are cases where the integral cannot be expressed in closed form or by a special function, and we must resort to numerical evaluation of the integral. We now summarize some ways this can be accomplished. Recall from calculus that an integral represents the area under a curve and that the simplest way to compute the area is to split it into rectangles and sum their individual areas (Figure 1–32a). If the widths of the rectangles are small enough, the sum of their areas gives the approximate value of the integral. This method is called *rectangular integration*.

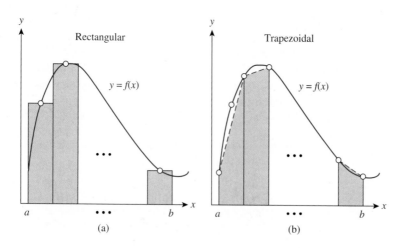

FIGURE 1–32

Illustration of (a) rectangular and (b) trapezoidal numerical integration.

A more sophisticated method is to use trapezoidal elements (Figure 1–32b). MATLAB implements trapezoidal integration with the `trapz` function. Its syntax is `trapz(x,y)`, where the array `y` contains the function values at the points contained in the array `x`. You cannot directly specify a function to integrate with the `trapz` function; you must first compute and store the function's values ahead of time in an array. MATLAB also has the `quad` function, which can accept a function directly. However, it cannot handle arrays of values. So, the functions complement each other.

Recall from calculus that another approach to numerical integration is *Simpson's rule*, which divides the integration range into an even number of panels and uses a different quadratic function to represent the integrand for each panel. A quadratic function has three parameters, and Simpson's rule computes these parameters by requiring that the quadratic pass through the function's three points corresponding to the two adjacent panels. To obtain greater accuracy, polynomials of a degree higher than 2 can be used. The MATLAB function `quad` implements an adaptive version of Simpson's rule by varying the panel width. The term *quad* is an abbreviation of *quadrature*, which is a term for the process of measuring areas.

The MATLAB function `quad(f,a,b)` computes the integral of the function `f` between the limits *a* and *b*. The input `f`, which represents the integrand $f(x)$, is either a function handle of the integrand function (the preferred method) or the name of the function as a character string (i.e., placed in single quotes). The function $y = f(x)$ must accept a vector argument *x* and must return the vector result *y*. Because the `quad` function calls the integrand function using vector arguments, you must always use array operations when defining the function.

The following example shows how this is done.

TABLE 1–5

MATLAB Function for $x \tan x$

```
function xt = xtan(x)
xt = x.*tan(x);
```

EXAMPLE 1–16   Numerical Evaluation of an Integral

Determine the solution of Equation 1–53 at $x = 1$ if $y(0) = 0$.

$$y' = x \tan(x) \tag{1–53}$$

SOLUTION   The equation can be solved with direct integration.

$$y(1) = \int_0^1 x \tan(x)\,dx \tag{1–54}$$

Unfortunately, this integral does not have a closed-form solution (a computer package will express the answer in terms of an infinite series). Thus, we must use a numerical method. We demonstrate two ways to use the `quad` function.

1. To use a function file, define the integrand with a user-defined function, as shown by the function file in Table 1–5.
    The quad function is called as follows: `quad(@xtan,0,1)`. The result is $y(1) = 0.4281$.
2. Using an anonymous function, the program is

$$\texttt{quad(@(x)x.*tan(x),0,1)}$$

The result is $y(1) = 0.4281$. The advantage of using an anonymous function is that you need not create and save a function file. However, for complicated integrand functions, using a function file is preferable.

Table 1–6 shows how to use the other packages to evaluate this integral. Because of numerical round-off error, you may obtain a result having a very small imaginary part, which we have ignored.

TABLE 1–6

Computer Evaluation of the Definite Integral Given by Equation 1–54

MATLAB Symbolic Math Toolbox

```
syms x
int(x*tan(x),x, 0, 1);
double(ans)
```

MuPAD

```
int(x*tan(x), x):
subs(%, x = 1):
float(%)
```

Maple

```
evalf(Int(x*tan(x),x=0..1))
```

Mathematica

```
Integrate[x*Tan[x],{x,0,1}]//N
```

Result for all programs:
0.4281

Considerations for Computer Solution of a Differential Equation

The best method for solving a differential equation depends on several considerations.

1. Is a closed-form (symbolic) solution required, or is it acceptable to obtain a numerical solution at only a single point or as a plot? Often it requires some effort to obtain a closed-form solution, even if one is obtainable. If the end result is only used to obtain the solution at a single point or to plot the solution, then it is usually easier to use a computer program to solve the equation numerically.

2. If a closed-form solution is required, are the initial conditions, boundary conditions, or equation constants given as specific numerical values or in general form? The solution for some equations has different forms for different initial conditions, boundary conditions, or different parameter values. For example, consider the equation $dy/dt = c^2 - y^2(t)$, where c is a constant. If $y^2(0) \neq c^2$ and $c \neq 0$, the solution is

$$y(t) = c\frac{1 + Ae^{-2ct}}{1 - Ae^{-2ct}} \qquad A = \frac{y(0) - c}{y(0) + c} \qquad \text{(1–55)}$$

However, if $c = 0$, the solution has a different form, which is

$$y(t) = \frac{y(0)}{1 + y(0)t} \tag{1-56}$$

3. If a closed-form solution is required but the equation is not solvable (as is the case with many nonlinear equations), consider replacing the nonlinear equation with a linear equation by using a suitable approximation for the nonlinear term. For example, consider the equation $y' + y + 4\sin y = 0$. If y is small, we may replace $\sin y$ with y using the first nonzero term in the Taylor series expansion for $\sin y \approx y - y^3/6 + \cdots$. The differential equation becomes $y' + 5y = 0$, whose solution is $y(x) = y(0)e^{-5x}$ as long as y is small.

4. Computer symbolic solutions are not yet infallible, so be sure to check the solution by substituting it into the differential equation and by checking to see if it satisfies the initial or the boundary conditions.

Section Review

1–29C Can every integral be found in an extensive table of integrals? Why or why not?

1–30C Define symbolic processing.

1–31C Can every linear first-order, ordinary differential equation be solved in closed form? Why or why not?

1–8 ▪ SUMMARY

An equation that involves the derivatives or differentials of one or more functions is called a *differential equation.*

Variables and Functions A quantity that can assume various values during a study is called a *variable.* A variable whose value can be changed arbitrarily is called an *independent variable or argument.* A variable whose value depends on the value of other variables and thus cannot be varied independently is called a *dependent variable* or a *function.* The range of values a variable can assume between the two specified numbers constitute the *interval* of that variable.

Origin of Differential Equations The description of most scientific problems involves relations that relate the *changes* in some key variables to each other. Usually, the smaller the chosen increment of the independent variable, the more general and accurate is the description. In the limiting case of *infinitesimal changes* in variables, we obtain differential equations that provide precise mathematical formulations for the physical principles and laws by representing the rates of changes as derivatives.

Continuity A function y is said to be *continuous* at a number a if (1) the function is defined at that number, (2) the limit $\lim_{x \to a} y(x)$ exists, and (3) this limit is equal to the value of the function at a. If a function is not continuous at a, then

it is said to be *discontinuous* at a or to have a *discontinuity* at a. A function is said to be continuous on an interval if it is continuous at every number in that interval.

Derivatives The **derivative** of a function y at a point is equivalent to the slope of the tangent line to the graph of the function at that point and is defined as

$$y'(x) = \lim_{\Delta x \to 0} \frac{y(x + \Delta x) - y(x)}{\Delta x} = \lim_{\Delta x \to 0} \frac{\Delta y}{\Delta x} = \frac{dy}{dx}$$

A function is said to be *differentiable* at x if this limit exists. A function is said to be differentiable on an interval if it is differentiable at every number in that interval. The increment Δx of the independent variable x is also represented by dx, which is called the *differential* of the independent variable. Then the differential dy of the dependent variable y is defined as $dy = y'(x)dx$.

When a function depends on two or more independent variables, it is possible to take the derivative of the function with respect to one variable while holding the other variables constant. Such derivatives are called partial derivatives and are denoted using the symbol ∂. For functions that depend on a single variable only, the partial derivatives and the ordinary derivatives are identical. The inverse process of differentiation is *integration*. The order of a derivative decreases by one each time it is integrated.

Differential Equations   A differential equation that involves only ordinary derivatives of one or more dependent variables with respect to a single independent variable is called an *ordinary differential equation*, and a differential equation that involves partial derivatives with respect to two or more independent variables is called a *partial differential equation*. Therefore, problems that involve a single independent variable result in ordinary differential equations, and problems that involve two or more independent variables result in partial differential equations.

Classification of Ordinary Differential Equations   The order of the highest derivative in an equation is the *order* of that differential equation. A differential equation is said to be in the *standard form* if the coefficient of its highest derivative is one. A differential equation is said to be *linear* if the dependent variable and all of its derivatives are of the first degree and if their coefficients depend on the independent variable only. In other words, a differential equation is linear if it can be written in a form that does not involve (1) any powers of the dependent variable or its derivatives, (2) any products of the dependent variable or its derivatives, and (3) any other nonlinear functions of the dependent variable. Otherwise, it is *nonlinear*. A linear differential equation of order n can be expressed in the most general form as

$$y^{(n)} + f_1(x)y^{(n-1)} + \cdots + f_{n-1}(x)y + f_n(x)y = R(x)$$

A differential equation that cannot be put into this form is nonlinear.

A linear differential equation in y is said to be *homogeneous* as well if $R(x) = 0$. Otherwise, it is *nonhomogeneous*. A differential equation is said to have *constant coefficients* if the coefficients of all the terms that involve the dependent variable or its derivatives are constants. If, after cleared of any common factors, any of the terms with the dependent variable or its derivatives involve the independent variable as a coefficient, that equation is said to have *variable coefficients*.

Differential equation models that involve two or more unknown functions in two or more coupled differential equations are called *systems of differential equations*.

Classification of Solutions   Differential equations may have multiple solutions. Any function that satisfies the differential equation on an interval is called a *solution* of that differential equation. A solution that involves one or more arbitrary constants represents a family of functions that satisfy the differential equation and is called a *general solution* of that equation.

A solution is referred to as *the general solution or the complete solution* if every solution of the equation can be obtained by assigning particular values to the arbitrary constants.

Such a solution is called a *particular solution* or a *specific solution*. A solution that cannot be obtained from the general solution by assigning particular values to the arbitrary constants is called a *singular solution*.

When solving a differential equation, it is very desirable to obtain a closed-form solution. If the unknown function can be expressed in terms of the independent variable, then the solution is said to be *explicit*; otherwise, the solution is *implicit*.

Initial Conditions and Boundary Conditions   To obtain a unique solution to a problem, we need to specify some conditions in addition to the governing differential equation. These conditions are called *initial conditions* if all of them are specified at the same value of the independent variable and *boundary conditions* if they are specified at two or more values of the independent variable. A differential equation accompanied by a set of initial conditions is called an *initial-value problem*; whereas, a differential equation accompanied by a set of boundary conditions is called a *boundary-value problem*.

Solution by Direct Integration   A differential equation involves derivatives of various orders of a function, and thus, integration is often utilized in the solution of a differential equation. The differential equations that have a single term that involves derivatives and no terms that involve the unknown function as a factor can be solved by *direct integration, assuming* the integrations can be performed.

When solving a differential equation by direct integration, all of the terms in the equation are integrated one by one using the rules of integration, and an integration constant is added. Even when a differential equation cannot be solved by direct integration, it may still be possible to reduce its order by successive integrations.

Computer Methods   Computer programs are useful for solving problems of the type encountered in this chapter. These tasks include plotting solutions, performing symbolic evaluation of the integrals required to solve equations using the direct integration method, interpreting solutions in terms of the special functions of mathematics, and numerical evaluation of integrals. *Symbolic processing* describes how a computer program produces a solution to a problem in symbolic or closed form; that is, as a mathematical formula. Symbolic processing programs can perform algebraic and trigonometric manipulations, solve algebraic and differential equations, and evaluate integrals, for example.

Some integrals cannot be evaluated in closed form, but they have been approximated with infinite series. The resulting functions are called the *special functions of mathematics* to distinguish them from the elementary functions (such as the exponential, logarithmic, and trigonometric functions). They can be evaluated with the popular computer programs. However, there are cases where the integral cannot be expressed in closed form or by a special function, and we must resort to numerical evaluation of the integral. Computer packages provide several ways of doing this.

Choice of Solution Method The best method for solving a differential equation depends on several considerations. Is a closed-form (symbolic) solution required, or is it acceptable to obtain a numerical solution only at a single point or as a plot? If a closed-form solution is required, are the initial conditions, boundary conditions, or equation constants given as specific numerical values or in general form?

The solution for some equations has different forms for different initial or boundary conditions, or different parameter values. If a closed-form solution is required but the equation is not solvable (as is the case with many nonlinear equations), consider replacing the nonlinear equation with a linear equation by using a suitable approximation for the nonlinear term, such as $\sin \theta \approx \theta$ for θ small.

PROBLEMS

1–1 Differential Equations in Sciences and Engineering

1–32C Discuss when it is more appropriate to use a rather simplistic model in place of a more realistic but very complex model.

1–2 How Do Differential Equations Arise?

1–33 A rock of mass m is thrown up into the air from the ground with a specified initial velocity V_i at time zero. Using Newton's second law of motion, obtain a differential equation that describes the position z of the rock relative to the ground level as a function of time. Take the upward direction to be positive.

1–34 A heavy object of mass m is suspended in a room through a linear spring whose spring constant is k. Initially, the object is supported so that the spring is at its free length (neither stretched nor compressed), which is taken to be $x = 0$. At time zero, the support is removed, and the object is allowed to oscillate under the combined influence of both gravity and spring forces. Using Newton's second law of motion, obtain the differential equation that describes the position x of the mass m relative to the undisturbed endpoint of the spring as a function of time.

1–35 Consider a small, hot metal object that is initially ($t = 0$) at a temperature of $T_i = 200°C$. The object is allowed to cool in an environment at $T_0 = 25°C$. The specific heat of the object is $c = 0.45$ kJ/kg°C and the convection heat-transfer coefficient during the process is $h = 0.01$ $kW/m^2°C$. Derive the differential equation that describes the temperature of the ball as a function of time, $T(t)$.

1–36 It is observed that (for some periods of time) the rate of change of population of human societies, animal species, insects, and bacteria colonies increases at a rate proportional to the population itself. Letting $N(t)$ denote the population at time t and k be the constant of proportionality, obtain the differential equation that describes the change in population with time.

1–37 It has been observed that radioactive materials (such as plutonium, radium, and the carbon isotope C^{14}) naturally decay to form another element or another isotope of the same element at a rate proportional to the amount of the radioactive material present. Letting $M(t)$ be the amount of the radioactive material at the time t and k be a positive constant that represents the fraction of the material that decays per unit time, obtain the differential equation that describes the change in M with time.

1–3 A Brief Review of Basic Concepts

1–38C Can an equation involve more than one independent variable? Can it involve more than one dependent variable? Give examples.

1–39C What is the geometrical interpretation of derivatives?

1–40C Consider a function $f(x)$ whose tangent line becomes parallel to the x-axis at $x = 5$. What can you say about the first derivative of the function at that point?

1–41C Consider a function $f(x)$ whose tangent line makes an angle of 45° with the x-axis at $x = 0$. What can you say about the first derivative of the function at that point?

1–42C Consider a function $f(x)$ whose tangent line becomes perpendicular to the x-axis at $x = 2$. What can you say about the first derivative of the function at that point?

1–43C Consider a function $f(x, y)$ and its partial derivative $(\partial f/\partial y)_x$. Under what conditions is this partial derivative equal to the total derivative df/dy?

1–44C Consider a function $f(x)$ and its derivative df/dx. Will this derivative still be a function of x?

1–45C An ideal gas is a gas that obeys the relation $Pv = RT$, where P is the absolute pressure, v is the specific volume (or inverse of density), T is the absolute temperature, and R is the gas constant. For an ideal gas, show that (a) the $P = $ constant lines on a $T–v$ diagram are straight lines and (b) the high pressure lines are steeper than the low pressure lines.

1–46C How is integration related to differentiation?

Determine the intervals in which the following functions are continuous.

1–47 (a) $x^2 - 1$ (b) $\sqrt{x}$

     (c) $\dfrac{x}{\sin 2x}$ (d) $\dfrac{e^{2x}}{x(x-1)}$

1–48 (a) -2 (b) xe^{3x}

     (c) $\dfrac{\cos x}{x^2}$ (d) $\dfrac{x^2}{e^x - 4}$

1–49 Consider a gas that obeys the van der Waals equation of state given as $(P + a/v^2)(v - b) = RT$, where P is the absolute pressure, v is the specific volume (or inverse of density), T is the absolute temperature, R is the gas constant, and a and b are two constants. Derive a relation for the slope of the $v = $ constant lines on a $T–P$ diagram for this gas.

1–50 Plot a function $f(x)$ in the interval $0 < x < 5$ such that (a) its first derivative is always negative, (b) its first and second derivatives are always positive, and (c) its first and second derivatives are always positive (except at $x = 3$, where both derivatives are zero).

1–51 Plot a function $f(x)$ in the interval $0 < x < 5$ such that (a) its first derivative is always positive, (b) its first and second derivatives are always negative, and (c) its first and second derivatives are always negative (except at $x = 3$, where both derivatives are zero).

1–52 Determine the ordinary and partial derivatives of the function $f = 5x^2 \sin 2t + xe^{-2x} - 4t$ with respect to x.

1–53 Take the derivatives of the following functions with respect to x. (*Note*: x and t are independent variables.)

     (a) $f_1 = 7x^4 - \sin 3x^3 + 2e^{-3x}$
     (b) $f_2 = 7x^4 - t \sin 3x^3 + t^2 e^{-3x}$
     (c) $f_3 = 7x^4 - x \sin 3t^3 + t^2 e^{-3t}$

1–54 Take the derivatives of the functions in Problem 1–53 with respect to t.

Determine the derivative of the following functions.

1–55 (a) $\ln(x^2 + 1)$ (b) $x^4 \cos 2x$

     (c) $\dfrac{5x}{2x^3 \sin x}$ (d) $\ln(e^{2x})$

1–56 (a) $e^{2x}(2x - 1)^2$ (b) $xe^{3x} \sin 2x$

     (c) $\dfrac{x^2}{\ln x^2}$ (d) $\dfrac{x \cos 2x}{\sqrt{\ln x^2}}$

Perform the following integrations.

1–57 (a) $\displaystyle\int_1^3 [x^{2t} + \sin 2\omega t + 3t^2 x] dx$

     (b) $\displaystyle\int [y''(x) + 3e^{-2tx} + \cosh 2\omega x] dx$

1–58 (a) $\displaystyle\int \left[\dfrac{a}{x^3} - x \cos 3x + x^2 e^{-2x} \right] dx$

     (b) $\displaystyle\int_{-1}^1 [xe^{-3x} + \sinh 2x - 1] dx$

     (c) $\displaystyle\int_3^x [y'(x) + t \ln 2x] dx$

     (d) $\displaystyle\int [2y''(x)y'''(x) + \sin x \cosh \omega t] dx$

1–59 (a) $\displaystyle\int [3x^4 + xe^{2x} + \cosh 3x] dx$

     (b) $\displaystyle\int_2^4 \left[\dfrac{a}{x} + 4 \sin 3x \cos 3x - \sinh 2x \right] dx$

     (c) $\displaystyle\int_x^8 [y''(x) + t^3 \sin 2\omega x + e^{-2tx}] dx$

     (d) $\displaystyle\int \left[4y(x)y'(x) + xy''(x) + \dfrac{be^{-3t}}{x^2} \right] dx$

1–4   Classification of Differential Equations

1–60C How do you recognize a linear, homogeneous differential equation?

1–61C How do differential equations with constant coefficients differ from those with variable coefficients?

1–62C Consider a function $y(x)$ and its slope $y' = 5$. Is this relation a differential equation? Explain.

Determine the order of each of the differential equations below, whether they are linear or nonlinear, and whether they have constant or variable coefficients.

1–63 (a) $y'' + 2y' = \sin x + 1$

     (b) $y''' + y'e^{-2x} \sin x = 0$

     (c) $y''' + y'' \sin 2x + x^4 y = 0$

     (d) $xy'' + 3xy' - xy = \sin 3x$

     (e) $y'' + e^{2x-y} = 0$

1–64 (a) $y' + 7y' = xe^{-2x}$

     (b) $y' + x^3 y = 0$

     (c) $y'' + 3y' + e^{-3x}y = 0$

     (d) $yy'' + 2xe^x y'y - 5y = 0$

     (e) $y''' + 2y'' + e^x \sin y = 0$

1–5 Solutions of Differential Equations

1–65C How do the solutions of algebraic and differential equations differ?

1–66C Clarify the difference between *a solution* of a differential equation and *the general solution* of a differential equation.

1–67C What is the difference between the implicit and the explicit solutions of a differential equation?

Show that the given functions are solutions of the given differential equation in each problem.

1–68 $x^2y'' - 2xy' - 4y = 0$, $y_1 = e^{-\ln x}$, and $y_2 = x^4$

1–69 $y'' + y = 0$, $y_1 = \sin x$, and $y_2 = \dfrac{\sin 2x}{\sin x}$

1–70 $x^2y'' + 5xy' + 4y = 0$, $y_1 = \dfrac{1}{x^2}$, and $y_2 = \dfrac{\ln x}{x^2}$

1–71 $y'' - y = 0$, $y_1 = e^x$, $y_2 = e^{-x}$, and $y_3 = \cosh x$

1–72 $x^2y'' + 3xy' + y = 0$, $y_1 = \dfrac{1}{x}$, $y_2 = \dfrac{\ln x}{x}$, and $y_3 = e^{-\ln x} \ln x$

1–73 $y'' - 4y' + 4y = 0$, $y_1 = e^{2x}$, $y_2 = xe^{2x}$, and $y_3 = 5xe^{-\ln x}e^{2x}$

1–74 $y'' - 2y' + 3y = 0$, $y_1 = e^x \sin \sqrt{2}x$, and $y_2 = 3e^x(\sin \sqrt{2}x + \cos \sqrt{2}x)$

1–75 $y'' - 9y = 0$, $y_1 = e^{3x}$, $y_2 = e^{-3x}$, and $y_3 = e^{5-3x}$

1–76 A rock of mass m is thrown up in to the air from the ground with a specified initial velocity V_i at time zero. Taking the z axis to be the vertical upward direction with its origin at the initial position of the rock, obtain two mathematical expressions to serve as initial conditions to the governing differential equation for the function $z(t)$, where t is the independent variable time.

1–77 Consider a parachute cruising in the air downward at a constant velocity of V_0 starting at time zero. The motion of the parachute can be described by a second-order linear differential equation for $z(t)$, where z is the vertical distance of the parachute from the ground level and t is the independent variable time. If it is known that the parachute hits the ground at time t_0, obtain two mathematical expressions to serve as the boundary conditions for the governing differential equation.

1–6 Solving Differential Equations by Direct Integration

1–78C Consider a fifth-order linear and nonhomogeneous differential equation that can be solved by direct integration. How many arbitrary constants will the solution involve?

Determine which of the following differential equations can be solved by direct integration. Obtain the general solution of those that can.

1–79 (a) $y'' = 0$ (b) $y'' + 4ye^{-3x} = 0$

(c) $y'' - 4xe^{-4x}y = 0$ (d) $y'' - xy = 0$

(e) $4y'y'' - 8x^3 = 0$

1–80 (a) $y''' = 0$ (b) $y''' - 5y = 0$

(c) $y''' - 5x = 0$ (d) $y''' - y'' = 0$

(e) $2y''y''' - 8e^{-2x} = 0$

1–81 (a) $y'' - ax = 0$ (b) $y''' + 4y \sinh 2x = 0$

(c) $y'' - b \ln ax = 0$ (d) $y' - e^y \cos x = 0$

(e) $xy'y'' - 8x^4 = 0$

1–7 Introduction to Computer Methods

1–82C Describe a situation where the closed-form solution of a differential equation is not needed because the plot of the solution contains enough information.

1–83C How small must θ be (in radians) for the approximation as $\sin \theta \approx \theta$ to be accurate to 5%?

1–84 Plot the solution $V(t) = (\sqrt{V(0)} - 0.0215t)^2$ developed in Example 1–15, where $V(t)$ is the liquid volume in the pot in cups. Use $V(0) = 36$ cups. Plot the solution until $V(t) = 0$.

1–85 The function $y = -2xe^{2x} + 2x - 3$ is the solution of the differential equation

$$y'' - 4y' + 4y = 8x - 20$$

For the initial conditions, use $y(0) = -3$, $y'(0) = -2$. Plot the solution for $0 \le x \le 1$.

1–86 The equation

$$\frac{dy}{dx} = x^2e^{-2x}$$

has the solution

$$y(x) = \frac{1}{4} - \frac{1}{4}e^{-2x}(1 + 2x + 2x^2) + y(0)$$

Plot the solutions for three values of $y(0)$: 0, 5, and 10 on the same graph. Choose an appropriate upper limit for x.

1–87 Solve the following equation to obtain the value $y(\sqrt{2\pi})$ if $y(0) = 0$.

$$y' = \sin x^2$$

1-88 Use a computer package to evaluate numerically the following integral.

$$\int_0^1 \sqrt{x^4 + 5}$$

1-89 Use a computer package to obtain the closed-form solution of the integrals given in Problem 1-57.

1-90 Use a computer package to obtain the closed-form solution of the integrals given in Problem 1-58.

1-91 Use a computer package to obtain the closed-form solution of the integrals given in Problem 1-59.

1-92 Use a computer package to obtain the closed-form solutions of the equations given in Problem 1-79.

1-93 Use a computer package to obtain the closed-form solutions of the equations given in Problem 1-80.

1-94 Use a computer package to obtain the closed-form solutions of the equations given in Problem 1-81.

Review Problems

Determine the values of m for which the given differential equations have a solution of the form e^{mx}.

1-95 (a) $y'' + y = 0$
(b) $y'' + 2y' + y = 0$
(c) $y'' - y = 0$

1-96 (a) $y'' + \lambda^2 y = 0$
(b) $y'' - 4y' + 4y = 0$
(c) $y'' - \lambda^2 y = 0$

1-97 (a) $y'' + 5y' + 4y = 0$
(b) $y'' + 6y' + 9y = 0$
(c) $y'' + y' + 3y = 0$

1-98 (a) $y'' - 6y' + 9y = 0$
(b) $y'' + 3y' + 4y = 0$
(c) $y'' - 6y' + 4y = 0$

1-99 (a) $y'' + 10y' + 25y = 0$
(b) $y'' + 5y' + 25y = 0$
(c) $y'' + 10y' - 25y = 0$

Determine the values of r for which the given differential equations have a solution of the form x^r.

1-100 (a) $x^2 y'' + y = 0$
(b) $x^2 y'' + xy' = 0$

1-101 (a) $x^2 y'' + 3xy' - 2y = 0$
(b) $x^2 y'' + xy' - 2y = 0$

1-102 (a) $2x^2 y'' + 6y' + 2y = 0$
(b) $x^2 y'' - y = 0$

1-103 (a) $-2x^2 y'' + 6xy' - 12y = 0$
(b) $x^2 y'' + 5xy' + 4y = 0$

1-104 A rock is thrown up into the air from the ground with a specified initial velocity of $V_i = 15$ m/s at time zero. The governing differential equation of this process is

$$\frac{d^2 z(t)}{dt^2} = -g$$

where z is the vertical upward direction with its origin at the initial position of the rock and g is the gravitational acceleration. By solving the differential equation and applying the boundary conditions, obtain a general relation for $z(t)$, and determine the position of the rock after 3 s for $g = 9.81$ m/s².

1-105 Consider a parachute cruising in the air downward at a constant velocity of V_0 starting at time zero at a height of 20 m above the ground. The motion of the parachute can be described by the differential equation

$$\frac{dz(t)}{dt} = a$$

where z is the vertical distance of the parachute from the ground level, t is the independent variable time, and a is a constant. If it is known that the parachute hits the ground at time $t_0 = 8$ s, determine the value of a and obtain the function $z(t)$ by solving the governing differential equation.

1-106 Consider a homogeneous, spherical radioactive material of radius $R = 0.04$ m, which is generating heat at a constant rate of $g_0 = 4 \times 10^7$ W/m³. The heat generated is dissipated to the environment steadily. The outer surface of the sphere is maintained at a uniform temperature of 80°C, and the thermal conductivity of the sphere is $k = 15$ W/m°C. The sphere temperature changes in the radial direction only, and thus, $T = T(r)$. The temperature distribution within the sphere is governed by the differential equation

$$\frac{1}{r^2}\frac{d}{dr}\left(r^2\frac{dT(r)}{dr}\right) + \frac{g_0}{k} = 0$$

Solving this differential equation and applying appropriate boundary conditions, obtain a relation for the temperature distribution $T(r)$ in the sphere. Also, determine the temperature in the middle of the sphere.

1–107 A long, homogeneous resistance wire of radius $R = 5$ mm is being used to heat the air in a room by the passage of electric current. Heat is generated in the wire uniformly as a result of resistance heating at a rate of $g_0 = 5 \times 10^7$ W/m^3. If the temperature of the outer surface of the wire remains at 180°C, determine the temperature at $r = 2.5$ mm after steady operation conditions are reached. Take the thermal conductivity of the wire to be $k = 8$ W/m°C. The temperature distribution within wire is governed by the differential equation

$$\frac{1}{r}\frac{d}{dr}\left(r\frac{dT(r)}{dr}\right) + \frac{g_0}{k} = 0$$

1–108 Consider a large plane wall of thickness $L = 0.2$ m. The surfaces of the wall are maintained at temperatures $T_1 = 80$°C and $T_2 = 10$°C at $x = 0$ and $x = L$, respectively. There is no heat generation in the wall. The temperature within the wall varies in the x direction only and is governed by the differential equation

$$\frac{d^2T(x)}{dx^2} = 0$$

Develop a relation for the steady-state temperature distribution $T(x)$ in the wall.

1–109 Consider a large plane wall of thickness $L = 0.5$ m. The wall surface at $x = 0$ is insulated, while the surface at $x = L$ is maintained at a temperature of 30°C. The thermal conductivity of the wall is $k = 30$ W/m°C, and heat is generated in the wall at a rate of $g(x) = g_0 e^{0.02x}$, where $g_0 = 7 \times 10^4$ W/m^3. The temperature within the wall varies in the x direction only and is governed by the differential equation

$$\frac{d^2T(x)}{dx^2} + \frac{g(x)}{k} = 0$$

Develop a relation for the steady-state temperature distribution $T(x)$ in the wall, and determine the temperature of the insulated surface. (*Note*: At an insulated surface, the temperature gradient dT/dx is zero.)

1–110 Chemists and engineers must be able to predict the changes in chemical concentration in a reaction. A model used for many single-reactant processes is

$$\text{Rate of change of chemical concentration} = \frac{dC}{dt} = -kC^n$$

where C is the chemical concentration and k is the rate constant. The order of the reaction is the value of the exponent n.

(a) Suppose that $n = 2$. In this case, the differential equation for C is nonlinear. Sometimes we can obtain a solution more easily by transforming variables. Use the substitution $y(t) = 1/C(t)$ to convert the differential equation into a linear equation, solve the equation for y, and then find the solution in terms of C.

(b) Obtain the solution by another method.

(c) The following formula describes the gas-phase decomposition of nitrogen dioxide into nitric oxide and oxygen at 300°C, which is a second-order reaction ($n = 2$).

$$2NO_2 \rightarrow 2NO + O_2$$

From experimental data, the value of k was estimated to be $k = 0.5444$ per second. Determine the concentration after 5 s if $C(0) = 0.01$ mol/L.

1–111 A model used for many third-order, single-reactant processes is

$$\text{Rate of change of chemical concentration} = \frac{dC}{dt} = -kC^3$$

where C is the chemical concentration and k is the rate constant. This is a nonlinear equation.

(a) To obtain a linear equation, use the substitution $y(t) = 1/C^2$ to convert the differential equation into a linear equation, solve the equation for y, and then find the solution in terms of C.

(b) Obtain the solution by another method.

FIRST-ORDER DIFFERENTIAL EQUATIONS

I
n many practical problems, the rate of change (the first derivative) of a quantity depends on the quantity itself as well as on the independent variable. Such problems often can be described by the differential equation $y' = f(x, y)$, where y' is the first derivative and $f(x, y)$ represents the remaining terms.

The simple appearance of first-order differential equations may mislead some people to believe that they are easy to solve. Sometimes they are. But often, solving a first-order differential equation is no less challenging than solving a higher-order equation. No general method exists for solving all first-order differential equations exactly. The existing solution methods are applicable to certain classes of differential equations, and thus, it is necessary to classify and study them in separate groups.

In this chapter, we will learn how to recognize the different types of first-order differential equations and how to solve each type. First, we will consider *linear* first-order equations, since they always can be solved using a systematic approach. We then discuss applications of such equations. Then we will consider *nonlinear* equations and discuss the existence of solutions in a given region. In particular, we will examine equations that are either *separable, homogeneous*, or *exact*, because such equations can be solved analytically whether they are linear or not.

Some equations can be made exact through the use of *integrating factors*. Considering that the first derivative is simply the slope of the unknown function, approximate solution curves can be obtained by *graphical methods* even when the differential equation cannot be solved analytically. At the end of this chapter, we will describe a systematic approach for solving first-order equations. You will soon realize that solving a differential equation often requires certain tricks, manipulations, and ingenuity.

There are several available computer packages that can perform these manipulations for you in certain cases. At the end of this chapter, we show how to use these packages to obtain exact solutions and how to implement the graphical methods introduced earlier in the chapter.

Finally, when all else fails, we can use a computer to obtain a numerical solution to a differential equation. These methods are discussed in Chapter 9.

Objectives

When you have finished this chapter, you should be able to:

1. classify first-order differential equations as either separable, homogeneous, or exact,

2. use an integrating factor to solve a linear first-order differential equation,

3. solve a separable equation or an exact equation by direct integration, and

4. use a computer package to obtain closed form solutions of first-order differential equations with specified or unspecified initial conditions, and to generate contour and direction field plots.

2–1 ▪ AN OVERVIEW OF FIRST-ORDER DIFFERENTIAL EQUATIONS

By definition, first-order differential equations involve only first derivatives. Considering y to be the dependent variable (i.e., the function we want to determine) and x to be the independent variable, a first-order differential equation can be expressed in the most general form as

$$f(x, y, y') = 0 \qquad (2\text{–}1)$$

Thus, a first-order differential equation is *any* equation that involves the variables x, y, and y' in *any* form, such as

$$3y' + \sin(2xy') - 5x^2 y^2 + 3 = 0$$

In this chapter, we will limit the discussion to equations in which y' can be expressed explicitly in terms of x and y for simplicity. That is, we will consider equations of the form

$$y' = f(x, y) \qquad (2\text{–}2)$$

where $f(x, y)$ is a specified function. The first thought that comes to mind when solving Equation 2–2 is to *integrate* it and obtain

$$y = \int f(x, y)\,dx + C \qquad (2\text{–}3)$$

where C is the integration constant. The integration on the right side (in general) cannot be performed unless the function f depends on x only. Therefore, although integrating the differential equation removes the derivative, it does not give the solution in the real sense because the right side now involves the integral of the unknown function y. In other words, in most cases, integration merely converts a *differential* equation into an *integral* equation. For the special case of f being a function of x only or just being a constant, then $y' = f(x)$, and the solution of the differential equation is obtained by simply performing the indicated integration

$$y(x) = \int f(x)\,dx + C$$

Figure 2–1 gives a specific example.

Any general solution of a first-order differential equation will involve an arbitrary constant C. The specific solution of an initial-value problem is obtained by determining C using the initial condition expressed as

$$y = y_0 \quad \text{at} \quad x = x_0$$

or

$$y(x_0) = y_0 \qquad (2\text{–}4)$$

Recall that a first-order differential equation with an initial condition forms an initial-value problem.

You will see in the next section that the solution of linear equations is straightforward. But this is not the case for nonlinear equations (unless they are in certain forms such as exact, separable, or homogeneous).

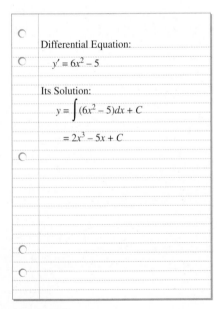

FIGURE 2–1

First-order differential equations of the form $y' = f(x)$ can be solved by direct integration.

Differential Equation:

$$y' = 6x^2 - 5$$

Its Solution:

$$y = \int (6x^2 - 5)\,dx + C$$

$$= 2x^3 - 5x + C$$

It is worth noting that when solving a first-order differential equation either x or y can be selected as the dependent variable. *Interchanging* the dependent and the independent variables sometimes may offer some simplification in the solution. For example, the nonlinear differential equation

$$\frac{dy}{dx} = y^2 \qquad (2\text{-}5)$$

also can be expressed for $y \neq 0$ as

$$\frac{dx}{dy} = \frac{1}{y^2}$$

which is linear in x. Figure 2–2 shows another example.

The solution methods for the first-order differential equations discussed here also can be used to solve higher-order equations if they involve two successive derivatives and they do not involve the unknown function as a factor. For example, by letting $u = y''$, the third-order differential equation

$$y''' + 3y'' = 5x^3 \qquad (2\text{-}6)$$

can be expressed as $u' + 3u = 5x^3$ which is a first-order equation in u. Once u is available, y can be determined by two successive integrations.

Section Review

Problems Denoted with a C are Conceptual Problems for Discussion

2–1C   What kind of differential equations are classified as being first-order?

2–2C   Can a first-order differential equation involve (a) y'', (b) y'^2, or (c) $\sqrt{(y')}$

2–2 ▪ LINEAR FIRST-ORDER EQUATIONS

A linear first-order differential equation can be expressed in general form as

$$y' + P(x)y = R(x) \qquad (2\text{-}7)$$

where P and R are two specified functions of x which are assumed to be continuous in the interval of interest. Note that a linear equation cannot involve any nonlinear terms (such as y', yy', y^3, or $\sin(y')^2$.

Integrating Factor

Equation 2–7 could be solved in a straightforward manner if we could somehow express its left side as the derivative of a single term. It turns out that we can always do that by multiplying the equation by a suitable factor. To determine this factor, we multiply Equation 2–7 by a function $\mu(x)$. This gives

$$\mu(x)y' + \mu(x)P(x)y = \mu(x)R(x) \qquad (2\text{-}8)$$

Noting that

$$[\mu(x)y]' = \mu(x)y' + \mu'(x)y \qquad (2\text{-}9)$$

and comparing it to Equation 2–8, we conclude that if the left side of Equation 2–7 is to be expressed as $[\mu(x)y]'$, then the function $\mu(x)$ must satisfy the condition $\mu'(x) = \mu(x)P(x)$.

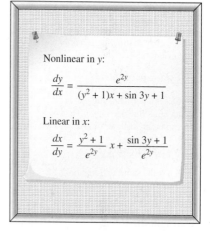

Nonlinear in y:

$$\frac{dy}{dx} = \frac{e^{2y}}{(y^2 + 1)x + \sin 3y + 1}$$

Linear in x:

$$\frac{dx}{dy} = \frac{y^2 + 1}{e^{2y}}x + \frac{\sin 3y + 1}{e^{2y}}$$

FIGURE 2–2

Some nonlinear equations can be made linear by simply interchanging the dependent and the independent variables.

Let $v(x)$ be another integrating factor that includes the integration constant C_1. Then,

$$\ln|v(x)| = \int P(x)dx + C_1$$

Take the exponential of both sides,

$$v(x) = e^{\int P(x)dx + C_1}$$

$$= e^{C_1} e^{\int P(x)dx}$$

$$= C_2\mu(x)$$

where $\mu(x)$ is given by Equation 2-10 and $C_2 = e^{C_1}$ is a constant which is never zero. Multiplying Equation 2-7 by $v(x)$ gives

$$[C_2\mu(x)y]' = C_2\mu(x)\,R(x)$$

But C_2 is a constant, and can be taken out of the derivative. Then C_2 can be divided out to give

$$[\mu(x)y]' = \mu(x)R(x)$$

which is the same as Equation 2-11.

FIGURE 2–3

Proof that the integration constant in the integrating factor can be taken to be zero without any loss in generality.

For $\mu(x) \neq 0$ on the interval under consideration, this equation can be rearranged as

$$\frac{\mu'(x)}{\mu(x)} = P(x)$$

Thus,

$$\int \frac{d\mu}{\mu} = \int P(x)\,dx$$

Then the function $\mu(x)$ is determined by integration to be

$$\ln|\mu(x)| = \int P(x)\,dx + C_1$$

Taking the exponential of both sides of this equation and noting that $e^{\ln\mu} = \mu$ for $\mu > 0$ yields

$$\mu(x) = e^{\int P(x)dx} \tag{2–10}$$

provided that the integral exists. Here we dropped the absolute value sign since the right side of Equation 2–10 is always positive, and thus, $\mu(x)$ must be a positive quantity. We also dropped the integration constant C because it need not to be included in this case, as illustrated in Figure 2–3.

The function $\mu(x)$ defined by Equation 2–10 is called an **integrating factor**. We can express Equation 2–7 with the help of the integrating factor, as shown in Figure 2–4. Thus,

$$[\mu(x)y]' = \mu(x)R(x) \tag{2–11}$$

which is in a readily integrable form. Integrating both sides yields

$$\mu(x)y = \int \mu(x)R(x)\,dx + C$$

Solving for y, we have

$$y = \frac{1}{\mu(x)}\left[\int \mu(x)R(x)\,dx + C\right] \tag{2–12}$$

where the integrating factor $\mu(x)$ is given by Equation 2–10, and the arbitrary constant C is to be determined from the initial condition. Equation 2–12 is of great significance, since it is an explicit relation for the general solution of first-order linear differential equations.

Note that Equation 2–7 is in the *standard form*, since the coefficient of y' is one. Therefore, when using this procedure for solving a differential equation, we should make sure that the equation is in the standard form before we attempt to identify $P(x)$ and determine the integrating factor $\mu(x)$ from Equation 2–10. Also note that $P(x)$ is the coefficient of y when it appears on the left side of the equation, and its sign must be included when determining the integrating factor, as shown in Figure 2–5. For example, $P(x) = -2x$ for the equation $y' - 2xy = 3$.

Linear Differential Equation:

$$y' + P(x)y = R(x)$$

Multiplying by $\mu(x)$ and rearranging,

$$[\mu(x)y]' = \mu(x)\,R(x)$$

FIGURE 2–4

Multiplying a first-order linear equation by the integrating factor $\mu(x)$ enables us to express its left side as the derivative of a single term.

The steps involved in the solution of first-order linear differential equations can be summarized as follows.

Step 1. Check to make sure that the coefficient of y' is one. If it is not, divide each term in the equation by that coefficient to make it one.

Step 2. Determine the integrating factor $\mu(x)$ from Equation 2–10, and mutiply the differential equation by it.

Step 3. Express the left side of the equation as $[\mu(x)y]'$, and integrate both sides of the equation.

Step 4. Divide the resulting equation by $\mu(x)$ to obtain an explicit expression for y.

Step 5. Apply the initial condition to determine the integration constant C.

Students are encouraged to master the method by actually carrying out the steps outlined here when solving a problem instead of simply using Equation 2–12 to determine the solution by direct substitution.

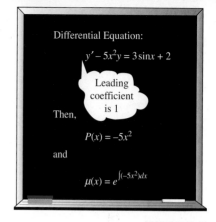

FIGURE 2–5

Proper identification of $P(x)$ when determining the integrating factor.

EXAMPLE 2–1   Use of an Integrating Factor

Solve the following linear initial-value problem:

$$y' - 3y = -9x$$

$$y(2) = 13$$

SOLUTION   Noting that the coefficient of y' is already one, we have $P(x) = -3$. Then the integrating factor is determined from Equation 2–10 to be

$$\mu(x) = e^{\int P(x)\,dx} = e^{\int (-3)\,dx} = e^{-3x}$$

Multiplying the differential equation by e^{-3x} yields

$$e^{-3x}y' - 3e^{-3x}y = -9xe^{-3x}$$

or

$$[e^{-3x}y]' = -9xe^{-3x} \qquad\qquad \text{(2–13)}$$

Integrating, we have

$$e^{-3x}y = \int (-9xe^{-3x})\,dx = e^{-3x}(3x + 1) + C$$

Solving for y, we have

$$y = 3x + 1 + Ce^{3x}$$

Applying the initial condition $y(2) = 13$, we have

$$13 = 3 \times 2 + 1 + Ce^{3\times 2} \rightarrow C = 6e^{-6}$$

Substituting, we have

$$y = 6e^{3x-6} + 3x + 1 \qquad\qquad \text{(2–14)}$$

which is the desired solution.

A Special Case: Equations with Constant Coefficients and Constant Right-Hand Side

Many problems of practical interest result in linear first-order differential equations with constant coefficients, and involve a constant on their right-hand side. Taking the leading coefficient to be $a = 1$, such equations can be expressed as

$$y' + by = c \qquad (2\text{--}15)$$

where b and c are constants. The solution of this differential equation with the initial condition $y(0) = y_0$ is obtained by the usual procedure to be

$$\mu(x) = e^{\int P(x)\,dx} = e^{\int b\,dx} = e^{bx}$$

$$e^{bx}\frac{dy}{dx} + e^{bx}by = ce^{bx}$$

$$\frac{d}{dx}\left[e^{bx}y\right] = ce^{bx}$$

$$e^{bx}y = \frac{c}{b}e^{bx} + C$$

$$y = \frac{c}{b} + Ce^{-bx} \qquad (2\text{--}16)$$

Applying the initial condition $y(0) = y_0$,

$$y_0 = \frac{c}{b} + C \rightarrow C = y_0 - \frac{c}{b}$$

Substituting,

$$y = \frac{c}{b}(1 - e^{-bx}) + y_0 e^{-bx} \qquad (2\text{--}17)$$

For the special case of $c = 0$ the solution reduces to

$$y = y_0 e^{-bx} \qquad (2\text{--}18)$$

For positive values of b, this equation represents exponential decay with x from the initial value of y_0. For negative values of b, it represents exponential growth. These results are summarized in Figure 2–6.

Initial-Value Problem:

$$y' + by = c$$
$$y(0) = y_0$$

Its Solution:

$$y = \frac{c}{b}(1 - e^{-bx}) + y_0 e^{-bx}$$

Special case: If $c = 0$, then

$$y = y_0 e^{-bx}$$

FIGURE 2–6

The solution of linear first-order differential equations with constant coefficients.

Existence and Uniqueness of Solutions

Our discussion of linear first-order differential equations will not be complete without a discussion on the generality of the solution given by Equation 2–12. This solution should be quite general and complete, considering that we started with the general form of the equation with general functions $P(x)$ and $R(x)$, requiring them only to be continuous. Thus we are justified in saying that a linear first-order differential equation *always* has a solution, and that *every* solution is included in Equation 2–12.

The foregoing demonstrations and arguments can be summarized in the following theorem on the *existence* and *uniqueness* of the solution of first-order linear differential equations.

THEOREM 2–1   Existence and Uniqueness for Linear First-Order Equations

If the functions $P(x)$ and $R(x)$ are continuous on the open interval I containing the point x_0, then the first-order linear differential equation

$$y' + P(x)y = R(x)$$

with

$$y(x_0) = y_0$$

has a unique solution on I, given by

$$y = \frac{1}{\mu(x)} \left[\int \mu(x)R(x)\,dx + C \right] \qquad \text{(Equation 2–12)}$$

where $\mu(x) = e^{\int P(x)\,dx}$ and the arbitrary constant C is determined from the initial condition $y(x_0) = y_0$, provided that the required integrations can be performed.

Theorem 2–1 clearly states that under the specified conditions the linear first-order initial-value problem *has* a solution, and that the solution is *unique*.

It is easy to verify that the differential Equation 2–7 has at least one solution by simply substituting Equation 2–12 into it. With the constant C determined from the initial condition, Equation 2–12 also represents a unique function (a continuous function in the open interval I passing through y_0). Further, all possible solutions of the differential equation are included in Equation 2–12. Therefore, Equation 2–12 represents *the general solution* of a linear first-order differential equation under the conditions of $P(x)$ and $R(x)$ being continuous. In other words, the differential Equation (2–7) has *no* singular solutions.

As an example, consider the differential equation $y' + 0.2y = 0$ in the interval $0 < x < \infty$. Its general solution is, from Equation 2–18, $y(x) = y_0 e^{-0.2x}$, and is plotted in Figure 2–7 for different values of y_0. Note that $P(x) = 0.2$

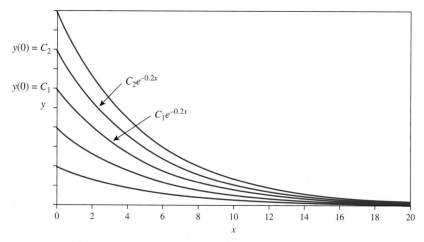

FIGURE 2–7

Solution curves of the differential equation $y' + 0.2y = 0$.

and $R(x) = 0$, which are continuous in the interval $0 < x < \infty$. Therefore, for a given initial condition $y(x_0) = y_0$, this differential equation has a unique solution, which is the solution curve passing through the point (x_0, y_0). In other words, no other solution curve will pass through the point (x_0, y_0). Also, the general solution $y(x) = Ce^{-0.2x}$ contains *all* the solutions to the differential equation, and thus there are no singular solutions.

Discontinuous Functions Probably you are wondering what will happen if the functions $P(x)$ or $R(x)$ are not continuous. First of all, Theorem 2–1 will still be applicable in any interval in which the functions $P(x)$ and $R(x)$ are continuous. Problems may arise only at the points of discontinuity. If the interval of interest lies on the part of the interval in which both $P(x)$ and $R(x)$ are continuous, then we can simply ignore any discontinuities in the functions since, as far as we are concerned, the functions $P(x)$ and $R(x)$ are continuous. Otherwise, we have to deal with discontinuities. This is illustrated below with an example.

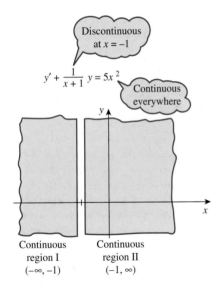

FIGURE 2–8

The coefficients $P(x)$ and $Q(x)$ of a differential equation can be treated as continuous in any region that does not include any points discontinuity.

EXAMPLE 2–2   Finding a Unique Solution

Solve the following initial-value problem:

$$(x + 1)y' + y = 5x^2(x + 1)$$

$$y(2) = 3$$

SOLUTION In its present form, the coefficient of y' is not one. Therefore, we first need to divide both sides of the equation by $x + 1$, which is the coefficient of y'. This yields

$$y' + \frac{1}{x + 1}y = 5x^2$$

Of course, this division is valid for $x + 1 \neq 0$ or $x \neq -1$.

Now we have $P(x) = 1/(x + 1)$ which is continuous everywhere except at $x = -1$, and $R(x) = 5x^2$ which is continuous over the entire real axis. Thus, we need to be careful when dealing with $P(x)$ at $x = -1$. We can avoid the point of discontinuity by choosing the interval to be either $-\infty < x < -1$ or $-1 < x < \infty$. By Theorem 2–1, an initial-value problem that involves the given differential equation has a unique solution in either interval (Figure 2–8). Considering that $x_0 = 2$ lies in the interval $-1 < x < \infty$, our initial-value problem will have a unique solution in that interval.

The solution of this linear first-order initial-value problem is determined by following the routine procedure,

$$\mu(x) = e^{\int P(x)dx} = e^{\int \frac{dx}{x+1}} = e^{\ln|x+1|} = |x + 1|$$

$$[\,|x + 1|y\,]' = |x + 1|5x^2dx$$

$$|x + 1|y = 5\int |x + 1|x^2dx + C$$

For $x > -1$, we have $|x + 1| = x + 1$. Then the solution in the interval $-1 < x < \infty$ becomes

$$(x + 1)y = 5\int (x^3 + x^2)dx + C = 5\left(\frac{x^4}{4} + \frac{x^3}{3}\right) + C$$

$$y = \frac{5x^3(3x + 4)}{12(x + 1)} + C$$

$$y(2) = 3 \rightarrow 3 = \frac{5 \times 8(6 + 4)}{12(2 + 1)} + \frac{C}{3} \rightarrow C = -\frac{73}{3}$$

Substituting,

$$y = \frac{5x^3(3x + 4)}{12(x + 1)} - \frac{73}{3(x + 1)}$$

which is the desired solution.

Discussion To gain a better understanding of the solution, we plot the *solution curves* in both intervals $-\infty < x < -1$ and $-1 < x < \infty$ in Figure 2–9. Each solution curve is a plot of the solution for a particular value of C, which depends on the given value of y at a particular value of x. Note that in either interval, only *one* curve passes through a specified x value, indicating the *uniqueness* of the solution of the initial-value problem in either interval in which both $P(x)$ and $R(x)$ are continuous. Also note that the solution curves diverge as $x \rightarrow -1$ from either direction.

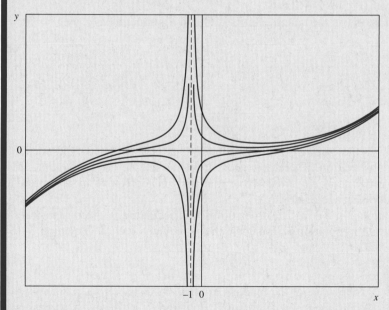

FIGURE 2–9
The solution curves of the linear differential equation discussed in Example 2–2.

Section Review

2–3C Under what conditions can a linear first-order differential equation be solved by direct integration?

2–4C What is the role of the integrating factor in the solution of first-order linear differential equations?

2–5C Under what conditions does a linear first-order initial-value problem have a solution? When is this solution unique?

2–6C Are the following equations linear?

(a) $y' + xe^y = 2$ (b) $y' - x^2y + xy^2 = 5$

2–7 Solve the following equations

(a) $y' - 3xy = 2x$ (b) $(1 - x^2)y' - 2y = 0$

(*Answers:* (a) $y = -\frac{2}{3} + Ce^{\frac{3}{2}x^2}$ (b) $= C\frac{x+1}{x-1}$)

2–8 Solve the following initial-value problems

(a) $y' + y = 0$ $y(0) = 1$ (b) $y' + 3(y - 1) = 2x$ $y(0) = 4$

(*Answers:* (a) $y = e^{-x}$ (b) $y = \frac{7}{9} + \frac{2}{3}x + \frac{29}{9}e^{-3x}$)

2–3 ▪ APPLICATIONS OF FIRST-ORDER LINEAR EQUATIONS

In many problems encountered in physical, biological, and social sciences it is observed that the rate of change of a quantity is proportional to the quantity itself (Figure 2–10).

That is, if y is the quantity of interest and t is time, then

$$\frac{dy}{dt} \propto y$$

or,

$$\frac{dy}{dt} = ky \tag{2-19}$$

$\frac{\Delta y}{\Delta t} = ky$				
y	Δt	Δy	$\Delta y/\Delta t$	k
100	1	10	10	0.1
200	1	20	20	0.1
300	1	30	30	0.1

FIGURE 2–10

In many physical problems, the rate of change of a quantity is proportional to the quantity itself.

where k is the constant of proportionality that is determined experimentally or by observation. Therefore, such problems are described by first-order linear differential equations. Note that the first derivative dy/dt represents the rate of change of y with t.

Equation 2–19 is a first-order differential equation with constant coefficients, and its solution is, as shown in the previous section (Equation 2–18),

$$y = y_0e^{kt} \tag{2-20}$$

where y_0 is the value of the function at time $t = 0$. Therefore, a quantity that changes according to the differential Equation 2–19 during a process will increase (or decrease if k is negative) exponentially during that process.

The problems encountered in physical sciences usually involve quantities that change continuously. But many problems encountered in biological sciences involve quantities that change discretely or discontinuously. For example, the population of an animal species or a bacteria colony changes by whole number amounts. However, when the population is very large, the population of a species can be considered to be a continuous function of time with reasonable accuracy. As such, the rates of change can be expressed as derivatives. Consequently, the population change of a species can be described by a differential equation.

Next, we will discuss a variety of such problems from various fields.

EXAMPLE 2–3 Population Growth: Malthusian Law

It is observed that for certain periods of time, the rate of change of population of human societies, animal species, insects, and bacteria colonies increases at a rate proportional to the population itself. Letting $N(t)$ denote the population at time t, obtain the differential equation that describes the change in population with time, and discuss its solution. Assume the initial population at time $t = 0$ is N_0.

SOLUTION Noting that the rate of change of population is proportional to the population itself, the differential equation that describes the change of population with time can be expressed as

$$\frac{dN}{dt} = kN \tag{2-21}$$

where k is the net rate of population, which is the difference between the rates of birth and death. The value of the constant k for various countries is often calculated, and used as a measure of comparison for the population growth of those countries for certain years, decades, or even centuries. For example, a k value of 0.015/year represents a population growth rate of 15 people per year per 1000 people.

Equation 2–21 is a first-order linear equation with constant coefficients. The initial condition is specified to be $N(0) = N_0$. Then the solution of this initial-value problem is, from Equation 2–20,

$$N = N_0 e^{kt} \tag{2-22}$$

Thus, the assumption that population increases at a rate proportional to the population yields that the population grows exponentially with time. This model of population change is called the **exponential growth** or **the Malthusian law** after the British economist Thomas Malthus (1766–1834) who first observed this phenomenon. Despite its simplicity, the Malthusian law is shown to be remarkably accurate for predicting the population growth of humans, several animal species, and colonies of bacteria at least for limited periods of time. But for very large values of t, it predicts that the population of a certain species will approach infinity (Figure 2–11). This is obviously quite unrealistic because of the limitations on living space, food supply, and other resources. A more realistic model for population growth, called the *logistic growth law*, is discussed later in this chapter.

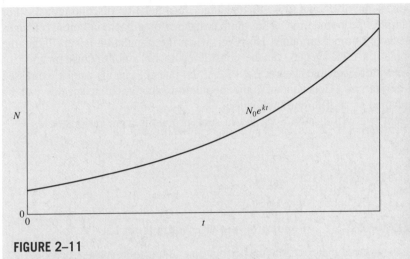

FIGURE 2–11
Malthusian law of population growth.

Estimating the Response Time with the Time Constant

As the following examples will show, there are many applications of the equation $y' + by = c$ in which the constant b is positive and the independent variable is time t. In this case the solution given by Equation 2–17 can be interpreted as follows. The solution expressed in terms of t is

$$y(t) = \frac{c}{b}(1 - e^{-bt}) + y_0 e^{-bt}$$

We immediately note that since $b > 0$, the exponential term e^{-bt} will disappear as $t \to \infty$. Thus, the final value, or *steady-state solution*, of y is c/b regardless of the value of the initial condition y_0. But suppose we wanted an estimate of how long it takes for y to reach the steady-state solution. The answer $t = \infty$ is of no practical use. To obtain an answer, first rewrite the solution by collecting the exponential terms to obtain

$$y(t) = \frac{c}{b} + \left(y_0 - \frac{c}{b}\right)e^{-bt} = y_{ss} + \Delta e^{-bt}$$

where we have defined $y_{ss} = c/b$ (the steady-state solution), and $\Delta = y_0 - y_{ss}$, which is the difference between the initial and final values of y. Noting that $e^{-4} \approx 0.02$ to two decimal places, and that $e^{-bt} \approx e^{-4}$ when $t = 4/b$, we can see that when $t = 4/b$,

$$y(4/b) - y_{ss} = 0.02\Delta$$

That is, when $t = 4/b$, only 2% remains of the original difference between the initial value y_0 and the final value $y_{ss} = c/b$. Thus we may use the value $4/b$ as an estimate of how long it takes for the solution to reach the steady state value.

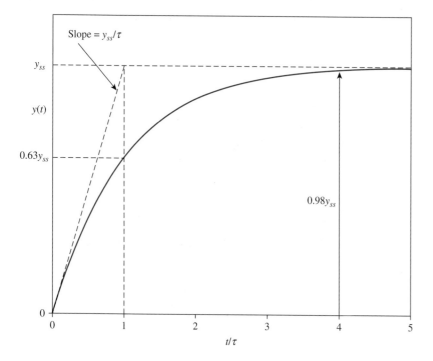

FIGURE 2–12

The response of a first-order linear equation with zero initial condition.

For the case under consideration, $b > 0$, and it is common to define a new term τ to be

$$\tau = \frac{1}{b}$$

(2-23)

The term τ is called the **time constant**. Thus, we may use the term 4τ as an estimate of how long it takes for the solution to reach the steady-state value.

Figure 2–12 shows the solution in terms of τ for the case where $y_0 = 0$. Note that the solution reaches 63% of the final value at $t = \tau$ because $e^{-1} = 0.37$ to two decimal places and thus $1 - e^{-1} = 0.63$ to two decimal places. Note also that

$$\frac{dy}{dt} = -b\Delta e^{-bt} = -\frac{\Delta}{\tau} e^{-t/\tau}$$

and thus, $y'(0) = -\Delta/\tau = y_{ss}/\tau$ if $y_0 = 0$. This relation is useful for estimating τ from experimental data if the data covers only a short time span.

Why use the 2% criterion as a measure of how close the solution is to the steady-state value? It is a common choice, but some people use a 1% criterion. Since $e^{-5} = 0.01$ to two decimal places, these people may use the term 5τ as an estimate of how long it takes for the solution to reach the steady-state value.

What if $c = 0$? In this case the solution is

$$y(t) = y_0 e^{-bt} = y_0 e^{-t/\tau}$$

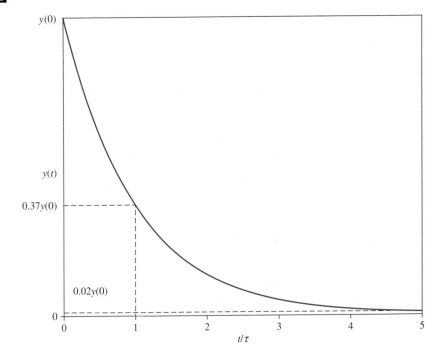

FIGURE 2–13

The homogeneous solution of a first-order linear equation.

Since $e^{-t/\tau} \approx e^{-4} \approx 0.02$ we may say that the solution has decayed to 2% of its initial value when $t = 4\tau$. This is often used as an estimate how long it will take for the solution to disappear. The 1% value is also used. This corresponds to $t = 5\tau$. Figure 2–13 illustrates the solution. Note also that the solution is 37% of its initial value at $t = \tau$ because $e^{-1} \approx 0.37$.

A linear first-order equation can always be put into the following form.

$$\tau \frac{dy}{dt} + y = R(t)$$

In this form, where the coefficient of y is 1, the time constant can always be recognized as the coefficient of the derivative.

EXAMPLE 2–4   **Radioactive Decay and Radioactive Carbon Dating**

It has been observed that radioactive materials such as plutonium, radium, and carbon isotope C^{14} naturally decay to form another element or another isotope of the same element at a rate proportional to the amount of the radioactive material present. Thus, the process of radioactive decay can be described by the first-order linear differential equation:

$$\frac{dM}{dt} = -kM \qquad (2\text{–}24)$$

where $M(t)$ is the amount of the radioactive material at time t and k is a positive constant called the *decay constant* of the material that represents the fraction of the material that decays per unit time. The negative sign is due to the fact that $M(t)$ is decreasing with time. Consequently, dM/dt must be a negative quantity.

An archaeologist discovered certain bones whose C^{14} content is measured to be 8% of that encountered in living animals. Taking the decay constant of C^{14} to be $k = 1.24 \times 10^{-4}$ per year, estimate the age of these bones.

SOLUTION Equation 2–24 is a first-order linear equation with constant coefficients. Taking the amount of the radioactive material at time $t = 0$ to be M_0, the solution of this initial-value problem becomes, from Equation 2–20,

$$M(t) = M_0 e^{-kt} \qquad (2\text{--}25)$$

Thus, if the initial mass of the radioactive material M_0 and the decay constant k are known, the remaining mass of the radioactive material at any time t can be determined from Equation 2–25. Note that the exponent kt must be a nondimensional quantity. Therefore, if k is given per year, then t must be expressed in years.

The solution above can also be expressed explicitly for time as

$$t = -\frac{1}{k} \ln \frac{M(t)}{M_0} \qquad (2\text{--}26)$$

The rate of decay of a radioactive material dM/dt is proportional to its mass $M(t)$, which is decreasing with time. Consequently, the decaying process is fast at the beginning but slows down with time. Instead of using the time constant $\tau = 1/k$ to estimate the decay rate, physicists measure the decay rate of radioactive materials by the **half-life** of the material, which is defined as *the time required for half of the mass of a radioactive material to decay* (Figure 2–14).

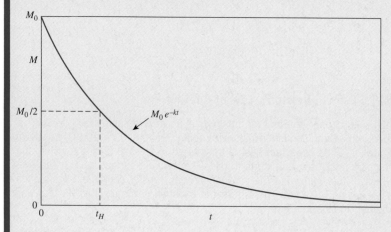

FIGURE 2–14

The decay of radioactive materials with time and the half-life t_H.

A relation for half-life is easily determined by substituting $M(t) = \frac{1}{2}M_0$ into Equation 2–25 and solving for t. It yields

$$t_H = \frac{\ln 2}{k} \qquad (2\text{–}27)$$

The half life of many radioactive substances have been measured in laboratories, and are tabulated in various handbooks. Knowing t_H, the decay k can easily be calculated from Equation 2–27.

An interesting application area of radioactive decay is **radiocarbon dating**, which is based on the decay of the radioactive isotope of carbon C^{14}. This method is commonly used to estimate the age of certain plant or animal remains as well as other archaeological artifacts. The method is based on the observation that a small fraction of the carbon atoms in any living creature is made up of C^{14}. This fraction remains relatively constant during the lifetime of the creature because the creature continually takes in new carbon from its environment through eating and breathing, and the fraction of C^{14} in the atmosphere essentially remains constant.

When a living creature dies, it stops taking in new carbon, including C^{14}, and its C^{14} content starts to be depleted by radioactive decay (Figure 2–15).The half-life of C^{14} is known to be about 5568 years, and its decay constant to be about 1.24×10^{-4} per year. Then the time passed since the death of the creature can be calculated from Equation 2–25 by measuring the remaining fraction of C^{14}.

The amount of C^{14} in the atmosphere is constantly replenished through the conversion of nitrogen to C^{14} by cosmic rays in the atmosphere, and thus the ratio of C^{14} to ordinary carbon in the atmosphere remains essentially constant. The small variations over centuries is taken into account through tables of correction factors.

In light of this background, the age of the bones discovered by the archaeologist is determined from Equation 2–26 by noting that $M(t)/M_0 = 0.08$,

$$t = -\frac{1}{k}\ln\frac{M(t)}{M_0} = -\frac{1}{1.24 \times 10^{-4}/\text{year}}\ln 0.08 = 20{,}369 \text{ years}$$

Thus, the animal that carried those bones died over 20 thousand years ago.

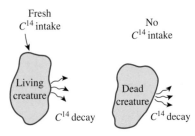

FIGURE 2–15

When a living creature dies, it stops taking in new C^{14}, and its C^{14} content starts to decrease by radioactive decay.

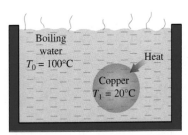

FIGURE 2–16

A copper sphere dropped into boiling water (Example 2–5).

EXAMPLE 2–5   **Newton's Law of Cooling**

A small solid copper ball that is initially ($t = 0$) at a temperature $T_1 = 20°C$ is dropped into a large container filled with boiling water at $T_0 = 100°C$, as shown in Figure 2–16. As expected, heat is transferred to the ball from the water, and the temperature of the ball starts to rise. The mass m, surface area A, the specific heat of the ball c and the convection heat transfer coefficient h are such that $\lambda = hA/mc = 0.1 \text{ s}^{-1}$. The differential equation governing this process was determined in Chapter 1 to be

$$\frac{dT}{dt} = \lambda(T_0 - T)$$

or in standard form as

$$\frac{1}{\lambda}\frac{dT}{dt} + T = T_0$$

Thus, we see that the time constant is $\tau = 1/\lambda = mC/hA$. From this we can tell that a sphere having a large mass m or a large specific heat C will heat up more slowly. This makes sense because more energy is required to increase the temperature of such a sphere. Similarly, a sphere having a small surface area A will also heat up more slowly because the heat must be transferred through a smaller surface area.

For our specific problem $T_0 = 100°C$ and

$$T(0) = T_1 = 20°C$$

Determine the temperature of the ball at $t = 20$ s by solving this initial-value problem.

SOLUTION This is a first-order linear initial-value problem, and its solution is

$$T(t) = T_0 - (T_0 - T_1)e^{-\lambda t} \qquad \text{(2–28)}$$

Substituting the specified values, the temperature of the ball 20 seconds after it is dropped into the boiling water is determined to be

$$T(20) = 100 - (100 - 20)e^{-1 \times 20} \cong 89.2°C$$

Note that the temperature of the ball will approach the boiling water temperature of $100°C$ as $t \to \infty$.

EXAMPLE 2–6   Absorption of Light

The absorption coefficient of water for red light is about 0.5 m^{-1}. Determine how far the red light will travel in water before 90% of it is absorbed.

SOLUTION The absorption of radiation was discussed in Chapter 1, and the governing differential equation was determined to be (Equation 1–8)

$$\frac{dE}{ds} = -\alpha E$$

where α is the absorption coefficient, s is the distance traveled in the direction of the beam, and E is the radiant energy of the red light. This is a first-order linear equation with a constant coefficient, and its solution from Equation 2–20 is $E(s) = E_0 e^{-\alpha s}$ or

$$\frac{E(s)}{E_0} = e^{-\alpha s}$$

where E_0 is the radiant energy of the beam when it strikes the medium at $s = 0$. The ratio $E(s)/E_0$ will be 0.1 at a location s when 90% of the radiation is absorbed. Thus,

$$0.1 = e^{-0.5s} \to s \cong 4.64 \text{ m}$$

Therefore, 90% of the red light will be absorbed by water before it travels a distance of 4.64 m (Figure 2–17).

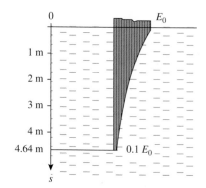

FIGURE 2–17

The absorption of light in water (Example 2–6).

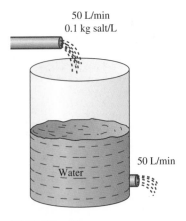

50 L/min
0.1 kg salt/L

50 L/min

Water

FIGURE 2–18

Schematic for Example 2–7.

EXAMPLE 2–7   **Mixing of a Brine Solution**

Consider a tank that contains 1000 liters (L) of pure water and is connected to supply and discharge lines as shown in Figure 2–18. At $t = 0$, both the supply and discharge lines are opened, and brine (water-salt solution) containing 0.1 kg of salt per liter enters the tank at a rate of 50 L/min. Brine leaves the tank at a rate of 50 L/min after it is thoroughly mixed with the water in the tank. Assume that the dissolved salt does not change the volume of the water. As expected, the salt content in the tank increases with time even if the water level remains constant. Obtain a relation for the amount of salt in the tank at any time t, and determine the maximum amount of salt the tank will eventually contain.

SOLUTION   Let M be the mass of salt in the tank at any time t. The conservation of mass principle for the salt in the tank can be expressed as

$$\frac{dM}{dt} = (50 \text{ L/min})(0.1 \text{ kg/L}) - (50 \text{ L/min})\left(\frac{M}{1000} \text{ kg/L}\right)$$

This reduces to

$$\frac{dM}{dt} + 0.05M = 5 \qquad \textbf{(2–29)}$$

This is the differential equation that describes the variation of salt in the tank with time. The initial condition for this problem is $M(0) = 0$ since the tank initially contains no salt. Note that this is a first-order linear initial-value problem with constant coefficients, and its solution is, from Equation 2–17,

$$M = 100(1 - e^{-0.05t}) \qquad \textbf{(2–30)}$$

Note that as $t \to \infty$, the term $e^{-0.05t}$ becomes zero and we obtain $M = 100$ kg. This is the maximum amount of salt that the tank can contain under the specified conditions. The solution is graphed in Figure 2–19. Because the time constant is $1/0.05 = 20$, it will take about 80 s for M to reach 100 kg.

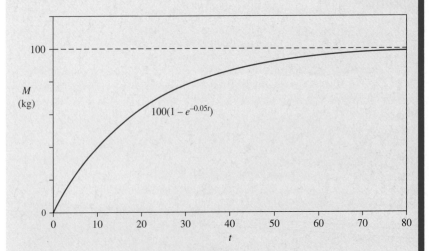

FIGURE 2–19

The increase in the amount of salt in the tank with time (Example 2–7).

EXAMPLE 2–8   Free Falling of Bodies with Air Resistance

The motion of rigid bodies along a straight line can be described by *Newton's second law of motion* expressed in the scalar form as

$$F = ma \quad \text{or} \quad F = m\frac{dV}{dt}$$

where F is the net force acting an the body and m, a, and V are the mass, acceleration, and the velocity of the body, respectively.

The two forces acting on freely falling bodies in the atmosphere are the *gravitational force* or its *weight* as $W = mg$ and the *air resistance*, which is a function of the velocity. For freely falling bodies, these two forces act in opposite directions, and the net force acting on the body is the difference between the two. At low velocities, the air resistance is approximately proportional to the velocity, and in such cases Newton's second law can be expressed as (Figure 2–20).

$$m\frac{dV}{dt} = mg - kV \tag{2–31}$$

or

$$\frac{dV}{dt} + \frac{k}{m}V = g \tag{2–32}$$

where k is a constant of proportionality that is determined experimentally. The gravitational acceleration has the value $g = 9.8 \text{ m/s}^2$ at sea level, and decreases with elevation. But for small elevations relative to the radius of the earth, the value of g can be assumed to be constant as 9.8 m/s^2.

Consider a body of mass m that is dropped from rest at $t = 0$. The body falls under the influence of gravity, and the air resistance that opposes the motion is assumed to be proportional to velocity. Letting x be the vertical distance and taking the positive direction of x axis to be downward with the origin at the initial position of the body, obtain relations for the velocity and position of the body as a function of time t.

SOLUTION   With the stated assumptions, the initial-value problem that describes this motion for times before the body strikes the ground is Equation 2–32 with the initial condition $V(0) = 0$. This is a first-order linear initial-value problem with constant coefficients, and its solution (from Equation 2–17) is

$$V(t) = \frac{mg}{k}(1 - e^{-kt/m}) \tag{2–33}$$

which is the desired relation for velocity as a function of time. Note that as $t \to \infty$, the velocity approaches the constant value of

$$V_\infty = \frac{mg}{k}$$

which is called the **terminal velocity** (Figure 2–21). A freely falling body reaches this velocity when the air resistance equals the weight of the body. Note that the terminal velocity depends only on the weight of the body and the coefficient of resistance k. It is independent of the initial velocity $V(0)$.

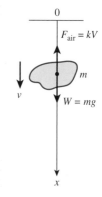

FIGURE 2–20

The gravity and air-resistance forces acting on a freely falling body.

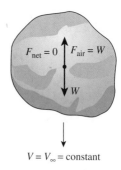

FIGURE 2–21

A freely falling body reaches its terminal velocity when the air resistance equals the weight of the body.

Rearranging Equation 2–33 as

$$\frac{m}{k}\frac{dV}{dt} + V = \frac{mg}{k}$$

we see that the time constant is $\tau = m/k$. Thus it will take about $t = 4\tau = 4m/k$ for the velocity to reach 98% of the terminal velocity.

The distance the body drops is obtained from the definition of velocity $V = dx/dt$ and the condition $x(0) = 0$. Integrating $dx = V dt$ after substituting the V expression from Equation 2–33 and applying the initial condition yields

$$x(t) = \int_0^t \frac{mg}{k}(1 - e^{-kt/m})dt = \frac{mg}{k}\left[t - \frac{m}{k}(1 - e^{-kt/m})\right] \qquad (2\text{–}34)$$

which is the desired relation for the position of the body as a function of time. Since $e^{-4} \approx 0.02$, when the ball reaches 98% of its terminal velocity, it will have fallen a distance equal to $x(4\tau) = x(4m/k)$, or

$$x\left(\frac{4m}{k}\right) = 3.02g\frac{m^2}{k^2}$$

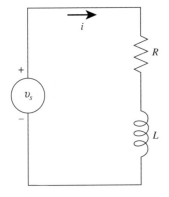

FIGURE 2–22

Representation of a solenoid circuit.

EXAMPLE 2–9   Model of a Starter Solenoid

The circuit shown in Figure 2–22 is a model of a solenoid, such as that used to engage the gear of a car's starter motor with the engine's flywheel. The solenoid is constructed by winding wire around an iron core to make an electromagnet. The resistance R is that of the wire and the inductance L is due to the electromagnetic effect. Switching on the supply voltage v_s activates the magnet, which moves the starter gear. Develop a model of the current i assuming that $v_s = V$, a constant. Determine the steady-state value of the current. How long will it take for the current to reach its steady-state value?

SOLUTION Using Kirchhof's voltage law, which states that the sum of voltages around a loop must be zero because of conservation of energy, we obtain the following model of the current i.

$$v_s - Ri - L\frac{di}{dt} = 0$$

If $v_s = V$, a constant, the equation becomes

$$\frac{di}{dt} + \frac{R}{L}i = \frac{V}{L}$$

This is an initial-value problem whose solution (from Equation 2–17) is

$$i(t) = i(0)e^{-Rt/L} + \frac{V}{R}(1 - e^{-Rt/L}) = \frac{V}{R}(1 - e^{-Rt/L})$$

if $i(0) = 0$. The steady-state current is V/R. The time constant for this model is $\tau = L/R$. Thus, because $1 - e^{-4} \approx 0.98$, the solenoid current will reach 98% of its final value V/R at $t = 4\tau = 4L/R$.

Section Review

2–9C What is the Malthusian law of population growth? Why is it not very realistic?

2–10C What is the basis of radioactive carbon dating? Why is C^{14} suitable for that purpose?

2–11C Determine the time constant τ for each of the following equations.

(a) $6\dfrac{dy}{dt} + y = 10$ (b) $6\dfrac{dy}{dt} + 3y = 10$ (c) $10\dfrac{dy}{dt} + 2y = t^2$

(*Answers:* (a) 6 (b) 2 (c) 5)

2–12 Determine the ratio of C^{14} content of bones that are 2000 years old to that of bones in living animals. (*Answer:* 78%)

2–4 ▪ NONLINEAR FIRST-ORDER DIFFERENTIAL EQUATIONS

Linear first-order initial-value problems are relatively easy to solve because there is an analytic expression for the general solution of such problems. Also, the solution of such problems is unique over the entire interval in which the coefficients $P(x)$ and $R(x)$ are continuous. These features are real luxuries when it comes to nonlinear initial-value problems. Thus when dealing with nonlinear problems, it becomes very important to determine whether a solution exists in a specified region, and if it does, whether it is unique. Finding the solution is yet another matter, assuming there is a solution. In this section, we will discuss the general characteristics of nonlinear initial-value problems. In the following sections, we will solve those that have certain special forms.

Many problems encountered in practice are linear in nature, and thus result in linear differential equations that are easy to solve. But many other problems of practical interest are nonlinear in nature, and thus result in nonlinear differential equations. No general procedure exists for the solution of nonlinear equations, and little can be said about the general characteristics of such equations. Therefore, the analytic study of nonlinear equations is limited to certain types for which exact solutions are available. When feasible, some nonlinear equations can be linearized by using some approximations that yield reasonably accurate results. When the nonlinear equation cannot be solved exactly or by linearizing, numerical methods discussed in Chapter 9 are often the best means of obtaining a solution.

Considering that a nonlinear initial-value problem may not even have a solution in a specified region, it is advisable to check if a solution *exists* in that region before attempting to solve an initial-value problem. Also, considering that a solution obtained may not be the only solution to a nonlinear problem, it may be necessary to check for the *uniqueness* of the solution in the specified region. The following theorem provides the necessary tools to check the existence and the uniqueness of the solution to a given nonlinear first-order initial-value problem (Figure 2–23).

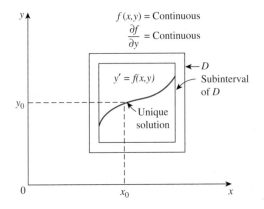

FIGURE 2–23

The existence and uniqueness for nonlinear initial-value problems $y' = f(x, y)$ with $y(x_0) = y_0$.

THEOREM 2–2   Existence and Uniqueness for Nonlinear First-Order Equations

If $f(x, y)$ is a continuous function on some rectangle D containing the point (x_0, y_0), then the first-order differential equation

$$y' = f(x, y)$$

with

$$y(x_0) = y_0$$

has at least one solution in a subinterval of D containing the point (x_0, y_0). Furthermore, the solution is unique if $\partial f / \partial y$ is also continuous in D.

The proof of the theorem is lengthy and is omitted, but can be found in theoretical texts. Note that Theorem 2–2 states the *sufficient* conditions for a nonlinear first-order initial-value problem to have a unique solution in some interval. Therefore, a problem that does not satisfy the conditions of this theorem may still have a unique solution.

Although the conditions of the theorem appear to be too restrictive, they are satisfied by any differential equation that accurately describes a physical problem that possesses a unique solution.

Theorem 2–2 states the conditions under which a first-order nonlinear differential equation possesses a unique solution but makes no reference to how to find the solution or how to determine the region in which the solution exists.

Linear equations yield general solutions that contain all the solutions to the equation. However, this is not usually the case with nonlinear equations. Also, unlike linear equations, the solutions of nonlinear equations are often in a form that cannot be expressed explicitly in terms of the independent variable. That is, the solutions are often in implicit form.

In the following sections, we discuss some solution methods that are applicable to both linear and nonlinear equations. Thus, in the case of linear equations, a choice for the solution method exists. As you will see, equations that are exact or separable can be put into a form that can be solved by direct integration.

Section Review

2–13C Under what conditions does the nonlinear equation $y' = f(x, y)$ have a solution in a specified region? When is this solution unique?

2–14C Is there a general procedure for solving first-order nonlinear differential equations?

2–15 For the following equations, approximately determine the region in the xy-plane where the existence and uniqueness of a solution through any specified point is guaranteed by the existence and uniqueness theorem.

(a) $y' = \dfrac{1}{x + y}$ (b) $y' = \sqrt{x^2 - y^2}$

(*Answers:* (a) A unique solution exists near any point in the xy-plane where $x \neq -y$. (b) A unique solution exists near any point in the xy-plane where $x > y$ or $x > -y$.)

2–16 For the following equations, approximately determine the region in the xy-plane where the existence of a solution is guaranteed. Also determine the region where the solution is unique.

(a) $y' = y$ $y(1) = 2$ (b) $y' = \sqrt{x - y}$ $y(0) = 1$

(*Answers:* (a) A solution exists and is unique in some neighborhood of $x = 1$. (b) There is no guarantee that a unique solution exists in some neighborhood of $x = 0$.)

2–5 ▪ SEPARABLE FIRST-ORDER EQUATIONS

The first-order differential equation in the standard form

$$y' = h(x, y)$$

is said to be **separable** if $h(x, y)$ can be expressed as the ratio a function of x and a function of y (Figure 2–24). That is,

$$h(x, y) = \frac{f(x)}{g(y)}$$

for separable equations, and thus,

$$y' = \frac{f(x)}{g(y)} \tag{2–35}$$

or

$$g(y)y' = f(x) \tag{2–36}$$

For example, the equation

$$y' = \frac{x^2 y^3}{(x - 2)e^{-2y}}$$

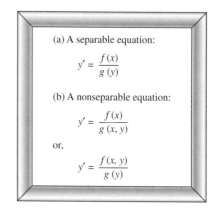

(a) A separable equation:

$$y' = \frac{f(x)}{g(y)}$$

(b) A nonseparable equation:

$$y' = \frac{f(x)}{g(x, y)}$$

or,

$$y' = \frac{f(x, y)}{g(y)}$$

FIGURE 2–24

A differential equation is separable if its right side can be expressed as a ratio of a function of x and a function of y.

is separable since it can be rearranged and expressed as

$$\frac{e^{-2y}}{y^3} y' = \frac{x^2}{x - 2}$$

for $y \neq 0$ and $x \neq 2$.

Thus, the variables x and y of a separable equation can be separated from each other by algebraic manipulations such that one side of the equation involves only y while the other side involves only x.

Integrating Equation 2–36 with respect to x yields

$$\int g(y) y' dx = \int f(x) dx + C$$

or

$$\int g(y) dy = \int f(x) dx + C \qquad \textbf{(2–37)}$$

since $y' dx = dy$. Note that the coefficient of dy involves only the variable y while the coefficient of dx involves only the variable x.

Equation 2–37 involves two integrations, and you may be tempted to use two integration constants C_1 and C_2. However, C_1 and C_2 are two arbitrary constants, and we can conveniently combine them into a single arbitrary constant C whose value can be determined by applying the initial condition (Figure 2–25).

There are three observations that can be made from Equation 2–37. First, the integrals appearing in this equation may be impossible to perform analytically, and it may become necessary to perform one or both integrations numerically. Second, the final solution will most likely be in an *implicit* form, and it may not be possible to express y explicitly in terms of x or to express x explicitly in terms of y. Third, expressing a given first-order differential equation in separable form often requires dividing both sides of the equation by a function $P(x)$ or $Q(y)$ or even $P(x)Q(y)$. Such divisions are performed under the assumption that $P(x)$ or $Q(y)$ is not zero in the interval of interest, since division by zero is not allowed. The one-parameter solutions obtained in this manner also reflect this assumption. These solutions may not include the solution of the differential equation that corresponds to the x and y values that make the factor zero, and it may be necessary to investigate the form the differential equation will take and its solutions in this case. Such solutions are the *singular* solutions of the differential equation if they cannot be obtained from a general one-parameter family of solutions, and if meaningful, should be included in the solution. The solution procedure of separable equations is illustrated below with examples.

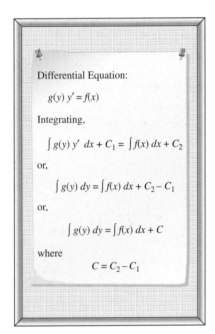

Differential Equation:

$$g(y) \, y' = f(x)$$

Integrating,

$$\int g(y) \, y' \, dx + C_1 = \int f(x) \, dx + C_2$$

or,

$$\int g(y) \, dy = \int f(x) \, dx + C_2 - C_1$$

or,

$$\int g(y) \, dy = \int f(x) \, dx + C$$

where

$$C = C_2 - C_1$$

FIGURE 2–25

In an equation that involves several indefinite integrals, all the integration constants can be combined into one.

EXAMPLE 2–10   Separable Equation

Solve the following initial-value problem using separation of variables. $y' = 2xy^2, y(2) = 1$.

SOLUTION Dividing both sides of the equation by y^2 gives

$$\frac{1}{y^2} y' = 2x$$

or

$$\int \frac{dy}{y^2} = \int 2x \, dx + C$$

The differential equation is now in the separated form since one side of the equation involves only y while the other side involves only x. The solution is obtained by integration to be (Figure 2–26),

$$-\frac{1}{y} = x^2 + C$$

or

$$y = \frac{-1}{x^2 + C}$$

The constant C is determined by applying the initial condition $y(2) = 1$, so

$$1 = \frac{-1}{2^2 + C} \rightarrow C = -5$$

Substituting,

$$y = \frac{-1}{x^2 - 5}$$

which is the desired solution in explicit form. Note that in obtaining this solution we divided both sides of the original differential equation by y^2, which is zero at $y = 0$. Thus we should investigate if we lost (or gained) any solutions by this division. We can show by direct substitution that $y = 0$ is a solution of the original differential equation, but it does not satisfy the initial condition. It is a singular solution since it cannot be obtained from the previous solution.

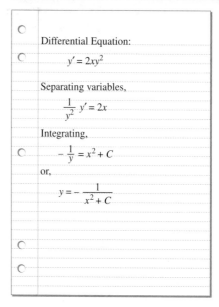

Differential Equation:

$$y' = 2xy^2$$

Separating variables,

$$\frac{1}{y^2} y' = 2x$$

Integrating,

$$-\frac{1}{y} = x^2 + C$$

or,

$$y = -\frac{1}{x^2 + C}$$

FIGURE 2–26

A separable equation can be solved by direct integration after the variables are separated.

EXAMPLE 2–11   Population Growth: Logistic Law

It is mentioned in Example 2–3 that the exponential growth model of population becomes unrealistic for large values of time, and a more realistic model is needed if it is to be applicable over a much larger time interval. The simplest way to account for the possible decline of the population N when it becomes very large is to make the factor k in Equation 2–21 linearly dependent on the population size N as

$$k(N) = a - bN$$

where a and b are two positive constants. This expression says that the growth rate decreases as N increases and becomes negative when $N > a/b$. Then the differential equation governing the population growth becomes (Figure 2–27)

$$N' = (a - bN)N \tag{2–38}$$

This model of population growth is due to the Belgian mathematician P.F. Verhulst (1804–1849), and is called the **logistic growth**. The value of the constant b is very small relative to a so that for small values of N the term bN is negligible. As N gets larger, the term bN starts to become significant and slows down the rate of growth by decreasing the value of $k(N)$. For even

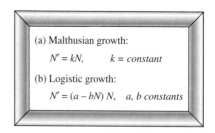

(a) Malthusian growth:

$$N' = kN, \qquad k = constant$$

(b) Logistic growth:

$$N' = (a - bN) N, \quad a, b \ constants$$

FIGURE 2–27

Two models of population growth and the corresponding differential equations.

larger values of N, the term bN becomes larger than a, and the rate of population growth $k(N)$ becomes negative.

Equation 2–38 is more realistic than Equation 2–21, but it is also more complex and its solution is more involved. This example demonstrates that better mathematical models of real world situations come at the expense of added labor.

Biologists have noticed that the population growth of fruit flies is in good agreement with the logistic law of growth expressed by Equation 2–38 with a and b being two experimentally determined constants. Taking the population at time $t = 0$ to be N_0, determine the population $N(t)$ as a function of time, and sketch the plot.

SOLUTION The mathematical formulation of this problem can be expressed as $N' = (a - bN)N$ with $N(0) = N_0$, which is a first-order nonlinear, initial-value problem. It is a relief to notice that the variables of the differential equation are separable.

Before we separate the variables and formally solve the problem, let us see what happens when the right side of the differential equation is zero. The right side will be zero when either $N = 0$ or $N = a/b$. For either case, the differential equation will reduce to $N' = 0$, which means that the population will not increase or decrease with time. In other words, for these two cases the population remains constant, and the solution $N = 0$ and $N = a/b$ are called the **equilibrium solutions**. On the N axis, the population values corresponding to these populations are called **equilibrium points** or **critical points**. We can disregard the case $N = 0$ as trivial. Then the point $N = a/b$ becomes the only meaningful equilibrium solution of the differential equation. Also, if $N_0 = a/b$, then $N = a/b$ will be the solution of the initial value problem, and the population will remain constant at the value of N_0.

When N is neither 0 nor a/b, the term $(a - bN)N$ is not zero, and the differential equation in this case can be expressed in separated form as

$$\frac{1}{(a - bN)N} N' = 1$$

Integrate both sides using the fact that $N'dt = dN$ to obtain

$$\int \frac{1}{(a - bN)N} N' dt = \int \frac{dN}{(a - bN)N} = \int dt + C$$

or

$$\frac{1}{a} \ln \left| \frac{N}{a - bN} \right| = t + C_1$$

Rearranging,

$$\left| \frac{N}{a - bN} \right| = e^{at + aC_1}$$

or

$$\frac{N}{|a - bN|} = Ce^{at}$$

since N is a positive quantity and $C = e^{aC_1}$. The constant C is determined by applying the initial condition $N(0) = N_0$ to be

$$\frac{N_0}{|a - bN_0|} = C$$

Substituting for C and assuming that the signs of $a - bN$ and $a - bN_0$ are the same, we obtain

$$N = \frac{aN_0}{bN_0 + (a - bN_0)e^{-at}}$$

which is the desired solution. It is plotted in Figure 2–28 for different values of N_0. From this plot, we can see that if $N_0 < a/b$ then N always will be less than a/b. Also, if $N_0 > a/b$ then N always will be greater than a/b. This verifies our assumption that the signs of $a - bN$ and $a - bN_0$ are the same.

Note that as $t \to \infty$, the factor $e^{-at} \to 0$ and $N(t)$ will asymptotically approach a/b, regardless of the value of N_0. Thus we call $N = a/b$ the saturation level, and we say that it is an asymptotically stable solution of the logistic population growth equation.

This solution suggests that in cases where the logistic law is applicable, the population of a certain insect colony will reach its equilibrium level of a/b after a sufficient time even if the initial population is very low (but nonzero). Likewise, dumping a large number of insects into an area will have no effect on the insect population in that area in the long run.

More realistic (but more complex) population models are available to offer more accurate solutions to population related problems, including extinction. Some of these are presented in the exercises.

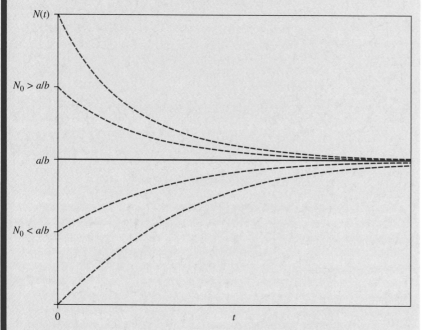

FIGURE 2–28

The logistic law of population growth for different values of N_0.

EXAMPLE 2–12   Population Growth: A Qualitative Study

Consider a fishery in which the population of the fish obeys the logistic law of growth, and assume that fish are caught continuously at a constant rate of k that is independent of the fish population. The differential equation governing the fish population N in this case can be expressed as

$$N' = (a - bN)N - k \tag{2-39}$$

where a, b, and k are positive constants. The presence of the constant k in the equation raises some interesting possibilities, including extinction if k is large. This equation can be solved by the method of separation of variables, but many interesting aspects of the problem can be understood by carefully studying the differential equation only. Answer the following questions without solving the differential equation:

(a) If $k < a^2/4b$, show that there are two equilibrium points N_1 and N_2 where $N_1 < N_2$. Also show that N_1 is unstable and N_2 is stable.
(b) If $k = a^2/4b$, show that there is only one equilibrium point and it is semi-stable.
(c) If $k > a^2/4b$, show that there are no equilibrium points and extinction will occur at this fishing rate regardless of the initial value of the fish population.

SOLUTION   (a) Equilibrium points are the points at which the rate of change of population is zero. That is, they are the points at which $N' = 0$. They are determined by setting N' in Equation 2–39 equal zero, $(a - bN)N - k = 0$ or,

$$N^2 - \frac{a}{b}N + \frac{k}{b} = 0$$

whose roots are

$$N_{1,2} = \frac{a \pm \sqrt{a^2 - 4kb}}{2b} \tag{2-40}$$

For $a^2 > 4kb$ (or $k < a^2/4b$), this quadratic equation has two real roots, which are

$$N_1 = \frac{a - \sqrt{a^2 - 4kb}}{2b} \quad \text{and} \quad N_2 = \frac{a + \sqrt{a^2 - 4kb}}{2b}$$

where $N_1 < N_2$. A plot of N' versus N is given in Figure 2–29a. Note that for $N = 0$, we have from Equation 2–39 that $N' = -k$. Therefore, the curve intersects the N' axis at $-k$. Also, note that the curve intersects the N axis at two points, indicating that $N' = 0$ at these two points; thus, they are the equilibrium points. This is expected, since the equation $N' = 0$ is a quadratic equation in N, which has two real roots in this case. Thus, the plot of N' on the $N' - N$ plane is a parabola that intersects the N' axis at $-k$ and the N axis at N_1 and N_2.

The equilibrium point N_1 is unstable since (1) N' is negative for $N < N_1$, meaning that the population will decrease (move away from N_1 to the left) if N is slightly less than N_1 and (2) N' is positive for $N > N_1$, meaning that the population will increase (move away from N_1 to the right) if N is slightly more

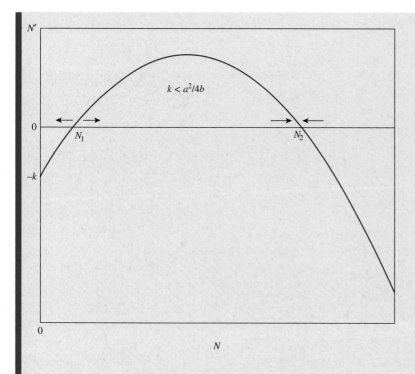

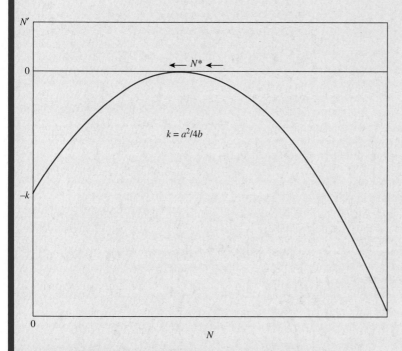

FIGURE 2–29 (a), (b) (*continued*)

A plot of N' versus N for (a) $k < a^2/4b$, (b) $k = a^2/4b$, and (c) $k > a^2/4b$.

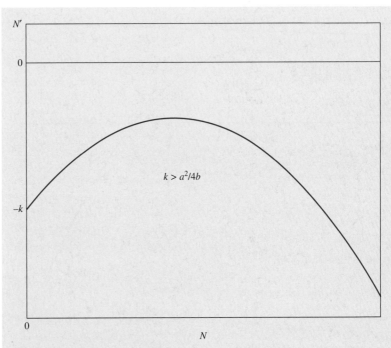

FIGURE 2–29 (c) (Continued)

than N_1. Likewise, the equilibrium point N_2 is stable since (1) N' is positive for $N < N_2$, meaning that the population will increase (move to the right towards N_2) if N is slightly less than N_2 and (2) N' is negative for $N > N_2$, meaning that the population will decrease (move to the left towards N_2) if N is slightly more than N_2.

Note that if the initial population $N_0 > N_1$, then the population will eventually increase to N_2 and stabilize there. But if $N_0 < N_1$, then extinction is inevitable.

(b) When $k = a^2/4b$, the roots of the equation $N' = 0$ are, from Equation 2–40, $N_1 = N_2 = a/2b = N^*$.

Therefore, $N^* = a/2b$ is the only root, and thus the only equilibrium point in this case. This is a semi-stable equilibrium point, however, since N' is negative for all values of N except $N = N^*$, at which point it is zero. This means that if the initial population $N_0 > N^*$, then the population will eventually decrease to N^* and stabilize there. But if $N_0 < N^*$, then the population will decrease until extinction occurs. This is also illustrated in Figure 2–29b.

(c) When $k > a^2/4b$, we can see from Equation 2–40 that both roots of the equation $N' = 0$ are complex. That is, there are no real roots in this case. Thus, the graph of N' on the $N' - N$ plane will never intersect the N axis, as shown in Figure 2–29c. This means that N' can never be positive or zero. Therefore, there will be no equilibrium points in this case, and the population will decrease until extinction occurs regardless of the initial value of the population.

The analysis above indicates that this fishery cannot accommodate fishing rates $k > a^2/4b$ under the specified conditions.

EXAMPLE 2–13   Velocity of a Rocket

The Aerobee is a two-stage rocket used for atmospheric research. The first stage has a thrust T of 217 kN and a lift-off mass of $m = 3839$ kg. Aerodynamic drag force D depends on the square of velocity as follows. $D = \rho C_D A v^2 / 2$ where ρ is the atmospheric mass density, A is the cross-sectional area of the rocket (the area perpendicular to the flow), and C_D is the drag coefficient. For the Aerobee, $A = 0.114$ m^2 and $C_D = 0.4$, and for the lower atmosphere, $\rho = 1.204$ kg/m^3. Thus, the drag force in newtons is $D = 0.027v^2$, where v is in meters per second (m/s).

(a) Obtain the equation of motion for the velocity v. (b) Determine the rocket velocity after 5 s.

SOLUTION   Assuming the rocket moves only vertically, the free-body diagram can be drawn as shown in Figure 2–30.

From Newton's law of motion,

$$m\frac{dv}{dt} = T - mg - D = T - mg - \frac{1}{2}\rho C_D A v^2$$

This can be put into the simpler form

$$\frac{dv}{dt} = B - Cv^2 \qquad B = \frac{T}{m} - g \qquad C = \frac{\rho C_D A}{2m}$$

This equation is separable as

$$\frac{1}{B - Cv^2}\frac{dv}{dt} = 1$$

or

$$\frac{dv}{B - Cv^2} = dt$$

This can be integrated to obtain

$$\frac{1}{\sqrt{BC}}\tanh^{-1}\frac{v}{\sqrt{B/C}} = t + C_1$$

If $v(0) = 0$, then the constant of integration C_1 is zero, and the solution is

$$v(t) = \sqrt{\frac{B}{C}}\tanh\left(\sqrt{BC}t\right)$$

This solution assumes that the rocket mass m is constant. Of course, as the rocket burns fuel its mass decreases. Thus, this solution will underestimate the actual velocity and can be used to determine whether or not the rocket can achieve some desired velocity.

(b) Substituting the values for the Aerobee, we obtain $B = 46.715$, $C = 7 \times 10^{-6}$, and $v(t) = 2583 \tanh(0.018t)$. Thus, $v(5) = 231$ m/s.

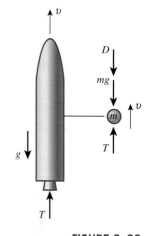

FIGURE 2–30
An ascending rocket and its free-body diagram.

Orthogonal Trajectories and Differential Equations

Two lines intersecting at right angles are said to be **orthogonal** at the point of intersection. You will recall from geometry that if the slope of one curve is m, then the slope of the curve orthogonal to it at that point is $-1/m$, as

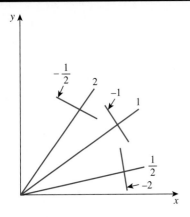

FIGURE 2–31

Orthogonal lines intersect at right angles, and the slope of one line at the intersection point is the negative reciprocal of the slope of the other line.

shown in Figure 2–31. Extending his definition, a family of curves in the xy-plane expressed as $F(x, y) = C$ are said to be **orthogonal trajectories** of another family of curves $G(x, y) = K$ if each member of one family intersects each member of the other family at right angles. In other words, the slope of a curve at any point (x, y) is the negative reciprocal of the slope of another curve that belongs to the other family.

Noting that dy/dx or y' represents the slope of a curve, and using subscripts 1 and 2 to denote the two families, we have

$$y_1' = -\frac{1}{y'_2} \tag{2–41}$$

Although it appears that orthogonal trajectories are of interest in geometry only, the problem of finding orthogonal trajectories of a given family of curves arises in many important physical problems. For example, the lines of electric force in a 2-D electric field are orthogonal trajectories of constant potential lines. The lines of heat flow in a 2-D heat transfer problem are orthogonal trajectories of constant temperature lines. The streamlines in 2-D fluid flow problem are orthogonal trajectories of constant potential lines.

EXAMPLE 2–14   **Orthogonal Trajectories for a Family of Straight Lines**

Determine the orthogonal trajectories of a family of straight lines passing through the origin.

SOLUTION   The mathematical formulation of a family of straight lines passing through the origin is $y = kx$. Differentiating both sides of the equation with respect to x yields $y' = k$. Eliminating the constant k through the substitution $k = y/x$ yields $y' = y/x$. Either of the last two equations is the differential equation of the straight lines passing through the origin. Thus, the slope of the lines at any point (x, y) is simply y/x. The negative reciprocal of this slope is $-x/y$, which is the slope of the orthogonal trajectories of this family of lines passing through the origin. Thus, the differential equation of the orthogonal trajectories is $y' = -x/y$, or $yy' = -x$, which is a separable equation. Integrating gives

$$\frac{y^2}{2} = -\frac{x^2}{2} + C_1$$

or

$$x^2 + y^2 = C^2 \tag{2–42}$$

where $C^2 = 2C_1$. This equation represents a family of concentric circles of radius C whose center is at the origin, as shown in Figure 2–32. Thus, any straight line passing through the origin is orthogonal or perpendicular to any circle whose center is at the origin.

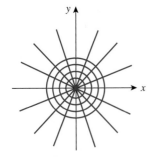

FIGURE 2–32

Orthogonal trajectories of a family of straight lines passing through the origin are the family of concentric circles whose center is at the origin.

Transforming Nonseparable Equations into Separable Ones

A nonseparable differential equation can sometimes be transformed into a separable one by changing the variable. There are no general rules on how to select the new variable, and there is no guarantee that this method will always work. The general appearance of the differential equation is often the only clue we have when trying this method. If the equation involves repeated combinations of x and y in a certain form, this combination is an obvious choice for the first trial for the new variable.

As a special case, the differential equation of the form

$$y' = f(ax + by + c) \tag{2-43}$$

can always be transformed into a separable form by defining a new variable v as

$$v = ax + by + c \tag{2-44}$$

Then $y = (v - ax - c)/b$ and

$$y' = \frac{1}{b}(v' - a)$$

Substituting $f(v)$ for y' and solving for v' gives $v' = a + bf(v)$ or,

$$\frac{v'}{a + bf(v)} = 1 \tag{2-45}$$

which is a separable equation in the variables v and x (Figure 2–33).

A nonseparable equation:

$$y' = \frac{(2x + y - 1)^2}{e^{4x + 2y - 2}} - 2x - y + 1$$

Change of variables:

$$v = 2x + y - 1$$

A separable equation:

$$v' = 2 + \frac{v^2}{e^{2v}} - v$$

FIGURE 2–33

A differential equation that appears to be nonseparable may be converted to a separable one by a suitable change of variable.

EXAMPLE 2–15   Transforming an Equation into a Separable One

Solve the following differential equation, $y' = (2x + 2y + 3)^2 + 4x + 4y + 6$.

SOLUTION   This differential equation is not linear or separable, but can be transformed into a separable one by substitution $v = 2x + 2y + 3$. It yields, from Equation 2–45,

$$\frac{v'}{2 + 2(v^2 + 2v)} = 1$$

Since $v'dx = dv$, integrating with respect to x gives

$$-\frac{1}{2(v + 1)} = x + C$$

or,

$$v = -1 - \frac{1}{2(x + C)}$$

The desired solution is obtained by back substitution as

$$2x + 2y + 3 = -1 - \frac{1}{2(x + C)}$$

or

$$y = -2 - x - \frac{1}{4(x + C)}$$

Homogeneous Differential Equations

The best-known class of differential equations that can be reduced to a separable form is the homogeneous equation. A first-order differential equation is said to be **homogeneous** if it can be expressed as

$$y' = f\left(\frac{y}{x}\right) \tag{2-46}$$

That is, the function f of a homogeneous equation can be expressed as $f(v)$, where $v = y/x$. For example, the equation

$$y' = \frac{x^3 - y^3}{x^2 y} \tag{2-47}$$

is homogeneous since its right side can be expressed as a function of v alone (Figure 2–34). We can rearrange the right hand side of Equation 2–47 as

$$\frac{x^3 - y^3}{x^2 y} = \frac{x^3}{x^2 y} - \frac{y^3}{x^2 y} = \frac{x}{y} - \left(\frac{y}{x}\right)^2 = \frac{1}{v} - v^2 \tag{2-48}$$

So the equation becomes

$$y' = \frac{1}{v} - v^2$$

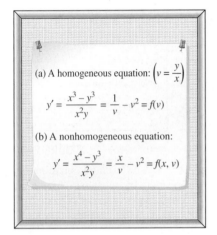

(a) A homogeneous equation: $\left(v = \dfrac{y}{x}\right)$

$$y' = \frac{x^3 - y^3}{x^2 y} = \frac{1}{v} - v^2 = f(v)$$

(b) A nonhomogeneous equation:

$$y' = \frac{x^4 - y^3}{x^2 y} = \frac{x}{v} - v^2 = f(x, v)$$

FIGURE 2–34

A first-order differential equation is homogeneous if the transformation $v = y/x$ reduces its right side to a function of v alone.

The reader should be aware that term homogeneous is used in a different meaning here than it is in Chapter 1 with regard to linear homogeneous equations. This dual usage is unfortunate, and it may at times be confusing. But the context usually makes it clear which meaning is intended.

The homogeneity of simple equations can easily be determined by inspection. But for complicated equations, we may need to apply the homogeneity test expressed as follows: in the differential equation, replace all the x's by λx, and all the y's by λy, and simplify. If, after simplification, all the λ's cancel out and we end up with the original equation, then the differential equation is homogeneous. Otherwise, it is not. For example, the equation

$$\frac{dy}{dx} = \frac{x^3 - y^3}{x^2 y}$$

is homogeneous since the substitution $x \rightarrow \lambda x$ and $y \rightarrow \lambda y$ yields

$$\frac{d(\lambda y)}{d(\lambda x)} = \frac{(\lambda x)^3 - (\lambda y)^3}{(\lambda x)^2 (\lambda y)} \rightarrow \frac{\lambda}{\lambda} \frac{dy}{dx} = \frac{\lambda^3 x^3 - \lambda^3 y^3}{\lambda^3 x^2 y} \rightarrow \frac{dy}{dx} = \frac{x^3 - y^3}{x^2 y}$$

which is the original equation.

As a practical rule, an equation that involves powers of x and y is homogeneous if, on the right side, the sum of the powers of x and y of each term in the numerator and the denominator are identical (Figure 2–35). In this example, the sum of the powers of x and y is 3 for every term in the numerator and the denominator.

For an equation of the form $y' = f(x, y)$ another way of stating the homogeneity test is to require that

$$f(\lambda x, \lambda y) = f(x, y) \tag{2-49}$$

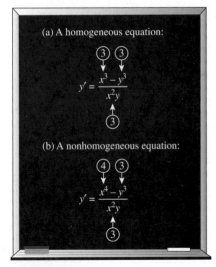

(a) A homogeneous equation:

$$y' = \frac{x^3 - y^3}{x^2 y}$$

(b) A nonhomogeneous equation:

$$y' = \frac{x^4 - y^3}{x^2 y}$$

FIGURE 2–35

For homogeneous equations, the sum of the powers of x and y of each term in the numerator and the denominator of the right side are identical.

Once it is determined that an equation is homogeneous, its reduction to separable form and its solution is straightforward. We first define a new variable $v = y/x$. Then $y = xv$, and its derivative with respect to x is

$$y' = xv' + v \qquad (2\text{-}50)$$

Substituting into Equation 2–46 gives

$$xv' + v = f(v) \qquad (2\text{-}51)$$

Rearranging gives

$$\frac{1}{x} = \frac{v'}{f(v) - v} \qquad (2\text{-}52)$$

which is a separable equation. Its solution is obtained by integration with respect to x to be

$$\int \frac{dx}{x} = \int \frac{v' dx}{f(v) - v} + C \qquad (2\text{-}53)$$

or

$$\ln|x| = \int \frac{dv}{f(v) - v} + C \qquad (2\text{-}54)$$

since $v' dx = dv$. Here C is the integration constant. The final form of the solution is obtained by replacing v by y/x after the integrations are performed.

Again we note that the integrals in Equation 2–54 may not be possible to perform analytically. Also, even if the integral can be evaluated, an explicit relation for x or y may not be possible to obtain. The one thing that we are sure of is that a homogeneous equation can always be reduced to a separable equation. We also could use the transformation $u = x/y$ to reduce a homogeneous equation to a separable one.

Sometimes two or more solution methods are applicable to a differential equation. Although all methods will give the same result, one method may be easier to apply than others.

EXAMPLE 2–16   A Homogeneous Equation

Solve the following differential equation:

$$y' = \frac{y - x}{y + x}$$

SOLUTION By inspection, we recognize this equation to be homogeneous since, on the right side, all the terms on the numerator and the denominator are of the first degree (Figure 2–36). Therefore, by taking $v = y/x$ or $y = xv$, this equation can be rearranged as

$$(xv)' = \frac{x\left(\frac{y}{x} - 1\right)}{x\left(\frac{y}{x} + 1\right)} = \frac{\frac{y}{x} - 1}{\frac{y}{x} + 1}$$

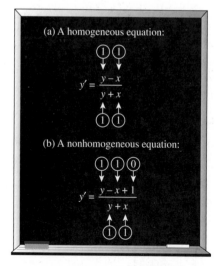

(a) A homogeneous equation:

$$y' = \frac{y - x}{y + x}$$

(b) A nonhomogeneous equation:

$$y' = \frac{y - x + 1}{y + x}$$

FIGURE 2–36

The differential equation solved in Example 2–16 is homogeneous since all the terms in the numerator and the denominator are of first degree.

or

$$xv' + v = \frac{v - 1}{v + 1}$$

Separating the variables gives

$$\frac{1}{x} = -\frac{v + 1}{v^2 + 1}v'$$

Integrating with respect to x,

$$\ln|x| = -\frac{1}{2}\ln|v^2 + 1| - \tan^{-1}v + C$$

or

$$\ln\left|x\sqrt{v^2 + 1}\right| + \tan^{-1}v = C$$

where C is the arbitrary integration constant. Back substituting $v = y/x$, we obtain

$$\ln\left|\sqrt{y^2 + x^2}\right| + \tan^{-1}\frac{y}{x} = C$$

Note that the solution is implicit since neither variable can be expressed explicitly in terms of the other.

This differential equation is a good example of why you need to be familiar with the solution methods presented in this chapter, despite having the availability of modern computer tools. Several symbolic processing programs were unable to obtain the solution.

Section Review

2–17C When is a first-order differential equation separable, and when is it not separable?

2–18C What is the general procedure for solving separable first-order differential equations?

2–19C How do the Malthusian and logistic growth models differ?

2–20 Solve the following equations by separating the variables.

(a) $yy' = x^3 + 1$ (b) $(x + 2)y' = y^2 + 2$

(*Answers:* (a) $y(x) = \pm\sqrt{2x^4 + 8x + C}$ (b) $y(x) = \sqrt{2}\tan[\sqrt{2}\ln(x + 2) + C]$)

2–21 Solve the following equations by first transferring them into separable form, and then separating the variables.

(a) $\dfrac{dy}{dx} = (x + y + 1)^2 - (x + y)$ *Hint:* Let $u = x + y$

(b) $\dfrac{dy}{dx} = \dfrac{10}{(x + y)e^{x+y}} - 1$ *Hint:* Let $u = x + y$

(*Answers:* (a) $y(x) = \dfrac{7}{2\sqrt{7}}\tan\left[\dfrac{7(x + C)}{2\sqrt{7}}\right] - x - \dfrac{1}{2}$

(b) $(x + y - 1)e^{x+y} = 10x + C)$)

2–22 Solve the following initial-value problems by using the separation of variables method.

(a) $y' + 2xy = 0$, $y(0) = 1$ (b) $y' = e^{2y}\cos 2x$, $y(\pi/2) = 0$

$\left(\text{Answers: (a) } |y| = Ce^{-x^2} \quad \text{(b) } y = \ln\dfrac{1}{\sqrt{1 - \sin 2x}}\right)$

2–6 ▪ EXACT FIRST-ORDER DIFFERENTIAL EQUATIONS

The first-order differential equation $y' = f(x, y)$ can also be expressed as

$$M(x, y) + N(x, y)y' = 0 \tag{2–55}$$

A general solution of this equation will involve the variables x and y as well as an arbitrary constant C and can be expressed implicitly as

$$S(x, y) = C \tag{2–56}$$

Differentiating this equation with respect to x yields

$$\frac{dS(x, y)}{dx} = \frac{\partial S}{\partial x} + \frac{\partial S}{\partial y}y' = 0 \tag{2–57}$$

Considering that differentiation and integration are inverse processes, the integral of Equation (2–57), which is a differential equation, must be Equation 2–56. Therefore, Equation 2–57 is in a form that can be directly integrated to yield $S(x, y) = C$, and is called an exact differential equation.

Comparison of Equation 2–55 and Equation 2–57 suggests the following definition.

Definition of An Exact Differential Equation
A first-order differential equation that can be expressed in the form

$$M(x, y) + N(x, y)y' = 0 \tag{2–58}$$

is called an exact differential equation in a region D if there exists a function $S(x, y)$ such that

$$\frac{\partial S(x, y)}{\partial x} = M(x, y) \tag{2–59}$$

and

$$\frac{\partial S(x, y)}{\partial y} = N(x, y) \tag{2–60}$$

for all (x, y) in that region.

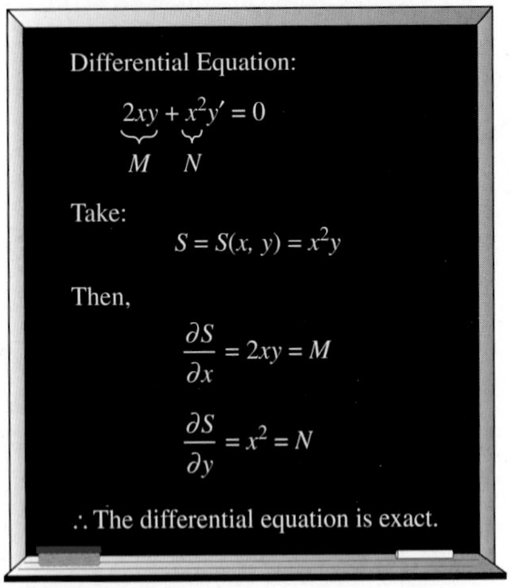

FIGURE 2–37

Demonstrating the exactness of the differential equation discussed in Example 2–17.

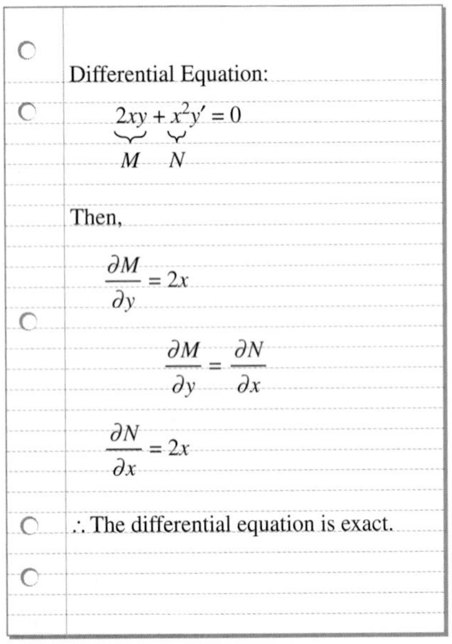

FIGURE 2–38

The use of Theorem 2–3 to check for the exactness of a given differential equation.

EXAMPLE 2–17   An Exact Differential Equation

Show that the differential equation $2xy + x^2y' = 0$ is exact, and then solve it.

SOLUTION   Comparing the given equation with Equation 2–58 and noting that the coefficient of y' is N, we have $M = 2xy$ and $N = x^2$. After some trial and error, we observe that $M = 2xy$ is the partial derivative of the function x^2y with respect to x, and $N = x^2$ is the partial derivative of the same function with respect to y. Therefore, the given differential equation is exact (Figure 2–37), and it can be expressed as

$$\frac{d(x^2y)}{dx} = 0$$

This result can easily be verified by performing the indicated derivative. Thus, the compact differential equation above equivalent to the original differential equation, and its solution is obtained by direct integration to be $x^2y = C$, where C is the arbitrary integration constant. For $x \neq 0$, the solution can also be expressed as $y = C/x^2$. We could also solve this differential equation using other methods such as the separation of variables.

We determined the exactness of the differential equation in Example 2–17 by inspection because it was a simple one. If fact, we simply assumed the equation to be exact, guessed the solution, and then verified that the equation was indeed exact. This is undoubtedly a very cumbersome way of determining exactness of a given equation. If the equation were not exact, we would have to try every conceivable function first before we could make that claim. Obviously, we need a more systematic criterion to determine the exactness of a differential equation. Such a criterion is provided by the following theorem.

THEOREM 2–3   Exactness of Differential Equations

If the partial derivatives $\partial M(x, y)/\partial y$ and $\partial N(x, y)/\partial x$ are continuous in a rectangular region D, then the differential equation

$$M(x, y) + N(x, y)y' = 0$$

is exact in that region if and only if

$$\frac{\partial M(x, y)}{\partial y} = \frac{\partial N(x, y)}{\partial x} \tag{2–61}$$

at every point in D (Figure 2–38).

Proof This theorem is proved in two parts. First we will show that if the differential equation is exact, then Equation 2–61 holds. Recalling that for exact differential equations, we have $M = \partial S/\partial x$, $N = \partial S/\partial y$, and

$$M(x, y) = \frac{\partial S(x, y)}{\partial x} \rightarrow \frac{\partial M(x, y)}{\partial y} = \frac{\partial^2 S(x, y)}{\partial x \partial y}$$

$$N(x, y) = \frac{\partial S(x, y)}{\partial y} \rightarrow \frac{\partial N(x, y)}{\partial x} = \frac{\partial^2 S(x, y)}{\partial y \partial x}$$

and thus,

$$\frac{\partial M(x, y)}{\partial y} = \frac{\partial N(x, y)}{\partial x}$$

since $\partial M/\partial y$ and $\partial N/\partial x$ are said to be continuous and the order of differentiation is immaterial for continuous functions. This completes the first part of the proof.

Next we will show that if $\partial M/\partial y = \partial N/\partial x$ then the differential equation is exact. In other words, there exists a function $S(x, y)$ such that

$$\frac{\partial S(x, y)}{\partial x} = M(x, y) \tag{2-62}$$

and

$$\frac{\partial S(x, y)}{\partial y} = N(x, y) \tag{2-63}$$

Integrating Equation 2–62 with respect to x holding y constant yields

$$S(x, y) = \int M(x, y)\,dx + g(y) \tag{2-64}$$

where $g(y)$ is an arbitrary function of y that is to be determined. Note that when performing integrations with respect to one of the variables, it is necessary to express the integration constant as a function of the variables that are held constant during integration for generality. The validity of this process can easily be verified by taking the partial derivative of Equation 2–64 with respect to x and observing that it yields the original differential equation since $dg(y)/dx = 0$.

Taking the partial derivative of Equation 2–64 with respect to y holding x constant gives

$$\frac{\partial S(x, y)}{\partial y} = \frac{\partial}{\partial y} \int M(x, y)\,dx + \frac{dg(y)}{dy} = \int \frac{\partial M(x, y)}{\partial y}\,dx + \frac{dg(y)}{dy}$$

since $\partial M/\partial y$ is a continuous function and thus the order of differentiation and integration can be interchanged. Also, we used the ordinary derivative for the function $g(y)$ since partial and ordinary derivatives are identical for functions that depend on a single variable only. Substituting $\partial S(x, y)/\partial y = N(x, y)$ and rearranging,

$$\frac{dg(y)}{dy} = N(x, y) - \int \frac{\partial M(x, y)}{\partial y}\,dx \tag{2-65}$$

The left side of this equation depends on y only; thus, the right side of it should also depend on y (at most) for the equality to hold, despite its appearance which suggests otherwise. This is done by showing that the derivative of the right side with respect to x is zero:

$$\frac{\partial N(x, y)}{\partial x} - \frac{\partial M(x, y)}{\partial y} = 0$$

This is indeed the case, since it is given that $\partial N/\partial x = \partial M/\partial y$. Thus, the right side of Equation 2–65 depends on y only, and $g(y)$ is obtained by integrating this equation with respect to y as

$$g(y) = \int \left[N(x, y) - \int \frac{\partial M(x, y)}{\partial y} dx \right] dy \qquad (2\text{–}66)$$

Substituting this into Equation 2–64, we obtain

$$S(x, y) = \int M(x, y) dx + \int \left[N(x, y) - \int \frac{\partial M(x, y)}{\partial y} dx \right] dy \qquad (2\text{–}67)$$

Then the solution becomes

$$S(x, y) = C \qquad (2\text{–}68)$$

where the constant C is to be determined from the initial condition. Note that we disregarded the integration constant when determining $g(y)$ in Equation 2–66 without any loss in generality. (Had we included an integration constant in Equation 2–66, we would absorb it in the integration constant of Equation 2–68.) This completes the second part of the proof.

The second part of the proof is a systematic approach for obtaining $S(x, y)$, and thus it is the description of a solution method for exact differential equations. Although Equation 2–67 together with Equation 2–68 can be used as a general formula for the solution, it is more instructive to go through the solution steps outlined in the proof above.

EXAMPLE 2–18   Application of the Exactness Test

Show that the differential equation $2x + 2yy' = 0$ is exact, and then solve it.

SOLUTION   In this case, we have $M = 2x$ and $N = 2y$. Applying the test of exactness (Equation 2–61),

$$\frac{\partial M(x, y)}{\partial y} = 0 = \frac{\partial N(x, y)}{\partial x}$$

Thus, the differential equation is exact. Also, both $\partial M/\partial y$ and $\partial N/\partial x$ are continuous over the entire xy-plane, and the solution is applicable to any region. Following the procedure described in the proof of Theorem 2–3, the solution is found as follows. From Equation 2–62,

$$\frac{\partial S(x, y)}{\partial y} = M(x, y) = 2x$$

Integrating with respect to x, we have $S(x, y) = x^2 + g(y)$. Differentiating with respect to y holding x constant, we have

$$\frac{\partial S(x, y)}{\partial y} = 0 + \frac{dg(y)}{dy}$$

Also, $\partial S(x, y)/\partial y = N = 2y$. From these two equations we have,

$$\frac{dg(y)}{dy} = 2y$$

and thus, $g(y) = y^2$. Substituting into the $S(x, y)$ relation, we obtain $S(x, y) = x^2 + y^2$. Thus, the solution of the differential equation in implicit form is $x^2 + y^2 = C$, where C is an arbitrary constant to be determined from the initial condition. We could, of course, start the solution by integrating $\partial S/\partial y = N$ with respect to y. In this case the integration would involve the unknown function $h(x)$, which would be determined in the same manner as $g(y)$, as illustrated in Figure 2–39. This problem could also be solved by other methods, such as the separation of variables. All approaches give the same result.

The solution represents circles of radius $R = \sqrt{C}$, as shown in Figure 2–40. Therefore, once the initial condition $y(x_0) = y_0$ is specified, the desired solution is also specified to be the circle, centered at the origin, that passes through the point (x_0, y_0).

EXAMPLE 2–19   Another Exact Differential Equation

Solve the following initial-value problem.

$$y' = -\frac{2e^{2x}\sin y + 2xy}{e^{2x}\cos y + x^2}, \quad y(0) = \frac{\pi}{2}$$

SOLUTION   The given differential equation can be rearranged as

$$(2e^{2x}\sin y + 2xy) + (e^{2x}\cos y + x^2)y' = 0$$

This time we have $M = 2e^{2x}\sin y + 2xy$ and $N = e^{2x}\cos y + x^2$. This differential equation is exact since, from Equation 2–61,

$$\frac{\partial M(x, y)}{\partial y} = 2e^{2x}\cos y + 2x = \frac{\partial N(x, y)}{\partial x}$$

The solution of the rearranged differential equation is identical to the solution of the original equation, except at the points where the denominator is zero. The solution of this problem is found as follows. From Equation 2–62, we have

$$\frac{\partial S(x, y)}{\partial x} = M(x, y) = 2e^{2x}\sin y + 2xy$$

Integrating gives

$$S(x, y) = e^{2x}\sin y + x^2 y + g(y)$$

Differentiating with respect to y holding x constant, we have

$$\frac{\partial S(x, y)}{\partial y} = e^{2x}\cos y + x^2 + \frac{dg(y)}{dy}$$

Differential Equation:

$$\underbrace{2x}_{M} + \underbrace{2yy'}_{N} = 0$$

Take

$$\frac{\partial S}{\partial y} = N = y$$

Integrate with respect to y,

$$S = y^2 + h(x)$$

Differentiate with respect to x,

$$\frac{\partial S}{\partial x} = \frac{\partial h}{\partial x}$$

Also

$$\frac{\partial S}{\partial x} = M = 2x$$

Therefore,

$$\frac{dh}{dx} = 2x$$

$$h = x^2$$

Substituting,

$$S = x^2 + y^2$$

Thus the solution is

$$x^2 + y^2 = C$$

FIGURE 2–39

Alternative solution for Example 2–18.

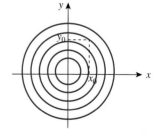

FIGURE 2–40

Solution curves for the differential equation solved in Example 2–18.

Also,

$$\frac{\partial S(x, y)}{\partial y} = N = e^{2x}\cos y + x^2$$

From these two equations, we have

$$\frac{dg(y)}{dy} = 0$$

and thus, $g(y) = C_1 = 0$. Substituting into the $S(x, y)$ relation gives $S(x, y) = e^{2x}\sin y + x^2 y$. Thus, the solution of the differential equation in implicit form is $e^{2x}\sin y + x^2 y = C$, where C is an arbitrary constant and is determined from the initial condition to be

$$e^0 \sin\frac{\pi}{2} + 0 = C \rightarrow C = 1$$

Substituting, we obtain $e^{2x}\sin y + x^2 y = 1$.

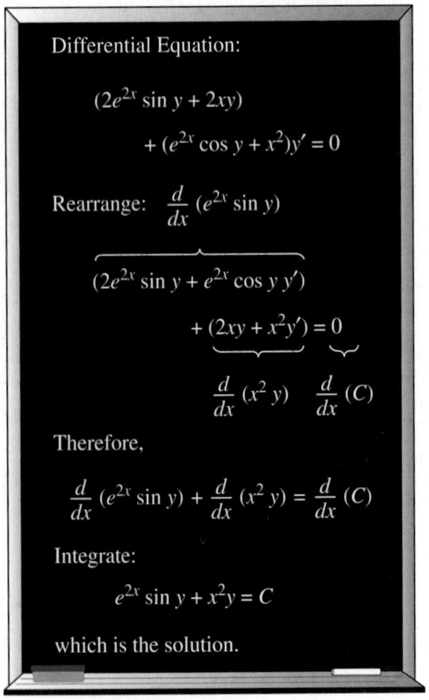

Alternative Solution: Method of Grouping

The solution procedure outlined in Example 2–19 is quite systematic and is applicable to any exact differential equation. However, it is lengthy, and requires considerable care and patience. For those with little patience and a lot of intuition, there is a very attractive alternative procedure. This method is called the **method of grouping** and is based on expressing the differential equation as the sum of derivatives of terms. For example, the differential equation from Example 2–19 can be rearranged (Figure 2–41) quite arbitrarily, as

$$\frac{d}{dx}(e^{2x}\sin y) + \frac{d}{dx}(x^2 y) = \frac{d}{dx}(C)$$

which is in a directly integrable form. So integrating each term yields $e^{2x}\sin y + x^2 y = C$, which is identical to the solution obtained previously.

Integrating Factors

The differential equation

$$y + 2xy' = 0 \tag{2-69}$$

is not exact since $\partial M/\partial y = 1$ and $\partial M/\partial y \neq \partial N/\partial x$. Therefore, this equation cannot be solved using the procedure discussed in the preceding section.

Now let us multiply each term of this equation by y. We get

$$y^2 + 2xyy' = 0 \tag{2-70}$$

This equation is now exact since $\partial M/\partial y = 2y = \partial N/\partial x$ (Figure 2–42). Therefore, it can be solved using the procedure discussed earlier.

Equations 2–69 and 2–70 are essentially equivalent, and they have the same solutions (except at the zeros of the factor). Yet, one is exact, but the other is not. This example suggests that an equation that is not exact may be converted to an exact one by multiplying it by a suitable factor. Such factors, if they exist, are called **integrating factors**, and are denoted by $\mu(x, y)$.

Differential Equation:

$$(2e^{2x}\sin y + 2xy)$$

$$+ (e^{2x}\cos y + x^2)y' = 0$$

Rearrange: $\dfrac{d}{dx}(e^{2x}\sin y)$

$$(2e^{2x}\sin y + e^{2x}\cos y\, y')$$

$$+ (2xy + x^2 y') = 0$$

$$\frac{d}{dx}(x^2 y) \quad \frac{d}{dx}(C)$$

Therefore,

$$\frac{d}{dx}(e^{2x}\sin y) + \frac{d}{dx}(x^2 y) = \frac{d}{dx}(C)$$

Integrate:

$$e^{2x}\sin y + x^2 y = C$$

which is the solution.

FIGURE 2–41

Details of the method of grouping for Example 2–19.

(a) An Inexact Equation:

$$y + 2xy' = 0$$

(b) An Exact Equation (after multiplying by y):

$$y^2 + 2xyy' = 0$$

FIGURE 2–42

An inexact differential equation can be made exact by multiplying it through a suitable integrating factor.

Integrating factors, in general, may depend on both x *and* y. No simple general procedure exists for their determination, except for some special cases (such as for linear equations discussed in Section 2–2).

Section Review

2–23C When is a first-order differential equation homogeneous, and when is it non-homogeneous?

2–24C How are first-order homogeneous differential equations solved?

2–25 Determine if the following equations are homogeneous.

(a) $\dfrac{dy}{dx} = \dfrac{x + y}{x - y}$ (b) $\dfrac{dy}{dx} = \dfrac{x + 1}{x^2 + y}$

(*Answers:* (a) Homogeneous (b) Not homogeneous.)

2–26 Solve the following homogeneous (or reducible to homogeneous) initial value problems.

(a) $\dfrac{dy}{dx} = \dfrac{y}{x} - 1, \ \ y(1) = 0$ (b) $\dfrac{dy}{dx} = \dfrac{x^3 - xy^2}{x^2y}, \ \ y(1) = 1$

(*Answers:* (a) $y(x) = -x \ln x$ (b) $y(x) = \pm \dfrac{\sqrt{2x^4 + 2}}{2x}$)

2–7 ▪ GRAPHICAL METHODS

It is often impossible to obtain analytic solutions to nonlinear equations. In such cases, it is desirable to get at least a sense of how the solution behaves, or to determine the solution approximately. A graphical method is one such approach, and it enables us to determine the solution of a nonlinear initial-value problem approximately in a graphical form.

Now let us re-examine the first-order differential equation $y' = f(x, y)$ from a geometrical point of view. Recall that y' represents the slope of a line tangent to the solution function y (which is yet unknown) at any point (x, y). Then the values of the function $f(x, y)$ at any point (x, y) represent the slope of y at that point. Therefore, the values of y' at any point on the xy-plane can be represented by line segments at a sufficient number of points on the xy-plane. Such a plot is called the **direction field** or the **slope field** of the differential equation. For example, the direction field of the equation $y' = 2xy$ is given in Figure 2–43. In this case, $f(x, y) = 2xy$, and the slope of line segment at any point (x, y) is simply $2xy$. Thus, at $(1, 3)$ it is 6, at $(-2, 4)$ it is -16, and at $(-3, -2)$ it is 12. The slope is zero anywhere on the x or the y axis ($y = 0$ or $x = 0$).

Once the direction field is available, the solution curve of a problem with the initial condition $y(x_0) = y_0$ is obtained by marking the point (x_0, y_0), and then drawing a curve that passes through this point and remains parallel to the line segments as closely as possible, as shown in Figure 2–43 for the case where $y(0) = 0.52$. More accurate solution curves are obtained by drawing shorter line segments at smaller intervals in x.

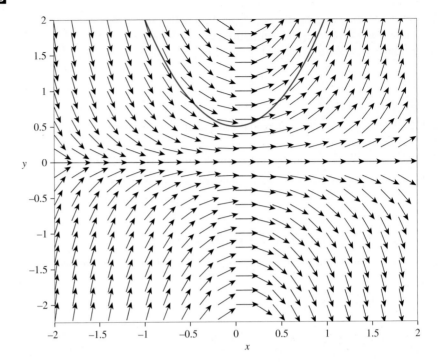

FIGURE 2–43

A plot of the direction field of
the differential equation $y' = 2xy$.

The curves $f(x, y) = C$, where C is a constant, represent curves of constant slope, and are called **isoclines**. The direction fields can be constructed by plotting the isoclines first. The isoclines of the equation $y' = 2xy$ are the family of curves $2xy = C$, some of which are plotted in Figure 2–44.

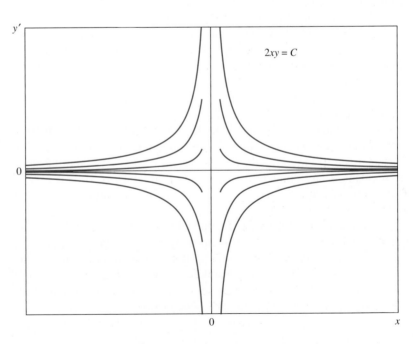

FIGURE 2–44

Some isoclines of the differential
equation $y' = 2xy$ (curves of $2xy = C$).

EXAMPLE 2–20   A Graphical Solution Method

Obtain the solution of the initial-value problem $y' = 0.2y + 0.04$, $y(0) = 1$ using a graphical method, and compare the solution obtained to the exact solution.

SOLUTION   In this case we have $f(x, y) = 0.2y + 0.04$, and thus the general equation of the isoclines is $0.2y + 0.04 = C$, or $y = 5C - 0.2$, which represents straight horizontal lines. Thus the slope of the line segments remain constant on any line parallel to the x-axis. Calculating the slope at various points and representing them by short line segments, we obtain the direction field as shown in Figure 2–45. The approximate graphical solution of the given problem is then obtained by plotting a curve that remains parallel to these line segments and passes through the point $y(0) = 1$ or $(0, 1)$.

For comparison purposes, we can also solve this problem exactly. This is a first-order linear differential equation with constant coefficients, and the initial condition is specified to be $y(0) = 1$. Then the solution of this initial-value problem is, from Equation 2–17,

$$y = 1.2e^{0.2x} - 0.2$$

This solution is also plotted in Figure 2–45. A comparison of the approximate and exact solution curves reveals a close match in this case. The agreement can be improved by using a finer mesh in the construction of the direction fields.

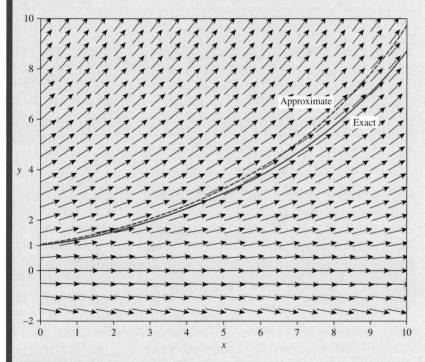

FIGURE 2–45

The direction field, the graphical solution (the dashed line), and the exact solution (the solid line) of the problem $y' = 0.2y + 0.04$, $y(0) = 1$.

Section Review

2–27C Why are graphical methods used to solve first-order differential equations?

2–28C Define direction field, and explain how it is used to solve first-order differential equations graphically.

2–29C Define isoclines, and explain how they are used to solve first-order differential equations graphically.

- Is direct integration applicable?

- Is the equation linear?

- Is the equation separable? Can it be made separable?

- Is the equation homogeneous? Can it be made homogeneous?

- Is the equation exact? Can it be made exact?

- Is the equation in a special form?

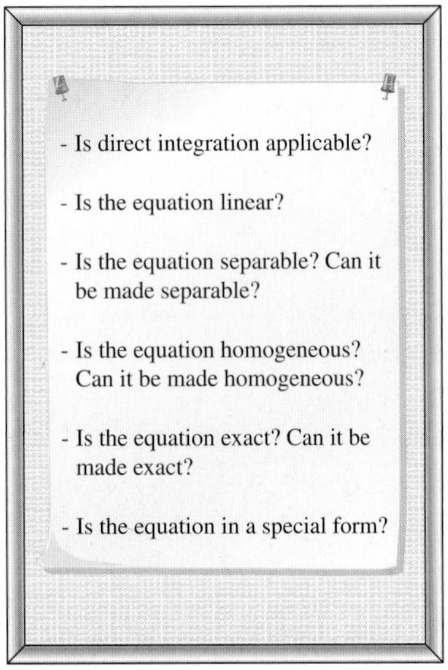

FIGURE 2–46

A systematic approach to solving first-order differential equations.

2–8 ▪ A SYSTEMATIC APPROACH TO SOLVING FIRST-ORDER EQUATIONS

So far, we have considered several different methods for solving first-order differential equations. These methods are sufficient to solve many equations encountered in practice, but there is no guarantee that a given equation can be solved by any of these methods. Sometimes one or more methods are applicable, but other times, none of the methods presented in this chapter may seem to work. In either case, it is always a good practice to approach the problems in a systematic manner.

In this section, we will describe a step approach for solving first-order equations of the form $y' = f(x, y)$ or higher-order equations that can be reduced to that form after a change of variable. We will assume that the differential equation satisfies the requirements for the existence of a solution in the interval of interest. The suggested approach involves asking the following questions until we get a satisfactory answer (Figure 2–46).

Step 1. Can the equation be solved by direct integration?

Many differential equations encountered in practice are in a form that can be integrated directly, and integration is the most direct way of solving differential equations. First-order equations of the form $y' = f(x)$ can always be solved by direct integration, provided that the integration can be performed.

Step 2. Is the equation linear?

A linear equation can always be solved in a straightforward manner, assuming the required integrations can be performed. Therefore, one of the first things we should do when solving a differential equation is to check for linearity.

Step 3. Is the equation separable?

The method that is closest to direct integration is the method of separation of variables. An equation is separable if it can be rearranged such that one side of the equation involves only the variable y while the other side involves only x. Once the variables are separated, the solution is obtained by direct integration.

Step 4. Is the equation homogeneous? If not, can it be made homogeneous?

An equation that is not separable can always be converted to a separable one by defining a new variable as $v = y/x$ if the equation is homogeneous. It is also possible to convert some nonhomogeneous equations to homogeneous ones if the equations are in certain forms.

Step 5. Is the equation exact? If not, can it be made exact?

We can apply the test of exactness to the given equation to determine if it is exact. The exact equations can be solved in a straightforward manner. If the equation is not exact, we can check if the equation can be made exact by finding an integrating factor.

Step 6. Is the equation in special form?

An equation that fails all the tests above can still be solved in a systematic manner if it belongs to a class of well-known equations, such as the Bernoulli and Ricati equations (see Problems 2–199 through 2–211).

The form of a differential equation may also suggest certain tricks or transformations that will enable us to obtain an analytical solution. If nothing seems to work, then we will have to resort to graphical or numerical solution methods to obtain an approximate solution.

EXAMPLE 2–21   **A Systematic Approach to Solving a Differential Equation**

Determine the solution of the differential equation $y' = e^{x + \ln x - y}$

SOLUTION   The first thing we do is check the order of the given equation. It is a first-order equation since it does not involve any second or higher order derivatives. Next we check if it can be solved by direct integration. We quickly discard this possibility since the right hand side of the equation involves a nonlinear function (exponential, in this case) of y. The equation does not seem to be separable in its present form, but this may change if we simplify the equation. Noting that $e^{a+b} = e^a e^b$ and $e^{\ln x} = x$, the given equation can be expressed as

$$y' = e^{x + \ln x - y} = e^x e^{\ln x} e^{-y}$$

or $y' = xe^x e^{-y}$.

Now the equation is in a separable form and it can be rearranged as $e^y y' = xe^x$. Integrating with respect to x gives $e^y = xe^x - e^x + C$. Noting that $\ln e^y = y$ and taking the logarithm of both sides gives $y = \ln(xe^x - e^x + C)$, which is the desired solution.

If the equation was not separable, we would check to see if it is homogeneous through a change of variable. If it is neither homogeneous nor exact, we would attempt to make it exact by finding an integrating factor that depends on only x or y. If this fails also and we do not recognize the given equation as being one of the special differential equations, we would have no choice but to consider a graphical or numerical method and settle for an approximate solution.

2–9 ▪ COMPUTER METHODS FOR FIRST-ORDER EQUATIONS

In this section, we show how to use the popular computer packages to solve the types of problems presented in this chapter. These applications are the following.

1. Obtaining closed form solutions with
   (a) unspecified initial conditions
   (b) specified initial conditions
2. Generating contour plots
3. Obtaining direction field plots

Obtaining Closed-Form Solutions

Symbolic processing programs use the procedures presented in this chapter to obtain closed form solutions. They are not perfect; sometimes they fail to obtain a solution even though one exists. Sometimes a solution will be obtained if you express the equation in a different form. For example, it helps to avoid fractions, so you may be able to obtain a solution of the equation $y'(x) = -B(x, y)/A(x, y)$ by expressing it in the form $A(x, y)y'(x) + B(x, y) = 0$.

Problems Having Unspecified Initial Conditions Consider the equation given in Example 2–15:

$$y' = (2x + 2y + 3)^2 + 4x + 4y + 6 \qquad (2\text{–}71)$$

A computer solution can be found as shown in Table 2–1. It is

$$y = -(2 + x) - \frac{1}{4(x + C)} = -\frac{4x^2 + 4(2 + C)x + 1 + 8C}{4(x + C)}$$

where C is a constant of integration. Note how MuPAD, Maple, and Mathematica require you to specify that y is a function of x with the notation $y(x)$ or $y[x]$, whereas MATLAB uses the simpler notation y.

Problems Having Specified Initial Conditions A solution can be obtained for a given initial condition. Consider the equation given in Example 2–2.

$$(x + 1)y' + y = 5x^2(x + 1) \qquad y(2) = 3 \qquad (2\text{–}72)$$

A computer solution can be found as shown in Table 2–2. It is

$$y = \frac{5x^3(3x + 4)}{12(x + 1)} - \frac{73}{3(x + 1)} = \frac{15x^4 + 20x^3 - 292}{12(x + 1)}$$

TABLE 2–1

Computer Solution of Equation 2–71

MATLAB Symbolic Math Toolbox
`dsolve('Dy=(2*x+2*y+3)^2+4*x+4*y+6','x')`

MuPAD
`eqn:= ode({y'(x)=(2*x+2*y(x)+3)^2+4*x+4*y(x)+6},y(x))` `solve(eqn)`

Maple
`ode:= diff(y(x),x) =(2*x+2*y(x)+3)^2 +4*x+4*y(x)+6` `dsolve(ode)`

Mathematica
`DSolve [y'[x]==(2*x+2*y[x]+3)^2+4*x+4*y[x]+6,y[x],x]`

TABLE 2–2

Computer Solution of Equation 2–72

MATLAB Symbolic Math Toolbox

```
dsolve('(1+x)*Dy+y=5*x^2*(x+1)','y(2)=3','x')
```

MuPAD

```
eqn := ode({(x+1)*y'(x)+y(x)=5*x^2*(x+1),y(2)=3},y(x))
solve(eqn)
```

Maple

```
ode := (1+x)*diff(y(x),x)+y(x)= 5*x^2x(x+1)
ic: = y(2)=3
dsolve ({ode, ic})
```

Mathematica

```
DSolve[{(x+1)*y'[x]+ y[x]  == 5*x^2*(x+1),  y[2]  == 3},y[x],x]
```

Note the different ways in which the initial conditions are specified in the various computer packages. In some packages the initial conditions are specified along with the equation.

Generating Contour Plots

Contour plots represent the solution curves of a differential equation. These plots can be generated with a computer package. Consider the equation treated in Example 2–19.

$$(e^{2x} \cos y + x^2)y'(x) + 2e^{2x} \sin y + 2xy = 0$$

The solution was found to be

$$e^{2x} \sin y + x^2y = C \tag{2-73}$$

where C is the integration constant. Table 2–3 shows how to obtain the solution curves for $0 \le x \le 3$, $0 \le y \le 3$, and different values of C. Figure 2–47 shows the plot generated by MATLAB.

Obtaining Direction Field Plots

As we saw in Section 2–7, it is often impossible to obtain a closed form solution to a differential equation, and in such cases, it is often possible to obtain a sense of the solution's behavior by examining a plot of the direction field. The plot is also useful even for equations whose solution is known, because it shows the general behavior of the solution for arbitrary initial conditions.

Consider the equation $y' = -xy$. Table 2–4 shows how to obtain the direction field plot with the various packages. The plot in Figure 2–48 was created with MATLAB. The arrows show the direction that the solution y moves if x changes. For example, at the point $x = 1$, $y = 1$, the slope is $y' = -(1)(1) = -1$, so if x increases, y will decrease.

TABLE 2–3

Computer Generated Contour Plot of Equation 2–73

MATLAB

```
% f is the solution for the integration constant C.
% Note: you must use array operations.
f = @(x,y)exp(2*x).*sin(y)+ x.^2.*y;
[X,Y] = meshgrid(0:0.1:3,0:0.1:3);
% Plot for C = 2 to 100 in steps of 10.
C = 2:10:100;
contour (X,Y,f(X,Y),L)
```

MuPAD

```
plot(plot::Implicit2d(exp(2*x)*sin(y)+x^2*y,x = 0..3,
 y = 0..3, Contours = [2,20,50,100]))
```

Maple

```
with(plots)
contourplot(exp(2*x)*sin(y)+x^2*y,x=0..3,y=0..3,
 Contours = [20,50,100])
```

Mathematica

```
ContourPlot[Exp[2*x]*Sin[y]+x^2*y,{x,0,3},{y,0,3},
 Contours->{20,50,100}]
```

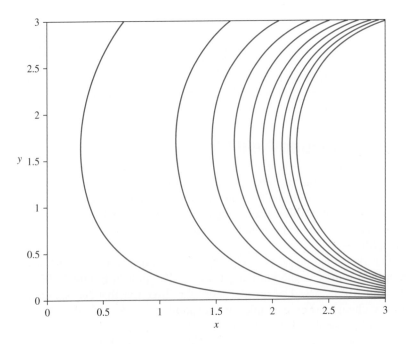

FIGURE 2–47

Contour Plot of Equation 2–68.

TABLE 2–4

Computer Generated Direction Field Plot of the Equation $y' = -xy$

MATLAB

```
[X,Y]= meshgrid(-2:0.2:2,-2:0.2:2);
S=-X.*Y;
L=sqrt(1+S.^2);% L is used to scale the arrow lengths.
quiver(X,Y,1./L,S./L),axis tight, xlabel('x'),ylabel('y')
```

MuPAD

```
field:= plot::VectorField2d([1,-x*y],x = -2..2,y = -2..2,
  Mesh=[25,25]):
```

Maple

```
with(DEtools)
dfieldplot(y'(x)=-x*y(x),y(x),x = -2..2,y = -2..2,
  axes = boxed)
```

Mathematica

```
VectorFieldPlot [{1,-x*y},{x,-2,3},{y,-1,2},\[Continuation]
ScaleFunction-> (1&), Axes->True,Frame->True]
```

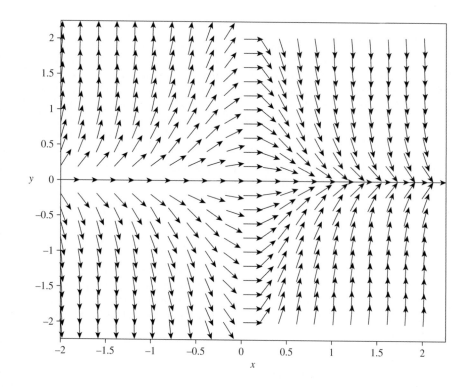

FIGURE 2–48

Direction Field Plot of the
Equation $y' = -xy$.

2–10 · SUMMARY

A first-order differential equation involves only the first-order derivatives, and it can be expressed as $y' = f(x, y)$. A general solution of a first-order differential equation involves an arbitrary constant C. The solution of an initial-value problem is obtained by determining C using the initial condition expressed as $y = y_0$ at $x = x_0$ or

$$y(x_0) = y_0 \tag{2-4}$$

Linearity A first-order differential equation is said to be linear if it is linear in y. A linear equation does not involve any powers, products, or other nonlinear functions of y or y' and can be expressed as

$$y' + P(x)y = R(x) \tag{2-7}$$

where P and R are specified functions of x which are continuous in the interval of interest. If an equation cannot be put into this form, then it is nonlinear.

Integrating Factor A linear first-order differential equation always can be solved in a straightforward manner by the use of an integrating factor defined as

$$\mu(x) = e^{\int P(x)\,dx} \tag{2-10}$$

Then the general solution of a linear first-order equation can be expressed as

$$y = \frac{1}{\mu(x)} \left[\int \mu(x)R(x)\,dx + C \right] \tag{2-12}$$

where the arbitrary constant C is determined from the initial condition.

Constant Coefficient Case Many problems of practical interest result in linear first-order differential equations with constant coefficients and right-hand side, and they can be expressed as

$$y' + by = c \tag{2-15}$$

The solution of this differential equation with the initial condition $y(0) = y_0$ is

$$y = \frac{c}{b}(1 - e^{-bx}) + y_0 e^{-bx} \tag{2-17}$$

For the special case of $c = 0$, it becomes

$$y = y_0 e^{-bx} \tag{2-18}$$

Uniqueness Condition Theorem 2–1 states that if the functions $P(x)$ *and* $Q(x)$ are continuous on an open interval I containing the point x_0, then the first-order linear initial-value problem

$$y' + P(x)y = R(x), \, y(x_0) = y_0$$

has a unique solution on I, given by

$$y = \frac{1}{\mu(x)} \left[\int \mu(x)R(x)\,dx + C \right]$$

where $\mu(x) = e^{\int P(x)\,dx}$ is the integrating factor.

Theorem 2–2 states that if $f(x, y)$ is a continuous function on some rectangle D containing the point (x_0, y_0). Furthermore, the solution is unique if $\partial f/\partial y$ is also continuous in D.

Separable Equations The first-order differential equation $y' = h(x, y)$ is said to be separable if its right side can be expressed as the ratio of a function of x and a function of y yielding $y' = f(x)/g(x)$ then a separable equation can be expressed as

$$g(y)y' = f(x) \tag{2-36}$$

Its solution is obtained by direct integration to be

$$\int g(y)\,dy = \int f(x)\,dx + C \tag{2-37}$$

since $y'\,dx = dy$.

Homogeneous Separable Case The best known class of differential equation that can be reduced to a separable form is the homogeneous equation. A first-order differential equation is said to be homogeneous if it can be expressed as

$$y' = f\left(\frac{y}{x}\right) \tag{2-46}$$

As a practical rule, an equation is homogeneous if, on the right side, the sum of the powers of x and y of each term in the numerator and the denominator are identical. Or we can apply the homogeneity test: in the differential equation, replace all x's by λx, and all the y's by λy, and simplify. If, after simplification, all the λ's cancel out and we end up with the original equation, then the differential equation is homogeneous. Otherwise, it is not.

Exact Differential Equation A first-order differential equation that can be expressed in the form $M(x, y) + N(x, y)y' = 0$ is called an exact differential equation in a region D if there exists a function $S(x, y)$ such that

$$\frac{\partial S(x, y)}{\partial x} = M(x, y) \quad \text{and} \quad \frac{\partial S(x, y)}{\partial y} = N(x, y)$$

for all (x, y) in that region. Theorem 2–3 states that If the partial derivatives $\partial M(x, y)/\partial y$ and $\partial N(x, y)/\partial x$ are continuous in a rectangular region D, then $M(x, y) + N(x, y)y' = 0$ is an exact differential equation in that region if and only if

$$\frac{\partial M(x, y)}{\partial y} = \frac{\partial N(x, y)}{\partial x}$$

at every point in D.

Some History for Perspective

All of the symbolic methods presented in this chapter were developed long ago, because people had no other way of solving differential equations. Some numerical methods were known, but they were very tedious to use before the advent of the digital computer. In fact, the present day symbolic processing programs use a set of rules based on the methods of this and later chapters.

Here are the famous contributors mentioned in this chapter.

Jakob Bernoulli (1654–1705), Swiss mathematician. He first analyzed the differential equation that is named for him. He also developed the method of separation of variables. Other members of the Bernoulli family were also prominent mathematicians (see Problems 2–199 to 2–205).

Jacopo Francesco Riccati (1676–1754), Italian mathematician. He first studied the differential equation that is named for him (see Problems 2–206 to 2–211).

Gottfried Wilhelm Leibniz (1646–1716), German mathematician. He developed the infinitesimal calculus independently from Newton, and his notation was widely adopted. He also developed several mechanical calculators and

refined the binary number system, which is the basis of digital computers.

Thomas Malthus (1766–1834), British economist. He wrote *An Essay on the Principle of Population*, in which he developed theories of population growth or decay.

Isaac Newton (1643–1727), English physicist, mathematician, and astronomer, among other pursuits. He is perhaps the most famous scientist of all time. He developed the calculus independently from Leibniz. He developed the basic principles of classical mechanics, including his law of gravitation and his laws of motion. He experimented with optics and developed his law of cooling and Newton's method for finding the roots of a function.

Evangelista Torricelli (1608–1647), Italian physicist and mathematician. He invented the barometer and discovered Torricelli's law, which relates the flow rate of a fluid through an opening to the height of the fluid.

Pierre Francois Verhulst (1804–1849), Belgian mathematician. He developed and solved the logistic differential equation model of population growth.

PROBLEMS

2–1 An Overview of First-Order Differential Equations

2–30C Can a first-order differential equation involve (a) $\sin y'$, (b) $e^{y'}$, or (c) y?

2–31C Can a general first-order differential equation be solved by direct integration? Under what conditions will this be the case?

2–32C Is the differential equation $dy/dx = xy^2$ equivalent to $dx/dy = 1/xy^2$?

2–33C Under what conditions does a linear first-order initial-value problem with constant coefficients have a solution? When is this solution unique?

2–34C How many integration constants does the general solution of a linear first-order differential equation involve?

2–35C Under what conditions does a linear first-order initial-value problem have singular solutions?

Determine if the following first-order differential equations are linear.

2–36 (a) $y' + 3x^2 y = \sin x$ (b) $2y' + 3x\sqrt{y} = e^x$

2–37 (a) $y' + e^x y = 2\sqrt{x}$ (b) $y'y^2 + \cos y = x$

2–38 (a) $xy'^2 + x^2 y = 1$ (b) $y' - 5x \sin y = 0$

2–39 (a) $yy' + xy = x$ (b) $y'^2 - y^2 = x^2$

2–40 (a) $y' - (y - x)^2 = 0$ (b) $y' - 3e^{xy} = x^3$

Solve the following linear first-order differential equations showing all of the steps involved.

2–41 (a) $2xy' - y = x^2$ (b) $y' + \dfrac{1}{x}y = e^x$

2–42 (a) $y' + 4xy = 2x$ (b) $y' - 4y = xe^{4x}$

2–43 (a) $y' + \left(3 - \dfrac{1}{x}\right)y = x^2 - x$

(b) $y' + (\tanh x)y = 2x$

2–44 (a) $(x^2 - 1)y' + 2xy = 4$ (b) $x^2 y' + 2xy = 1$

2–45 (a) $y' + \dfrac{2}{x}y + x^2 = \sin 2x$ (b) $y' + \dfrac{2}{x}y = \dfrac{e^{2x}}{x}$

2–46 (a) $xy' + (1 + x)y = 2$ (b) $y' + \dfrac{1}{x}y = e^x$

Solve the following linear first-order initial-value problems showing all the steps involved.

2–47 (a) $y' - 2y = e^x$ (b) $(x^2 - 1)y' - xy = 1$
$\quad\quad y(1) = 2$ $\quad\quad\quad\quad y(2) = 3$

2–48 (a) $\cos xy' - \sin xy = 4$ (b) $xy' + y = (x + 1)^2$
$\quad\quad y(\pi) = 1$ $\quad\quad\quad\quad y(1) = 2$

2–49 (a) $x^2 y' + xy = 4$ (b) $y' + \dfrac{1}{x - 4}y = x^4$
$\quad\quad y(1) = 3$ $\quad\quad\quad\quad y(2) = 8$

2–50 (a) $y' - \dfrac{2x}{2-x^2}y = e^x$ (b) $xy' + 4y = \cos x$

$\quad\quad y(2) = 4$ $\quad\quad\quad\quad\quad y(0) = 1$

2–51 By considering x to be the dependent variable instead of y, solve the following initial-value problem,

$$\frac{dy}{dx} = \frac{y^2}{1-x}, \quad y(0) = 1$$

2–52 By considering x to be the dependent variable instead of y, solve the following initial-value problem,

$$\frac{dy}{dx} = \frac{e^y}{e^{-y} + 2x}, \quad y(0) = 0$$

2–53 Show that if $y_1(x)$ is a solution of the linear homogeneous first-order equation $y' + P(x)y = 0$, then $Cy_1(x)$, where C is an arbitrary constant, is also a solution of that equation.

2–54 Show that if $y_1(x)$ is a solution of the nonlinear homogeneous first-order equation $y' + P(x)y^2 = 0$, then $Cy_1(x)$, where C is an arbitrary constant, is not a solution of that equation.

2–55 Show that if $y_1(x)$ is a solution of the linear nonhomogeneous first-order equation $y' + P(x)y = Q(x)$, then $Cy_1(x)$, where C is an arbitrary constant, is not a solution of that equation.

2–3 Applications of First-Order Linear Equations

2–56C Obtain a relation for the distance a light beam with absorption coefficient a travels in a medium before half of it is absorbed?

2–57C Define the terminal velocity for a rain droplet. Does this velocity depend on the height at which the droplet is formed?

2–58 In a large fishery with plenty of food supply, it is observed that the fish population doubles every year when no fish are caught. Taking the initial number of fish in the fishery to be N_0 and assuming Malthusian law of growth, obtain a relation for the number of fish as a function of time if fish is continuously caught at a rate of $0.002N_0$ per day.

2–59 It is observed that the population of certain bacteria colony doubles every 3 hours. Assuming the Malthusian growth law population is valid, determine how long it will take for the original population to quadruple.

2–60 Consider a country whose population is growing at a rate of 0.2 percent per year. If this rate of growth remains constant, in how many years will the population of that country double?

2–61 State whether any of the following equations has a time constant. If so, calculate its time constant.

(a) $6\dfrac{dy}{dt} + y^2 = 10$ (b) $10\dfrac{dy}{dt} + 2y = \sin t$

(c) $10\left(\dfrac{dy}{dt}\right)^2 + 2y = t^2$

2–62 Given the equation

$$6\frac{dy}{dt} + 3y = 0$$

and the initial condition $y(0) = 10$, without solving the equation, determine how long will it take for $y(t)$ to reach approximately $y = 3.7$? How long to reach $y = 0.2$?

2–63 Given the equation

$$15\frac{dy}{dt} + 3y = 24$$

and the initial condition $y(0) = 0$, determine the following.

(a) What is the steady-state value of y?
(b) Without solving the equation, determine how long will it take for $y(t)$ to reach approximately $y = 5.04$? How long to reach $y = 7.84$?

2–64 The half life of radium 226 is about 1600 years. Determine the decay constant of radium 226 and the fraction of radium 226 that decays in 100 years.

2–65 A small copper ball that is initially at a temperature $T_1 = 30$ is dropped into ice water at $t = 0$. It is observed that the temperature of the ball drops to 20°C at $t = 1$ min. Using Newton's law of cooling, determine temperature of the ball at $t = 2$ min.

2–66 A grape 1 cm in diameter that is initially at a uniform temperature of 20°C is placed in a refrigerator such that $\lambda = hA/mc = 0.003 \text{ s}^{-1}$. Using Newton's law of cooling, determine the temperature of the grape after 10 minutes.

2–67 A hot aluminum plate that is initially at a uniform temperature of 250°C is cooled by exposing it to an air stream at 50°C. The various parameters involved in the process are such that $\lambda = hA/mc = 0.001 \text{ s}^{-1}$. Using Newton's law of cooling, determine the time required to cool the plate to 100°C.

2–68 The absorption coefficient of water for green light is about 0.03 m^{-1}. Determine the fraction of green light absorbed after it travels 30 m in water.

2–69 Red light with a wavelength of $1.22 \ \mu\text{m}$ enters a 2–m deep pond at an angle of 45°. The absorption coefficient of water at this wavelength is 0.5 m^{-1}. Determine the fraction of the light that will reach the bottom of the pond.

2–70 A tank holds 200 l of brine that contains 10 kg of salt. Now pure water runs into the tank at a rate of 5 l per minute and the well-stirred mixture drains out of the tank at the same rate. Determine the amount of the salt in the tank after 30 min. How long will it take for the amount of the salt in the tank to drop to 1 kg?

2–71 Repeat Problem 2–70 assuming the drain valve is closed.

2–72 A body of mass $m = 5$ kg is dropped from the top of a 50-m high building. It strikes the hard ground with a perfectly elastic collision that reverses its direction of motion but does not change the magnitude of the velocity when the strike occurs. Assuming the air resistance to be proportional to the velocity of the body, with a proportionality constant $k = 2$ N·s/m, and taking $g = 9.75$ m/s^2, determine how high the body will bounce after striking the ground.

2–73 A spherical body of mass m, whose density is ρ_b, is released from rest into water and allowed to sink. While gravity is pulling the body down, a buoyancy force, which is defined by $\rho_w g v$, where ρ_w is the water density (kg/m^3), g is the gravitational constant (m/s^2), and v is the volume of body immersed in water (m^3) is pushing the body up. Assuming that the water resistance due to viscous effects is proportional to the velocity of the body with a proportionality constant k, derive the equation of motion of the body in terms of the given parameters. Also, determine the terminal sinking velocity of the body by taking $t \to \infty$. Finally, plot the velocity of the body as a function of time by taking $m = 15$ kg, $\rho_b = 2000$ kg/m^3, $\rho_w = 1000$ kg/m^3, $k = 15$ N·s/m, and $g = 9.81$ m/s^2.

2–74 The RL circuit shown in Figure 2–22 has the following values: $R = 10^4\ \Omega$, $L = 0.003$ H, and $v_s = 10$ V.

    (a) If the current is initially zero when the voltage is applied, determine the steady-state value of the current.

    (b) Without solving the differential equation, determine approximately how long it will take for the current to reach its steady-state value.

2–75 A sum of $10,000 is deposited into a savings account at an interest rate of 4% compounded continuously. Determine the amount of money in the account in eight years. What would your answer be if money is continuously withdrawn from the account at a rate of $1 per day? Set up the appropriate differential equations in both cases, and solve them.

2–76 A sum of $5,000 is deposited into a savings account at an interest rate of 10% compounded continuously. At the same time, money is withdrawn from the account continuously at a rate of $2 per day. By solving the governing differential equation, determine how long it will take for the balance of the account to be zero.

2–77 A sum of money A is deposited into a savings account with interest compounded continuously. If the money in the account is doubled at the end of the fifth year, determine the interest rate.

2–4 Nonlinear First-Order Differential Equations

For the first-order differential equations given, approximately determine the region in the xy-plane where the existence and uniqueness of a solution through any specified point is guaranteed by the existence and uniqueness theorem.

2–78 (a) $y' = \dfrac{x}{y}$ (b) $y' = y(1 - x^2)$

2–79 (a) $y' = xy$ (b) $y' = \dfrac{xy}{y^2 - 1}$

2–80 (a) $y' = \dfrac{1}{\sqrt{x^2 + y^2}}$ (b) $y' = 1 + xy$

For the first-order initial-value problems given, approximately determine the region in the xy-plane where the existence of a solution is guaranteed. Also, determine the region where the solution is unique.

2–81 (a) $y' = \sqrt{x^2 - y^2}$ (b) $y' = \dfrac{x}{y}$

     $y(0) = 1$ $y(1) = 3$

2–82 (a) $y' = \dfrac{2xy}{x^2 + y^2}$ (b) $y' = x^2 y^3$

     $y(2) = 4$ $y(0) = 0$

2–83 (a) $y' = \dfrac{1}{x^3 + y^3}$ (b) $y' = \dfrac{2xy}{1 - (x^2 + y^2)}$

     $y(0) = 2$ $y(1) = 2$

2–5 Separable First-Order Equations

2–84C Define orthogonality for two intersecting curves. Also define orthogonal trajectories.

2–85C Is it possible to convert a nonseparable equation into a separable one? How?

Solve the following first-order differential equations by separating the variables.

2–86 (a) $y' + 2e^{x+y} = 0$ (b) $y' = \dfrac{\sin x}{\sin y}$

2–87 (a) $xy'^2 = 1 - y^2$ (b) $y' = ay - bxy$

2–88 (a) $(x^2 - 1)y' = 3y$ (b) $y' = x^3 y^3$

2–89 (a) $y' = x \sin x \cos y$ (b) $yy' = e^{x+y+1}$

2–90 (a) $y' = e^{-y}(x + e^{-x})$ (b) $xyy' = \sqrt{1 - y^2}$

Solve the following first-order differential equations by first transforming them into separable form, and then separating the variables.

2–91 (a) $\dfrac{dy}{dx} = \dfrac{2 + (y - x)e^{3(y-x)}}{(y - x)e^{3(y-x)}} = \dfrac{2}{(y - x)e^{3(y-x)}} + 1$

     (b) $\dfrac{dy}{dx} = \sqrt{x + 2y - 3}$

2-92 (a) $\dfrac{dy}{dx} = (x - y)^2$

(b) $\dfrac{dy}{dx} = \dfrac{4e^{y-2x}}{x^2 - 4xy + 4y^2} + \dfrac{1}{2}$

$\qquad = \dfrac{4}{(x - 2y)^2 e^{2x-y}} + \dfrac{1}{2}$

Solve the following first-order initial-value problems by using the separation of variables method.

2-93 (a) $y' - 4xy^2 = x$ $\qquad$ (b) $x^2 y' = 1 - y^2$
$\qquad\quad\ y(1) = 0$ $\qquad\qquad\qquad\ y(1) = 0$

2-94 (a) $y' = 2(x - y)^2$ $\qquad$ (b) $y' = x^2 y^3$
$\qquad\quad\ y(0) = 0$ $\qquad\qquad\qquad\ y(-2) = 1$

2-95 (a) $y' = 3x^2 y,\ y(2) = 1$

(b) $y' = \dfrac{x \sin x}{y \cos x},\ y(\pi/2) = 0$

Solve the following first-order differential equations using two different methods.

2-96 (a) $y' + by = 0$ $\qquad$ (b) $y' = \dfrac{y}{1 - x^2}$

2-97 (a) $y' = 6x^3 y$ $\qquad$ (b) $y' + by = c$

2-98 A spherical tank of radius R is initially filled with water. Now a hole of radius r is opened at the bottom of the tank, and water is allowed to drain out. According to Torricelli's law, the water leaves the opening at a velocity of $V = \sqrt{2gy}$, where y is the height of the water above the hole at that moment, and g is gravitational acceleration. Obtain a relation for the depth of water as a function of time t, and determine how long it will take for the tank to drain completely.

2-99 Repeat Problem 2–98 for an inverted conical tank if a hole is opened at its bottom.

2-100 Logistic population growth with a threshold is described by the differential equation

$$\frac{dN}{dt} = -(a - bN)N$$

Obtain a general solution of this equation, and plot the population growth (or decline) for several initial population values N_0. Determine the threshold value of N_0 below which growth will not occur and certain species will become extinct.

2-101 A more realistic but more complex model for population growth is one that does not allow unbounded growth but allows extinction. Such a model is described by adding another factor to the differential equation in the above problem so that the rate of growth becomes negative when N is large. It is expressed as

$$\frac{dN}{dt} = -(a - bN)(1 - cN)N$$

Obtain a general solution of this differential equation and determine its equilibrium solutions.

2-102 In a large fishery, it is observed that the fish population grows according to the logistic law when no fish are caught. Obtain a relation for number of fish as function of time if fish are continuously caught at a constant rate of f.

2-103 The first stage of a two-stage rocket has a thrust T of 300 kN and a lift-off mass of $m = 5000$ kg. Aerodynamic drag force D for this particular rocket depends on the square of velocity as $D = 0.027v^2$, where v is in meters per second.

(a) Obtain the equation of motion and solve it for the velocity $v(t)$.

(b) Determine the rocket velocity after 4 s.

2-104 The first stage of a two-stage rocket has a thrust T of 300 kN and a lift-off mass of $m = 5000$ kg. Aerodynamic drag force D depends on the square of velocity as $D = \rho C_D A v^2/2$, where ρ is the atmospheric mass density, A is the cross-sectional area of the rocket (the area perpendicular to the flow), and C_D is the drag coefficient. For this particular rocket, $A = 0.2$ m^2, $C_D = 0.5$, and for the lower atmosphere, $\rho = 1.204$ kg/m^3.

(a) Obtain the equation of motion and solve it for the velocity $v(t)$.

(b) Determine the rocket velocity after 3 s.

2-105 Determine the orthogonal trajectories of the one-parameter family of curves for (a) $x^2 - y^2 = C$ and (b) $x^2 + y^2 - 2kx = 0$.

2-106 Determine the orthogonal trajectories of the one-parameter family of curves for (a) $y = ky^2$ and (b) $x^2 + 4xy - y^2 + 1 = C$.

Separable Homogeneous First-Order Differential Equations

2-107C What is the criteria for homogeneity for first-order differential equations?

2-108C Can a homogeneous first-order differential equation always be transformed into a separable one? How?

Determine if the following first-order differential equations are homogeneous.

2-109 (a) $\dfrac{dy}{dx} = \dfrac{x^2 - y^2}{xy}$ $\qquad$ (b) $\dfrac{dy}{dx} = \dfrac{x^3 - 2xy^2}{x^2 + y}$

2-110 (a) $\dfrac{dy}{dx} = \dfrac{x^3 + x^2 y}{2xy^2 - y^3}$ $\qquad$ (b) $\dfrac{dy}{dx} = x^2 - \dfrac{y^3}{x}$

2-111 (a) $\dfrac{dy}{dx} = \dfrac{x^4 - 3x^2 y^2 + y^4}{xy^3 - 4y^4}$ $\qquad$ (b) $\dfrac{dy}{dx} = x^3 - y^3$

Solve the following first-order homogeneous (or reducible to homogeneous) differential equations.

2–112 (a) $\dfrac{dy}{dx} = \dfrac{x}{x+y}$ (b) $\dfrac{dy}{dx} = \dfrac{x^2 y}{x^3 + 3y^3}$

2–113 (a) $\dfrac{dy}{dx} = \dfrac{2x^2 - y^2}{x^2}$ (b) $\dfrac{dy}{dx} = \dfrac{x + 2y}{2x - y}$

2–114 (a) $\dfrac{dy}{dx} = \dfrac{x^2 - 6y^2}{2xy}$ (b) $\dfrac{dy}{dx} = \dfrac{x^2 - 2xy}{x^2 + y^2}$

2–115 (a) $\dfrac{dy}{dx} = \dfrac{2x^2 y}{x^3 - y^3}$ (b) $\dfrac{dy}{dx} = \dfrac{-2x + 3y}{x - 2y}$

2–116 (a) $xy\dfrac{dy}{dx} = y^2 + x\sqrt{x^2 + y^2}$ (b) $x\dfrac{dy}{dx} = y - 4xe^{2y/x}$

2–117 (a) $\dfrac{dy}{dx} = \dfrac{y - 10\sqrt{4x^2 - y^2}}{x}$ (b) $\dfrac{dy}{dx} = \dfrac{x - y}{x}$

Solve the following first-order homogeneous (or reducible to homgeneous) initial-value problems.

2–118 (a) $\dfrac{dy}{dx} = \dfrac{x^2 - y^2}{2xy}$, $y(1) = 0$

     (b) $\dfrac{dy}{dx} = \dfrac{x - y}{x + y}$, $y(0) = 0$

2–119 (a) $\dfrac{dy}{dx} = \dfrac{y}{x + y}$, $y(0) = 1$

     (b) $\dfrac{dy}{dx} = \dfrac{2xy - y^2}{3x^2}$, $y(8) = 1$

2–120 (a) $\dfrac{dy}{dx} = \dfrac{x + 2y}{2x - y}$, $y(1) = 0$

     (b) $\dfrac{dy}{dx} = \dfrac{y - \sqrt{x^2 + xy - y^2}}{x}$, $y(1) = 0$

*Some nonhomogeneous first-order equations can be readily converted to homogeneous equations by changing the variables. One class of such equations is the **linear fraction equation**, expressed as*

$$y' = \frac{ax + by + c}{Ax + By + C}$$

This nonhomogeneous equation can be converted to the following homogeneous equation

$$y' = \frac{aX + bY}{AX + BY}$$

by defining two new variables as $x = X + x_0$ and $y = Y + y_0$ where

$$x_0 = \frac{Bc - bC}{Ab - aB} \quad \text{and} \quad y_0 = \frac{aC - Ac}{Ab - aB}$$

with $Ab - aB \neq 0$. Using this technique, solve the following equations.

2–121 (a) $\dfrac{dy}{dx} = \dfrac{-2x + 3y + 1}{x - 1}$ (b) $\dfrac{dy}{dx} = \dfrac{x + 2y - 3}{x - y}$

2–122 $\dfrac{dy}{dx} = \dfrac{3x - 4y - 5}{x + 2y}$

2–123 (a) $\dfrac{dy}{dx} = \dfrac{x + y}{x - 4}$ (b) $\dfrac{dy}{dx} = \dfrac{x + 2y - 1}{y}$

2–6 Exact First-Order Differential Equations

2–124C When is a first-order differential equation exact, and when is it inexact?

2–125C When integrating Equation 2–58, why did we use the arbitrary function $g(y)$ instead of the arbitary constant C?

2–126C What is the method of grouping? Does it work for inexact first-order differential equations?

Determine whether or not the first-order differential equations given are exact.

2–127 (a) $3x + 1 + (3y - 1)y' = 0$
     (b) $3y - 1 - (3x + 1)y' = 0$

2–128 (a) $y^2 - 2x + (2xy - e^y)y' = 0$
     (b) $y^2 - 2xyy' = 0$

2–129 (a) $e^y\sin x + 2 - (e^y\cos x)y' = 0$
     (b) $e^x\sin y - (e^x\cos x)y' = 0$

2–130 (a) $2x + y + (x - 2y)y' = 0$
     (b) $x + 2y + (x - 2y)y' = 0$

2–131 (a) $x^2 + \sin x - (y^2 - \cos y)y' = 0$
     (b) $x^2 + \sin y - (y^2 - \cos x)y' = 0$

2–132 (a) $\dfrac{dy}{dx} = \dfrac{x - y - 1}{x + y + 1}$ (b) $\dfrac{dy}{dx} = \dfrac{x + y - 1}{x + y + 1}$

2–133 (a) $\dfrac{dy}{dx} = \dfrac{-2xe^y}{x^2 e^y + 1}$ (b) $\dfrac{dy}{dx} = \dfrac{2xe^x}{x^2 e^y + 1}$

2–134 (a) $\dfrac{dy}{dx} = -\dfrac{2x\sin 2y + xe^x}{e^{2y} - x^2\cos 2y}$

     (b) $\dfrac{dy}{dx} = \dfrac{2x\sin 2y + xe^x}{x^2\cos 2y - e^{2y}}$

Solve the following initial-value problems after showing that the differential equation is exact.

2–135 $(2x^2 + 1) + (4y^3 - 2y + 1)y' = 0$, $y(0) = 1$

2–136 $(3x^2\sin y + xe^x) + (x^3\cos y - y^2 + 1)y' = 0$, $y(1) = -2$

2–137 $(2x + 3y - 1) + (3x - 2y + 3)y' = 0$, $y(0) = 0$

2–138 $(3x^2 y + e^x\sin y) + (x^3 + e^x\cos y)y' = 0$, $y(0) = \pi/2$

2–139 $y' = \dfrac{x^2 e^x + 1}{y^2 e^y - 1}$, $y(0) = 4$

2–140 $y' = \dfrac{2x - 3y - 1}{3x - 2y + 1}$, $y(-2) = 3$

2–7 Graphical Methods

Sketch the direction field of the following differential equations, and plot the solution that satisfies the specified initial conditions.

2–141 (a) $y' = x^2 + y^2$, $y(2) = 4$
(b) $y' = xy + 2$, $y(1) = 2$

2–142 (a) $y' = x^2 - y^2$, $y(1) = 1$ (b) $y' = xy$, $y(2) = 6$

2–143 (a) $y' = \sqrt{y}$, $y(3) = 2$ (b) $y' = \dfrac{x}{y}$, $y(1) = 1$

2–144 (a) $y' = y$, $y(0) = -1$
(b) $y' = \dfrac{1}{y}$, $y(2) = 1$

2–145 (a) $y' = x - y$, $y(2) = 3$
(b) $y' = 0.5y^{1/3}$, $y(1) = 0.5$

2–9 Computer Methods for First-Order Equations

Solve the following equations by computer.

2–146 $(x^2 - 1)y' + 2xy = 4$

2–147 $y' = x \sin x \cos y$

2–148 $y' = \sqrt{x + 2y - 3}$

2–149 $y' = \dfrac{x^2 y}{x^3 + 3y^3}$

Solve the following equations by computer.

2–150 $x^2 y' + xy = 4$, $y(0) = 3$

2–151 $y' = 2(x - y)^3$, $y(0) = 0$

2–152 $y' = \dfrac{x^3 - xy^2}{y^3}$, $y(0) = -1$

Use a computer to plot the direction field for the following problems.

2–153 $y' = x^2 - y^2$

2–154 $y' = 0.5y^{1/3}$

2–155 $y' = \sqrt{y}$

Use a computer to plot the contour plot for the following problems. Use five contours having equally spaced values of C.

2–156 The solution of $4yy' = x$ has the form $4y^2 - x^2 = C$.

2–157 The solution of $4yy' + x = 0$ has the form $4y^2 + x^2 = C$.

2–158 The solution of $yy' = 2$ has the form $y^2 = 4x + C$.

Review Problems

Solve the following linear first-order differential equations, which involve hump discontinuities in the functions $P(x)$ or $Q(x)$. (Hint: If $x = a$ is a point of discontinuity, solve the differential equation twice for $x < a$ and $x > a$, and then combine the solutions.)

2–159 $y' - 4y = f(x)$, where $f(x) = \begin{cases} 0, x < 0 \\ 10, x \geq 0 \end{cases}$

2–160 $y' + f(x)y = 0$, where $f(x) = \begin{cases} 0, x < 1 \\ 2x, x \geq 1 \end{cases}$

2–161 $y' + y = f(x)$, where $f(x) = \begin{cases} -x, x < 0 \\ x, x \geq 0 \end{cases}$

2–162 $y' + f(x)y = 1$, where $f(x) = \begin{cases} -1, x < 0 \\ 1, x \geq 0 \end{cases}$

2–163 Temperature measurements are based on heat transfer between the sensor of a measurement device such as an ordinary thermometer or the junction of a thermocouple, and the medium whose temperature is to be measured. Once the sensor or thermometer is brought into contact with the medium, the sensor quickly receives (or loses, if it is warmer) heat and reaches thermal equilibrium with the medium. At this time, the medium and the sensor are at the same temperature. The time required for the temperature equilibrium to be established may vary from a fraction of a second to several minutes. Because of its small size and high conductivity, the sensor can be assumed to be at a uniform temperature at the all times, and Newton's law of cooling is applicable.

Thermocouples are commonly used to measure the temperature of gas streams. The characteristics of the thermocouple junction and the gas flow are such that $\lambda = hA/mc = 0.02s^{-1}$. Initially, the thermocouple junction is at temperature T_i, and the gas stream at T_0. Determine how long it will take for the thermocouple to sense 95% of the initial temperature difference between the junction and the gas.

2–164 A body of mass m at the top of a 100-m high tower is thrown vertically upwards into the air with an initial velocity of 10 m/s. Assume the air resistance F_D acting on the body to be proportional to the velocity V, so that $F_D = kV$. Taking $g = 9.75$ m/s^2 and $k/m = 5$ s, determine (a) how high the body will reach above the tower, (b) how long it will take for the body to hit the ground, and (c) the velocity of the body when it hits the ground.

2–165 Repeat Problem 2–164 assuming the body is thrown upwards at 30° from the horizontal instead of vertically.

2–166 Consider a body of mass m that is dropped from rest at $t = 0$. The body falls under the influence of gravity, and the air resistance F_D that opposes the motion is assumed to be proportional to the square of the velocity such that $F_D = kV^2$.

Let x be the vertical distance and take the positive direction of the x axis to be downward with the origin at the initial position of the body. Obtain relations for the velocity and position of the body as a function of time t.

2–167 Assuming that the rate of change of price P of merchandise is proportional to the difference between demand D and supply S at any time t, the differential equations that describe the price fluctuations with time can be expressed as

$$\frac{dP}{dt} = k(D - s)$$

where k is the constant of proportionality whose value depends on the particular merchandise. Solve the differential equation above by expressing the supply and demand as simply linear functions of price, as $S = aP - b$ and $D = e - fP$.

2–168 A chemical reaction that involves the interaction of two substances A and B to form a new compound X is called a second order reaction. In such cases, it is observed that the rate of reaction (or the rate at which the new compound is formed) is proportional to the product of remaining amounts of the two original substances. If one molecule of A and one molecule of B combine to form one molecule of X, (i.e., the reaction equation is $A + B \rightarrow X$), then the differential equation that describes this specific reaction can be expressed as

$$\frac{dx}{dt} = k(a - x)(b - x)$$

where k is a positive constant, a and b are the initial concentrations of the reactants A and B, respectively, and $x(t)$ is the concentration of the new compound at any time t. Assuming there is no compound X present initially, obtain a relation for $x(t)$. What happens when $t \rightarrow \infty$?

2–169 Repeat the Problem 2–168, assuming that the initial concentration of the first reacting substance is twice the initial concentration of the second substance so that $a = 2b$.

2–170 Show that any separable first-order differential equation is necessarily exact.

2–171 Find the value of the constant a such that the differential equation

$$2x + ay - 2 + (3x - 4y - 3)y' = 0$$

is exact, and then solve it.

2–172 Find the value of the constant b such that the differential equation

$$4x^2 + by + (2x - 3y^2 + 1)y' = 0$$

is exact, and then solve it.

2–173 Find the function $f(x)$ such that the differential equation

$$e^x \sin x + f(x)y^2 - 3 + (2xy - y^2)y' = 0$$

is exact, and then solve it.

2–174 Show that the differential equation $M(x, y)dx + N(x, y)dy = 0$ has an integrating factor that is a function of xy if the quantity h depends on xy only where

$$h = \frac{1}{xM - yN}\left(\frac{\partial N}{\partial x} - \frac{\partial M}{\partial y} \right)$$

2–175 A 2 m^3 tank is divided into two equal parts by a permeable partition. Initially each part contains a solution of different concentrations, C_1 and C_2. Show that the concentration in part 1 is governed by the differential equation

$$\frac{d^2C_1}{dt^2} + 2k\frac{dC_1}{dt} = 0$$

where k is the constant of proportionality, and solve this differential equation by reducing it to first-order.

Solve the following differential equations using any applicable method. Also, determine the integration constant when an initial condition is specified.

2–176 $y' - 2y = y^3$, $\quad y(0) = 1$

2–177 $(e^x + 1)y' = e^y + 1$, $\quad y(1) = 0$

2–178 $y' = e^{\ln x - y + 2}$

2–179 $y' = \dfrac{y + \sqrt{x^2 - 8xy}}{x}$

2–180 $xy' + y = x - 1$, $\quad y(2) = 3$

2–181 $y' = \dfrac{x^2 + xy + y^2}{x^2}$, $\quad y(1) = 0$

2–182 $y' = \dfrac{1}{e^y - x}$, $\quad y(1) = 0$

2–183 $y' = \dfrac{2x^2y^3 - y^5}{x^5}$

2–184 $y'' - 2y' = x + 1$

2–185 $y'' + yy' = 0$

2–186 $4y'y'' = x - 1$, $\quad y(0) = 0, y'(0) = 1/4$

2–187 $y''' + y'' = e^x$

Any nth-order differential equation that contains only two consecutive derivatives of unknown function y, but not y itself, can be reduced to a first-order differential equation through the transformation $v = y^{(n-1)}$. For example, the transformation $v = y''$ reduces the third-order differential equation $y''' = f(x, y'')$ into the first-order equation $v' = f(x, v)$. Also, a second-order differential equation that does not contain the independent variable x can be reduced to a first-order one by the transformation $v = y'$. This transformation reduces the second-order equation

$$y'' = f(y, y')$$

to

$$v\frac{dv}{dy} = f(y, u)$$

which is a first-order differential equation in v with y as the independent variable. This equation can be solved, assuming its solution exists, using any of the applicable methods discussed in this chapter. Solve the following initial-value or boundary-value problems by first reducing the differential equations to a first-order.

2–188 $y''' = 3y'' - 9x$, $y(0) = 1$, $y'(1) = 5$,
$y''(2) = 13$

2–189 $2y'' = \dfrac{y'^2 + 1}{y}$, $y(0) = 1$, $y'(0) = 0$

2–190 $y'' + y^2 y' = 0$, $y(0) = 1$, $y'(0) = -1/3$

2–191 $y'' = x^2 + 1$, $y(0) = 0$, $y'(2) = 2$

2–192 $y'' + 4yy' = 0$, $y(1) = 1$, $y'(1) = 2$

2–193 $y''' + \dfrac{1}{x + 1}y'' = -2$, $y(0) = -1$,
$y'(0) = 1$, $y''(0) = 0$

2–194 $y'' + y' = e^{3x}$, $y(1) = -1$, $y'(0) = 4$

2–195 $y'' + y' + y'^2 = 0$, $y(0) = -1$, $y'(1) = 1$

2–196 $y'' + (y' - 1)^2 - y'^2 = 2$, $y(0) = 0$, $y'(1) = 0$

2–197 $x^2 y'' = y'$, $y(0) = 1$, $y'(1) = 0$

2–198 $y'' + 3y'^2 = y'$, $y(1) = 1$, $y'(0) = 1$

The first-order equations of the form $y' + P(x)y = R(x)y^n$ are called **Bernoulli equations** after Jakob Bernoulli (1654–1705). When $n = 0$ or $n = 1$, a Bernoulli equation becomes a linear equation that can be solved in a straightforward manner. But when $n \neq 0$ or $n \neq 1$, the Bernoulli equation

is nonlinear. Nonlinear equations, in general, are difficult to solve. However, as Leibniz showed in 1696, the transformation $v = y^{(1-n)}$ reduces the Bernoulli equation to a linear equation in v. The proof is straightforward and is left as an exercise to the student.

Solve the following nonlinear first-order differential equations using the transformation. When an initial condition is specified, also determine the integration constant.

2–199 $y' - y = y^4$, $y(0) = 1$

2–200 $y' + 2y = -4y^3$, $y(0) = 1$

2–201 $y' - \dfrac{y}{x^2 - 1} = y^2$

2–202 $y' - (a - by)y = 0$, $y(0) = 100$

2–203 $y' - (a - by^2)y = 0$

2–204 $y' - \dfrac{1}{x}y = y^2$, $y(1) = 0$

2–205 Show that the transformation $v = y^{1-n}$ reduces the Bernoulli equation to a linear equation in v.

The first-order equations of the form $y' + P(x)y^2 + Q(x)y = R(x)$ are called **Riccati equations**, after Italian mathematician J. F. Riccati (1676–1754). If y_1 is a solution of this equation, then the transformation $y = y_1 + 1/z$ reduces this equation to the following linear first-order equation in z,

$$z' + [2y_1 P(x) + Q(x)]z = -P(x)$$

This can be shown easily by substituting y and y' expressions into the original equation and simplifying. Using the given particular solution and the transformation $y = y_1 + 1/z$, solve the following nonlinear first-order differential equations.

2–206 $y' + y^2 + (2x - 4)y = 4(x - 1)$, $y_1 = -x$

2–207 $y' = 2y + y^2$, $y_1 = 0$

2–208 $y' = 2(1 - y) - (1 - y)^2$, $y_1 = 1$

2–209 $y' = 2e^{-2x}y^2 + y - e^{2x}$, $y_1 = e^{2x}$

2–210 $y' = 3(x - y) - (x - y)^2 + 1$, $y_1 + x$

2–211 Show that if $y_1(x)$ is a solution, the transformation $y = y_1 + 1/z$ reduces the Riccati equation into a linear equation in z.

SECOND-ORDER LINEAR DIFFERENTIAL EQUATIONS

3

*F*irst-order linear differential equations always can be solved in a systematic manner through the use of an integrating factor, as discussed in Chapter 2, and it does not make much difference if the coefficients are constant or variable so long as the integrations can be performed. But this is not the case with the *second (or higher) order* linear differential equations, since no general procedure exists to solve such equations unless the coefficients are constant or they meet certain conditions. Many differential equations that arise in sciences and engineering are second-order linear equations with constant coefficients, and thus, it is important that we master the solution procedure for such equations. This is precisely what we intend to do in this chapter.

Although most definitions, theorems, and procedures described in this chapter are quite general, we will primarily focus on the *second-order linear equations with constant coefficients* for two reasons: (1) such equations are the ones scientists and engineers are most likely to encounter in practice and (2) new concepts are easier to demonstrate and learn on simpler equations. We will extend the analysis to higher-order linear equations with constant coefficients in Chapter 4 and to linear equations with variable coefficients in Chapter 5 by introducing the method of series solutions. This three-chapter sequence provides a fairly complete coverage of linear equations.

We start this chapter by reviewing the basic definitions and theorems related to linear differential equations (such as *linear and homogeneous equations, linear dependence and independence*, the *superposition principle*, and *reduction of order*). We continue with the *characteristic equation* and discuss the solution procedure for second-order linear homogeneous equations with constant coefficients. We then introduce the methods of *undetermined coefficients* and *variation of parameters* to determine the particular solutions corresponding to the nonhomogeneous terms. Then we discuss the *Euler equation*, which is a linear equation with variable coefficients of a special form, since it always can be transformed into equations with constant coefficients. Finally, we apply the solution procedure to various second-order linear differential equations with constant coefficients that frequently arise in practice. These applications include mechanical vibrations and oscillations in electrical circuits.

Objectives

When you have finished this chapter, you should be able to:

1. use the Wronskian to determine if two solutions are linearly independent,

2. identify a fundamental set of solutions of a linear homogeneous second-order equation,

3. use the reduction of order method to obtain a second fundamental solution when one solution is known,

4. obtain the general solution of a second-order linear homogeneous equation with constant coefficients,

5. obtain the particular solution of a second-order linear nonhomogeneous equation with constant coefficients using the method of undetermined coefficients and the method of variation of parameters,

6. solve the second-order Euler equation,

7. apply the chapter results to analyze applications in mechanical vibrations and oscillations in electrical circuits, and

8. use a computer package to obtain the closed-form solution of a second-order equation.

3–1 ▪ INTRODUCTION TO SECOND-ORDER LINEAR EQUATIONS

You will recall from Chapter 1 that a differential equation is said to be **linear** if it does not involve any powers, products, or other nonlinear functions of dependent variable y or its derivatives. The second-order linear differential equation can be written in the most general form as

$$y'' + P(x)y' + Q(x)y = R(x) \tag{3–1}$$

where P, Q, and R are given functions, which are constants or depend only on the independent variable x. Note that a linear equation does not involve any nonlinear functions of the independent variable (such as x^2, e^x, or $x^2 \sin x$).

The function $R(x)$ represents all of the terms that do not involve the dependent variable y or any of its derivatives and is called the **nonhomogeneous term**. A linear differential equation is said to be **nonhomogeneous** when $R(x) \neq 0$ and **homogeneous** when $R(x) = 0$. Thus, second-order linear homogeneous equations can be written in the most general form as

$$y'' + P(x)y' + Q(x) = 0 \tag{3–2}$$

When solving a linear, nonhomogeneous equation, it is often convenient to consider the homogeneous part of the equation separately. This is done by simply setting $R(x)$ equal to zero. The resulting equation is called the **related homogeneous equation** or **complementary equation** of the given differential equation (Figure 3–1). Therefore, Equation 3–2 is the related homogeneous equation of Equation 3–1.

Linear differential equations are also classified with respect to the coefficients of the dependent variable y and its derivatives. If these coefficients are simply constants, the equation is said to have **constant coefficients**. If one or more coefficients depend on the independent variable x, then the equation is said to have **variable coefficients**. Therefore, the second-order linear differential equation with constant coefficients can be expressed in the most general form as

$$y'' + by' + cy = R(x) \tag{3–3}$$

where b and c are two real constants (such as 3, −4.2, 3/5, or even zero). Note that the nonhomogeneous term still can be a function of x. For example,

$$y'' - 2y' + 6.8y = x^3 + e^{-2x} - 1 \tag{3–4}$$

is a second-order linear equation with *constant coefficients*; whereas,

$$y'' - 2xy' + 6.8y = x^3 + e^{-2x} - 1 \tag{3–5}$$

is a second-order linear equation with *variable coefficients* (Figure 3–2).

The distinction between linear equations with constant or variable coefficients is very important because the solution procedures of these two classes of linear equations are very different. But the fundamental theorems associated with linear equations that we will discuss next are applicable to both classes.

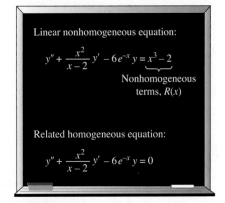

FIGURE 3–1

A linear, nonhomogeneous equation and its related homogeneous equation.

(a) With constant coefficients:

$$y'' + 6y' - 2y = xe^{-2x}$$

(b) With variable coefficients:

$$y'' - 6x^2y' - \frac{2}{x-1}y = xe^{-2x}$$

FIGURE 3–2

A linear, nonhomogeneous equation with (a) constant coefficients and (b) variable coefficients.

In Chapter 2, we have shown that a first-order linear differential equation with a specified initial condition (i.e., a first-order linear, initial-value problem) has a unique solution in an interval in which the coefficients are continuous. It turns out that this is also the case with the higher-order linear, initial-value problems, except that now we need to specify an additional initial condition for each additional order. (Two initial conditions for a second-order equation, three initial conditions for a third-order equation, etc.) The *existence and uniqueness* of the solution of second-order linear, initial-value problems is expressed by the following theorem. The proof can be found in specialized references.

THEOREM 3–1   Existence and Uniqueness

If the functions $P(x)$, $Q(x)$, and $R(x)$ are continuous on an interval $x_1 < x < x_2$ and x_0 is any point in this interval, then the differential equation

$$y'' + P(x)y' + Q(x)y = R(x)$$

has a unique (one and only one) solution on this interval that satisfies the two initial conditions:

$$y(x_0) = y_0 \quad \text{and} \quad y'(x_0) = y_0'$$

Therefore, even if we do not know how to solve the second-order linear differential equation yet, we know at least that there is a solution and it is unique in an interval, provided that the coefficients are continuous in that interval and the two initial conditions are specified at a point in that interval. Note that the differential equation must be in the *standard form* (the leading coefficient being 1) for this theorem to be applicable. If it is not, we should divide each term by the coefficient of y'' to put it into that form (Figure 3–3). Once the coefficient of y'' is 1, then the coefficient of y' is $P(x)$, the coefficient of y is $Q(x)$, and all of the remaining terms are $R(x)$.

Theorem 3–1 reassures us that, once we find a function that satisfies both the differential equation and the initial conditions, the search for the solution is over. There is no other function that will satisfy the differential equation and the initial conditions, as illustrated in the following examples.

Given differential equation:

$$2xy'' - 8x^2 y = 6$$

Its standard form:

$$y'' - 4xy = \frac{3}{x}$$

$$\underset{1}{\uparrow}$$

FIGURE 3–3

A second-order differential equation can be put into the standard form by dividing each term by the coefficient of y''.

EXAMPLE 3–1   Existence of a Solution

Show that the given initial-value problem has a unique solution, and determine the interval of that solution.

$$y'' + \frac{3x}{x - 1}y' - 5y = \cos x - 2$$

$$y(5) = 3 \quad \text{and} \quad y'(5) = -1$$

SOLUTION This is an *initial-value problem*, since both conditions are specified at the same x value, $x_0 = 5$. The differential equation is *second order*

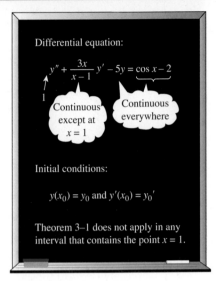

Differential equation:

$$y'' + \frac{3x}{x-1} y' - 5y = \cos x - 2$$

Continuous except at $x = 1$

Continuous everywhere

Initial conditions:

$$y(x_0) = y_0 \text{ and } y'(x_0) = y_0'$$

Theorem 3–1 does not apply in any interval that contains the point $x = 1$.

FIGURE 3–4

An initial-value problem will have a unique solution in any interval provided that the differential equation does not involve any discontinuities in that interval.

because the highest derivative is y''; *linear* as it involves no powers, products, or nonlinear functions of y and its derivatives; *nonhomogeneous* since the right-hand side is nonzero and the terms on the right side do not involve the dependent variable y or any of its derivatives; and is in the *standard form* since the coefficient of y'' is one. Comparing it with Equation 3–1 we see that

$$P(x) = \frac{3x}{x-1}, \quad Q(x) = -5, \quad \text{and} \quad R(x) = \cos x - 2$$

The functions $Q(x)$ and $R(x)$ are continuous, but the function $P(x)$ is discontinuous at $x = 1$. Therefore, $P(x)$ is continuous in any interval that does not contain the point $x = 1$ (Figure 3–4). Specifically, it is continuous in two intervals: $-\infty < x < 1$ and $1 < x < \infty$.

Considering that the initial conditions are specified at $x_0 = 5$, which is in the second interval, Theorem 3–1 guarantees that this initial-value problem has a unique solution in the interval $1 < x < \infty$.

EXAMPLE 3–2   **Zero Solution**

Determine the solution of the following initial-value problem:

$$y'' + 3xy' - 5y = 0$$
$$y(2) = 0 \quad \text{and} \quad y'(2) = 0$$

SOLUTION This is an *initial-value problem*, since both conditions are specified at the same x value. The differential equation is *second order* because the highest derivative is y''; *linear* as it involves no powers, products, or other nonlinear functions of y and its derivatives; *homogeneous* since every term involves the dependent variable y or one of its derivatives; and is the *standard form* since the coefficient of y'' is 1. Furthermore, the coefficients of the differential equation do not involve any discontinuities; therefore, the interval of the solution is $-\infty < x < \infty$.

We note that the point $x_0 = 2$ (or any other point) is in this interval. Thus, according to Theorem 3–1, this initial-value problem has one and only one solution, which is determined by inspection to be $y = 0$ since the function $y = 0$ satisfies both the differential equation and the initial conditions.

Differential equation:

$$y'' + P(x)y' + Q(x)y = 0$$

Initial conditions:

$$y(x_0) = 0 \text{ and } y'(x_0) = 0$$

Solution:

$$y = 0$$

FIGURE 3–5

The trivial solution $y = 0$ is the only solution of this linear, homogeneous equation with continuous coefficients and zero initial conditions.

You may be tempted to try some other functions to see if the initial-value problem in Example 3–2 possesses any other solutions since $y = 0$ is, after all, a trivial solution. But Theorem 3–1 says that any such attempt will be a waste of time, because the initial-value problem has only one solution and we already found one solution, which is $y = 0$.

We generalize this finding as follows (Figure 3–5). In an interval that contains the point x_0 and in which the coefficients of the differential equation in the standard form are continuous, the trivial solution $y = 0$ is the only solution of a second-order linear, homogeneous initial-value problem whose initial conditions are $y(x_0) = 0$ and $y'(x_0) = 0$.

For linear, homogeneous equations with constant coefficients, $R(x) = 0$, and the coefficients are naturally continuous in $-\infty < x < \infty$. Thus, the solution of such equations are valid for all x. We do not need to specify an interval in this case. More generally, if the coefficients and the nonhomogeneous terms are continuous over the entire x axis, then x_0 can be any point, and the solution is valid for all x.

Distinction should be made between the *solution of a differential equation* and *one of an initial-value problem*. A second-order differential equation involves y''; thus, it is natural to expect the solution y to involve two integrations and two arbitrary constants C_1 and C_2. Considering that these arbitrary constants can take on an infinite number of values, a second-order linear differential equation will have an infinite number of different solutions. To determine the values of the two arbitrary constants C_1 and C_2, we need to specify two conditions (such as the value of the unknown function or its first derivative at some point or points), and we require the solution to satisfy these conditions. These two conditions will give us two equations for the determination of C_1 and C_2.

One possibility is to specify both conditions at the same point x_0. In this case, we will have an *initial-value problem*, which is guaranteed by Theorem 3–1 to have a unique solution in an interval that contains the point x_0 under stated conditions. Therefore, out of an infinite number of solution curves, one and only one curve will satisfy the two specified initial conditions, yielding a unique solution to the initial-value problem. Considering that the two initial conditions $y(x_0) = y_0$ and $y'(x_0) = y_0'$ can be interpreted as the values of the solution curve and its slope at the point x_0, we conclude that no two solution curves will have the same slope at their point of interception.

We cannot help wondering what will happen if the two conditions are specified at different points, say at x_1 and x_2. In this case, we will have a *boundary-value problem*, and Theorem 3–1 gives no assurances that this boundary-value problem will have a unique solution or any solution at all (Figure 3–6). But it will suffice to say that a boundary-value problem will have a unique solution only when the two boundary conditions yield unique values for the arbitrary constants C_1 and C_2.

(a) Initial-value problem:

$$y'' + 2y' - 3x^2 y = x^3 e^{-x}$$

$$y(0) = 2, \quad y'(0) = -5$$

$y(x)$ exists and is unique.

(b) Boundary-value problem:

$$y'' + 2y' - 3x^2 y = x^3 e^{-x}$$

$$y(0) = 2, \quad y'(8) = 3$$

$y(x)$ may not be unique; it may not even exist.

FIGURE 3–6

When the functions $P(x)$, $Q(x)$, and $R(x)$ are continuous, Theorem 3–1 guarantees the existence and uniqueness of the solution of an initial-value problem, but no such guarantee exists for boundary-value problem.

EXAMPLE 3–3   Steady Heat Conduction Through a Plain Wall

Under steady conditions, the temperature distribution in a plain wall of thickness L shown in Figure 3–7 is governed by the following second order differential equation $y'' = 0$ where y represents the temperature of the wall at location x. Determine the general solution (the temperature distribution in the wall), and the specific solution for the following cases:

(a) Initial conditions $y(0) = 10$ and $y'(0) = -5$
(b) Boundary conditions $y(0) = 10$ and $y(L) = 0$
(c) Boundary conditions $y'(0) = -5$ and $y'(L) = 10$
(d) Boundary conditions $y'(0) = -5$ and $y'(L) = 5$

SOLUTION   This is a simple second-order, linear, homogeneous differential equation with constant coefficients. The functions $P(x) = Q(x) = R(x) = 0$

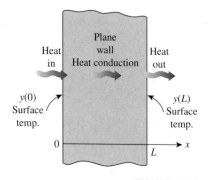

FIGURE 3–7

The plane wall discussed in Example 3–3.

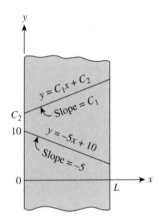

FIGURE 3–8

Any straight line is a solution of the differential equation $y'' = 0$, but only one of those lines will satisfy the initial conditions $y(0) = 10$ and $y'(0) = 5$.

in this case and are continuous over the entire x axis. Therefore, at least mathematically, the solution is not limited to any finite interval. However, the differential equation describes the temperature distribution in the medium $0 \leq x \leq L$; thus, we will limit the solution to this interval only.

The differential equation is in a readily integrable form. Therefore, we obtain the general solution by two simple successive integrations:

$$y' = C_1 \tag{3–6}$$

and

$$y = C_1 x + C_2 \tag{3–7}$$

where C_1 and C_2 are arbitrary constants. Note that the general solution of this second-order differential equation involves two arbitrary constants as expected.

The general solution in this case resembles the general formula of a straight line whose slope C_1 and whose value at $x = 0$ is C_2. Therefore, any straight line is a solution of the differential equation $y'' = 0$ (Figure 3–8). Note that the solution lines may intersect each other. That is, different solutions may have the same value at the same point. But they never may have the same slope at the point of intersection and still remain different solutions.

(a) The solution that satisfies the specified initial conditions is obtained by applying the two conditions to the general solution, and solving for C_1 and C_2.

$$y'(0) = -5 \rightarrow C_1 = -5$$
$$y(0) = 10 \rightarrow 10 = -5.0 + C_2 \rightarrow C_2 = 10$$

Therefore, $y(x) = -5x + 10$, which is the equation of a specific line. No other solution line will satisfy these two initial conditions, according to Theorem 3–1. Therefore, this is the unique solution of the specified initial-value problem (Figure 3–8).

(b) The solution that satisfies the specified boundary conditions is obtained by applying the conditions to the general solution to determine C_1 and C_2:

$$y(0) = 10 \rightarrow 10 = C_1 \cdot 0 + C_2 \rightarrow C_2 = 10$$
$$y(L) = 0 \rightarrow 0 = C_1 \cdot L + 10 \rightarrow C_1 = -\frac{10}{L}$$

Therefore, $y(x) = -(10/L)\, x + 10$, which is again the equation of a specific line. The boundary-value problem has a unique solution in this case. Physically, this problem corresponds to specifying the temperature of the wall on both surfaces.

(c) The solution that satisfies the specified boundary conditions is obtained by applying them to the general solution to determine C_1 and C_2:

$$y'(0) = -5 \rightarrow C_1 = -5$$
$$y'(L) = 10 \rightarrow C_1 = 10$$

which is impossible, since C_1 cannot be -5 and 10 at the same time. Therefore, this boundary-value problem has no solution. Physically, this corresponds to supplying heat to the plane wall from both sides and expecting the temperature of the wall to remain steady (not to change with time). This will never happen.

(d) The solution that satisfies the specified boundary conditions is obtained by applying them to the general solution to determine C_1 and C_2:

$$y'(0) = -5 \rightarrow C_1 = -5$$
$$y'(L) = -5 \rightarrow C_1 = -5$$

Therefore, $y(x) = -5x + C_2$, which is not a unique solution since C_2 is arbitrary. The solution represents the family of straight lines whose slope is -5. Physically, this problem corresponds to requiring that the rate of heat supplied to the wall at $x = 0$ be equal to the rate of heat removal from the other side of the wall at $x = L$. This is not enough information to fix the temperature distribution in the wall. So it is not surprising that the solution of this boundary-value problem is not unique.

We observe the following from the preceding example:

1. The general solution of a second-order linear differential equation involves two arbitrary constants.
2. An initial-value problem has a unique solution when the differential equation is linear, homogeneous, and has continuous coefficients.
3. A boundary-value problem may have a unique solution, an infinite number of solutions, or no solution at all depending on the specified boundary conditions (Figure 3–9). These conclusions are reaffirmed in the following sections.

$$y'' = 0 \rightarrow y = C_1 x + C_2$$

$$\left. \begin{array}{l} y(0) = 10 \\ y'(L) = 0 \end{array} \right\} \quad y(x) = \text{unique}$$

$$\left. \begin{array}{l} y'(0) = -5 \\ y'(L) = 10 \end{array} \right\} \quad y(x) = \text{nonexistent}$$

$$\left. \begin{array}{l} y'(0) = -5 \\ y'(L) = -5 \end{array} \right\} \quad y(x) = \text{not unique}$$

FIGURE 3–9

A boundary-value problem may have a unique solution, infinitely many solutions, or no solutions at all.

Section Review

Problems Denoted with a C are Conceptual Problems for Discussion

3–1C   How do you identify the homogeneous terms in a differential equation?

3–2C   How do you obtain the related homogeneous equation of a given differential equation?

3–3C   Can a differential equation be classified as being an equation with constant coefficients even if the nonhomogeneous term is not a constant?

3–4C   What is the difference between the solution of a differential equation and the solution of an initial-value problem?

3–5C   Under what conditions does a second-order linear boundary-value problem have a unique solution?

3–6   Determine if the following second-order differential equations are (1) linear or nonlinear, (2) homogeneous or nonhomogeneous, and (3) with constant or variable coefficients.

(a) $y'' + 3yy' = 6x^2$ (b) $y'' - 3y = e^{2x}$

(c) $x^2 y'' + xy' + y = 0$ (d) $y'' + xy' - 3y = \sin 2x$

(*Answers:* (a) $y'' + 3yy' = 6x^2$; nonlinear, nonhomogeneous, constant coefficients (b) $y'' - 3y = e^{2x}$; linear, nonhomogeneous, constant coefficients (c) $x^2 y'' + xy' + y = 0$; linear, homogeneous, variable coefficients (d) $y'' + xy' - 3y = \sin 2x$; linear, nonhomogeneous, variable coefficients)

3–7 Determine the interval in which the initial-value problems given are guaranteed to have a unique solution.

(a) $y'' + 3y' = \cos x$, $y(\pi) = 0$, and $y'(\pi) = -2$

(b) $x^2y'' + 2xy' - y = e^x$, $y(0) = 2$, and $y'(0) = 5$

(*Answers:* (a) Unique solution in the interval $-\infty < x < +\infty$. (b) Theorem 3–1 guarantees nothing.)

3–8 By differentiating the following functions twice and eliminating the constants C_1 and C_2, determine the second-order differential equation satisfied by the family of functions below.

(a) $y = C_1 e^{-2x} + C_2 e^{2x}$ (b) $y = C_1 x + C_2$

(*Answers:* (a) $y'' - 4y = 0$ (b) $y'' = 0$)

Functions:

$$y_1 = 3e^x$$
$$y_2 = 2e^x$$

Their ratio:

$$\frac{y_1}{y_2} = \frac{3e^x}{2e^x} = \frac{3}{2} = \text{constant}$$

(Linearly dependent)

FIGURE 3–10

Two functions are linearly independent if their ratio is a constant.

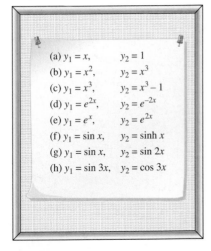

(a) $y_1 = x$, $y_2 = 1$
(b) $y_1 = x^2$, $y_2 = x^3$
(c) $y_1 = x^3$, $y_2 = x^3 - 1$
(d) $y_1 = e^{2x}$, $y_2 = e^{-2x}$
(e) $y_1 = e^x$, $y_2 = e^{2x}$
(f) $y_1 = \sin x$, $y_2 = \sinh x$
(g) $y_1 = \sin x$, $y_2 = \sin 2x$
(h) $y_1 = \sin 3x$, $y_2 = \cos 3x$

FIGURE 3–11

Examples of linearly independent function pairs.

3–2 ▪ LINEAR INDEPENDENCE AND THE WRONSKIAN OF FUNCTIONS

The expression $C_1 y_1 + C_2 y_2$ where C_1 and C_2 are arbitrary constants is called a *linear combination* of the two functions y_1 and y_2. Therefore, the expression $C_1 x + C_2$ is a linear combination of the functions $y_1 = x$ and $y_2 = 1$. Next we discuss the linear dependence and independence of functions.

*Two functions are said to be **linearly dependent** in an interval $x_1 < x < x_2$ if one function is a constant multiple of the other for all values of x in that interval. Otherwise, they are said to be **linearly independent**.*

In other words, two functions are linearly dependent in an interval if their ratio is a constant in that interval (Figure 3–10). Otherwise, they are linearly independent. For example, the functions $y_1 = x$, and $y_2 = 1$ are linearly independent, since $y_1/y_2 = x/1 = x$, which is a variable. But functions $5x$ and $-2x$ are linearly dependent in any interval, since $y_1/y_2 = 5x/(-2x) = -2.5$, which is a constant. Some common pairs of functions that are linearly independent in any interval are given in Figure 3–11. Note that two functions are linearly dependent in a specified interval I if their ratio is a constant for all x in that interval.

Linear independence also can be expressed more formally as

Two functions y_1 and y_2 are linearly independent in an interval $x_1 < x < x_2$ if the equation

$$C_1 y_1 + C_2 y_2 = 0$$

is satisfied for all x in that interval only when $C_1 = C_2 = 0$.

If this equation can be satisfied for all x with one or both of the coefficients C_1 and C_2 being nonzero, then the two functions are linearly dependent in that interval.

EXAMPLE 3–4   **Linearly Independent Functions**

Determine if the following pairs of functions are linearly dependent or independent for $-\infty < x < +\infty$.

(a) $y_1 = 6x$ and $y_2 = 2$
(b) $y_1 = x^2$ and $y_2 = x^3$
(c) $y_1 = e^x$ and $y_2 = e^{-x}$
(d) $y_1 = e^x$ and $y_2 = e^{2x}$
(e) $y_1 = \sin x$ and $y_2 = \cos x$
(f) $y_1 = x$ and $y_2 = x + 1$

SOLUTION   All of these pairs of functions are linearly independent, since the ratio of the two functions in each pair depends on x (i.e., it is not a constant), as illustrated here:

(a) $\dfrac{y_1}{y_2} = \dfrac{6x}{2} = 3x$

(b) $\dfrac{y_1}{y_2} = \dfrac{x^2}{x^3} = \dfrac{1}{x}$

(c) $\dfrac{y_1}{y_2} = \dfrac{e^x}{e^{-x}} = e^{2x}$

(d) $\dfrac{y_1}{y_2} = \dfrac{e^x}{e^{2x}} = e^{-x}$

(e) $\dfrac{y_1}{y_2} = \dfrac{\sin x}{\cos x} = \tan x$

(f) $\dfrac{y_1}{y_2} = \dfrac{x}{x + 1}$

The Wronskian of Two Functions

Linear dependence or independence of two functions can be determined easily by taking their ratio. But this simple approach will not work when we need to determine the linear independence of three or more functions. Therefore, we need a more systematic procedure to determine the linear independence of functions.

Consider two differentiable functions y_1 and y_2. From the definition of linear independence, these two functions are linearly independent in an interval if the equation

$$C_1 y_1 + C_2 y_2 = 0 \tag{3–8}$$

is satisfied for all x in that interval if and only if $C_1 = C_2 = 0$. We now take the derivative of this equation and obtain

$$C_1 y_1' + C_2 y_2' = 0 \tag{3–9}$$

These two equations form a system of two equations in two unknowns that can be solved for C_1 and C_2. To eliminate C_2, we multiply the first equation by y_2' and the second one by y_2 and subtract. We obtain

$$C_1(y_1 y_2' - y_1' y_2) = 0 \tag{3–10}$$

Similarly, multiplying the first equation by y_1', the second one by y_1, and subtracting gives

$$C_2(y_1 y_2' - y_1' y_2) = 0 \qquad (3\text{--}11)$$

Note that the factor $y_1 y_2' - y_1' y_2$ is the same in both equations. If this factor is not zero, then the only way these two equations can be satisfied is $C_1 = C_2 = 0$, since for a product to be zero at least one of its factors must be zero. To facilitate ease of use with any number of functions, this factor is denoted by W and often expressed in the determinant form as

$$W(y_1, y_2) = \begin{vmatrix} y_1 & y_2 \\ y_1' & y_2' \end{vmatrix} = y_1 y_2' - y_1' y_2 \qquad (3\text{--}12)$$

The function $W(y_1, y_2)$ is called the **Wronskian** of the functions y_1 and y_2 after the Polish mathematician J.M. Wronski (1776–1853). The linear dependence and independence of two functions can be defined as follows with the help of their Wronskian (Figure 3–12).

Two functions are linearly dependent in a interval if their Wronskian is zero in that interval for all x. Otherwise, they are linearly independent.

Note that the Wronskian of two functions can be zero for some x values and nonzero for others in a specified interval $x_1 < x < x_2$. To be linearly dependent, the Wronskian of the two functions must be zero for all x in that interval.

The use of the Wronskian is unnecessary when determining the linear independence of two functions, since it is much easier just to take the ratio of the two functions. The real value of the Wronskian will be apparent when we discuss the linear independence of three or more functions. The Wronskian also plays an important role in the theory of linear differential equations, as you will see later in this chapter.

If $W(y_1, y_2) = \begin{vmatrix} y_1 & y_2 \\ y_1' & y_2' \end{vmatrix}$

$= y_1 y_2' - y_1' y_2$

$\neq 0$

then linearly independent.

FIGURE 3–12

Two functions are linearly independent if their Wronskian is not identically zero.

EXAMPLE 3–5   **Wronskian of Two Functions**

Calculate the Wronskian of the pairs of functions given, and determine if they are linearly dependent or independent on the entire x axis.

(a) $y_1 = x + 1$, and $y_2 = x^2$
(b) $y_1 = \sin x$, and $y_2 = \cos x$
(c) $y_1 = x^3$, and $y_2 = -2x^3$

SOLUTION   The Wronskian of each pair of functions is determined from the definition of Wronskian, $W(y_1, y_2) = y_1 y_2' - y_1' y_2$.

(a)
$$\begin{aligned} W(y_1, y_2) &= (x + 1)(x^2)' - (x + 1)' x^2 \\ &= (x + 1)(2x) - x^2 \\ &= x(x + 2) \end{aligned}$$

The Wronskian becomes zero at the two points $x = 0$ and $x = -2$. But still, these two functions are linearly independent in any interval, even if the interval contains the point 0 and –2. This is because the Wronskian must be zero for all x in an interval for the functions to be linearly dependent in that interval.

(b)
$$W(y_1, y_2) = \sin x(\cos x)' - (\sin x)' \cos x$$
$$= \sin x(-\sin x) - \cos x \cos x$$
$$= -(\sin^2 x + \cos^2 x) = -1 \neq 0$$

Therefore, these two functions are linearly independent.

(c)
$$W(y_1, y_2) = x^3(-2x^3)' - (x^3)'(-2x^3)$$
$$= x^3(-6x^2) - (3x^2)(-2x^3)$$
$$= -6x^5 + 6x^5 = 0$$

The Wronskian of these two functions is identically zero; thus, these functions are linearly dependent in any interval.

Linear Independence and the Wronskian of *n* Functions

The study of second- and higher-order differential equations often requires the determination of the linear independence of three or more functions. Therefore, we extend this discussion on linear independence to a set of n functions.

We first define the *linear combination* of n functions $y_1, y_2, \ldots, y_n$ as

$$C_1y_1 + C_2y_2 + \cdots + C_ny_n$$

where $C_1, C_2, \ldots, C_n$ are arbitrary constants. The linear independence of n functions is defined as follows.

The n functions $y_1, y_2, \ldots, y_n$ are linearly independent in an interval $x_1 < x < x_2$ if the equation

$$C_1y_1 + C_2y_2 + \cdots + C_ny_n = 0$$

is satisfied for all x in that interval only when $C_1 = C_2 = \cdots = C_n = 0$. Otherwise, these n functions are said to be linearly dependent in that interval.

Therefore, the n functions $y_1, y_2, \ldots, y_n$ are linearly dependent if the equation above can be satisfied for all x in the specified interval with at least one of the coefficients $C_1, C_2, \ldots, C_n$ being nonzero.

It is left as an exercise for the student to show that if n functions are linearly dependent, then at least one of those functions can be expressed as a linear combination of the others. Conversely, if one of the functions in a set of n functions can be expressed as a linear combination of the others, then these functions are linearly dependent in that interval. To be more specific, if two of the n functions are linearly dependent, then these n functions are linearly dependent. For example, the two functions x and $5x$ are linearly dependent in any interval. Then it follows that any set of n functions that contain these two functions are also linearly dependent in any interval.

The linear dependence of n specified functions can sometimes be determined by inspection (Figure 3–13), but this is more the exception

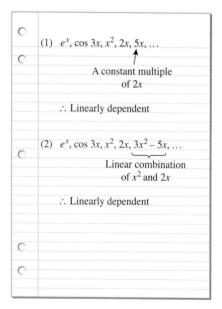

(1) $e^x, \cos 3x, x^2, 2x, 5x, \ldots$

A constant multiple
of $2x$

∴ Linearly dependent

(2) $e^x, \cos 3x, x^2, 2x, 3x^2 - 5x, \ldots$

Linear combination
of x^2 and $2x$

∴ Linearly dependent

FIGURE 3–13

The linear dependence of n functions can sometimes be determined by inspection.

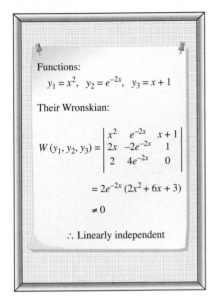

FIGURE 3–14

Three (or more) functions are linearly independent if their Wronskian is not identically zero.

than the rule. A systematic procedure to determine whether n given functions are linearly independent involves the evaluation of their Wronskian, as expressed here.

The n functions $y_1, y_2, \ldots, y_n$ each possessing $(n-1)$th derivatives on an interval $x_1 < x < x_2$ are linearly independent on this interval if their Wronskian

$$W(y_1, y_2, \ldots, y_n) = \begin{vmatrix} y_1 & y_2 & \cdots & y_n \\ y_1' & y_2' & \cdots & y_n' \\ \cdot & \cdot & \cdots & \cdot \\ \cdot & \cdot & \cdots & \cdot \\ y_1^{(n-1)} & y_2^{(n-1)} & \cdots & y_n^{(n-1)} \end{vmatrix}$$ (3–13)

is not identically zero on that interval.

Notice that the Wronskian of n functions $W(y_1, y_2, \ldots, y_n)$ is, in general, a function of x. Therefore, it may be zero for some x and nonzero for others in a specified interval $x_1 < x < x_2$. To be linearly dependent, the Wronskian of the functions must be zero for all x. That is, the Wronskian must be identically zero (Figure 3–14). Students may refer to Section 7–5 for a review of determinants and matrices.

EXAMPLE 3–6   **Linearly Independent Functions**

Determine if the functions 1, $2x$, and $\sin x$ are linearly dependent or independent over the entire x axis, $-\infty < x < +\infty$.

SOLUTION   Taking $y_1 = 1$, $y_2 = 2x$, and $y_3 = \sin x$, the Wronskian of these three functions are determined from Equation 3–13 by forming the 3×3 determinant and evaluating its value. It gives

$$W(y_1, y_2, y_3) = \begin{vmatrix} y_1 & y_2 & y_3 \\ y_1' & y_2' & y_3' \\ y_1'' & y_2'' & y_3'' \end{vmatrix} = \begin{vmatrix} 1 & 2x & \sin x \\ 0 & 2 & \cos x \\ 0 & 0 & -\sin x \end{vmatrix} = -2\sin x$$

which is not identically zero (i.e., It is not zero for all x. It is zero only for $x = 0, \pi, 2\pi, 3\pi, \ldots$). Therefore, these three functions are linearly independent.

Section Review

3–9C   Are the functions $y_1 = 0$ and $y_2 = f(x)$ linearly dependent or independent? Answer the same question for the functions $y_1 = 1$ and $y_2 = f(x)$.

3–10C   Consider two functions y_1 and y_2 whose Wronskian is zero for some x and nonzero for other x values. Are these two functions linearly dependent or independent?

3–11 Determine if the following pairs of functions y_1 and y_2 are linearly dependent or independent (1) by inspection, and (2) by determining their Wronskian.

(a) $y_1 = x + 1$ and $y_2 = x^2 - 1$ (b) $y_1 = \sin(\alpha + \beta)$ and $y_2 = \sin \alpha + \sin \beta$

(*Answers:* (a) $W = (x + 1)^2 \neq 0$ so the functions y_1 and y_2 are linearly independent. (b) $W = 0$ so the functions y_1 and y_2 are linearly dependent.)

3–12 Determine if the following functions are linearly dependent or independent by determining their Wronskian.

$$y_1 = x + 1, \ y_2 = x^3, \text{ and } y_3 = x^2 - 1$$

(*Answer:* $W = -2x^3 - 6x^2 - 6x \neq 0$ which indicates that y_1, y_2 and y_3 are linearly independent.)

3–3 ▪ THEORY OF HOMOGENEOUS EQUATIONS

Let us reexamine the solution of the second-order, linear, homogeneous differential equation $y'' = 0$ discussed in Example 3–3 one more time. The general solution of this equation was given by

$$y = C_1 y_1 + C_2 y_2$$

where $y_1 = x$ and $y_2 = 1$. We can easily verify by direct substitution that both y_1 and y_2 satisfy the differential equation. A constant multiple of either solution also satisfies the differential equation as well as their sum $y_1 + y_2$. In general, the linear combination $C_1 y_1 + C_2 y_2$ satisfies the differential equation for any values of the constants C_1 and C_2 (Figure 3–15). Not only that, the linear combination $C_1 y_1 + C_2 y_2$ contains all the solutions of the differential equation. That is, any solution of the differential equation $y'' = 0$ can be obtained from the general solution by assigning suitable values to the constant C_1 and C_2.

The foregoing intuitive discussion leads to the following important theorem.

If $y_1 = x$ and $y_2 = 1$ are two solutions of the linear homogeneous equation

$$y'' = 0,$$

so are

$$y_3 = 2x \ \ (= 2y_1)$$
$$y_4 = 5 \ \ (= 5y_2)$$
$$y_5 = x + 1 \ \ (= y_1 + y_2)$$
$$y_6 = 3x - 4 \ \ (= 3y_1 - 4y_2)$$

and, in general,

$$y = C_1 x + C_2$$

FIGURE 3–15

The superposition principle.

THEOREM 3–2 Superposition Principle

If y_1 and y_2 are two solutions of the linear homogeneous equation

$$y'' + P(x)y' + Q(x)y = 0$$

then the linear combination

$$y = C_1 y_1 + C_2 y_2$$

where C_1 and C_2 are arbitrary constants, is also a solution of this equation.

Proof This theorem is easily proved by differentiating equation

$$y = C_1 y_1 + C_2 y_2$$

twice and substituting the results into the differential equation:

$$y' = C_1 y_1' + C_2 y_2'$$
$$y'' = C_1 y_1'' + C_2 y_2''$$

Thus,

$$y'' + Py' + Qy = (C_1y_1'' + C_2y_2'') + P(C_1y_1' + C_2y_2') + Q(C_1y_1 + C_2y_2)$$

$$= C_1(y_1'' + Py_1' + Qy_1) + C_2(y_2'' + Py_2' + Qy_2)$$

$$= C_1 \cdot 0 + C_2 \cdot 0$$

$$= 0$$

since y_1 and y_2 are solutions. Thus, they satisfy the differential equation. This completes the proof.

The superposition principle can be expressed in simpler words.

If a function is a solution of a linear homogeneous differential equation, a constant multiple of it is also a solution. If two functions are solutions of a linear, homogenous differential equation, their sum is also a solution of that differential equation.

Note that the superposition principle is applicable to linear homogeneous differential equations only. It is not applicable to nonlinear equations or to nonhomogeneous equations even when they are linear. This is illustrated below with examples.

EXAMPLE 3–7   Superposition Principle (Homogeneous Equations)

Verify that e^{-2x} is a solution of the differential equation $y'' - 4y = 0$, and show that $5e^{-2x}$ is also a solution of this equation.

SOLUTION We first notice that the differential equation is linear and homogeneous. We can verify by direct substitution that e^{-2x} is a solution of the given equation,

$$y'' - 4y = (e^{-2x})'' - 4e^{-2x}$$

$$= 4e^{-2x} - 4e^{-2x}$$

$$= 0 \quad (Checks)$$

Now we substitute $5e^{-2x}$ into the differential equation

$$y'' - 4y = (5e^{-2x})'' - 4(5e^{-2x})$$

$$= 20e^{-2x} - 20e^{-2x}$$

$$= 0 \quad (Checks)$$

Therefore, $5e^{-2x}$ (which is constant multiple of e^{-2x}) is also a solution of the given differential equation. This is expected, since (according to Theorem 3–2, a constant multiple of a solution of a linear homogeneous differential equation is also a solution (Figure 3–16).

The function e^{-2x} is a solution of the linear homogeneous equation

$$y'' - 4y = 0$$

So is $5e^{-2x}$.

FIGURE 3–16

A constant multiple of a solution of a *linear homogeneous* equation is also a solution.

EXAMPLE 3–8   Superposition Principle (Homogeneous Equations)

Verify that e^{-2x} and e^{2x} are solutions of the differential equation $y'' - 4y = 0$. Also show that $e^{-2x} + e^{2x}$ is also a solution of this equation.

SOLUTION   We first notice that the differential equation is linear and homogeneous. We can verify by direct substitution that both e^{-2x} and e^{2x} are solutions of the given equation,

$$
\begin{aligned}
y'' - 4y &= (e^{-2x})'' - 4e^{-2x} \\
&= 4e^{-2x} - 4e^{-2x} \\
&= 0 \quad (Checks)
\end{aligned}
$$

$$
\begin{aligned}
y'' - 4y &= (e^{2x})'' - 4e^{2x} \\
&= 4e^{2x} - 4e^{2x} \\
&= 0 \quad (Checks)
\end{aligned}
$$

Now we substitute $e^{-2x} + e^{2x}$ into the differential equation

$$
\begin{aligned}
y'' - 4y &= (e^{-2x} + e^{2x})'' - 4(e^{-2x} + e^{2x}) \\
&= 4e^{-2x} + 4e^{2x} - 4e^{-2x} - 4e^{2x} \\
&= 0 \quad (Checks)
\end{aligned}
$$

Therefore, $e^{-2x} + e^{2x}$ is also a solution of the given differential equation. This is expected, since (according to Theorem 3–2), the sum of the two solutions of a linear homogeneous differential equation is also a solution (Figure 3–17).

Because e^{-2x} and e^{2x} are solutions of the linear homogeneous equation

$$y'' - 4y = 0$$

so is $e^{-2x} + e^{2x}$.

FIGURE 3–17

The sum of the two solutions of a *linear homogeneous* equation is also a solution.

EXAMPLE 3–9   Superposition Principle (Nonhomogeneous Equations)

Verify that e^{-2x} is a solution of the differential equation $y'' - 3y - e^{-2x} = 0$, and check if $5e^{-2x}$ is also a solution of this equation.

SOLUTION   We first notice that this is a linear but nonhomogeneous differential equation because the last term does not involve y or any of its derivatives. We can verify by direct substitution that e^{-2x} is a solution of the given equation:

$$
\begin{aligned}
y'' - 3y - e^{-2x} &= (e^{-2x})'' - 3e^{-2x} - e^{-2x} \\
&= 4e^{-2x} - 3e^{-2x} - e^{-2x} \\
&= 0 \quad (Checks)
\end{aligned}
$$

Now we substitute $5e^{-2x}$ into the differential equation:

$$
\begin{aligned}
y'' - 3y - e^{-2x} &= (5e^{-2x})'' - 3(5e^{-2x}) - e^{-2x} \\
&= 20e^{-2x} - 15e^{-2x} - e^{-2x} \\
&= 4e^{-2x} \\
&\neq 0 \quad (Does\ not\ check)
\end{aligned}
$$

The function e^{-2x} is a solution of the linear nonhomogeneous equation

$$y'' - 4y = e^{-2x}$$

but $5e^{-2x}$ is not.

FIGURE 3–18

The superposition principle is not applicable to *nonhomogeneous* equation.

The function x is a solution of the nonlinear equation

$$y'' + x^2y' - y^2 = 0$$

but $2x$ is not.

FIGURE 3–19

The superposition principle is not applicable to *nonlinear* equations.

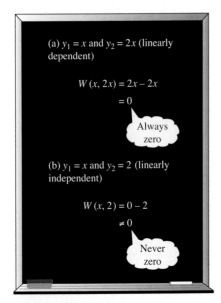

FIGURE 3–20

Abel's identity for the differential equation $y'' = 0$ whose fundamental solutions are x and 1.

Therefore, $5e^{-2x}$ is not a solution of the given differential equation. This is not surprising since the differential equation is not homogeneous, and the superposition principle is not applicable to nonhomogeneous equations even when they are linear (Figure 3–18).

EXAMPLE 3–10   Superposition Principle and Nonlinear Equations

Verify that $y = x$ is a solution of the differential equation $y'' + x^2y' - y^2 = 0$ and check if $2x$ is also a solution of this equation.

SOLUTION   First notice that this is a nonlinear differential equation because the last term involves a power of y. We can verify by direct substitution that x is a solution of the given equation:

$$y'' + x^2y' - y^2 = (x)'' + x^2(x)' - (x)^2$$
$$= 0 + x^2 - x^2$$
$$= 0 \qquad (Checks)$$

Now we substitute $2x$ into the differential equation,

$$y'' + x^2y' - y^2 = (2x)'' + x^2(2x)' - (2x)^2$$
$$= 0 + 2x^2 - 4x^2$$
$$\neq 0 \qquad (Does\ not\ check)$$

Therefore, $2x$ is not a solution of the given differential equation. Again, this is not surprising since the differential equation is nonlinear, and the superposition principle is not applicable to nonlinear equations (Figure 3–19).

It seems like a second-order linear homogeneous differential equation has infinite number of solutions, but most of these solutions differ by a constant factor. Then we cannot help wondering how many of these solutions are *fundamental* solutions from which other solutions can be obtained by the superposition principle. In other words, we would like to know how many linearly independent solutions a linear homogeneous differential equation can have. It turns out that the number of linearly independent solutions a linear homogeneous equation can have is equal to the order of the differential equation. But before we prove it, we will develop an important relation.

THEOREM 3–3   Abel's Identity

Consider the second-order, linear, homogeneous differential equation

$$y'' + P(x)y' + Q(x)y = 0$$

whose coefficients $P(x)$ and $Q(x)$ are continuous in an interval $x_1 \leq x \leq x_2$, and let y_1 and y_2 be any two solutions of this differential equation in this interval. Then the Wronskian of y_1 and y_2 is either always zero (indicating these two solutions are linearly dependent) or never zero (indicating these two solutions are linearly independent) (Figure 3–20).

Proof Since y_1 and y_2 are solutions, they satisfy the differential equation:

$$y_1'' + P(x)y_1' + Q(x)y_1 = 0$$
$$y_2'' + P(x)y_2' + Q(x)y_2 = 0$$

Multiplying the first equation by y_2, the second one by y_1, and subtracting the first one from the second gives

$$(y_1y_2'' - y_1''y_2) + P(x)(y_1y_2' - y_1'y_2) = 0$$

or

$$W' + P(x)W = 0 \qquad (3\text{-}14)$$

since by definition of the Wronskian, $W = y_1y_2' - y_1'y_2$, and

$$W' = y_1'y_2' + y_1y_2'' - y_1''y_2 - y_1'y_2' = y_1y_2'' - y_1''y_2$$

Equation 3–14 is a first-order linear differential equation, and its solution is

$$\boxed{W = Ke^{-\int P(x)dx}} \qquad (3\text{-}15)$$

where K is a constant and W is the Wronskian $W(y_1, y_2)$. The exponential function in this relation is never zero since $P(x)$ is a continuous function and thus the integral $\int P(x)dx$ cannot become infinite. Therefore, the only way the Wronskian W can be zero is if $K = 0$, in which case W is identically zero. If $K \neq 0$, then W is never zero in the interval in which $P(x)$ is continuous. This completes the proof.

Equation 3–15 was first derived by the Norwegian mathematician N.H. Abel (1802–1829), and is known as **Abel's formula**. It enables us to determine the Wronskian of two linearly independent solutions of a second-order linear, homogeneous equation with continuous coefficients to within a constant factor.

Theorem 3–3 indicates that $W(y_1, y_2)$ cannot be zero for some x and nonzero for other x values in an interval in which the coefficients $P(x)$ and $Q(x)$ of a linear, homogeneous, differential equation are continuous. Therefore, when determining linear independence of two solutions in a specified interval, it is sufficient to evaluate $W(y_1, y_2)$ at any convenient point x_0 in that interval since, if $W(y_1, y_2)$ at x_0, it is zero for all x, and y_1 and y_2 are linearly independent. Likewise, if $W(y_1, y_2) \neq 0$ at x_0, then y_1 and y_2 are linearly independent in that interval.

EXAMPLE 3–11   Application of Abel's Formula

Determine the Wronskian of the solutions $y_1 = x^{1/3}$ and $y_2 = 1/x$ of the differential equation

$$x^2y'' + \frac{5}{3}xy' - \frac{1}{3}y = 0$$

in the interval $0 < x < \infty$ using (a) the Wronskian formula and (b) Abel's formula.

SOLUTION This is a second-order, linear, homogeneous equation, and it can be put into the standard form by dividing each term by the coefficient of y'', which is x^2:

$$y'' + \frac{5}{3x} y' - \frac{1}{3x^2} y = 0$$

Therefore, $P(x) = 5/3x$ and $Q(x) = -1/3x^2$, which are continuous in any interval that does not contain the point $x = 0$. Therefore, we expect the Wronskian $W(y_1, y_2)$ to be identically zero or never to be zero on the interval $0 < x < \infty$.

(a) From the Wronskian formula, we have

$$W(y_1, y_2) = y_1 y_2' - y_1' y_2 = x^{1/3}\left(-\frac{1}{x^2}\right) - \left(\frac{1}{3} x^{-2/3}\right)\frac{1}{x} = -\frac{4}{3} x^{-5/3} \neq 0$$

(b) From Abel's formula, we have

$$W(y_1, y_2) = K e^{-\int P(x)dx} = K e^{-\int \frac{5}{3x}dx} = K e^{-\frac{5}{3}\ln x} = K x^{-5/3}$$

Thus, $K = -4/3$. Note that $W(y_1, y_2)$ is never zero in $0 < x < \infty$, indicating that these two solutions are linearly independent.

We will use Abel's formula to prove the following important theorem.

THEOREM 3–4   General Solution of Homogeneous Equations

The second-order, linear, homogeneous differential equation

$$y'' + P(x)y' + Q(x)y = 0$$

whose coefficients $P(x)$ and $Q(x)$ are continuous in an interval $x_1 < x < x_2$ always possesses two solutions y_1 and y_2 that are linearly independent in that interval. Furthermore, any solution of this differential equation in that interval can be expressed uniquely as a linear combination of these two solutions as

$$y = C_1 y_1 + C_2 y_2 \tag{3–16}$$

which is the general solution.

Proof The first part of this theorem is easily proved by showing that two solutions exist whose Wronskian is not zero. Consider a point x_0 and the following two initial-value problems of the given differential equation in the interval $x_1 < x < x_2$:

1. $y'' + P(x)y' + Q(x)y = 0$ with $y(x_0) = 1, y'(x_0) = 0$
2. $y'' + P(x)y' + Q(x)y = 0$ with $y(x_0) = 0, y'(x_0) = 1$

According to Theorem 3–1, each of these initial-value problems has a unique solution. We now let y_1 and y_2 be the solution of the first and the second initial-value problems, respectively. Using the given initial conditions, the Wronskian of these two solutions at the point x_0 is determined to be

$$W[y_1(x_0), y_2(x_0)] = y_1(x_0)y_2'(x_0) - y_1'(x_0)y_2(x_0) = 1 \times 1 - 0 \times 0 = 1$$

which is not zero. Thus we conclude that solutions y_1 and y_2 exist, and they are linearly independent because their Wronskian is not identically zero. This completes the proof of the first part.

To prove the second part, let y_1 and y_2 be two linearly independent solutions and let y_3 be any other solution. From Abel's formula, we have

$$W(y_1, y_2) = y_1y_2' - y_1'y_2 = K_1 e^{-\int P(x)dx} \neq 0 \qquad \textbf{(3–17)}$$

where $K_1 \neq 0$. Similarly,

$$W(y_1, y_3) = y_1y_3' - y_1'y_3 = K_2 e^{-\int P(x)dx} \qquad \textbf{(3–18)}$$

$$W(y_2, y_3) = y_2y_3' - y_2'y_3 = K_3 e^{-\int P(x)dx} \qquad \textbf{(3–19)}$$

Multiplying Equation 3–18 by y_2 and Equation 3–19 by y_1 and subtracting, we have

$$(y_1y_2' - y_1'y_2)y_3 = K_3 e^{-\int P(x)dx} y_1 - K_2 e^{-\int P(x)dx} y_2$$

Replacing the terms in the parentheses by their equivalent from Equation 3–17, we have

$$K_1 e^{-\int P(x)dx} y_3 = K_3 e^{-\int P(x)dx} y_1 - K_2 e^{-\int P(x)dx} y_2$$

Cancelling the exponential term and dividing by K_1,

$$y_3 = \frac{K_3}{K_1}y_1 - \frac{K_2}{K_1}y_2 \qquad \textbf{(3–20)}$$

or, $y_3 = C_1y_1 + C_2y_2$, where we have defined $C_1 = K_3/K_1$ and $C_1 = -K_2/K_1$. Thus any solution y_3 can be expressed as a linear combination of y_1 and y_2. This completes the proof.

In the light of this theorem, we conclude that $y = C_1y_1 + C_2y_2$ is **the general solution** since it contains all the solutions of the differential equation in the specified interval. Any solution of the equation can be obtained from the general solution by assigning suitable values to the constants C_1 and C_2.

Thus the solution set y_1 and y_2 is referred to as a **fundamental set** of solutions that is defined as a set of two linearly independent solutions of a second-order linear, homogeneous equation on an interval. Note that a differential equation can have several fundamental sets of solutions, as shown in Figure 3–21,

Differential equation:
$$y'' - y = 0$$

Fundamental sets of solutions:

(1) e^x and e^{-x}

(2) $2e^x$ and $5e^{-x}$

(3) $-e^x$ and $3e^x + 2e^{-x}$

(4) $\dfrac{e^x + e^{-x}}{2}$ and $\dfrac{e^x - e^{-x}}{2}$

(5) $\cosh x$ and $\sinh x$

(6) $\cosh x$ and e^x

(7) $3\sinh x$ and $e^x - 4e^{-x}$

FIGURE 3–21

A second-order, linear, homogeneous equation with continuous coefficients may have several sets of fundamental solutions, and any of those sets can be used to construct the general solution of the differential equation.

and any of these sets can be used to construct the general solution. It can be shown that all the general solutions obtained using different sets of fundamental solutions are equivalent to each other.

EXAMPLE 3–12   Fundamental Sets of Solutions

It can be shown by direct substitution that the functions e^x, e^{-x}, $2e^x - 3e^{-x}$, $\cosh x$, and $\sinh x$ are solutions of the differential equation $y'' - y = 0$. Also, it can be verified by inspection that the ratio of any two of these functions is a variable. Therefore, any two of these functions are linearly independent of each other and form a fundamental set of solutions. Then it follows that the general solution of the given differential equation can be expressed as $y = C_1 y_1 + C_2 y_2$, where y_1 and y_2 are any two of the solution functions given. Therefore, the general solution can be taken to be $y = C_1 e^x + C_2 e^{-x}$ or $y = K_1 \cosh x + K_2 \sinh x$, where C_1, C_2, K_1, and K_2 are arbitrary constants. Show that these two general solutions are equivalent to each other.

SOLUTION   Using the definitions of hyperbolic functions $\cosh x$ and $\sinh x$, the second solution can be expressed as

$$y = K_1 \cosh x + K_2 \sinh x$$

$$= K_1 \left(\frac{e^x + e^{-x}}{2} \right) + K_2 \left(\frac{e^x - e^{-x}}{2} \right)$$

$$= \left(\frac{K_1}{2} + \frac{K_2}{2} \right) e^x + \left(\frac{K_1}{2} - \frac{K_2}{2} \right) e^{-x}$$

$$= C_1 e^x + C_2 e^{-x}$$

where $C_1 = (K_1 + K_2)/2$ and $C_2 = (K_1 - K_2)/2$. Therefore, the two general solutions are equivalent to each other, and we can construct the general solution of a second-order, linear, homogeneous equation using any two of its solutions that are linearly independent.

The student can also verify that the Wronskian of any three of the given solutions is zero, indicating that only two solutions of a second-order, linear, homogeneous equation can be linearly independent. Theorem 3–4 is analogous to a theorem in vector algebra (Figure 3–22). Any vector in a plane can be expressed as a linear combination of two vectors in that plane that are not parallel to each other (i.e., that are linearly independent).

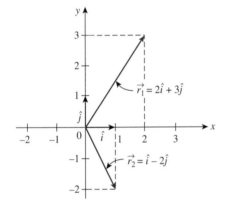

FIGURE 3–22

In vector algebra, all vectors in a plane can be expressed as a linear combination of the two linearly independent unit vectors $\hat{\imath}$ and $\hat{\jmath}$.

Theorem 3–4 ensures the existence of two linearly independent solutions. It also ensures that in a set of any number of solutions only two can be linearly independent. It guarantees, for example, that the equation $y'' - 4y = 0$ has two linearly independent solutions that can be taken to be e^{-2x} and e^{2x}, and also guarantees that any solution of this differential equation can be obtained from these solutions. Thus solving a second-order, linear, homogeneous equation is equivalent to finding two linearly independent solutions. Then the general solution of this differential equation is easily obtained from Equation 3–16.

Section Review

3–13C Does a differential equation have to be linear and homogeneous for the super-position principle to be applicable?

3–14C For what kind of differential equation is a constant multiple of a solution also a solution?

3–15C For what kind of differential equation is the sum of two solutions also a solution?

3–16C Consider a second-order, linear, homogeneous equation with continuous coefficients and its two solutions y_1 and y_2, which are linearly independent. Can this differential equation have a solution that cannot be expressed as $C_1y_1 + C_2y_2$ where C_1 and C_2 are constants?

3–17 For each of the following second-order differential equations, let y_1 be a solution of the equation. Determine by inspection if ky_1, where k is a constant, is also a solution of that equation.

    (a) $y'' + e^y y' - 2y = 6$ (b) $y'' - 2y' + y = x^3 \cos 2x$

    (c) $y'' - 5x^2 y' = 0$ (d) $y'' - y = 0$

(*Answers:* (a) and (b) The equation is a nonhomogeneous differential equation, and therefore, ky_1 is *not* a solution. (c) and (d) The equation is a linear, homogeneous differential equation, and therefore, ky_1 is a solution.)

3–18 For each of the following second-order differential equations, let y_1 and y_2 be solutions of the equation. Determine by inspection if $y_1 + y_2$ is also a solution of that equation.

    (a) $y'' + y' \cos y + 8xy = 0$ (b) $y'' + 6y' + 9\sqrt{y} = x^3$

    (c) $x^3 y'' - xy' = 0$ (d) $y'' + k^2 y = 0$

(*Answers:* (a) and (b) The equation is a nonlinear differential equation, and therefore, $y_1 + y_2$ is *not* a solution. (c) and (d) The equation is a linear, homogeneous differential equation, and therefore, $y_1 + y_2$ is also a solution.)

3–19 Consider the following second-order, linear, homogeneous equations and two of their solutions y_1 and y_2 for $x > 0$. Identify the pair of solutions whose Wronskian $W(y_1, y_2)$ is never zero for $x > 0$ by inspection. Verify your findings by actually calculating $W(y_1, y_2)$ for each case.

    (a) $y'' - 4y = 0$, $y_1 = e^{2x}$ and $y_2 = -3e^{2x}$

    (b) $y'' - 4y = 0$, $y_1 = e^{2x}$ and $y_2 = e^{-2x}$

    (c) $y'' - 4y = 0$, $y_1 = 3e^{-2x}$ and $y_2 = e^{3-2x}$

(*Answers:* (a) y_1 and y_2 are linearly dependent and $W = 0$. (b) y_1 and y_2 are linearly independent and $W = -4$. (c) y_1 and y_2 are linearly dependent and $W = 0$.)

3–20 Consider the following second-order linear, homogeneous, equations and two of their solutions y_1 and y_2 for $x > 0$. Determine if y_1 and y_2 form a fundamental set of solutions. If they do, develop a relation for $y(x)$ that contains all solutions of the differential equation.

    (a) $y'' - y = 0$, $y_1 = e^x$ and $y_2 = e^{-x}$

    (b) $y'' - y = 0$, $y_1 = \sinh x$ and $y_2 = \cosh x$

    (c) $y'' - y = 0$, $y_1 = e^x$ and $y_2 = \cosh x$

(*Answers:* (a) $W = -2 \neq 0$, $y(x) = C_1y_1 + C_2y_2 = C_1e^x + C_2e^{-x}$
(b) $W = -1 \neq 0$, $y(x) = C_1y_1 + C_2y_2 = C_1 \sinh x + C_2 \cosh x$
(c) $W = -1 \neq 0$, $y(x) = C_1e^x + C_2 \cosh x$)

3–4 · REDUCTION OF ORDER

Before we start actually solving differential equations, we have one more item to consider: reducing a second-order, linear, homogeneous equation to a first-order one when one of its solutions is known. This method of reducing the order of a differential equation by one when one of its solutions is available is called **reduction of order**. It was developed by the French mathematician Jean d'Alembert (1717–1783).

Let y_1 be a nontrivial ($y_1 \neq 0$) solution of the second-order linear homogeneous equation

$$y'' + P(x)y' + Q(x)y = 0$$

Then we know that Cy_1, where C is constant, is also solution of this equation. Now we wonder if vy_1, where v is a function of x, also can be a solution of this differential equation. If it is, vy_1 will be a linearly independent solution of y_1 since the ratio of these two solutions is v, which is not a constant. Therefore, finding the function v is equivalent to obtaining the second linearly independent solution of the given differential equation.

Now we will assume that $y = vy_1$ is a solution of the differential equation, and attempt to determine the function v. Taking the first and second derivatives of $y = vy_1$, $y' = v'y_1 + vy_1'$ and $y'' = v''y_1 + v'y_1' + v'y_1' + vy_1''$. Substitution into the differential equation and rearranging,

$$y_1 v'' + [2y_1' + P(x)y_1]v' + [y_1'' + P(x)y_1' + Q(x)y_1]v = 0$$

The quantity in the last parentheses is zero since y_1 is a solution. Dividing the remaining terms by y_1 yields

$$v'' + \left[P(x) + \frac{2y_1'}{y_1} \right]v' = 0$$

or taking $w = v'$,

$$w' + \left[P(x) + \frac{2y_1'}{y_1} \right]w = 0 \qquad \textbf{(3–21)}$$

which is a first-order linear homogeneous equation in w. Its solution is

$$w = Ce^{-\int(P(x)+2y_1'/y_1)\,dx} = Ce^{-2\int(y_1'/y_1)\,dx}e^{-\int P(x)\,dx}$$

Since

$$e^{-2\int(y_1'/y_1)\,dx} = e^{-2\int(1/y_1)\,dy_1} = e^{-2\ln|y_1|} = \frac{1}{y_1^2}$$

we have

$$w = \frac{C}{y_1^2}e^{-\int P(x)\,dx} \qquad \textbf{(3–22)}$$

where C is an arbitrary constant, which we will take to be $C = 1$. Then v is obtained by integrating Equation 3–22 to be

$$v = \int \frac{e^{-\int P(x)\,dx}}{y_1^2}\,dx \qquad \textbf{(3–23)}$$

Therefore, the function v can be determined from the above formula (Figure 3–23). It is not necessary to memorize this formula, however, since it is just as easy to substitute vy_1 into the given differential equation and follow through these logical steps.

Once v and thus vy_1 are available, the second linearly independent solution of the differential equation becomes $y_2 = vy_1$. Then the general solution can be expressed as

$$y = C_1y_1 + C_2vy_1 \tag{3-24}$$

Note that if we kept the integration constant C in Equation 3–22, the general solution would involve C_2C in place of C_2. But this is of no significance since we can rename C_2C as another arbitrary constant, say C_3. Therefore, we can always ignore the integration constant (or assign any convenient value to it) when determining v. Also note that y_1 and y_2 are linearly independent since their ratio is $y_2/y_1 = v$, which is never a constant. This is because the integrand of Equation 3–23 will never be zero. In other words, the expression for v will always involve the independent variable x.

We summarize the method of reduction of order in the following theorem:

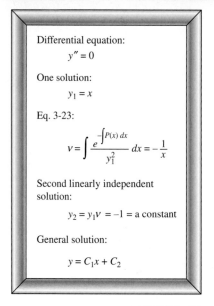

Differential equation:
$$y'' = 0$$

One solution:
$$y_1 = x$$

Eq. 3-23:

$$v = \int \frac{e^{-\int P(x)\,dx}}{y_1^2}\,dx = -\frac{1}{x}$$

Second linearly independent solution:

$$y_2 = y_1v = -1 = \text{a constant}$$

General solution:

$$y = C_1x + C_2$$

FIGURE 3–23

Finding the second linearly independent solution of a differential equation by the method of reduction of order.

THEOREM 3–5   Reduction of Order

If y_1 is a known nonzero solution of the second-order linear homogeneous differential equation

$$y'' + P(x)y' + Q(x)y = 0$$

whose coefficients $P(x)$ and $Q(x)$ are continuous in an interval $x_1 < x < x_2$, then $y_2 = vy_1$, where

$$v = \int \frac{e^{-\int P(x)dx}}{y_1^2}\,dx$$

is also a solution that is linearly independent of y_1 in that interval. Furthermore, the general solution of this differential equation in the given interval is

$$y = C_1y_1 + C_2vy_1$$

Note that the method of reduction of order is not a complete method for solving differential equations since it requires one of the solutions to be available before this method can be applied. However, this method is very attractive when one solution is somehow determined by another method or simply by inspection.

EXAMPLE 3–13   Reduction of Order

Given that $y_1 = x$ is a solution of the differential equation

$$x^2y'' - 4xy' + 4y = 0$$

find a second linearly independent solution by the method of reduction of order in the interval $x > 0$.

SOLUTION This is a second-order linear homogeneous equation, and we seek its second linearly independent solution in the form $y = vy_1 = vx$. Taking its first and second derivatives,

$$y_2' = v'x + v$$
$$y_2'' = v''x + v' + v' = v''x + 2v'$$

Substituting into the differential equation,

$$x^2(v''x + 2v') - 4x(v'x + v) + 4vx = 0$$

which simplifies to $v'' - 2v'/x = 0$ or $w' - 2w/x = 0$, where $w = v'$. This is a first-order linear differential equation, and its solution is $w = x^2$. Then v is determined by integration to be $v = x^3/3$. Note that we suppressed the integration constant since it is immaterial. Then the second linearly independent solution becomes $y_2 = vy_1 = x^4/3$. Note that the functions x and x^4 are linearly independent, as expected. Finally, the general solution of this differential equation for $x > 0$ can be expressed as $y = C_1x + C_2x^4$, where C_1 and C_2 are arbitrary constants. Note that we absorbed the constant factor 1/3 in the arbitrary constant C_2.

Section Review

3–21C What is the practical value of the method of reduction of order? When would you consider using this method?

3–22 Using the one solution given, determine the second linearly independent solution of the given second-order linear homogeneous equation by the method of reduction of order.

$$y'' - y = 0, \qquad y_1 = e^x$$

(*Answer:* $y_2 = -\frac{1}{2}e^{-x}$. The general solution is $y = C_1e^x + C_2e^{-x}$)

3–5 ▪ HOMOGENEOUS EQUATIONS WITH CONSTANT COEFFICIENTS

So far we discussed the theory of second-order, linear, homogeneous equations, and learned about the properties of their solutions. Now we are going to learn how to actually solve such equations. It turns out that linear homogeneous equations can be solved easily in a systematic manner if their coefficients are constant. However, except for some specialized cases, no simple procedures exist for the solution of such equations when their coefficients are variable. In this section we will consider linear homogeneous equations with constant coefficients. Equations with variable coefficients, which are usually solved in terms of infinite series, will be considered in Chapter 5.

Consider the second-order, linear, homogeneous equation with constant coefficients,

$$ay'' + by' + cy = 0 \qquad \qquad \text{(3–25)}$$

where the coefficients a, b, and c are real constants (the nonzero leading coefficient always can be made 1 by dividing each term by a. Considering that constant coefficients are continuous functions over the interval $-\infty < x < \infty$ (the entire x axis), the solutions of such equations are valid in any interval, and thus we do not need to specify an interval for the solution. We can summarize the key theorems in this case as follows:

A second-order, linear, homogeneous equation with constant coefficients always possesses two linearly independent solutions y_1 and y_2 that are applicable to any interval, and its general solution is expressed as $y = C_1 y_1 + C_2 y_2$, where C_1 and C_2 are arbitrary constants (Figure 3–24).

The big question is, of course, how to find the two solutions y_1 and y_2. A careful examination of Equation 3–25 reveals that adding the solution function and its derivatives after multiplying them by some constants yields zero for all x. Thus we conclude that the solution function and its derivatives must differ, at most, by a constant multiple only. The only elementary function whose derivatives are constant multiples of itself is the exponential function e^{mx}, where m is a constant. This is easily verified by observing that the functions

$$y = e^{mx} \tag{3-26}$$

$$y' = me^{mx} \tag{3-27}$$

$$y'' = m^2 e^{mx} \tag{3-28}$$

differ from each other by m or m^2, which are constants. Therefore, we will assume the solution of Equation 3–25 to be of the form e^{mx} (Figure 3–25). Substituting this function into Equation 3–25 yields

$$a(e^{mx})'' + b(e^{mx})' + c(e^{mx}) = 0$$

which simplifies to $e^{mx}(am^2 + bm + c) = 0$. But the exponential function e^{mx} cannot be zero if the solution is to be a general one. Then we must have

$$am^2 + bm + c = 0 \tag{3-29}$$

This quadratic algebraic equation is called the **characteristic equation** (or the auxiliary equation) since it yields the acceptable values of m that characterize the solution of the given differential equation. A comparison of the characteristic equation and the differential equation suggests a straightforward way of obtaining the characteristic equation: in the differential equation, replace y'' by m^2, y' by m, and y by 1 (Figure 3–26). This procedure will convert the differential equation into the characteristic equation.

You will recall from algebra that an nth degree polynomial equation has n roots. Therefore, the characteristic equation will have two roots m_1 and m_2 since it involves a second-degree polynomial in m. These two roots are determined from the quadratic formula as

$$m_1 = \frac{-b + \sqrt{b^2 - 4ac}}{2a} \quad \text{and} \quad m_2 = \frac{-b - \sqrt{b^2 - 4ac}}{2a} \tag{3-30}$$

Differential equation:
$$y'' = 0$$

Two linearly independent solutions:
$$y_1 = x \text{ and } y_2 = 1$$

General solution:
$$y = C_1 x + C_2 \cdot 1$$

Valid for:
$$-\infty < x < \infty$$

FIGURE 3–24

A second-order linear, homogeneous equation with constant coefficients possesses two linearly independent solutions whose linear combination gives the general solution for all x.

If
$$y = e^{-3x}$$

Then
$$y' = -3e^{-3x} = -3y$$
$$y'' = 9e^{-3x} = 9y$$

FIGURE 3–25

The exponential function e^{mx} differs from its derivatives by a constant only, making it the ideal choice for the trial solution for linear homogeneous differential equations with constant coefficients.

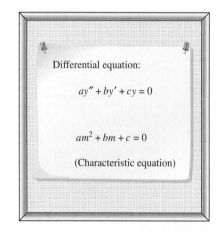

FIGURE 3–26

The characteristic equation of a second-order equation can be obtained easily by replacing y'' with m^2, y' with m, and y with 1.

Quadratic equation:

$$am^2 + bm + c = 0$$

The roots:

$$m_{1,2} = \frac{-b \pm \sqrt{b^2 - 4ac}}{2a}$$

Three cases:

(1) $b^2 - 4ac > 0 \rightarrow m_1 \neq m_2$ (real)

(2) $b^2 - 4ac = 0 \rightarrow m_1 = m_2$ (real)

(3) $b^2 - 4ac < 0 \rightarrow m_1 \neq m_2$ (complex)

FIGURE 3–27

A little refresher from algebra.

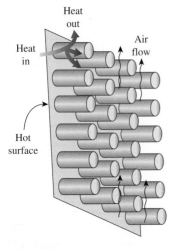

FIGURE 3–28

Pin fins are commonly used in practice to increase the rate of heat transfer from hot surfaces.

This gives the two allowable values of m, and thus, the solutions are

$$y_1 = e^{m_1 x} \quad \text{and} \quad y_2 = e^{m_2 x} \tag{3-31}$$

If m_1 and m_2 are real and distinct, the two solutions above are linearly independent, and we can readily form the general solution. But m_1 and m_2 can be equal to each other. They will even be complex numbers if $b^2 - 4ac$ is negative. The nature of the solution is different for different cases, and we need to consider each case separately (Figure 3–27).

Case 1: Real and Unequal Roots ($m_1 \neq m_2$)

As you will recall from algebra, when $b^2 - 4ac > 0$ the roots of the characteristic equation $am^2 + bm + c = 0$ will be real and unequal. Then $m_1 \neq m_2$, and the two solutions $e^{m_1 x}$ and $e^{m_2 x}$ are linearly independent since their ratio is $e^{m_1 x}/e^{m_2 x} = e^{(m_1 - m_2)x}$, which is not a constant. Then the general solution becomes

$$y = C_1 e^{m_1 x} + C_2 e^{m_2 x} \tag{3-32}$$

EXAMPLE 3–14   **A Homogeneous Equation with $m_1 \neq m_2$**

Determine the general solution of the differential equation $y'' + y' - 2y = 0$.

SOLUTION This is a second-order, linear, homogeneous equation with constant coefficients, and its characteristic equation is obtained by replacing y'' by m^2, y' by m, and y by 1 to be $m^2 + m - 2 = 0$, which can be factored as $(m - 1)(m + 2) = 0$.

The roots of this equation are $m_1 = 1$ and $m_2 = -2$, which are real and unequal. Thus the general solution of the given differential equation is, from Equation 3–32, $y = C_1 e^x + C_2 e^{-2x}$. We can show by direct substitution that this general solution as well as the individual solutions e^x and e^{-2x}, satisfy the differential equation.

EXAMPLE 3–15   **Heat Transfer from Fins (Part 1)**

Aluminum pin fins of uniform diameter D and length L are frequently used in practice to enhance heat transfer from hot surfaces by providing additional surface area for heat transfer to take place, as shown in Figure 3–28. The base of the fin is in perfect contact with the hot surface, and thus the temperature of the fin base is the same as the temperature of the hot surface. Heat is first conducted from the hot surface to the fin through its base. As heat flows towards the tip of the fin, part of it is transferred to the surrounding air through the outer surface of the fin. As a result of this heat loss, the temperature of the fin decreases away from the base.

By applying the conservation of energy principle to a differential cross-section of the fin (Figure 3–29) and utilizing Fourier's law of heat conduction and Newton's law of cooling, the differential equation that governs the temperature distribution $T(x)$ along the fin under steady operation in a medium that is at 0°C is determined to be

$$T'' - \lambda T = 0 \tag{3-33}$$

where $\lambda = 4h/kD$. Here h is the heat transfer coefficient between the fin and the surrounding medium, and k is the thermal conductivity of the fin material. Note that λ is a positive quantity.

Taking $L = 0.5$ m, $\lambda = 4\,\text{m}^{-1}$, the temperature of the fin base to be $T(0) = 200°C$, and the slope of the temperature profile at the base to be $T'(0) = -480°C/m$, determine the temperature distribution along the fin. Also determine the value of the temperature at the end of the fin, $x = L = 0.5$ m.

SOLUTION This is an initial-value problem since both conditions are specified at the same point. It can be formulated as

$$T'' - 4T = 0$$

$$T(0) = 200$$

$$T'(0) = -480$$

The differential equation is a second-order, linear, homogeneous equation with constant coefficients, and its characteristic equation is $m^2 - 4 = 0$. The roots of this equation are $m_1 = -2$ and $m_2 = 2$, which are real and unequal. Thus the general solution of the differential equation is, from Equation 3–32,

$$T(x) = C_1 e^{-2x} + C_2 e^{2x} \qquad \textbf{(3–34)}$$

Its derivative with respect to x is

$$T'(x) = -2C_1 e^{-2x} + 2C_2 e^{2x} \qquad \textbf{(3–35)}$$

The arbitrary constants are determined by applying the initial conditions:

$$T(0) = 200 \rightarrow C_1 + C_2 = 200$$
$$T'(0) = -480 \rightarrow -2C_1 + 2C_2 = -480$$

since $e^0 = 1$. Solving these two equations simultaneously for the two unknowns yields $C_1 = 220$ and $C_2 = -20$. Substituting these values into Equation 3–34 yields the solution of this initial-value problem,

$$T(x) = 220e^{-2x} - 20e^{2x} \qquad \textbf{(3–36)}$$

The value of the temperature at any location x along the fin can be determined by substituting that x value into the solution Equation 3–36. Thus the temperature of the fin at $x = L = 0.5$ m is

$$T(0.5) = 220e^{-2 \times 0.5} - 20e^{2 \times 0.5} = 26.57°C$$

Therefore, the temperature of the fin drops from 200 at its base to 26.57 at its tip as a result of heat transfer from the fin to its surrounding medium (Figure 3–30).

Alternative Solution You may be wondering what would happen if we had expressed the general solution in terms of the hyperbolic functions $\cosh 2x$ and $\sinh 2x$ instead of the exponential functions e^{2x} and e^{-2x}. After all, these two family of functions are closely related to each other by

$$\cosh mx = \frac{e^{mx} + e^{-mx}}{2} \quad \text{and} \quad \sinh mx = \frac{e^{mx} - e^{-mx}}{2} \qquad \textbf{(3–37)}$$

We can show by direct substitution that both $\cosh 2x$ and $\sinh 2x$ satisfy the differential equation, and thus they are solutions. Further, these two solutions are linearly independent since their ratio $(\sinh 2x)/\cosh 2x = \tanh 2x$ is not a

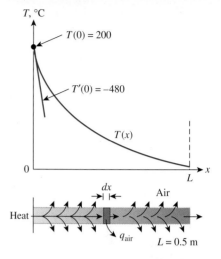

FIGURE 3–29

The differential element and the initial conditions for the single-pin fin discussed in Example 3–15.

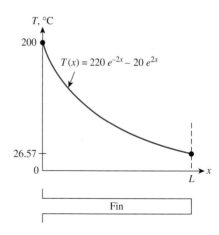

FIGURE 3–30

The variation of the temperature along the pin fin discussed in Example 3–15.

constant. Then we can express the general solution of the same differential equation as

$$T(x) = D_1 \cosh 2x + D_2 \sinh 2x \tag{3–38}$$

where D_1 and D_2 are arbitrary constants. But we know that a second-order, linear, homogeneous equation with constant coefficients can have only two linearly independent solutions, and the general solution that is constructed using these two solutions contains all the solutions of the differential equation. In other words, the two different looking general solutions must be equivalent to each other. Using the definitions of the hyperbolic functions (Equation 3–37), we can show that this is indeed the case. We will demonstrate this on the initial-value problem.

The derivative of Equation 3–38 with respect to x is

$$T'(x) = 2D_1 \sinh 2x + 2D_2 \cosh 2x$$

The arbitrary constants are again determined by applying the initial conditions. Noting that $\cosh 0 = 1$ and $\sinh 0 = 0$,

$$T(0) = 200 \rightarrow D_1 = 200$$
$$T'(0) = -480 \rightarrow 2D_2 = -480 \rightarrow D_2 = -240$$

Substituting these values into Equation 3–38 yields the solution of the given initial-value problem,

$$T(x) = 200 \cosh 2x - 240 \sinh 2x \tag{3–39}$$

To show that this solution is equivalent to the solution obtained earlier (Equation 3–36), we replace the hyperbolic functions above by their equivalents in terms of the exponential functions. We obtain

$$T(x) = 200 \frac{e^{2x} + e^{-2x}}{2} - 240 \frac{e^{2x} - e^{-2x}}{2} = 220e^{-2x} - 20e^{2x}$$

which is identical to the first solution obtained. This should reaffirm our belief that once we determine the general solution of a linear, homogeneous differential equation, any solution of that equation, no matter how different it may appear, can be obtained from that general solution as a special case (Figure 3–31).

Differential equation:
$$T'' - 4T = 0$$

Roots of characteristic equation:
$$m_1 = 2, \quad m_2 = -2$$

Possible forms of general solution:

$$T = A_1 \sinh 2x + A_2 \cosh 2x$$
$$T = B_1 \sinh 2(L - x) + B_2 \cosh 2(L - x)$$
$$T = C_1 e^{-2x} + C_2 e^{2x}$$
$$T = D_1 e^{-2(L - x)} + D_2 e^{2(L - x)}$$

FIGURE 3–31

A second-order, linear, homogeneous differential equation with constant coefficients has only two linearly independent solutions, but they can be expressed in various forms. Although all are equivalent, some forms may be more convenient to use than others in a given problem.

EXAMPLE 3–16   Heat Transfer from Fins (Part 2)

Solve the problem described in preceding example by replacing the initial conditions by the boundary conditions $T(0) = 200$ and $T(0.5) = 26.57°C$.

SOLUTION This is a boundary-value problem since the two conditions are specified at different points. It can be formulated as

$$T'' - 4T = 0$$
$$T(0) = 200$$
$$T(0.5) = 26.57$$

The general solution of the differential equation is independent of the initial or boundary conditions, and it was determined to be $T(x) = C_1e^{-2x} + C_2e^{2x}$. The arbitrary constant in this case are determined by applying the boundary conditions:

$$T(0) = 200 \rightarrow C_1 + C_2 = 200$$
$$T(0.5) = 26.57 \rightarrow C_1e^{-2\times0.5} + C_2e^{2\times0.5} = 26.57$$

Solving these two equations simultaneously for the two unknowns yields $C_1 = 220$ and $C_2 = -20$. Substituting these values into the general solution yields the solution of this boundary-value problem, $T(x) = 220e^{-2x} - 20e^{2x}$, which is the same as the solution of the initial-value problem (Figure 3–30). This is not surprising since we chose the boundary condition at $x = L = 0.5$ to be the value of the temperature obtained from the previous solution. Thus we can fix a specific solution curve of a second order linear differential equation by either specifying the value of solution and its slope at the same points (a boundary-value problem). Note that if we used a different temperature at $x = 0.5$, we would obtain a different solution.

Case 2: Real and Equal Roots ($m_1 = m_2$)

When $b^2 - 4ac = 0$, the roots of the characteristic equation $am^2 + bm + c = 0$ will be real and equal to each other. From Equation 3–30, they are determined to be $m_1 = m_2 = m = -b/2a$. Then the two solutions corresponding to each one of them become identical,

$$y_1 = e^{m_1x} = e^{m_2x} = e^{mx} = e^{-(b/2a)x}$$

Therefore, the characteristic equation gives only one solution in this case. The second linearly independent solution is determined by applying the method of reduction of order to be $y_2 = v(x)y_1$, where from Equation 3–23,

$$v(x) = \int \frac{e^{-\int P(x)dx}}{y_1^2} dx = \int \frac{e^{-\int (b/a)dx}}{[e^{-\int(b/2a)x}]^2} dx = \int \frac{e^{-\int(b/a)x}}{e^{-\int(b/a)x}} dx = \int dx = x$$

Here we intentionally ignored the integration constants for simplicity since they are of no consequence, as explained in Section 3–4. Therefore, the second solution is

$$y_2 = vy_1 = xy_1 = xe^{-mx} \tag{3–40}$$

We can check by direct substitution that y_2 satisfies the differential equation (Equation 3–33), and thus it is a solution. Not only that, y_1 and y_2 are linearly independent since $y_2/y_1 = x$, which is not a constant. Then the general solution in the case of real and equal roots becomes (Figure 3–32). $y = C_1e^{mx} + C_2xe^{mx}$, or

$$y = (C_1 + C_2x)e^{mx} \tag{3–41}$$

Thus, we conclude that when the characteristic equation has real and equal roots, the second linearly independent solution is obtained by multiplying the first one by x.

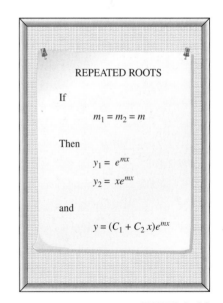

REPEATED ROOTS

If

$$m_1 = m_2 = m$$

Then

$$y_1 = e^{mx}$$
$$y_2 = xe^{mx}$$

and

$$y = (C_1 + C_2 x)e^{mx}$$

FIGURE 3–32

When the roots of the characteristic equation are real and equal, the second linearly independent solution is obtained by multiplying the first one by x.

EXAMPLE 3–17   **Homogeneous Equations with Repeated Roots**
$(m_1 = m_2)$

Determine the general solution of the differential equation $y'' + 6y' + 9y = 0$.

SOLUTION   This is a second-order linear homogeneous equation with constant coefficients, and its characteristic equation is

$$m^2 + 6m + 9 = 0$$

which can be factored as

$$(m + 3)^2 = 0$$

The roots of this equation are $m_1 = m_2 = m = -3$, which are real and equal. Thus one solution of the given equation is e^{-3x}, and the second linearly independent solution is xe^{-3x}. Then the general solution becomes (Equation 3–41) $y = C_1 e^{-3x} + C_2 x e^{-3x}$. We can check by direct substitution that the functions e^{-3x} and xe^{-3x}, as well as any linear combination of them, satisfy the given differential equation. Furthermore, any solution of the differential equation can be obtained from the general solution above by assigning suitable values to the constants C_1 and C_2.

Case 3: Complex Roots $(m_{1,2} = \alpha \pm i\beta)$

When $b^2 - 4ac < 0$, the roots of the characteristic equation $am^2 + bm + c = 0$ will be complex since Equation 3–30 will involve the square root of a negative number. It is clear from these equations that the roots are necessarily complex conjugates of each other. That is, $m_1 = \alpha + i\beta$ and $m_2 = \alpha - i\beta$, where $i = \sqrt{-1}$, $\alpha = -b/2a$, and $\beta = \sqrt{4ac - b^2}/2a$. Noting that $e^{c+d} = e^c e^d$, the two solutions corresponding to the two roots of the characteristic equation are $y_1 = e^{m_1 x} = e^{(\alpha + i\beta)x} = e^{\alpha x} e^{i\beta x}$ and $y_2 = e^{m_2 x} = e^{(\alpha - i\beta)x} = e^{\alpha x} e^{-i\beta x}$. These two solutions are linearly independent since their ratio is $y_1/y_2 = e^{i\beta x}/e^{-i\beta x} = e^{2i\beta x}$, which is not constant. Thus, the general solution is

$$y = A e^{\alpha x} e^{i\beta x} + B e^{\alpha x} e^{-i\beta x}$$
$$= e^{\alpha x}(A e^{i\beta x} + B e^{-i\beta x}) \tag{3–42}$$

where A and B are arbitrary constants. The general solution in Equation 3–42 involves complex functions, and we would like to express it in terms of real functions. To do this, we need to have a better understanding of the function e^{ix}, where x is a negative or positive number, and be able to manipulate it.

You may recall from calculus that the Taylor series expansion of the exponential function is

$$e^x = \sum_{n=0}^{\infty} \frac{x^n}{n!} \tag{3–43}$$

Replacing x by ix and rearranging yields

$$e^{ix} = \sum_{n=0}^{\infty} \frac{(ix)^n}{n!} = 1 + \frac{ix}{1!} - \frac{x^2}{2!} - \frac{ix^3}{3!} + \frac{x^4}{4!} - \cdots$$

$$= \sum_{n=0}^{\infty} \frac{(-1)^n x^{2n}}{(2n)!} + i \sum_{n=1}^{\infty} \frac{(-1)^{n-1} x^{2n-1}}{(2n - 1)!} \tag{3–44}$$

$$= \cos x + i \sin x \tag{3–45}$$

since the two series in Equation 3–44 are the Taylor series expansions of $\cos x$ and $\sin x$, respectively. Likewise,

$$e^{-ix} = \cos x - i \sin x \qquad \textbf{(3–46)}$$

since $\cos(-x) = \cos x$ and $\sin(-x) = -\sin x$. Equations 3–45 and 3–46 are known as *Euler's identities*.

With the help of these relations, the terms in the parentheses of Equation 3–42 can be expressed as

$$\begin{aligned} Ae^{i\beta x} + Be^{-i\beta x} &= A(\cos \beta x + i \sin \beta x) + B(\cos \beta x - i \sin \beta x) \\ &= (A + B)\cos \beta x + i(A - B)\sin \beta x \\ &= C_1 \cos \beta x + C_2 \sin \beta x \qquad \textbf{(3–47)} \end{aligned}$$

where $C_1 = A + B$ and $C_2 = i(A - B)$ are two arbitrary constants. Then the general solution of the differential equation can be expressed as (Figure 3–33)

$$y = e^{\alpha x}(C_1 \cos \beta x + C_2 \sin \beta x) \qquad \textbf{(3–48)}$$

which involves real functions only.

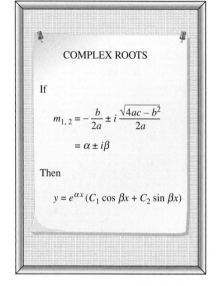

COMPLEX ROOTS

If

$$m_{1,2} = -\frac{b}{2a} \pm i\frac{\sqrt{4ac - b^2}}{2a}$$

$$= \alpha \pm i\beta$$

Then

$$y = e^{\alpha x}(C_1 \cos \beta x + C_2 \sin \beta x)$$

FIGURE 3–33
When the roots of the characteristic equation are complex, the general solution is still real and involves the periodic functions sine and cosine.

EXAMPLE 3–18   A Homogeneous Equation with Complex Roots

Determine the general solution of the differential equation

$$y'' - 2y' + 3y = 0.$$

SOLUTION This is a second-order, linear, homogeneous equation with constant coefficients, and its characteristic equation is $m^2 - 2m + 3 = 0$, whose roots are

$$m_{1,2} = \frac{-b \pm \sqrt{b^2 - 4ac}}{2a} = \frac{2 + \sqrt{4 - 12}}{2} = 1 \pm i\sqrt{2}$$

Therefore, $\alpha = 1$ and $\beta = \sqrt{2}$, and the general solution is, from Equation 3–48, $y = e^x(C_1 \cos \sqrt{2}x + C_2 \sin \sqrt{2}x)$, where C_1 and C_2 are arbitrary constants.

SPECIAL CASE: Purely Imaginary Roots

When the coefficient b in the characteristic equation $am^2 + bm + c = 0$ is $b = 0$, the two roots are $m_{1,2} = \pm\sqrt{-c/a}$. Thus if the ratio c/a is positive, the two roots will be purely imaginary and they can be expressed as $m_{1,2} = \pm i\sqrt{c/a}$. In this case the form of the solution from Equation 3–48 is $y = C_1 \cos \beta x + C_2 \sin \beta x$, where $\beta = \sqrt{c/a}$. The solution is a constant amplitude oscillation with a radian frequency of $\sqrt{c/a}$.

The case with purely imaginary roots occurs frequently in the analysis of mechanical objects whose motion consists of an oscillation or vibration. The next two examples illustrate two applications in which oscillations occur.

EXAMPLE 3–19   **Equation of Motion of a Pendulum**

The pendulum shown in Figure 3–34a consists of a concentrated mass m_C a distance L_C from point O, attached to a rod of length L_R and inertia I_{RG} about its mass center. The inertia of the concentrated mass m_C about point O is $m_C L_C^2$. (a) Obtain the equation of motion. (b) Discuss the case where the rod's mass m_R is small compared to the concentrated mass. (c) Determine the equation of motion for small angles θ.

SOLUTION (a) From physics you may recall the parallel-axis theorem for moments of inertia, which says that the rod's moment of inertia about point O is

$$I_{RO} = I_{RG} + m_R \left(\frac{L_R}{2} \right)^2$$

Thus the entire pendulum's inertia about point O is

$$I_O = I_{RO} + m_C L_C^2 = I_{RG} + m_R \left(\frac{L_R}{2} \right)^2 + m_C L_C^2$$

The distance L is the distance between point O and the mass center G of the entire pendulum. The moment M_O about point O is caused by the perpendicular component of the total weight $(m_C + m_R)g$ acting through the mass center at G (see Figure 3–34b), and is $-(m_C + m_R)gL \sin \theta$. The desired equation of motion is obtained from the basic law of motion for rotation about a fixed point O, which is

(mass moment of inertia about a fixed point O) $\times$ (angular acceleration)
= sum of moments about point O

This gives the equation of motion:

$$I_O \ddot{\theta} = M_O = -(m_C + m_R)gL \sin \theta = -mgL \sin \theta$$

where $m = m_C + m_R$. However the distance L between point O and the mass center G of the entire pendulum is not given, but can be calculated as follows (Figure 3–34c). If the entire pendulum mass were concentrated at G, the weight force would produce the same moment about point O as the real pendulum. Thus, taking moments about point O, we have

$$mgL = m_C g L_C + m_R g \left(\frac{L_R}{2} \right)$$

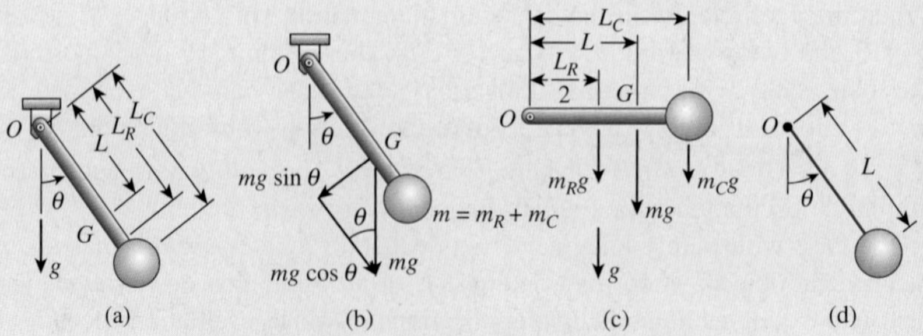

FIGURE 3–34
A rod-and-bob pendulum.

(a)   (b)   (c)   (d)

Solve for L to obtain

$$L = \frac{m_C L_C + m_R L_R/2}{m_C + m_R}$$

(b) If we neglect the rod's mass m_R compared to the concentrated mass m_C, we can take $m_R = I_{RG} = 0$, $m = m_C$, $L = L_C$, and $I_O = mL^2$. In this case, the equation of motion reduces to $mL^2\ddot{\theta} = -mgL\sin\theta$. Canceling one L and the m we obtain $L\ddot{\theta} = -g\sin\theta$. This is a model for a pendulum whose mass is concentrated at a distance L from the pivot point, like that shown in Figure 3–34d. Note that this equation of motion is independent of the value of m.

(c) For small angles, $\sin\theta \approx \theta$ if θ is in radians. Substituting this approximation into the equation gives $L\ddot{\theta} = -g\theta$. This is a linear second order equation with constant coefficients. The characteristic equation is $L\beta^2 = -g$. The roots are imaginary: $\beta = \pm i\sqrt{g/L}$. The solution has the form

$$\theta(t) = C_1\sin\sqrt{\frac{g}{L}}t + C_2\cos\sqrt{\frac{g}{L}}t$$

The oscillation frequency is $\sqrt{g/L}$ radians/time, and the period is $2\pi\sqrt{L/g}$. Thus a longer pendulum will have a longer period.

EXAMPLE 3–20   Equation of Motion of a Rolling Ship

Figure 3–35a shows the cross-section view of a ship undergoing rolling motion. Archimedes' principle states that the buoyancy force B equals the weight of the displaced liquid. In order to float, B must equal the ship's weight $W = mg$. Thus, $B = W = mg$. The *metacenter M* is the intersection point of the line of action of the buoyancy force and the ship's centerline. The distance h of M from the mass center G is called the *metacentric height*. Obtain the equation describing the ship's rolling motion in terms of θ.

SOLUTION Use the following principle from Newton's laws of motion.

(mass moment of inertia about the mass center G) × (angular acceleration)
    = sum of moments about point G

From the force diagram in Figure 3–35b we obtain

$$I_G\ddot{\theta} = M_G = -(B\sin\theta)h$$

where I_G is the ship's mass moment of inertia about point G. With $B = mg$, we obtain $I_G\ddot{\theta} = -mgh\sin\theta$. This has the same form as the pendulum equation of Example 3–19, and we can obtain a linear model using the same approximation $\sin\theta \approx \theta$. This gives $I_G\ddot{\theta} = -mgh\theta$. This model neglects drag on the ship's hull as it rolls, but we can use the solution of this equation to obtain a preliminary estimate of the roll frequency of the ship.

The characteristic equation is $I_G p^2 = -mgh$. The roots are imaginary: $p = \pm i\sqrt{mgh/I_G}$. The solution has the form

$$\theta(t) = C_1\sin\sqrt{\frac{mgh}{I_G}}t + C_2\cos\sqrt{\frac{mgh}{I_G}}t$$

The oscillation frequency is $\sqrt{mgh/I_G}$ radians/time, and the period is $2\pi\sqrt{I_G/mgh}$.

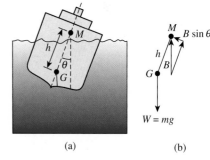

(a)   (b)

FIGURE 3–35

Rolling motion of a ship.

TABLE 3–1

The General Solution of Second-Order, Linear, Homogeneous Differential Equations with Constant Coefficients.

Differential equation: $ay'' + by' + cy = 0$

Characteristic equation: $am^2 + bm + c = 0$

Characteristic roots: $m_{1,2} = \dfrac{-b \pm \sqrt{b^2 - 4ac}}{2a}$

Nature of m_1 and m_2	The General Solution
Case 1: Real and Unequal $(m_1 \neq m_2)$ $b^2 - 4ac > 0$	$y = C_1 e^{m_1 x} + C_2 e^{m_2 x}$
Case 2: Real and Equal $(m_1 = m_2 = m)$ $b^2 - 4ac = 0$	$y = C_1 e^{mx} + C_2 x e^{mx}$
Case 3: Complex Conjugates $(m_{1,2} = \alpha + i\beta)$ $b^2 - 4ac < 0$	$y = e^{\alpha x}(C_1 \cos \beta x + C_2 \sin \beta x)$

The reader should always keep in mind that the solution procedures presented in this section apply to second-order, linear, homogeneous equations with constant coefficients. In Table 3–1 we summarize the solutions of such equations for the three different cases for easy reference.

Section Review

3–23C Consider a second-order, linear, homogeneous equation with constant coefficients. If the functions y_1, y_2, and y_3 all satisfy this equation, can we say that any one of these functions must be a linear combination of the other two?

3–24C Does there exist a second-order, linear, homogeneous equation with constant coefficients that is satisfied by the functions e^{2x}, e^{-2x}, and e^{3x}?

3–25C When the roots of the characteristic equation of a second-order, linear, homogeneous equation with constant coefficients are complex, are they necessarily conjugates of each other?

3–26 Determine the general solution of the given second-order, linear, homogeneous equations with constant coefficients.

(a) $y'' + y = 0$ (b) $y'' + 2y' + y = 0$ (c) $y'' - y = 0$

(*Answers*: (a) $y = C_1 \cos x + C_2 \sin x$ (b) $y = (C_1 + C_2 x)e^{-x}$ (c) $y = C_1 e^x + C_2 e^{-x}$)

3–27 Determine the specific solution of the following initial-value problem.

$$y'' + 4y = 0, \qquad y(\pi) = 0 \quad \text{and} \quad y'(\pi) = 1$$

(*Answer*: $y = \dfrac{1}{2} \sin 2x$)

3–28 Determine the specific solution of the following boundary-value problem.

$$y'' - y = 0, \qquad y(0) = 100 \quad \text{and} \quad y(5) = 0$$

(*Answer*: $y = \dfrac{100}{\sinh 5} \sinh(5 - x)$)

3–6 ▪ THEORY OF LINEAR NONHOMOGENEOUS EQUATIONS

So far we have limited the discussion to linear, homogeneous equations because they are easier to solve. Now we extend the discussion to nonhomogeneous equations. In this section we will discuss the basic theory of nonhomogeneous equations, and in the next two sections we will present two methods of solving such equations.

Second-order, linear, nonhomogeneous equations can be expressed as

$$y'' + P(x)y' + Q(x)y = R(x) \qquad \text{(3–49)}$$

where the functions $P(x), Q(x)$, and $R(x)$ are assumed to be continuous on the interval of interest. Its related homogeneous equation is obtained by setting $R(x) = 0$,

$$y'' + P(x)y' + Q(x)y = 0 \qquad \text{(3–50)}$$

The solutions of nonhomogeneous equations are closely associated with their related homogeneous equations. The first step in solving a nonhomogeneous equation is to obtain the solution of its related homogeneous equation and express this solution as

$$y_h = C_1 y_1 + C_2 y_2 \qquad \text{(3–51)}$$

where y_1 and y_2 are a fundamental set of solutions of the homogeneous equation. The function y_h represents the general solution of the related homogeneous equation, and is referred to as the **homogeneous solution** or the **complementary solution**. In contrast, a function that does not involve any arbitrary constants and satisfies the entire nonhomogeneous equation is called a **particular solution**. The next step is to modify the homogeneous solution so that it satisfies the given nonhomogeneous equation. This is done in accordance with the following theorem:

THEOREM 3–6 General Solution of Linear, Nonhomogeneous Equations

If y_p is a particular solution of the linear nonhomogeneous equation

$$y'' + P(x)y' + Q(x)y = R(x)$$

where the functions $P(x)$, $Q(x)$, and $R(x)$ are continuous in an interval $x_1 < x < x_2$ and y_h is the general solution of its related homogeneous equation, then the general solution of this nonhomogeneous equation in that interval is

$$y = y_h + y_p = C_1 y_1 + C_2 y_2 + y_p \qquad \text{(3–52)}$$

where y_1 and y_2 are a fundamental set of solutions of related homogeneous equation, and C_1 and C_2 are arbitrary constants.

Proof Let y_p be a particular solution of the nonhomogeneous equation and y be any solution of it. Then naturally each solution will satisfy the differential equation: $y_p'' + Py_p' + Qy_p = R$, and $y'' + Py' + Qy = R$. Now we

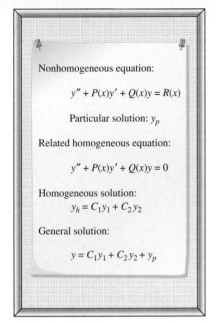

FIGURE 3–36

The general solution of a linear nonhomogeneous equation is obtained by adding the homogeneous solution y_h and a particular solution y_p that is a function satisfying the nonhomogeneous equation.

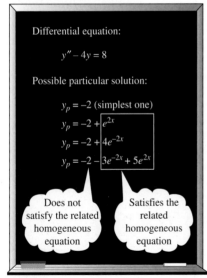

FIGURE 3–37

The particular solution of a differential equation is not unique, and any particular solution will do the job. However, it is more convenient to use the simplest one in the solution.

subtract the first equation from the second one. The nonhomogeneous terms will cancel out during this process and we will obtain

$$(y - y_p)'' + P(y - y_p)' + Q(y - y_p) = 0$$

Thus, the function $y - y_p$ satisfies the related homogeneous equation, and it must be equal to its general solution, $y - y_p = y_h$. Or, after rearranging, we have $y = y_h + y_p$. This completes the proof (Figure 3–36).

Therefore, once the general solution of the related homogeneous equation is available, all we need to do is determine a particular solution y_p that satisfies the given nonhomogeneous equation to construct its general solution (Figure 3–36).

EXAMPLE 3–21   Solving a Nonhomogeneous Equation

Determine the general solution of the differential equation $y'' - 4y = 8$.

SOLUTION This is a second-order, linear, nonhomogeneous differential equation with constant coefficients. Its related homogeneous equation $y'' - 4y = 0$, whose general solution was determined in Example 3–14 to be $y(x) = C_1 e^{-2x} + C_2 e^{2x}$. Now we need to find a particular solution that satisfies the original nonhomogeneous equation. By inspection we see that $y = -2$ satisfies the given equation. Therefore, $y_p = -2$. Then the general solution of the given nonhomogeneous equation becomes, from Equation 3–52, $y(x) = C_1 e^{-2x} + C_2 e^{2x} - 2$, where C_1 and C_2 are arbitrary constants.

We can show by direct substitution that this solution satisfies the given differential equation. Furthermore, all solutions of the given differential equation can be obtained from this solution by assigning suitable values to C_1 and C_2. Note that any solution of a nonhomogeneous equation will involve the particular solution since it is the only function that will cancel the nonhomogeneous term when the solution is substituted into the differential equation.

To prevent any confusion, we should point out that a particular solution is not unique. There are many solutions that will satisfy the given nonhomogeneous equation, and any of them can serve as a particular solution. In Example 3–21 we could have chosen the particular solution to be $y_p = -2 + e^{2x}$ since a linear combination of any two solutions is also a solution. This can be checked easily by direct substitution. A different choice for a particular solution does not affect the general solution since the functions that involve any solution of the related homogeneous equation can be combined with the homogeneous solution $y_h = C_1 y_1 + C_2 y_2$, leaving only the simplest particular solution to stand apart from y_h (Figure 3–37).

The nonhomogeneous term $R(x)$ often involves several terms, and in such cases it is sometimes easier to find a particular solution corresponding to each nonhomogeneous term, and then to add them up. In other words, to apply the superposition principle. We express this in the following theorem.

THEOREM 3–7   Superposition Principle for Particular Solutions

If y_{p1} is a particular solution of

$$y'' + P(x)y' + Q(x)y = R_1(x) \qquad \text{(3–53)}$$

and y_{p2} is a particular solution of

$$y'' + P(x)y' + Q(x)y = R_2(x) \qquad \text{(3–54)}$$

then $y_{p1} + y_{p2}$ is a particular solution of

$$y'' + P(x)y' + Q(x)y = R_1(x) + R_2(x) \qquad \text{(3–55)}$$

Proof   Substituting the sum of the two particular solutions into Equation 3–53 gives

$$(y_{p1}'' + y_{p2}'') + P(y_{p1}' + y_{p2}') + Q(y_{p1} + y_{p2}) = R_1(x) + R_2(x)$$

which can be rearranged as

$$(y_{p1}'' + Py_{p1}' + Qy_{p1}) + (y_{p2}'' + Py_{p2}' + Qy_{p2}) = R_1(x) + R_2(x)$$

But the terms in the first parentheses equal $R_1(x)$ since y_{p1} is a solution of Equation 3–53, and the terms in the second parentheses equal $R_2(x)$ since y_{p2} is a solution of Equation 3–54. Thus the last equation satisfied. This completes the proof.

This theorem is the result of linearity of the differential equation, and can be extended to equations whose nonhomogeneous term involves any number of terms.

EXAMPLE 3–22   Superposition of Particular Solutions

It is known that $y_{p1} = -2$ is a particular solution of $y'' - 4y = 8$. It is also known that $y_{p2} = x/2$ is a particular solution of $y'' - 4y = -2x$. Show that $y_p = -2 + x/2$ is a particular solution of $y'' - 4y = 8 - 2x$.

SOLUTION   This result follows directly from the superposition principle of a particular solution and can be verified by direct substitution (Figure 3–38):

$$y_p'' - 4y_p = (-2 + x/2)'' - 4(-2 + x/2)$$
$$= 0 + 8 - 2x$$
$$= 8 - 2x$$

Thus, y_p satisfies the equation.

If
$$y'' - 4y = 8 \;\rightarrow\; y_{p1} = -2$$
and
$$y'' - 4y = -2x \;\rightarrow\; y_{p2} = x/2$$
Then
$$y'' - 4y = 8 - 2x \;\rightarrow\; y_{p3} = -2 + x/2$$

FIGURE 3–38

The superposition principle for particular solutions.

Note that the term *particular solution* is also used to refer to a specific solution that satisfies a set of initial or boundary conditions in addition to the differential equation. But the context usually clarifies the intended use.

In the following two sections we discuss two systematic ways of determining the particular solution y_p of nonhomogeneous equations: *The method of undetermined coefficients* and *the method of variation of parameters*.

Section Review

3–29C Can any function that satisfies the given nonhomogeneous equation, including a constant, be taken as the particular solution y_p for use in the general solution relation?

3–30C Do you think there may exist a linear nonhomogeneous differential equation whose particular solution is $y_p = 0$?

3–31C What is the practical value of the superposition principle for the particular solutions?

3–32 Determine the general solutions of the given second-order, linear, nonhomogeneous equations with constant coefficients using the given particular solution, and express them in the simplest form.

$$\text{(a) } y'' - y = 2, y_p = -2 \qquad \text{(b) } y'' - y = 2, y_p = -2 + 3e^x$$

(*Answers*: (a) $y = C_1e^x + C_2e^{-x} - 2$ (b) $y = C_1e^x + C_2e^{-x} - 2$)

3–7 ▪ NONHOMOGENEOUS EQUATIONS: THE METHOD OF UNDETERMINED COEFFICIENTS

Probably the simplest method of obtaining a particular solution to the nonhomogeneous differential equation with constant coefficients $y'' + by' + cy = R(x)$ is the **method of undetermined coefficients**. This method is based on making an *educated guess* for the general form of particular solution y_p that involves some unknown constant coefficients, and then determining these coefficients by requiring the guessed solution to satisfy the nonhomogeneous differential equation.

Although it may appear like this method is not well founded since it involves guessing the particular solution, there is a well-developed procedure for the method of undetermined coefficients when the differential equation has constant coefficients, and the nonhomogeneous term $R(x)$ is in a suitable form. The basic requirement on $R(x)$ is for it to have only a finite number of linearly independent derivatives. This requirement is satisfied by a nonhomogeneous term that consists of

1. a constant, k
2. a polynomial, $P_n(x)$
3. an exponential function, e^{kx}
4. the functions $\sin \alpha x$ or $\cos \alpha x$

or a finite number of the products of these functions. Therefore, the general form of a nonhomogeneous term suitable for the method of undetermined coefficients is $e^{kx}P_n(x)\cos \alpha x$ or $e^{kx}P_n(x)\sin \alpha x$. The method of undetermined coefficients can be applied in these cases in a straightforward manner (Figure 3–39). Here k and α are real constants, n is a nonnegative integer, and $P_n(x)$ is polynomial of degree n.

Although the functions listed above are rather limited, a large class of problems encountered in practice involve these simple functions only, and thus this short list covers a large number of problems of practical interest. If the differential equation has variable coefficients, then there is no guarantee that this method will work. Or, if the nonhomogeneous term involves functions such as

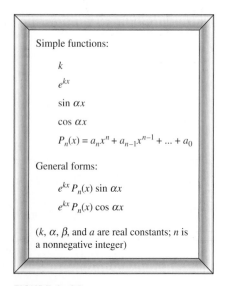

FIGURE 3–39

The forms of the nonhomogeneous terms for which the method of undetermined coefficients is applicable.

Simple functions:

k

e^{kx}

$\sin \alpha x$

$\cos \alpha x$

$P_n(x) = a_nx^n + a_{n-1}x^{n-1} + \ldots + a_0$

General forms:

$e^{kx}P_n(x)\sin \alpha x$

$e^{kx}P_n(x)\cos \alpha x$

(k, α, β, and a are real constants; n is a nonnegative integer)

$1/x$, $\ln x$, or $\tan x$, which possess infinitely many linearly independent derivatives, the method of undetermined coefficients is impractical since the particular solution needs to be taken as an infinite series with an infinite number of unknown constants. In such cases, the method of variation of parameters, which is discussed in the next section, should be used. We now discuss various aspects of the method of undetermined coefficients with examples.

EXAMPLE 3–23   Particular Solutions Where $R(x) = e^{kx}$

Find a particular solution of the differential equation $y'' - 4y = 10e^{3x}$.

SOLUTION   Finding a particular solution to a differential equation is equivalent of finding a function that satisfies the given differential equation. In this case, we should choose a function y_p such that when we subtract four times the function itself from its second derivative we should obtain $10e^{3x}$. Obviously, this will be the case only if the function y_p and its derivatives involve a constant multiple of the exponential function e^{3x}. Therefore, an intelligent choice for the particular solution is (Figure 3–40) $y_p = Ae^{3x}$, where A is a constant coefficient that is to be determined, giving rise to the name *the method undetermined coefficients*. The first and the second derivatives of y_p are

$$y_p' = 3Ae^{3x}$$

$$y_p'' = 9Ae^{3x}$$

Substituting y_p and y_p'' into the differential equation, we have $9Ae^{3x} - 4Ae^{3x} = 10e^{3x}$ or $5Ae^{3x} = 10e^{3x}$. The only A value that will satisfy the last expression is $A = 2$. Therefore, a particular solution of the given differential equation is $y_p = 2e^{3x}$. Note that during the solution we guessed the general form of the function that may satisfy the given differential equation, and took a constant multiple of it as the particular solution. Then we determined the unknown coefficient and thus the specific form of the particular solution by requiring the assumed function to satisfy the differential equation. These are typical steps involved in the method of undetermined coefficients.

   Note also that unlike homogeneous solutions, a constant multiple of a particular solution is not a particular solution.

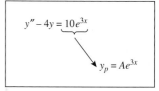

FIGURE 3–40

The general form of the particular solution corresponding to an exponential function is a constant multiple of that exponential function.

EXAMPLE 3–24   Particular Solutions Where $R(x) = \sin \alpha x$ or $\cos \alpha x$

Find a particular solution of the differential equation $y'' + y' - 3y = 6 \sin 2x$.

SOLUTION   This time the nonhomogeneous term is $R(x) = 6 \sin 2x$. In the previous example the particular solution turned out to be a constant multiple of $R(x)$, and thus we tempted to try $y_p = A \sin 2x$ for the particular solution. Substituting this function and derivatives into the given differential equation will yield

$$-4A \sin 2x + 2A \cos 2x - 3A \sin 2x = 6 \sin 2x$$

or,

$$2A \cos 2x - 7A \sin 2x = 6 \sin 2x \tag{3–56}$$

This equation will be satisfied for all x if and only if (1) the coefficients of $\cos 2x$ are the same on both sides, and (2) the coefficients of $\sin 2x$ are the same on both sides of the equal sign. The first requirement gives $A = 0$ whereas the second requirement gives $A = -6/7$. This obviously is contradiction, and leads us to believe that the particular solution cannot be of the form $A \sin 2x$ since no A value will satisfy Equation 3–56.

What went wrong here? How come an idea that worked so well in the previous example failed in this example? The answer is simple: In the previous example the derivatives of assumed form of y_p did not yield any functions that are linearly independent of y_p, but in this example it did. More specifically, the derivatives of $y_p = A e^{kx}$ involve constant multiples of e^{kx}. Thus the left side of the differential equation involves only the function e^{kx} after substitution, which is the function on the right side. But the derivatives of $y_p = A \sin kx$ involve not only $\sin kx$ but also $\cos kx$ which is linearly independent of $\sin kx$. Therefore, the particular solution in this case may involve both of these functions, and its proper form is (Figure 3–41) $y_p = A \sin 2x + B \cos 2x$. Substituting y_p, y_p', and y_p'' into the differential equation, we have

$$(-4A \sin 2x - 4B \cos 2x) + (2A \cos 2x - 2B \sin 2x)$$
$$-3(A \sin 2x + B \cos 2x) = 6 \sin 2x$$

or

$$(-7A - 2B) \sin 2x + (2A - 7B) \cos 2x = 6 \sin 2x$$

Equating the coefficient of $\sin 2x$ and $\cos 2x$ on both sides gives $-7A - 2B = 6$ and $2A - 7B = 0$, whose solution is $A = -42/53$ and $B = -12/53$. Therefore, a particular solution of the given differential equation is

$$y_p = -\frac{42}{53} \sin 2x - \frac{12}{53} \cos 2x$$

Well, it looks like our second choice for y_p worked but there is so much guesswork involved. How can we be sure the function we obtained is the right answer? The rule is very simple and reassuring: If *we get an answer, it is always the correct answer* (assuming of course no algebra mistakes are made) (Figure 3–42).

This example shows that the selected form of the particular solution should include not only the nonhomogeneous term $R(x)$ but also the linearly independent functions its derivatives yield.

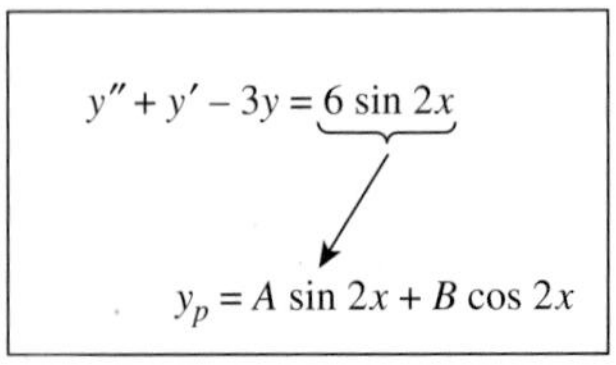

$$\boxed{y'' + y' - 3y = \underbrace{6 \sin 2x}}$$
$$y_p = A \sin 2x + B \cos 2x$$

FIGURE 3–41

The general form of the particular solution corresponding to a sine (or cosine) function involves both the sine and cosine functions.

If the method of undetermined coefficients results in a meaningful answer for the particular solution, it is always the correct answer.

FIGURE 3–42

A simple rule that relieves anxiety.

EXAMPLE 3–25   Particular Solutions Where $R(x)$ Is a Polynomial

Find a particular solution of the differential equation $y'' + 2y' - 4y = 8x^2$.

SOLUTION This time the nonhomogeneous term is $R(x) = 8x^2$. Again the first thought that comes to mind for the general form of the particular solution is $y_p = Ax^2$, which is a constant multiple of $R(x)$. However, we suspect that this will not work since the first and second derivatives of Ax^2 are $2Ax$ and $2A$, which are not constant multiples of Ax^2. In other words, the functions Ax^2, $2Ax$ and $2A$, are linearly independent. Therefore, the proper form of the particular solution is a linear combination of these three functions (Figure 3–43): $y_p = Ax^2 + Bx + C$, where A, B, and C are unknown constants. To determine them, we take the first and second derivatives of y_p and substitute into the given differential equation:

$$2A + 2(2Ax + B) - 4(Ax^2 + Bx + C) = 8x^2$$

or

$$-4Ax^2 + (4A - 4B)x + (2A + 2B - 4C) = 8x^2$$

This equation will be satisfied for all x if and only if the coefficients of each power of x are the same on both sides of the equation. Noting that $8x^2$ can be viewed as $8x^2 + 0x + 0$, this requirement gives the following three equations,

$$-4A = 8$$

$$4A - 4B = 0$$

$$2A + 2B - 4C = 0$$

whose solution is $A = -2$, $B = -2$, and $C = -2$. Therefore, a particular solution of the given differential equation is $y_p = -2x^2 - 2x - 2$. This result can be checked easily by direct substitution into the differential equation.

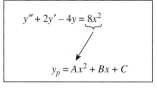

FIGURE 3–43

The general form of the particular solution corresponding to x^n is a polynomial of degree n.

Discussion 1

We found out that if we assume too few terms for y_p we end up with a contradiction. What if we did the opposite? That is, what if we assume too many terms for y_p? For example, what would happen if we assumed $y_p = Ax^3 + Bx^2 + Cx + D$ in this example? We can find out very easily by substituting this form of y_p into the differential equation, and solve for the four unknown coefficients. Not surprisingly, we would obtain zero for the coefficient of x^3, and end up with the particular solution determined earlier.

Thus, we conclude that *there is no harm in assuming too many terms for* y_p, *except that we will have to do extra work just to find out that we assumed too many terms* (Figure 3–44).

In the method of undetermined coefficients, assuming too few terms for y_p results in contradiction; assuming too many terms results in zero coefficients for the unnecessary terms.

FIGURE 3–44

Another simple rule for peace of mind.

Discussion 2

Now let us try to find a particular solution of the differential equation whose nonhomogeneous term is modified as $y'' + 2y' - 4y = 8x^2 - 3x + 1$. This problem is identical to the previous one, except that the nonhomogeneous term $R(x)$ now involves two additional terms. But $R(x)$ is still a second degree polynomial, and the first and second derivatives of the functions x^2 and $8x^2 - 3x + 1$ involve the same linearly independent functions. Therefore, the general form of the particular solution in this case is also $y_p = Ax^2 + Bx + C$.

It is left as an exercise to the student to show that the particular solution this time is

$$y_p = -2x^2 - \frac{5}{4}x - \frac{15}{8}$$

Thus, we conclude that *the general form of the particular solution corresponding to R(x) being an nth-degree polynomial or a single term that involves the nth power of x is the same, and it is an nth-degree polynomial whose coefficients are to be determined* (Figure 3–45).

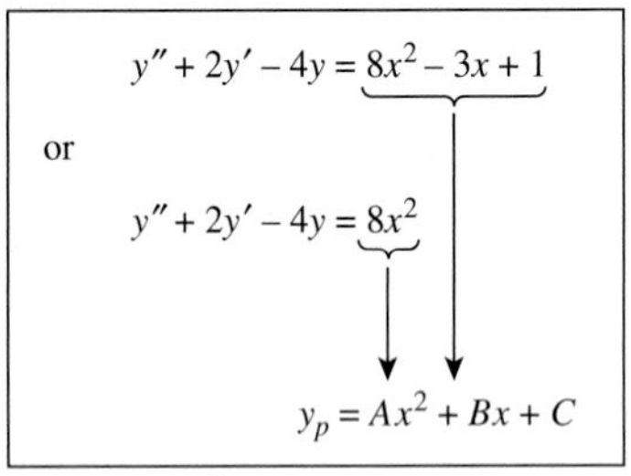

$$y'' + 2y' - 4y = \underbrace{8x^2 - 3x + 1}$$

or

$$y'' + 2y' - 4y = \underbrace{8x^2}$$

$$\downarrow \qquad \downarrow$$

$$y_p = Ax^2 + Bx + C$$

FIGURE 3–45

The general form of the particular solution corresponding to x^n or $P_n(x)$ is a polynomial of degree n.

Differential equation:

$$y'' + 2y' - 4y = \underbrace{x^2 + 2} - \underbrace{3\sin 2x} + \underbrace{e^{-x}}$$

$$y_{p1} = Ae^{-x}$$

$$y_{p2} = B_1 \sin 2x + B_2 \cos 2x$$

$$y_{p3} = C_1 x^2 + C_2 x + C_3$$

Particular solution:

$$y_p = y_{p1} + y_{p2} + y_{p3}$$

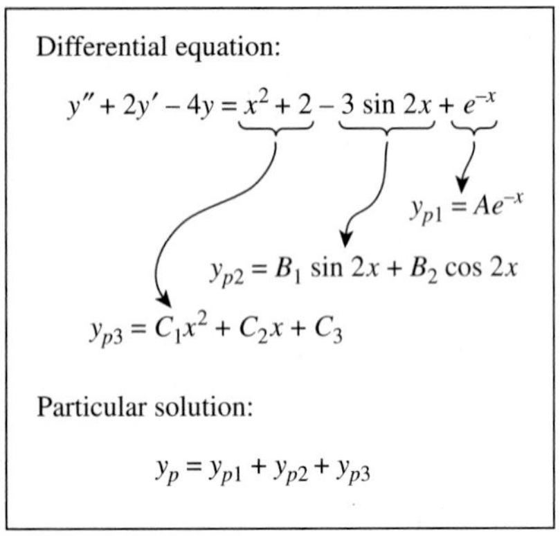

FIGURE 3–46

The superposition of the particular solutions when the nonhomogeneous term involves three terms of different nature.

EXAMPLE 3–26   Superposition of Particular Solutions

Find a particular solution of the differential equation

$$y'' + 2y' - 4y = 8x^2 - 3x + 1 + 2\sin x + 4\cos x - 6e^{2x}$$

SOLUTION It is hard not to notice that the nonhomogeneous term $R(x)$ involves many terms in this case, and we would expect the general form of the particular solution to be rather complicated. In cases like this the first thing we do is group the terms on the right side such that the general form of the particular solution involves the smallest number of unknown coefficients.

For example, if we consider the first three terms together as a second-degree polynomial, the particular solution corresponding to these three terms will be $Ax^2 + Bx + C$, which involves only three unknown coefficients. However, if we consider each term separately, we would have to introduce six unknown coefficients to cover the first three terms on the right side. Also considering $\sin x$ and $\cos x$ as another group we can express the given differential equation as

$$y'' + 2y' - 4y = (8x^2 - 3x + 1) + (2\sin x + 4\cos x) - (6e^{2x})$$

The proper form of the particular solution of this equation is (Figure 3–46).

$$y_p = (A_1 x^2 + A_2 x + A_3) + (B_1 \sin x + B_2 \cos x) + Ce^{2x}$$

where the A's, B's, and C are unknown constants.

Now we could substitute y_p and its derivatives into the given differential equation and try to determine the unknown coefficients. However, this will require dealing with rather lengthy expressions and solving six equations with six unknowns. A more practical approach would be to split the given equation into three equations each containing only one group of nonhomogeneous terms, determining the particular solution for each case, and combining them by applying the superposition principle. The three equations and their assumed particular solutions are

1. $y'' + 2y' - 4y = 8x^2 - 3x + 1,$ $y_{p1} = A_1 x^2 + A_2 x + A_3$

2. $y'' + 2y' - 4y = 2\sin x + 4\cos x,$ $y_{p2} = B_1 \sin x + B_2 \cos x$

3. $y'' + 2y' - 4y = -6e^{2x},$ $y_{p3} = Ce^{2x}$

The first equation has the particular solution

$$y_{p1} = -2x^2 - \frac{5}{4}x - \frac{15}{8}$$

Following the same procedure, the reader can easily verify that the particular solutions of the second and the third equations are

$$y_{p2} = -\frac{2}{29}\sin x - \frac{24}{29}\cos x$$

$$y_{p3} = \frac{3}{2}e^{2x}$$

Then the particular solution of the given differential equation is constructed using the superposition principle, giving

$$y_p = y_{p1} + y_{p2} + y_{p3}$$

$$= -2x^2 - \frac{5}{4}x - \frac{15}{8} - \frac{2}{29}\sin x - \frac{24}{29}\cos x + \frac{3}{2}e^{2x}$$

Again, we can check this result by substituting it directly into the given differential equation.

EXAMPLE 3–27   Particular Solutions That Are a Product of Functions

Find a particular solution of the equation $y'' + 2y' - 4y = xe^{2x} + 5e^{2x}$.

SOLUTION   This equation differs from the previous one in that the first term on the right side involves the product of two functions. To get a sense about the appropriate form of the particular solution corresponding to the first term, we take its first and second derivatives and identify the linearly independent functions they involve:

$$R_1(x) = xe^{2x}$$
$$R_1'(x) = e^{2x} + 2xe^{2x}$$
$$R_1''(x) = 2e^{2x} + 2e^{2x} + 4xe^{2x}$$

We recognize two linearly independent functions in these equations as: e^{2x} and xe^{2x}. Therefore, the proper form of the particular solution corresponding to $R_1(x) = xe^{2x}$ is a linear combination of these two functions:

$$y_p = Axe^{2x} + Be^{2x} = (Ax + B)e^{2x} \tag{3–57}$$

where A and B are unknown constants. The second term on the right side $5e^{2x}$ would contribute a constant times e^{2x}, which is already included in the particular solution. Therefore, Equation 3–57 is the general form of the particular solution of the given equation. We now take the first and second derivatives of y_p and substitute into the given differential equation.

$$[(4A + 4B)e^{2x} + 4Axe^{2x}] + 2[(A + 2B)e^{2x} + 2Axe^{2x}]$$
$$- 4[Be^{2x} + Axe^{2x}] = xe^{2x} + 5e^{2x}$$

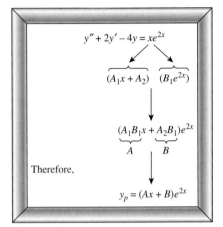

FIGURE 3–47

The form of the particular solution corresponding to a product can be taken as the product of the particular solutions corresponding to each factor and then simplified to avoid nonlinear algebraic equations.

Equating the coefficients of the functions on both sides of this equation yields

$$e^{2x}: 6A + 4B = 5$$

$$xe^{2x}: 4A = 1$$

whose solution is $A = 1/4$, $B = 7/8$. Therefore, the particular solution of the given differential equation is

$$y_p = \left(\frac{1}{4}x + \frac{7}{8}\right)e^{2x}$$

Again, we can check this result by substituting it into the given differential equation. This is sufficient proof that our result is correct.

Discussion Note that we could also determine the general form of the particular solution corresponding to the product xe^{2x} by determining the form of the particular solutions corresponding to each factor, and then taking their product. In this case it would be (Figure 3–47).

$$y_p = (A_1x + A_2)(B_1e^{2x})$$
$$= (A_1B_1x + A_2B_1)e^{2x}$$
$$= (Ax + B)e^{2x}$$

where we took $A = A_1B_1$ and $B = A_2B_1$. Thus, we obtained the same general form for the particular solution.

The procedure described previously can be used for more complicated products, and the simplified form of the particular solution that involves the minimum number of unknowns can then be used as the desired form of the particular solution. For example, the general form of the particular solution corresponding to $R(x) = x^2e^{-3x} \sin 2x$ is

$$y_p = (A_1x^2 + A_2x + A_3)(B_1 \sin 2x + B_2 \cos 2x)C_1e^{-3x}$$

$$= (A_1B_1C_1x^2 + A_2B_1C_1x + A_3B_1C_1)e^{-3x} \sin 2x$$

$$+ (A_1B_2C_1x^2 + A_2B_2C_1 + A_3B_2C_1)e^{-3x} \cos 2x$$

$$= (D_1x^2 + D_2x + D_3)e^{-3x} \sin 2x + (E_1x^2 + E_2x + E_3)e^{-3x} \cos 2x$$

Note that number of unknown constants is the same in both the initial and the final forms of the particular solution. However, the final form is definitely preferable in calculations because it will yield six *linear* algebraic equations for unknown coefficients that are easy to solve. The initial form of the particular solution will result in six *nonlinear* algebraic equations for the determination of six unknown constants, which are much more complicated and difficult to solve.

EXAMPLE 3–28 Particular Solutions Where $R(x)$ Is a Solution of a Related Homogeneous Equation

Find a particular solution of the differential equation $y'' - 4y = e^{2x}$.

SOLUTION This equation looks exactly like the first example of this section, except the nonhomogeneous term involves e^{2x} instead of e^{3x}. Thus, we follow exactly the same procedure and assume the particular solution to be $y_p = Ae^{2x}$. Taking the second derivative of y_p and substituting into the given equation yields $4Ae^{2x} - 4Ae^{2x} = e^{2x}$, or $0 = e^{2x}$, which is impossible (Figure 3–48).

What went wrong this time? The assumed form of the particular solution yielded zero on the left side, indicating that it is a solution of the related homogeneous equation $y'' - 4y = 0$. Indeed, the general solution of the related homogeneous equation is $y_h = C_1e^{2x} + C_2e^{-2x}$.

Clearly, the homogeneous term e^{-2x} is a solution of the homogeneous equation, verifying our suspicion. A solution of the homogeneous equation will always yield zero on the left side, and thus can never be a solution of the given nonhomogeneous equation.

This situation can be resolved by applying the method of variation of parameters discussed in the next section, and result is

$$y_p = Axe^{2x} \tag{3–58}$$

which is x times the initially assumed solution. Now substituting this form of the particular solution together with its second derivative into the given differential equation and solving for A yields $A = 0.25$. Thus the particular solution we are looking for is $y_p = 0.25xe^{2x}$.

Differential equation:

$$y'' - 4y = e^{2x}$$

Taking $y_p = Ae^{2x}$ gives

$$0 = Ae^{2x}$$

Therefore, e^{2x} is a homogeneous solution.

FIGURE 3–48

The assumed form of a particular solution that happens to be a solution of the related homogeneous equation will always yield zero on the left side of the differential equation.

The procedure described above for handling nonhomogeneous terms when they are solutions of the related homogeneous equation is quite general and can be expressed as follows: *When a nonhomogeneous term is a solution of the related homogeneous equation, multiply the initially assumed form of the particular solution by the independent variable* x (Figure 3–49).

EXAMPLE 3–29 Particular Solutions Where $R(x)$ and $xR(x)$ Are Solutions of a Related Homogeneous Equation

Find a particular solution of the differential equation $y'' - 4y' + 4y = e^{2x}$.

SOLUTION Again we first assume that the particular solution will be of the form $y_p = Ae^{2x}$. But substituting this function and its derivatives into the differential equation yields $0 = e^{2x}$, which suggests that e^{2x} must be a solution of the related homogeneous equation. Therefore, in light of the previous example, we modify the particular solution by multiplying it by x and obtain $y_p = Axe^{2x}$. But this modified form also yields what we do not want to see: $0 = e^{2x}$. Again this suggests that xe^{2x} must also be a solution of the related

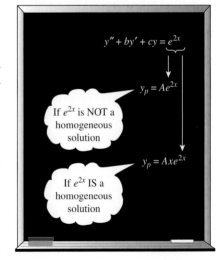

FIGURE 3–49

The assumed form of a particular solution that happens to be a solution of the related homogeneous equation should be modified by multiplying it by the independent variable x.

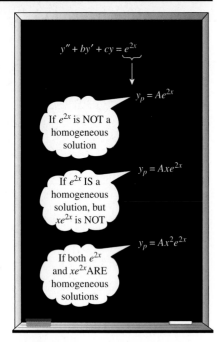

FIGURE 3–50

The assumed form of a particular solution that happens to be a solution of the related homogeneous equation should be modified by multiplying it by x^k, where x is the independent variable and k is the smallest positive integer that eliminates such duplication.

homogeneous equation. We can verify this by finding the general solution of the related homogeneous equation, $y'' - 4y' + 4y = 0$. Indeed, the characteristic equation is $m^2 - 4m + 4 = 0$, whose roots are $m_1 = m_2 = m = 2$. Thus $m = 2$ is a repeated root, and the general solution of the related homogeneous equation is $y_h = C_1 e^{2x} + C_2 x e^{2x}$, which explains why e^{2x} and $x e^{2x}$ yielded zero on the left side when substituted into the given equation. So we just continue multiplying the assumed form of the particular solution by x until it is no longer a solution of the homogeneous part of the equation. So we try

$$y_p = Ax^2 e^{2x} \qquad (3\text{--}59)$$

Substituting this form of the particular solution together with its first and second derivatives into the given differential equation and solving for A yields $A = 0.5$. Thus the particular solution we are looking for is $y_p = 0.5 x^2 e^{2x}$. We can summarize the lessons we learned from the preceding two examples as follows: *When a nonhomogeneous term is a solution of the related homogeneous equation, multiply the initially assumed form of the particular solution by the lowest power of the independent variable x such that no term in the particular solution will be a solution of the homogeneous equation* (Figure 3–50).

EXAMPLE 3–30   **General Solution of A Nonhomogeneous Equation**

Find the general solution of the differential equation $y'' - y' = x + 2$.

SOLUTION   First we find the general solution of the homogeneous part of the equation $y'' - y' = 0$. Its characteristic equation is $m^2 - m = 0$, whose roots are $m_1 = 0$ and $m_2 = 1$. Thus, the general solution of the related homogeneous equation is

$$y_h = C_1 e^{0x} + C_2 e^{1x} = C_1 + C_2 e^x$$

For the particular solution, we would normally try $y_h = Ax + B$. But any constant (C_1 or B) is a solution of the homogeneous equation, and thus, we need to modify the particular solution by multiplying it by x. Then the proper form of the particular solution in this case would be $y_p = x(Ax + B)$, whose first and second derivatives are $y'_p = 2Ax + B$ and $y'_p = 2A$. Substituting them into the differential equation yields $(2A) - (2Ax + B) = x + 2$ or $-2Ax + (2A - B) = x + 2$. Setting the coefficients of each power x on both sides equal to each other yields

$$-2A = 1$$

$$2A - B = 2$$

whose solution is $A = -0.5$ and $B = -3$. Thus, the particular solution is $y_p = x(-0.5x - 3)$. Then the general solution becomes $y = y_h + y_p = C_1 + C_2 e^x - 0.5x^2 - 3x$.

Note that a constant A is always solution of the homogeneous part of the differential equation $y'' + ay' = R(x)$ since both derivatives of a constant are zero, satisfying the related homogeneous equation automatically. Also, the first-degree polynomial $Ax + B$ is always a solution of the homogeneous part of the differential equation $y'' = R(x)$ since the second derivatives of a first-degree polynomial is zero. Therefore when $R(x)$ is a polynomial, we will need to multiply the assumed form of the particular solution by x in the first case, and by x^2 in the second case (Figure 3–51).

(1) $y'' + by' + cy = x + 2$

$\downarrow$

$y_p = Ax + B$

(2) $y'' + by' = x + 2$ ($c = 0$)

$\downarrow$

$y_p = x(Ax + B)$

(3) $y'' = x + 2$ ($b = c = 0$)

$\downarrow$

$y_p = x^2(Ax + B)$

FIGURE 3–51

The form of the particular solution of $y'' + by' + cy = E_x + F$ depends on whether b or c are zero.

EXAMPLE 3–31 An Initial-Value Problem

The differential equation that governs the temperature distribution along a fin in a medium of temperature T_{air} is given by $T'' - \lambda(T - T_{air}) = 0$, which is a nonhomogeneous equation. Determine the temperature distribution along the fin for $\lambda = 4$, $T(0) = 200°C$, $T'(0) = -420°C/m$, and $T_{air} = 20°C$.

SOLUTION This is an initial-value problem since both conditions are specified at the same point. It can be formulated as

$$T'' - 4T = -80$$

$$T(0) = 200$$

$$T'(0) = -420$$

The differential equation is a second-order, linear, nonhomogeneous equation with constant coefficients, and its characteristic equation is $m^2 - 4 = 0$. The roots of this equation are $m_1 = -2$ and $m_2 = 2$, which are real and unequal. Thus, the general solution of the related homogeneous equation is, (from Equation 3–32), $T(x) = C_1 e^{-2x} + C_2 e^{2x}$. The right side of the equation is a constant, and a constant is not a solution of the related homogeneous equation. Therefore, the proper form of the particular solution in this case is $y_p = A$. Substituting into the differential equation, $0 - 4A = -80$, which gives $y_p = A = 20$. Thus, the general solution of the given differential equation is $T(x) = C_1 e^{-2x} + C_2 e^{2x} + 20$. The derivative of the general solution is $T'(x) = -2C_1 e^{-2x} + 2C_2 e^{2x}$.

The arbitrary constants are determined by applying the initial conditions:

$$T(0) = 200 \rightarrow C_1 + C_2 = 200$$

$$T'(0) = -420 \rightarrow -2C_1 + 2C_2 = -420$$

since $e^0 = 1$. Solving these two equations simultaneously for the two unknowns yields $C_1 = -195$ and $C_2 = -15$. Substituting these values into the general solution gives the solution of this initial-value problem (Figure 3–52).

$$T(x) = 195e^{-2x} - 15e^{2x} + 20$$

Note that the initial conditions are applied to the *general solution* of the initial-value problem. The initial or boundary conditions should never be applied to only the homogeneous solution or only the particular solution. This is because the initial or boundary conditions are to be satisfied by the solution of entire differential equation, not just part of it.

Differential equation:

$$y'' - 4y = -80$$

Homogeneous solution:

$$y_h = C_1 e^{-2x} + C_2 e^{2x}$$

General solution:

$$y = C_1 e^{-2x} + C_2 e^{2x} + 20$$

Now we can apply the initial conditions.

FIGURE 3–52

The initial or boundary conditions should be applied to the general solution of the differential equation, not just to its homogeneous solution.

The points made in the foregoing examples can be summarized as follows:

1. The method of undetermined coefficients is not a general method for finding the particular solutions of nonhomogeneous equations. It is simple and straightforward, but its use is limited to linear equations with constant coefficients whose nonhomogeneous terms are of the form $e^{\alpha x}P_n(x)\sin \beta x$ or $e^{\alpha x}P_n(x)\cos \beta x$ where α and β are real constants and $P_n(x)$ is a polynomial of degree n.

2. The general form of particular solution y_p corresponding to a nonhomogeneous function $R(x)$ that is not a solution of the related homogeneous equation is the linear combination of $R(x)$ and the linearly independent functions its derivatives involve. If any of the functions in the particular solution is also a solution of the related homogeneous equations, the initially assumed form of the particular solution should be multiplied by the lowest power of x that will eliminate any duplication of solutions. The general form of the particular solutions corresponding to several functions are given in Table 3–2.

3. A differential equation, whose nonhomogeneous term $R(x)$ contains many terms, can be split into several equations each containing only a portion of $R(x)$. The particular solution in this case is obtained by superposition by adding up the particular solutions of the simpler equations.

TABLE 3–2

The General Form of The Particular Solution Corresponding to Some Function in The Nonhomogeneous Term*

Specified Function, $R(x)$	Corresponding Particular Solution, y_p
a (a constant)	A's (constants)
ax^n or $P_n(x) = a_n x^n + a_{n-1}x^{n-1} + \cdots + a_0$	$A_n x^n + A_{n-1}x^{n-1} + \cdots + A_0$
$a\sin kx$ or $a\cos kx$ or $a\sin kx + b\cos kx$	$A\sin kx + B\cos kx$
$e^{cx}P_n(x)$	$e^{cx}(A_n x^n + A_{n-1}x^{n-1} + \cdots + A_0)$
$ae^{cx}\sin kx$ or $ae^{cx}\cos kx$ or $ae^{cx}\sin kx + be^{cx}\cos kx$	$e^{cx}(A\sin kx + B\cos kx)$
$e^{cx}P_n(x)\sin kx$ or $e^{cx}Q_n(x)\cos kx$ or $e^{cx}P_n(x)\sin kx + e^{cx}Q_n(x)\cos kx$	$e^{cx}(A_n x^n + A_{n-1}x^{n-1} + \cdots + A_0)\sin kx$ $+ e^{cx}(B_n x^n + B_{n-1}x^{n-1} + \cdots + B_0)\cos kx$

*If y_p or any term in y_p is a solution of related homogeneous equation, multiply y_p by lowest power of x to eliminate such duplication.

4. A nonhomogeneous equation may have several particular solutions, and any of them will do the job. Any combination of a particular solution and a solution of the related homogeneous equation is also a particular solution.

5. The method of undetermined coefficients is self correcting. When too few terms are assumed for the particular solution, a contradiction results. When too many terms are assumed, zeros occur for the coefficients of unnecessary terms. Getting unique values for the unknown coefficients is a sure sign that assumed form of the particular solution is correct.

6. Any initial or boundary conditions should be applied to the general solution of the nonhomogeneous equation, which is the sum of the homogeneous solution and the particular solution. They should never be applied to the general solution of the related homogeneous equation alone.

Section Review

3–33C Under what conditions is the general form of a particular solution y_p corresponding to a nonhomogeneous term $R(x)$ of the form $AR(x)$, where A is a constant?

3–34C Are the general forms of the particular solution y_p corresponding to nonhomogeneous terms x^3 and $x^3 - 4x + 2$ different?

3–35C Why is the method of undetermined coefficients not suitable when the nonhomogeneous term involves the function $\ln x$?

3–36C In the method of undetermined coefficients, what happens if we assume too many terms for the general form of the particular solution? What happens if we assume too few terms?

3–37 Using the method of undetermined coefficients, determine the general solution of the following second-order linear nonhomogeneous equations.

(a) $y'' - 4y = 4e^{3x}$

(b) $y'' - 4y = -3x^2e^{3x}$

(c) $y'' - 4y = 2e^{2x}$

(d) $y'' - 4y = 5e^{-2x}\cos 3x$

(*Answers:* (a) $y = C_1e^{-2x} + C_2e^{2x} + \dfrac{4}{5}e^{3x}$

(b) $y = C_1e^{-2x} + C_2e^{2x} + \left(-\dfrac{3}{5}x^2 + \dfrac{36}{25}x - \dfrac{186}{125}\right)e^{3x}$

(c) $y = C_1e^{-2x} + C_2e^{2x} + \dfrac{1}{2}xe^{2x}$

(d) $y = C_1e^{-2x} + C_2e^{2x} - \dfrac{1}{15}(3\cos 3x + 4\sin 3x)e^{-2x})$

3–38 Determine the specific solution of the following initial-value problem. Use the method of undetermined coefficients to find the particular solution.

$$y'' + 16y = \sin 2x - 3\cos 2x, \; y(\pi/2) = 1, \text{ and } y'(\pi/2) = 0$$

(*Answer:* $y = \dfrac{3}{4}\cos 4x + \dfrac{1}{24}\sin 4x - \dfrac{1}{4}\cos 2x + \dfrac{1}{12}\sin 2x)$

3–8 ▪ NONHOMOGENEOUS EQUATIONS: THE METHOD OF VARIATION OF PARAMETERS

The method of undetermined coefficients, discussed in the previous section, determines a particular solution of a nonhomogeneous equation in a simple and straightforward way, but it lacks generality because it has two severe limitations: the differential equation must have constant coefficients, and the nonhomogeneous terms must be of the form $e^{\alpha x}P_n(x)\sin \beta x$ or $e^{\alpha x}P_n(x)\cos \beta x$ where α and β are real constants and $P_n(x)$ is a polynomial of degree n.

In this section we will describe an alternative general method for finding a particular solution of a given nonhomogeneous equation. It is called the method of **variation of parameters**, which is applicable to equations with constant or variable coefficients and to nonhomogeneous terms that can be of any form. However, it requires the general solution of the related homogeneous equation to be available. The method is first developed by J. L. Lagrange (1736–1813), and is also known as **Lagrange's method**.

Consider the second-order, linear, nonhomogeneous differential equation in the standard form (the leading coefficient is one),

$$y'' + P(x)y' + Q(x)y = R(x) \tag{3-60}$$

where the functions P, Q, and R are continuous in the interval of interest. We know that the related homogeneous equation $y'' + P(x)y' + Q(x)y = 0$ has two linearly independent solutions y_1 and y_2 in this interval, and the general solution of the related homogeneous equation can be expressed as

$$y_h = C_1y_1 + C_2y_2 \tag{3-61}$$

The basic idea behind the method of variation of parameters is to seek a particular solution of the form

$$y_p = u_1y_1 + u_2y_2 \tag{3-62}$$

which is obtained by replacing the constant parameters C_1 and C_2 in the homogeneous solution by the variable functions u_1 and u_2, and then determining these two functions such that Equation 3–62 satisfies the nonhomogeneous equation (Figure 3–53).

To determine the two unknown functions we need two equations. One equation is obtained by requiring y_p to satisfy the differential Equation 3–60. The other equation is obtained by requiring these two functions to satisfy a condition that we are free to impose. We will make that choice when appropriate such that it greatly simplifies the determination of u_1 and u_2.

Differentiating Equation 3–62 with respect to x gives

$$y_p' = (u_1' y_1 + u_2' y_2)+(u_1y_1' + u_2y_2') \tag{3-63}$$

We now impose a second condition by requiring the terms in the first parentheses to vanish,

$$u_1' y_1 + u_2' y_2 = 0 \tag{3-64}$$

With this condition in effect, differentiating Equation 3–63 with respect to x gives

$$y_p'' = u_1' y_1' + u_2' y_2' + u_1y_1'' + u_2y_2'' \tag{3-65}$$

Notice that the y_p'' expression above involves only the first derivatives of u_1 and u_2 as a result of the second condition we imposed. We now substitute the y_p'', y_p', and y_p expressions into the differential Equation (3–60) and rearrange the terms to obtain

$$u_1(y_1'' + Py_1' + Qy_1) + u_2(y_2'' + Py_2' + Qy_2) + u_1' y_1' + u_2' y_2' = R(x)$$

Homogeneous solution:

$$y_h = C_1y_1 + C_2y_2$$

Form of particular solution:

$$y_p = u_1y_1 + u_2y_2$$

FIGURE 3–53

The method of variation of parameters is based on replacing the constant parameters C_1 and C_2 in the homogeneous solution by the variable ones u_1 and u_2.

But the terms in the two parentheses are zero, since y_1 and y_2 are solutions of the related homogeneous equation. Then this equation simplifies to

$$u_1' y_1' + u_2' y_2' = R(x) \tag{3-66}$$

Equations 3–64 and 3–66 form a system of two equations for the two unknowns u_1' and u_2'. Solving these two equations simultaneously yields

$$u_1' = -\frac{y_2 R(x)}{y_1 y_2' - y_1' y_2} \quad \text{and} \quad u_2' = \frac{y_1 R(x)}{y_1 y_2' - y_1' y_2} \tag{3-67}$$

where the denominator $y_1 y_2' - y_1' y_2$ is the Wronskian $W(y_1, y_2)$, which is never zero in the specified interval since y_1 and y_2 are linearly independent solutions of the related homogeneous equation. Thus, the functions u_1 and u_2 can be determined uniquely from Equations 3–67 by integration, as

$$u_1 = -\int \frac{y_2 R(x)}{y_1 y_2' - y_1' y_2} dx \quad \text{and} \quad u_2 = \int \frac{y_1 R(x)}{y_1 y_2' - y_1' y_2} dx \tag{3-68}$$

The integration constants k_1 and k_2 in Figure 3–54 are of no significance and can be taken to be zero with no loss in generality, as shown in that figure.

We summarize the method of variation of parameters in the following theorem (Figure 3–55).

THEOREM 3–8 Variation of Parameters

If the functions y_1 and y_2 are linearly independent homogeneous solutions of the equation

$$y'' + P(x)y' + Q(x)y = R(x) \tag{3-61}$$

where the functions P, Q, and R are continuous in the interval of interest, then a particular solution of this nonhomogeneous differential equation is given by

$$y_p = u_1 y_1 + u_2 y_2 \tag{3-63}$$

where

$$u_1 = -\int \frac{y_2 R(x)}{y_1 y_2' - y_1' y_2} dx \quad \text{and} \quad u_2 = \int \frac{y_1 R(x)}{y_1 y_2' - y_1' y_2} dx \tag{3-68}$$

Once a particular solution is available, the general solution of the nonhomogeneous equation can be determined from

$$y = C_1 y_1 + C_2 y_2 + y_p$$
$$= C_1 y_1 + C_2 y_2 + u_1 y_1 + u_2 y_2 \tag{3-69}$$

Sometimes the particular solution obtained in this manner involves terms that are constant multiples of the homogeneous solutions y_1 and y_2. Such terms can be dropped from the solution, since the homogeneous solution involves the same terms with arbitrary constants. For example, if the

Homogeneous solution:

$$y_h = C_1 y_1 + C_2 y_2$$

Particular solution:

$$y_p = (u_1 + k_1)y_1 + (u_2 + k_2)y_2$$

General solution:

$$y = y_h + y_p$$
$$= C_1 y_1 + C_2 y_2$$
$$\quad + (u_1 + k_1)y_1 + (u_2 + k_2)y_2$$
$$= (C_1 + k_1)y_1 + (C_2 + k_2)y_2 + u_1 y_1 + u_2 y_2$$
$$= D_1 y_1 + D_2 y_2 + u_1 y_1 + u_2 y_2$$

FIGURE 3–54

The integration constants, k_1 and k_2, of the functions u_1 and u_2 in Equation 3–68 can be dropped, since these constants simply introduce constant multiples of the homogeneous solution, and they can always be absorbed by the arbitrary constants of the homogeneous solution.

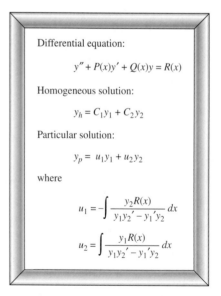

Differential equation:

$$y'' + P(x)y' + Q(x)y = R(x)$$

Homogeneous solution:

$$y_h = C_1 y_1 + C_2 y_2$$

Particular solution:

$$y_p = u_1 y_1 + u_2 y_2$$

where

$$u_1 = -\int \frac{y_2 R(x)}{y_1 y_2' - y_1' y_2} dx$$

$$u_2 = \int \frac{y_1 R(x)}{y_1 y_2' - y_1' y_2} dx$$

FIGURE 3–55

The basic steps involved in finding a particular solution using the method of variation of parameters.

homogeneous and the particular solutions are $y_h = C_1 e^{2x} + C_2 e^{-3x}$ and $y_p = 2x^2 + 1 + 5e^{-3x}$, then the general solution can be expressed as

$$y = y_h + y_p$$
$$= C_1 e^{2x} + C_2 e^{-3x} + 2x^2 + 1 + 5e^{-3x}$$
$$= C_1 e^{2x} + (C_2 + 5)e^{-3x} + 2x^2 + 1$$
$$= C_1 e^{2x} + D_2 e^{-3x} + 2x^2 + 1$$

since an arbitrary constant plus a number is still an arbitrary constant.
  To summarize,

1. The method of undetermined coefficients is easier to use, since it involves differentiation instead of integration and should be preferred when the coefficients of the differential equation are constants and the nonhomogeneous term $R(x)$ is in the proper form.
2. If the coefficients of the differential equation are constant but $R(x)$ is not in the proper form, then the particular solution can be determined by the method of variation of parameters after solving the related homogeneous equation.
3. If the coefficients of the equation are variable, the solution in general is difficult to find and usually involves infinite series.
4. If only one of the solutions of the related homogeneous equation is available, the second homogeneous solution together with a particular solution can be obtained by applying the method of reduction of order to the given nonhomogeneous equation.

EXAMPLE 3–32   Variation of Parameters

Determine the general solution of the equation $y'' - 2y' + y = e^x/x$ for $x > 0$.

SOLUTION The leading coefficient of the differential equation is 1, and thus, its nonhomogeneous term is $R(x) = e^x/x$. This function is not in a suitable form for the method of undetermined coefficients, so we use the method of variation of parameters to determine its particular solution. But first, we need to find the general solution of its related homogeneous equation. The characteristic equation of the related homogeneous equation is $m^2 - 2m + 1 = 0$. The roots of this equation are $m_1 = m_2 = 1$, which are real and equal. Thus, the general solution of the related homogeneous equation is $y_h = C_1 e^x + C_2 x e^x$. Taking $y_1 = e^x$ and $y_2 = x e^x$, the Wronskian of these two functions (which is also the denominator of the u_1 and u_2 expressions) is

$$W(y_1, y_2) = y_1 y_2' - y_1' y_2 = e^x(e^x + x e^x) - x e^{2x} = e^{2x}$$

Substituting this into Equation 3–68, the functions u_1 and u_2 are determined to be

$$u_1 = -\int \frac{y_2 R(x)}{y_1 y_2' - y_1' y_2} dx = -\int \frac{x e^x e^x}{e^{2x} x} dx = -\int dx = -x$$

and

$$u_2 = \int \frac{y_1 R(x)}{y_1 y_2' - y_1' y_2} dx = \int \frac{e^x}{e^{2x}} \frac{e^x}{x} dx = \int \frac{1}{x} dx = \ln x$$

Thus, the particular solution (from Equation 3–62) is

$$y_p = u_1 y_1 + u_2 y_2$$

$$= -xe^x + xe^x \ln x$$

We could verify this result by substituting it into the given differential equation.
 Finally, the general solution of the differential equation obtained by combining the homogeneous solution with this particular solution (from Equation 3–69) is

$$y = C_1 y_1 + C_2 y_2 + y_p = C_1 e^x + C_2 xe^x - xe^x + xe^x \ln x$$

$$= C_1 e^x + (C_2 - 1)xe^x + xe^x \ln x$$

or

$$y = C_1 e^x + C_2 xe^x + xe^x \ln x$$

where we have replaced $C_2 - 1$ with C_2. The integrals to determine the functions u_1 and u_2 turned out to be easy in this case. This is more the exception than the rule, however.

Section Review

3–39C   What are the limitations of the method of undetermined coefficients?

3–40C   What is the method of variation of parameters based on?

3–41   Using the method of variation of parameters, determine the particular solution of the following second-order, linear, nonhomogeneous equations below. Check the result in part (a) using the method of undetermined coefficients.

   (a) $y'' - y' - 2y = e^{3x}$ (b) $y'' - y' - 2y = 2^x$

(*Answers:* (a) $y = C_1 e^{-x} + C_2 e^{2x} + \frac{1}{4} e^{3x}$

(b) $y = C_1 e^{-x} + C_2 e^{2x} + \dfrac{2^x}{(\ln 2 - 2)(\ln 2 + 1)})$

3–9 ▪ THE EULER EQUATION

So far in this chapter, the emphasis has been on linear equations with *constant* coefficients because a systematic procedure exists for solving such equations. There is no simple procedure for solving linear equations with *variable* coefficients, however, except for some certain types. One type of linear differential equation that is appropriate to discuss in this chapter (because it always can be converted into an equation with constant coefficients) is the

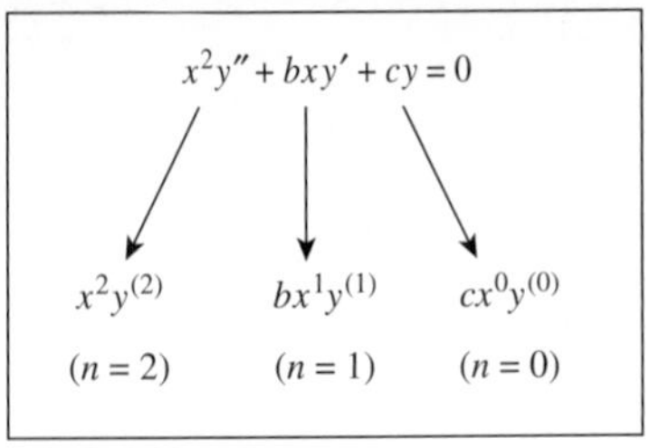

$$x^2 y'' + bxy' + cy = 0$$

$$x^2 y^{(2)} \qquad bx^1 y^{(1)} \qquad cx^0 y^{(0)}$$

$$(n = 2) \qquad (n = 1) \qquad (n = 0)$$

FIGURE 3–56

Each term of a homogeneous Euler equation is of the form $kx^n y^{(n)}$ where k is a constant and n is a nonnegative integer.

Euler equation (also called Euler-Cauchy equation or equidimensional equation), which is expressed as

$$x^2 y'' + bxy' + cy = r(x) \tag{3–70}$$

where b and c are constants.[1] The characteristic feature of this equation is that the coefficient of y is a constant, the coefficient of y' is a constant times x, and in general, the coefficient of nth derivative of y is a constant multiple of the nth power of x. That is, each term on the left side is of the form $kx^n y^{(n)}$ where k is a constant (Figure 3–56). The Euler equation can be put into the standard form by dividing each term by coefficient of highest derivative,

$$y'' + \frac{b}{x} y' + \frac{c}{x^2} y = R(x), \qquad x \neq 0 \tag{3–71}$$

where $R(x) = r(x)/x^2$. Clearly the coefficients of this equation are not continuous at $x = 0$, and thus we should exclude this point from any interval for the fundamental theorems discussed earlier in this chapter to be applicable. Also, to avoid the nuisance of an absolute value sign, we will consider only the interval $x > 0$ unless we state otherwise.

The Euler equation always can be transformed into an equation with constant coefficients through the transformation $x = e^t$, as stated in the following theorem.

THEOREM 3–9　The Euler Equation

The transformation $x = e^t$ will always convert the Euler equation

$$x^2 y'' + bxy' + cy = r(x)$$

into the following equation with constant coefficients

$$\ddot{y} + (b - 1)\dot{y} + cy = r(e^t)$$

where the overdot denotes differentiation with respect to t.

Proof　Noting that for $x > 0$ we have $t = \ln x$ and applying the chain rule, we have

$$\frac{dy}{dx} = \frac{dy}{dt}\frac{dt}{dx} = \frac{1}{x}\frac{dy}{dt}$$

and

$$\frac{d^2 y}{dx^2} = \frac{d}{dx}\left(\frac{dy}{dx}\right) = \frac{d}{dx}\left(\frac{1}{x}\frac{dy}{dt}\right) = \frac{1}{x}\frac{d}{dx}\left(\frac{dy}{dt}\right) - \frac{1}{x^2}\frac{dy}{dt}$$

$$= \frac{1}{x}\frac{d}{dt}\left(\frac{dy}{dt}\right)\frac{dt}{dx} - \frac{1}{x^2}\frac{dy}{dt} = \frac{1}{x^2}\frac{d^2 y}{dt^2} - \frac{1}{x^2}\frac{dy}{dt}$$

$$= \frac{1}{x^2}\left(\frac{d^2 y}{dt^2} - \frac{dy}{dt}\right)$$

---

[1] The Euler equation presented here is a *single* equation and is different than the Euler equations that describe fluid flow, and the Euler equations that describe the rotation of a rigid body.

Substituting these two expressions into the Euler equation yields

$$\frac{d^2y}{dt^2} - \frac{dy}{dt} + b\frac{dy}{dt} + cy = r(e^t)$$

or

$$\ddot{y} + (b-1)\dot{y} + cy = r(e^t) \tag{3-72}$$

This completes the proof.

If we had assumed $x < 0$ and used the transformation $-x = e^t$, we would still obtain the same result. Note that the right side of Equation 3–72 also becomes a function of t by replacing all occurrences of x by e^t. This theorem can be extended to Euler equations of any order.

Once an Euler equation is converted into an equation with constant coefficients, it can be solved in a routine manner by forming the characteristic equation of its homogeneous part,

$$m^2 + (b-1)m + c = 0 \tag{3-73}$$

and finding its roots. Finally the desired solution is obtained by the back transformation $t = \ln x$. The procedure is illustrated below with an example.

EXAMPLE 3–33   An Euler Equation

Determine the general solution of the differential equation $x^2y'' - 2xy' - 4y = 0$, for $x > 0$ using the transformation $x = e^t$.

SOLUTION   We recognize this equation immediately as being an Euler equation, since each term on the left side is of the form of $kx^ny^{(n)}$ for $n = 0$, 1, and 2. The transformation $x = e^t$ will reduce this Euler equation to (see Equation 3–72)

$$\ddot{y} - 3\dot{y} - 4y = 0$$

which is a second-order, linear, homogeneous equation with constant coefficients. Its characteristic equation is $m^2 - 3m - 4 = 0$, whose roots are $m_1 = -1$ and $m_2 = 4$, which are real distinct. Thus, the general solution of the transformed equation is $y(t) = C_1e^{-t} + C_2e^{4t}$.

Noting that $e^{\ln z} = z$, the back transformation $t = \ln x$ yields (Figure 3–57)

$$y(x) = C_1e^{-\ln x} + C_2e^{4\ln x}$$

$$= C_1e^{\ln\frac{1}{x}} + C_2e^{\ln x^4}$$

$$= \frac{C_1}{x} + C_2x^4$$

which is the general solution of the given differential equation.

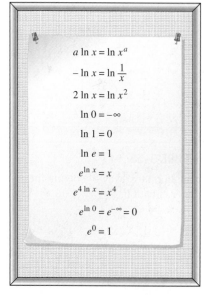

$$a\ln x = \ln x^a$$
$$-\ln x = \ln\frac{1}{x}$$
$$2\ln x = \ln x^2$$
$$\ln 0 = -\infty$$
$$\ln 1 = 0$$
$$\ln e = 1$$
$$e^{\ln x} = x$$
$$e^{4\ln x} = x^4$$
$$e^{\ln 0} = e^{-\infty} = 0$$
$$e^0 = 1$$

FIGURE 3–57

Just in case you forgot these useful relations about logarithmic and exponential functions.

An Alternative Solution Method

Now we consider an alternative to the previous procedure by assuming the solution to be of the form x^r, where r is a constant. We suspect that the function x^r might be a solution for certain values of r, since when the derivatives $y' = rx^{r-1}$ and $y'' = r(r-1)x^{r-2}$ are substituted into the differential equation, the terms x^2y'', xy', and y will all involve the same power of x, which can be factored out. If we obtain two different values of r and thus two linearly independent solutions at the end, this procedure will give us the general solution.

Therefore, we guess the solution to be of the form $y = x^r$ and substitute it and its derivatives into the homogeneous part of the Euler equation (Equation 3–70) to obtain

$$r(r - 1)x^r + brx^r + cx^r = 0$$

$$[r^2 + (b - 1)r + c]x^r = 0$$

or

$$r^2 + (b - 1)r + c = 0 \tag{3–74}$$

since $x \neq 0$ and thus x^r cannot be zero. Note that Equation 3–74 is equivalent to the characteristic equation of the transformed equation with constant coefficients, and the two roots of this quadratic equation are (Figure 3–58)

$$r_{1,2} = \frac{-(b - 1) \pm \sqrt{(b - 1)^2 - 4c}}{2} \tag{3–75}$$

Again, the two roots can be real and unequal, real and equal, or complex, depending on whether $(b - 1)^2 - 4c$ positive, zero, or negative. We now consider each case separately.

Case 1: Real and Unequal Roots $(r_1 \neq r_2)$

In this case, the two linearly independent solutions are x^{r_1} and x^{r_2}, and the general solution of the homogeneous part of the (second order) Euler equation is

$$y = C_1 x^{r_1} + C_2 x^{r_2}, \quad x > 0 \tag{3–76}$$

Case 2: Real and Equal Roots $(r_1 = r_2 = r)$

In this case, the procedure described previously gives only one solution, x^r. The other linearly independent solution can be obtained from the method of reduction of order to be $x^r \ln x$. Then the general solution of the homogeneous part of the Euler equation is

$$y = C_1 x^r + C_2 x^r \ln x, x > 0 \tag{3–77}$$

Case 3: Complex Roots $(r_{1,2} = \alpha \pm i\beta)$

In this case, the two roots are necessarily complex conjugates of each other and can be expressed as $r_{1,2} = \alpha \pm i\beta$. Noting that $x^r = e^{\ln x^r} = e^{r \ln x}$, the general solution of the homogeneous part in this case can be expressed as

$$y = Ax^{r_1} + Bx^{r_2}$$

$$= Ae^{r_1 \ln x} + Be^{r_2 \ln x}$$

$$= Ae^{(\alpha + i\beta)\ln x} + Be^{(\alpha - i\beta)\ln x}$$

$$= e^{\alpha \ln x}[Ae^{i\beta \ln x} + Be^{-i\beta \ln x}]$$

Euler equation:

$$x^2 y'' + bxy' + cy = 0$$

Substitute: $y = x^r$

Obtain:

$$r^2 + (b - 1)r + c = 0$$

whose roots are

$$r_{1,2} = \frac{-(b - 1) \pm \sqrt{(b - 1)^2 - 4c}}{2}$$

FIGURE 3–58

An alternative way of solving the Euler equation.

But $e^{\alpha \ln x} = x^{\alpha}$, and from Equation 3–47, we have

$$Ae^{i\beta \ln x} + Be^{-i\beta \ln x} = C_1 \cos(\beta \ln x) + C_2 \sin(\beta \ln x)$$

Therefore, the general solution of the homogeneous part of the Euler equation can be expressed as

$$y = x^{\alpha}[C_1 \cos(\beta \ln x) + C_2 \sin(\beta \ln x)] \qquad \textbf{(3–78)}$$

where C_1 and C_2 are constants (Figure 3–59).

The solutions given in these cases are valid only in the region $x > 0$, since x^r (when r is not an integer) and $\ln x$ are not defined for $x \le 0$. However, we can show in a straightforward manner that the change of variable $t = -x$ (where $t > 0$) converts the homogeneous Euler equation into

$$t^2 \frac{d^2 y}{dt^2} + bt \frac{dy}{dt} + cy = 0, \quad t > 0 \qquad \textbf{(3–79)}$$

which is identical to the original homogeneous Euler equation. Thus the solutions above are valid for $x < 0$ also provided that we use $-x$ for x. In other words, we use the absolute value of x since $|x| = x$ for $x > 0$, and $|x| = -x$ for $x < 0$. We summarize these results in Theorem 3–10.

Euler equation:

$$x^2 y'' + bxy' + cy = 0$$

Substitute: $y = x^r$,

$$r^2 + (b-1)r + c = 0$$

General solution:

(1) $r_1 \ne r_2$, real

$$y = C_1 x_{r_1} + C_2 x_{r_2}$$

(2) $r_1 = r_2 = r$, real

$$y = (C_1 + C_2 \ln x)\, x^r$$

(3) $r_{1,2} = \alpha \pm i\beta$, complex

$$y = x^{\alpha}[C_1 \cos(\beta \ln x) + C_2 \sin(\beta \ln x)]$$

FIGURE 3–59

The general solution of the homogeneous Euler equation for $x > 0$ for different cases.

THEOREM 3–10   General Solution of the Euler Equation

The substitution $y = x^r$ into the second-order homogeneous Euler equation

$$x^2 y'' + bxy' + cy = 0$$

produces

$$r^2 + (b-1)r + c = 0$$

whose roots are r_1 and r_2. The general solution of this homogeneous Euler equation in any interval not containing the origin is

$$y = C_1 |x|^{r_1} + C_2 |x|^{r_2} \qquad (r_1 \ne r_2,\ real) \qquad \textbf{(3–80)}$$
$$y = (C_1 + C_2 \ln |x|)\,|x|^r \qquad (r_1 = r_2 = r,\ real) \qquad \textbf{(3–81)}$$
$$y = |x|^{\alpha}[C_1 \sin(\beta \ln |x|) + C_2 \cos(\beta \ln |x|)] \quad (r_{1,2} = \alpha \pm i\beta,\ complex) \qquad \textbf{(3–82)}$$

where C_1 and C_2 are constants. For $x > 0$, the absolute value sign can be dropped.

For nonhomogeneous Euler equations, we determine the homogeneous solution as described previously, and find a particular solution using the method of variation of parameters. Note that the equation should be put into the standard form first by dividing each term by the coefficient of y'' so that we correctly identify the nonhomogeneous term $R(x)$. Normally, the method of undetermined coefficients is not applicable in this case, since the Euler equation has variable coefficients, unless we transform the entire equation into one with constant coefficients through the transformation $x = e^t$.

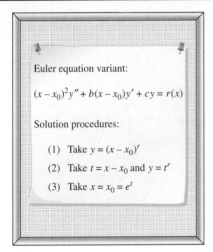

Euler equation variant:

$$(x - x_0)^2 y'' + b(x - x_0)y' + cy = r(x)$$

Solution procedures:

(1) Take $y = (x - x_0)^r$

(2) Take $t = x - x_0$ and $y = t^r$

(3) Take $x = x_0 = e^t$

FIGURE 3–60

Three different ways of solving the Euler equation in $x - x_0$ instead of x.

The substitution

$$y = x^r$$

gives the solution of the Euler equation

$$x^2 y'' + bx y' + cy = 0$$

directly and easily.

FIGURE 3–61

Something worth remembering.

As a final point, an Euler equation of the form

$$(x - x_0)^2 y'' + b(x - x_0)y' + cy = r(x) \qquad \text{(3–83)}$$

can be solved exactly the same way by taking $y = (x - x_0)^r$ instead of $y = x^r$. Then we can use Theorem 3–10 for the homogeneous solution by replacing all occurrences of x by $x - x_0$. An alternative procedure is to make a change of variable $t = x - x_0$, which will convert Equation 3–83 into the standard form of the Euler equation. As another alternative, the transformation $x - x_0 = e^t$ will reduce Equation 3–83 to a linear equation with constant coefficients, which can then be solved in a routine manner (Figure 3–60).

EXAMPLE 3–34 **The Euler Equation: Comparing Solution Methods**

Determine the general solution of the Euler equation $x^2 y'' - 2xy' - 4y = 0$ for $x > 0$ by taking $y = x^r$.

SOLUTION This is the Euler equation we solved in Example 3–33 by first converting it to an equation with constant coefficients. Now we will solve it using the alternative method so that we can compare the two methods.

Taking $y = x^r$ and substituting it and its derivatives $y' = rx^{r-1}$ and $y'' = r(r - 1)x^{r-2}$ into the given equation yields

$$r(r-1)x^2 x^{r-2} - 2rxx^{r-1} - 4x^r = 0$$

$$[r(r - 1) - 2r - 4]x^r = 0$$

or

$$r^2 - 3r - 4 = 0$$

since $x \neq 0$ and thus x^r cannot be zero. Note that the previous equation is identical to the characteristic equation obtained in Example 3–33. It can be expressed as $(r + 1)(r - 4) = 0$, whose roots are $r_1 = -1$ and $r_2 = 4$, which are real and distinct. Thus, the general solution of this Euler equation (from Equation 3–80) is $y = C_1/x + C_2 x^4$, which is identical to the solution obtained in Example 3–33.

Comparing the two solution methods, one would conclude that the approach used in this example is much easier and straightforward, since it does not involve any transformations and it does not require memorizing the general form of the transformed equation with constant coefficients or lengthy manipulations (Figure 3–61).

EXAMPLE 3–35 **The Euler Equation: Repeated Roots**

Determine the general solution of the differential equation $x^2 y'' + 3xy' + y = 0$ for $x > 0$, by taking $y = x^r$.

SOLUTION We recognize this equation immediately as being an Euler equation, since each term on the left side of the $kx^n y^{(n)}$ for $n = 0, 1$, and 2. Taking $y = x^r$

and substituting it and its derivatives $y' = rx^{r-1}$ and $y'' = r(r-1)x^{r-2}$ into the given differential equation yields

$$r(r-1)x^2x^{r-2} + 3rxx^{r-1} + x^r = 0$$

$$[r(r-1) + 3r + 1]x^r = 0$$

or

$$r^2 + 2r + 1 = 0$$

since $x \neq 0$, and thus, x^r cannot be zero. It can be expressed as $(r+1)^2 = 0$, whose roots are $r_1 = r_2 = -1$, which are real and equal. Thus, the general solution of this Euler equation (from Equation 3–81) is $y = (C_1 + C_2 \ln x)/x$.

EXAMPLE 3–36   The Euler Equation: Particular Solution

Determine the general solution of the following Euler equation for $x > 0$.

$$x^2y'' - 2xy' - 4y = 10x$$

SOLUTION The solution of the homogeneous part of this equation was determined in Example 3–33 to be $y_h = C_1/x + C_2x^4$. Now we need to find a particular solution. The first thing that comes to mind is to take $y_p = Ax + B$ and apply the method of undetermined coefficients, since the right side of the equation involves a polynomial that is not a solution of the related homogeneous equation. However, there is no guarantee that it will work, because the differential equation has variable coefficients and it is not in the standard form. Thus, we will use the method of variation of parameters to determine the particular solution.

Dividing both sides of the equation by x^2 yields

$$y'' - \frac{2}{x}y' - \frac{4}{x^2}y = \frac{10}{x}$$

Thus, $R(x) = 10/x$. Also from the homogeneous solution, we have $y_1 = 1/x$ and $y_2 = x^4$. Therefore,

$$W(y_1, y_2) = y_1y_2' - y_1'y_2 = \frac{1}{x}(4x^3) - \left(-\frac{1}{x^2}\right)x^4 = 5x^2$$

Substituting this into Equations 3–68, the functions u_1 and u_2 are determined to be

$$u_1 = -\int \frac{y_2R(x)}{y_1y_2' - y_1'y_2}\,dx = -\int \frac{x^4}{5x^2}\frac{10}{x}\,dx = -\int 2x\,dx = -x^2$$

and

$$u_2 = \int \frac{y_1R(x)}{y_1y_2' - y_1'y_2}\,dx = \int \frac{1}{x}\frac{1}{5x^2}\frac{10}{x}\,dx = \int \frac{2}{x^4}\,dx = -\frac{2}{3x^3}$$

Thus, the particular solution (from Equation 3–62) is

$$y_p = u_1 y_1 + u_2 y_2 = -x^2 \frac{1}{x} - \frac{2}{3x^3} x^4 = -\frac{5}{3} x$$

Finally, the general solution of the differential equation is obtained by combining the homogeneous solution with this particular solution: $y = C_1/x + C_2 x^4 - 5/3x$. We can check this result by substituting it into the given differential equation.

Section Review

3–42C When is a differential equation an Euler equation? How do you recognize it?

3–43C Can we always reduce Euler equations to linear equations with constant coefficients?

3–44 Determine the general solution of the following second-order Euler equations for $x > 0$, and specify the interval in which the solution is valid.

(a) $x^2 y'' + y = 0$ (b) $x^2 y'' + y = x + 1$

(*Answers*: (a) $y = x^{1/2} \left[C_1 \cos \left(\frac{\sqrt{3}}{2} \ln x \right) + C_2 \sin \left(\frac{\sqrt{3}}{2} \ln x \right) \right]$

(b) $y = x^{1/2} \left[C_1 \cos \left(\frac{\sqrt{3}}{2} \ln x \right) + C_2 \sin \left(\frac{\sqrt{3}}{2} \ln x \right) \right] + x + 1$)

3–10 · APPLICATIONS OF SECOND-ORDER LINEAR EQUATIONS WITH CONSTANT COEFFICIENTS

In this chapter, the emphasis has been on the solution of second-order linear equations with constant coefficients of the form

$$ay'' + by' + cy = r(x) \tag{3–84}$$

where a, b, and c are constants and $r(x)$ is a continuous function in the interval of interest. Many important problems in science and engineering that seem unrelated can be described by this equation, differing only in the nature of the quantities represented by y, x, the coefficients, and the function $r(x)$. But the solution procedure and the form of the general solution is the same no matter what these symbols represent. Therefore, it is no coincidence that people in different branches of science take the same differential equations course and use the information to solve seemingly unrelated problems in their own disciplines. This shows what a powerful and indispensable tool mathematics is for scientists and engineers in all branches.

In this section, we will study in some detail two important applications in mechanical and electrical engineering that result in Equation 3–84: *mechanical vibrations* and *electrical circuits*.

Mechanical Vibrations

Before we consider some specific cases, we would like to derive the differential equation that governs vibrational motions. Any equation that deals with motion is derived using Newton's second law of motion. It is normally expressed in vector form since it involves quantities that possess both magnitude and direction. However, it also can be expressed in the scalar form when the direction of motion is fixed (that is, in a straight line).

The momentum of a body in any direction at any time t is the product of its mass m and velocity v at that time in that direction. We can express Newton's second law as

The rate of change of momentum with time in any direction is equal to the net force acting on the body in that direction.

Taking the x axis as the direction of motion, this can be expressed mathematically as

$$\frac{d(mv)}{dt} = F_{net}, \; v = \frac{dx}{dt}$$

where m is the body's mass and F_{net} is the net force in the x direction.

If the mass m is constant, then $d(mv)/dt = m\,dv/dt$ and

$$m\frac{d^2x}{dt^2} = F_{net} \qquad \text{(3–85)}$$

since $dv/dt = d^2x/dt^2$, the acceleration in the x direction. The net force is a positive quantity if it acts in the positive x direction, and it is a negative quantity if it acts in the negative x direction (Figure 3–62).

Next we will analyze the vertical motion of a mass suspended by a linear spring under various conditions. But first we will derive the differential equation that governs the vertical motion of a mass m that is suspended by a spring after it is disturbed from its equilibrium position.

Differential Equation of Mechanical Vibrations

Consider a spring firmly attached to fixed point (such as a ceiling). When the spring carries no weight, it is neither compressed nor stretched and is said to be at its *free length*, and its free end is at the *natural* or *unstretched* position. We assume that the spring is a *linear spring*, which means that its resisting force F is proportional to the distance s the spring is either stretched or compressed from its free length, so that $F = ks$. The constant of proportionality k is called the **spring constant**.

When a body of mass m is attached to lower end of the spring and the spring is released, the spring will stretch, and its endpoint will move downward under the influence of the force of gravity acting on the mass. The spring will resist stretching, however, and if we gently let the endpoint move down until this resistance force equals the force of gravity, the mass will stop moving downwards and will assume a static equilibrium position a distance L from its unstretched length. At this point, the weight mg equals the spring force kL. Thus, the length of the spring will increase by $L = mg/k$ as a result (Figure 3–63).

We now choose this static position of the mass to be the origin of the x-axis that extends in the vertical direction and take the positive direction to be downward. If the mass is somehow disturbed by an external effect, we would expect the mass to oscillate (vibrate) about the equilibrium position at $x = 0$.

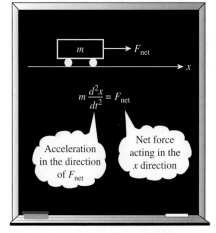

FIGURE 3–62

Newton's second law of motion in the x direction.

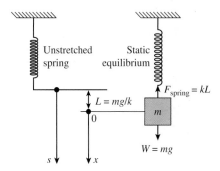

FIGURE 3–63

A mass suspended by a linear spring will fall downward as a result of gravity (*weight*) and will reach a static position a distance $L = mg/k$ from its unstretched length.

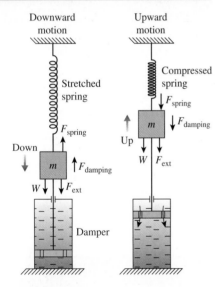

FIGURE 3–64

The forces that act on a mass suspended by a spring in vertical motion.

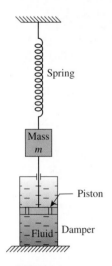

FIGURE 3–65

Example of a spring-mass-damper system.

Now we will identify the forces that may act on the mass during this motion (Figure 3–64).

1. **Weight** The force of gravity acting on a mass is equal to its weight W and is expressed as

$$W = mg \qquad (3\text{–}86)$$

where g is local acceleration of gravity. At sea level, its value is approximately $g = 9.8$ m/s^2. Note that weight always acts downward (the positive x direction), and thus, it is a positive quantity.

2. **Spring Force** We know from experience that it becomes more and more difficult to stretch a spring further and further. That is, the more stretched the spring is, the greater the force needed to stretch it further. For relatively small displacements, the spring acts like a linear spring. This principle is known as **Hooke's law** after Robert Hooke (1635–1703). The spring constant is a measure of stiffness of the spring, and has the unit force per unit length, such as N/m where N $=$ kg · m/s^2 is the force unit called a *newton*. For example, the spring constant of a spring that is stretched 0.01 meter by a 50–N force is $k = 5000$ N/m. The spring force tries to restore the spring to its free length, and thus, it exerts a *restoring force*. It acts upwards when the spring is stretched (pulling the mass up) and downwards when it is compressed (pushing the mass down). In other words, the spring force is positive when s is negative, and it is negative when s positive. Thus, it can be expressed as

$$F_{\text{spring}} = -k(L + x) \qquad (3\text{–}87)$$

since $s = L + x$ in our case (see Figure 3–63). Note that this relation is applicable to a spring whether it is stretched or compressed. A negative result indicates that the spring force will act upwards (in the negative x direction), and a positive result will indicate the force will act downwards (in the positive x direction). This relation also can be used for springs that are stretched or compressed horizontally by taking $L = 0$. When the mass suspended by the spring is in equilibrium, the magnitudes of the spring force and the weight of the mass must be the same, since the net force acting on the mass is zero at equilibrium. Therefore,

$$kL = mg \qquad (3\text{–}88)$$

since we took $x = 0$ to be where the spring force balances the weight.

3. **Damping Force** When a body moves in a medium that contains a fluid, a *friction force* develops between the body and the surrounding fluid that always opposes the motion (it acts upward when the mass moves downwards, and it acts downwards when the mass moves upwards). In some systems, a component (such as a shock absorber or dashpot) is connected to the system to damp any undesired motion intentionally (Figure 3–64). This resistance force, which is also called the **damping force**, is observed to be proportional to some power of velocity. At low velocities, the friction can be approximated with reasonable accuracy by

a force whose magnitude is proportional to the magnitude of velocity, and whose direction is opposite to the direction of motion. In such cases it can be represented mathematically as

$$F_{\text{damping}} = -cv = -c\frac{dx}{dt} \tag{3–89}$$

where c is a positive constant called the **damping constant**. It has the unit of force per velocity (N · s/m). Note that when the mass moves downward (in the positive x direction), dx/dt is positive (and thus the friction force is negative), indicating that it will act upward (in the negative x direction). When the mass moves upward, dx/dt is negative (and thus the friction force is positive), indicating that it will act downward. Thus, Equation 3–89 will always give the correct magnitude and direction for the force. The system that consists of a mass suspended on a spring and connected to a damper or dashpot is frequently referred to as a *spring-mass-damper* system (Figure 3–65).

4. **External Force** Any force imposed on the mass by an external source other than the spring and damping forces (such as an electric or magnetic field, hitting the mass by a hammer, or pulling it by hand) is called an **external force** and is denoted by F_{ext}. The external force may be a constant, a periodic function, or any arbitrary function of x, v, or t. The external force is a positive quantity when it acts in the positive x direction and is a negative quantity when it acts in the negative x direction. The resultant of all of the forces acting on a body is the **net force**, which is obtained by adding all of these forces, paying particular attention to their signs (directions),

$$F_{\text{net}} = W + F_{\text{spring}} + F_{\text{damping}} + F_{\text{ext}}$$

$$= mg - k(L + x) - c\frac{dx}{dt} + F_{\text{ext}}$$

$$= -kx - c\frac{dx}{dt} + F_{\text{ext}} \tag{3–90}$$

since $kL = mg$ from Equation 3–88. Thus, the weight force cancels the portion of the spring force that holds the mass in static equilibrium. Therefore, we can neglect the weight of a body when formulating dynamic problems involving suspended masses if we take the unstretched position of the spring as the position at which the spring holds the mass in static equilibrium. Substituting this result into Newton's second law expression (Equation 3–85) yields the linear, constant-coefficient equation:

$$m\frac{d^2x}{dt^2} + c\frac{dx}{dt} + kx = F_{\text{ext}}$$

or

$$m\ddot{x} + c\dot{x} + kx = F_{\text{ext}} \tag{3–91}$$

where the overdot indicates time derivative. This equation is derived using a vertical spring-mass-damper system, but is also applicable to such systems of any orientation, including horizontal ones (Figure 3–66).

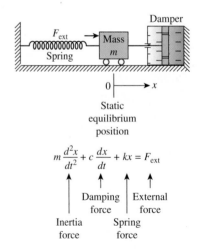

FIGURE 3–66

The differential equation that governs the motion of a spring-mass-damper system on any straight line ($x = 0$ is the static equilibrium position of the mass, and $x(t)$ is the position of the mass at time t).

Note that if we assumed the spring force to be proportional to a different power of x than one or the damping force to be proportional to a different power of velocity than one, we would end up instead with a nonlinear differential equation, which may not even be possible to solve analytically. Thus, when we make simplifying assumptions, one of our goals is to reduce the problem to a mathematically manageable one.

When $c = 0$, we have no friction or damping, and the motion is called **undamped**. Otherwise, it is said to be **damped**. When $F_{net} = 0$, there is no external force, and the motion is called **free** or **unforced**. Otherwise, the motion is said to be **forced**. As you would expect, the general solution of Equation 3–91 will involve two arbitrary constants. Thus, we can specify two initial conditions: the initial displacement x_0 and the initial velocity v_0 to obtain a unique solution to a problem.

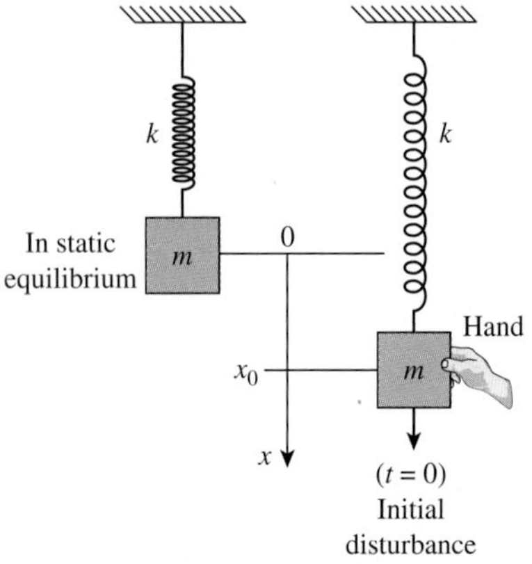

FIGURE 3–67

The schematic of a spring-mass-damper system that is undergoing free vibrations with no damping.

EXAMPLE 3–37 Undamped Free Vibrations

Consider a frictionless spring-mass system that is in static equilibrium. At $t = 0$, mass is pulled down to location x_0 and then released with a velocity of v_0, as shown in Figure 3–67.

The mass starts to vibrate as a result. Taking the equilibrium position of the mass to be $x = 0$ and the downward direction to be positive, determine the position of the mass as a function of time, $x(t)$. Also determine the amplitude and the period of the vibrations.

SOLUTION There is no external force to oppose the motion, and thus, Equation 3–91 in this case reduces to $m\ddot{x} + kx = 0$ with $x(0) = x_0$ and $x(0) = v_0$. Dividing the equation by m and letting $\omega_0 = \sqrt{k/m}$, its characteristic equation becomes $r^2 + \omega_0^2 = 0$, whose roots are $r = \pm i\omega_0$. Thus, the general solution of the differential equation is

$$x(t) = C_1 \cos \omega_0 t + C_2 \sin \omega_0 t \tag{3–92}$$

where C_1 and C_2 are arbitrary constants. They are determined from the initial conditions to be $C_1 = x_0$ and $C_2 = v_0/\omega_0$. Subsituting, the solution of this initial-value problem is determined to be

$$x(t) = x_0 \cos \omega_0 t + \frac{v_0}{\omega_0} \sin \omega_0 t \tag{3–93}$$

This obviously is a periodic motion because of the periodic nature of the sine and cosine functions. For convenience in discussions, we would like to express this solution in terms of a single trigonometric function as

$$x(t) = A \cos(\omega_0 t - \phi) \tag{3–94}$$

To determine A and ϕ, we make use of the trigonometric identity for $\cos(\omega_0 t - \phi)$,

$$x(t) = A \cos(\omega_0 t - \phi) = A \cos \omega_0 t \cos \phi + A \sin \omega_0 t \sin \phi \tag{3–95}$$

Comparing Equations 3–93 and 3–95, we have

$$A \cos \phi = x_0 \quad \text{and} \quad A \sin \phi = \frac{v_0}{\omega_0} \tag{3–96}$$

Squaring and adding each equation and using the identity $\sin^2\phi + \cos^2\phi = 1$, we have

$$\left(\frac{v_0}{\omega_0}\right)^2 + x_0^2 = A^2\sin^2\phi + A^2\cos^2\phi = A^2$$

Choosing the positive square root for A gives

$$A = \sqrt{\left(\frac{v_0}{\omega_0}\right)^2 + x_0^2} \qquad \text{(3-97)}$$

The angle ϕ is called the **phase angle**, and can be determined by dividing the second equation in Equation 3–96 by the first equation to obtain

$$\frac{\sin\phi}{\cos\phi} = \tan\phi = \frac{v_0}{\omega_0 x_0}$$

and thus

$$\phi = \tan^{-1}\frac{v_0}{\omega_0 x_0} \qquad \text{(3-98)}$$

provided that the angle is in the correct quadrant; that is, satisfies Equations 3–96. The angle obtained using Equations 3–98 may differ by π from the angle obtained using Equations 3–96 since $\tan(\phi + \pi) = \tan\phi$. Thus we may need to add or subtract π from the angle obtained using Equation 3–98 to ensure that it is in the quadrant specified by Equations 3–96. Since we chose A to be positive, the correct quadrant of ϕ can be determined from the signs of $\sin\phi$ and $\cos\phi$ given by Equations 3–96. The solution is

$$x(t) = A\cos(\omega_0 t - \phi) = \sqrt{\left(\frac{v_0}{w_0}\right)^2 + x_0^2}\cos(\omega_0 t - \phi) \qquad \text{(3-99)}$$

It is plotted in Figure 3–68.
Differentiating Equation 3–99 twice gives the acceleration

$$\ddot{x}(t) = -A\omega_0^2\cos(\omega_0 t - \phi) = -\omega_0^2 x(t)$$

Oscillatory motion such as this, where the acceleration is in the opposite direction of the displacement and proportional to the square of the frequency, is called **simple harmonic motion**. Noting that the cosine of an angle cannot be greater than 1, the factor A corresponds to the maximum displacement, which is called the **amplitude** of the vibrations. The mass will continuously oscillate between the positions $x = A$ and $x = -A$. Noting that $\cos\alpha = 1$ only when $\alpha = 2\pi$ (or more generally when $\alpha = 2n\pi$ where n is an integer), the values of t at which the mass will be at its highest position are determined from $\omega_0 t - \phi = 2n\pi$, which yields

$$t = \frac{2n\pi + \phi}{\omega_0} \qquad n = 0,1,2,3,\dots \qquad \text{(3-100)}$$

The time during which a cycle is completed is called the **period** of the motion and can be determined from the previous relation by taking the difference

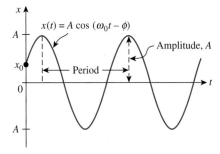

FIGURE 3–68

Undamped free vibrations (a simple harmonic motion).

between the times at which two consecutive maximums occur. Substituting 1 and 0 for n in Equation 3–100 and subtracting yields the period of the oscillations to be

$$T = \frac{2\pi}{\omega_0} \text{ s/cycle} \tag{3–101}$$

The **frequency** of the oscillations is the number of oscillations per unit time and is equal to the inverse of the period:

$$f = \frac{1}{T} = \frac{\omega_0}{2\pi} \text{ cycle/s} \tag{3–102}$$

Its unit is cycles per second, which is called a hertz (Hz). Note that in the absence of any external effects, the frequency depends on the characteristics of the mass and the spring only and is independent of the initial conditions and gravity. The frequency ω_0 is an example of a **circular frequency**, which has units of radians per second. The term $\omega_0 = \sqrt{k/m}$ is referred to as the **natural circular frequency** or just the **natural frequency** of the system. For example, for $m = 0.1$ kg, $k = 1000$ N/m, $x_0 = 0.02$ m, and $v_0 = 0$, the relations yield $A = 0.02$ m, $\sqrt{k/m} = 100 \text{ s}^{-1}$, $\phi = 0$, $T = 0.0628$ s, and $f = 15.9$ Hz. The equation of the displacement as a function of time is $x(t) = 0.02\cos(100t)$, where t is in seconds and x in meters.

EXAMPLE 3–38   Undamped Forced Vibrations: Beats

Sometimes, spring-mass-damper systems involve external forces imposed on the mechanical system. In many practical applications, such forces are periodic in nature and can be expressed as $F_0\cos\omega t$ or $F_0\sin\omega t$ (or other periodic functions), where ω is the circular frequency of the imposed force and F_0 is its amplitude. This is the kind of external force a system would experience when it is attached to rotating machinery having a slight imbalance, for example. The vibrations the system will undergo in this case are forced vibrations, since they are caused by an external effect.

Consider a spring-mass system that is initially at a static equilibrium ($x(0) = 0$ and $\dot{x}(0) = 0$). The system is now subjected to a periodic external force $F_0\cos\omega t$, as shown in Figure 3–69.

Assuming the system involves no friction or damping ($c = 0$), obtain a relation for the position of the mass relative to its equilibrium position as a function of time for the case where $\omega \neq \omega_0$.

SOLUTION   There is no damping to oppose the motion but there is an external force in this case, and thus Equation 3–91 becomes $m\ddot{x} + kx = F_0\cos\omega t$. Dividing it by m to put it into standard form and letting $\omega_0 = \sqrt{k/m}$ we obtain:

$$\ddot{x} + \omega_0^2 x = \frac{F_0}{m}\cos\omega t \tag{3–103}$$

The solution of the homogeneous part of this equation was determined in Example 3–37 to be (Equation 3–92)

$$x_h = C_1\cos\omega_0 t + C_2\sin\omega_0 t \tag{3–104}$$

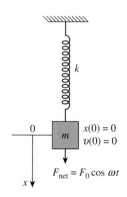

FIGURE 3–69

The schematic of a spring-mass system that is undergoing forced vibrations with no damping.

We take the particular solution to be $x_p = A\cos\omega t$, since $\omega \neq \omega_0$, and thus, $\cos\omega t$ is not a solution of the homogeneous part of the equation. Also, we did not include the $\sin\omega t$ term in the particular solution, since the differential equation does not involve odd orders of derivatives, and thus, the derivatives will not yield a sine function on the left side. Substituting this particular solution into the differential equation, solving for A, and back substituting yields

$$x_p = \frac{F_0/m}{\omega_0^2 - \omega^2}\cos\omega t \qquad (3\text{–}105)$$

Then the general solution is determined by adding the homogeneous and the particular solutions:

$$x(t) = C_1\cos\omega_0 t + C_2\sin\omega_0 t + \frac{F_0/m}{\omega_0^2 - \omega^2}\cos\omega t \qquad (3\text{–}106)$$

Applying the initial conditions $x(0) = 0$ and $\dot{x}(0) = 0$, the arbitrary constants are determined to be $C_1 = -F_0/m(\omega_0^2 - \omega^2)$ and $C_2 = 0$. Thus, the general solution is

$$x(t) = \frac{F_0/m}{\omega_0^2 - \omega^2}(\cos\omega t - \cos\omega_0 t) \qquad (3\text{–}107)$$

which is the difference of two periodic functions of different periods but the same amplitude.

Now let us investigate what happens when the frequency of the imposed force is close to the natural frequency of the system, $\omega \approx \omega_0$. Taking $\alpha = \frac{1}{2}(\omega_0 + \omega)$ and $\beta = \frac{1}{2}(\omega_0 - \omega)$ and using the trigonometric identity

$$\cos(\alpha - \beta) - \cos(\alpha + \beta) = 2\sin\alpha\sin\beta \qquad (3\text{–}108)$$

the general solution also can be expressed as

$$x(t) = \left[\frac{2F_0/m}{\omega_0^2 - \omega^2}\sin\frac{\omega_0 - \omega}{2}t\right]\sin\frac{\omega_0 + \omega}{2}t \qquad (3\text{–}109)$$

When $\omega \approx \omega_0$, we will have $\omega_0 + \omega \gg |\omega_0 - \omega|$. As a result, the function $\sin\frac{\omega_0 + \omega}{2}t$ will be *rapidly* oscillating with a circular frequency $(\omega_0 + \omega)/2$, while the function $\sin\frac{\omega_0 - \omega}{2}t$ will be *slowly* oscillating with a circular frequency $(\omega_0 - \omega)/2$. Then, we can view Equation 3–109 as

$$x(t) = A(t)\sin\frac{\omega_0 + \omega}{2}t \qquad (3\text{–}110)$$

where $\sin\frac{\omega_0 + \omega}{2}t$ is a rapidly oscillating function whose amplitude $A(t)$ is a slowly varying periodic function that is equal to the terms in the brackets in Equation 3–109. A vibrating motion such as this with a slowly but periodically varying amplitude is called a **beat** and is illustrated in Figure 3–70.

This phenomena is frequently encountered in acoustics when two instruments of nearly identical frequencies are played simultaneously. It yields sound waves (vibrations) whose amplitude varies periodically. Each cycle corresponds to a beat that is noticeable to an ordinary ear. The case $\omega = \omega_0$ is considered in the next example.

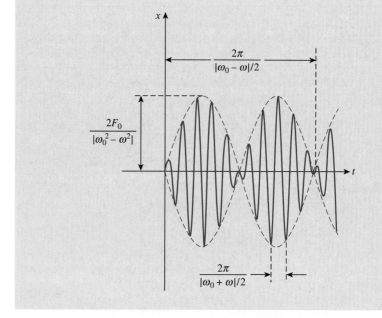

FIGURE 3–70

Forced vibrations with a periodically varying amplitude (beats).

EXAMPLE 3–39   Undamped Forced Vibrations: Resonance

Solve Example 3–38 for the special case where $\omega = \omega_0$.

SOLUTION In this case, the differential equation, the initial conditions, and the homogeneous solution remain the same, but the particular solution should be taken as $x_p = t(A \sin \omega_0 t + B \cos \omega_0 t)$ since the nonhomogeneous term $F_0 \cos \omega_0 t$ is a solution of the related homogeneous equation. Substituting this particular solution into the differential equation and solving for the unknown coefficients yield $A = F_0 / 2m\omega_0$ and $B = 0$. Thus, the particular solution is

$$x_p = \frac{F_0}{2m\omega_0} t \, \sin \omega_0 t \tag{3–111}$$

Then the general solution is determined by adding the homogeneous and the particular solution to obtain

$$x(t) = C_1 \cos \omega_0 t + C_2 \sin \omega_0 t + \frac{F_0}{2m\omega_0} t \sin \omega_0 t$$

Applying the initial conditions $x(0) = 0$ and $\dot{x}(0) = 0$, the arbitrary constants are determined to be $C_1 = C_2 = 0$. Thus, the general solution is

$$x(t) = \frac{F_0}{2m\omega_0} t \, \sin \omega_0 t \tag{3–112}$$

The most striking feature of this solution is the factor t, which causes the displacement to become unbounded as $t \to \infty$, as shown in Figure 3–71.

Again, we can view the final form of the general solution as

$$x(t) = A(t) \sin \omega_0 t \tag{3–113}$$

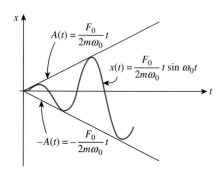

FIGURE 3–71

Forced vibrations with a continuously increasing amplitude (resonance).

This is a sinusoidal function of frequency ω_0 and amplitude $A(t) = (F_0/2m\omega_0)t$, which increases with time. This phenomena of ever-increasing amplitude is known as **resonance**. In this case the resonance is referred to as *pure resonance* or *undamped resonance* since the motion is assumed not to involve any friction or damping. Equation 3–112 implies that the amplitude of the motion will approach infinity as $t \to \infty$. However, in practice the system will collapse at some time $t = t_f$ as a result of these violent vibrations, and this equation will not apply for $t > t_f$. Also, the linear spring force assumption becomes invalid for large amplitudes.

The resonance phenomenon appears only in the particular solution, and it will occur no matter what the initial conditions are. This is because the particular solution with the factor t will dominate the motion for large t regardless of the values of the constants C_1 and C_2 in the homogeneous solution.

In practice, resonance also occurs to a certain degree in systems whose damping is not large enough to offset it, and there are several spectacular examples of structures whose destruction was caused by resonance. A large structure has many components, each with a different natural frequency. It is very unlikely that the entire structure will resonate as a result of a periodic external force. However, the resonance of some key components is sufficient to destroy the entire structure.

For example, the Broughton Bridge near Manchester, England collapsed in 1831 as a result of soldiers marching over the bridge in step, causing it to resonate. Thus, it is a universal practice now for soldiers to march out of step when crossing bridges. Another example is the collapse of the Tacoma Narrows bridge in Washington State on November 7, 1940, which was the third largest suspension bridge in the world. The violent resonance oscillations in this case were caused by the winds. Several other recent disasters were caused by resonance, which makes it a serious consideration in the design of the mechanical systems, airplane wings, buildings, hanging dance floors, and bridges.

The following argument may shed some light on resonance phenomena. A system has the minimum resistance to oscillations at its natural frequency ω_0, since it will oscillate at ω_0 when it is not disturbed. When an external effect forces the system to oscillate at a different frequency, the system will resist because it does not feel comfortable oscillating at a different (unnatural) frequency. But when the external effect forces the system to oscillate at its natural frequency, the system will gladly cooperate since the request is in perfect compliance with its intrinsic characteristics.

Resonance occurs because the external force always acts in the same direction as the velocity, thus increasing the amplitude. The result of the resonance is not always destruction. It is used to create some very desirable effects in acoustics, seismography, and electronics.

EXAMPLE 3–40   Damped Free Vibrations

Any system with moving parts will involve friction; thus, any vibrating system in practice will involve some damping. The numerical value of the damping constant c gives an idea about the magnitude of damping. Consider a spring-mass-damper

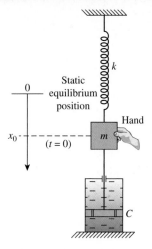

FIGURE 3–72

The schematic of a spring-mass-damper system that is undergoing free vibrations with damping.

system that is in static equilibrium. At $t = 0$, the mass is pulled down to location x_0 and then released with a velocity of v_0, as shown in Figure 3–72. Taking the equilibrium position of the mass to be $x = 0$ and the downward direction to be positive, determine the position of the mass as a function of time, $x(t)$.

SOLUTION There is no external force applied; thus, Equation 3–91 reduces in this case to $m\ddot{x} + c\dot{x} + kx = 0$ with $x(0) = x_0$ and $\dot{x}(0) = v_0$. The differential equation is linear, homogeneous, and has constant coefficients. Its characteristic equation is $mr^2 + cr + k = 0$ whose roots are

$$r_1 = \frac{-c + \sqrt{c^2 - 4mk}}{2m} \quad \text{and} \quad r_2 = \frac{-c - \sqrt{c^2 - 4mk}}{2m}$$

Thus, the nature of the solution will depend on whether $c^2 - 4mk$ is positive, zero, or negative. Next we will consider each case separately.

Case 1: $c^2 - 4mk > 0$ *(Overdamped Motion)*

In this case, the roots are real and distinct, and thus the general solution is

$$x(t) = C_1 e^{r_1 t} + C_2 e^{r_2 t} \tag{3–114}$$

Considering that $\sqrt{4mk} < c$ and thus $\sqrt{c^2 - 4mk} < c$, both exponents are negative in this case regardless of the initial conditions. As t increases, both terms will decay because of the negative exponents, and $x(t)$ will approach zero as $t \to \infty$. That is, the mass will move towards its static equilibrium position without oscillating. The mass is said to be **overdamped** in this case because of the large damping constant and thus a large damping force. The exact form of the displacement function will depend on the initial conditions.

Three possibilities are plotted in Figure 3–73 for a fixed initial position x_0 but different initial velocities. Curve (a) will occur if v_0 is applied in the positive x direction. The mass will move further down under the influence of the initial velocity, but will move back to its static equilibrium position at $x = 0$ as a result of the restoring force of the spring. A large damping force will prevent any oscillations. For curve (b) the initial velocity is zero. For curve (c) the initial velocity is directed in the negative x direction. In this case the mass passes through the equilibrium position and then returns to it.

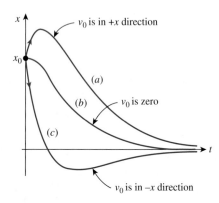

FIGURE 3–73

Three possibilities for overdamped and critically damped motion, depending on the direction of the initial velocity v_0.

Case 2: $c^2 - 4mk = 0$ *(Critically Damped Motion)*

In this case, the roots are real and equal; and thus the general solution is

$$x(t) = (C_1 + C_2 t)e^{-ct/2m} \tag{3–115}$$

The mass is said to be **critically damped** in this case because the damping force is just enough to prevent the onset of any oscillations. A slightly smaller value of the damping constant c will allow oscillations, and a slightly larger value of c will cause the motion to be overdamped. Thus, this is the borderline case between the overdamped and underdamped motions. Again as t increases, both terms will decay because of the negative exponent, and $x(t)$ will approach zero $t \to \infty$. Although the factor t in the second term will cause it to increase as t increases, the exponential factor decreases faster than this increase, and as a result, the mass will move towards its static equilibrium position at $x = 0$. This is because the series expansion for e^{at} is

$$e^{at} = 1 + at + \frac{(at)^2}{2!} + \cdots + \frac{(at)^n}{n!} + \cdots$$

Thus,

$$\lim_{t \to \infty} te^{-at} = \lim_{t \to \infty} \frac{t}{e^{at}} = \lim_{t \to \infty} \frac{t}{1 + at + \frac{(at)^2}{2!} + \cdots + \frac{(at)^n}{n!} + \cdots} = 0$$

The exact form of the displacement function will depend on the initial conditions. The three possibilities discussed in Case 1 and plotted in Figure 3–73 are also applicable in this case.

Case 3: $c^2 - 4mk < 0$ (*Underdamped or Oscillatory Motion*)

In this case the roots are

$$r_{1,2} = -\frac{c}{2m} \pm i\frac{\sqrt{4mk - c^2}}{2m} = -\frac{c}{2m} \pm i\sqrt{\frac{k}{m} - \frac{c^2}{4m^2}}$$

and the solution is

$$x(t) = e^{-ct/2m}\left(C_1 \cos\sqrt{\frac{k}{m} - \frac{c^2}{4m^2}}\, t + C_2 \sin\sqrt{\frac{k}{m} - \frac{c^2}{4m^2}}\, t\right) \quad \text{(3–116)}$$

In this case, the mass will oscillate because of the sine and cosine functions, but the amplitude of the oscillations will get smaller and smaller as t increases because of the exponential factor $e^{-ct/2m}$. Although the motion is oscillatory, it is not periodic; that is, the time between the peaks is not constant. Because of the oscillations, the mass is said to be **underdamped** in this case. This is due to a relatively small damping constant and thus a small damping force. Equation 3–116 also can be expressed as

$$x(t) = Ae^{-ct/2m}\cos\left(\sqrt{\frac{k}{m} - \frac{c^2}{4m^2}}\, t - \phi\right) \quad \text{(3–117)}$$

where $A = \sqrt{C_1^2 + C_2^2}$ and ϕ is the angle whose sine and cosine are given by $\sin\phi = C_1/A$ and $\cos\phi = C_2/A$. Equation 3–117 is plotted in Figure 3–74.

Noting that since the cosine of an angle cannot be greater than 1, the factor $Ae^{-ct/2m}$ corresponds to the maximum displacement; thus, a plot of this factor together with its negative counterpart forms an envelope to surround the oscillations, as shown in Figure 3–74.

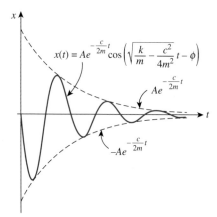

FIGURE 3–74

Free vibrations in the presence of damping (underdamped motion).

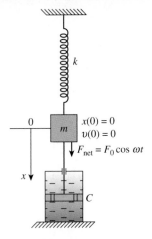

FIGURE 3–75

The schematic of a spring-mass-damper system that is undergoing forced vibrations with damping.

EXAMPLE 3–41   **Damped Forced Vibrations**

Consider a spring-mass-damper system that is initially at static equilibrium ($x(0) = 0$ and $\dot{x}(0) = 0$). The system is now subjected to a periodic external force $F_0 \cos \omega t$, as shown in Figure 3–75.

Obtain a relation for the position of the mass relative to its equilibrium position as a function of time in the presence of damping $c \neq 0$.

SOLUTION   There is both damping and external force applied in this case; thus, Equation 3–91 applies as

$$m\ddot{x} + c\dot{x} + kx = F_0 \cos \omega t$$

Dividing it by m to put it into standard form and letting $\omega_0 = \sqrt{k/m}$, we have

$$\ddot{x} + \frac{c}{m}\dot{x} + \omega_0^2 x = \frac{F_0}{m}\cos \omega t \qquad (3\text{–}118)$$

The solution of the homogeneous part of this equation was determined in the previous example to be

$$x_h = C_1 e^{r_1 t} + C_2 e^{r_2 t} \qquad (3\text{–}119)$$

where r_1 and r_2 are

$$r_{1,2} = \frac{-c \pm \sqrt{c^2 - 4mk}}{2m}$$

which may be real and distinct, real and equal, or complex, depending on whether $c^2 - 4mk$ is positive, zero, or negative. We take the particular solution to be

$$x_p = A\cos \omega t + B\sin \omega t$$

Substituting this particular solution into the differential equation, solving for A and B, and substituting them back into the particular solution relation yields

$$x_p = \frac{F_0}{m^2(\omega_0^2 - \omega^2)^2 + c^2\omega^2}\left[m(\omega_0^2 - \omega^2)\cos \omega t + c\omega \sin \omega t\right] \qquad (3\text{–}120)$$

The particular solution can be expressed in a more convenient form as

$$x_p = \frac{F_0 \cos(\omega t - \phi)}{\sqrt{m^2(\omega_0^2 - \omega^2)^2 + c^2\omega^2}} \qquad (3\text{–}121)$$

where

$$\phi = \tan^{-1}\frac{c\omega}{m(\omega_0^2 - \omega^2)} \qquad 0 \leq \phi \leq \pi$$

Note that the particular solution is a simple harmonic function of period $2\pi/\omega$ and amplitude $F_0/\sqrt{m^2(\omega_0^2 - \omega^2) + c^2\omega^2}$, which are constant. Thus, the system has the same frequency as the forcing function, but lags behind by the

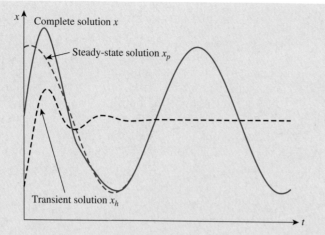

FIGURE 3–76

In forced vibrations with damping, the homogeneous solution is due to the initial disturbance (initial conditions), and it is damped out leaving the particular solution that is due to the external force (the nonhomogeneous term) as the only solution of the equation.

phase angle. The general solution is obtained by combining the homogeneous and the particular solutions:

$$x = x_h + x_p = (C_1 e^{r_1 t} + C_2 e^{r_2 t}) + \frac{F_0 \cos(\omega t - \phi)}{\sqrt{m^2(\omega_0^2 - \omega^2)^2 + c^2\omega^2}} \qquad \textbf{(3–122)}$$

Again, the homogeneous part of the solution is due to the initial disturbance, and it always decays quickly with time as a result of damping. As $t \rightarrow \infty$, we will have $x_h \rightarrow \infty$; thus,

$$x(t) = \frac{F_0 \cos(\omega t - \phi)}{\sqrt{m^2(\omega_0^2 - \omega^2)^2 + c^2\omega^2}} \quad \text{as} \quad t \rightarrow \infty \qquad \textbf{(3–123)}$$

Therefore, it is appropriate to refer to the homogeneous solution as the **transient solution** and the particular solution as the **steady-state solution**, since x_h dies out after a while but x_p persists indefinitely (Figure 3–76).

Discussion

You are probably wondering if we can have resonance in the presence of damping, $c \neq 0$. First of all, we will never have pure resonance since the nonhomogeneous term $F_0 \cos \omega t$ will never be a solution of the related homogeneous equation. Thus, the particular solution corresponding to it will never involve that factor. Therefore, the displacements of a spring-mass-damper system are always bounded. But under some conditions, the amplitude may increase so much that it may do the same damage as pure resonance, as we will explain. The steady-state solution (Equation 3–123) can be rearranged as

$$x(t) = A\cos(\omega t - \phi) \qquad \textbf{(3–124)}$$

where

$$A = \frac{F_0}{\sqrt{m^2(\omega_0^2 - \omega^2)^2 + c^2\omega^2}} \qquad \textbf{(3–125)}$$

is the amplitude of the oscillations since $0 \leq \cos \alpha \leq 1$ for any angle α. The first thing we would like to know is if the amplitude A would ever become infinite, so we look at its denominator. Clearly, the denominator cannot be zero even when $\omega = \omega_0$; thus, the amplitude cannot become infinity. This eliminates the possibility of pure resonance as long as $c \neq 0$. The case $c = 0$ is not a realistic possibility, since every system inherently involves some damping. Next we would like to know how large A can become, since an amplitude larger than a safe level is as destructive as pure resonance. To find out, we need to determine the ω value that minimizes the denominator $Z = m^2(\omega_0^2 - \omega^2)^2 + c\omega^2$, since the amplitude will be a maximum when its denominator is a minimum. The ω value that minimizes the denominator Z is determined by taking the derivative of Z with respect to ω while holding k, c, and ω_0 constant and then setting it equal to zero. Solving the resulting expression for ω yields $\omega = 0$ and

$$\omega^2 = \omega_0^2 - \frac{c^2}{2m^2} = \frac{k}{m}\left(1 - \frac{c^2}{2k}\right) \tag{3-126}$$

The second derivative of Z at this ω value is positive if $2mk - c^2 > 0$, indicating that this ω value minimizes the denominator Z and thus maximizes the amplitude A (Figure 3–77).

But if $c^2/2mk > 1$, then $\omega = 0$ will give the maximum amplitude. Substituting the ω relation in Equation 3–126 into Equation 3–125 yields the maximum amplitude to be

$$A_{max} = \frac{F_0}{c\omega_0} = \frac{F_0}{c}\sqrt{\frac{m}{k}} \tag{3-127}$$

Note that the smaller the damping constant, the larger the amplitude. The amplitude will tend to infinity as $t \to \infty$. Also, systems with a large natural frequency tend to allow small amplitudes. The variation of amplitude with circular frequency of the applied force is plotted in Figure 3–78 for $m = 1$, $k = 1$, and $F_0 = 1$. Note that, for $c > \sqrt{2km}$, the amplitude always decreases with increasing ω.

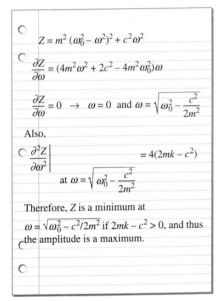

FIGURE 3–77

Demonstrating that the amplitude is a maximum at $\omega = \sqrt{\omega_0^2 - c^2/2m^2}$.

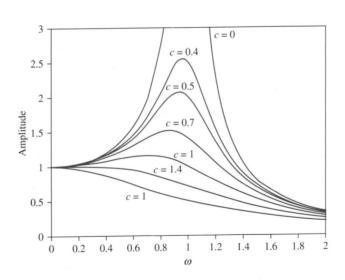

FIGURE 3–78

The variation of amplitude A with frequency of the external force for $m = k = F_0 = 1$ for various damping coefficients.

Electrical Circuits

Another important application of second order linear differential equations with constant coefficients is simple series electric circuits, also called series *RLC* circuits, which are frequently encountered in electrical engineering. Such a circuit typically involves a *resistor* whose resistance is R ohms (Ω), a *capacitor* whose capacitance is C farads (F), and an *inductor* whose inductance is L henries (H), as shown in Figure 3–79.

The voltage $E(t)$ is supplied to the circuit by a battery, a generator, radio or TV signals, or simply by the household electricity. A battery supplies a constant voltage of magnitude E_0, whereas a generator supplies a periodic voltage that can be expressed as $E_0 \cos \omega t$ or $E_0 \sin \omega t$, where the constant E_0 is the amplitude of the voltage in volts (V) and ω is its (circular) frequency. The quantity of primary interest in this electric circuit is the current, which is defined as the amount of electrical charge Q flowing per unit time,

$$I = \frac{dQ}{dt} \tag{3-128}$$

The current I that flows through a circuit is determined from **Kirchhoff's law**: *The sum of the voltage drops in a single-loop circuit is equal to the applied voltage.* You will recall from physics that the voltage drop across a resistor is proportional to the current and is expressed as

$$E_{\text{drop,resistor}} = IR \quad (\text{volt} = \text{ampere} \times \text{ohm}) \tag{3-129}$$

where the constant of proportionality R is called the **resistance** whose unit is the *ohm*. Inductors are coils made using highly conducting materials (such as copper) and are commonly used in electric motors and transformers. An inductor offers practically no resistance to electron flow when the current is constant. But it resists changes in current; thus, causing a voltage drop across the inductor that is proportional to the rate of change of current. Thus, we have

$$E_{\text{drop,inductor}} = L\frac{dI}{dt} \quad (\text{volt} = \text{henry} \times \text{ampere/s}) \tag{3-130}$$

where the constant of proportionality L is called the **inductance** whose unit is the *henry*. A capacitor can be viewed as a storage device that can regulate the current flow in a circuit by storing electrical charge Q or releasing it. The amount of electrical change stored on a capacitor at any instant is proportional to the voltage drop across it and can be expressed as

$$Q = CE_{\text{drop,capacitor}}$$

or

$$E_{\text{drop,capacitor}} = \frac{Q}{C} \quad (\text{volt} = \text{coloumb/farad}) \tag{3-131}$$

where the constant C is called the **capacitance** whose unit is the *farad*. Then from Kirchhoff's law, the differential equation that governs the variation of current flow in a closed circuit with time becomes

$$L\frac{dI}{dt} + RI + \frac{1}{C}Q = E(t) \tag{3-132}$$

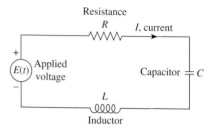

FIGURE 3–79

An *RLC* (resistance-inductance-capacitance) circuit.

This differential equation is not in a useful form, since it involves two dependent variables I and Q. However, we can reduce the number of dependent variables to one by eliminating I using the relation $I = dQ/dt$:

$$L\frac{d^2Q}{dt^2} + R\frac{dQ}{dt} + \frac{1}{C}Q = E(t) \tag{3-133}$$

The differential equation in the other dependent variable I can be obtained by differentiating Equation 3–132 with respect to t and again using the relation $I = dQ/dt$ (Figure 3–80),

$$L\frac{d^2I}{dt^2} + R\frac{dI}{dt} + \frac{1}{C}I = \frac{dE(t)}{dt} \tag{3-134}$$

The electrical properties R, L, and C, in general, may depend on the current. Thus Equations 3–133 and 3–134 may become nonlinear. However, the dependence of these properties on the current is very mild, and they can be treated as constants in most practical problems. Therefore, these two equations are second-order linear differential equations with constant coefficients. The resemblance between Equations 3–133 and 3–91 that governs the mechanical vibrations is striking. Although physically they are worlds apart, mathematically they are identical, and thus, they have the same form of solution. The solutions obtained earlier for mechanical systems as well as the concepts such as beat, resonance, natural frequency, damped oscillations, critical damping, and steady-state solution are also applicable to electrical systems with proper interpretation. The one-to-one correspondence between the mechanical and electrical quantities is called **electromechanical analogy**, and is given in Table 3–3.

The general solution of the differential equation will involve two arbitrary constants that can be determined from two initial conditions. For Equation 3–133, we need to specify the initial charge in the capacitor and the initial current flowing through the circuit:

$$Q(0) = Q_0 \quad \text{and} \quad I(0) = I_0$$

In $I(t)$ and $Q(t)$:

$$L\frac{dI}{dt} + RI + \frac{1}{C}Q = E(t)$$

In $Q(t)$ only:

$$L\frac{d^2Q}{dt^2} + R\frac{dQ}{dt} + \frac{1}{C}Q = E(t)$$

In $I(t)$ only:

$$L\frac{d^2I}{dt^2} + R\frac{dI}{dt} + \frac{1}{C}I = \frac{dE(t)}{dt}$$

FIGURE 3–80

Various forms of the differential equation that describes an *RLC* circuit.

TABLE 3–3

Electromechanical Analogy

Mechanical System	Electrical System
$m\ddot{x} + c\dot{x} + kx = F(t)$	$L\ddot{Q} + R\dot{Q} + \frac{1}{C}Q = E(t)$
Mass, m(kg) Damping constant, c(N · s/m) Spring Constant, k(N/m)	Inductance, L(H) Resistance, $R(\Omega)$ Reciprocal of Capacitance, 1/C (1/F)
Applied Force, F(N) Displacement, x(m)	Applied Voltage, E(V) Charge, Q(C)
Velocity, $v = \dot{x}$(m/s)	Current, $I = \dot{Q}$(A)

For Equation 3–134, we also need to specify the derivative of the current at $t = 0$, which is determined from Equation 3–132 to be

$$\dot{I}(0) = \frac{1}{L}\left[E(0) - RI_0 - \frac{1}{C}Q_0 \right] \qquad \text{(3–135)}$$

Also, if we solve the differential equation for Q, we can always determine I from $I = dQ/dt$. Likewise when I is known, we can determine Q by integration.

EXAMPLE 3–42   Response of an *RLC* Circuit

Determine the steady-state current in an *RLC* circuit for an applied periodic voltage of the form $E(t) = E_0 \sin \omega t$.

SOLUTION   Noting that $E(t) = E_0 \sin \omega t$, the differential equation governing the current flow in the circuit (from Equation 3–134) is

$$L\ddot{I} + R\dot{I} + \frac{1}{C}I = \omega E_0 \cos \omega t$$

which is analogous to the differential equation solved in Example 3–41,

$$m\ddot{x} + c\dot{x} + kx = F_0 \cos \omega t$$

Thus, the general form of the solution of this equation is identical to the solution of Example 3–41 (Equation 3–121), except now we need to replace m by L, c by R, k by $1/C$, ω_0^2 by $1/LC$, and F_0 by ωE_0. The result is, after some simplifications,

$$I(t) = \frac{E_0 \cos(\omega t - \phi)}{\sqrt{R^2 + \left(\omega L - \dfrac{1}{\omega C} \right)^2}} \qquad \text{(3–136)}$$

where

$$\phi = \tan^{-1}\frac{\omega RC}{1 - LC\omega^2}$$

The quantity $Z = \sqrt{R^2 + (\omega L - 1/\omega C)^2}$ in the denominator represents the effective resistance of the circuit to electron flow in ohms and is called the **impedance** of the circuit.

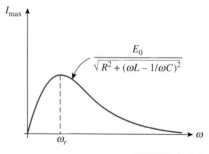

In analogy with mechanical systems, the impedance becomes minimum when $\omega = \omega_r = 1/\sqrt{LC}$. This can be verified easily by taking the derivative of Z with respect to ω, setting it equal to zero, and solving for ω. This value of the frequency of the applied voltage is called the **resonance frequency** since it maximizes the current (Figure 3–81).

Resonance proves to be very destructive in most mechanical systems, and thus it is something to be avoided. In electrical systems, however, the operation of many devices is based on the resonance phenomenon; thus, it is something to be sought. In a simple radio, for example, the tuning dial varies the

FIGURE 3–81

The variation of the maximum current with the frequency of the applied voltage for fixed values of E_0, R, and L.

capacitance C of the circuit without altering R and L. Therefore, adjusting the dial is equivalent to specifying the periodic signal whose frequency ω will maximize the current. If we want to tune in on a station that broadcasts radio signals at frequency ω_1 and provides periodic input voltage signals of the form $E_0 \sin \omega_1 t$, we set the value of the capacitance to $C_1 = 1/L\omega_1^2$, so this particular signal will cause the smallest impedance (thus the largest current) in the circuit. (The parasitic effects of the broadcast at nearby frequencies can be suppressed by other circuitry.) This signal is then amplified and sent to a speaker that converts these signals to sound waves whose amplitude is proportional to the amplitude of electrical signals.

Section Review

3–45C Define the amplitude, frequency, and period of vibration. When is a vibrational motion simple harmonic?

3–46C Explain frequency, circular frequency, and natural frequency. Point out the differences and similarities between them.

3–47C Can actual systems have pure resonance? Explain.

3–48 Consider a $m = 0.2$ kg mass suspended by a spring whose spring constant is $k = 500$ N/m. The mass is now pulled down 1 cm, and then released with zero initial velocity. Neglecting any friction, determine the natural frequency, period, and the amplitude of the resulting motion.

(*Answers:* $\omega_0 = 31.62 \text{ s}^{-1}$, $T = \dfrac{2\pi}{31.62 \text{ s}^{-1}} \approx 0.20 \text{ s}$, $A = 1$ cm)

3–49 In electrical terms, what is the function of a tuning dial of a radio?

3–50 If the variation of the current with time $I(t)$ in an RLC circuit is known, explain how you would determine the variation of the charge in the capacitor with time, $Q(t)$.

3–11 ▪ COMPUTER METHODS FOR SECOND-ORDER LINEAR EQUATIONS

The systematic methods developed in this chapter for solving second-order linear differential equations have been incorporated into symbolic processing programs. Thus, you should not expect such a program to be able to solve an equation that cannot be solved by one of more of the methods developed in this chapter. The advantages of using such a program are that the program can obtain solutions more quickly and they save us the trouble of doing tedious integrations and algebraic manipulations. However, they are not infallible, and you sometimes will find that they cannot solve a solvable equation. For this reason, you still need to be familiar with the methods of this chapter.

As a first introduction to solving a second-order equation, consider the specific Euler equation

$$x^2 y'' - 2xy' - 4y = 10x \tag{3–137}$$

TABLE 3–4

Computer Solution of Equation 3–137

MATLAB Symbolic Math Toolbox
`dsolve('x^2*D2y-2*x*Dy-4*y=10*x','x')`

MuPAD
`eqn := ode({x^2*y''(x) -2*x*y'(x)-4*y(x)=10*x},y(x)):` `solve(eqn)`

Maple
`ode := x^2*y''(x)-2*x*y'(x)-4*y(x)=10*x` `dsolve(ode)`

Mathematica
`DSolve[x^2*y''[x] -2*x*y'[x]-4*y[x]==10*x,y[x],x]`

which was solved in Example 3–36. The general solution is

$$y = \frac{C_1}{x} + C_2 x^4 - \frac{5}{3}x$$

Table 3–4 shows how to obtain a computer solution of this equation for arbitrary initial conditions.

Damped Forced Vibrations with Derivative Input

Section 3–10 treated the solution of the damped oscillator equation

$$m\ddot{x} + c\dot{x} + kx = F_{ext}$$

where the external force F_{ext} is harmonic, that is, sinusoidal or cosinusoidal. There are applications, however, where the external force is of the form $F_{ext} = ay(t) + b\dot{y}(t)$. As a simple example to illustrate the solution of this equation, suppose that $m = 1$, $c = 3$, $k = 2$, $a = 1$, $b = 1$, and $y(t) = te^{-5t}$. Then the equation is

$$\ddot{x} + 3\dot{x} + 2x = y + \dot{y} = te^{-5t} + e^{-5t} - 5te^{-5t} = (1 - 4t)e^{-5t}$$

Thus, with zero initial conditions, for example, the problem to be solved is

$$\ddot{x} + 3\dot{x} + 2x = (1 - 4t)e^{-5t}, x(0) = \dot{x}(0) = 0 \qquad \textbf{(3–138)}$$

The solution is

$$x = \frac{1}{9}e^{-2t} - \frac{1}{3}te^{-5t} - \frac{1}{9}e^{-5t}$$

This solution can be found by computer using the code listed in Table 3–5. These solutions are based on the variation of parameters method described in Section 3–8 and summarized in Theorem 3–8.

TABLE 3-5

Computer Solution of Equation 3-138

MATLAB Symbolic Math Toolbox

```
dsolve('D2x+3*Dx+2*x=(1-4*t)
 *exp(-5*t)','x(0)=0','Dx(0)=0','t')
```

MuPAD

```
eqn:=ode({x''(t)+3*x'(t)+2*x(t)=(1-4*t)*exp(-4*t),x(0)=0,
 x'(0)=0},x(t))
solve(eqn)
```

Maple

```
ode := x''(t)+3*x'(t)+2*x(t)=(1-4*t)*exp(-5*t)
ics := x(0)=0,x'(0)=0
dsolve({ode,ics})
```

Mathematica

```
ode = x''[t]+3*x'[t]+2*x[t]==(1-4*t)*Exp[-5*t]
DSolve[{ode,x[0]==0,x'[0]==0},x[t],t]
```

EXAMPLE 3-43   A Vehicle Suspension Model

One application where the external force is of the form $ay(t) + b\dot{y}(t)$ occurs is the *quarter-car model* of a vehicle suspension is shown in Figure 3–82. In this simplified model, the masses of the wheel, tire, and axle are neglected, and the mass m represents one fourth of the vehicle mass. The spring constant k models the combined stiffness of both the tire and the suspension spring. The damping constant c models the shock absorber. The equilibrium position of m when $y = 0$ is $x = 0$. The road surface displacement $y(t)$ can be derived from the road surface profile and the car's speed. Obtain the equation of motion.

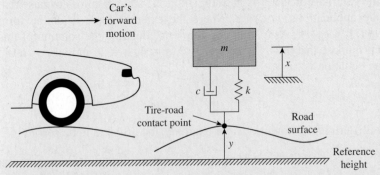

FIGURE 3–82

Quarter-car model of a vehicle suspension system.

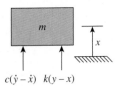

FIGURE 3–83

Free-body diagram of the quarter-car suspension model.

SOLUTION Figure 3–83 shows the free-body diagram, which is drawn assuming that $\dot{y} > \dot{x}$ and $y > x$. Only the dynamic spring force is shown because the static spring force is canceled by the gravity force mg. From this free-body diagram, we obtain the equation of motion:

$$m\ddot{x} = c(\dot{y} - \dot{x}) + k(y - x)$$

Putting this in standard form gives

$$m\ddot{x} + c\dot{x} + kx = ky + c\dot{y} \qquad (3\text{--}139)$$

EXAMPLE 3–44   Vehicle Response to a Bump

Suppose the vehicle shown in Figure 3–82 encounters a half-meter high bump one meter in length while moving at 18 m/s (about 40 mph). The bump profile is given by

$$y(z) = 5.437ze^{-4z}$$

where z is the horizontal distance traveled by the vehicle while going over the bump. The displacement $y(t)$ felt by the suspension is related to $y(z)$ through the vehicle speed $z = vt$, where $v = 18$ m/s. Thus,

$$y(t) = 97.858te^{-72t}$$

The following values are representative of a real suspension: $m = 240$ kg, which represents one-fourth of the vehicle mass, $c = 5000$ N·s/m, and $k = 16\,000$ N/m. For these values, the right hand side of Equation 3–139 reduces to

$$ky + c\dot{y} = (489\,290 - 33\,663\,152t)e^{-72t}$$

The equation of motion becomes

$$240\ddot{x} + 5000\dot{x} + 16\,000x = (489\,290 - 33\,663\,152t)e^{-72t}$$

This is of the same form as Equation (3–138) and can be solved by computer using the same methods listed in Table 3–5. Because the numerical values are cumbersome, we will not display the code required to find this solution. The solution is plotted along with the bump profile in Figure 3–84. From the plot, you can see that, although the bump height is 0.5 m, the maximum displacement of the chassis is only about 0.22 m. So the suspension has done a good job in reducing the effect of the bump on the passenger compartment.

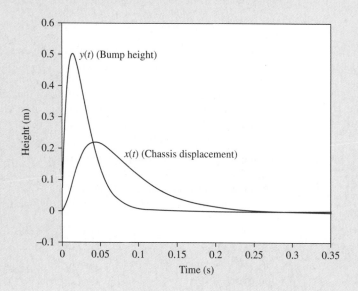

FIGURE 3–84

Bump response of a vehicle suspension.

3–12 ▪ SUMMARY

Terminology for Second-Order Equations A differential equation is said to be *linear* if it does not involve any powers, products, or other nonlinear functions of the dependent variable y or its derivatives. A second-order linear differential equation can be expressed as

$$y'' + P(x)y' + Q(x)y = R(x) \tag{3-1}$$

The function $R(x)$ represents all the terms that do not involve the dependent variable of any of its derivatives, and is called the *nonhomogeneous term*. A linear differential equation is said to be *nonhomogeneous* when $R(x) \neq 0$ and *homogeneous* when $R(x) = 0$. The equation that is obtained by setting $R(x)$ equal to zero is called the *related homogeneous equation* or *complementary equation*. If the coefficients of the dependent variable and its derivatives are constants, the equation is said to have *constant coefficients*. If one or more coefficients depend on the independent variable x, then the equation is said to have *variable coefficients*.

Existence and Uniqueness The *existence and uniqueness theorem* states that if the functions $P(x)$, $Q(x)$, and $R(x)$ are continuous on an interval and the point x_0 is in this interval, then the second-order linear differential Equation 3–1 has a unique solution on this interval, that satisfies the two initial conditions specified at x_0.

Linear Independence The expressions $C_1 y_1 + C_2 y_2$ where C_1 and C_2 are arbitrary constants is called a *linear combination* of the two functions y_1 and y_2. Two functions are said to be *linearly dependent* in an interval $x_1 < x < x_2$ if one function is a constant multiple of the other for all values of x in that interval. Otherwise, the functions are *linearly independent*. Alternately, two functions are also said to be linearly independent in an interval $x_1 < x < x_2$ if the equation

$$C_1 y_1 + C_2 y_2 = 0 \tag{3-8}$$

is satisfied for all x in that interval only when $C_1 = C_2 = 0$.

Independence Test with the Wronskian The linear independence of two functions also can be expressed in terms of their *Wronskian*, defined as

$$W(y_1, y_2) = \begin{vmatrix} y_1 & y_2 \\ y_1' & y_2' \end{vmatrix} = y_1 y_2' - y_1' y_2 \tag{3-12}$$

Two functions are linearly dependent in an interval if their *Wronskian* in that interval is zero for all x. Otherwise, they are independent.

The expression $C_1 y_1 + C_2 y_2 + \cdots + C_n y_n$, where C_1, $C_2, \ldots, C_n$ are arbitrary constants, is called a *linear combination* of the n functions $y_1, y_2, \ldots, y_n$. The n functions y_1, $y_2, \ldots, y_n$ are said to be *linearly independent* in an interval $x_1 < x < x_2$ if the equation

$$C_1 y_1 + C_2 y_2 + \cdots + C_n y_n = 0$$

is satisfied for all x in that interval only when $C_1 = C_2 = \cdots = C_n = 0$. Otherwise, these n functions are said to be *linearly dependent* in that interval. The linear independence of n functions also can be expressed in terms of their *Wronskian*, defined as

$$W(y_1, y_2 \ldots, y_n) = \begin{vmatrix} y_1 & y_2 & \cdots & y_n \\ y_1' & y_2' & \cdots & y_n' \\ \vdots & \vdots & \vdots & \vdots \\ y_1^{(n-1)} & y_2^{(n-1)} & \cdots & y_n^{(n-1)} \end{vmatrix} \tag{3-13}$$

The n functions are linearly dependent in an interval if their Wronskian in that interval is zero for all x. Otherwise, they are linearly independent.

Superposition Principle If a function is a solution of a linear homogeneous differential equation, a constant multiple of it is also a solution. If two functions are solutions of a linear, homogeneous differential equation, a linear combination of them is also a solution of that differential equation. This is known as the *superposition principle*. The superposition principle is applicable to linear homogeneous equations only. It is not applicable to nonhomogeneous equations even if they are linear.

Fundamental Solution Set The Wronskian of two solution functions of a second-order linear homogeneous equation with continuous coefficients is either always zero, or never zero. This is known as *Abel's identity*. A second-order, linear, homogeneous equation whose coefficients are continuous on an interval always possesses two solutions: y_1 and y_2. These are linearly independent in that interval. Furthermore, any other solution of this differential equation in that interval can be expressed uniquely as a linear combination of these two solutions as

$$y = C_1 y_1 + C_2 y_2 \tag{3-16}$$

which called *the general solution*, since it contains all the solutions of the differential equation in the specified interval. Any set of two linearly independent solutions of a linear homogeneous equation on an interval is called a *fundamental set of solutions*. A differential equation may have several sets of fundamental solutions, and any of these sets can be used to construct the general solution.

Reduction of Order Method When one fundamental solution of a second-order linear homogeneous equation with continuous coefficients is known, another one can be determined by the method of *reduction of order* from

$$v = \int \left[\frac{e^{\int P(x)dx}}{y_1^2} \right] dx$$

where y_1 is a known nonzero solution. Then the second solution is $y_2 = vy_1$.

TABLE 3–6

Differential equation: $ay'' + by' + cy = 0$
Characteristic equation: $am^2 + bm + c = 0$
Characteristic roots: $m_{1,2} = \dfrac{-b \pm \sqrt{b^2 - 4ac}}{2a}$

Nature of m_1 and m_2	The General Solution
Case 1: Real and Unequal ($m_1 \neq m_2$) $b^2 - 4ac > 0$	$y = C_1 e^{m_1 x} + C_2 e^{m_2 x}$
Case 2: Real and Equal ($m_1 = m_2 = m$) $b^2 - 4ac = 0$	$y = C_1 e^{mx} + C_2 x e^{mx}$
Case 3: Complex Conjugates ($m_{1,2} = \alpha + i\beta$) $b^2 - 4ac < 0$	$y = e^{\alpha x}(C_1 \cos \beta x + C_2 \sin \beta x)$

General Solution of A Second-Order Linear Homogeneous Equation A second-order, linear, homogeneous equation with constant coefficients always possesses two linearly independent solutions y_1 and y_2 that are valid on any interval, and its general solution is expressed as $y = C_1 y_1 + C_2 y_2$ where C_1 and C_2 are arbitrary constants. The general solution of a second-order, linear, homogeneous equation for different cases is summarized in Table 3–6.

General Solution of A Second-Order Linear, Nonhomogeneous Equation The general solution of linear, nonhomogeneous equation is obtained by combining the general solution of the related homogeneous equation, called the *homogeneous solution* or the *complementary solution* y_h, with a function that satisfies the given nonhomogeneous equation, called a *particular solution* y_p as

$$y = y_h + y_p = C_1 y_1 + C_2 y_2 + y_p \qquad (3\text{--}52)$$

where y_1 and y_2 are a fundamental set of solutions of the related homogeneous equation, and C_1 and C_2 are arbitrary constants.

The nonhomogeneous term $R(x)$ often involves several terms, and in such cases, it is much easier to find a particular solution corresponding to each nonhomogeneous term and then to add them up according to the *superposition principle*.

There are two ways to determine the particular solution y_p of nonhomogeneous equations: the method of undetermined coefficients and the method of variation of parameters.

Method of Undetermined Coefficients The method of *undetermined coefficients* is based on making an educated guess for the general form of the particular solution y_p, which involves some unknown constant coefficients, and then determining these coefficients by requiring the guessed solution to satisfy the nonhomogeneous differential equation. The basic requirement on the nonhomogeneous term $R(x)$ is for it to have only a finite number of linearly independent derivatives. Thus, the general form of a nonhomogenous term suitable for the method of undetermined coefficients is $e^{kx} P_n(x) \sin \alpha x$ or $e^{kx} P_n(x) \cos \alpha x$. Here k and α are real constants, n is a positive integer, and $P_n(x)$ is a polynomial of degree n.

If a particular solution turns out to be a homogeneous solution, it should be modified by multiplying it by the lowest power of x that will eliminate such duplication. The method of undetermined coefficients is self correcting. When too few terms are assumed for the particular solution, it results in a contradiction. When too many terms are assumed, it yields zeros for the coefficients of unnecessary terms. Getting unique values for the unknown coefficients is a sure sign that the assumed form of the particular solution is correct. Any initial or boundary conditions should be applied to the general solution of the given nonhomogeneous equation that is the sum of the homogeneous solution and the particular solution.

Method of Variation of Parameters The method of *variation of parameters* is applicable to equations with constant or variable coefficients and to nonhomogeneous terms that can be of any form. But it requires the general solution of the related homogeneous equation to be available. For second-order linear equations, the particular solution is determined from

$$y_p = u_1 y_1 + u_2 y_2 \qquad (3\text{--}62)$$

where

$$u_1 = -\int \frac{y_2 R(x)}{y_1 y_2' - y_1' y_2} dx \text{ and } u_2 = \int \frac{y_1 R(x)}{y_1 y_2' - y_1' y_2} dx \qquad (3\text{--}68)$$

Solution of The Euler Equation There is no general procedure for solving linear equations with variable coefficients, except for some certain types. One such equation is the *Euler* *equation*, which can always be converted into an equation with constant coefficients. The general term of the Euler equation is of the form $kx^m y^{(m)}$ where k is a constant and m is an integer. The second-order Euler equation is expressed as

$$x^2 y'' + bxy' + cy = r(x) \tag{3-70}$$

where b and c are constants. The Euler equation always can be transformed into an equation with constant coefficients through the transformation $x = e^t$.

It is often much easier to solve the Euler equations by taking the solution to be of the form $y = x^r$. The substitution $y = x^r$ gives the following characteristic equation. $r^2 + (b - 1)r + c = 0$ whose roots are r_1 and r_2. Then the general solution of a second-order homogeneous Euler equation in any interval not containing the origin is

$$y = C_1 |x|^{r_1} + C_2 |x|^{r_2}, \ (r_1 \neq r_2, \text{real}) \tag{3-80}$$

$$y = (C_1 + C_2 \ln|x|)|x|^r, \ (r_1 = r_2 = r, \text{real}) \tag{3-81}$$

$$y = |x|^\alpha [C_1 \cos(\beta \ln|x|) + C_2 \sin(\beta \ln|x|)],$$

$$(r_{1,2} = \alpha \pm i\beta, \text{complex}) \tag{3-82}$$

where C_1 and C_2 are constants. For $x > 0$, the absolute value sign can be dropped. The general solution of a second-order homogeneous Euler equation for $x > 0$ also can be determined from the general solution of a second-order, linear, homogeneous equation with constant coefficients that has the same characteristic equation by replacing all occurrences of x in the solution with $\ln x$.

Two important applications of second-order linear equations with constant coefficients are mechanical vibrations and electrical circuits.

Historical Notes
The following is a summary of the famous mathematicians and scientists cited in this chapter.

Niels Henrik Abel (1802–1829) Norwegian mathematician. Besides Abel's identity (Theorem 3–3), he developed a proof of the binomial theorem for all numbers, and at age 19, invented group theory to demonstrate that there is no general alebraic solution of any polynomial equation of fifth degree or higher.

Augustin-Louis Cauchy (1789–1857) Prolific French mathematician who, among other contributions, initiated rigorous formulation and proofs of the theorems of infinitesimal calculus. The Cauchy probability distribution, the Cauchy sequence, and other mathematical concepts are named for him.

Jean-Baptiste le Rond d'Alembert (1717–1783) French mathematician and physicist. He developed a method for solving the wave equation, which is a partial differential equation that describes vibrations (waves) in a string and other objects. He also developed d'Alembert's principle, which is an alternative statement of the classical laws of motion.

Robert Hooke (1635–1703) English scientist and architect. Although perhaps best known for his law of elasticity (Hooke's law), at age thirty he published the first scientific best seller, *Micrographia*, which described his observations with a microscope and generated public interest in the then new science of microscopy. He proposed the biological term *cell*.

Gustav Robert Kirchhoff (1824–1887) German physicist. He contributed to the fundamental understanding of electrical circuits with his voltage and current laws. He also contributed to spectroscopy and suggested the term *black body radiation*.

Joseph-Louis Lagrange (1736–1813) Born in Turin, Piedmont but worked in Prussia and France. He developed the method of variation of parameters for solving differential equations. His treatise on analytical mechanics (1788) was a major contribution to the development of mathematical physics in the nineteenth century. Among other contributions, he developed the method of Lagrange multipliers used in the calculus of variations, and Lagrange's equations, which are an alternative to Newton's laws in formulating the equations of motion.

Józef Maria Hoene-Wroński (1776–1853) Polish mathematician and philosopher. The importance of his determinant, the Wronskian, was discovered only after his death.

PROBLEMS

3–1 Introduction to Second-Order Linear Equations

3–51C How do you decide whether a given differential equation is linear or nonlinear?

3–52C When dealing with second- or higher-order linear equations, why do we distinguish between constant versus variable coefficients?

3–53C What do you look for when deciding if a given equation is in the standard form?

3–54C Under what conditions is a linear initial-value problem guaranteed to have a unique solution in a specified interval?

3–55C For what kind of initial-value problems is the solution $y = 0$ the only solution?

Determine if the following second-order differential equations are (1) *linear or nonlinear,* (2) *homogeneous or nonhomogeneous, and* (3) *with constant or variable coefficients.*

3–56 (a) $y'' + 2y^2y' + 2y = xe^{-3x}$

(b) $y'' + 5y' - ky = 0$

(c) $y'' - 3y' + xy = 0$

(d) $y'' + y' = x^2 \cos x$

3–57 (a) $y'' - 5y' + \cos y = x + 1$ (b) $y'' = 0$

(c) $y'' + 2x^2y' + 5y = 0$ (d) $y'' + e^xy = \dfrac{1}{x}$

3–58 (a) $y'' + e^y y' - 2y = 6$

(b) $y'' - 2y' + y = x^3 \cos 2x$

(c) $y'' - 5x^2 y' = 0$

(d) $y'' - y = 0$

3–59 (a) $y'' + \dfrac{1}{y} = 1$

(b) $y'' + 8y' - e^{\ln y} = 0$

(c) $y'' - \sin 2xy' + y = 0$

(d) $y'' + y = 7$

Determine the interval in which the initial-value problems below are guaranteed to have a unique solution.

3–60 (a) $y'' = 0$, $y(0) = 0$, and $y'(0) = -4$

(b) $(x - 1)^2 y'' + 2xy' - y = e^{-x}$, $y(-2) = 3$, and $y'(-2) = -7$

3–61 (a) $y'' + xy' - 3y = x^2 e^{3x}$, $y(-1) = 1$, and $y'(-1) = 4$

(b) $(x - 2)y'' + 6xy = 2$, $y(0) = -2$, and $y'(0) = 0$

3–62 (a) $x(x - 3)y'' + xy' - 2(x - 3)y = -3x^2$, $y(1) = 2$, and $y'(1) = -5$

(b) $y'' - 5y = \ln x$, $y(5) = 3$, and $y'(5) = 1$

3–63 (a) $y'' + 4y = e^{2x} \cos x$, $y(0) = 0$, and $y'(0) = -1$

(b) $(x^2 - 4)y'' - 3xy' - 2y = 0$, $y(1) = 0$, and $y'(1) = 7$

The general solution of a second-order, linear, homogeneous equation involves a family of functions with two arbitrary constants C_1 and C_2. Solving a differential equation is equivalent to finding this family of functions, which may not be easy to do. The reverse problem of finding the differential equation whose solution is known is much easier since it involves differentiation instead of integration.

By differentiating the following functions twice and eliminating the constants C_1 and C_2, determine the second-order differential equation satisfied by the given family of functions.

3–64 (a) $y = C_1 \sinh 2x + C_2 \cosh 2x$

(b) $y = C_1 e^{2x} + C_2 x e^{2x}$

3–65 (a) $y = C_1 e^{-x} \sin 3x + C_2 e^{-x} \cos 3x$

(b) $y = C_1 \dfrac{\sin x}{\sqrt{x}} + C_2 \dfrac{\cos x}{\sqrt{x}}$

3–66 (a) $y = \dfrac{C_1}{x} + C_2 \dfrac{\ln x}{x}$

(b) $y = C_1 x^2 + C_2 x$

3–67 (a) $y = \dfrac{C_1}{x} + C_2 x^4$

(b) $y = C_1 \sin 2x + C_2 \cos 2x$

3–2 Linear Independence and The Wronskian Functions

3–68C If two functions y_1 and y_2 are linearly dependent in an interval, does y_1 have to be a constant multiple of y_2 for all x in that interval?

3–69C Is $y = 3x$ a linear combination of $y_1 = x$ and $y_1 = x^2$?

3–70C If three functions are linearly dependent in an interval, does one of them have to be a constant multiple of one of the other two in that interval?

3–71C Consider five functions whose Wronskian is zero for some x and nonzero for other x values. Are these five functions linearly dependent or independent?

Determine if the following pairs of functions y_1 and y_2 are linearly dependent or independent (1) *by inspection and* (2) *by determining their Wronskian.*

3–72 (a) $y_1 = x + 1$ and $y_2 = x^2 - 1$

(b) $y_1 = \sin \alpha + \cos \beta$ and $y_2 = \sin \alpha + \sin \beta$

3–73 (a) $y_1 = e^x + e^{-x}$ and $y_2 = \cosh x$

(b) $y_1 = x^3$ and $y_2 = -x^3$

3–74 (a) $y_1 = x^2$ and $y_2 = 2$

(b) $y_1 = xe^x$ and $y_2 = e^x$

3–75 (a) $y_1 = e^x - e^{-x}$ and $y_2 = \cosh x$

(b) $y_1 = x$ and $y_2 = 1/x$

3–76 (a) $y_1 = |x|$ and $y_2 = x$

(b) $y_1 = e^{-2x}$ and $y_2 = e^{2x}$

3–77 (a) $y_1 = e^x \sin 2x$ and $y_2 = e^x \cos 2x$

(b) $y_1 = x^3$ and $y_2 = x^3 - 1$

3–78 (a) $y_1 = |x| + 2$ and $y_2 = x + 2$

(b) $y_1 = \sin^2 x + \cos^2 x$ and $y_2 = -5$

3–79 (a) $y_1 = e^{-2\ln x}$ and $y_2 = 5/x^2$

(b) $y_1 = \sin(\alpha + \beta)$ and $y_2 = \sin\alpha + \sin\beta$

3–80 Consider three functions y_1, y_2, and y_3. Show that if the pairs y_1, y_2 and y_2, y_3 are linearly independent so is the pair y_1, y_3.

Determine if the following functions are linearly dependent or independent by determining their Wronskian.

3–81 $y_1 = e^x + e^{-x}$, $y_2 = 5$, and $y_3 = \cosh x$

3–82 $y_1 = x^2$, $y_2 = 5$, and $y_3 = x^2 - 1$

3–83 $y_1 = e^x - e^{-x}$, $y_2 = e^{2x}$, and $y_3 = \cosh x$

3–84 $y_1 = |x|$, $y_2 = x$, and $y_3 = 1$

3–85 $y_1 = e^x\sin 2x$, $y_2 = e^x\cos 2x$ and $y_3 = e^x$

3–86 $y_1 = x^3$, $y_2 = x^3 - 2$, and $y_3 = 1$

3–87 $y_1 = e^{-2\ln x}$, $y_2 = x^2$, and $y_3 = 5/x^2$

3–88 $y_1 = e^x$, $y_2 = xe^x$, and $y_3 = x^2e^x$

3–89 $y_1 = 2x$, $y_2 = e^{2x}$, and $y_3 = e^{-2x}$

3–3 Theory of Homogeneous Equations

3–90C If the functions y_1 and y_2 are two solutions of a second-order, linear, homogeneous equation with continuous coefficients, can the Wronskian of y_1 and y_2 be zero for some x and nonzero for other x values?

3–91C How many different solutions can a second-order, linear, homogeneous equation with continuous coefficients can have? How many of these solutions can be linearly independent?

3–92C What is the fundamental set of solutions of second-order, linear, homogeneous equation? How is it used to construct the general solution?

For each of the following second-order differential equations, let y_1 be a solution of the equation. Determine by inspection if ky_1, where k is a constant, is also a solution of that equation.

3–93C (a) $y'' - 2y' - 3y = 0$

(b) $y'' = e^{2x}$

(c) $y'' - y^2 = 0$

(d) $x^2y'' + (x - 1)y = 1$

3–94 (a) $y'' + x^2y = x + 1$

(b) $y'' + 3(x^2 + 1)y' - 7y = 0$

(c) $y'' - 2yy' - 3y = 0$

(d) $x^2y'' - 5y = 0$

3–95 (a) $y'' + 3xy' - 2y^2 = 0$

(b) $y'' - (2x + 1)y = x + 1$

(c) $x^2y'' + xy' + 3y = 0$

(d) $y'' - 2y' + 5y = 0$

3–96 (a) $y'' + x^2y = x - 2$

(b) $y'' + y' + y = 0$

(c) $y'' + \dfrac{1}{x - 1}y' - 8y = 0$

(d) $y'' - y^3 = 0$

For each of the following second-order differential equations, let y_1 and y_2 be solutions of the equation. Determine by inspection if $y_1 + y_2$ is also a solution of that equation.

3–97 (a) $y'' + 3y' - y = 0$

(b) $y'' - y' = e^{2x}$

(c) $y'' + 5y^2 = 0$

(d) $x^2y'' + xy = -3$

3–98 (a) $y'' - x(x + 1)y = e^x$

(b) $y'' - 2y' + 3e^xy = 0$

(c) $y'' - 3y^2y' = 0$

(d) $x^2y'' + 2y' = 0$

3–99 (a) $y'' - 2y' + 3x^xy^2 = 0$

(b) $y'' - x(x^2 - 1)y' - 2y = 0$

(c) $x^2y'' - 4y = 0$

(d) $y'' + y' - e^y = 0$

3–100 (a) $y'' + y = x$

(b) $y'' - (\sin x)y' = x^2e^{-2x}$

(c) $x^2y'' + xy' - 2y = 0$

(d) $y'' + \sin y = 0$

Consider the following second-order, linear, homogeneous equations and two of their solutions y_1 and y_2 for $x > 0$. Identify the pair of solutions whose Wronskian $W(y_1, y_2)$ is never zero for $x > 0$ by inspection. Verify your findings by actually calculating $W(y_1, y_2)$ for each case.

3–101 (a) $x^2y'' + 5xy' - 3y = 0$, $y_1 = x^{1/3}$, and $y_2 = 2/x$

(b) $x^2y'' + 5xy' - 3y = 0$, $y_1 = 1/x$, and $y_2 = -1/x$

(c) $x^2y'' + 5xy' - 3y = 0$, $y_1 = 3x^{1/3}$, and $y_2 = 1/x^{-1/3}$

3–102 (a) $x^2y'' - 2xy' - 4y = 0$, $y_1 = -1/x$, and $y_2 = x^4$

(b) $x^2y'' - 2xy' - 4y = 0$, $y_1 = e^{-\ln x}$, and $y_2 = 3/x$

(c) $x^2y'' - 2xy' - 4y = 0$, $y_1 = 2x^4$, and $y_2 = -4e^{4\ln x}$

3–103 (a) $y'' + y = 0$, $y_1 = \sin x$, and $y_2 = \cos x$

(b) $y'' + y = 0$, $y_1 = -3\sin x$, and $y_2 = \dfrac{\sin 2x}{\cos x}$

(c) $y'' + y = 0$, $y_1 = \dfrac{\sin x}{\tan x}$, and $y_2 = 2\cos x$

3–104 (a) $x^2y'' + 5xy' + 4y = 0$, $y_1 = \dfrac{1}{x^2}$, and $y_2 = \dfrac{\ln x}{x^2}$

(b) $x^2y'' + 5xy' + 4y = 0$, $y_1 = \dfrac{1}{x^2}$, and $y_2 = -2x^{-2}$

(c) $x^2y'' + 5xy' + 4y = 0$, $y_1 = \dfrac{5\ln x}{x^2}$, and $y_2 = \dfrac{\ln x^3}{x^2}$

Consider the following second-order, linear, homogeneous equations and two of their solutions y_1 and y_2 in $x > 0$. Determine if y_1 and y_2 form a fundamental set of solutions. If they do, develop a relation for $y(x)$ that contains all solutions of the differential equation.

3–105 (a) $x^2y'' + 3xy' + y = 0$, $y_2 = \dfrac{1}{x}$, and $y_2 = \dfrac{\ln x}{x}$

(b) $x^2y'' + 3xy' + y = 0$, $y_1 = \dfrac{2}{x}$, and $y_2 = \ln xe^{-\ln x}$

(c) $x^2y'' + 3xy' + y = 0$, $y_1 = -\dfrac{1}{x}$, and $y_2 = \dfrac{3}{x}$

3–106 (a) $y'' - 4y' + 4y = 0$, $y_1 = e^{2x}$, and $y_2 = xe^{2x}$

(b) $y'' - 4y' + 4y = 0$, $y_1 = 3e^{2x}$, and $y_2 = xe^{-\ln x}e^{2x}$

(c) $y'' - 4y' + 4y = 0$, $y_1 = 2xe^{2x}$, and $y_2 = 3xe^{2x}$

3–107 (a) $y'' - 2y' + 3y = 0$, $y_1 = e^x \sin \sqrt{2}x$, and $y_2 = e^x \cos \sqrt{2}x$

(b) $y'' - 2y' + 3y = 0$, $y_1 = e^x \sin \sqrt{2}x$, and $y_2 = e^{x-1} \cos \sqrt{2}x$

(c) $y'' - 2y' + 3y = 0$, $y_1 = e^x \cos \sqrt{2}x$, and $y_2 = 3e^x\left(\sin \sqrt{2}x + \cos \sqrt{2}x\right)$

3–108 (a) $y'' - 9y = 0$, $y_1 = e^{3x}$, and $y_2 = e^{-3x}$

(b) $y'' - 9y = 0$, $y_1 = e^{-3x}$, and $y_2 = e^{5-3x}$

(c) $y'' - 9y = 0$, $y_1 = \sinh 3x$, and $y_2 = \sinh 3x + e^{-3x}$

3–4 Reduction of Order

3–109C Is the method of reduction of order applicable to linear but nonhomogeneous equations?

Using the one solution given, determine the second linearly independent solution of the following second-order, linear, homogeneous equations by the method of reduction of order.

3–110 $y'' + 4y = 0$, $y_1 = \cos 2x$

3–111 $y'' + 2y' + y = 0$, $y_1 = e^{-x}$

3–112 $y'' - 4y' + 4y = 0$, $y_1 = e^{2x}$

3–113 $y'' - 4y = 0$, $y_1 = e^{2x}$

3–114 $y'' + y = 0$, $y_1 = \cos x$

3–115 $y'' + 9y = 0$, $y_1 = \sin 3x$

3–116 $x^2y'' + xy' + \left(x^2 - \dfrac{1}{4}\right)y = 0$, $y_1 = \dfrac{\cos x}{\sqrt{x}}$

3–117 $x^2y'' + 3xy' + y = 0$, $y_1 = \dfrac{1}{x}$

3–118 $x^2y'' + xy' = 0$, $y_1 = 1$

3–119 $y'' - \dfrac{2x}{x-1}y' - 4y = 0$, $y_1 = x$

3–120 $x^2y'' + 5xy' + 4y = 0$, $y_1 = \dfrac{1}{x^2}$

3–121 $x^2y'' + 5xy' - 3y = 0$, $y_1 = x^{1/3}$

3–5 Homogeneous Equations with Constant Coefficients

3–122C Do you think there exists a second-order, linear, homogeneous equation with constant coefficients that is satisfied by the functions e^{2x}, e^{-3x}, and $5e^{2x} - 8e^{-3x}$?

3–123C Do you think there exists a second-order, linear, homogeneous equation with constant coefficients that is satisfied by the functions x, $x + 1$ and x^2?

3–124C Do you think there exists a second-order, linear, homogeneous equation with constant coefficients that is satisfied by the function $\sin x$, $\cos x$ and $\tan x$?

3–125C What is the rationale for assuming the solutions of second-order, linear, homogeneous equation with constant coefficients to be of the form e^{mx} where m is a constant?

3–126C Explain the physical significance of the characteristic equation and its roots for second-order, linear, homogeneous equation with constant coefficients.

3–127C When the roots of the characteristic equation corresponding to a second-order, linear, homogeneous equation with constant coefficients are equal, we took the second linearly independent solution to be xe^{mx}, and it worked. Do you think functions of a different form such as x^2e^{mx} or e^{mx}/x could also be taken as the second linearly independent solution?

3–128C Consider the family of curves $f(x) = C_1y_1 + C_2y_2$ where C_1 and C_2 are arbitrary constants, and y_1 and y_2 are the fundamental solutions of a second-order, linear, homogeneous equation with constant coefficients. Can any two of these curves have the same slope at their point of intersection?

Determine the general solution of the following second-order, linear, homogeneous equations with constant coefficients.

3–129 (a) $y'' + \lambda^2y = 0$

(b) $y'' - 4y' + 4y = 0$

(c) $y'' - \lambda^2y = 0$

3–130 (a) $y'' + 5y' + 4y = 0$

(b) $y'' + 6y' + 9y = 0$

(c) $y'' + y' + 3y = 0$

3–131 (a) $y'' - 6y' + 9y = 0$

(b) $y'' + 3y' + 4y = 0$

(c) $y'' - 6y' - 4y = 0$

3–132 (a) $y'' + 10y' + 25y = 0$

(b) $y'' + 5y' + 25y = 0$

(c) $y'' + 10y' - 25y = 0$

Determine the specific solution of the following initial-value problems.

3–133 $y'' - 4y = 0$, $y(0) = 0$, and $y'(0) = 1$

3–134 $y'' + 3y' - 4y = 0$, $y(1) = 2$, and $y'(1) = -3$

3–135 $2y'' + y' - y = 0$, $y(0) = -5$, and $y'(0) = 6$

3–136 $y'' - 6y' + 9y = 0$, $y(-2) = 1$, and $y'(-2) = 0$

3–137 $y'' + 4y' + 20y = 0$, $y(\pi/2) = 0$, and $y'(\pi/2) = 2$

Determine the specific solution of the following boundary-value problems.

3–138 $y'' + 2y' + y = 0$, $y(0) = 0$, and $y(2) = 6$

3–139 $y'' - 3y' - 4y = 0$, $y(1) = 1$, and $y'(4) = 0$

3–140 $y'' - 9y = 0$, $y(0) = 6$, and $y(10) = 0$

3–141 Consider a pin fin of diameter $D = 3$ cm, length $L = 15$ cm, and thermal conductivity $k = 237$ W/m·°C. The base of the fin is maintained at 100°C, and the entire fin is dissipating heat to the surrounding air at a rate of 340 W. The heat-transfer coefficient between the fin and the air at 0°C is $h = 25$ W/m²·°C. Noting that Fourier's law of heat conduction at the fin base can be expressed as

$$Q_{\text{base}} = -k\left(\frac{\pi D^2}{4}\right) T'(L)$$

determine the temperature distribution along the fin.

3–142 Determine the temperature at the middle of the fin discussed in Problem 3–141, and the slope of the temperature profile at the tip of the fin.

3–143 Consider a pin fin of diameter $D = 0.4$ cm, length $L = 40$ cm, and thermal conductivity $k = 220$ W/m·°C. The base of the fin is maintained at 200°C, and heat loss from the fin tip is assumed to be negligible. The heat transfer coefficient between the fin and the air is $h = 35$ W/m²·°C.

Noting that Fourier's law of heat conduction at the fin base can be expressed as

$$Q_{\text{base}} = -k\left(\frac{\pi D^2}{4}\right) T'(L)$$

determine the temperature distribution along the fin.

3–6 Theory of Nonhomogeneous Equations

3–144C Can a function that appears in the homogeneous solution be a particular solution? Explain.

3–145C Can a nonhomogeneous equation have more than one particular solution? If yes, does that mean that the general solution of a nonhomogeneous equation is not unique?

3–146C How can you tell if a particular solution is in its simplest form?

Determine the general solutions of the following second-order, linear, nonhomogeneous equations with constant coefficients

using the given particular solution, and express them in the simplest form.

3–147 (a) $y'' + y = 2e^x$, $y_p = e^x$

(b) $y'' + y = 2e^x$, $y_p = e^x - 5 \sin x$

3–148 (a) $y'' - y' = x - 3$, $y_p = -\frac{1}{2}x^2 + 2x$

(b) $y'' - y' = x - 3$, $y_p = -\frac{1}{2}x^2 + 2x - 34$

3–149 (a) $y'' + 4y' + 4y = 2e^{-2x}$, $y_p = x^2 e^{-2x}$

(b) $y'' + 4y' + 4y = 2e^{-2x}$, $y_p = x(1 + x)e^{-2x}$

3–150 (a) $y'' + 2y' + 3y = 6$, $y_p = 2$

(b) $y'' + 2y' + 3y = 6$, $y_p = 2 + e^{-x} \sin \sqrt{2}x$

3–151 (a) $y'' = x^2 - 1$, $y_p = \frac{1}{12}x^4 - \frac{1}{2}x^2$

(b) $y'' = x^2 - 1$, $y_p = \frac{1}{12}x^4 - \frac{1}{2}x^2 + 3x - 5$

3–152 If $y_{p1} = -1/3$ is a particular solution of $y'' - 9y = 3$ and $y_{p2} = -x/9$ is a particular solution of $y'' - 9y = x$, determine the general solution of $y'' - 9y = 3 + x$.

3–153 If $y_{p1} = 2x^2 + x$ is a particular solution of $y'' + 4y = 8x^2 + 4x + 4 + 10e^x$ and $y_{p2} = 2e^x$ is a particular solution of $y'' + 4y = 10e^x$, determine the general solution of $y'' + 4y = 8x^2 + 4x + 10e^x$.

3–154 If $y_{p1} = -\frac{1}{3}x + 1$ is a particular solution of $y'' + 6y' + 9y = 7 - 3x - 2e^{-x}$ and $y_{p2} = -2e^{-2x}$ is a particular solution of $y'' + 6y' + 9y = -2e^{-2x}$, determine the general solution of $y'' + 6y' + 9y = 3x + 11 - 2e^{-2x}$.

3–155 If $y_{p1} = -2 \sin 2x$ is a particular solution of $y'' + y = 6 \sin 2x$ and $y_{p2} = 2$ is a particular solution of $y'' + y = 2$, determine the general solution of $y'' + y = 6 \sin 2x + 2$.

3–7 Nonhomogeneous Equations: The Method of Undetermined Coefficients

3–156C Under what conditions is the general form of a particular solution y_p corresponding to a nonhomogeneous term $R(x)$ of the form $AxR(x)$, where A is a constant?

3–157C Under what conditions is the general form of a particular solution y_p corresponding to a nonhomogeneous term $R(x)$ of the form $Ax^2R(x)$, where A is a constant?

3–158C Under what conditions is the general form of a particular solution y_p corresponding to a nonhomogeneous term $R(x) = \sin x$ of the form $A \sin x$, where A is a constant?

3–159C Why is the general form of a particular solution y_p corresponding to a nonhomogeneous term x^5 taken as a fifth-degree polynomial instead of just Ax^5 where A is a constant?

Using the method of undetermined coefficients, determine the general solution of the following second-order, linear, nonhomogeneous equations.

3–160 (a) $y'' + 9y = 2\sin x$
(b) $y'' + 9y = 2x\cos x$
(c) $y'' + 9y = -3x\cos 3x$
(d) $y'' + 9y = xe^x \sin 2x - 5\sin 2x + 3\cos 2x$

3–161 (a) $y'' - 4y' + 4y = -2e^{3x}$
(b) $y'' - 4y' + 4y = 2e^{2x+3}$
(c) $y'' - 4y' + 4y = 5xe^{2x}$
(d) $y'' - 4y' + 4y = e^x \cos 2x$

3–162 (a) $y'' - 2y' + 2y = x^2 + 1$
(b) $y'' - 2y' + 2y = \sin x + \cos 2x$
(c) $y'' - 2y' + 2y = e^x \sin x$
(d) $y'' - 2y' + 2y = x^3 e^x$

3–163 (a) $y'' - 3y' = x - 2$
(b) $y'' - 3y' = (x - 1)e^x$
(c) $y'' - 3y' = x^2 - 1$
(d) $y'' - 3y' = xe^x \sin 2x$

3–164 (a) $y'' - 6y' + 10y = 20$
(b) $y'' - 6y' + 10y = x^2 e^x$
(c) $y'' - 6y' + 10y = e^{3x} \cos x$
(d) $y'' - 6y' + 10y = x^2 \sin 2x + \cos 2x$

3–165 (a) $y'' + y = 2\sin x - 3\cos x$
(b) $y'' + y = x^2 + 5 - e^x$
(c) $y'' + y = (x^2 - 1)e^x$
(d) $y'' + y = e^{2x} \sin 3x$

3–166 (a) $y'' = 5$ (b) $y'' = -3x^2 e^x$
(c) $y'' = 2x^2 - 3$ (d) $y'' = 8\cos 2x$

Determine the specific solution of the following initial-value problems. Use the method of undetermined coefficients to find the particular solution.

3–167 $y'' - 2y' + 2y = x^3 - 5$, $y(0) = 6$, and $y'(0) = 0$

3–168 $y'' - 3y' = x + 3 - 2e^{2x}$, $y(0) = 0$, and $y'(0) = 0$

3–169 $y'' - y = 4e^x + x\cos x$, $y(0) = 1$, and $y'(0) = -2$

3–170 $y'' + 4y = 3\sin 2x$, $y(\pi) = 0$, and $y'(\pi) = 1$

3–8 Nonhomogeneous Equations: The Method of Variation Of Parameters

3–160C Can we apply the method of variation of parameters by using any two homogeneous solution functions in Equation 3–62 instead of using the two fundamental solutions?

Using the method of variation of parameters, determine the particular solution of the following second-order, linear, nonhomogeneous equations. Check the result in part (a) using the method of undetermined coefficients.

3–171 (a) $y'' - 4y = xe^{2x}$ (b) $y'' - 4y = x - x^2$

3–172 (a) $y'' + 9y = \cos 2x$ (b) $y'' + 9y = \dfrac{1}{\cos 3x}$

3–173 (a) $y'' - 4y' + 5y = e^{2x} \cos 3x$
(b) $y'' - 4y' + 5y = e^{2x} \tan x$

3–174 (a) $y'' + y' = x^3 - 1$ (b) $y'' + y' = \dfrac{2}{x} - \dfrac{2}{x^a}$

3–175 (a) $y'' - 4y' = x + 5$
(b) $y'' - 4y' = \dfrac{2x - 3}{(x - 2)^a}$

3–176 (a) $y'' = x^2 e^x$ (b) $y'' = \dfrac{1}{x^a}$

3–177 (a) $y'' - 2y' + y = e^{2x} + 8$
(b) $y'' - 2y' + y = \dfrac{6e^x}{x^a}$

3–9 The Euler Equation

3–178C Why is the solution of Euler equation not valid at $x = 0$?

3–179C Describe two systematic ways of solving the Euler equation. Which approach is more practical?

Determine the general solution of the second-order Euler equations, and specify the interval in which the solution is valid.

3–180 (a) $x^2 y'' + xy' = 0$ (b) $x^2 y'' + xy' = \ln x$

3–181 (a) $x^2 y'' + 3xy' - 2y = 0$
(b) $(x - 1)^2 y'' + 3(x - 1)y' - 2y = 6$

3–182 (a) $x^2 y'' + xy' - 2y = 0$
(b) $(x + 2)^2 y'' + (x + 2)y' - 2y = x - 2$

3–183 (a) $2x^2 y'' + 6xy' + 2y = 0$
(b) $2x^2 y'' + 6xy' + 2y = 4x^2$

3–184 (a) $x^2 y'' - y = 0$ (b) $x^2 y'' - y = (x^2 + 1)\sin x$

3–185 (a) $-2x^2 y'' + 6xy' - 12y = 0$
(b) $-2x^2 y'' + 6xy' - 12y = x - 1$

3–186 (a) $x^2 y'' + 5xy' + 4y = 0$
(b) $x^2 y'' + 5xy' + 4y = xe^x$

3–10 Application of Second-Order Linear Equations with Constant Coefficients

3–10–1 Mechanical Vibrations

3–187C Write the differential equation that governs the motion of a *horizontal* spring-mass-damper system, and explain the physical significance of each term. Also explain when each term will drop out of the equation. How would you choose the location $x = 0$ in this case?

3–188C How does undamped motion differ from damped one? How do free vibrations differ from forced vibrations?

3–189C When do forced vibrations without damping result in beats? When do they result in resonance?

3–190C Describe overdamped, critically damped, and underdamped motion.

3–191C How does underdamped motion differ from simple harmonic motion?

3–192C For a fixed damping, which system is more susceptible to vibrations with a large amplitude: a system with a small or large natural frequency?

3–193 A $m = 0.5$ kg mass is suspended by a spring that stretched 0.2 cm under the influence of the weight of this mass. The mass is now pulled down and released. At time $t = 0$, the mass is observed to pass through its static equilibrium position with a velocity of 10 m/s. Neglecting any friction, determine the natural frequency, period, and the amplitude of the resulting motion.

3–194 For the identity $A \cos(\omega t - \phi_1) = B \sin(\omega t - \phi_2)$ to hold, determine what B and ϕ_2 must be in terms of A and ϕ_1.

3–195 A $m = 1$ kg mass hangs on a spring that is stretched 1 cm under the influence of the weight of this mass. A periodic external force of $F(t) = 200 \cos \omega t$ is now applied on the mass that was initially in static equilibrium. Neglecting any friction, obtain a relation for the displacement of the mass as a function of time, $x(t)$. Also, determine the value of ω that will cause resonance to occur.

3–196 Consider a mass of m suspended by a spring that has a spring constant of k. A periodic external force of $F(t) = F_0 \cos \omega t + F_1$ is now applied on the mass that was initially in static equilibrium. Neglecting any friction, obtain a relation for the displacement of the mass as a function of time, $x(t)$. Also, determine the value of ω that will cause resonance to occur.

3–197 Consider a mass of m suspended by a spring that has a spring constant k. A periodic external force of $F(t) = F_0 \sin \omega t$ is now applied to the mass, which was initially in static equilibrium. Use the values $\omega = 20$, $\omega_0 = 30$, $m = 1$, and $F_0 = 100$. Neglecting any friction, obtain a relation for the velocity of the mass as a function of time, $v(t)$. Also determine the maximum value of the velocity v_{max} and the time difference between the occurence of two maximum velocities.

3–198 A $m = 5$ kg mass hangs on a spring that is stretched 2 cm under the influence of the weight of this mass. The mass is attached to a damper with a damping constant of $c = 200$ N·s/m. The mass is now pulled down 1 cm and then released with zero initial velocity. Determine how far the mass will be from its static equilibrium position at time $t = 0.05$ s.

3–199 A $m = 0.5$ kg mass hangs on a spring that is stretched 0.2 cm under the influence of the weight of this mass. The mass is attached to a damper with a damping constant of $c = 2000$ N·s/m. The mass is now pulled down 2 cm and then released with a downward velocity of 20 m/s. Determine if the mass will ever pass through its static equilibrium position. If it does, determine the time and the velocity of the mass at that instant.

3–200 A $m = 4$ kg mass hangs on a spring that is stretched 3 cm under the influence of the weight of this mass. The mass is attached to a damper with a damping constant of $c = 5000$ N·s/m. The mass is now pulled down 5 cm and then released with an upward velocity of 30 m/s. Determine the maximum displacement of the mass from its static equilibrium position during the entire motion.

3–201 A $m = 5$ kg mass hangs on a spring that is stretched 2 cm under the influence of the weight of this mass. The mass is attached to a damper with a damping constant of $c = 200$ N·s/m. A periodic external force of $F(t) = 200 \cos \omega t$ is now applied on the mass which was initially in static equilibrium. Obtain a relation for the displacement of the mass as a function of time, $x(t)$. Also, determine the value of ω that will cause the amplitude of the motion to be a maximum.

3–202 In Figure P3–202 the mass m is in equilibrium at the point E (where $x = 0$). Neglecting any friction on the inclined surface, derive the differential equation of motion.

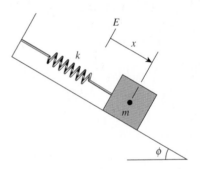

FIGURE P3–202

3–203 In Figure P3–203, the left-hand end of spring k_1, whose displacement is y, is driven by the rotating cam. The displacement $y(t)$ is a given function of time. When $x = y = 0$, both springs are at their free length. Neglect any friction on the surface and derive the differential equation of motion in terms of x.

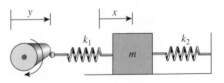

FIGURE P3–203

3–204 An object of mass m and weight W drops from a height h on to a platform that is supported by a spring, as shown in Figure P3–204.

(a) Determine the expression for the velocity v of the mass when it strikes the platform.

(b) Assuming that the mass does not rebound from the platform and that the spring is at its free length when $x = 0$, determine the maximum compression in the spring in terms of the parameters m, g, k, and h.

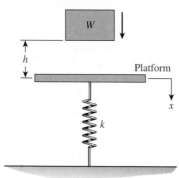

FIGURE P3–204

3–205 A box car of mass 18 000 kg hits a shock absorber at the end of the track while moving at 1.3 m/s, as shown in Figure P3–205. The stiffness of the absorber is $k = 73\,000$ N/m and the damping constant is $c = 88\,000$ N · s/m. Let x be the displacement of the boxcar after it contacts the shock absorber (positive to the right). Note that $x = 0$ corresponds to the spring being at its free length. Assume that the boxcar does not rebound from the absorber. Determine the maximum spring compression.

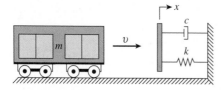

FIGURE P3–205

3–206 The rod Figure P3–206 has a mass moment of inertia I_O about the point O. The applied force f pushes the rod tip to the right. Assume that the resulting displacement x is small enough so that its motion is essentially horizontal. When $x = 0$, the springs are at their free length. Derive the differential equation of motion in terms of x.

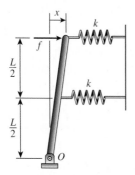

FIGURE P3–206

3–207 In Figure P3–207 note that, for small values of ϕ, the motion of the attachment point of the spring and damper is approximately horizontal; its displacement is $L_1\phi$, and its velocity is $L_1\dot{\phi}$. By summing moments about point O, derive the differential equation of motion in terms of ϕ.

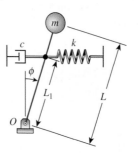

FIGURE P3–207

3–208 A motor is supported by a cantilever beam of length L, as shown in part (a) of Figure P3–208. It can be shown from mechanics of materials that the end of the beam will deflect a vertical distance x when a force f is applied to the end, such that

$$x = \frac{4L^3}{Ewh^3}f$$

where E is Young's modulus of elasticity for the beam material, w is the beam width, and h is the beam thickness. Thus, the beam acts like a spring with a spring constant k given by

$$k = \frac{f}{x} = \frac{Ewh^3}{4L^3}$$

and the beam-motor system may be represented as the equivalent system shown in part (b) of the figure, assuming that the beam mass is small compared to the motor mass. Assume that the motor can be considered to be a point mass at the end of the beam. How much will the system's natural frequency ω_o decrease if the beam length L is doubled?

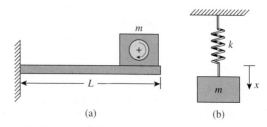

(a)   (b)

FIGURE P3–208

3–209 A motor of mass m is supported by a cantilever beam of length L, as shown in part (a) of Figure P3–209. The beam acts like a spring of stiffness k, that resists the vertical displacement of the motor. The beam-motor system may be represented as the equivalent system shown in part (b) of the figure, assuming that the beam mass is small compared to the motor mass. Assume that the motor can be considered to be a point mass at the end of the beam. If the motor is unbalanced, it will exert a vertical force f on the end of the beam of the form $f(t) = b\omega^2 \sin \omega t$, where ω is the motor speed in circular units and b is a constant that depends on the amount of unbalance. Thus, the equation of motion is $m\ddot{x} + kx = b\omega^2 \sin \omega t$. Assuming the initial conditions are zero, derive the expression for the solution $x(t)$.

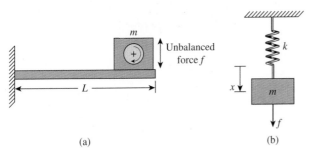

(a)

(b)

FIGURE P3–209

3–210 A dimensionless ratio, called the **damping ratio**, is frequently used in the analysis of second-order, linear, differential equations. The damping ratio of the equation $m\ddot{x} + c\dot{x} + kx = F_{\text{ext}}$ is defined as

$$\zeta = \frac{c}{2\sqrt{mk}}$$

where ζ is the Greek letter zeta.

(a) Express the characteristic equation and the characteristic roots of the above differential equation in terms of only two dimensionless parameters ζ and the natural frequency $\omega_0 = \sqrt{k/m}$, assuming that the characteristic roots are complex.

(b) Show that the roots are complex if $\zeta < 1$, real and equal if $\zeta = 1$, and real and unequal if $\zeta > 1$.

3–211 Express the homogeneous solution of the differential equation $m\ddot{x} + c\dot{x} + kx = F_{\text{ext}}$ in terms of the two dimensionless parameters, the damping ratio $\zeta = c/2\sqrt{mk}$ and the natural frequency $\omega_0 = \sqrt{k/m}$ and the two initial conditions x_0 and v_0.

3–210 In the following equation, the right-hand side is a constant b: $m\ddot{x} + c\dot{x} + kx = b$. For the case where the initial conditions are zero, express the solution of this differential equation in terms of b and the two dimensionless parameters, the damping ratio ζ and the natural frequency $\omega_0 = \sqrt{k/m}$.

3–212 In the following equation, the right-hand side is sinusoidal with an amplitude A and circular frequency ω: $m\ddot{x} + c\dot{x} + kx = A \sin \omega t$.

For the case where the initial conditions are zero, express the *steady-state* solution of this differential equation in terms of A, the ratio $\Delta = A/k$, and the two dimensionless parameters, the damping ratio $\zeta = c/2\sqrt{mk}$ and the **frequency ratio** r, defined as $r = \omega/\omega_0$, where $\omega_0 = \sqrt{k/m}$.

3–10–2   Electrical Circuits

3–213C How is the resonance frequency of a series RLC circuit calculated?

3–214 Consider a series RLC circuit with negligible resistance ($R = 0$) and no imposed voltage. The initial charge in the capacitor is Q_0, and the initial current is zero. By solving the governing differential equation and letting $\omega_0^2 = 1/LC$, obtain relations for the charge in the capacitor $Q(t)$ and the current in the circuit $I(t)$ as functions of time.

3–215 Consider a series RLC circuit with negligible resistance ($R = 0$) and a periodically changing applied voltage of the form $E(t) = E_0 \cos \omega t$. By solving the governing differential equation and letting $\omega_0^2 = 1/LC$, obtain a relation for the charge in the capacitor $Q(t)$ as a function of time. Investigate what happens to the charge in the capacitor as $t \to \infty$ for the special case of $\omega = \omega_0$.

3–216 Consider a series RLC circuit with no imposed voltage. By solving the governing differential equation, obtain relations for the charge in the capacitor $Q(t)$ as a function of time corresponding to the three cases of $R^2 - 4L/C$ being positive, negative, and zero.

3–217 Extend Problem 3–216 to solve for the current in the circuit $I(t)$.

3–11   Computer Problems

Use a computer to determine the general solution of the following second-order, linear, homogeneous equations with constant coefficients.

3–218 $y'' + 5y' + 4y = 0$

3–219 $y'' + 6y' + 9y = 0$

3–220 $y'' + 6y' + 13y = 0$

3–221 $y'' + 4y = 0$

Use a computer to determine the specific solution of the following initial-value problems.

3–222 $y'' + 4y = 0$, $y(\pi) = 0$, and $y'(\pi) = 1$

3–223 $2y'' + y' - y = 0$, $y(0) = -5$, and $y'(0) = 6$

3–224 $y'' - 6y' + 9y = 0$, $y(-2) = 1$, and $y'(-2) = 0$

3–225 $y'' + 4y' + 20y = 0$, $y(\pi/2) = 0$, and $y'(\pi/2) = 2$

Use a computer to determine the specific solution of the following boundary-value problems.

3–226 $y'' - y = 0$, $y(0) = 100$, and $y(5) = 0$

3–227 $y'' + 2y' + y = 0$, $y(0) = 0$, and $y(2) = 6$

Use a computer to determine the general solution of the following second-order, linear, nonhomogeneous equations.

3–228 $y'' - 4y = 4e^{3x}$

3–229 $y'' - 4y = -3x^2 e^{3x}$

3–230 $y'' + 9y = 2 \sin x$

3–231 $y'' + 9y = 2x\cos x$

3–232 $y'' - 4y' + 4y = 5xe^{2x}$

3–233 $y'' - 3y' = xe^x \sin 2x$

3–234 $y'' - 2y' + 2y = \sin x + \cos 2x$

Use a computer to determine the specific solution of the following initial-value problems.

3–235 $y'' + 16y = \sin 2x - 3\cos 2x$, $y(\pi/2) = 1$, and $y'(\pi/2) = 0$

3–236 $y'' - 2y' + 2y = x^3 - 5$, $y(0) = 6$, and $y'(0) = 0$

Use a computer to determine the general solution of the following second-order Euler equations.

3–237 $y'' + y = 0$

3–238 $x^2 y'' + 3xy' - 2y = 0$

Review Problems

3–239 Show that if n functions are linearly dependent in an interval, then at least one of those functions can be expressed as a linear combination of the remaining functions in that interval.

3–240 Show that if one function in a set of n functions can be expressed as a linear combination of the remaining functions in an interval, then these n functions are linearly dependent in that interval.

Determine the general solution of the following linear equations for $x > 0$. Also, determine the arbitrary constants in the general solution when initial conditions are specified.

3–241 $y'' - 16y = 0$

3–242 $y'' - y' = xe^{2x}\cos x$

3–243 $y'' + y' = 0$

3–244 $y'' = \dfrac{1}{x} + x\sin x$

3–245 $2x^2 y'' + 5xy' = x^2 - 1$

3–246 $y'' + y' + y = x^3 - 2$

3–247 $y'' + 2y' = 0$

3–248 $x^2 y'' + xy' = \dfrac{1}{x} - 2$

3–249 $y'' - 6y' + 9y = 0$

3–250 $y'' - 3y' + 3y = 0$

3–251 $y'' + y' = 0$, $y(0) = 0$, $y'(0) = 1$

3–252 $y'' + y = 4e^{3x} - x$

3–253 $y'' - 4y' = x + 1$

3–254 $y'' - 4y' + 3y = -e^{2x} - 1$

3–255 $y'' - y' = x^2 + 1 - e^x \sin x$

3–256 $y'' + y = x\sin x$

3–257 $y'' - 9y' + 8y = x^2 e^{3x}$

3–258 $y'' + 16y = xe^{2x} - 1$

3–259 $y'' - y = 0$, $y(0) = 1$, $y'(0) = 0$

3–260 $y'' + 9y' = x^2 \cos 2x$

3–261 $x^2 y'' - 3xy' + y = 0$

3–262 $y' + y = 1$, $y(\pi) = y'(\pi) = 0$

3–263 $x^2 y'' + 4y = 0$

3–264 $x^2 y'' + y = 0$

3–265 $y'' + 4y' + 1 = x^2 - 1$, $y(0) = 0$, $y'(0) = 1$

3–266 A mass of m which is suspended by a spring with $k = 2000$ N/m is initially at static equilibrium. A periodic external force of $F(t) = 50\cos 10t$ is now applied, and the mass is observed to resonate under the influence of this force. Determine the value of the mass m.

3–267 A $m = 2$ kg mass hangs on a spring that is stretched 0.2 cm under the influence of the weight of this mass. The mass is attached to a damper with a damping constant of $c = 500$ N·s/m. A periodic external force of $F(t) = 50\sin 10t$ is now applied to the mass, which was initially in static equilibrium. Obtain a relation for the velocity of the mass as a function of time, $v(t)$. Also, determine the maximum value of the velocity $v_{\max}$ and the time difference between the two maximum velocities.

3–268 Consider a pendulum of length L and mass m balanced *vertically*, that is initially displaced from its *vertical* static equilibrium position by an angle θ_0. Neglecting any resistance and noting that $\sin\theta \cong \theta$ for small angles, derive the differential equation that governs the swinging motion of the pendulum, and solve it for the angular displacement θ, assuming that the pendulum is released with zero velocity.

3–269 Consider a series *RLC* circuit with inductance $L = 0.1$ H, resistance $R = 2 \times 10^{-5}$ F and an applied voltage of $E(t) = 5\cos 60t$. Determine the steady-state current in the circuit, $I(t)$. Also, determine the value of the capacitance C that will maximize this current, holding R and L constant.

3–270 Consider a series *RLC* circuit with resistance $R = 10^3 \ \Omega$, inductance $L = 0.5$ H, capacitance $C = 5 \times 10^{-6}$ F; and no applied voltage. The initial charge in the capacitor is $Q_0 = 8 \times 10^{-4}$ C. The on/off switch is turned on at time $t = 0$, and current starts to flow through the circuit. Determine how long it will take for the maximum current in the circuit to decrease by half.

HIGHER-ORDER LINEAR DIFFERENTIAL EQUATIONS

4

The natures of first- and second-order, linear differential equations are quite different; therefore, there is little in common between their solution procedures. For example, first-order, linear equations always can be solved in a straightforward manner, assuming the integrations they involve can be performed. However, for second-order, linear equations, this is the case only for equations with constant coefficients. Even then, the solution can be rather involved if the equation is nonhomogeneous.

It is very fortunate that there is a close parallel between second- and higher-order linear equations. The theory of higher-order, linear equations is analogous to that of second-order, linear equations. In this chapter, we basically extend the theory associated with second-order, linear equations to higher-order, linear equations. The proofs presented in Chapter 3 for the second-order case can be extended to higher-order equations by generalizing the procedure. Therefore, the proofs for the higher-order case will not be presented here.

The second- and higher-order, linear, differential equations are like a high-rise building with identical floor plans. If one masters the second floor thoroughly, he or she should have no problem getting around in the upper floors.

The section titles in this chapter are essentially identical to those in the previous chapter. Any section in this chapter is a natural extension of the corresponding section in the previous chapter, and these two chapters can be covered in parallel if desired. When studying a section in this chapter, it is advisable first to review the corresponding section in the previous chapter.

■ ■ ■ ■ ■ ■ ■

Objectives

When you have finished this chapter, you should be able to:

1. extend the methods of Chapter 3 for second-order equations to higher-order equations,

2. use the Wronskian to determine if solutions are linearly independent,

3. identify a fundamental set of solutions of a linear homogeneous higher-order equation,

4. use the reduction of order method to reduce the equation order when one fundamental solution is known,

5. obtain the general solution of a higher-order linear homogeneous equation with constant coefficients,

6. obtain the particular solution of a higher-order linear nonhomogeneous equation with constant coefficients using the method of undetermined coefficients and the method of variation of parameters,

7. solve the nth-order Euler equation, and

8. use a computer package to obtain the closed-form solution of higher-order equations.

4–1 ▪ INTRODUCTION TO HIGHER-ORDER LINEAR EQUATIONS

The terminology of higher-order equations is the same as that of second-order equations. For example, we mentioned several times that a differential equation is **linear** if it does not involve any powers, products, or other nonlinear functions of the dependent variable y or its derivatives. The nth-order, linear differential equation can be written in the most general form as

$$y^{(n)} + P_1(x)y^{(n-1)} + \cdots + P_{n-1}(x)y' + P_n(x)y = R(x) \qquad (4\text{–}1)$$

where $P_1, P_2, \ldots, P_n$ are given functions that may only depend on the independent variable x. Note that a linear equation does not involve any nonlinear functions of the dependent variable (such as yy', y'^2, or e^y), but it may involve nonlinear functions of the independent variable (such as x^2, e^x, or $x^2 \sin x$).

The function $R(x)$ represents all of the terms that do not involve the dependent variable y or any of its derivatives and is called the **nonhomogeneous term**. A linear differential equation is said to be **nonhomogeneous** when $R(x) \neq 0$ and **homogeneous** when $R(x) = 0$. Thus, the nth-order linear homogeneous equation can be written in the most general form as

$$y^{(n)} + P_1(x)y^{(n-1)} + \cdots + P_{n-1}(x)y' + P_n(x)y = 0 \qquad (4\text{–}2)$$

When solving a linear, nonhomogeneous equation, it is often convenient to consider the homogeneous part of the equation separately. This is done by simply setting $R(x)$ equal to zero. The resulting equation is called the **related homogeneous equation** or **complementary equation** of the given differential equation. Therefore, Equation 4–2 is the related homogeneous equation of Equation 4–1.

Linear differential equations are also classified with respect to the coefficients of the dependent variable y and its derivatives. If these coefficients are simply some constants, the equation is said to have **constant coefficients**. If one or more coefficients depend on the independent variable x, then the equation is said to have **variable coefficients**. Therefore, the nth-order, linear differential equation with constant coefficients can be expressed in the most general form as

$$y^{(n)} + a_1 y^{(n-1)} + \cdots + a_{n-1}y' + a_n y = R(x) \qquad (4\text{–}3)$$

where $a_1, a_2, \ldots, a_n$ are real constants (such as 3, -4.2, 3/5, or even zero). Note that the nonhomogeneous term $R(x)$ still can be a function of x.

In Chapter 3, we stated that a second-order, linear differential equation has a unique solution in an interval $x_1 < x < x_2$ in which the coefficients of the equation are continuous, provided that two initial conditions are specified at a point x_0, where x_0 is any point in this interval. The *existence and uniqueness* of the solution of an nth-order, linear initial-value problem is expressed in a similar manner by Theorem 4–1.

This theorem guarantees that an nth-order, linear differential equation has a solution that is unique in an interval, provided that the coefficients are continuous in that interval and the n initial conditions are specified at a point in that interval (Figure 4–1). Note that the differential equation must be in the *standard form* (the leading coefficient being one) for this theorem

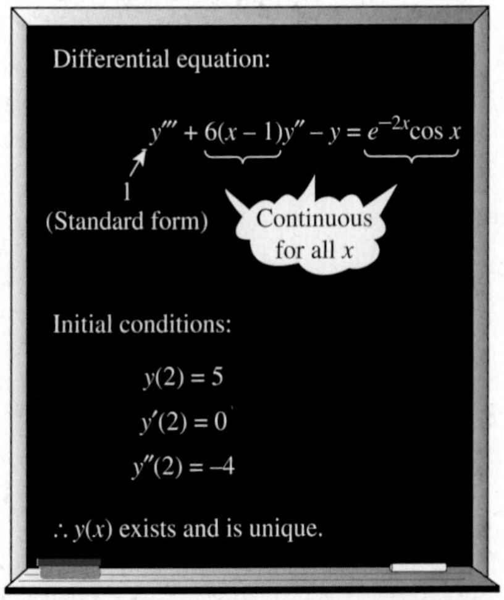

Differential equation:

$$y''' + 6(x-1)y'' - y = e^{-2x}\cos x$$

(Standard form) — Continuous for all x

Initial conditions:

$$y(2) = 5$$
$$y'(2) = 0$$
$$y''(2) = -4$$

$\therefore y(x)$ exists and is unique.

FIGURE 4–1

A third-order, linear, initial-value problem that satisfies the conditions of Theorem 4–1 in the interval $-\infty < x < \infty$ and thus has a unique solution in that interval.

THEOREM 4–1 Existence and Uniqueness

If the functions $P_1(x), P_2(x), \ldots, P_n(x)$ and $R(x)$ are continuous on an interval $x_1 < x < x_2$ and x_0 is any point in this interval, then the differential equation

$$y^{(n)} + P_1(x)y^{(n-1)} + \cdots + P_{n-1}(x)y' + P_n(x)y = R(x)$$

has a unique (one and only one) solution on this interval that satisfies the n initial conditions:

$$y(x_0) = y_0, y'(x_0) = y_0, \ldots, y^{(n-1)}(x_0) = y_0^{(n-1)}$$

where $y_0, y_0', \ldots, y_0^{(n-1)}$ are specified real constants.

to be applicable. Theorem 4–1 reassures us that once we find a function that satisfies both the differential equation and the initial conditions, the search for a solution is over. There is no other function that will satisfy the differential equation and the specified initial conditions.

EXAMPLE 4–1 Existence of a Solution

Show that the following initial-value problem has a unique solution, and determine the interval of that solution.

$$y''' - \frac{2x}{x^2 - 4}y'' + 3y = \frac{x + 1}{x^2} + e^x$$

$$y(1) = 0, y'(1) = -3, \quad \text{and} \quad y''(1) = 5$$

SOLUTION This is an *initial-value problem* since all of the conditions are specified at the same x value at $x_0 = 1$. The differential equation is *third order* since the highest derivative is y'''; *linear* since it involves no powers, products, or nonlinear functions of y and its derivatives; *nonhomogeneous* since the terms on the right side do not involve the dependent variable y or any of its derivatives; and is in the *standard form* since the coefficient of y''' is 1. Comparing it with Equation 4–1, we see that

$$P_1(x) = -\frac{2x}{x^2 - 4}, P_2(x) = 0, P_3(x) = 3, \quad \text{and} \quad R(x) = \frac{x + 1}{x^2} + e^x$$

The functions $P_2(x)$ and $P_3(x)$ are continuous, but the function $P_1(x)$ is discontinuous at $x = 2$ and $x = -2$, since it becomes infinity at these points. The function $R(x)$ is discontinuous at $x = 0$. Therefore, the existence and uniqueness theorem applies to this equation in any interval that does not contain the points $x = -2, 0$ and 2. Specifically, $R(x)$ is continuous in the intervals $-\infty < x < -2$, $-2 < x < 0$, $0 < x < 2$, and $2 < x < \infty$.

Considering that the initial conditions are specified at $x_0 = 1$, Theorem 4–1 guarantees that this initial-value problem has a unique solution in the interval $0 < x < 2$.

As a direct consequence of this theorem, we can say that the trivial solution $y = 0$ is the only solution of an *n*th-order, linear, homogeneous, differential equation with continuous coefficients whose initial conditions are all equal to zero.

For linear homogeneous equations of any order with constant coefficients, $R(x) = 0$ and the coefficients are naturally continuous in $-\infty < x < \infty$; thus, the solutions of such equations are valid for all x. We do not need to specify an interval in this case. More generally, if the coefficients and the nonhomogeneous terms are continuous over the entire x axis, then x_0 can be any point, and the solution is valid over the entire x axis.

Note that Theorem 4–1 guarantees the existence and uniqueness of the solution of an nth-order initial-value problem under specified conditions. No such guarantees exist for boundary-value problems. A boundary-value problem will have a unique solution only when the specified boundary conditions yield unique values for the arbitrary constants in the general solution.

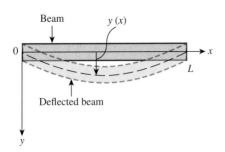

Beam $y(x)$

Deflected beam

FIGURE 4–2

The deflection of a beam under the influence of its own weight (Example 4–2).

EXAMPLE 4–2   The Deflection of a Beam Under its Own Weight

The deflection of a homogeneous horizontal beam with a uniform cross section and length L is governed by the fourth-order differential equation

$$y^{(iv)} = \frac{\rho g}{EI} \qquad (4\text{–}4)$$

where ρ is the mass density of the beam, g is the gravitational acceleration, E is the Young's modulus of the beam material (which is a measure of its stiffness), and I is the moment of inertia of the cross section of the beam about a horizontal line passing through its center ($I = \pi r^4/4$ for circular cross sections of radius r).

The function y denotes the deflection of the beam at any location x, as shown in Figure 4–2. Determine (a) the general solution and (b) the specific solution for the case of fixed-fixed beam (both ends of the beam are firmly attached).

SOLUTION This is a simple fourth-order, linear, nonhomogeneous differential equation with constant coefficients. The coefficients and the nonhomogeneous term are continuous functions over the entire x axis. Therefore, at least mathematically, the solution is not limited to any finite interval. However, the differential equation describes the deflection of the beam in $0 \leq x \leq L$. Thus, we will limit the solution into this interval only on physical grounds.

(a) The differential equation is in a readily integrable form. Therefore, we obtain the general solution by four simple successive integrations:

$$y''' = \frac{\rho g}{EI} x + C_1$$

$$y'' = \frac{\rho g}{2EI} x^2 + C_1 x + C_2$$

$$y' = \frac{\rho g}{6EI} x^3 + \frac{1}{2} C_1 x^2 + C_2 x + C_3$$

$$y = \frac{\rho g}{24EI} x^4 + \frac{1}{6} C_1 x^3 + \frac{1}{2} C_2 x^2 + C_3 x + C_4 \qquad (4\text{–}5)$$

where C_1, C_2, C_3, and C_4 are arbitrary constants. Note that the general solution of this second-order differential equation involves four arbitrary constants as expected.

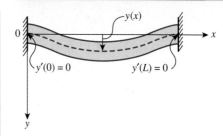

(b) A well-supported beam cannot deflect at the point of support. Therefore, its deflection at both ends must be zero, so $y(0) = y(L) = 0$. Furthermore, the ends of a tightly connected beam cannot rotate freely, and thus, the deflection curve must be horizontal (zero slope) at the ends, as shown in Figure 4–3. Therefore, the other two boundary conditions must be $y'(0) = y'(L) = 0$. Applying these four boundary conditions gives four equations for the determination of the four arbitrary constants C_1, C_2, C_3, and C_4. Solving for them and substituting their values into the general solution, the specific solution of this boundary-value problem is determined to be

$$y = \frac{\rho g L^4}{24EI}\left[\left(\frac{x}{L}\right)^4 - 2\left(\frac{x}{L}\right)^3 + \left(\frac{x}{L}\right)^2\right] \tag{4-6}$$

This solution involves no arbitrary constants. Thus, it is a unique solution of the given boundary-value problem.

FIGURE 4–3

When the ends of the beam in Example 4–2 are firmly attached, the deflection curve will have to be horizontal at both ends.

Section Review

Problems Denoted with a C are Conceptual Problems for Discussion

4–1C At least how many different arbitrary constants does the solution of an nth-order, linear differential equation involve?

4–2C How many initial conditions must be specified to guarantee the existence of a unique solution for an nth-order, linear differential equation in a specified interval?

4–3 Determine if the following differential equations are (1) linear or nonlinear, (2) homogeneous or nonhomogeneous, and (3) whether they have constant or variable coefficients.

(a) $y''' + 3yy' = 6x^2$ (b) $y''' - 3y = e^{2x}$

(c) $x^3 y''' + xy' + y = 0$ (d) $y''' + xy' - 3y = \sin 2x$

(*Answers:* (a) nonlinear, nonhomogeneous, constant coefficients (b) linear, nonhomogeneous, constant coefficients (c) linear, homogeneous, variable coefficients (d) linear, nonhomogeneous, variable coefficients)

4–4 Determine the interval in which the following initial-value problems are guaranteed to have a unique solution.

(a) $y''' + 3y' = \cos x$, $y(\pi) = 0$, and $y'(\pi) = -2$

(b) $x^3 y''' + 2xy' - y = e^x$, $y(0) = 2$, and $y'(0) = 5$

(*Answers:* (a) $-\infty < x < +\infty$ (b) Considering that the initial conditions are specified at $x = 0$, Theorem 4–1 guarantees nothing.)

4–2 ▪ THEORY OF HOMOGENEOUS EQUATIONS

The superposition principle discussed in Chapter 3 in connection with second-order, linear, homogeneous equations is applicable to linear, homogeneous equations of any order, as expressed in Theorem 4–2.

Therefore, if a function is a solution of a linear, homogeneous differential equation, a constant multiple of it is also a solution. If two functions are

THEOREM 4–2   Superposition Principle

If $y_1, y_2, \ldots, y_n$ are n solutions of the linear homogeneous equation

$$y^{(n)} + P_1(x)y^{(n-1)} + \cdots + P_{n-1}(x)y' + P_n(x)y = 0$$

then the linear combination

$$y = C_1 y_1 + C_2 y_2 + \cdots + C_n y_n \tag{4–7}$$

where $C_1, C_2, \ldots, C_n$ are arbitrary constants, is also a solution of this equation.

solutions of a linear, homogeneous differential equation, their sum is also a solution of that differential equation.

Note that the superposition principle is applicable to linear, homogeneous differential equations only. It is not applicable to nonlinear equations or to nonhomogeneous equations (even when they are linear).

Abel's identity is also applicable to higher-order linear, homogeneous equations and can be generalized as follows in Theorem 4–3.

THEOREM 4–3   Abel's Identity

Consider the nth-order linear, homogeneous differential equation

$$y^{(n)} - P_1(x)y^{(n-1)} + \cdots + P_{n-1}(x)y' + P_n(x)y = 0,$$

whose coefficients $P_1, P_2, \ldots, P_n$ are continuous in an interval $x_1 < x < x_2$, and let $y_1, y_2, \ldots, y_n$ be any n solutions of it in this interval. Then the Wronskian of $y_1, y_2, \ldots, y_n$ is either always zero (indicating these n solutions are linearly dependent) or never zero (indicating these n solutions are linearly independent).

The Wronskian of any n solutions of an nth-order, linear homogeneous equation with continuous coefficients can be determined within a constant factor K from *Abel's formula*, which is expressed as

$$W(y_1, y_2, \ldots, y_n) = Ke^{-\int P_1(x)dx} \tag{4–8}$$

Theorem 4–3 indicates that $W(y_1, y_2, \ldots, y_n)$ cannot be zero for some x and nonzero for other x values in an interval in which the coefficients P_1, $P_2, \ldots, P_n$ of a linear, homogeneous differential equation are continuous. Therefore, when determining the linear independence of n solutions in a specified interval, it is sufficient to evaluate $W(y_1, y_2, \ldots, y_n)$ at any convenient point x_0 in that interval, since if $W(y_1, y_2, \ldots, y_n) = 0$ at x_0, it is zero for all x. Likewise, if $W(y_1, y_2, \ldots, y_n) \neq 0$ at x_0, then it is nonzero for all x and $y_1, y_2, \ldots, y_n$ are linearly independent in that interval.

The fundamental theorem of the general, linear, homogenous equation can be expressed as given in Theorem 4–4.

THEOREM 4–4   General Solution of Homogeneous Equations

The nth-order linear, homogeneous differential equation

$$y^{(n)} + P_1(x)y^{(n-1)} + \cdots + P_{n-1}(x)y' + P_n(x)y = 0$$

whose coefficients $P_1, P_2, \ldots, P_n$ are continuous in an interval $x_1 < x < x_2$, always possesses n solutions $y_1, y_2, \ldots, y_n$ that are linearly independent in that interval. Furthermore, any solution of this differential equation in that interval can be expressed uniquely as a linear combination of these n solutions as

$$y = C_1 y_1 + C_2 y_2 + \cdots + C_n y_n \qquad \text{(4–9)}$$

*which is the **general solution** of this differential equation.*

Therefore, the solution $y = C_1 y_1 + C_2 y_2 + \cdots + C_n y_n$ contains *all* of the solutions of the differential equation in the specified interval. Any solution of the equation can be obtained from the general solution by assigning suitable values to the constants $C_1, C_2, \ldots, C_n$. Thus, the solution set $y_1, y_2, \ldots, y_n$ is referred to as **a fundamental set** of solutions of the differential equation in that interval (Figure 4–4).

Theorem 4–4 ensures the existence of n linearly independent solutions. It also ensures that *only* n solutions can be linearly independent. Thus, solving an nth-order, linear, homogeneous equation is equivalent to finding its n linearly independent solutions. Then the general solution of this differential equation is obtained easily from Equation 4–9.

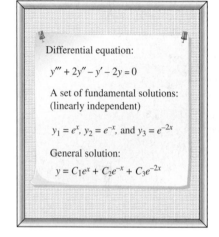

Differential equation:

$$y''' + 2y'' - y' - 2y = 0$$

A set of fundamental solutions:
(linearly independent)

$$y_1 = e^x,\ y_2 = e^{-x},\ \text{and}\ y_3 = e^{-2x}$$

General solution:

$$y = C_1 e^x + C_2 e^{-x} + C_3 e^{-2x}$$

FIGURE 4–4

A third-order linear, homogeneous equation with continuous coefficients has three linearly independent solutions. Their linear combination gives the general solution.

Section Review

4–5C For what kind of differential equation is the sum of the solutions also a solution?

4–6C Can the Wronskian of the three linearly independent solutions of a third-order linear, homogeneous equation with continuous coefficients be zero for some x and nonzero for other x values?

4–7 Consider the following linear, homogeneous equations and their solution in $x > 0$. Identify the solutions whose Wronskian is never zero for $x > 0$ by inspection. Verify your findings by calculating their Wronskian for each case.

(a) $y''' - 3y'' + 3y' = 0$, for e^x, xe^x, and $x^2 e^x$

(b) $y''' - 3y'' + 3y' = 0$, for e^x, $2e^x$, and $-3x^2 e^x$

(*Answers:* (a) $W = 2e^{3x}$, which is never zero for $x > 0$. (b) The solutions e^x, $2e^x$, and $-3x^2 e^x$ are linearly dependent since $2e^x$ is a constant multiple of e^x, so $W = 0$.)

4–8 Consider the following linear, homogeneous equations and their solution for $x > 0$. Identify the solutions whose Wronskian is never zero for $x > 0$ by inspection. Verify your findings by calculating their Wronskian for each case.

(a) $x^3 y''' + 2x^2 y'' - 2xy' = 0$, for $\dfrac{1}{x}$, x^2, and 1

(b) $x^3 y''' + 2x^2 y'' - 2xy' = 0$, for $e^{-\ln x}$, x^2, and 5

(*Answers:* (a) $W = -6/x^2$, which is never zero for $x > 0$. (b) The solutions are linearly independent, since $W = -30/x^2 \neq 0$.)

4–9   Consider the following linear, homogeneous equations and their solutions for $x > 0$. Determine if the given solutions form a fundamental set of solutions. If they do, develop a relation for y that contains all of the solutions of the differential equation.

(a) $x^3 y''' + 3x^2 y'' - 6xy' - 6y = 0$, for $\dfrac{1}{x}$, $\dfrac{1}{x^2}$, and x^3

(b) $x^3 y''' + 3x^2 y'' - 6xy' - 6y = 0$, for $\dfrac{2}{x}$, $x^4 e^{-\ln x}$, and x^3

(*Answers:* (a) $W = -\dfrac{20}{x^3}$, which is never zero for $x > 0$, and $y = \dfrac{C_1}{x} + \dfrac{C_2}{x^2} + C_3 x^3$.

(b) $W = 0$, so these solutions do not form a fundamental set for $x > 0$.)

4–3 ▪ REDUCTION OF ORDER

The method of reduction of order is applicable to linear differential equations of any order. If y_1 is a known nontrivial ($y_1 \neq 0$) solution of an nth-order linear homogeneous equation, then the substitution of $y = v y_1$ (where v is a function of the independent variable x) reduces the given equation into a linear homogeneous equation of order $n - 1$ in v'. Therefore, applying the method of reduction of order reduces an nth-order equation in y to an $(n - 1)$th-order equation in $w = v'$. We present this result in Theorem 4–5.

THEOREM 4–5   Reduction of Order

If y_1 is a nontrivial solution of the nth-order linear homogeneous equation

$$y^{(n)} + P_1(x)y^{(n-1)} + \cdots + P_{n-1}(x)y' + P_n(x)y = 0$$

then the substitution of $y = v y_1$ reduces this equation to a linear, homogeneous equation of order $n-1$ in v'.

If a solution of the $(n - 1)$th-order equation in w can be found by inspection or other means, the method of reduction of order can be applied again to obtain an $(n - 2)$th-order linear, homogeneous equation. We can continue in this manner as long as we can find solutions to the successive reduced equation. This method is also applicable to nonhomogeneous equations.

Although it is possible, at least in principle, to reduce an nth-order linear equation to a first-order one by repeated application of the method of reduction of order, it is rarely practical to do so. For equations of third or higher order, the reduced equation is at least second-order, which is usually no easier to solve than the original equation.

Equations with constant coefficients can be solved in a systematic manner without the use of the method of reduction of order. However, equations with variable coefficients must normally be solved by infinite series or numerical methods, unless they are in a special form. Reducing the order of such equations by one often does not result in any significant simplification.

Section Review

4–10 Using the one solution given, determine the other linearly independent solutions of the following linear, homogeneous equation by the method of reduction of order.

$$y''' - y' = 0, \; y_1 = e^x$$

(*Answer:* $1, e^x, e^{-x}$)

4–4 ▪ HOMOGENEOUS EQUATIONS WITH CONSTANT COEFFICIENTS

Consider the general nth-order linear, homogeneous equation with constant coefficients:

$$a_0 y^{(n)} + a_1 y^{(n-1)} + \cdots + a_{n-1} y' + a_n y = 0 \qquad \text{(4–10)}$$

where the coefficients $a_0, a_1, \ldots, a_n$ are real constants. (The nonzero leading coefficient can always be made 1 by dividing each term by a_0.)

Considering that constant coefficients are continuous functions over the interval $-\infty < x < \infty$, the solutions of such equations are valid in any interval. Thus, we do not need to specify an interval for the solution. We can summarize the key theorems in this case as

An nth*-order, linear, homogeneous equation with constant coefficients always possesses n linearly independent solutions* $y_1, y_2, \ldots, y_n$ *that are applicable to any interval, and its general solution is expressed as*

$$y = C_1 y_1 + C_2 y_2 + \cdots + C_n y_n \qquad \text{(4–11)}$$

where $C_1, C_2, \ldots, C_n$ *are arbitrary constants (Figure 4–5).*

Again, the solution functions and their derivatives must differ, at most, by a constant multiple only. Therefore, we assume the solution to be of the form e^{mx}, where m is a constant. Substituting this function into Equation 4–10 yields

$$e^{mx}(a_0 m^n + a_1 m^{n-1} + \cdots + a_{n-1} m + a_n) = 0 \qquad \text{(4–12)}$$

However, the exponential function e^{mx} cannot be zero. Then we must have

$$a_0 m^n + a_1 m^{n-1} + \cdots + a_{n-1} m + a_n = 0 \qquad \text{(4–13)}$$

This nth-order polynomial equation is called the **characteristic equation** or the *auxiliary equation,* since it yields the acceptable values of m that characterize the solution of the given differential equation. A comparison of the characteristic equation and the differential equation suggests a straightforward way of obtaining the characteristic equation: In the differential equation, replace $y^{(n)}$ by m^n, $y^{(n-1)}$ by $m^{(n-1)}$, and so on (Figure 4–6). This procedure will convert the differential equation into the characteristic equation.

You will recall from algebra that an nth-degree polynomial has n zeros. Therefore, the characteristic equation of an nth-order, linear, homogeneous equation will have n roots: $m_1, m_2, \ldots, m_n$. Corresponding to these n roots, there are n solutions:

$$y_1 = e^{m_1 x}, y_2 = e^{m_2 x}, \ldots, y_n = e^{m_n x}$$

Third order differential equation:

$$y''' + 2y'' - y' - 2y = 0$$

Linearly independent solutions:

$$y_1 = e^x, y_2 = e^{-x}, y_3 = e^{-2x}$$

General solution:

$$y = C_1 e^x + C_2 e^{-x} + C_3 e^{-2x}$$

Valid for:

$$-\infty < x < \infty$$

FIGURE 4–5

An nth-order linear homogeneous equation with constant coefficients possesses n linearly independent solutions whose linear combination gives the general solution for all x.

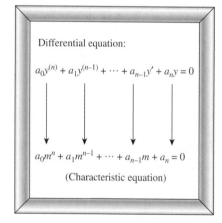

Differential equation:

$$a_0 y^{(n)} + a_1 y^{(n-1)} + \cdots + a_{n-1} y' + a_n y = 0$$

$$a_0 m^n + a_1 m^{n-1} + \cdots + a_{n-1} m + a_n = 0$$

(Characteristic equation)

FIGURE 4–6

The characteristic equation of an nth-order equation can be obtained easily by replacing $y^{(n)}$ by m^n for $n = n, n - 1, \ldots, 2, 1, 0$.

If the n roots are real and distinct, the n solutions are linearly independent, and we can readily form the general solution. Some of the roots, however, may be repeated, and some even may be complex. The solution procedure for each case closely parallels the corresponding second-order case discussed in Chapter 3. We will consider each case separately, but first, we will present some discussion on finding the roots of the characteristic equations of higher-order equations.

Finding the Roots of Polynomial Equations

Solving higher-order linear differential equations with constant coefficients requires us to find the roots of the characteristic equation. Once the roots are available, the general solution then can be constructed in a systematic manner following the procedure for the constant-coefficient, second-order case described in Section 3–5 of Chapter 3. The characteristic equation of an nth-order differential equation involves an nth-order polynomial called the **characteristic polynomial**.

For $n = 2$, both roots of the polynomial equation can be determined easily from the quadratic formula. There are similar formulas for $n = 3$ and $n = 4$, but they are not easy to use. Thus, for $n \geq 3$, the most practical thing to do is to calculate the roots with a calculator or a computer program. Most modern engineering calculators can do this, and in Section 4–9, we show how to use the popular computer packages to find the roots.

A Special Case: Real Integer Roots

When all of the roots of the characteristic equation are real integers, the characteristic equation will be of the form

$$(r - r_1)(r - r_2) \cdots (r - r_n) = r^n + a_1 r^{n-1} + \cdots + a_n \qquad \text{(4–14)}$$

where the coefficients $a_1, a_2, \ldots, a_n$ are integers. Furthermore, the constant term a_n is the product of the roots (Figure 4–7). Therefore, the roots must be the factors of a_n. This suggests that when the characteristic equation involves integer coefficients and a leading coefficient 1, we can try the factors of the constant term as possible roots as a first guess if we do not have a calculator or computer handy.

As an example, consider the third-order polynomial equation:

$$r^3 - 5r^2 - 8r + 12 = 0 \qquad \text{(4–15)}$$

which has integer coefficients and a leading coefficient of 1. The factors of the constant term 12 are $\pm 1, \pm 2, \pm 3, \pm 4, \pm 6$, and ± 12. Therefore, we can try these factors as the first guesses for the roots. We will find that all three roots of this equation are integers, and they are 1, -2, and 6.

Sometimes when a polynomial is missing some terms, it can be reduced to a lower-order polynomial. For example, the polynomial: $r^4 + 7r^2 + 10 = 0$ is missing the r^3 and r terms. So it can be solved for r^2 using the quadratic formula as follows.

$$r^2 = \frac{-7 \pm \sqrt{49 - 40}}{2} = -2, -5$$

Thus, the roots are $\pm i\sqrt{2}$ and $\pm i\sqrt{5}$.

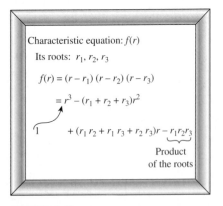

Characteristic equation: $f(r)$

Its roots: r_1, r_2, r_3

$f(r) = (r - r_1)(r - r_2)(r - r_3)$

$= r^3 - (r_1 + r_2 + r_3)r^2$

$1 \qquad + (r_1 r_2 + r_1 r_3 + r_2 r_3)r - \underbrace{r_1 r_2 r_3}_{}$

Product of the roots

FIGURE 4–7

When the leading coefficient is 1, the constant term in the characteristic equation is the product of its roots.

Constructing the General Solution

Next, we discuss how to construct the general solution of a higher-order, linear, homogeneous equation with constant coefficients, assuming the roots of its characteristic equation have already been found. Again, we consider three cases: real and distinct roots, real and repeated roots, and complex roots.

Case 1: Real and Distinct Roots

If the n roots of the characteristic equation $m_1, m_2, \ldots, m_n$ are real and different, then the n solutions of the given nth-order differential equation are

$$e^{m_1 x}, e^{m_2 x}, \ldots, e^{m_n x}$$

We can argue intuitively that no two such solutions are a constant multiple of each other (since no two roots are identical) and no solution can be expressed as a linear combination of the other solution. Therefore, these n solutions are linearly independent, and the general solution is

$$y = C_1 e^{m_1 x} + C_2 e^{m_2 x}, \ldots, C_n e^{m_n x} \qquad \text{(4–16)}$$

We can verify that these n solutions are indeed linearly independent by determining their Wronskian.

EXAMPLE 4–3   **Homogeneous Equation: Real and Distinct Roots**

Determine the general solution of the differential equation $y''' + 6y'' + 8y' - 3y = 0$.

SOLUTION This is a third-order, linear, homogeneous equation with constant coefficients, and its characteristic equation is $m^3 + 6m^2 + 8m - 3 = 0$. The leading coefficient of the characteristic equation is 1, and all other coefficients are real integers. Therefore, if we do not have a calculator or computer handy, we can try the factors of the constant term, which are ± 1 and ± 3 as possible solutions. Dividing the characteristic equation by $m + 3$ gives the quadratic equation $m^2 + 3m - 1 = 0$ whose roots are

$$m_{2,3} = \frac{-3 \pm \sqrt{13}}{2} = -1.5 \pm \sqrt{3.25}$$

All three roots are real and distinct. Therefore, the general solution of the given equation is

$$y = C_1 e^{-3x} + C_2 e^{-(1.5+\sqrt{3.25})x} + C_3 e^{-(1.5-\sqrt{3.25})x}$$

where C_1, C_2, and C_3 are arbitrary constants. Note that a third-order, linear, homogeneous equation with constant coefficients has three linearly independent solutions, and its general solution is the linear combination of them.

Case 2: Repeated Roots

When one or more roots of the characteristic equation are repeated two or more times, Equation 4–16 cannot be the general solution since it will now involve fewer than n linearly independent solutions. In Chapter 3, we have seen that if m_1 is a repeated root of the characteristic equation of a second-order differential equation, then $xe^{m_1 x}$ is a solution of the differential equation in addition to $e^{m_1 x}$. We can show using the method of reduction of order that if m_1 is a three-fold (triple) repeated root, then $x^2 e^{m_1 x}$ also would be a solution. We generalize this as

If m_1 is a k-fold repeated root of the characteristic equation, then

$$e^{m_1 x}, xe^{m_1 x}, x^2 e^{m_1 x}, \ldots, x^{k-1} e^{m_1 x} \qquad (4\text{--}17)$$

are the k linearly independent solutions corresponding to this root (Figure 4–8).

For example, the general solution of a sixth-order, linear, homogeneous equation with constant coefficients whose characteristic equation has a triple root m_1, a double root m_2, and a distinct root m_3 is

$$y = (C_1 e^{m_1 x} + C_2 xe^{m_1 x} + C_3 x^2 e^{m_1 x}) + (C_4 e^{m_2 x} + C_5 xe^{m_2 x}) + C_6 e^{m_3 x}$$
$$= (C_1 + C_2 x + C_3 x^2)e^{m_1 x} + (C_4 + C_5 x)e^{m_2 x} + C_6 e^{m_3 x} \qquad (4\text{--}18)$$

Note that the part of the general solution corresponding to a k-fold root m is obtained by multiplying e^{mx} by a polynomial of degree $(k-1)$ with arbitrary constant coefficients.

REPEATED ROOTS

If
$$m_1 = m_2 = \cdots = m_k$$
Then
$$y_1 = e^{m_1 x}$$
$$y_2 = xe^{m_1 x}$$
$$y_3 = x^2 e^{m_1 x}$$
$$\vdots$$
$$y_k = x^{k-1} e^{m_1 x}$$
and
$$y = (C_1 + C_2 x + \cdots + C_k x^{k-1})e^{m_1 x}$$

FIGURE 4–8
The k linearly independent solutions corresponding to a k-fold repeated real root of the characteristic equation.

EXAMPLE 4–4   Homogeneous Equation: Repeated Real Roots

Determine the general solution of the differential equation $y^{(iv)} + 8y''' + 18y'' + 16y' + 5y = 0$.

SOLUTION This is a fourth-order, linear, homogeneous equation with constant coefficients, and its characteristic equation is $m^4 + 8m^3 + 18m^2 + 16m + 5 = 0$. This is a fourth-degree polynomial equation; thus, it has four roots. They are determined to be -1, -1, -1, and 5. Note that -1 is a triple (three-fold) root, whereas 5 is a single root. All roots are real. Therefore, the general solution of the given equation is $y = (C_1 + C_2 x + C_3 x^2)e^{-x} + C_4 e^{5x}$, where C_1, C_2, C_3, and C_4 are arbitrary constants. Note that a fourth-order, linear, homogeneous equation with constant coefficients has four linearly independent solutions, and its general solution is the linear combination of them.

Case 3: Complex Roots

You will recall from algebra that, if a polynomial equation has real coefficients, any complex roots that it may have must occur in conjugates. That is, if $\alpha + i\beta$ is a root, so is $\alpha - i\beta$. We have seen in the previous chapter with regard to second-order equations that the general solution corresponding to a pair of conjugate roots of the characteristic equation is

$$y = e^{\alpha x}(C_1 \cos \beta x + C_2 \sin \beta x) \qquad (4\text{--}19)$$

Thus, the two linearly independent solutions corresponding to a pair of complex conjugate roots are

$$e^{\alpha x} \cos \beta x \quad \text{and} \quad e^{\alpha x} \sin \beta x$$

This is the case no matter what the order of the differential equation is. Linearly independent solutions corresponding to other pairs of complex conjugates roots are determined in the same manner.

If a complex root $\alpha + \beta i$ is repeated k times, its conjugate $\alpha - \beta i$ also must be repeated k times, assuming the coefficients of the characteristic equation are real. The procedure for repeated roots discussed earlier also applies to complex roots. Thus, the part of the general solution corresponding to a k-fold complex conjugate pair $\alpha \pm \beta i$ is

$$y = e^{\alpha x}(C_1 \cos \beta x + C_2 \sin \beta x) + xe^{\alpha x}(C_3 \cos \beta x + C_4 \sin \beta x) + \cdots + x^{k-1}e^{\alpha x}(C_{2k-1} \cos \beta x + C_{2k} \sin \beta x) \qquad \text{(4–20)}$$

where $C_1, C_2, \ldots, C_{2k}$ are arbitrary constants (Figure 4–9).

EXAMPLE 4–5   Homogeneous Equation: Repeated Complex Roots

Determine the general solution of the differential equation: $y^{(iv)} + 18y'' + 81y = 0$.

SOLUTION   This is a fourth-order linear, homogeneous equation with constant coefficients, and its characteristic equation is $m^4 + 18m^2 + 81 = (m^2 + 9)^2 = 0$ whose four roots are $-3i, -3i, 3i,$ and $3i$. We notice that the complex conjugate pair $\pm 3i$ is a two-fold root of the characteristic equation. Therefore, the general solution of the given differential equation is $y = (C_1 \cos 3x + C_2 \sin 3x) + x(C_3 \cos 3x + C_4 \sin 3x)$, where $C_1, C_2, C_3,$ and C_4 are arbitrary constants. Note that a fourth-order, linear, homogeneous equation with constant coefficients has four linearly independent solutions, and its general solution is the linear combination of them.

Often the laws of physics result in a set of coupled, multiple differential equations of first or second-order. To obtain a solution in such cases, it is sometimes easier to reduce the entire set of equations to a single, higher-order equation. Example 4–6 illustrates this method.

EXAMPLE 4–6   A Speaker Model

A speaker utilizes a magnet, a coil, and a cone to convert electrical energy into mechanical energy (sound waves) by causing the coil to move the cone. The operation of a speaker is illustrated by Figure 4–10. A stereo or radio amplifier produces a current in a coil that is attached to a diaphragm in the cone. This causes the coil and diaphragm to move relative to the permanent magnet. The motion of the diaphragm produces air-pressure waves, which are sound.

(a) Develop a model of the speaker system.
(b) Obtain the characteristic roots and the form of the homogeneous solution for the following parameter values.

$m = 0.002 \text{ kg}$ $k = 4 \times 10^5 \text{ N/m}$
$K_f = 16 \text{ N/A}$ $K_b = 13 \text{ V} \cdot \text{s/m}$
$R = 12 \text{ }\Omega$ $L = 10^{-3} \text{ H}$

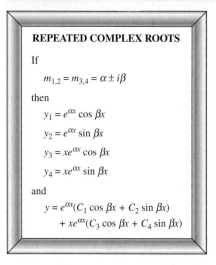

REPEATED COMPLEX ROOTS

If

$$m_{1,2} = m_{3,4} = \alpha \pm i\beta$$

then

$$y_1 = e^{\alpha x} \cos \beta x$$
$$y_2 = e^{\alpha x} \sin \beta x$$
$$y_3 = xe^{\alpha x} \cos \beta x$$
$$y_4 = xe^{\alpha x} \sin \beta x$$

and

$$y = e^{\alpha x}(C_1 \cos \beta x + C_2 \sin \beta x) + xe^{\alpha x}(C_3 \cos \beta x + C_4 \sin \beta x)$$

FIGURE 4–9

The four linearly independent solutions corresponding to a two-fold repeated pair of complex conjugate roots of the characteristic equation.

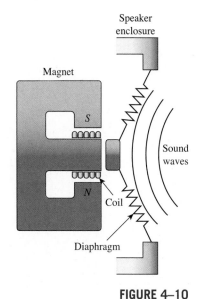

FIGURE 4–10

Diagram of a speaker.

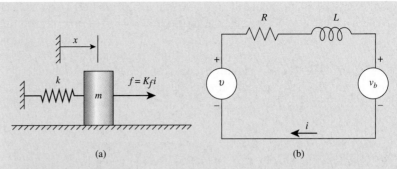

FIGURE 4–11
Models of the mechanical and electrical subsystems of a speaker.

SOLUTION (a) Figure 4–11 shows a simplified model of the mechanical subsystem. The mass m represents the combined mass of the diaphragm and the coil. The spring constant depends on the material properties of the diaphragm. The force f is the magnetic force, which is related to the coil current i by $f = nBLi = K_f i$, where n is the number of turns in the coil and B is the magnetic field strength. Here $K_f = nBL = 16$ N/A. From Newton's law

$$m\frac{d^2x}{dt^2} = -kx + K_f i \qquad (4\text{-}21)$$

Figure 4–11b shows the electrical subsystem. The coil's inductance and resistance are L and R. The coil experiences a back emf voltage v_b, because it is a current conductor moving in a magnetic field. This back emf voltage is given by $v_b = K_b dx/dt$. The voltage v is the signal from the amplifier. From Kirchhoff's voltage law, we have

$$v = L\frac{di}{dt} + Ri + K_b\frac{dx}{dt} \qquad (4\text{-}22)$$

The speaker model consists of Equations 4–21 and 4–22.

(b) These equations are not in the form that enables us to compute the characteristic roots. To do this, we must reduce the equations to a single equation. Solve Equation 4–21 for i to obtain

$$i = \frac{1}{K_f}\left(m\frac{d^2x}{dt^2} + kx \right) \qquad (4\text{-}23)$$

Then differentiate Equation 4–23, as

$$\frac{di}{dt} = \frac{1}{K_f}\left(m\frac{d^3x}{dt^3} + k\frac{dx}{dt} \right) \qquad (4\text{-}24)$$

Substitute these expressions in Equation 4–22:

$$v = L\left[\frac{1}{K_f}\left(m\frac{d^3x}{dt^3} + k\frac{dx}{dt} \right)\right] + R\left[\frac{1}{K_f}\left(m\frac{d^2x}{dt^2} + kx \right)\right] + K_b\frac{dx}{dt} \qquad (4\text{-}25)$$

Collect terms to obtain

$$mL\frac{d^3x}{dt^3} + mR\frac{d^2x}{dt^2} + (kL + K_b K_f)\frac{dx}{dt} + kRx = K_f v \qquad (4\text{-}26)$$

Thus, we have obtained a third-order equation. The characteristic equation is

$$mL\beta^3 + mR\beta^2 + (kL + K_bK_f)\beta + kR = 0$$

The model has three roots, and it is not possible to obtain a simple closed-form expression for these roots. So we must use the parameter values given in the problem. The equation becomes

$$2\beta^3 + 0.024\beta^2 + 608\beta + 4.8 \times 10^6 = 0$$

The roots are $\beta = -8715$ and $\beta = -1643 \pm 16\,513i$. These roots give a homogeneous solution of the form

$$x(t) = C_1e^{-8715t} + C_2e^{-1643t} \sin 16\,513t + C_3e^{-1643t} \cos 16\,513t$$

The term C_1e^{-8715t} will disappear first (after approximately $t = 4(1/8715) = 4.6 \times 10^{-4}$ s). The solution will oscillate with a frequency of 16 513 rad/s before disappearing after approximately $t = 4(1/1643) = 0.024$ s.

EXAMPLE 4–7   Effects of Ground Motion on a Two-Story Building

Figure 4–12 is a representation of a two-story building. The floor masses are m_1 and m_2. Each floor is supported by six columns. When the ground moves horizontally due to an earthquake, the floors also move horizontally, and the columns act like springs and resist this motion. The total horizontal stiffnesses of each set of six columns are k_1 and k_2. The horizontal ground motion is y.

(a) Develop a model of the building's response to the motion y.
(b) For the case where the masses are identical ($m_1 = m_2 = m$) and the stiffnesses are identical ($k_1 = k_2 = k$), obtain a single equation model of the building and find its homogeneous solution.

SOLUTION   (a) The floors' motion is more easily visualized by the representation shown in Figure 4–13 as two blocks sliding on a frictionless surface and driven by the motion $y(t)$. The free-body diagrams are shown in Figure 4–14.

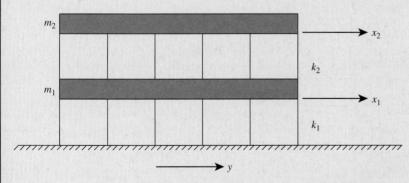

FIGURE 4–12

A two-story building. The floor masses are m_1 and m_2. The horizontal ground motion is y. The total horizontal stiffnesses of each set of six columns are k_1 and k_2.

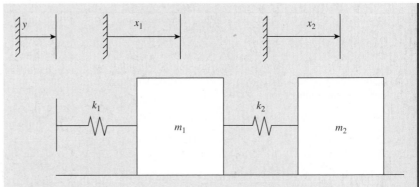

FIGURE 4–13

Model of a two-story building to analyze the effects of ground motion and column stiffness.

for the case where $y > x_1 > x_2$. From these diagrams and Newton's laws, we obtain the following equations of motion:

$$m_1 \ddot{x}_1 = -k_2(x_1 - x_2) + k_1(y - x_1)$$

$$m_2 \ddot{x}_2 = k_2(x_1 - x_2)$$

(b) For identical masses and stiffnesses, these become

$$m \ddot{x}_1 + 2kx_1 - kx_2 = ky$$

$$m \ddot{x}_2 - kx_1 + kx_2 = 0$$

Divide each equation by m and let $\alpha = k/m$. The result is

$$\ddot{x}_1 + 2\alpha x_1 - \alpha x_2 = \alpha y \qquad \text{(4–27)}$$

$$\ddot{x}_2 - \alpha x_1 + \alpha x_2 = 0 \qquad \text{(4–28)}$$

To obtain a single equation in terms of x_1, differentiate Equation 4–27 twice to obtain

$$\frac{d^4 x_1}{dt^4} + 2\alpha \frac{d^2 x_1}{dt^2} - \alpha \frac{d^2 x_2}{dt^2} = \alpha \frac{d^2 y}{dt^2}$$

Substitute for $\ddot{x}_2$ from Equation 4–28 and for x_2 from Equation 4–27 to obtain

$$\frac{d^4 x_1}{dt^4} + 3\alpha \frac{d^2 x_1}{dt^2} + \alpha^2 x_1 = \alpha^2 y + \alpha \frac{d^2 y}{dt^2} \qquad \text{(4–29)}$$

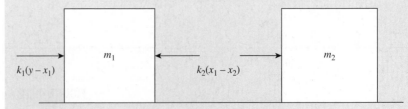

FIGURE 4–14

Free-body diagrams of the two floors.

This is the desired equation. Its characteristic equation is $\beta^4 + 3\alpha\beta^2 + \alpha^2 = 0$. Because there is no β^3 or β term, this equation is quadratic in β^2, and we may use the quadratic formula to obtain.

$$\beta^2 = \frac{-3\alpha \pm \sqrt{9\alpha^2 - 4\alpha^2}}{2} = \frac{-3 \pm \sqrt{5}}{2}\alpha = -0.3820\alpha, -2.618\alpha$$

Thus, the characteristic roots are

$$\beta = \pm i0.618\sqrt{\frac{k}{m}}, \pm i1.618\sqrt{\frac{k}{m}}$$

Because these roots are imaginary, the homogeneous solution has the form

$$x_1(t) = C_1 \sin 0.618\sqrt{\frac{k}{m}}t + C_2 \cos 0.618\sqrt{\frac{k}{m}}t$$

$$+ C_3 \sin 1.618\sqrt{\frac{k}{m}}t + C_4 \cos 1.618\sqrt{\frac{k}{m}}t$$

The solution contains oscillations with radian frequencies of $0.618\sqrt{k/m}$ and $1.618\sqrt{k/m}$. Note that we must specify four initial conditions to evaluate the solution.

Section Review

4–11C Consider a third-order linear homogeneous equation with constant coefficients. If the functions y_1, y_2, and y_3 all satisfy this equation, can we say that any one of these functions must be a linear combination of the other two?

4–12C Do you think there exists a third-order linear, homogeneous equation with constant coefficients that is satisfied by the functions e^{2x}, e^{-2x}, e^{-3x}, and e^{3x}?

4–13 Determine the general solution of the following linear homogeneous equations with constant coefficients.

(a) $y^{(iv)} - y = 0$ (b) $y''' + 3y'' + 4y' + 12y = 0$

(*Answers:* (a) $y = C_1 \sin x + C_2 \cos x + C_3 e^{-x} + C_4 e^x$ (b) $y = C_1 e^{-3x} + C_2 \sin 2x + C_3 \cos 2x$)

4–14 Determine the specific solution of the following initial-value problem.

$$y^{(iv)} - 81y = 0, y(\pi) = y'(\pi) = y''(\pi) = 0 \text{, and } y'''(\pi) = 1$$

(*Answer:* $y(x) = \frac{1}{54}\{\sinh[3(x - \pi)] + \sin 3x\}$)

4–5 · THEORY OF NONHOMOGENEOUS EQUATIONS

The general nth-order, linear, nonhomogeneous equation can be expressed as

$$y^{(n)} + P_1(x)y^{(n-1)} + \cdots + P_{n-1}(x)y' + P_n(x)y = R(x)$$

where the functions $P_1(x), P_2(x), \ldots, P_n(x)$ and $R(x)$ are assumed to be continuous on the interval of interest. Its related homogeneous equation is obtained by setting $R(x) = 0$,

$$y^n + P_1(x)y^{(n-1)} + \cdots + P_{n-1}(x)y' + P_n(x)y = 0$$

The solution of a nonhomogeneous equation is closely associated with the solution of its related homogeneous equation. The first step in solving a nonhomogeneous equation is to obtain the solution of its related homogeneous equation and express it as

$$y_h = C_1 y_1 + C_2 y_2 + \cdots + C_n y_n$$

where $y_1, y_2, \ldots, y_n$ are a fundamental set of solutions of the homogeneous equation. The function y_h represents the general solution of the related homogeneous equation and is referred to as the **homogeneous solution** or the **complementary solution**. In contrast, a function that does not involve any arbitrary constants and satisfies the entire nonhomogeneous equation is called a **particular solution**. The next step is to modify the homogeneous solution so that it satisfies the given nonhomogeneous equation. This is done in accordance with Theorem 4–6.

Nonhomogeneous equation:

$$y^{(n)} + P_1(x)y^{(n-1)} + \cdots + P_n(x)y = R(x)$$

Particular solution: y_p

Related homogeneous equation:

$$y^{(n)} + P_1(x)y^{(n-1)} + \cdots + P_n(x)y = 0$$

Homogeneous solution:

$$y_h = C_1 y_1 + C_2 y_2 + \cdots + C_n y_n$$

General solution:

$$y = C_1 y_1 + C_2 y_2 + \cdots + C_n y_n + y_p$$

FIGURE 4–15

The general solution of linear, nonhomogeneous equations is obtained by adding the homogeneous solution y_h and a particular solution y_p, which is a function that satisfies the nonhomogeneous equation.

THEOREM 4–6   General Solution of Linear Nonhomogeneous Equations

If y_p is a particular solution of the linear nonhomogeneous equation

$$y^{(n)} + P_1(x)y^{(n-1)} + \cdots + P_{n-1}(x)y' + P_n y = R(x)$$

where the functions $P_1(x), P_2(x), \ldots, P_n(x)$ and $R(x)$ are continuous in an interval $x_1 < x < x_2$ and y_h is the general solution of its related homogeneous equation, then the general solution of this nonhomogeneous equation in that interval is

$$\begin{aligned} y &= y_h + y_p \\ &= C_1 y_1 + C_2 y_2 + \cdots + C_n y_n + y_p \end{aligned} \quad \text{(4–30)}$$

where $y_1, y_2, \ldots, y_n$ are a fundamental set of solutions of the related homogeneous equation and $C_1, C_2, \ldots, C_n$ are arbitrary constants.

Therefore, once the general solution of the related homogeneous equation is available, all we need to do is determine a particular solution y_p that satisfies the given nonhomogeneous equation to construct its general solution (Figure 4–15).

The nonhomogeneous term $R(x)$ often involves several terms, and in such cases, it is much easier to find a particular solution corresponding to each nonhomogeneous term, and then to add them up. In other words, apply the superposition principle. We express this in the following theorem (Figure 4–16).

If

$$y''' - 4y = 8 \rightarrow y_{p1} = -2$$

and

$$y''' - 4y = -2x \rightarrow y_{p2} = x/2$$

Then

$$y''' - 4y = 8 - 2x \rightarrow y_p = -2 + x/2$$

FIGURE 4–16

Example of the superposition principle for particular solutions.

THEOREM 4–7   Superposition Principle for Particular Solutions

If y_{p1} is a particular solution of

$$y^{(n)} + P_1(x)y^{(n-1)} + \cdots + P_{n-1}(x)y' + P_n(x)y = R_1(x) \quad \text{(4–31)}$$

and y_{p2} is a particular solution of

$$y^{(n)} + P_1(x)y^{(n-1)} + \cdots + P_{n-1}(x)y' + P_n(x)y = R_2(x) \quad \text{(4–32)}$$

then $y_{p1} + y_{p2}$ is a particular solution of

$$y^{(n)} + P_1(x)y^{(n-1)} + \cdots + P_{n-1}(x)y' + P_n(x)y = R_1(x) + R_2(x) \quad \text{(4–33)}$$

Next we discuss the methods of undetermined coefficients and variation of parameters for the determination of the particular solution in a systematic manner.

4–6 ▪ NONHOMOGENEOUS EQUATIONS: THE METHOD OF UNDETERMINED COEFFICIENTS

The method of undetermined coefficients described in Chapter 3 for second-order, linear differential equations is also applicable to higher-order equations without any modifications. When deciding the general form of a particular solution corresponding to a nonohomogeneous term, it makes no difference whether the equation is second-order or any order. Thus, we can use Table 3–2 for the proper form of the particular solution regardless of the order of the differential equation (Figure 4–17).

Of course, all of the limitations of this method still apply. For example, the method is easy and straightforward, but it is limited to linear equations with constant coefficients whose nonhomogeneous terms involve one of the following:

1. A constant, k
2. An exponential function, e^{kx}
3. A polynomial $P_n(x)$
4. The functions $\sin \beta x$ or $\cos \beta x$
5. A finite number of their products

Also, if any term in the assumed form of the particular solution y_p is a solution of the related homogeneous equation, then the indicated form of y_p should be multiplied by the lowest integer power of the independent variable x until every term in y_p differs from every term in the homogeneous solution. If the differential equation involves variable coefficients or nonhomogeneous terms that are not suitable for the method of undetermined coefficients, then the method of variation of parameters discussed in the next section should be used.

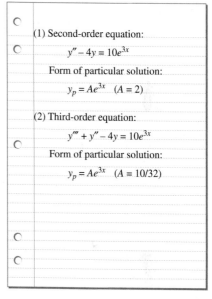

(1) Second-order equation:

$$y'' - 4y = 10e^{3x}$$

Form of particular solution:

$$y_p = Ae^{3x} \quad (A = 2)$$

(2) Third-order equation:

$$y''' + y'' - 4y = 10e^{3x}$$

Form of particular solution:

$$y_p = Ae^{3x} \quad (A = 10/32)$$

FIGURE 4–17

The general form of the particular solution does not depend on the order of the differential equation.

EXAMPLE 4–8   Particular Solutions: e^{kx}

Find a particular solution of the differential equation: $y''' + y'' - 4y = 10e^{3x}$.

SOLUTION   This example is similar to Example 3–24, except the differential equation is third-order in this case instead of being second order. Again, we assume the particular solution corresponding to the exponential nonhomogeneous term $10e^{3x}$ to be of the form $y_p = Ae^{3x}$, where A is a constant coefficient that is to be determined. Taking the second and third derivatives of y_p and substituting them into the differential equation gives

$$27Ae^{3x} + 9Ae^{3x} - 4Ae^{3x} = 10e^{3x}$$

or $32Ae^{3x} = 10e^{3x}$. The only A value that will satisfy the last expression is $A = 10/32$. Therefore, a particular solution of the given differential equation is $y_p = (10/32)e^{3x}$. Note that the order of the differential equation was not a consideration in selecting the general form of the particular solution.

EXAMPLE 4–9   **General Solution of a Nonhomogeneous Equation**

Find the general solution of the differential equation:

$$y^{(iv)} = x + 2$$

SOLUTION This example is similar to Example 3–27. Again, we first find the general solution of the homogeneous part of the equation $y^{(iv)} = 0$. Its characteristic equation is $m^4 = 0$, whose roots are $m_1 = m_2 = m_3 = m_4 = 0$. Therefore, $m = 0$ is a four-fold repeated root. Thus, the general solution of the related homogeneous equation is $y_h = c_1 + c_2 x + c_3 x^2 + c_4 x^3$, since $e^0 = 1$. We also could obtain this result by direct integration. For the particular solution, we would normally try $y_p = Ax + B$. However, any constant or a linear function of x is a solution of the homogeneous equation; thus, we need to modify the particular solution by multiplying it by the lowest integer power of the independent variable x until every term in y_p differs from every term in the homogeneous solution. The particular solution will meet this requirement if it does not involve any powers of x lower than x^4. Therefore, we must multiply the assumed form of the particular solution by x^4 to prevent any overlap with the homogeneous solution. Thus, the proper form of the particular solution in this case is $y_p = x^4(Ax + B)$, whose fourth derivative is $y_p^{(iv)} = 120Ax + 24B$. Substituting this into the differential equation yields $120Ax + 24B = x + 2$.

Setting the coefficients of each power of x on both sides equal to each other gives $A = 1/120$ and $B = 1/12$. Thus, the particular solution is

$$y_p = \frac{x^4}{120}(x + 10)$$

Then the general solution becomes

$$y = y_h + y_p$$

$$= c_1 + c_2 x + c_3 x^2 + c_4 x^3 + \frac{x^4}{120}(x + 10)$$

Note that there are no common terms in the homogeneous and the particular solutions.

Section Review

4–15C Do we need to modify the method of undetermined coefficients when dealing with third- or higher-order linear equations?

4–16 Using the method of undetermined coefficients, determine the general solution of the following linear, nonhomogeneous equations.

(a) $y''' - y = 4e^{3x}$ (b) $y''' - y = -3x^2 e^{3x}$

(*Answers:* (a) $y(x) = C_1 e^x + e^{-x/2}\left(C_2 \cos\frac{\sqrt{3}}{2}x + C_3 \sin\frac{\sqrt{3}}{2}x\right) + \frac{2}{13}e^{3x}$

(b) $y(x) = C_1 e^x + e^{-x/2}\left(C_2 \cos\frac{\sqrt{3}}{2}x + C_3 \sin\frac{\sqrt{3}}{2}x\right) + \left(-\frac{3}{26}x^2 + \frac{81}{338}x - \frac{1485}{8788}\right)e^{3x})$

4–7 ▪ NONHOMOGENEOUS EQUATIONS: THE METHOD OF VARIATION OF PARAMETERS

The method of undetermined coefficients is quite simple and straightforward, but it lacks generality because it has two severe limitations: The differential equation should have constant coefficients and the nonhomogeneous terms should be of the form

$$e^{\alpha x} P_n(x) \sin \beta x \quad \text{or} \quad e^{\alpha x} P_n(x) \cos \beta x$$

where α and β are real constants and $P_n(x)$ is a polynominal of degree n. The method of variation of parameters, which was discussed in Chapter 3 in connection with second-order linear equations, is also applicable to higher-order equations with constant or variable coefficients and to nonhomogeneous terms that can be of any form. However, it requires the general solution of the related homogeneous equation to be available. Also, its complexity increases considerably as the order of the differential equation increases, making it impractical for higher-order equations. We now develop the general formulation associated with the method of variation of parameters, which is an extension of the development for the second-order case described in the previous chapter.

Consider the nth-order linear, nonhomogeneous differential equation in the standard form (the leading coefficient is 1),

$$y^{(n)} + P_1(x)y^{(n-1)} + \cdots + P_n(x)y = R(x) \tag{4–34}$$

where the functions $P_1(x), P_2(x), \ldots, P_n(x)$ and $R(x)$ are continuous in the interval of interest. We know that the related homogeneous equation of Equation 4–34 has n linearly independent solutions $y_1, y_2, \ldots, y_n$ in this interval, and the general solution of the related nonhomogeneous equation can be expressed as

$$y_h = C_1 y_1 + C_2 y_2 + \cdots + C_n y_n \tag{4–35}$$

Knowing the homogeneous solution, we now assume the particular solution to be of the form (Figure 4–18).

$$y_p = u_1 y_1 + u_2 y_2 + \cdots + u_n y_n \tag{4–36}$$

which is obtained by replacing the constant parameters $C_1, C_2, \ldots, C_n$ in the homogeneous solution by the variable functions $u_1, u_2, \ldots, u_n$, which depend on x. These n functions must be such that Equation 4–36 satisfies the given nonhomogeneous equation.

To determine the n unknown functions, we need n equations. One equation is obtained by requiring y_p to satisfy the differential Equation 4–34. The other equations are obtained by requiring these n functions to satisfy conditions that we are free to impose. We will make those choices when appropriate such that we greatly simplify the determination of $u_1, u_2, \ldots, u_n$.

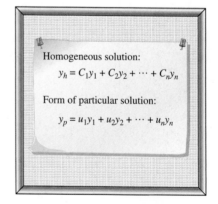

Homogeneous solution:
$$y_h = C_1 y_1 + C_2 y_2 + \cdots + C_n y_n$$

Form of particular solution:
$$y_p = u_1 y_1 + u_2 y_2 + \cdots + u_n y_n$$

FIGURE 4–18

The method of variation of parameters is based on replacing the constant parameters in the homogeneous solution by the variable ones.

The basic idea behind the choices turns out to be suppressing the terms that give rise to second- or higher-order derivatives of $u_1, u_2, \ldots, u_n$.

Differentiating Equation 4–36 gives

$$y_p' = (u_1 y_1' + u_2 y_2' + \cdots + u_n y_n') + (u_1' y_1 + u_2' y_2 + \cdots + u_n' y_n) \quad \text{(4–37)}$$

To avoid second derivatives in later steps, we require the terms in the first parentheses (those involving the first derivatives of $u_1, u_2, \ldots, u_n$) to vanish, giving

$$u_1' y_1 + u_2' y_2 + \cdots + u_n' y_n = 0 \quad \text{(4–38)}$$

We continue differentiation in this manner and obtain $y_p'', y_p''', \ldots, y_p^{(n-1)}$, each time requiring the terms that involve $u_1', u_2', \ldots, u_n'$ to vanish. These conditions we impose on the derivatives of y_p give us $n - 1$ equations:

$$u_1' y_1^{(m)} + u_2' y_2^{(m)} + \cdots + u_n' y_n^{(m)} = 0, \, m = 0, 1, 2, \ldots, n - 2 \quad \text{(4–39)}$$

The nth condition (and thus the nth equation) comes from the requirement that y_p satisfies the given differential equation. Noting that $y_1, y_2, \ldots, y_n$ are solutions of the related homogeneous equation and using the conditions just developed, this requirement gives

$$u_1' y_1^{(n-1)} + u_2' y_2^{(n-1)} + \cdots + u_n' y_n^{(n-1)} = R(x) \quad \text{(4–40)}$$

Equations 4–39 and 4–40 give us n simultaneous linear algebraic equations for the determination of the n unknowns $u_1', u_2', \ldots, u_n'$. Denoting u_i' by w_i for $i = 1, 2, 3, \ldots, n$ for simplicity, this system of n equations with n unknowns can be expressed as

$$y_1 w_1 + y_2 w_2 + \cdots + y_n w_n = 0$$

$$y_1' w_1 + y_2' w_2 + \cdots + y_n' w_n = 0$$

$$\vdots \quad \text{(4–41)}$$

$$y_1^{(n-1)} w_1 + y_2^{(n-1)} w_2 + \cdots + y_n^{(n-1)} w_n = R(x)$$

You will recall from algebra that a system of n equations with n unknowns is guaranteed to have a solution if the coefficient determinant (the determinant of the coefficient matrix) is nowhere zero in the interval of interest. This condition is automatically satisfied in our case, since $y_1, y_2, \ldots, y_n$ are n linearly independent solutions of the related homogeneous equation and the coefficient determinant is simply the Wronskian $W(y_1, y_2, \ldots, y_n)$, which is never zero and is expressed as

$$W(y_1, y_2, \ldots, y_n) = \begin{vmatrix} y_1 & y_2 & \cdot & \cdot & y_n \\ y_1' & y_2' & \cdot & \cdot & y_n' \\ \cdot & \cdot & \cdot & \cdot & \cdot \\ \cdot & \cdot & \cdot & \cdot & \cdot \\ y_1^{(n-1)} & y_1^{(n-1)} & \cdot & \cdot & y_n^{(n-1)} \end{vmatrix} \quad \text{(4–42)}$$

Then the n unknown functions $w_1, w_2, \ldots, w_n$ can be determined systematically using Cramer's rule to be

$$w_k = \frac{R(x)W_k(x)}{W(y_1, y_2, \ldots, y_n)}, \quad k = 1, 2, \ldots, n \qquad \text{(4-43)}$$

where $W_k(x)$ is the determinant obtained by deleting the kth column and the last row from $W(y_1, y_2, \ldots, y_n)$ and multiplying it by $(-1)^{n-k}$. Therefore, if $W(y_1, y_2, \ldots, y_n)$ is a 4×4 determinant, then $W_1(x)$, $W_2(x)$, and $W_3(x)$ are 3×3 determinants. Also, for simplicity, the Wronskian $W(y_1, y_2, \ldots, y_n)$ can be determined from Abel's formula as

$$W(y_1, y_2, \ldots, y_n) = Ke^{-\int P_1(x)dx} \qquad \text{(4-44)}$$

where $P_1(x)$ is the coefficient function of $y^{(n-1)}$ of the differential equation in the standard form. The constant K can be obtained from Equation 4–44 by evaluating this determinant at a convenient point (such as $x = 0$) in the interval of interest.

Once $w_1, w_2, \ldots, w_n$ are available, the functions $u_1, u_2, \ldots, u_n$ are determined by integration to be

$$u_k(x) = \int w_k(x)dx = \int \frac{R(x)W_k(x)}{W(y_1, y_2, \ldots, y_n)}dx, \quad k = 1, 2, \ldots, n \qquad \text{(4-45)}$$

The integration constants are of no significance and can be taken to be zero with no loss in generality. Finally, the particular solution is obtained by substituting these functions into Equation 4–36. Note that some or all of the k integrals in Equation 4–45 may not be possible to perform analytically. In such cases, we may have to resort to numerical integration.

We summarize the method of variation of parameters in Theorem 4–8.

THEOREM 4–8   Variation of Parameters

If the functions $y_1, y_2, \ldots, y_n$ are a fundamental set of solutions of the related homogeneous equation of

$$y^{(n)} + P_1(x)y^{(n-1)} + \cdots + P_n(x)y = R(x) \qquad \text{(4-46)}$$

where the functions $P_1, P_2, \ldots, P_n$ and R are continuous in the interval of interest, then a particular solution of this nonhomogeneous differential equation is given by

$$y_p = u_1y_1 + u_2y_2 + \cdots + u_ny_n \qquad \text{(4-47)}$$

where

$$u_k = \int \frac{R(x)W_k(x)}{W(y_1, y_2, \ldots, y_n)}dx, \quad k = 1, 2, \ldots, n \qquad \text{(4-48)}$$

Here $W(y_1, y_2, \ldots, y_n)$ is the Wronskian of the fundamental set of solutions, and $W_k(x)$ is the determinant obtained by deleting the kth column and the last row from $W(y_1, y_2, \ldots, y_n)$ and multiplying it by $(-1)^{n-k}$.

Once a particular solution is available, the general solution of the nonhomogeneous equation can be determined from

$$y = C_1 y_1 + C_2 y_2 + \cdots + C_n y_n + y_p \qquad (4\text{-}49)$$

Note that the function $R(x)$ in the previous relations represents the nonhomogeneous term of the differential equation in the standard form. Also note that the method of undetermined coefficients is much easier to use and thus should be preferred whenever it is applicable.

EXAMPLE 4–10   Variation of Parameters

Determine the general solution of the differential equation $y''' + 2y'' = e^x$ using (a) the method of undetermined coefficients and (b) the method of variation of parameters for the particular solution.

SOLUTION The leading coefficient of the differential equation is 1; thus, its nonhomogeneous term is $R(x) = e^x$. First we will find its homogeneous solution. The characteristic equation of the related homogeneous equation is $m^3 + 2m^2 = 0$ or $m^2(m + 2) = 0$. The roots of this equation are 0, 0, and –2. Noting that $m = 0$ is a double root, we have $y_1 = e^0 = 1$, $y_2 = xe^0 = x$, and $y_3 = e^{-2x}$. Thus, the general solution of the related homogeneous equation is $y_h = C_1 + C_2 x + C_3 e^{-2x}$.

(a) The proper form of the particular solution corresponding to the nonhomogeneous term $R(x) = e^x$ is $y_p = Ae^x$. Note that the assumed form of the particular solution does not duplicate any function in the homogeneous solution. Substituting this into the given differential equation and solving for the undetermined coeffecient yields $A = 1/3$. Therefore, the particular solution is $y_p = e^x/3$. The general solution of the given differential equation is the sum of the homogeneous and the particular solutions: $y(x) = C_1 + C_2 x + C_3 e^{-2x} + e^x/3$.

(b) Before we apply the method of variation of parameters, we determine the Wronkskian $W(y_1, y_2, y_3)$ and the functions W_1, W_2, and W_3 as

$$W(y_1, y_2, y_3) = \begin{vmatrix} 1 & x & e^{-2x} \\ 0 & 1 & -2e^{-2x} \\ 0 & 0 & 4e^{-2x} \end{vmatrix} = 4e^{-2x}$$

$$W_1(x) = (-1)^{3-1} \begin{vmatrix} x & e^{-2x} \\ 1 & -2e^{-2x} \end{vmatrix} = -2xe^{-2x} - e^{-2x}$$

$$W_2(x) = (-1)^{3-2} \begin{vmatrix} 1 & e^{-2x} \\ 0 & -2e^{-2x} \end{vmatrix} = 2e^{-2x}$$

$$W_3(x) = (-1)^{3-3} \begin{vmatrix} 1 & x \\ 0 & 1 \end{vmatrix} = 1$$

The functions u_1, u_2, and u_3 are determined by substituting these quantities into Equation 4–45:

$$u_1 = \int \frac{R(x)W_1(x)}{W(y_1, y_2, y_3)} dx = \int \frac{e^x(-2xe^{-2x} - e^{-2x})}{4e^{-2x}} dx = -\frac{1}{2}xe^x + \frac{1}{4}e^x$$

$$u_2 = \int \frac{R(x)W_2(x)}{W(y_1, y_2, y_3)} dx = \int \frac{e^x(2e^{-2x})}{4e^{-2x}} dx = \frac{1}{2}e^x$$

$$u_3 = \int \frac{R(x)W_3(x)}{W(y_1, y_2, y_3)} dx = \int \frac{e^x(1)}{4e^{-2x}} dx = \frac{1}{12}e^{3x}$$

Thus, the particular solution (from Equation 4–38) is

$$y_p = u_1 y_1 + u_2 y_2 + u_3 y_3$$

$$= \left(-\frac{1}{2}xe^x + \frac{1}{4}e^x\right) + \frac{1}{2}e^x x + \frac{1}{12}e^{3x}e^{-2x}$$

$$= \frac{1}{3}e^x$$

which is the same result obtained with the method of undetermined coefficients (but with much more effort). The general solution is also the same as the one obtained in part (a).

Section Review

4–17 Do we need to modify the method of variation of parameters when dealing with third- or higher-order linear equations? If so, how?

4–18 Using the method of variation of parameters, determine the particular solution of the following linear, nonhomogeneous equations. Check your results in part (a) using the method of undetermined coefficients. You may have to leave the integrals in part (b) unevaluated.

(a) $y''' - y = e^{3x}$ (b) $y''' - y = \dfrac{1}{\sin x}$

(*Answers:* (a) $y_p = \dfrac{1}{26}e^{3x}$

(b) $y_p = u_1 y_1 + u_2 y_2 + u_3 y_3$

$$= \left(\frac{1}{3}\int \frac{e^{-x}}{\sin x}dx\right)(e^x) + \left[-\frac{\sqrt{3}}{9}\int \frac{e^{x/2}}{\sin x}\left(3\cos\frac{\sqrt{3}}{2}x + \sqrt{3}\sin\frac{\sqrt{3}}{2}x\right)dx\right]\left(e^{-x/2}\sin\frac{\sqrt{3}}{2}x\right)$$

$$+ \left[-\frac{\sqrt{3}}{9}\int \frac{e^{x/2}}{\sin x}\left(-3\sin\frac{\sqrt{3}}{2}x + \sqrt{3}\cos\frac{\sqrt{3}}{2}x\right)dx\right]\left(e^{-x/2}\cos\frac{\sqrt{3}}{2}x\right))$$

4–8 · THE EULER EQUATION

One type of linear differential equation with variable coefficients that can always be converted into an equation with constant coefficients is the **Euler equation**, which can be expressed in the most general form as

$$x^n y^{(n)} + a_1 x^{n-1} y^{(n-1)} + \cdots + a_{n-1}xy' + a_n y = R(x) \qquad \text{(4–50)}$$

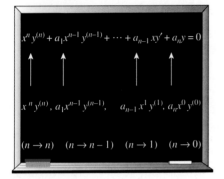

FIGURE 4–19

Each term of a homogeneous Euler equation is of the form $kx^m y^{(m)}$, where k is a constant and m is a nonnegative integer.

where $a_1, a_2, \ldots, a_n$ are constants. The characteristic feature of this equation is that the coefficient of y is a constant, the coefficient of y' is a constant times x, and (in general) the coefficient of nth derivative of y is a constant multiple of the nth power of x. That is, each term on the left side is of the form $kx^m y^{(m)}$, where k is a constant and m is a nonnegative integer (Figure 4–19). If we express the Euler equation in the standard form by dividing each term by the leading coefficient, which is x^n, all other coefficients will involve a power of x in their denominators. These coefficients obviously will be discontinuous at $x = 0$.

THEOREM 4–9   Euler Equations

The transformation $x = e^t$ will always convert the nth-order Euler equation

$$x^n y^{(n)} + a_1 x^{n-1} y^{(n-1)} + \cdots + a_{n-1} xy' + a_n y = R(x)$$

into an nth-order linear equation with constant coefficients.

Consider Theorem 4–9. We proved this theorem in Chapter 3 for $n = 2$, and that proof can be extended to higher orders. Once an Euler equation is converted into an equation with constant coefficients, it can be solved in a routine manner by forming the characteristic equation of its homogeneous part and finding its roots. Finally, the desired solution is obtained by the reverse transformation $t = \ln x$.

For higher-order equations, the transformation indicated in Theorem 4–9 to obtain the transformed equation with constant coefficients is quite lengthy and tedious. A shortcut is to use the alternative transformation $y = x^r$. This results in an nth-degree polynomial equation in r, which happens to be the characteristic equation of the transformed equation with constant coefficients (Figure 4–20). Once we determine the n roots $r_1, r_2, \ldots, r_n$, we can proceed to determine the general solution of the transformed Euler equation with constant coefficients, as explained in earlier sections. We can even apply the methods of undetermined coefficients or variation of parameters to determine the particular solution of the nonhomogeneous equation. Finally, the reverse transformation $t = \ln x$ willl give the general solution of the given Euler equation.

As a more straightforward alternative, we can forget about the transformation in Theorem 4–9 and assume directly the solution to be of the form $y = x^r$, where r is a constant, as explained in Section 3–9 of Chapter 3 for the second-order case (Figure 4–20). Substitute $y = x^r$ and its derivatives into the homogeneous part of the Euler equation. Such Euler equations will involve only real functions.

If the n roots $r_1, r_2, \ldots, r_n$, are all real and distinct, then the n linearly independent solutions are

$$x^{r_1}, x^{r_2}, \ldots, x^{r_n} \tag{4–51}$$

The substitution

$$y = x^r$$

into the Euler equation

$$x^n y^{(n)} + a_1 x^{n-1} y^{(n-1)} + \cdots + a_n y = 0$$

gives the characteristic equation:

$$r^n + b_1 r^{n-1} + \cdots + b_{n-1} r + b_n = 0$$

FIGURE 4–20

An alternative way of obtaining the characteristic equations of the transformed equation with constant coefficients of the Euler equation.

If r_1 is a k-fold repeated root, then the k linearly independent solutions corresponding to this root are (Figure 4–21)

$$x^{r_1}, (\ln x)x^{r_1}, (\ln x)^2 x^{r_1}, \dots, (\ln x)^{k-1}x^{r_1} \qquad (4\text{-}52)$$

If the complex conjugate pair $r_{1,2} = \alpha \pm i\beta$ is k-fold repeated root, then the $2k$ linearly independent solutions corresponding to this pair are

$$x^\alpha \cos(\beta \ln x), x^\alpha \sin(\beta \ln x),$$

$$(\ln x)\, x^\alpha \cos(\beta \ln x), (\ln x)\, x^\alpha \sin(\beta \ln x),$$

$$\vdots \qquad\qquad \vdots$$

$$(\ln x)^{k-1}\, x^\alpha \cos(\beta \ln x), (\ln x)^{k-1}\, x^\alpha \sin(\beta \ln x) \qquad (4\text{-}53)$$

Note that $\ln x$ plays the role of the independent variable x in equations with constant coefficients. So it is no surprise that the transformation $t = \ln x$ converts the Euler equations into an equation with constant coefficients. The solutions given in Equation 4–53 are also applicable for $x < 0$ if all occurrences of x in the relations are replaced by $|x|$.

The general solutions of a homogeneous Euler equation for $x > 0$ also can be determined from the general solution of a linear, homogeneous equation with constant coefficients that has the same characteristic equation by replacing all occurrences of x in the solution by $\ln x$.

For nonhomogeneous Euler equations, we determine the homogeneous solution as described previously and find a particular solution using the method of variation of parameters, since the coefficients of the Euler equation are variable. Note that the equation should be put into the standard form first by dividing each term by the leading coefficient so that we correctly identify the nonhomogeneous term $R(x)$.

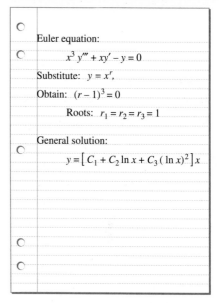

Euler equation:

$$x^3 y''' + xy' - y = 0$$

Substitute: $y = x^r$,

Obtain: $(r-1)^3 = 0$

Roots: $r_1 = r_2 = r_3 = 1$

General solution:

$$y = \left[C_1 + C_2 \ln x + C_3 (\ln x)^2 \right] x$$

FIGURE 4–21

Obtaining the general solution of a third-order homogeneous Euler equation when r is a triple root.

EXAMPLE 4–11   A Third-Order Euler Equation

Determine the general solution of the differential equation $x^3 y''' - 2xy' + 4y = 0$ for $x > 0$ taking $y = x^r$.

SOLUTION   We recognize this equation immediately as being an Euler equation, since each term on the left side is of the form $kx^m y^{(m)}$ for $m = 0$, 1, and 3. Taking $y = x^r$ and substituting it and its derivatives $y' = rx^{r-1}$ and $y''' = r(r-1)(r-2)x^{r-3}$ into the given differential equation yields

$$r(r-1)(r-2)x^3 x^{r-3} - 2rxx^{r-1} + 4x^r = 0$$

or $[r(r-1)(r-2) - 2r + 4]x^r = 0$, which gives $r^3 - 3r^2 + 4 = 0$ since x^r cannot be zero. The roots of the equation are 2, 2, and -1. Noting that 2 is a double root, the general solution of this Euler equation is

$$y = (C_1 + C_2 \ln x)x^2 + \frac{C_3}{x}$$

Section Review

4–19C How do you recognize an nth-order differential equation as being an Euler equation?

4–20C Can we always reduce the Euler equation to a linear equation with constant coefficients regardless of its order?

4–21 Determine the general solution of the following Euler equation for $x > 0$.

$$x^3 y''' + x^2 y'' + 4y = 0$$

(*Answer:* $y(x) = \dfrac{C_1}{x} + x^{3/2} \left[C_1 \cos\left(\dfrac{\sqrt{7}}{2} \ln x \right) + C_2 \sin\left(\dfrac{\sqrt{7}}{2} \ln x \right) \right]$)

4–9 ▪ COMPUTER METHODS FOR HIGHER-ORDER EQUATIONS

Although the theory of higher-order equations is similar to that of second-order equations, there is a big difference between the two when it comes to applying the methods, because the algebra required becomes much more tedious as the equation order increases. However, there are powerful computer methods available to assist with this algebra.

For example, solving for the characteristic roots is more difficult. Formulas exist for finding the roots of third- and fourth-order polynomials, but they are cumbersome to use. In addition, it has been proved that no formula can be found for polynomials of fifth order and higher. So we must use a numerical root-finding procedure for those cases.

The solution of an nth-order equation will contain n integration constants, which must be found from the n initial conditions or boundary conditions. To find these requires the solution of n algebraic equations. A related problem involves the evaluation of the determinant given by the Wronskian.

In this section, we illustrate the appropriate computer methods useful for solving higher-order equations.

EXAMPLE 4–12   **Root Finding**

Consider the following third-order equation for the function $y(x)$: $y''' + 10y'' + 29y' + 20y = 0$. The initial conditions are $y(0) = 1$, $y'(0) = 0$, $y''(0) = 0$. Obtain its solution.

SOLUTION   The characteristic equation is

$$m^3 + 10m^2 + 29m + 20 = 0$$

Its roots can be found as shown in Table 4–1. They are $m = -1$, -4, and -5.

TABLE 4–1

Computer Solution for the Roots of $m^3 + 10m^2 + 29m + 20 = 0$

MATLAB

```
roots([1,10,29,20])
```

MuPAD

```
numeric::polyroots(m^3 +10*m^2+29*m+20)
```

Maple

```
solve(m^3 + 10*m^2 + 29*m + 20)
```

Mathematica

```
Roots[m^3+10*m^2+29*m+20==0,m]
```

Thus, the form of the solution is

$$y(x) = C_1 e^{-x} + C_2 e^{-4x} + C_3 e^{-5x} \qquad \textbf{(4–54)}$$

To compute the three coefficients, use the given initial conditions to obtain

$$y(0) = C_1 + C_2 + C_3 = 1$$

$$y'(0) = -C_1 - 4C_2 - 5C_3 = 0$$

$$y''(0) = C_1 + 16C_2 + 25C_3 = 0$$

These are three linear algebraic equations in three unknowns. They can be solved in several ways. One way is to write out each of the three equations and then solve them as a set. This method is illustrated in Table 4–2. The other way is to express the three equations as a single matrix equation: $\mathbf{AC} = \mathbf{b}$ where

$$\mathbf{A} = \begin{bmatrix} 1 & 1 & 1 \\ -1 & -4 & -5 \\ 1 & 16 & 25 \end{bmatrix}$$

$$\mathbf{C} = \begin{bmatrix} C_1 \\ C_2 \\ C_3 \end{bmatrix} \quad \mathbf{b} = \begin{bmatrix} 1 \\ 0 \\ 0 \end{bmatrix}$$

This method is shown for all four packages in Table 4–2. The solution is $C_1 = 1.667$, $C_2 = -1.667$, and $C_3 = 1$.

TABLE 4–2

Computer Solution for the Coefficients of Equation (4–54)

MATLAB

```
A = [1,1,1;-1,-4,-5;1,16,25];
B = [1;0;0];
C = A\b
```

MuPAD

```
eqn1 := C1+C2+C3=1:
eqn2 := -C1-4*C2-5*C3=0:
eqn3 := C1+16*C2+25*C3=0:
numeric::linsolve([eqn1,eqn2,eqn3],[C1,C2,C3])
```

or

```
A := matrix([[1,1,1],[-1,-4,-5],[1,16,25]]):
B := matrix([[1],[0],[0]]):
linalg::matlinsolve(A, b)
```

Maple

```
eqn1 := C1+C2+C3=1:
eqn2 := -C1-4*C2-5*C3=0:
eqn3 := C1+16*C2+25*C3=0:
solve({eqn1, eqn2, eqn3},[C1, C2, C3])
```

or

```
A := Matrix([[1,1,1],[-1,-4,-5],[1,16,25]]):
b := Matrix([[1],[0],[0]]):
LinearAlgebra[LinearSolve](A,b)
```

Mathematica

```
A={{1,1,1},{-1,-4,-5},{1,16,25}};
LinearSolve[N[A],N[b]]
```

The Wronskian can be evaluated by computer. For example, the following equation was solved in Example 4–10.

$$y''' + 2y'' = e^x$$

The solution is

$$C_1 + C_2 x + C_3 e^{-2x} + \frac{1}{3}e^x$$

This can be found as shown in Table 4–3.

The Wronskian is

$$W(y_1, y_2, y_3) = \begin{vmatrix} 1 & x & e^{-2x} \\ 0 & 1 & -2e^{-2x} \\ 0 & 0 & 4e^{-2x} \end{vmatrix} = 4e^{-2x} \qquad (4\text{–}55)$$

This evaluation is shown in Table 4–4.

TABLE 4–3

Computer Solution of $y''' + 2y'' = e^x$

MATLAB Symbolic Math Toolbox

```
dsolve('D3y+2*D2y=exp(x)','x')
```

MuPAD

```
eqn:=ode(y'''(x)+2*y''(x)=exp(x),y(x)):
solve (eqn)
```

Maple

```
eqn := y'''(x)+2*y''(x)=exp(x)
dsolve(eqn)
```

Mathematica

```
DSolve[y'''[x]+2*y''[x]==Exp[x],y[x],x]
```

TABLE 4–4

Computer Evaluation of the Wronskian Equation (4–55)

MATLAB Symbolic Math Toolbox

```
syms W x
W = [1,x,exp(-2*x);0,1,-2*exp(-2*x);0,0,4*exp(-2*x)];
det(W)
```

MuPAD

```
W := matrix([[1,x,exp(-2*x)],[0,1,-2*exp(-2*x)],
 [0,0,4*exp(-2*x)]])
linalg::det(W)
```

Maple

```
W := Matrix([[1,x,exp(-2*x)],[0,1,-2*exp(-2*x)],[0,0,
 exp(-2*x)]])
with(LinearAlgebra);Determinant(W)
```

Mathematica

```
W = {{1,x,Exp[-2*x]},{0,1,-2*Exp[-2*x]},{0,0,Exp[-2*x]}};
Det[W]
```

4–10 · SUMMARY

Linear Equation Terminology A differential equation is said to be *linear* if it does not involve any powers, products, or nonlinear functions of the dependent variable y or its derivatives. The nth-order linear differential equation can be written in the most general form as

$$y^{(n)} + P_1(x)y^{(n-1)} + \cdots$$
$$+ P_{n-1}(x)y' + P_n(x)y = R(x) \qquad (4\text{–}1)$$

where the coefficients $P_1, P_2, \ldots, P_n$ may depend on x only. The function $R(x)$ represents all of the terms that do not involve the dependent variable y or any of its derivatives and is called the *nonhomogeneous term*. A linear differential equation is said to be *nonhomogeneous* when $R(x) \neq 0$ and *homogeneous* when $R(x) = 0$. The equation that is obtained by setting $R(x)$ equal to zero is called the *related homogeneous equation* or *complementary equation*. If the coefficients of the dependent variable y and its derivatives are constants, the equation is said to have *constant coefficients*. If one or more coefficients depend on the independent variable x, then the equation is said to have *variable coefficients*.

Existence and Uniqueness of Solutions The *existence and uniqueness* of the solution of the *n*th-order, linear, initial-value problems is expressed by Theorem 4–1.

> If the functions $P_1(x), P_2(x), \ldots, P_n(x)$ and $R(x)$ are continuous on an interval $x_1 < x < x_2$ and x_0 is any point in this interval, then the *n*th-order linear Equation 4–1 has a unique solution on this interval that satisfies the *n* initial conditions
>
> $$y(x_0) = y_0', \ldots, y^{(n-1)}(x_0) = y_0^{(n-1)}$$
>
> where $y_0, y_0', \ldots, y_0^{(n-1)}$ are specified real constants.

Superposition Principle for Linear Homogeneous Equations If a function is a solution of a linear, homogeneous, differential equation, a constant multiple of it is also a solution. If *n* functions are solutions of a linear, homogeneous differential equation, their sum is also a solution of that differential equation. This is known as the *superposition principle* and is expressed by Theorem 4–2.

> If $y_1, y_2, \ldots, y_n$ are *n* solutions of an *n*th-order, linear, homogeneous equation, then the linear combination
>
> $$y = C_1 y_1 + C_2 y_2 + \cdots + C_n y_n \qquad \text{(4–7)}$$
>
> where $C_1, C_2, \ldots, C_n$ are arbitrary constants, is also a solution of this equation.

Abel's Identity For an *n*th-order, linear, homogeneous equation whose coefficients are continuous in the interval of interest, *Abel*'s identity is expressed in Theorem 4–3.

> The Wronskian of any *n* solutions $y_1, y_2, \ldots, y_n$ of an *n*th-order, linear, homogeneous equation is either always zero (indicating these *n* solutions are linearly dependent) or never zero (indicating these *n* solutions are linearly independent).

Fundamental Solution Set A linear, homogeneous, *n*th-order differential equation has *n* linearly independent solutions that form a *fundamental set of solutions*, as expressed in Theorem 4–4:

> An *n*th-order, linear, homogeneous differential equation whose coefficients are continuous in an interval $x_1 < x < x_2$ always possesses *n* solutions $y_1, y_2, \ldots, y_n$ that are linearly independent in that interval. Furthermore, any solution of this differential equation in that interval can be expressed uniquely as a linear combination of these *n* solutions as
>
> $$y = C_1 y_1 + C_2 y_2 + \cdots + C_n y_n \qquad \text{(4–9)}$$

which is called the general solution of the equation in that interval.

Reduction of Order When one of the nontrivial solutions of a linear homogeneous equation is known, its order can be reduced by one by the method of *reduction of order*. This is expressed by Theorem 4–5.

> If y_1 is a solution of an *n*th-order linear homogeneous equation. then the substitution $y = \nu y_1$, where ν is a function of *x*, reduces this equation to a linear homogeneous equation of order $n - 1$ in ν'.

Solution Forms for Distinct Real Roots An *n*th-order, linear, homogeneous equation with constant coefficients always possesses *n* linearly independent solutions $y_1, y_2, \ldots, y_n$, and its general solution is expressed as $y = C_1 y_1 + C_2 y_2 + \cdots + C_n y_n$ where $C_1, C_2, \ldots, C_n$ are arbitrary constants. If the *n* roots of the characteristic equation $m_1, m_2, \ldots, m_n$ are real and different, then *n* fundamental solutions of the given *n*th-order differential equation are $e^{m_1 x}, e^{m_2 x}, \ldots, e^{m_n x}$.

Solution Forms for Repeated Real Roots If m_1 is a *k*-fold repeated root of the characteristic equation, then *k* linearly independent solutions corresponding to this root are

$$e^{m_1 x}, x e^{m_1 x}, x^2 e^{m_1 x}, \ldots, x^{k-1} e^{m_1 x} \qquad \text{(4–17)}$$

The part of the general solution corresponding to a *k*-fold root *m* is obtained by multiplying e^{mx} by a polynomial of degree $k - 1$ with arbitrary constant coefficients.

Solution Forms for Complex Roots If a polynomial equation has real coefficients, then any complex roots that it may have must occur in conjugates. The general solution corresponding to a pair of conjugate root $\alpha \pm i\beta$ of the characteristic equation is

$$y = e^{\alpha x}(C_1 \cos \beta x + C_2 \sin \beta x) \qquad \text{(4–19)}$$

The part of the general solution corresponding to a *k*-fold complex conjugate pair $\alpha \pm \beta$ is

$$\begin{aligned} y = &\, e^{\alpha x}(C_1 \cos \beta x + C_2 \sin \beta x) \\ &+ x e^{\alpha x}(C_3 \cos \beta x + C_4 \sin \beta x) + \cdots \\ &+ x^{k-1} e^{\alpha x}(C_{2k-1} \cos \beta x + C_{2k} \sin \beta x) \qquad \text{(4–20)} \end{aligned}$$

where $C_1, C_2, \ldots, C_{2k}$ are arbitrary constants.

Homogeneous and Particular Solutions The general solution of a linear, nonhomogeneous equation is obtained by combining the general solution of the related homogeneous equation, called the *homogeneous solution* or the *complementary solution*, with a function that satisfies the given nonhomogeneous equation, called a *particular solution*, in accordance with Theorem 4–6.

> If y_p is a particular solution of an *n*th-order, linear, nonhomogeneous equation whose coefficients and

nonhomogeneous term $R(x)$ are continuous in an interval $x_1 < x < x_2$ and y_h is the general solution of its related homogeneous equation, then the general solution of this nonhomogeneous equation is

$$y = y_h + y_p = C_1y_1 + C_2y_2, \ldots, C_ny_n + y_p \quad \text{(4-30)}$$

where $y_1, y_2, \ldots, y_n$ are a fundamental set of solutions of the related homogeneous equation, and $C_1, C_2, \ldots, C_n$ are arbitrary constants.

Superposition Principle for Linear Nonhomogeneous Equations The nonhomogeneous term $R(x)$ often involves several terms. In such cases, it is much easier to find a particular solution corresponding to each nonhomogeneous term and then to add them up according to the *superposition principle* expressed by Theorem 4–7.

If y_{p1} is a particular solution of

$$y^{(n)} + P_1(x)y^{(n-1)} + \cdots + P_{n-1}(x)y' + P_n(x)y = R_1(x) \quad \text{(4-31)}$$

and y_{p2} is a particular solution of

$$y^{(n)} + P_1(x)y^{(n-1)} + \cdots + P_{n-1}(x)y' + P_n(x)y = R_2(x) \quad \text{(4-32)}$$

then $y_{p1} + y_{p2}$ is a particular solution of

$$y^{(n)} + P_1(x)y^{(n-1)} + \cdots + P_{n-1}(x)y' + P_n(x)y$$
$$= R_1(x) + R_2(x) \quad \text{(4-33)}$$

Method of Undetermined Coefficients There are two ways to determine the particular solution y_p of nonhomogeneous equations: the method of undetermined coefficients and the method of parameters. The method of undetermined coefficients discussed in Chapter 3 in conjunction with the second-order equations is also applicable to higher-order linear equations regardless of their order.

Method of Variation of Parameters The method of *variation of parameters* is applicable to equations with constant or variable coefficients and to nonhomogeneous terms, which can be of any form, but it requires the general solution of the related homogeneous equation to be available. For nth-order linear equations, it is summarized in Theorem 4–8.

If the functions $y_1, y_2, \ldots, y_n$ are a fundamental set of solutions of the related homogeneous equation of an nth order linear equation with continuous coefficients and nonhomogeneous term $R(x)$ in an interval $x_1 < x < x_2$, then a particular solution of this nonhomogeneous differential equation is given by

$$y_p = u_1y_1 + u_2y_2 + \cdots + u_ny_n \quad \text{(4-36)}$$

where

$$u_k = \int \frac{R(x)W_k(x)}{W(y_1, y_2, \ldots, y_n)} dx \quad k = 1, 2, \ldots n \quad \text{(4-45)}$$

Here $W(y_1, y_2, \ldots, y_n)$ is the Wronskian of the fundamental set of solutions, and $W_k(x)$ is the determinant obtained by deleting the kth column and the last row from $W(y_1, y_2, \ldots, y_n)$ and multiplying it by $(-1)^{n-k}$.

The Euler Equation There is no general procedure for solving linear equations with variable coefficients, except for some certain types. One such equation is the *Euler equation,* which can always be converted into an equation with constant coefficients. The general term of the Euler equation is of the form $kx^my^{(m)}$, where k is a constant and m is a nonnegative integer. The nth-order Euler equation is expressed as

$$x^ny^{(n)} + a_1x^{n-1}y^{(n-1)} + \cdots + a_{n-1}xy' + a_ny = R(x) \quad \text{(4-50)}$$

where $a_1, a_2, \ldots, a_n$ are constants. The Euler equation always can be transformed into an equation with constant coefficients through the transformation $x = e^t$, as stated in Theorem 4–9.

It is often much easier to solve the Euler equation by taking the solution to be of the form $y = x^r$. This transformation results in an nth-degree polynomial equation in r. If the n roots $r_1, r_2, \ldots, r_n$ are all real and distinct, then the n solutions

$$x^{r_1}, x^{r_2}, \ldots, x^{r_n} \quad \text{(4-51)}$$

form a fundamental set of solutions. If r_1 is a k-fold repeated real root, then the k linearly independent solutions corresponding to this root are

$$x^{r_1}, (\ln x)x^{r_1}, (\ln x)^2x^{r_1}, \ldots, (\ln x)^{k-1}x^{r_1} \quad \text{(4-52)}$$

If the complex conjugate pair $r_{1,2} = a \pm i\beta$ is a k-fold repeated root, then the $2k$ linearly independent solutions corresponding to these roots are

$$x^\alpha\cos(\beta\ln x), \qquad x^\alpha\sin(\beta\ln x),$$
$$(\ln x)x^\alpha\cos(\beta\ln x), \qquad (\ln x)x^\alpha\sin(\beta\ln x),$$
$$\cdots \qquad\qquad \cdots$$
$$(\ln x)^{k-1}x^\alpha\cos(\beta\ln x), \quad (\ln x)^{k-1}x^\alpha\sin(\beta\ln x) \quad \text{(4-53)}$$

The general solution of a homogeneous Euler equation for $x > 0$ also can be determined from the general solution of a linear, homogeneous equation with constant coefficients that has the same characteristic equation by replacing all occurrences of x in the solution by $\ln x$.

PROBLEMS

4–1 Introduction to Higher-Order Linear Equations

4–22C Under what conditions is an nth-order linear initial-value problem guaranteed to have a unique solution in a specified interval?

4–23C Find a third-order initial-value problem whose only solution is the trivial solution $y = 0$.

Determine if the following differential equations are (1) linear or nonlinear, (2) homogeneous or nonhomogeneous, and (3) whether they have constant or variable coefficients.

4–24 (a) $y''' + 2y^2y' + 2y = xe^{-3x}$
(b) $y''' + 5y' - ky = 0$
(c) $y''' - 3y' + xy = 0$
(d) $y''' + y' = x^2\cos x$

4–25 (a) $y^{(iv)} - 5y' + \cos y = x + 1$
(b) $y^{(iv)} = 0$
(c) $y^{(iv)} + 2x^2y' + 5y = 0$
(d) $y^{(iv)} + e^x y = \dfrac{1}{x}$

4–26 (a) $y''' + e^y y' - 2y = 6$
(b) $y''' - 2y' + y = x^3 \cos 2x$
(c) $y''' - 5x^2 y' = 0$
(d) $y''' - y = 0$

4–27 (a) $y^{(v)} + \dfrac{1}{y} = 1$
(b) $y^{(v)} - 8y' - e^{\ln y} = 0$
(c) $y^{(v)} - (\sin 2x)y' + y = 0$
(d) $y^{(v)} + y = 7$

Determine the interval in which the following initial-value problems are guaranteed to have a unique solution.

4–28 (a) $y''' = 0$, $y(0) = 0$, $y'(0) = -4$, and $y''(0) = 0$
(b) $(x - 1)^3 y''' + 2xy' - y = e^{-x}$,
$y(-2) = 3$, $y'(-2) = -7$, and $y''(-2) = 0$

4–29 (a) $y''' + xy' - 3y = x^2 e^{3x}$,
$y(-1) = 1$, $y'(-1) = 4$, and $y''(-1) = 0$
(b) $(x - 2)y''' + 6xy = 2$,
$y(0) = -2$, $y'(0) = 0$, and $y''(0) = 0$

4–30 (a) $x(x - 3)y''' + xy' - 2(x - 3) = -3x^2$,
$y(1) = 2$, $y'(1) = -5$, and $y''(1) = 0$
(b) $y''' - 5y = \ln x$, $y(5) = 3$, $y'(5) = 1$, and $y''(5) = 0$

4–31 (a) $y''' + 4y = e^{2x}\cos x$, $y(0) = 0$, $y'(5) = 1$, and $y''(5) = 0$
(b) $(x^2 - 4)y''' - 3xy' - 2y = 0$,
$y(1) = 0$, $y'(1) = 7$, and $y''(1) = 0$

4–2 Theory of Homogeneous Equations

4–32C How many different solutions can an nth-order linear homogeneous equation with continuous coefficients have? How many of these solutions can be linearly independent?

4–33C Consider a third-order linear homogeneous equation with continuous coefficients and three of its solutions y_1, y_2, and y_3 that are linearly independent. Can this differential equation have a solution that cannot be expressed as $y = C_1 y_1 + C_2 y_2 + C_3 y_3$ where C_1, C_2, and C_3 are constants?

Consider the following linear, homogeneous equations and their solution in $x > 0$. Identify the solutions whose Wronskian is never zero for $x > 0$ by inspection. Verify your findings by calculating their Wronskian for each case.

4–34 (a) $x^3 y''' - 3x^2 y'' + 6xy' - 6y = 0$; x, x^2, and x^3
(b) $x^3 y''' - 3x^2 y'' + 6xy' - 6y = 0$; x, $-x$, and x^3

4–35 (a) $y''' - y' = 0$; e^x, e^{-x}, and 1
(b) $y''' - y' = 0$; e^x, $2e^{2+x}$, and -5

4–36 (a) $x^3 y''' + 3x^2 y'' - 2xy = 0$; $\dfrac{1}{x}$, $\dfrac{\ln x}{x}$, and x^2
(b) $x^3 y''' + 3x^2 y'' - 2xy = 0$; $\dfrac{1}{x}$, $\dfrac{\ln x^2}{x}$, and $\dfrac{\ln x^3}{x}$

Consider the following linear, homogeneous equations and their solutions in $x > 0$. Determine if the given solutions form a fundamental set of solutions. If they do, develop a relation for y that contains all the solutions of the differential equation.

4–37 (a) $y^{(iv)} - y = 0$; 1, e^x, and e^{-x}
(b) $y^{(iv)} - y = 0$; 1, $\sinh x$, and $\cosh x$

4–38 (a) $y''' - y'' + y' - y = 0$; e^x, $\sin x$, and $\cos x$
(b) $y''' - y'' + y' - y = 0$; e^x, $\dfrac{\sin x}{\tan x}$, and $\cos x$

4–39 (a) $y''' - y'' + y' - y = 0$; e^x, xe^x, and e^{-x}
(b) $y''' - y'' + y' - y = 0$; xe^x, $e^{x+\ln x}$, and $3e^{-x}$

4–40 (a) $y''' - 4y'' + 4y' = 0$; 1, e^{2x}, and xe^{2x}
(b) $y''' - 4y'' + 4y' = 0$; -5, e^{2x+1}, and $e^{2x} + 15$

4–3 Reduction of Order

4–41C Is the method of reduction of order practical for third- or higher-order linear equations? Explain.

Using the one solution given, determine the other linearly independent solutions of the following linear homogeneous equations by the method of reduction of order.

4–42 $y^{(iv)} - 16y = 0$, $y_1 = e^{2x}$

4–43 $y''' + 9y' = 0$, $y_1 = 1$

4-44 $y^{(iv)} + 8y''' + 18y'' + 16y' + 5y = 0,\ y_1 = e^{-x}$

4-45 $x^3 y''' - 2xy' + 4y = 0,\ y_1 = x^2$

4-46 $x^2 y''' + 3xy'' + y' = 0,\ y_1 = 4$

4-4 Homogeneous Equations with Constant Coefficients

4-47C Do you think there exists a fourth-order, linear, homogeneous equation with constant coefficients that is satisfied by the functions e^{2x}, e^{-3x}, and $5e^{2x} - 8e^{-3x}$?

4-48C Do you think there exists a third-order, linear, homogeneous equation with constant coefficients that is satisfied by the functions x, $x + 1$, x^2, and $x^2 + 5$?

4-49C Do you think there exists a third-order, linear, homogeneous equation with continuous coefficients that is satisfied by the functions x, $\cos x$, $\tan x$, and $\cot x$?

4-50C When the roots of the characteristic equation corresponding to a fourth-order, linear, homogeneous equation with constant coefficients are equal, explain how you would form the general solution.

4-51C When all of the roots of the characteristic equation of a sixth-order, linear, homogeneous equation with constant coefficients are complex, are they necessarily in the form of conjugate pairs?

Determine the general solution of the following linear homogeneous equations with constant coefficients.

4-52 (a) $y''' - y' = 0$ (b) $y''' - 5y'' + 4y = 0$

4-53 (a) $y''' + 3y'' + 3y' + y = 0$
(b) $y''' + 6y'' + 9y' = 0$

4-54 (a) $y''' - y'' - y' + y = 0$
(b) $y''' + 3y'' + 4y = 0$

4-55 (a) $y''' - 2y''' + y' + 4y = 0$
(b) $y^{(iv)} + 4y''' + 12y'' + 16y' + 16y = 0$

Determine the specific solution of the following initial-value problems.

4-56 $y''' - 4y'' + 4y' = 0,\ y(0) = 0,\ y'(0) = 1,$ and $y''(0) = 0$

4-57 $y''' - y = 0,\ y(0) = 1,$ and $y'(0) = y''(0) = 0$

4-58 $y''' + 2y'' + y' - y = 0,$
$y(4) = y'(4) = y''(4) = 0$

4-59 $y''' - 3y'' + 3y' - y = 0,\ y(0) = 1,$ and $y'(0) = y''(0) = 0$

4-60 For the speaker model developed in Example 4-6, obtain the differential equation for the current $i(t)$.

4-61 For the speaker model developed in Example 4-6, obtain the form of the homogeneous solution for the following parameter values.

$$m = 0.003 \text{ kg} \qquad k = 5 \times 10^5 \text{ N/m}$$
$$K_f = 20 \text{ N/A} \qquad K_b = 20 \text{ V} \cdot \text{s/m}$$
$$R = 10\Omega \qquad L = 10^{-3} \text{ H}$$

4-62 For the two-story building model discussed in Example 4-7, obtain the fourth-order differential equation for the displacement x_2 of the second floor. Obtain its characteristic roots.

4-63 For the two-story building model discussed in Example 4-7, obtain its characteristic roots for the case where $m_1 = 2m$, $m_2 = m$ and $k_1 = 2k$, $k_2 = k$.

4-5 Theory of Nonhomogeneous Equations

4-64C Do we need to modify the superposition principle for the particular solutions when dealing with third- or higher-order linear equations?

4-6 Nonhomogeneous Equations: The Method of Undetermined Coefficients

4-65C Are the general forms of the particular solutions corresponding to the same nonhomogeneous term in a second- and a third-order linear homogeneous equation the same? If not, how do they differ?

Using the method of undetermined coefficients, determine the general solution of the following linear nonhomogeneous equations.

4-66 (a) $y''' + y' = 2\sin x$
(b) $y''' + y' = 2x\cos 3x$
(c) $y''' + y' = -3\cos 3x$
(d) $y''' + y' = xe^x \sin 2x - 5\sin 2x + 3\cos 2x$

4-67 (a) $y''' - 3y' + 2y = -2e^{3x}$
(b) $y''' - 3y' + 2y = 2e^{3-2x}$
(c) $y''' - 3y' + 2y = 5xe^{-2x}$
(d) $y''' - 3y' + 2y = e^x \cos 2x$

4-68 (a) $y''' - 2y'' = x^2 + 1$
(b) $y''' - 2y'' = \sin x + \cos 2x$
(c) $y''' - 2y'' = e^x \sin x$
(d) $y''' - 2y'' = x^3 e^x$

4-69 (a) $y^{(iv)} - y = x - 2$
(b) $y^{(iv)} - y = (x - 1)e^x$
(c) $y^{(iv)} - y = x^2 - 1$
(d) $y^{(iv)} - y = xe^x \sin 2x$

4-70 (a) $4y''' - 3y' - y = 20$
(b) $4y''' - 3y' - y = x^2 e^x$
(c) $4y''' - 3y' - y = e^{3x}\cos x$
(d) $4y''' - 3y' - y = x^2 \sin 2x$

4-71 (a) $y''' + 8y = 2\sin x - 3\cos x$
(b) $y''' + 8y = x^2 - e^x$
(c) $y''' + 8y = (x^2 - 1)e^x$
(d) $y''' + 8y = e^{2x}\sin 3x$

4–72 (a) $y''' = 5$ (b) $y''' = -3x^2e^x$
(c) $y''' = 2x^2 - 3$ (b) $y''' = 8\cos 2x$

4–73 For the two-story building model discussed in Example 4–7, obtain the form of the particular solution for the case where $y = 1$, $m_1 = m_2 = m$, and $k_1 = k_2 = k$.

4–74 For the two-story building model discussed in Example 4–7, obtain the form of the particular solution for the case where $y = \sin\left(\sqrt{\frac{k}{m}}t\right)$, $m_1 = m_2 = m$, and $k_1 = k_2 = k$.

4–7 Nonhomogeneous Equations: The Method of Variation of Parameters

4–75C Why does the method of variation of parameters become rather complicated for third- or higher-order equations?

Using the method of variation of parameters, determine the particular solution of the following linear nonhomogeneous equations. Check your results in part (a) using the method of undetermined coefficients. You may need to leave the integrals in part (b) unevaluated.

4–76 (a) $y^{(iv)} - 16y = xe^{2x}$ (b) $y^{(iv)} - 16y = \dfrac{e^{2x}}{x}$

4–77 (a) $y''' + 9y' = \cos 2x$ (b) $y''' + 9y' = \dfrac{1}{\cos 2x}$

4–78 (a) $y''' - 2y'' = e^{2x}\cos x$ (b) $y''' - 2y'' = \tan x$

4–79 (a) $y''' + y' = x^3 - 1$ (b) $y''' + y' = \dfrac{1}{x}$

4–80 (a) $y''' - y'' - 4y' - 6y = x + 5$
(b) $y''' - y'' - 4y' - 6y = \ln x$

4–81 (a) $y''' = x^2e^x$ (b) $y''' = \dfrac{1}{x^2}$

4–82 (a) $y''' - 2y' - 4y = e^{2x} + 8$
(b) $y''' - 2y' - 4y = \dfrac{e^{2x}}{x}$

4–8 The Euler Equation

4–83C Describe two systematic ways of obtaining the characteristic equation of the transformed equation with constant coefficients corresponding to a given Euler equation. Which approach is more practical?

4–84C When solving a third- or higher-order Euler equation using the substitution $y = x^r$, how would you handle a threefold repeated real root?

4–85C When solving a sixth-order Euler equation with real coefficients using the substitution $y = x^r$, how would you form the general solution if $\alpha \pm i\beta$ is a triple root?

Determine the general solution of the following Euler equations for $x > 0$.

4–86 $x^3y''' - 3x^2y'' + 6xy' - 6y = 0$

4–87 $x^3y''' + 3x^2y'' - 6xy' - 6y = 0$

4–88 $x^3y''' + x^2y'' = 0$

4–89 $2x^3y''' + 6xy' - 6y = 0$

4–90 $x^3y''' - 6y = 0$

4–91 $x^3y''' + 4x^2y'' - 6xy' - 12y = 0$

4–92 $x^3y''' + 3x^2y'' - 6y = 0$

Computer Problems

4–93 Use a computer or calculator to obtain the roots of the following equations.

(a) $r^3 + 16r^2 + 76r + 96 = 0$

(b) $r^3 + 9r^2 + 24r + 20 = 0$

(c) $5r^3 + 30r^2 + 60r + 40 = 0$

(d) $r^3 + 13r^2 + 119r + 267 = 0$

(e) $r^4 + 16r^3 + 194r^2 + 984r + 4005 = 0$

(f) $r^4 + 16r^3 + 158r^2 + 624r + 801 = 0$

(g) $r^4 + 12r^3 + 104r^2 + 408r + 1156 = 0$

Use a computer to determine the general solution of the following equations.

4–94 (a) $y^{(iv)} - y = 0$ (b) $y''' + 3y'' + 4y' + 12y = 0$

4–95 (a) $y''' - y'' - 4y' - 6y = x + 5$
(b) $y''' - y = e^{3x}$

4–96 (a) $x^3y''' + x^2y'' + 4y = 0$
(b) $x^3y''' + 4x^2y'' - 6xy' - 12y = 0$

Determine the specific solution of the following initial-value problems using a computer to solve for the undetermined coefficients.

4–97 $y''' - 4y'' + 4y' = 0$, $y(0) = 0$, $y'(0) = 1$, and $y''(0) = 0$

4–98 $y''' - 3y'' + 3y' - y = 0$, $y(0) = 1$, and $y'(0) = y''(0) = 0$

Use a computer to determine the Wronskian for each of the following problems.

4–99 (a) $y''' - 3y'' + 3y' = 0$; e^x, xe^x, and x^2e^x
(b) $y''' - 3y'' + 3y' = 0$; e^x, $2e^x$, and $-3x^2e^x$

4–100 (a) $x^3y''' + 2x^2y'' - 2xy' = 0$; $\dfrac{1}{x}$, x^2, and 1
(b) $x^3y''' + 2x^2y'' - 2xy' = 0$; $e^{-\ln x}$, x^2, and 5

Review Problems

4–101 Verify that if y_1 is solution of

$$y''' + P_1(x)y'' + P_2(x)y' + P_3(x)y = 0$$

then the substitution $y = u(x)y_1$ gives the following second-order, linear, homogeneous equation in u'.

$$y_1 u''' + (3y_1' + P_1 y_1)u'' + (3y_1'' + 2P_1 y_1' + P_2 y_1)u' = 0.$$

Determine the general solution of the following linear, homogeneous equations for $x > 0$. Also, determine the arbitrary constants in the general solution when initial conditions are specified.

4–102 $y^{(iv)} - 16y = 0$

4–103 $y''' - y' = xe^{2x} \cos x$

4–104 $y''' + 2y'' + y' = 0$

4–105 $y''' = \dfrac{1}{x} + x \sin x$

4–106 $2x^3 y''' + 5x^2 y'' = x^2 - 1$

4–107 $y''' + 2y'' + 6y' + 4y = x^3 - 2$

4–108 $y^{(iv)} + 2y'' + y = 0$

4–109 $x^3 y''' + x^2 y'' = \dfrac{1}{x} - 2$

4–110 $y''' - 6y'' + 9y' = 0$

4–111 $y''' - 3y'' + 3y' - y = 0$

4–112 $y''' + y' = 0$, $y(0) = 0$, $y'(0) = y''(0) = 1$

4–113 $y''' + y = 4e^{3x} - x$

4–114 $y''' - 4y'' = x + 1$

4–115 $y''' - 4y'' + 3y = -e^{2x} - 1$

4–116 $y^{(iv)} - y'' = x^2 + 1 - e^x \sin x$

4–117 $y^{(iv)} + y = x \sin x$

4–118 $y''' - 9y' + 8y = x^2 e^{3x}$

4–119 $y^{(iv)} + 16y = xe^{2x} - 1$

4–120 $y^{(iv)} - y = 0$, $y(0) = 1$,
$\quad y'(0) = y''(0) = 0$, $y'''(0) = 1$

4–121 $y''' + 9y' = x^2 \cos 2x$

4–122 $x^3 y''' + 3x^2 y'' - 3xy' + 3y = 0$

4–123 $y^{(iv)} + 64y = 1$,
$\quad y(0) = y'(0) = y''(0) = y'''(0) = 0$

4–124 $x^4 y^{(iv)} - 4x^2 y'' - 6y = 0$

4–125 $x^3 y''' + 6y = 0$

4–126 $y''' + 4y'' + 4y' = x^2 - 1$, $y(0) = 0$, $y'(0) = 1$,
$\quad y''(0) = 2$

LINEAR DIFFERENTIAL EQUATIONS: VARIABLE COEFFICENTS

5

So far, we have considered linear differential equations with *constant coefficients*, because many equations always can be solved in a systematic manner in terms of elementary functions (such as exponentials, trigonometric functions, and logarithms). We also have considered Euler's equation as a special case of an equation with variable coefficients.

Now we are in a position to handle linear differential equations with *variable coefficients*. Such equations rarely can be solved in terms of elementary functions, and thus, we need to investigate other methods of solution. One method that is successfully used to solve differential equations with variable coefficients is the *method of series solutions*. This method is used to find exact or approximate solutions to linear and nonlinear equations with constant or variable coefficients.

In this chapter, we will apply the method of series solutions to second-order linear differential equations with variable coefficients that can be expressed as

$$y'' + P(x)y' + Q(x)y = 0$$

Such equations frequently occur in physical sciences and engineering, and the method of series solutions for such equations is well developed. The procedures discussed in this chapter also can be extended to higher-order linear equations.

In this method, the solution of a differential equation is expressed in terms of an infinite series with adjustable coefficients. The evaluation of an infinite series at a specified point—at least in appearance—requires the calculation and addition of an infinite number of terms, which looks like an endless task. In practice, however, the evaluation of a finite number of terms in the series is sufficient, since the series used in the solution are convergent and the terms approach zero as the index of summation gets larger.

There is no standard procedure for applying the method of series solutions to second-order, linear differential equations with variable coefficients. Not all such equations can be solved by this method with ease. Thus, it is necessary to classify the equations and develop procedures applicable to each class. Equations with continuous coefficients $P(x)$ and $Q(x)$ are relatively easy and straightforward to solve. Any complications in the solution procedure are due to the presence of discontinuous or singular points of $P(x)$ or $Q(x)$.

Objectives

When you have finished this chapter, you should be able to:

1. manipulate power series, test for convergence, and compute the interval of convergence,

2. identify ordinary points and singular points of variable coefficient, second-order equations, and compute the radius of convergence,

3. obtain power series solutions of second-order equations about an ordinary point,

4. identify and solve Legendre's equation,

5. obtain series solutions about a regular singular point, using the method of Frobenius,

6. identify and solve Bessel's equations, and

7. use a computer package to obtain the solution as a power series or in terms of special functions.

We start this chapter with a brief review of power series, since they are the backbone of the method of series solutions. After demonstrating the method, we will apply it to equations whose coefficients $P(x)$ and $Q(x)$ have no singular points in the region of interest. Then, we will extend the analysis to equations whose coefficients have certain forms of singularities in the region of interest. Finally, we will apply the method of series solutions to some well-known second-order differential equations having variable coefficients, such as Legendre's equation and Bessel's equation.

5–1 · REVIEW OF POWER SERIES

Power series form the basis of the method of series solutions, and thus, a good understanding of power series, their properties, and the terminology associated with them is essential in the study of this method. In this section, we will review power series to the extent necessary to follow and understand the method of series solution.

A mathematical function that is expressed as the sum of several terms is called a **series**, and a function that is expressed as the sum of an infinite number of terms is called an **infinite series**. An infinite series whose terms involve the powers of the variable in the form x^n or $(x - x_0)^n$ where n is a nonnegative integer, is called a **power series** and is expressed as (Figure 5–1)

$$f(x) = \sum_{n=0}^{\infty} C_n x^n = C_0 + C_1 x + C_2 x^2 + C_3 x^3 + \cdots \tag{5–1}$$

or

$$f(x - x_0) = \sum_{n=0}^{\infty} C_n (x - x_0)^n = C_0 + C_1(x - x_0) + C_2(x - x_0)^2 + \cdots \tag{5–2}$$

where x_0 is a fixed value of x. Here the constants C_n are called **coefficients** of the power series, and the point $x = x_0$ is called the **center**.

The Equation 5–1 is frequently referred to as a *power series about the point $x = 0$*, and Equation 5–2 is a *power series about the point $x = x_0$*. The series in Equation 5–2 can be obtained from Equation 5–1 simply by replacing x with $(x - x_0)$. Therefore, for simplicity in notation, we will usually consider power series in x with the understanding that they readily can be converted to a series in $(x - x_0)$ using a simple change of variable.

Many familiar elementary functions have well-known power series representations some of which are

$$e^x = \sum_{n=0}^{\infty} \frac{x^n}{n!} = 1 + x + \frac{x^2}{2!} + \frac{x^3}{3!} + \cdots \tag{5–3}$$

$$\sin x = \sum_{n=0}^{\infty} (-1)^n \frac{x^{2n+1}}{(2n + 1)!} = x - \frac{x^3}{3!} + \frac{x^5}{5!} - \cdots \tag{5–4}$$

$$\sinh x = \sum_{n=0}^{\infty} \frac{x^{2n+1}}{(2n + 1)!} = x + \frac{x^3}{3!} + \frac{x^5}{5!} + \cdots \tag{5–5}$$

$$\cos x = \sum_{n=0}^{\infty} (-1)^n \frac{x^{2n}}{(2n)!} = 1 - \frac{x^2}{2!} + \frac{x^4}{4!} - \cdots \tag{5–6}$$

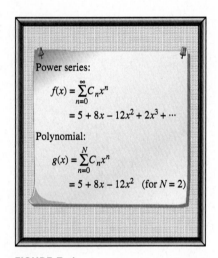

FIGURE 5–1

A power series is an infinite series whose terms are of the form $C_n x^n$, where n is an integer. A polynomial is a power series with a finite number of terms.

$$\cosh x = \sum_{n=0}^{\infty} \frac{x^{2n}}{(2n)!} = 1 + \frac{x^2}{2!} + \frac{x^4}{4!} + \cdots \tag{5-7}$$

$$\tan^{-1} x = \sum_{n=0}^{\infty} (-1)^n \frac{x^{2n+1}}{2n+1} = x - \frac{x^3}{3} + \frac{x^5}{5} - \cdots \tag{5-8}$$

Note that the factorial of n is the product $n! = 1 \cdot 2 \cdot 3, \ldots, n$, with $0! = 1$ by definition (Figure 5–2). Also note that $x^0 = 1$ for all x, including $x = 0$. A series representation is said to **converge** to the function it represents if the value of the series for a specific value of x approaches the value of the function as more terms are included in the series. The series in Equations 5–3 to 5–8 converge to their respective functions for real values of x.

The power series in Equations 5–3 through 5–8, as well as the power series of other functions, can be obtained from their Taylor series expansion about the point $x = 0$. The **Taylor series** of any function $f(x)$ about a point x_0 is expressed as the power series

$$f(x - x_0) = \sum_{n=0}^{\infty} \frac{f^{(n)}(x_0)}{n!}(x - x_0)^n$$

$$= f(x_0) + f'(x_0)(x - x_0) + \frac{f''(x_0)}{2!}(x - x_0)^2 + \cdots \tag{5-9}$$

provided that the derivatives $f', f'', \ldots, f^{(n)}$ exist (in other words, if the function is infinitely differentiable). The series expansion of elementary functions can be obtained from Equation 5–9 by performing the indicated differentiations at the point $x_0 = 0$ (see Figure 5–3).

The Greek symbol *sigma* in the power series notation

$$\sum_{n=0}^{\infty} C_n x^n$$

denotes *summation*, and n denotes the *index of summation* which serves as a counter. The index of summation is a dummy parameter (just like the dummy variable in a definite integral), and it makes no difference whether we denote it by n, m, i, j, or k. For example,

$$\sum_{n=2}^{4} n^2 x^n = 4x^2 + 9x^3 + 16x^4 = \sum_{i=2}^{4} i^2 x^i \tag{5-10}$$

Two power series are *identical* if they represent the same function. Therefore, if

$$\sum_{n=0}^{\infty} C_n x^n = \sum_{n=0}^{\infty} D_n x^n \tag{5-11}$$

for all x in some interval, then $C_n = D_n$ for all $n = 0,1,2,3, \ldots$. As a special case, if a power series is equal to zero for all x in some interval, then $C_n = 0$ for all $n = 0, 1, 2, 3 \ldots$.

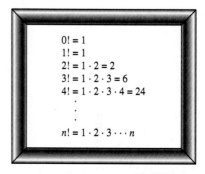

$0! = 1$
$1! = 1$
$2! = 1 \cdot 2 = 2$
$3! = 1 \cdot 2 \cdot 3 = 6$
$4! = 1 \cdot 2 \cdot 3 \cdot 4 = 24$
$\vdots$
$n! = 1 \cdot 2 \cdot 3 \cdots n$

FIGURE 5–2

The factorial function.

Polynomial:

$$f(x) = x^2 - 1$$

then

$$f'(x) = 2x$$
$$f''(x) = 2$$
$$f^{(n)}(x) = 0, \quad n = 3, 4, 5, \ldots$$

At $x = 0$:

$$f(0) = -1$$
$$f'(0) = 0$$
$$f''(0) = 2$$
$$f''(0) = 0, \quad n = 3, 4, 5, \ldots$$

Taylor series:

$$f(x - 0) = \sum_{n=0}^{\infty} \frac{f^{(n)}(0)}{n!}(x - 0)^n$$

$$= -1 + 0 + \frac{2}{2!}x^2$$

$$= x^2 - 1$$

$$= f(x)$$

FIGURE 5–3

Taylor series expansions of polynomials about the origin are equivalent to themselves.

A series expression can be manipulated just like a definite integral. For example,

$$\sum_{n=3}^{8} C_n x^n = \sum_{n=3}^{5} C_n x^n + \sum_{n=6}^{8} C_n x_n \tag{5-12}$$

$$\sum_{n=3}^{8} C_n x^n = \sum_{n=0}^{8} C_n x^n - \sum_{n=0}^{2} C_n x^n \tag{5-13}$$

$$\sum_{n=0}^{10} 2C_n x^n = 2\sum_{n=0}^{10} C_n x^n \tag{5-14}$$

$$x^2 \sum_{n=1}^{7} C_n x^n = \sum_{n=1}^{7} C_n x^{n+2} \tag{5-15}$$

Note that any quantity that does not depend on the index of summation can be moved into or out of summation sign, just like a quantity that does not depend on the integration variable can be moved into or out of the integration sign (Figure 5–4).

Sometimes, it is convenient to write out some of the terms in a summation individually and keep the remainder of the terms in the summation. For example,

$$\sum_{n=0}^{\infty} C_n x^{2n} = C_0 + C_1 x^2 + C_2 x^4 + \sum_{n=3}^{\infty} C_n x^{2n}$$

Shifting the Index of Summation

Often it is necessary to shift the index of summation, especially when combining series whose general terms are not of the same power. The index can be shifted forward or backward by any amount as long as equality is maintained. That is, both series have the same terms when expanded. For example, consider the following three representations of polynomials. They are identical despite the difference in their appearances.

$$f(x) = \sum_{n=2}^{4} (n + 1)x^2 = 3x^2 + 4x^3 + 5x^4 \tag{5-16}$$

$$f(x) = \sum_{i=0}^{2} (i + 3)x^{i+2} = 3x^2 + 4x^3 + 5x^4 \tag{5-17}$$

$$f(x) = \sum_{j=5}^{7} (j - 2)x^{j-3} = 3x^2 + 4x^3 + 5x^4 \tag{5-18}$$

Any two of these can be obtained from the other one by simply shifting the index. In this example, Equation 5–17 is obtained from Equation 5–16 by replacing n by $i + 2$, and Equation 5–18 is obtained from Equation 5–16 by replacing n by $j - 3$.

Let us say that we would like to re-express Equation 5–16 such that the power of x changes from n to $i + 2$. The easiest way to do this is to replace

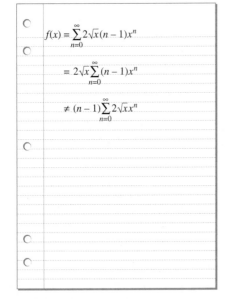

FIGURE 5–4

A quantity that does not depend on the index of summation can be moved into or out of the summation.

every occurrence of n in the series, including the ones under and above the summation sign, by $i + 2$. We obtain

$$f(x) = \sum_{i+2=2}^{i+2=4} (i + 2 + 1)x^{i+2} = \sum_{i=0}^{2} (i + 3)x^{i+2}$$

which is Equation 5–17. If we wish, we can switch back to the index n from i, so that

$$f(x) = \sum_{n=0}^{2} (n + 3)x^{n+2}$$

Of course we could avoid this step by replacing n at the beginning by $n + 2$ instead of by $i + 2$.

A practical rule on using the shift of the index is, when increasing the index in the expression by a number, decrease it from the limits on the summation by the same number, and vice versa (Figure 5–5). In the previous example, when we increased the index in the expression by 2, we also decreased both summation limits by 2. When dealing with infinite series, the upper limit of summation is not affected by the shifting process and always remains infinity, since infinity plus or minus a finite number is still infinity.

$$f(x) = \sum_{n=0}^{\infty} nx^{2n}$$

$$= \sum_{n=1}^{\infty} (n - 1)x^{2(n-1)}$$

$$= \sum_{n=2}^{\infty} (n - 2)x^{2(n-2)}$$

$$= \sum_{n=i}^{\infty} (n - i)x^{2(n-i)}$$

FIGURE 5–5

The index of summation n can be shifted by i by replacing occurrences of n with $n - i$.

EXAMPLE 5–1   Shifting the Index of Summation

Shift the index of summation of the series

$$f(x) = \sum_{n=1}^{\infty} n^2 \frac{(x - x_0)^{n+3}}{2^{n+1}}$$

so that the power of $(x - x_0)$ is n.

SOLUTION   By inspection, we see that we can achieve the desired shift by simply replacing all occurrences of n by $n - 3$, so

$$f(x) = \sum_{n-3=1}^{\infty} (n - 3)^2 \frac{(x - x_0)^{n-3+3}}{2^{n-3+1}} = \sum_{n=4}^{\infty} (n - 3)^2 \frac{(x - x_0)^n}{2^{n-2}}$$

which is the desired result (Figure 5–6). The equivalence of the two series easily can be verified by writing out the individual terms of both series and observing that the corresponding terms are exactly the same:

$$\sum_{n=1}^{\infty} n^2 \frac{(x - x_0)^{n+3}}{2^{n+1}} = \frac{(x - x_0)^4}{2^2} + 2^2 \frac{(x - x_0)^5}{2^3} + 3^2 \frac{(x - x_0)^6}{2^4} + \cdots$$

and

$$\sum_{n=4}^{\infty} (n - 3)^2 \frac{(x - x_0)^n}{2^{n-2}} = \frac{(x - x_0)^4}{2^2} + 2^2 \frac{(x - x_0)^5}{2^3} + 3^2 \frac{(x - x_0)^6}{2^4} + \cdots$$

Thus, the two power series are identical.

$$f(x) = \sum_{n=1}^{\infty} n^2 \frac{(x - x_0)^{n+3}}{2^{n+1}}$$

$$= \sum_{n=4}^{\infty} (n - 3)^2 \frac{(x - x_0)^n}{2^{n-2}}$$

FIGURE 5–6

Shifting the index of summation in Example 5–1 by 3.

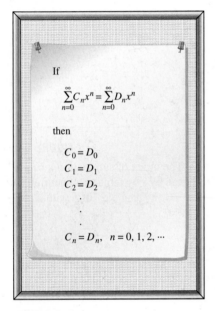

FIGURE 5–7

If two power series are equivalent, their corresponding coefficients must be equal for each power of x.

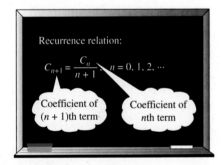

FIGURE 5–8

A relation that relates two or more coefficients of a series to each other is called a recurrence relation.

EXAMPLE 5–2   **Manipulating the Power Series**

Using the properties of equivalent series, determine the coefficients C_n in the power series expansion of the exponential function e^x:

$$e^x = \sum_{n=0}^{\infty} C_n x^n = C_0 + C_1 x + C_2 x^2 + C_3 x^3 + \cdots$$

SOLUTION   We easily can determine the first coefficient C_0 by evaluating both sides of the expression at $x = 0$. It yields

$$e^0 = C_0 + 0 + 0 + 0 + \cdots \rightarrow C_0 = 1$$

We now take the first derivative of both sides:

$$\frac{de^x}{dx} = 0 + C_1 + 2C_2 x + 3C_3 x^2 + \cdots + nC_n x^{n-1} + \cdots = \sum_{n-1}^{\infty} nC_n x^{n-1}$$

Noting that the first derivative of e^x is equal to e^x itself, their series expansions must also be equal, so

$$\sum_{n=1}^{\infty} nC_n x^{n-1} = \sum_{n=0}^{\infty} C_n x^n$$

To equate the powers of x on both sides, we shift the index of the first summation by 1 by replacing all occurrences of n by $n + 1$. We obtain

$$\sum_{n=0}^{\infty} (n + 1) C_{n+1} x^n = \sum_{n=0}^{\infty} C_n x^n$$

For this equality to hold for all x, the corresponding coefficients of the two series must be equal (Figure 5–7). This condition gives us the relation we are looking for:

$$(n + 1) C_{n+1} = C_n \quad \text{or} \quad C_{n+1} = \frac{C_n}{n + 1} \tag{5–19}$$

A relation such as Equation 5–19 that relates two or more coefficients of the power series to each other is called a **recurrence relation** (Figure 5–8). In this case, the recurrence relation relates a coefficient to the one before it. Thus, since the first coefficient is available ($C_0 = 1$), the remainder of the coefficients ($C_1, C_2, C_3, C_4, \ldots$) can be determined from the recurrence relation as

$$n = 0: \quad C_1 = \frac{C_0}{1} = \frac{1}{1!}$$

$$n = 1: \quad C_2 = \frac{C_1}{2} = \frac{1}{2!}$$

$$n = 2: \quad C_3 = \frac{C_2}{3} = \frac{1}{3!}$$

$$n = 3: \quad C_4 = \frac{C_3}{4} = \frac{1}{4!}$$

Generalizing, we obtain

$$C_n = \frac{C_0}{n!} = \frac{1}{n!}, \quad n = 1, 2, 3, 4, \dots \qquad \text{(5–20)}$$

Thus, we have determined all of the coefficients. Substituting these coefficients into the given power series yields

$$e^x = \sum_{n=0}^{\infty} \frac{x^n}{n!}$$

which is the Taylor series expansion about $x = 0$ of the exponential function.

Convergence of Power Series

When dealing with series, a matter of utmost importance is **convergence**. A series representation of a function is of little use if the series does not converge to the function. For example, the series representation of the elementary functions given in Equations 5–3 through 5–8 converge to the function they represent for all values of x. But the power series expansion of

$$\frac{1}{1-x} = \sum_{n=0}^{\infty} x^n = 1 + x + x^2 + x^3 + \cdots \qquad \text{(5–21)}$$

converges to $1/(1-x)$ only for the values of $|x| < 1$. For $x = 3$, for example, the series diverges (becomes infinite) instead of converging to the correct value of -0.5. Therefore, it is often necessary to speak of convergence in an interval or in a range of x values instead of the entire x axis (from $-\infty$ to $+\infty$).

The convergence of power series can be defined as follows:

A power series of the form $\sum_{n=0}^{\infty} C_n x^n$ is said to converge on an interval I if the limit $\lim_{n \to \infty} \sum_{k=0}^{n} C_k x^k$ exists for all x in that interval.

In other words, a power series converges at a given x if the sum of all of its terms is a finite number for that x value (Figure 5–9).

The easiest way to check the convergence of a power series is to apply the **ratio test**, which is based on comparing the nth and $(n + 1)$th terms of the series and taking the limit as $n \to \infty$ (Figure 5–10),

$$L = \lim_{n \to \infty} \left| \frac{C_{n+1} x^{n+1}}{C_n x^n} \right| = |x| \lim_{n \to \infty} \left| \frac{C_{n+1}}{C_n} \right| \qquad \text{(5–22)}$$

The power series converges for a given x value if $L < 1$ and diverges if $L > 1$. The ratio test fails if $L = 1$. In other words, the power series converges for a given x value if the absolute value of the terms decreases as n increases. That is, a power series will converge for a given x if its nth term approaches zero as $n \to \infty$.

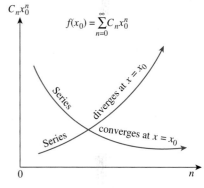

FIGURE 5–9

A power series is said to converge at a specified x value if the absolute value of the terms in the series decreases as the index n increases.

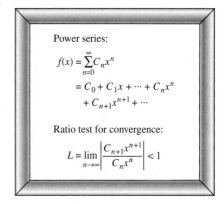

FIGURE 5–10

The ratio test for convergence is based on comparing the absolute values of the nth and $(n + 1)$th terms as $n \to \infty$.

EXAMPLE 5-3   **Convergence of Power Series**

Determine if the following power series converges at $x = 0.4$ and $x = -2$:

$$\frac{1}{(1 + x)^2} = \sum_{n \to 0}^{\infty} (-1)^n (n + 1) x^n = 1 - 2x + 3x^2 - 4x^3 + \cdots \qquad \text{(5-23)}$$

SOLUTION   Applying the ratio test, we have

$$L = \lim_{n \to \infty} \left| \frac{(-1)^{n+1}(n + 2)x^{n+1}}{(-1)^n(n + 1)x^n} \right| = |x| \lim_{n \to \infty} \left| \frac{n + 2}{n + 1} \right| = |x|$$

Thus, we have $L = |x|$ and this power series will converge for $|x| < 1$. Therefore, the given power series will converge for $x = 0.4$ but will diverge for $x = -2$.

EXAMPLE 5-4   **Interval of Convergence of Power Series**

Determine the range of x values for which the following power series converges:

$$f(x) = \sum_{n=1}^{\infty} (n + 2)(x + 3)^n$$

SOLUTION   Applying the ratio test, we have

$$L = \lim_{n \to \infty} \left| \frac{(n + 3)(x + 3)^{n+1}}{(n + 2)(x + 3)^n} \right| = |x + 3| \lim_{n \to \infty} \left| \frac{n + 3}{n + 2} \right| = |x + 3|$$

Thus, we have $L = |x + 3|$, and this power series will converge for $|x + 3| < 1$ or $-4 < x < -2$. It will diverge for all other values of x, specifically for $x < -4$ and $x = -4$ since the nth term of the series approaches infinity instead of zero, as $n \to \infty$.

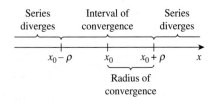

FIGURE 5-11

Geometrical representation of the interval of convergence and the radius of convergence.

On the x-axis, the open interval in which the power series $\sum_{n=0}^{\infty} C_n(x - x_0)^n$ converges is called the **interval of convergence**, and this interval can be determined from the ratio test. The interval of convergence often is described in terms of the **radius of convergence** ρ, which can be viewed as the distance between the center x_0 of the series and the closest point at which the series diverges (Figure 5-11). The interval of convergence of a power series of center x_0 is usually described in terms of the radius of convergence as $|x - x_0| < \rho$, as shown in Figure 5-11. For $\rho = 0$, the power series diverges for all except $x = x_0$. For $\rho = \infty$, the series converges for all x, and the interval of convergence in this case is the entire x axis. In general, ρ is a finite number, and the series converges for $|x - x_0| < \rho$ and diverges when $|x - x_0| > \rho$. At the end points $x = x_0 - \rho$ and $x = x_0 + \rho$, the series may converge or diverge. The convergence at these points can be checked separately by substituting these values into the series and taking the limit in each case.

The radius of convergence of a power series of the form $\sum_{n=0}^{\infty} C_n(x - x_0)^n$ can be determined directly from

$$\rho = \lim_{n \to \infty} \left| \frac{C_n}{C_{n+1}} \right| \tag{5-24}$$

But this relation is not applicable to series that involve exponents other than n, such as $\sum C_n(x - x_0)^{2n}$ or $\sum C_n(x - x_0)^{n^3}$.

EXAMPLE 5–5   **Radius of Convergence of Power Series**

Determine the radius of convergence and the interval of convergence of the power series

$$f(x) = \sum_{n=1}^{\infty} \frac{(x - 3)^n}{2^n}$$

using (a) the ratio test and (b) Equation 5–24.

SOLUTION   (a) Applying the ratio test, we have

$$L = \lim_{n \to \infty} \left| \frac{(n + 1)\text{th term}}{n\text{th term}} \right| = \lim_{n \to \infty} \left| \frac{(x - 3)^{n+1}/2^{n+1}}{(x - 3)^n/2^n} \right| = |x - 3| \lim_{n \to \infty} \frac{1}{2} = \frac{|x + 3|}{2}$$

The series will converge for $\frac{|x - 3|}{2} < 1$ or $|x - 3| < 2$. Thus, the interval of convergence is $1 < x < 5$, and the radius of convergence is $\rho = 2$, which is half the length of convergence interval.
 (b) Using Equation 5–24, the radius of convergence is determined to be

$$\rho = \lim_{n \to \infty} \left| \frac{C_n}{C_{n+1}} \right| = \lim_{n \to \infty} \frac{1/2^n}{1/2^{n+1}} = 2$$

The center of the power series is $x_0 = 3$, and thus, the interval of convergence is $x_0 - \rho < x < x_0 + \rho$ or $1 < x < 5$ (Figure 5–12).

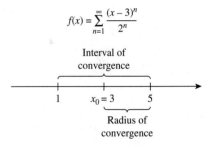

$$f(x) = \sum_{n=1}^{\infty} \frac{(x - 3)^n}{2^n}$$

Interval of convergence

FIGURE 5–12

The interval of convergence and the radius of convergence of the power series discussed in Example 5–5.

If the power series $f(x) = \sum_{n=1}^{\infty} a_n(x - x_0)^n$ and $g(x) = \sum_{n=1}^{\infty} b_n(x - x_0)^n$ both converge in the interval I, then their sum, difference, and product also will converge in that interval (Figure 5–13).

1. $f(x) + g(x) = \sum_{n=0}^{\infty} (a_n + b_n)(x - x_0)^n \tag{5-25}$

2. $f(x) - g(x) = \sum_{n=0}^{\infty} (a_n - b_n)(x - x_0)^n \tag{5-26}$

3. $f(x)g(x) = \sum_{n=0}^{\infty} (a_0 b_n + a_1 b_{n-1} + a_2 b_{n-2} + \cdots + a_n b_0)(x - x_0)^n \tag{5-27}$

If two power series converge in an interval, then

• their sum
• their difference
• their product

also converge in that interval.

FIGURE 5–13

Extending the convergence of power series.

Also for $g(x) \neq 0$, the two power series can be divided to yield

$$\frac{f(x)}{g(x)} = \frac{\sum_{n=0}^{\infty} a_n(x - x_0)^n}{\sum_{n=0}^{\infty} b_n(x - x_0)^n} = \sum_{n=0}^{\infty} C_n(x - x_0)^n \tag{5-28}$$

where the new coefficients C_n are determined by formally dividing the expanded forms of the two series, a process that is quite laborious and cumbersome. Also, the resultant series may have a smaller radius of convergence than either series, since $f(x)/g(x)$ may diverge at the zeros of $g(x)$.

Derivatives of Power Series

The power series is essentially a polynomial with an infinite number of terms, and thus, it is infinitely differentiable in its interval of convergence. The derivatives f', f'', $\ldots, f^{(n)}$ can be determined by term-by-term differentiation. The derivatives of $f(x)$, which are also power series, converge in the interval of convergence of $f(x)$. The first term of a power series (corresponding to $n = 0$) is the constant C_0, which drops out during differentiation. Therefore, the summation on the first derivative starts with $n = 1$ instead of $n = 0$. The value of n increases by one with each differentiation. If

$$f(x) = C_0 + C_1(x - x_0) + C_2(x - x_0)^2 + C_3(x - x_0)^3 + \cdots$$

$$= \sum_{n=0}^{\infty} C_n(x - x_0)^n$$

then

$$f'(x) = C_1 + 2C_2(x - x_0) + 3C_3(x - x_0)^2 + \cdots$$

$$= \sum_{n=1}^{\infty} C_n n(x - x_0)^{n-1} \tag{5-29}$$

$$f''(x) = 2C_2 + 2 \cdot 3 C_3(x - x_0) + \cdots$$

$$= \sum_{n=2}^{\infty} C_n(n - 1)n(x - x_0)^{n-2} \tag{5-30}$$

and so on. At $x = x_0$, we have $f(x_0) = C_0$, $f'(x_0) = C_1$, $f''(x_0) = 2C_2$, and (in general) $f^{(n)}(x_0) = n!C_n$. Solving for C_n, we have

$$C_n = \frac{f^{(n)}(x_0)}{n!} \tag{5-31}$$

Substituting this into the power series, we obtain

$$f(x) = \sum_{n=0}^{\infty} \frac{f^{(n)}(x_0)}{n!}(x - x_0)^n \tag{5-32}$$

which is the formula for the Taylor series expansion of the function $f(x)$.

Thus, if a function is infinitely differentiable at a point x_0, its Taylor series exists at that point. Also, if the Taylor series expansion of a function $f(x)$ at a point x_0 and its immediate vicinity exists, then that function is said to be **analytic** at that point. Therefore, *any function that is analytic at x_0 can be expressed as a power series of center x_0 with a nonzero radius of convergence.*

In light of this discussion, we can say that if the functions $f(x)$ and $g(x)$ are analytic at x_0, so are the functions $f(x) + g(x), f(x) - g(x), f(x) \cdot g(x)$, and even $f(x)/g(x)$—except when $g(x_0) = 0$. For example, the functions e^x, $\sin x$, $\cos x$, $\sinh x$, and $\cosh x$ are analytic everywhere. Also, every polynomial is analytic at every point. The sums, differences, products, and quotients (except at the zeros of the denominator) of polynomials are also analytic everywhere (Figure 5–14).

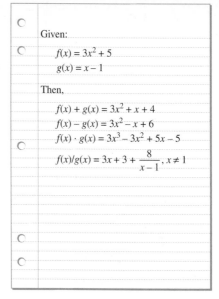

Given:

$f(x) = 3x^2 + 5$

$g(x) = x - 1$

Then,

$f(x) + g(x) = 3x^2 + x + 4$

$f(x) - g(x) = 3x^2 - x + 6$

$f(x) \cdot g(x) = 3x^3 - 3x^2 + 5x - 5$

$f(x)/g(x) = 3x + 3 + \dfrac{8}{x-1}, x \neq 1$

FIGURE 5–14

All polynomials: their sums, differences, products, and quotients (except at the zeros of the denominator) are analytic everywhere.

Section Review

Problems Denoted with a C are Conceptual Problems for Discussion

5–1C What is a power series? How does it differ from a polynomial?

5–2C In what ways are the index of a summation and the variable of a definite integral similar?

5–3C Consider a power series whose index of summation is n. Under what conditions can a factor inside the summation be moved outside of it?

5–4C Under what conditions are two power series identical?

5–5 Write out the first three terms of the following series while keeping the rest of the terms under the summation.

(a) $2\sum_{n=0}^{\infty} nx^n$ (b) $-3x\sum_{n=0}^{\infty} nC_n x^{2n}$

(*Answers:* (a) $2x + 4x^2 + 6x^3 + 2\sum_{n=0}^{\infty} nx^n$ and (b) $-3C_1 x^3 - 6C_2 x^5 - 9C_3 x^7 - 3x\sum_{n=4}^{\infty} nC_n x^{2n}$)

5–6 Shift the index of the following summations such that the power of x in each of them is n.

(a) $\sum_{n=0}^{\infty} \dfrac{x^{n+2}}{n!}$ (b) $\sum_{n=4}^{\infty} nC_n x^{n-3}$

(*Answers:* (a) $\sum_{n=2}^{\infty} \dfrac{x^n}{(n-2)!}$ (b) $\sum_{n=1}^{\infty} (n+3)C_{n+3} x^n$)

5–7 Prove that the following equality is correct.

$$\sum_{n=0}^{\infty} (n+2)x^n + 2\sum_{n=1}^{\infty} nx^n = 2 + \sum_{n=1}^{\infty} (3n+2)x^n = 0$$

5–8 Determine the interval of convergence and the radius of convergence of the following power series.

(a) $\sum_{n=0}^{\infty} nx^n$ (b) $\sum_{n=2}^{\infty} \dfrac{n+1}{2^n} x^{n-1}$

(*Answers:* (a) The interval of convergence is $[-1,1)$. (b) The interval of convergence is $[-2,2)$.)

5–2 ▪ INTRODUCTION TO POWER SERIES SOLUTIONS

The method of power series solution is based on assuming that a given differential equation has a series solution of the form

$$\sum_{n=0}^{\infty} C_n x^n \quad \text{or} \quad \sum_{n=0}^{\infty} C_n (x - x_0)^n$$

substituting this assumed solution into the given differential equation, performing the indicated derivations, and finally determining the unknown coefficients, C_n. We will demonstrate the method on some simple examples to familiarize ourselves with it and to gain a better understanding and appreciation of it before introducing the theory associated with it. We will do this first with equations having constant coefficients and then with equations having variable coefficients.

EXAMPLE 5–6   **Power Series Solution Method**

Solve the following initial-value problem assuming a power series solution,

$$y' - y = 0 \qquad y(0) = 1$$

SOLUTION This is a first-order, linear, homogeneous differential equation with constant coefficients, and its solution easily can be determined by separating the variables or by using the solution procedure for linear equations to be $y = e^x$. Now we will ignore this solution (we will even ignore the existence of the exponential function e^x), and we will attempt to solve this equation by assuming a power series solution of the form

$$y = \sum_{n=0}^{\infty} C_n x^n$$

Differentiating term by term, we have

$$y' = \sum_{n=1}^{\infty} n C_n x^{n-1}$$

Substituting into the differential equation, we have

$$\sum_{n=1}^{\infty} n C_n x^{n-1} - \sum_{n=0}^{\infty} C_n x^n = 0$$

Then equate the powers of x in both summations; we shift the index of the first summation by 1 and replace n by $n - 1$. It yields

$$\sum_{n=0}^{\infty} (n + 1) C_{n+1} x^n - \sum_{n=0}^{\infty} C_n x^n = 0$$

or

$$\sum_{n=0}^{\infty} [(n + 1) C_{n+1} - C_n] x^n = 0$$

This equation will be satisfied for all x if and only if the coefficient of each power of x is zero (Figure 5–15). This condition gives us an infinite number of equations for the determination of the expansion coefficients C_n: $(n + 1)C_{n+1} - C_n = 0$ or

$$C_{n+1} = \frac{C_n}{(n + 1)}, \qquad n = 0, 1, 2, 3, \ldots \qquad \text{(5–33)}$$

In this case, Equation 5–33 is the recurrence relation, and it relates any coefficient to the one before it. Thus, if the first coefficient C_0 is available, the remainder of the coefficients $(C_1, C_2, C_3, C_4, \ldots)$ can be determined from the recurrence relation, Equation 5–33:

$$n = 0: \qquad C_1 = \frac{C_0}{1} = \frac{C_0}{1!}$$

$$n = 1: \qquad C_2 = \frac{C_1}{2} = \frac{C_0}{2!}$$

$$n = 2: \qquad C_3 = \frac{C_2}{3} = \frac{C_0}{3!}$$

$$n = 3: \qquad C_4 = \frac{C_3}{4} = \frac{C_0}{4!}$$

Generalizing, we obtain

$$C_n = \frac{C_0}{n!}, \qquad n = 1, 2, 3, 4, \ldots$$

Thus, we have determined all of the coefficients in the assumed power series solutions except C_0. Substituting these coefficients into the solution and factoring out C_0, we obtain

$$Y = C_0\left[1 + \frac{x}{1!} + \frac{x^2}{2!} + \frac{x^3}{3!} + \cdots + \frac{x^n}{n!} + \cdots\right] = C_0\sum_{n=0}^{\infty}\frac{x^n}{n!}$$

Applying the initial condition $y(0) = 1$ yields $C_0 = 1$, since all of the terms in the series (except the first one) drop out at $x = 0$. Substituting, we obtain the series solution to be

$$y = \sum_{n=0}^{\infty}\frac{x^n}{n!} = e^x$$

since the series in the above relation is exactly the Taylor series expansion of the exponential function e^x. Thus, we obtained the same result with the power series solution method.

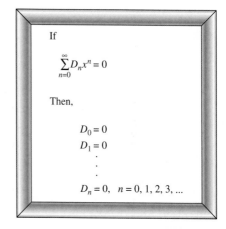

FIGURE 5–15

A power series will be equal to zero for all x if and only if the coefficient of each power of x is zero.

Of course, the procedure here is more complex than other methods, but our purpose is to demonstrate the new method and to build confidence that it really works before we apply it to problems that cannot be solved by any other analytic method.

EXAMPLE 5–7   Power Series Solution Method

Solve the following differential equation assuming a power series solution: $y'' + y = 0$.

SOLUTION   This is a linear, second-order, homogeneous differential equation with constant coefficients, and its general solution was determined in Chapter 3 to be

$$y = C_0 \sin x + C_1 \cos x$$

Now we will ignore this solution (we will even ignore the existence of the sine and cosine functions), and we will attempt to solve this equation by assuming a power series solution of the form

$$y = \sum_{n=0}^{\infty} C_n x^n$$

Differentiating twice term by term (Figure 5–16), we have

$$y' = \sum_{n=1}^{\infty} n C_n x^{n-1}$$

$$y'' = \sum_{n=2}^{\infty} n(n-1) C_n x^{n-2}$$

Substituting into the differential equation, we obtain

$$\sum_{n=2}^{\infty} n(n-1) C_n x^{n-2} + \sum_{n=0}^{\infty} C_n x^n = 0$$

To equate the powers of x in both summations, we shift the index of the first summation by 2 by replacing n by $n - 2$. This yields

$$\sum_{n=0}^{\infty} (n+2)(n+1) C_{n+2} x^n + \sum_{n=0}^{\infty} C_n x^n = 0$$

or

$$\sum_{n=0}^{\infty} [(n+2)(n+1) C_{n+2} + C_n] x^n = 0$$

This equation will be satisfied for all x if and only if the coefficient of each power of x is zero. This condition gives us an infinite number of equations for the determination of the expansion coefficients C_n: $(n+2)(n+1) C_{n+2} + C_n = 0$ or

$$C_{n+2} = \frac{C_n}{(n+2)(n+1)}, \qquad n = 0, 1, 2, 3, \ldots \tag{5–34}$$

In this case, Equation 5–34 is the recurrence relation, and it relates any coefficient to the second one before it. Thus, if the first two coefficients C_0 and C_1 are available, the remainder of the coefficients ($C_2, C_3, C_4, C_5, \ldots$) can be determined from the previous recurrence relation.

When n is even ($n = 2k = 2, 4, 6, \ldots$), the recurrence relation yields

$$C_2 = -\frac{C_0}{2 \cdot 1} = -\frac{C_0}{2!}$$

$$C_4 = -\frac{C_2}{4 \cdot 3} = \frac{C_0}{4!}$$

$$C_6 = -\frac{C_4}{6 \cdot 5} = -\frac{C_0}{6!}$$

FIGURE 5–16

The lower limit of the index of a power series may move up during differentiation, since the derivative of constant terms is zero.

If

$$y = \sum_{n=0}^{\infty} C_n x^n = 0$$

$$= C_0 + C_1 x + C_2 x^2 + \cdots$$

Then

$$y' = \sum_{n=0}^{\infty} n C_n x^{n-1}$$

$$= 0 + C_1 + 2C_2 x + 3C_3 x^2 + \cdots$$

$$= \sum_{n=1}^{\infty} n C_n x^{n-1}$$

Generalizing, we obtain

$$C_{n,\text{even}} = C_{2k} = (-1)^k \frac{C_0}{(2k)!}, \qquad k = 1, 2, 3, \ldots$$

When n is odd ($n = 2k + 1 = 3, 5, 7, \ldots$) the recurrence relation yields

$$C_3 = -\frac{C_1}{3 \cdot 2} = -\frac{C_1}{3!}$$

$$C_5 = -\frac{C_3}{5 \cdot 4} = \frac{C_1}{5!}$$

$$C_7 = -\frac{C_5}{7 \cdot 6} = -\frac{C_1}{7!}$$

Generalizing, we have

$$C_{n,\text{odd}} = C_{2k+1} = (-1)^k \frac{C_1}{(2k + 1)!}, \qquad k = 1, 2, 3, \ldots$$

Thus, we have determined all the coefficients in the assumed power series solution, except for C_0 and C_1. Substituting these coefficients into the solution and factoring out C_0 and C_1 yields (Figure 5–17)

$$
\begin{aligned}
y &= C_0 \left[1 - \frac{x^2}{2!} + \frac{x^4}{4!} - \cdots + (-1)^n \frac{x^{2n}}{(2n)!} + \cdots \right] \\
&\quad + C_1 \left[x - \frac{x^3}{3!} + \frac{x^5}{5!} - \cdots + (-1)^n \frac{x^{2n+1}}{(2n + 1)!} + \cdots \right] \\
&= C_0 \sum_{n=0}^{\infty} (-1)^n \frac{x^{2n}}{(2n)!} + C_1 \sum_{n=0}^{\infty} (-1)^n \frac{x^{2n+1}}{(2n + 1)!} \\
&= C_0 \cos x + C_1 \sin x
\end{aligned}
$$

(5–35)

since the two series in Equation 5–35 are exactly the Taylor series expansions of $\cos x$ and $\sin x$, respectively (recall that $0! = 1$, so there is no division by zero with the $n = 0$ term in the series expansion of the cosine). Thus, we obtained the same result with the power series solution method. Notice that the constant coefficients C_0 and C_1 are completely arbitrary and are determined from the initial conditions $y(0)$ and $y'(0)$. This is not surprising, since the general solution of a second-order, linear differential equation involves two arbitrary constants.

It is also worth noting that many properties of the functions $\cos x$ and $\sin x$ can be derived using their power series representations. We immediately see that $\cos 0 = 1$ and $\sin 0 = 0$. We also can show easily using term-by-term differentiation that $(\cos x)' = -\sin x$ and $(\sin x)' = \cos x$.

Ordinarily, the functions $\cos x$ and $\sin x$ are defined by referring to a right triangle in trigonometry. This example demonstrates that the power series solution of certain differential equations may also be used to define basic functions. For example, we can define $\cos x$ as the solution of the following initial-value problem.

$$y'' + y = 0 \quad \text{with} \quad y(0) = 1, y'(0) = 0$$

and $\sin x$ as the solution of the initial-value problem

$$y'' + y = 0 \quad \text{with} \quad y(0) = 0, y'(0) = 1$$

Indeed, many well-known functions such as the *Bessel functions* and *Legendre polynomials* are defined in this manner.

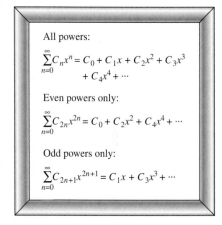

All powers:

$$\sum_{n=0}^{\infty} C_n x^n = C_0 + C_1 x + C_2 x^2 + C_3 x^3 + C_4 x^4 + \cdots$$

Even powers only:

$$\sum_{n=0}^{\infty} C_{2n} x^{2n} = C_0 + C_2 x^2 + C_4 x^4 + \cdots$$

Odd powers only:

$$\sum_{n=0}^{\infty} C_{2n+1} x^{2n+1} = C_1 x + C_3 x^3 + \cdots$$

FIGURE 5–17

All even powers of x can be represented by x^{2n}, and all odd powers of x can be represented by x^{2n-1}, where $n = 0, 1, 2, \ldots$.

EXAMPLE 5–8   **Power Series Solution Method**

Solve the following differential equation assuming a power series solution: $(x - 1)y' + 2y = 0$.

SOLUTION   This is a linear, first-order, homogeneous differential equation with variable coefficients, and its solution easily can be determined by separating the variables or by using the solution procedure for linear equations to be

$$y = \frac{C_0}{(x - 1)^2}$$

Now we will ignore the existence of this solution, and we will attempt to solve this equation by assuming a power series solution of the form

$$y = \sum_{n=0}^{\infty} C_n x^n$$

Differentiating term-by-term, we have

$$y' = \sum_{n=1}^{\infty} n C_n x^{n-1}$$

Substituting into the differential equation, we have

$$(x - 1) \sum_{n=1}^{\infty} n C_n x^{n-1} + 2 \sum_{n=0}^{\infty} C_n x^n = 0$$

or

$$\sum_{n=1}^{\infty} n C_n x^n - \sum_{n=1}^{\infty} n C_n x^{n-1} + 2 \sum_{n=0}^{\infty} C_n x^n = 0$$

To equate the powers of x in all summations, we shift the index of the middle summation by 1, replacing n with $n - 1$. We also replace $n = 0$ with $n = 1$ on the first summation with no effect on the sum, since this is equivalent to adding a zero to the series. This procedure yields

$$\sum_{n=0}^{\infty} n C_n x^n - \sum_{n=0}^{\infty} (n + 1) C_{n+1} x^n + 2 \sum_{n=0}^{\infty} C_n x^n = 0$$

or

$$\sum_{n=0}^{\infty} [n C_n - (n + 1) C_{n+1} + 2 C_n] x^n = 0$$

This equation will be satisfied for all x if and only if the coefficient of each power of x is zero. This condition gives us an infinite number of equations for the determination of the expansion coefficients C_n:

$$(n + 2) C_n - (n + 1) C_{n+1} = 0$$

or

$$C_{n+1} = \frac{n + 2}{n + 1} C_n, \qquad n = 0, 1, 2, 3, \ldots \qquad \text{(5–36)}$$

The recurrence relation in this case relates a coefficient to the one before it. Thus, the first coefficient C_0 is available, and the remainder of the coefficients $(C_1, C_2, C_3, C_4, \ldots)$ can be determined from the recurrence relation as

$$n = 0: \quad C_1 = \frac{2}{1}C_0 = 2C_0$$

$$n = 1: \quad C_2 = \frac{3}{2}C_1 = 3C_0$$

$$n = 2: \quad C_3 = \frac{4}{3}C_2 = 4C_0$$

$$n = 3: \quad C_4 = \frac{5}{4}C_3 = 5C_0$$

The pattern is now clear. Generalizing, we have

$$C_n = (n + 1)C_0, \quad n = 0, 1, 2, 3, 4, \ldots$$

Thus, we have determined all of the coefficients in the assumed power series solution, except C_0. Substituting these coefficients into the solution and factoring out C_0, we obtain

$$y = C_0[1 + 2x + 3x^2 + 4x^3 + \cdots + (n + 1)x^n + \cdots]$$

$$= C_0\sum_{n=0}^{\infty} (n + 1)x^n = \frac{C_0}{(x - 1)^2}$$

The series of this relation is exactly the binomial series expansion of $1/(x - 1)^2$. Thus, we obtained the same result with the power series solution method.

This solution is deceiving; however, since the power series solution here will diverge for $|x| > 1$ instead of converging to the value that would be obtained from $1/(x - 1)^2$. Thus, the power series solution here is valid for $|x| < 1$ (Figure 5–18). Yet, the solution procedure gives us no warning to this effect. This shows that there is more to the power series method than what is implied here, and we need to understand the underlying theory if we are to use this method effectively and with confidence.

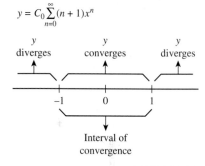

FIGURE 5–18

Series solutions of differential equations with variable coefficients in general do not converge for all values of x (Example 5–8).

In the following sections, we will discuss the fundamentals of the power series method and apply it to linear differential equations for which there are no other viable alternative solution methods. Some of these equations are frequently encountered in practice, and they are referred to by their names. The ones that are best known are listed here.

Bessel's equation: $\qquad x^2y'' + xy' + (x^2 - v^2)y = 0 \qquad$ **(5–37)**

An application of this equation to heat transfer is given in Section 5–7.

Legendre's equation: $\qquad (1 - x^2)y'' - 2xy' + \alpha(\alpha + 1)y = 0 \qquad$ **(5–38)**

This equation results when solving for the gravitational potential function in spherical coordinates.

The Euler equation: $\qquad x^2y'' + axy' + by = 0 \qquad$ **(5–39)**

This equation, also known as the Euler–Cauchy equation, is the simplest case of a second-order equation having regular singular points. Thus, it serves as a good introduction to the general case. It appears in applications involving the gravitational and electrostatic potential functions in spherical coordinates.

Airy's equation: $$y'' - xy = 0 \qquad \text{(5–40)}$$

This equation arises in optics.

Hermite's equation: $$y'' - 2xy' + 2\lambda y = 0 \qquad \text{(5–41)}$$

This equation results from the solution of the wave equation in quantum mechanics.

Chebyshev's equation: $$(1 - x^2)y'' - xy' + \lambda^2 y = 0 \qquad \text{(5–42)}$$

This equation occurs in polynomial curve-fitting applications.

Laguerre's equation: $$xy'' + (1 - x)y' + \lambda y = 0 \qquad \text{(5–43)}$$

This equation has nonsingular solutions only if λ is a non-negative integer.

Gauss's hypergeometric equation:

$$x(1 - x)y'' + [c - (a + b + 1)x]y' - aby = 0 \qquad \text{(5–44)}$$

Every second-order linear, ordinary differential equation with three regular, singular points can be transformed into this equation by a change of variables. See Section 5–3.

We will study some of these equations briefly, and some others in detail.

Section Review

5–9C Is the series solution method limited to differential equations with variable coefficients only or is it also applicable to equations with constant coefficients?

5–10 Solve the following differential equation using two different methods, one being the method using power series. Show that the two solutions are identical: $y'' + 4y = 0$.

(*Answer:* $y(x) = C_0 \left(1 - 2x^2 + \frac{2}{3}x^4 - \frac{4}{45}x^6 + \cdots \right) + C_1 \left(x - \frac{2}{3}x^3 + \frac{2}{15}x^5 - \frac{4}{315}x^7 + \cdots \right)$)

5–3 · ORDINARY VERSUS SINGULAR POINTS

In the preceding chapters, when solving linear equations with *constant* coefficients of the form

$$ay'' + by' + cy = 0 \qquad \text{(5–45)}$$

we simply talked about the *solution* of the equation without specifying any point or interval for it. This is because a constant coefficient (such as $a = 2$) represents a continuous line parallel to the x-axis, which extends from $-\infty$ to $+\infty$; no x value can make that coefficient zero. Consequently, the solutions obtained are valid for all x values. In the trivial case of a constant coefficient being zero (such as $b = 0$), the term with that coefficient simply disappears from the equation, and we have a simpler equation with continuous coefficients. However, when solving linear differential equations with variable coefficients, such as

$$a(x)y'' + b(x)y' + c(x)y = 0 \qquad \textbf{(5–46)}$$

we will have to think about *solutions about a point* (or alternatively, solutions *around* a point or a solution *in the neighborhood* or *vicinity* of a point). This will refer to a solution in an interval that contains that point (Figure 5–19). The interval in which the solution is applicable will rarely be the entire x axis. Consequently, a linear differential equation with variable coefficients may have different solutions around different points, or it may even have no solutions at all around some points. Therefore, we need to specify the interval or the point around which we would like to solve an equation with variable coefficients.

In the sections that follow, we will seek solutions to the differential equations with variable coefficients around a point x_0 in terms of $(x - x_0)^n$. As you will see, the solution of the equation around a point depends not only on the point itself, but also on the *nature* or *kind* of the point with respect to the differential equation. The solution method and the form of solution will be different for different kinds of points. Therefore, we need to identify the kind of point before we attempt to solve a given equation around that point.

A given second-order differential equation with variable coefficients can be expressed in the *standard form* (leading coefficient = 1) by dividing each term by $a(x)$, which is the coefficient of y''. After canceling any common factors, we obtain

$$y'' + P(x)y' + Q(x)y = 0 \qquad \textbf{(5–47)}$$

where $P(x) = b(x)/a(x)$ and $Q(x) = c(x)/a(x)$ in the most simplified form. In this and the following sections, we will limit the discussion to second-order differential equations for simplicity. However, any definitions and theorems readily can be extended to higher-order equations. A given point x_0 either can be ordinary or singular, depending on the behaviour of the coefficients $P(x)$ and $Q(x)$ of the differential equation at that point (Figure 5–20).

A point x_0 is called an **ordinary point** *of the differential equation if both of the functions $P(x)$ and $Q(x)$ are analytic at that point. A point x_0 is called a* **singular point** *of the differential equation if one or both of the functions $P(x)$ and $Q(x)$ are not analytic at that point.*

A singular point of a differential equation is further classified as follows: A singular point x_0 is called a **regular singular point** *of the differential equation if both of the functions*

$$(x - x_0)P(x) \quad \text{and} \quad (x - x_0)^2 Q(x) \qquad \textbf{(5–48)}$$

are analytic at that point. Otherwise, the point x_0 is called an **irregular singular point** *of the differential equation.*

In other words, a singular point x_0 is a regular singular point if the following limits exist (Figure 5–21).

$$\lim_{x \to x_0}(x - x_0)P(x) \quad \text{and} \quad \lim_{x \to x_0}(x - x_0)^2 Q(x) \qquad \textbf{(5–49)}$$

Thus the proper classification of a given point of a differential equation can be quite laborious and cumbersome since it requires the determination of whether two or more functions are analytic, which in turn requires the determination of whether the Taylor series of these functions converge at the specified point. We definitely need a break, and here it is.

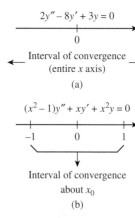

FIGURE 5–19

Solutions of linear differential equations with constant coefficients converge for all x, but solutions of differential equations with variable coefficients (in general) converge in an interval only.

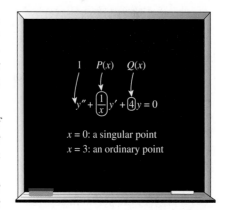

FIGURE 5– 20

A point is an ordinary point of differential equation if both $P(x)$ and $Q(x)$ are analytic at that point; otherwise, it is a singular point.

(a) $x = 0$ is a regular singular point of

$$y'' + \frac{1}{x}y' + \frac{3}{x^2}y = 0$$

since

$$xP(x) = 1, \quad x^2Q(x) = 3$$

(b) $x = 0$ is an irregular singular point of

$$y'' + \frac{1}{x^2}y' + \frac{3}{x^2}y = 0$$

since

$$xP(x) = \frac{1}{x} \quad x^2Q(x) = 3$$

FIGURE 5–21

The point $x = 0$ is a regular, singular point of the differential equation (a) but is an irregular singular point of equation (b).

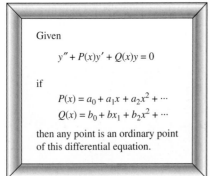

Given

$$y'' + P(x)y' + Q(x)y = 0$$

if

$$P(x) = a_0 + a_1x + a_2x^2 + \cdots$$
$$Q(x) = b_0 + bx_1 + b_2x^2 + \cdots$$

then any point is an ordinary point of this differential equation.

FIGURE 5–22

Any point is an ordinary point of a differential equation if the functions $P(x)$ and $Q(x)$ are polynomials.

Most functions $a(x)$, $b(x)$, and $c(x)$ encountered in practice are polynomials, and all polynomials (including their sums, differences, and products) are analytic functions. Then the functions $P(x)$ and $Q(x)$ are (at most) the quotients of two polynomials, which are still analytic everywhere except at the zeros of the denominators. The ordinary and singular points in this case can be defined as follows:

> *When $P(x)$ and $Q(x)$ are quotients of polynomials, the points at which the denominator of $P(x)$ or $Q(x)$ of a differential equation vanishes (becomes zero) are the singular points, and all other points are ordinary points of the differential equation.*

For the special case of $P(x)$ or $Q(x)$ of a differential equation being a polynomial, any point x is an ordinary point (Figure 5–22).

Probably you are wondering why we are distinguishing a regular singular point from an irregular one. After all, functions $P(x)$ and/or $Q(x)$ are infinite at a singular point no matter what kind it is. The reason is that a regular singularity is relatively weak or mild, and we can handle it with confidence; whereas, an irregular singularity is rather severe and difficult to handle. The definition of a regular singular point implies that at the point x_0 the singularity in $P(x)$ is no more severe than $(x - x_0)^{-1}$, and the singularity in $Q(x)$ is no more severe than $(x - x_0)^{-2}$.

EXAMPLE 5–9 **Ordinary Points**

Determine the ordinary and singular points of the following differential equation:

$$y'' - (x - 2)y' + (3x^2 - 2x + 5)y = 0$$

SOLUTION The differential equation is already in the standard form (the coefficient of y'' is 1), and we have

$$P(x) = -(x - 2) \quad \text{and} \quad Q(x) = 3x^2 - 2x + 5$$

both of which are polynomials. Therefore, all points are ordinary points of the differential equation, since polynomials are analytic everywhere.

EXAMPLE 5–10 **Regular and Irregular Singular Points**

Determine the ordinary and singular points of the following differential equation:

$$xy'' + \frac{2}{x - 1}y' + \frac{1}{x^2}y = 0$$

SOLUTION The differential equation can be put into the standard form by dividing each term by x (the coefficient of y''):

$$y'' + \frac{2}{x(x - 1)}y' + \frac{1}{x^3}y = 0$$

Thus, we have

$$P(x) = \frac{2}{x(x-1)} \quad \text{and} \quad Q(x) = \frac{1}{x^3}$$

both of which are expressed as the ratios of polynomials. By inspection, we see that $P(x)$ becomes zero at $x = 0$ and $x = 1$, and $Q(x)$ becomes zero at $x = 0$. Therefore, $x = 0$ and $x = 1$ are the singular points of this differential equation. All other points are ordinary points (Figure 5–23). Furthermore, the point $x = 1$ is a regular singular point, since

$$(x-1)P(x) = \frac{2}{x} \qquad \text{(analytic at } x = 1)$$

$$(x-1)^2 Q(x) = \frac{(x-1)^2}{x^3} \qquad \text{(analytic at } x = 1)$$

But the point $x = 0$ is an irregular singular point, since

$$xP(x) = \frac{2}{x-1} \qquad \text{(analytic at } x = 0)$$

$$x^2 Q(x) = \frac{1}{x} \qquad \text{(not analytic at } x = 0)$$

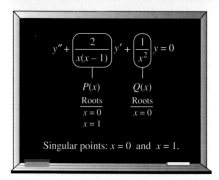

FIGURE 5–23

When $P(x)$ and $Q(x)$ are ratios of polynomials, the only singular points of a differential equation are the zeros of the denominators of $P(x)$ and $Q(x)$.

Determining a series solution to a differential equation is not complete without determining the interval in which the series converges. One way of determining the radius of convergence of the infinite series in the solution is to apply a convergence test directly to the series. A more practical way is to determine the radius of convergence of the functions $P(x)$ and $Q(x)$, and then to use the following theorem:

THEOREM 5–1 Radius of Convergence of Series Solutions

If x_0 is an ordinary point of the differential equation

$$y'' + P(x)y' + Q(x)y = 0$$

then the infinite series in the general solution of this differential equation has a radius of convergence that is at least as large as the smaller of the radii of convergence of the functions $P(x)$ and $Q(x)$.

The radii of convergence of the functions $P(x)$ and $Q(x)$ (in general) can be determined by applying the convergence test. But when both the numerators and the denominators of $P(x)$ and $Q(x)$ are polynomials (if they are expressed as ratios), the singular points of these two functions (including the complex ones) can be determined easily. Then the minimum radius of convergence of the series solution becomes the distance between the specified point and the nearest singular point of $P(x)$ or $Q(x)$. When determining this distance, we need to consider not only the real singular points but also the complex ones. This is illustrated with the following examples.

EXAMPLE 5–11   Radius of Convergence: Real Singular Points

Determine the radius of convergence of the series solution of the following differential equation about $x = 5$,

$$(x^2 - 9)y'' - xy' + \frac{1}{x}y = 0$$

SOLUTION The differential equation can be put into the standard form by dividing each term by

$$y'' - \frac{x}{x^2 - 9}y' + \frac{1}{x(x^2 - 9)}y = 0$$

Thus, we have

$$P(x) = -\frac{x}{x^2 - 9} \quad \text{and} \quad Q(x) = \frac{1}{x(x^2 - 9)}$$

both of which are expressed as the ratios of polynomials. By inspection, we see that $P(x)$ becomes zero at $x = 3$ and $x = -3$, and $Q(x)$ becomes zero at $x = 0$, $x = 3$, and $x = -3$. Therefore, $x = 0$, $x = 3$, and $x = -3$ are the singular points of this differential equation. (There are no complex singular points.) All other points are ordinary points.

The distance between the specified point $(x = 5)$ and the closest singular point $(x = 3)$ is 2. Therefore, this differential equation has a series solution about the point $x = 5$ with a radius of convergence of $\rho = 2$, as shown in Figure 5–24.

Note that the series solution of the same differential equation has different radii of convergence about different points. For example, $\rho = 7$ for $x_0 = -10$; $\rho = 1$ for $x_0 = 2$; and $\rho = 0$ for $x_0 = 3$.

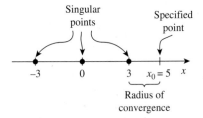

FIGURE 5–24

The radius of convergence of the series solution of the differential equation in Example 5–11 about the point $x_0 = 5$.

EXAMPLE 5–12   Radius of Convergence: Complex Singular Points

Determine the radius of convergence of the series solution of the following differential equation about $x = 0$:

$$(x^2 - 4x + 8)y'' - 3x^2y' + 4y = 0$$

SOLUTION The differential equation can be put into the standard form by dividing each term by $x^2 - 4x + 8$ (the coefficient of y''):

$$y'' - \frac{3x^2}{x^2 - 4x + 8}y' + \frac{4}{x^2 - 4x + 8}y = 0$$

Thus, we have

$$P(x) = -\frac{3x^2}{x^2 - 4x + 8} \quad \text{and} \quad Q(x) = \frac{4}{x^2 - 4x + 8}$$

both of which are expressed as the ratios of polynomials. By determining the roots of the denominator, we see that both $P(x)$ and $Q(x)$ become zero at $x = 2 + 2i$ and $x = 2 - 2i$ (Figure 5–25). Therefore, this differential equation has two singular points, both of which are complex. All other points (real or complex) are ordinary points.

The distance between the specified point ($x_0 = 0$) and either singular point is the length of the line connecting the two points, and is easily determined from Figure 5–25 to be $\sqrt{8}$. Therefore, this differential equation has a series solution about the point $x_0 = 0$ with a radius of convergence of $\rho = \sqrt{8}$.

Note again that the series solution of the same differential equation has different radii of convergence about different points. For example, $\rho = 2$ for $x_0 = 2$; $\rho = \sqrt{20}$ for $x_0 = -2$; and $\rho = \sqrt{13}$ for $x_0 = 5$.

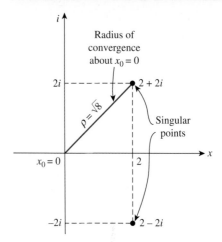

FIGURE 5–25

The radius of convergence of the series of the differential equation in Example 5–12 about the point $x_0 = 0$.

EXAMPLE 5–13   Radius of Convergence: Complex Singular Points

Determine the radius of convergence of the series solution of the differential equation

$$(x^2 + 4)y'' - 3y' + 4(x + 4)y = 0$$

for the assumed series solutions of (a) $\sum_{n=0}^{\infty} C_n x^n$ and (b) $\sum_{n=0}^{\infty} C_n(x - 3)^n$

SOLUTION   (a) The differential equation can be put into the standard form by dividing each term by $x^2 + 4$ (the coefficient of y''), giving

$$y'' - \frac{3}{x^2 + 4}y' + \frac{4(x + 4)}{x^2 + 4}y = 0$$

Thus, we have

$$P(x) = -\frac{3}{x^2 + 4} \quad \text{and} \quad Q(x) = \frac{4(x + 4)}{x^2 + 4}$$

both of which are expressed as the ratios of polynomials. By determining the roots of the denominator, we see that both $P(x)$ and $Q(x)$ become zero at $x = 2i$ and $x = -2i$ (Figure 5–26). Therefore, this differential equation has two singular points, both of which are complex. All other points (real or complex) are ordinary points.

The series solution of the form $\sum_{n=0}^{\infty} C_n x^n$ has the point $x_0 = 0$ as its center, and the radius of convergence is the distance between this point and either singular point. It easily is determined from Figure 5–26 to be 2. Therefore, the specified series solution will converge for $|x| < 2$.

(b) The series solution of the form $\sum_{n=0}^{\infty} C_n(x - 3)^n$ has the point $x_0 = 3$ as its center, and the radius of convergence this time is $\sqrt{13}$. Therefore, the series solution in this case will converge for $|x - 3| < \sqrt{13}$.

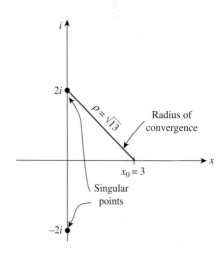

FIGURE 5–26

The radius of convergence of the series solution of the differential equation in Example 5–13 about the point $x_0 = 3$.

In the following sections, we will discuss solution procedures around ordinary points and regular singular points of given differential equations.

The proper classification of the point x_0 around which we are seeking a solution is extremely important in the solution. As you will see, a second-order differential equation is guaranteed to have two linearly independent power series solutions around an *ordinary* point. We can also solve a differential equation around a *regular singular* point by assuming a modified form of power series solutions. But the solution procedure around an *irregular singular* point is rather involved, and beyond the scope of this text.

We will also concentrate on homogeneous equations since most second-order, linear differential equations with variable coefficients encountered in practice are homogeneous. But the procedure described is equally applicable to the corresponding nonhomogeneous equations. The solution (in this case) can be determined by either applying the method directly to the nonhomogeneous equation or by determining separately the particular solution corresponding to the nonhomogeneous terms and then adding it to the solution of the homogeneous part of the differential equation.

Section Review

5–11 When solving linear differential equations with variable coefficients why do we seek solutions around a specified point instead of seeking a solution that is applicable everywhere?

5–12 How do the singular points of a linear, second-order differential equation differ from ordinary points?

5–13 Identify the ordinary and singular points of the following differential equations. Also, determine whether the singular points are regular or irregular.

$$\text{(a) } y'' - 4y' + 5y = 0 \qquad \text{(b) } xy'' + \frac{x}{x+1}y' - \frac{1}{x^2}y = 0$$

(*Answers:* (a) Every point in the interval $(-\infty, \infty)$ is an ordinary point, and there is no singular point. (b) $x = -1$ is a regular singular point, whereas $x = 0$ is an irregular singular point.)

5–14 Determine the radius of convergence of the series solution of the following differential equation about the specified ordinary point.

$$y'' + 3y' - 4y = 0, \qquad x_0 = 0$$

(*Answer:* The radius of convergence of the series solution is infinity.)

5–4 ▪ POWER SERIES SOLUTIONS ABOUT AN ORDINARY POINT

Before we attempt to solve a differential equation in the neighborhood of a specified point by the infinite series method, we need to know if a solution in that region exists, and if it does, whether it is unique. The following theorem addresses these concerns.

THEOREM 5–2   Series Solutions About Ordinary Points

If x_0 is an ordinary point of the differential equation

$$y'' + P(x)y' + Q(x)y = 0$$

then this differential equation has two linearly independent solutions y_1 and y_2, each of the form $\sum_{n=0}^{\infty} C_n(x - x_0)^n$. The general solution of this differential equation is

$$y = \sum_{n=0}^{\infty} C_n(x - x_0)^n$$

$$= C_0 y_1(x) + C_1 y_2(x) \qquad \text{(5–50)}$$

where C_0 and C_1 are two arbitrary constants that are determined from the initial conditions. The remaining coefficients in the series solution are determined by substituting the series solution into the differential equation. Furthermore, the radius of convergence of the series solution is at least as large as the distance from x_0 to the nearest real or complex singular point (Figure 5–27).

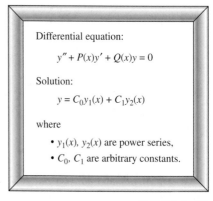

Differential equation:

$$y'' + P(x)y' + Q(x)y = 0$$

Solution:

$$y = C_0 y_1(x) + C_1 y_2(x)$$

where

- $y_1(x)$, $y_2(x)$ are power series,
- C_0, C_1 are arbitrary constants.

FIGURE 5–27

Solution about an ordinary point.

The proof of this theorem can be found in more advanced texts on differential equations. We now illustrate the solution procedure and the use of this theorem with examples.

EXAMPLE 5–14   Hermite's Equation

A differential equation that arises in quantum mechanics in the study of Schrödinger equation for a harmonic oscillator is Hermite's equation, which is

$$y'' - 2xy' + 2\lambda y = 0 \qquad \text{(5–51)}$$

where λ is a constant. Find a power series solution to this equation in powers of x (i.e., about the point $x_0 = 0$).

SOLUTION   This is a linear, second-order homogeneous differential equation with variable coefficients, and it is already in the standard form, since the leading coefficient is 1. Thus, $P(x) = -2x$, and $Q(x) = 2\lambda$, which are polynomials. Recalling that polynomials are analytic functions over the entire x-axis, any point is an ordinary point of this differential equation, including the point $x_0 = 0$. Then from Theorems 5–1 and 5–2, we conclude that this differential equation has a power series solution about any point and the radius of convergence of the series solution about any point is infinity (i.e., the solution converges for all x values).

We now assume a power series solution of the form

$$y = \sum_{n=0}^{\infty} C_n x^n$$

Differentiating twice and substituting the derivatives into the differential equation, we have

$$\sum_{n-2}^{\infty} n(n-1) C_n x^{n-2} - 2x \sum_{n-1}^{\infty} nC_n x^{n-1} + 2\lambda \sum_{n=0}^{\infty} C_n x^n = 0$$

Shifting the index of the first summation by 2 by replacing n with $n-2$ and rearranging the second term, we have

$$\sum_{n=2}^{\infty} (n+2)(n+1)C_{n+2} x^n - 2 \sum_{n=1}^{\infty} nC_n x^{n-1} + 2\lambda \sum_{n=0}^{\infty} C_n x^n = 0$$

Now the nth term of all three series involves the same power of x. But we cannot combine them under a single summation yet because the index of the second summation starts with $n = 1$ instead of 0. We can fix this problem easily by starting the second summation with $n = 0$ because the corresponding term will be zero because of the factor n in the summation. Thus,

$$\sum_{n=2}^{\infty} [(n+2)(n+1)C_{n+2} - 2nC_n + 2\lambda C_n] x^n = 0$$

This equation will be satisfied for all x if and only if the coefficient of each power of x is zero. This condition gives us an infinite number of equations for the determination of the expansion coefficients C_n.

$$(n+2)(n+1)C_{n+2} - 2nC_n + 2\lambda C_n = 0$$

or

$$C_{n+2} = \frac{2(\lambda - n)C_n}{(n+1)(n+2)}, \qquad n = 0, 1, 2, 3, \ldots$$

This is the recurrence relation, and it relates any coefficient to the second one before it. Thus if the first two coefficients C_0 and C_1 are available, the remainder of the coefficients (C_2, C_3, C_4, C_5, ...) can be determined from the recurrence relation. The first few of them are

$$C_2 = -\frac{2\lambda}{1 \cdot 2} C_0 = -\frac{2\lambda}{2!} C_0$$

$$C_3 = -\frac{2(\lambda - 1)}{2 \cdot 3} C_1 = -\frac{2(\lambda - 1)}{3!} C_1$$

$$C_4 = -\frac{2(\lambda - 2)}{3 \cdot 4} C_2 = \frac{2^2 \lambda(\lambda - 2)}{4!} C_0$$

$$C_5 = -\frac{2(\lambda - 3)}{4 \cdot 5} C_3 = \frac{2^2(\lambda - 1)(\lambda - 3)}{5!} C_1$$

$$C_6 = -\frac{2(\lambda - 4)}{5 \cdot 6} C_4 = -\frac{2^3 \lambda(\lambda - 2)(\lambda - 4)}{6!} C_0$$

$$C_7 = -\frac{2(\lambda - 5)}{6 \cdot 7} C_5 = -\frac{2^3(\lambda - 1)(\lambda - 3)(\lambda - 5)}{7!} C_1$$

Substituting these coefficients into the solution and factoring out C_0 and C_1, we obtain

$$y = C_0 \left[1 - \frac{2\lambda}{2!} x^2 + 2^2\lambda \frac{(\lambda - 2)}{4!} x^4 - \frac{2^3 \lambda(\lambda - 2)(\lambda - 4)}{6!} x^6 + \cdots \right]$$

$$+ C_1 \left[x - \frac{2(\lambda - 1)}{3!} x^3 + \frac{2(\lambda - 1)(\lambda - 3)}{5!} x^5 - \frac{2^3(\lambda - 1)(\lambda - 3)(\lambda - 5)}{7!} x^7 + \cdots \right]$$

$$= C_0 y_1(x) + C_1 y_2(x)$$

Generalizing the coefficients for the even and odd terms, the two independent solutions y_1 and y_2 also can be expressed in a more general form as

$$y = C_0 \left[1 + \sum_{n=1}^{\infty} (-1)^n \frac{2^n \lambda(\lambda - 2) \cdots (\lambda - 2n + 2)}{(2n)!} x^{2n} \right]$$
$$+ C_1 \left[x + \sum_{n=1}^{\infty} (-1)^n \frac{2^n \lambda(\lambda - 1)(\lambda - 3) \cdots (\lambda - 2n + 1)}{(2n + 1)!} x^{2n+1} \right] \quad \text{(5–52)}$$

The terms in the brackets are two linearly independent solutions of the Hermite's equation. Note that this solution is valid for any x value since Hermite's equation has no singular points.

When λ is a nonnegative integer, the terms in the first or the second series in the solution drop out for $n > \lambda$, yielding a polynomial of degree n in place of that infinite series. A constant multiple of the resulting polynomial of degree n (which is a solution of Hermite's equation) is known as the **Hermite polynomial**, and is denoted by $H_n(x)$. The constant multiple is chosen such that the coefficient of x^n is 2^n. The first four Hermite polynomials are given in Figure 5–28.

$\lambda = n$	C_0	C_1	$H_n(x)$
0	1	0	1
1	0	2	$2x$
2	-2	0	$4x^2 - 2$
3	0	-2	$8x^3 - 12x$

FIGURE 5–28

Determination of Hermite polynomials from Equation 5–52 by assigning positive integer values to λ and suitable values to C_0 and C_1 so that the coefficient of x^n is 2^n.

EXAMPLE 5–15   Airy's Equation

A differential equation that arises in optics in the study of light intensity is Airy's equation, which is $y'' - xy = 0$. Find a power series solution to this equation in powers of x (i.e., about the point $x_0 = 0$).

SOLUTION This is a linear second-order, homogeneous differential equation with variable coefficients, and it is already in the standard form since the leading coefficient is 1. Thus, $P(x) = 0$ and $Q(x) = -x$, which are polynomials. Recall that polynomials are analytic functions over all x, including the point $x_0 = 0$. Then from Theorems 5–1 and 5–2 we conclude that the radius of convergence of the series solutions about any point is infinity (i.e., the solution converges for all x values).

We now assume a power series solution of the form

$$y = \sum_{n=0}^{\infty} C_n x^n$$

Differentiating twice and substituting into the differential equation,

$$\sum_{n=2}^{\infty} n(n - 1) C_n x^{n-2} - x \sum_{n=0}^{\infty} C_n x^n = 0$$

or

$$\sum_{n=2}^{\infty} n(n - 1) C_n x^{n-2} - \sum_{n=0}^{\infty} C_n x^{n+1} = 0$$

To equate the powers of x in the two summations, we shift the index of the first summation by replacing n by $n + 2$ and shift the index of the second summation by 1, replacing n by $n - 1$,

$$\sum_{n=0}^{\infty} (n + 2)(n + 1) C_{n+2} x^n - \sum_{n=1}^{\infty} n C_{n-1} x^n = 0$$

or

$$2(1)C_2 + \sum_{n=1}^{\infty} [(n+2)(n+1)C_{n+2} - C_{n-1}]x^n = 0$$

For this equation to hold for any x value, the coefficient of each power of x, including the zeroth power, must be zero. This requirement yields $C_2 = 0$, and the recurrence relation is $(n+2)(n+1)C_{n+2} - C_{n-1} = 0$ or

$$C_{n+2} = \frac{1}{(n+1)(n+2)} C_{n-1}, \quad n = 0, 1, 2, 3, \ldots \quad \text{(5–53)}$$

The recurrence relation in this case relates any coefficients to the third one before it. Thus the coefficients $C_3, C_6, C_9, \ldots$ are determined in terms of C_0; the coefficients $C_4, C_7, C_{10}, \ldots$ are determined in terms of C_1; and the coefficients $C_5, C_8, C_{11}, \ldots$ are determined in terms of C_2, which is already determined to be zero. Therefore, $C_2 = C_5 = C_8 = C_{11} = \cdots = 0$. The first few coefficients are determined from the recurrence relation to be

$$C_3 = \frac{1}{2 \cdot 3} C_0 = \frac{1}{3!} C_0$$

$$C_4 = \frac{1}{3 \cdot 4} C_1 = \frac{2}{4!} C_1$$

$$C_6 = \frac{1}{5 \cdot 6} C_1 = \frac{4}{6!} C_0$$

$$C_7 = \frac{1}{6 \cdot 7} C_4 = \frac{10}{7!} C_1$$

Substituting these coefficients into the solution and factoring out C_0 and C_1, we obtain

$$y = C_0 \left[1 + \frac{1}{3!}x^3 + \frac{1 \cdot 4}{6!}x^6 + \cdots + \frac{1 \cdot 4 \cdots (3n-2)}{(3n)!}x^{3n} + \cdots \right]$$

$$+ C_1 \left[x + \frac{2}{4!}x^2 + \frac{2 \cdot 5}{7!}x^5 + \cdots + \frac{2 \cdot 5 \cdots (3n-1)}{(3n+1)!}x^{3n+1} + \cdots \right]$$

$$= C_0 y_1(x) + C_1 y_2(x)$$

Or, in a more general form,

$$y = C_0 \left[1 + \sum_{n=1}^{\infty} \frac{1 \cdot 4 \cdots (3n-2)}{(3n)!}x^{3n} \right]$$

$$+ C_1 \left[x + \sum_{n=1}^{\infty} \frac{2 \cdot 5 \cdots (3n-1)}{(3n+1)!}x^{3n+1} \right] \quad \text{(5–54)}$$

This is the general solution of Airy's equation, and $y_1(x)$ and $y_2(x)$ are the two linearly independent solutions of it. Note that this solution is valid for any x value since Airy's equation has no singular points.

Discussion We solved Airy's equation above about the ordinary point $x_0 = 0$ and obtained a solution of the form

$$y = \sum_{n=0}^{\infty} C_n x^n = C_0 y_1(x) + C_1 y_2(x)$$

where the two linearly independent solutions $y_1(x)$ and $y_2(x)$ can be found from Equation 5–54. This solution converges for any x value, since Airy's equation has no singular points, and thus, its radius of convergence is infinity.

Choosing $x_0 = 0$ has the advantage that it yields simpler expressions. Now let us investigate what would happen if we choose x_0 to be another ordinary point. This time, the solution would be of the form

$$y = \sum_{n=0}^{\infty} C_n(x - x_0)^n = C_0 y_3(x) + C_1 y_4(x)$$

which again converges for any x value. The two solutions are equivalent although they appear to be different. The functions $y_3(x)$ and $y_4(x)$ can be expressed as a linear combination of $y_1(x)$ and $y_2(x)$, since according to Theorem 5–3, a second-order differential equation can have only two linearly independent solutions in a specified interval of convergence (Figure 5–29). If desired, the solution in terms of $x - x_0$ can be obtained by either expressing the coefficient x in Airy's equation as $x_0 + (x - x_0)$ (which is the Taylor series expansion of the function x about the point x_0) and thus expressing the differential equation as $y'' - (x - x_0)y + x_0 y = 0$, or by defining a new variable as $t = x - x_0$ and assuming a solution of the form $y = \sum_{n=0}^{\infty} C_n t^n$.

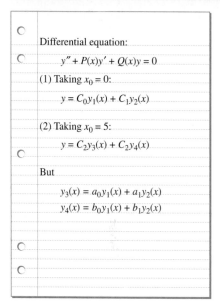

Differential equation:

$$y'' + P(x)y' + Q(x)y = 0$$

(1) Taking $x_0 = 0$:

$$y = C_0 y_1(x) + C_1 y_2(x)$$

(2) Taking $x_0 = 5$:

$$y = C_2 y_3(x) + C_2 y_4(x)$$

But

$$y_3(x) = a_0 y_1(x) + a_1 y_2(x)$$
$$y_4(x) = b_0 y_1(x) + b_1 y_2(x)$$

FIGURE 5–29

A second-order, linear, homogeneous differential equation may have independent solutions about different ordinary points within an interval of convergence, but all solutions can be expressed as a linear combination of the first two linearly independent solutions.

EXAMPLE 5–16 Chebyshev's Equation

The search for a polynomial that deviates the least from zero in the interval $-1 \le x \le 1$ (which makes it of great importance in numerical analysis) led to the study of Chebyshev's equation, which is

$$(1 - x^2)y'' - xy' + \lambda^2 y = 0 \tag{5-55}$$

where λ is a constant. Find a power series solution to this equation about the origin, $x_0 = 0$.

SOLUTION This is a linear, second-order, homogeneous differential equation with variable coefficients, and it can be put into the standard form by dividing each term by $1 - x^2$:

$$y'' - \frac{x}{1 - x^2}y' + \frac{\lambda^2}{1 - x^2}y = 0$$

Thus $P(x) = -x/(1 - x^2)$ and $Q(x) = \lambda^2/(1 - x^2)$, which are ratios of polynomials. By inspection, we see that the denominators of both $P(x)$ and $Q(x)$ become zero $x = \pm 1$. Therefore, the points $x = -1$ and $x = 1$ are the singular points of this differential equation; thus, a series solution obtained about the point $x_0 = 0$ will converge in the interval $-1 < x < 1$.

We now assume a power series solution of the form

$$y = \sum_{n=0}^{\infty} C_n x^n$$

Differentiating twice and substituting the derivatives into the differential equation, we have

$$(1 - x^2)\sum_{n=2}^{\infty} n(n - 1)C_n x^{n-2} - x\sum_{n=1}^{\infty} nC_n x^{n-1} + \lambda^2 \sum_{n=0}^{\infty} C_n x^n = 0$$

or

$$\sum_{n=2}^{\infty} n(n-1)C_n x^{n-2} - \sum_{n=2}^{\infty} n(n-1)C_n x^n - \sum_{n=1}^{\infty} nC_n x^n + \lambda^2 \sum_{n=0}^{\infty} C_n x^n = 0$$

Shifting the index of the first summation by replacing n with $n - 2$ and starting the two summations in the middle with $n = 0$ instead of 1 or 2 (since the additional terms corresponding to $n = 0$ or 1 will be zero because of the factors n and $n - 1$ in the summation), we have

$$\sum_{n=0}^{\infty} (n+2)(n+1)C_{n+2} x^n - \sum_{n=0}^{\infty} n(n-1)C_n x^n - \sum_{n=0}^{\infty} nC_n x^n + \lambda^2 \sum_{n=0}^{\infty} C_n x^n = 0$$

or

$$\sum_{n=0}^{\infty} \{(n+2)(n+1)C_{n+2} + [\lambda^2 - n(n-1) - n]C_n\}x^n = 0$$

This equation will be satisfied for all x if and only if the coefficient of each power of x is zero. This condition gives us an infinite number of equations for the determination of the expansion coefficients C_n:

$$(n+2)(n+1)C_{n+2} + [\lambda^2 - n(n-1) - n]C_n = 0$$

or

$$C_{n+2} = -\frac{\lambda^2 - n^2}{(n+1)(n+2)}C_n, \qquad n = 0, 1, 2, 3, \dots.$$

This is the recurrence relation, and it relates any coefficient to the second one before it. Thus, if the first two coefficients C_0 and C_1 are available, the remainder of the coefficients $(C_2, C_3, C_4, C_5, \dots)$ can be determined from the recurrence relation. The first few of them are

$$C_2 = -\frac{\lambda^2}{1 \cdot 2}C_0 = -\frac{\lambda^2}{2!}C_0$$

$$C_3 = -\frac{\lambda^2 - 1^2}{2 \cdot 3}C_1 = -\frac{\lambda^2 - 1}{3!}C_1$$

$$C_4 = -\frac{\lambda^2 - 2^2}{3 \cdot 4}C_2 = \frac{\lambda^2(\lambda^2 - 2^2)}{4!}C_0$$

$$C_5 = -\frac{\lambda^2 - 3^2}{4 \cdot 5}C_3 = \frac{(\lambda^2 - 1^2)(\lambda^2 - 3^2)}{5!}C_1$$

$$C_6 = -\frac{\lambda^2 - 4^2}{5 \cdot 6}C_4 = -\frac{\lambda^2(\lambda^2 - 2^2)(\lambda^2 - 4^2)}{6!}C_0$$

$$C_7 = -\frac{\lambda^2 - 5^2}{6 \cdot 7}C_5 = -\frac{(\lambda^2 - 1^2)(\lambda^2 - 3^2)(\lambda^2 - 5^2)}{7!}C_1$$

substituting these coefficients into the solution and factoring out C_0 and C_1, we obtain

$$y = C_0\left[1 - \frac{\lambda^2}{2!}x^2 + \frac{\lambda^2(\lambda^2 - 2^2)}{4!}x^4 - \frac{\lambda^2(\lambda^2 - 2^2)(\lambda^2 - 4^2)}{6!}x^6 + \cdots\right]$$

$$+ C_1\left[x - \frac{\lambda^2 - 1}{3!}x^3 + \frac{(\lambda^2 - 1)(\lambda^2 - 3^2)}{5!}x^5 - \frac{(\lambda^2 - 1)(\lambda^2 - 3^2)(\lambda^2 - 5^2)}{7!}x^7 + \cdots\right]$$

$$= C_0 y_1(x) + C_1 y_2(x)$$

Generalizing the coefficients for the even and odd terms, the solution can also be expressed in a more general form as

$$y = C_0\left[1 + \sum_{n-1}^{\infty}(-1)^n\frac{(\lambda^2 - 0^2)(\lambda^2 - 2^2)\cdots[\lambda^2 - (2n-2)^2]}{(2n)!}x^{2n}\right]$$

$$+ C_1\left[x + \sum_{n-1}^{\infty}(-1)^n\frac{(\lambda^2 - 1^2)(\lambda^2 - 3^2)\cdots[\lambda^2 - (2n-1)^2]}{(2n+1)}x^{2n+1}\right]$$

(5–56)

The terms in the brackets are the two linearly independent solutions y_1 and y_2 of the Chebyshev's equation. Note that this solution is valid for any x value in the interval $-1 < x < 1$.

When λ is a non-negative integer, either $y_1(x)$ or $y_2(x)$ becomes a polynomial of degree n in place of that infinite series. When multiplied by a suitable constant, the resulting polynomial of degree n (which is a solution of Chebyshev's equation) is called the **Chebyshev polynomial**, and is denoted by $T_n(x)$. The first four Chebyshev polynomials are given in Figure 5–30.

$\lambda = n$	$T_n(x)$
0	1
1	x
2	$2x^2 - 1$
3	$4x^3 - 3x$

FIGURE 5–30

The first four Chebyshev polynomials.

Section Review

5–15C Consider a linear, homogeneous, third-order differential equation with variable coefficients. How many arbitrary constants will the general solution involve about an ordinary point? What will the radius of convergence of this solution be?

5–16 Solve the following linear second-order differential equation about the specified ordinary point using the power series method. Also, determine the interval of convergence of the solution.

$$y'' - 4xy' + 4y = 0, x_0 = 0$$

(*Answer:* $y(x) = C_0\left(1 - 2x^2 - \frac{2}{3}x^4 - \frac{4}{15}x^6 - \frac{2}{21}x^8 - \cdots\right) + C_1x$

The interval of convergence is $(-\infty, \infty)$.)

5–17 Solve the following linear, second-order initial-value problem about the ordinary point $x_0 = 0$ using the power series method.

$$y'' + xy' + y = 0, \qquad y(0) = 0, \qquad y'(0) = 1$$

(*Answer:* $y(x) = x - \frac{1}{3}x^3 + \frac{1}{15}x^5 - \frac{1}{105}x^7 + \frac{1}{945}x^9 + \cdots$)

5–5 ▪ LEGENDRE'S EQUATION AND LEGENDRE POLYNOMIALS

Numerous problems of practical interest in physics and engineering involve spherical geometry, such as the temperature distribution in a spherical shell, and result in **Legendre's differential equation** (named after the French mathematician Adrien Marie Legendre, 1752–1833). This equation is

$$(1 - x^2)y'' - 2xy' + \alpha(\alpha + 1)y = 0$$

(5–57)

where α is a constant. Any series solution of Legendre's equation is called a **Legendre function** (of order α). When α is a nonnegative integer, some

Legendre functions reduce to polynomials, which are called **Legendre polynomials**. These special polynomials are widely used in polynomial representation of functions and in numerical integration in the Gaussian quadrature method because of their desirable behavior in the range $-1 \leq x \leq 1$. We discuss the solution of Legendre's equation in the following example.

EXAMPLE 5–17   **Legendre's Equation**

Find a power series solution to Legendre's differential equation about the origin, $x_0 = 0$.

SOLUTION   This is a linear second-order homogeneous, differential equation with variable coefficients, and it can be put into the standard form by dividing each term by $1 - x^2$,

$$y'' - \frac{2x}{1 - x^2}y' + \frac{\alpha(\alpha + 1)}{1 - x^2}y = 0$$

Thus, $P(x) = -2x/(1 - x^2)$ and $Q(x) = \alpha(\alpha + 1)/(1 - x^2)$, which are ratios of polynomials. By inspection, we see that the denominators of both $P(x)$ and $Q(x)$ become zero at $x = \pm 1$. Therefore, the points $x = -1$ and $x = 1$ are the singular points of this differential equation, and thus, a series solution obtained about the point $x_0 = 0$ will converge in the interval $-1 < x < 1$. The series solution will have a radius of convergence of at least 1.

We now assume a power series solution of the form

$$y = \sum_{n=0}^{\infty} C_n x^n$$

Differentiating twice and substituting the differentials into the differential equation, we have

$$(1 - x^2)\sum_{n=2}^{\infty} n(n - 1)C_n x^{n-2} - 2x\sum_{n=1}^{\infty} nC_n x^{n-1} + \alpha(\alpha + 1)\sum_{n=0}^{\infty} C_n x^n = 0$$

or

$$\sum_{n=2}^{n} n(n - 1)C_n x^{n-2} - \sum_{n=2}^{n} n(n - 1)C_n x^n - 2\sum_{n=1}^{n} nC_n x^n + \alpha(\alpha + 1)\sum_{n=0}^{n} C_n x^n = 0$$

Shifting the index of the first summation with 2 by replacing n by $n - 2$ and starting the two summations in the middle with $n = 0$ instead of 1 or 2 (since the additional terms corresponding to $n = 0$ or 1 will be zero because of the factors n and $n - 1$ in the summation), we have

$$\sum_{n=0}^{\infty} (n + 2)(n + 1)C_{n+2} x^n - \sum_{n=0}^{\infty} n(n - 1)C_n x^n - 2\sum_{n=0}^{\infty} nC_n x^n + \alpha(\alpha + 1)\sum_{n=0}^{\infty} C_n x^n = 0$$

or

$$\sum_{n=0}^{\infty} \{(n + 2)(n + 1)C_{n+2} + [\alpha(\alpha + 1) - n(n - 1) - 2n]C_n\}x^n = 0$$

This equation will be satisfied for all x if and only if the coefficient of each power of x is zero. This condition gives us an infinite number of equations for the determination of the expansion coefficients C_n's,

$$(n + 2)(n + 1)C_{n+2} + [\alpha(\alpha + 1) - n(n - 1) - 2n]C_n = 0$$

or

$$C_{n+2} = \frac{n(n+1) - \alpha(\alpha+1)}{(n+1)(n+2)} C_n \qquad n = 0, 1, 3, \ldots \qquad (5\text{--}58)$$

In this case Equation 5–58 is the recurrence relation, and it relates any coefficient to the second one before it. Thus, if the first two coefficients C_0 and C_1 are available, the remainder of the coefficients $C_2, C_3, C_4, C_5, \ldots$ can be determined from the recurrence relation.

The first few of them are

$$C_2 = \frac{0 \cdot 1 - \alpha(\alpha+1)}{1 \cdot 2} C_0 = -\frac{\alpha(\alpha+1)}{2!} C_0$$

$$C_3 = \frac{1 \cdot 2 - \alpha(\alpha+1)}{2 \cdot 3} C_1 = -\frac{(\alpha-1)(\alpha+2)}{3!} C_1$$

$$C_4 = \frac{2 \cdot 3 - \alpha(\alpha+1)}{3 \cdot 4} C_2 = \frac{\alpha(\alpha-2)(\alpha+1)(\alpha+3)}{4!} C_0$$

$$C_5 = \frac{3 \cdot 4 - \alpha(\alpha+1)}{4 \cdot 5} C_3 = (\alpha-1)(\alpha-3)(\alpha+2)\frac{(\alpha+4)}{5!} C_1$$

Substituting these coefficients into the solution and factoring out C_0 and C_1, we obtain

$$y = C_0\left[1 - \frac{\alpha(\alpha+1)}{2!}x^2 + \frac{\alpha(\alpha-2)(\alpha+1)(\alpha+3)}{4!}x^4 - \cdots\right]$$

$$+ C_1\left[x - \frac{(\alpha-1)(\alpha+2)}{3!}x^3 + \frac{(\alpha-1)(\alpha-3)(\alpha+2)(\alpha+4)}{5!}x^5 - \cdots\right]$$

$$= C_0 y_1(x) + C_1 y_2(x)$$

Generalizing the coefficients for the even and odd terms, the solution can also be expressed in a more general form as

$$y = C_0\left[1 + \sum_{m=1}^{\infty}(-1)^m\frac{\alpha(\alpha-2)(\alpha-4)\cdots(\alpha-2m+2)(\alpha+1)(\alpha+3)\cdots(\alpha+2m-1)}{(2m)!}x^{2m}\right]$$

$$+ C_1\left[x + \sum_{m=1}^{\infty}(-1)^m\frac{(\alpha-1)(\alpha-3)\cdots(\alpha-2m+1)(\alpha+2)(\alpha+4)\cdots(\alpha+2m)}{(2m+1)!}x^{2m+1}\right]$$

The terms in the brackets are the two linearly independent solutions y_1 and y_2 of Legendre's equation. Note that this solution is valid for any x value in the interval $-1 < x < 1$. It can be shown that both series diverge at the end points.

Legendre Polynomials

When α is equal to a nonnegative integer n, the two solutions $y_1(x)$ and $y_2(x)$ of Legendre's equation can be written as

$$y_1(x) = 1 + \sum_{m=1}^{\infty}(-1)^m\frac{n(n-2)(n-4)\cdots(n-2m+2)(n+1)(n+3)\cdots(n+2m-1)}{(2m)!}x^{2m}$$

and

$$y_2(x) = x + \sum_{m=1}^{\infty}(-1)^m\frac{(n-1)(n-3)\cdots(n-2m+1)(n+2)(n+4)\cdots(n+2m)}{(2m+1)!}x^{2m+1}$$

Clearly, when n is an even number, $y_1(x)$ will reduce to a polynomial of degree n since the factor $n - 2m + 2$ will be zero when $m = n/2 + 1$, and all the terms corresponding to larger values of the index m will contain this factor. For example, when n is 0, 2, and 4, $y_1(x)$ will reduce to

$$1, \quad 1 - 3x^2, \quad \text{and} \quad 1 - 10x^2 + \frac{35}{3}x^4$$

respectively. Likewise, when n is an odd number, $y_2(x)$ will reduce to a polynomial of degree n, since the factor $n - 2m + 1$ will be zero when $m = (n + 1)/2$, and all the terms corresponding to larger values of the index m will contain this factor. For example, when n is 1, 3, and 5, $y_1(x)$ will reduce to

$$x, \quad x - \frac{5}{3}x^3, \quad \text{and} \quad x - \frac{14}{3}x^3 + \frac{21}{5}x^5$$

respectively. Thus, we conclude that, when α is equal to a non-negative integer n, one of the solutions of Legendre's equations reduces to a polynomial of degree n. When multiplied by a suitable constant, the resulting polynomial of degree n (which is a solution of Legendre's equation) is called the **Legendre polynomial of order n** and is denoted by $P_n(x)$. This constant is selected such that the coefficient of the highest power of x in $P_n(x)$ is equal to

$$C_n = \frac{(2n)!}{2^n(n!)^2} \tag{5-59}$$

so that when $x = 1$ the polynomial will have the value 1. That is, $P_n(1) = 1$ for all values of n. The coefficients of other powers of x are determined from the recurrence relation (Equation 5–58) by replacing n by m and α by n,

$$C_{m-2} = -\frac{m(m + 1)}{(n - m + 2)(n + m - 1)}C_m \tag{5-60}$$

Note that n is the order of the Legendre polynomial, whereas m is the dummy index of the summation. For $m = n$, substitution of Equation 5–59 into Equation 5–60 yields

$$C_{n-2} = -\frac{n(n - 1)}{2(2n - 1)}C_n = -\frac{n(n - 1)}{2(2n - 1)}\frac{(2n)!}{2^n(n!)^2} = -\frac{(2n - 2)!}{2^n(n - 2)!(n - 1)!}$$

For $m = n - 2$, we will have

$$C_{n-4} = -\frac{(n - 2)(n - 3)}{4(2n - 3)}C_{n-2} = -\frac{(n - 2)(n - 3)}{4(2n - 3)}\frac{(2n - 2)!}{2^n(n - 2)!(n - 1)!}$$

$$= \frac{(2n - 4)!}{2^n 2!(n - 4)!(n - 2)!}$$

Generalizing for $m = n - 2k$,

$$C_{n-2k} = \frac{(-1)^k(2n - 2k)!}{2^n k!(n - k)!(n - 2k)!} \tag{5-61}$$

Then the Legendre polynomial of order n can be expressed as

$$P_n(x) = \sum_{k=0}^{N}\frac{(-1)^k(2n - 2k)!}{2^n k!(n - k)!(n - 2k)!}x^{n-2k}, \quad n = 0, 1, 2, \dots \tag{5-62}$$

where N is the greatest integer less than or equal to $n/2$. That is, $N = n/2$ when n is even, and $N = (n - 1)/2$ when n is odd. Note that Legendre polynomials of even order (such as $P_2, P_4, \ldots$) involve only the even powers of x, whereas Legendre polynomials of odd order (such as $P_3, P_5, \ldots$) involve only the odd powers of x. The first six Legendre polynomials can be expressed explicitly as

$$P_0(x) = 1 \qquad\qquad P_1(x) = x$$

$$P_2(x) = \frac{1}{2}(3x^2 - 1) \qquad\qquad P_3(x) = \frac{1}{2}(5x^3 - 3x)$$

$$P_4(x) = \frac{1}{8}(35x^4 - 30x^2 + 3) \qquad P_5(x) = \frac{1}{8}(63x^5 - 70x^3 + 15x)$$

A plot of the first few Legendre polynomials is given in Figure 5–31.

Unlike the Legendre functions, the Legendre polynomials converge at the end points $x = \pm 1$ as well as the interval in between. We can show that $P_n(1) = 1$ and $P_n(-1) = (-1)^n$ for any value of n. Therefore, $P_n(x)$ is the only solution of Legendre's equation that remains finite on the closed interval $-1 \leq x \leq 1$.

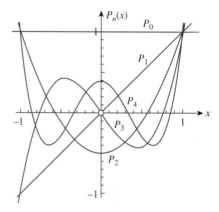

FIGURE 5–31

A plot of the first few Legendre polynomials.

EXAMPLE 5–18   Rodrigues Formula

Show that the Legendre polynomials can be generated in a systematic manner from the relation

$$P_n(x) = \frac{1}{2^n n!}\frac{d^n}{dx^n}[(x^2 - 1)^n], \qquad n = 0, 1, 2, 3, \ldots \tag{5-63}$$

which is known as **Rodrigues Formula**, after the French mathematician Olinde Rodrigues (1794–1851).

SOLUTION   Using the binomial expansion formula, $(x^2 - 1)^n$ can be expressed as

$$(x^2 - 1)^n = \sum_{k=0}^{n} \frac{(-1)^k n!}{k!(n - k)!}x^{2n-2k} \tag{5-64}$$

Substituting and noting that the derivative of a sum is equal to the sum of the derivatives (i.e., the derivative operator can be moved into or out of the summation), we have

$$P_n(x) = \frac{1}{2^n n!}\sum_{k=0}^{n} \frac{(-1)^k n!}{k!(n - k)!}\frac{d^n}{dx^n}(x^{2n-2k}) \tag{5-65}$$

Performing the differentiation, we obtain

$$\frac{d^n}{dx^n}(x^{2n-2k}) = (2n - 2k)\frac{d^{n-1}}{dx^{n-1}}(x^{2n-2k-1})$$

$$= (2n - 2k)(2n - 2k - 1)\frac{d^{n-2}}{dx^{n-2}}(x^{2n-2k-2})$$

$$= (2n - 2k)(2n - 2k - 1) \cdots (n - 2k - 1)x^{n-2k}$$

$$= \frac{(2n - 2k)!}{(n - 2k)!}x^{n-2k} \tag{5-66}$$

(a) $P_n(x) = \sum_{k=0}^{N} \dfrac{(-1)^k (2n - 2k)! x^{n-2k}}{2^n k! (n-k)! (n-2k)!}$

(b) $P_n(x) = \dfrac{1}{2^n n!} \dfrac{d^n}{dx^n} (x^2 - 1)^n$

(c) $P_n(x) = \dfrac{(2n-1)xP_{n-1} - (n-1)P_{n-2}}{n}$

with $P_0 = 1$ and $P_1 = x$.

FIGURE 5–32

Three ways of obtaining a Legendre polynomial: (a) series expansion, (b) Rodrigues formula, and (c) recurrence relation.

Also, when $m > n/2$ the derivative in the summation yields zero, since the exponent of x in this case becomes less than n, and the nth derivative of a polynomial of degree less than n is zero. Therefore, we can change the upper limit of the index of summation to N, which is the greatest integer less than or equal to $n/2$. Substitution of Equation 5–66 into Equation 5–65 yields (after some cancelations)

$$P_n(x) = \sum_{k=0}^{N} \frac{(-1)^k (2n - 2k)!}{2^n k! (n-k)! (n-2k)!} x^{n-2k}, \qquad n = 0, 1, 2, 3, \dots$$

which is the desired result.

Using the Rodrigues formula and going through some lengthy manipulations, we obtain the following recurrence relation for Legendre polynomials,

$$P_n(x) = \frac{(2n-1)xP_{n-1} - (n-1)P_{n-2}}{n} \qquad \text{(5–67)}$$

Thus knowing that $P_0(x) = 1$ and $P_1(x) = x$, we can determine all the Legendre polynomials using this recurrence relation (Figure 5–32).

EXAMPLE 5–19   Obtaining Legendre Polynomials

Determine the Legendre polynomial P_2 using (a) the Rodrigues formula and (b) the recurrence relation.

SOLUTION (a) Taking $n = 2$ and applying the Rodrigues formula (Equation 5–63), we have

$$P_2(x) = \frac{1}{2^2 2!} \frac{d^2}{dx^2} \big[(x^2 - 1)^2\big] = \frac{1}{8} \frac{d}{dx}\big[4x(x^2 - 1)\big] = \frac{1}{2}(3x^2 - 1)$$

(b) Noting that $P_0(x) = 1$ and $P_1(x) = x$, the recurrence relation (Equation 5–67) with $n = 2$ yields

$$P_2 = \frac{3xP_1 - P_0}{2} = \frac{1}{2}(3x^2 - 1)$$

Both methods gave the same result as expected.

Section Review

5–18C How are Legendre polynomials and Legendre functions related to each other?

5–19C Is the general solution of Legendre's equation obtained in Example 5–17 valid at $x = 2$? Why?

5–20 Determine the Legendre polynomial $P_3(x)$ using (a) the series expansion, (b) the Rodrigues formula, and (c) the recurrence relation.

(*Answer:* $P_3(x) = \frac{1}{2}(5x^3 - 3x)$)

5–6 · SERIES SOLUTIONS ABOUT A REGULAR SINGULAR POINT

We now consider the solutions of the general second-order, linear, differential equation with variable coefficients

$$y'' + P(x)y' + Q(x)y = 0 \qquad (5\text{–}68)$$

in the neighborhood of a regular point, x_0. For convenience we will assume that the regular singular point is at the origin, i.e., $x_0 = 0$. This assumption simplifies the problem, but does not cause any loss in generality since any singular point x_0 of a differential equation can be moved to the origin through the transformation $t = x - x_0$. We will also consider the interval $x > 0$ in the discussions to avoid the absolute value sign. This again is not a serious limitation since the interval $x < 0$ can be handled in the same manner by changing the variable $t = -x$ and performing the analysis for $t > 0$.

It follows from the definition of regular singular points that if $x_0 = 0$ is a regular singular point, then the functions $xP(x)$ and $x^2Q(x)$ are analytic, and they have Taylor series expansions at that point. Thus these two functions can be expressed as

$$p(x) = xP(x) = p_0 + p_1x + p_2x^2 + \cdots = \sum_{n=0}^{\infty} p_n x^n \qquad (5\text{–}69)$$

and

$$q(x) = x^2Q(x) = q_0 + q_1x + q_2x^2 + \cdots = \sum_{n=0}^{\infty} q_n x^n \qquad (5\text{–}70)$$

The functions $p(x)$ and $q(x)$ need not involve an infinite number of terms. In fact, these two functions in most familiar differential equations are polynomials with no more than two or three terms. For example, for Bessel's equation of order zero, we have

$$y'' + \frac{1}{x}y' + y = 0$$

We see at once by inspection that $p(x) = 1$ and $q(x) = x^2$, which are simple polynomials.

Multiplying Equation 5–68 by x^2 yields

$$x^2y'' + x^2P(x)y' + x^2Q(x)y = 0$$

This equation can be rearranged as

$$x^2y'' + x[xP(x)]y' + [x^2Q(x)]y = 0$$

or

$$x^2y'' + xp(x)y' + q(x)y = 0 \qquad (5\text{–}71)$$

which closely resembles the Euler equation discussed in Chapter 3. For the special case of $p(x)$ and $q(x)$ being constants, Equation 5–71 does become the Euler equation (Figure 5–33),

$$x^2y'' + p_0xy' + q_0y = 0 \qquad (5\text{–}72)$$

The solution of this equation is of the form x^r, where r is not necessarily an integer.

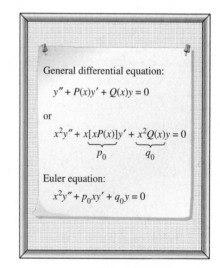

FIGURE 5–33

When the functions $xP(x)$ and $x^2Q(x)$ are constants, the second-order, linear, homogeneous, differential equation reduces to the Euler equation.

General differential equation:

$$y'' + P(x)y' + Q(x)y = 0$$

or

$$x^2y'' + x\underbrace{[xP(x)]}_{p_0}y' + \underbrace{x^2Q(x)}_{q_0}y = 0$$

Euler equation:

$$x^2y'' + p_0xy' + q_0y = 0$$

A careful examination of Equation 5–71 reveals that the coefficients of the differential equation appear as the product of the coefficients of the Euler equation and the coefficients of equations that have power series solutions. This observation suggests that we seek the solution of Equation 5–71 in the form

$$y = x^r \sum_{n=0}^{\infty} C_n x^n = \sum_{n=0}^{\infty} C_n x^{n+r} \tag{5–73}$$

that is, as a product of the Euler solution and a power series solution (Figure 5–34). The procedure of seeking a solution to a differential equation in the form of a product of an unknown power of x and a power series in x is known as the **method of Frobenius** after the German mathematician George F. Frobenius (1849–1917). We will see that in the neighborhood of a regular singular point, the differential Equation (5–68) has at least one solution of the form of Equation 5–73 and another solution of the same or modified form, depending on the values of r.

To determine the acceptable of r, we consider the differential equation in its general form (Equation 5–71), and substitute the expansions for $p(x)$ and $q(x)$ in Equations 5–69 and 5–70 into this equation. We obtain

$$x^2 y'' + x \sum_{n=0}^{\infty} p_n x^n y' + \sum_{n=0}^{\infty} q_n x^n = 0 \tag{5–74}$$

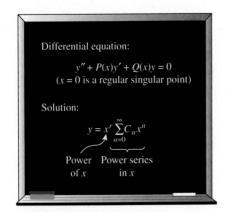

FIGURE 5–34

The solution of differential equation about the point $x = 0$, where $x = 0$ is a regular singular point, is in the form of a product of a power of x and a power series in x.

We now assume a solution of the form of Equation 5–73 with $C_0 \neq 0$, from which we obtain by differentiation:

$$y' = \sum_{n=0}^{\infty} (n + r) C_n x^{n+r-1}$$

and

$$y'' = \sum_{n=0}^{\infty} (n + r - 1)(n + r) C_n x^{n+r-2}$$

Substituting the expression for y, y', and, y'' into Equation 5–74 and setting the coefficient of x^r, which is the lowest power of x, equal to zero yields

$$[r^2 + (p_0 - 1)r + q_0]C_0 = 0$$

or

$$r^2 + (p_0 - 1)r + q_0 = 0 \tag{5–75}$$

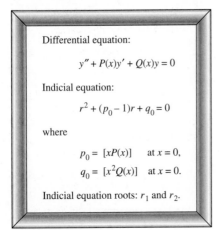

FIGURE 5–35

The indicial equation of a differential equation is a quadratic equation in r which involves the values of the functions $xP(x)$ and $x^2 Q(x)$ at $x = 0$.

since $C_0 \neq 0$. This is a quadratic equation in r and is called the **indicial equation** of the differential equation (Figure 5–35). It has two real or two complex roots r_1 and r_2, which are called the *exponents* of the regular singular point under consideration.

If the roots are complex, they are necessarily conjugate of each other. In this case the solution will be complex functions since they will involve complex exponents r_1 and r_2. However, we can still obtain real valued functions by separating the real and imaginary parts of the solution. When the roots r_1 and r_2 are real and unequal, we will always take r_1 to be the larger root.

When $p(x) = xP(x)$ and $q(x) = x^2Q(x)$ are polynomials, the constants p_0 and q_0 are simply the constants in those polynomials (the coefficients of x^0). Otherwise, they can be determined from the following limits:

$$p_0 = \lim_{x \to 0} xP(x) \quad \text{and} \quad q_0 = \lim_{x \to 0} x^2Q(x) \tag{5–76}$$

We now illustrate the determination of r_1 and r_2 with examples.

EXAMPLE 5–20   Indicial Equation and Its Roots

Show that the point $x = 0$ is a regular singular point of the differential equation

$$x^2y'' - 2x(x - 1)y' + x^2y = 0$$

and determine the roots of the indicial equation, r_1 and r_2.

SOLUTION This is a linear, second-order, homogeneous differential equation with variable coefficients, and it can be put into the standard form by dividing each term by x^2:

$$y'' - \frac{2(x - 1)}{x}y' + y = 0$$

Thus, $P(x) = -2(x - 1)/x$ which is a ratio of two polynomials, and $Q(x) = 1$, which is a polynomial. By inspection, we see that $Q(x)$ is analytic everywhere, but the denominator of $P(x)$ becomes zero at $x = 0$. Therefore, the point $x = 0$ is a singular point. This is a regular singular point, however, since both $p(x) = xP(x) = -2(x - 1) = 2 - 2x$ and $q(x) = x^2Q(x) = x^2$ are polynomials, and thus analytic functions.

From these two relations, we observe that $p_0 = 2$ and $q_0 = 0$. Substituting these values into the indicial equation $r^2 + (p_0 - 1)r + q_0 = 0$ yields $r^2 + r = 0$ or $r(r + 1) = 0$. The roots of this indicial equation easily are determined by inspection to be $r_1 = 0$ and $r_2 = -1$. Note that we denoted the larger root by r_1.

EXAMPLE 5–21   Shifting the Singular Point to the Origin

Show that the point $x = 1$ is a regular singular point of Legendre's equation:

$$(1 - x^2)y'' - 2xy' + \alpha(\alpha + 1)y = 0$$

where α is a constant. Shift this singular point to the origin through the transformation $t = x - 1$, and determine the roots of the indicial equation that belongs to the transformed equation.

SOLUTION This is a linear, second-order, homogeneous differential equation with variable coefficients, and it can be put into the standard form by dividing each term by $(1 - x^2)$:

$$y'' - \frac{2x}{1 - x^2}y' + \frac{\alpha(\alpha + 1)}{1 - x^2}y = 0 \tag{5–77}$$

Thus $P(x) = -2x/(1 - x^2)$ and $Q(x) = \alpha(\alpha + 1)/(1 - x^2)$, both of which are ratios of polynomials. By inspection, we see that the denominators of both

$P(x)$ and $Q(x)$ become zero at $x = \pm 1$. Therefore, the points $x = -1$ and $x = 1$ are the singular points of this differential equation. These are the regular singular points, however, since for $x_0 = 1$,

$$(x - x_0)P(x) = (x - 1)\frac{-2x}{1 - x^2} = \frac{2x}{x + 1}$$

and

$$(x - x_0)^2 Q(x) = (x - 1)^2\frac{\alpha(\alpha + 1)}{1 - x^2} = -\frac{(x - 1)\alpha(\alpha + 1)}{1 + x}$$

which are analytic at $x = 1$. We can show similarly that the point $x_0 = -1$ is also a regular singular point.

To shift the singular point $x_0 = 1$ to the origin, we apply the transformation $t = x - 1$. Substituting this into Equation 5–77 and rearranging, we obtain

$$y'' - \frac{2(t + 1)}{t(t + 2)}y' - \frac{\alpha(\alpha + 1)}{t(t + 2)}y = 0$$

where the primes in this case denote differentiation with respect to t. The point $t = 0$ is clearly one of the singular points. Thus, we accomplished our goal of shifting the regular singular point $x_0 = 1$ to the origin.

Before we can calculate the roots of the indicial equation, we need to determine the constants p_0 and q_0. Since $p(t)$ and $q(t)$ are not polynomials in this case, we need to determine those from Equations 5–65 and 5–66 by taking the following limits:

$$p_0 = \lim_{t \to 0} tP(t) = \lim_{t \to 0}\frac{2t(t + 1)}{t(t + 2)} = 1$$

and

$$q_0 = \lim_{t \to 0} t^2 Q(t) = \lim_{t \to 0}\frac{-t^2\alpha(\alpha + 1)}{t(t + 2)} = 0$$

Substituting these values into the indicial equation $r^2 + (p_0 - 1)r + q_0 = 0$ yields $r^2 + (1 - 1)r + 0 = 0$ or $r^2 = 0$. The roots of this indicial equation easily are determined by inspection to be $r_1 = r_2 = 0$. Note that the roots in this case are real and equal.

As a side note, it is more convenient to solve the equation

$$t(t + 2)y'' + 2(t + 1)y' - \alpha(\alpha + 1)y = 0 \tag{5–78}$$

than its equivalent

$$ty'' + \frac{2(t + 1)}{t + 2}y' - \frac{\alpha(\alpha + 1)}{t + 2}y = 0 \tag{5–79}$$

since, in the latter case, we will need to expand the terms in the denominator using the binomial expansion:

$$\frac{1}{1+x} = \sum_{n=0}^{\infty}(-1)^n x^n = 1 - x + x^2 - x^3 + \cdots$$

Thus,

$$\frac{1}{2+t} = \frac{1}{2(1+\frac{t}{2})} = \frac{1}{2}\sum_{n=0}^{\infty}(-1)^n\left(\frac{t}{2}\right)^n = \sum_{n=0}^{\infty}\frac{(-1)^n}{2^{n+1}}t^n$$

Substituting into Equation 5–79, we have

$$ty'' + (t+1)\sum_{n=0}^{\infty}\frac{(-1)^n}{2^n}t^n y' - \alpha(\alpha+1)\sum_{n=0}^{\infty}\frac{(-1)^n}{2^{n+1}}t^n y = 0 \qquad \textbf{(5–80)}$$

which is much more complex than the differential Equation 5–78.

The theory of the method of Frobenius is rather involved, and beyond the scope of an introductory text on differential equations. We summarize the results in the following theorem.

THEOREM 5–3   Series Solutions About Regular Singular Points

Let the point $x = 0$ be a regular singular point of the differential equation:

$$y'' + P(x)y' + Q(x)y = 0$$

and ρ be the smaller radius of convergence of two functions $p(x) = xP(x)$ and $q(x) = x^2Q(x)$. If r_1 and r_2 are the roots of the indicial equation:

$$r^2 + (p_0 - 1)r + q_0 = 0$$

where

$$p_0 = \lim_{x\to 0} xP(x) \quad and \quad q_0 = \lim_{x\to 0} x^2Q(x)$$

and $r_1 > r_2$ when the roots are real and unequal, then two linearly independent solutions $y_1(x)$ and $y_2(x)$ to this differential equation exist with a radius of convergence of ρ. For $x > 0$, they are the following forms (Figure 5–36):

CASE 1: $r_1 = r_2 + \lambda$ *(λ is a positive non-integer)*

$$y_1 = x^{r_1}\sum_{n=0}^{\infty}a_n x^n \qquad (a_0 \neq 0) \qquad \textbf{(5–81a)}$$

$$y_2 = x^{r_2}\sum_{n=0}^{\infty}b_n x^n \qquad (b_0 \neq 0) \qquad \textbf{(5–81b)}$$

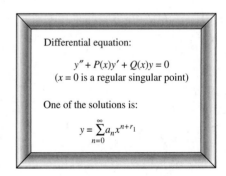

Differential equation:

$$y'' + P(x)y' + Q(x)y = 0$$
$(x = 0$ is a regular singular point)

One of the solutions is:

$$y = \sum_{n=0}^{\infty}a_n x^{n+r_1}$$

FIGURE 5–36

When $x = 0$ is a regular singular point, a second-order linear equation is guaranteed to have at least one solution of the form $\sum_{n=0}^{\infty}a_n x^{n+r_1}$ where r_1 is the larger root of the indicial equation.

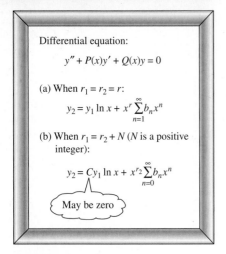

Differential equation:

$$y'' + P(x)y' + Q(x)y = 0$$

(a) When $r_1 = r_2 = r$:

$$y_2 = y_1 \ln x + x^r \sum_{n=1}^{\infty} b_n x^n$$

(b) When $r_1 = r_2 + N$ (N is a positive integer):

$$y_2 = Cy_1 \ln x + x^{r_2} \sum_{n=0}^{\infty} b_n x^n$$

May be zero

FIGURE 5–37

When $r_1 = r_2 = r$, the second linearly independent solution always involves a logarithmic term. When $r_1 = r_2 + N$, where N is a positive integer, then the second linearly independent solution involves a logarithmic term only when $C \neq 0$.

CASE 2: $r_1 = r_2 = r$

$$y_1 = x^r \sum_{n=0}^{\infty} a_n x^n \qquad (a_0 \neq 0) \tag{5–82a}$$

$$y_2 = y_1 \ln x + x^r \sum_{n=1}^{\infty} b_n x^n \tag{5–82b}$$

CASE 3: $r_1 = r_2 + N$ *(N is a positive integer)*

$$y_1 = x^{r_1} \sum_{n=0}^{\infty} a_n x^n \qquad (a_0 \neq 0) \tag{5–83a}$$

$$y_2 = Cy_1 \ln x + x^{r_2} \sum_{n=0}^{\infty} b_n x^n \qquad (b_0 \neq 0) \tag{5–83b}$$

where the constant C may be zero (Figure 5–37). Then the general solution of the differential equation for all three cases is expressed as

$$y = C_1 y_1(x) + C_2 y_2(x) \tag{5–84}$$

where the arbitrary constants C_1 and C_2 are determined from the initial and boundary conditions.

The proof of this theorem is given in more advanced texts on differential equations. Before we illustrate the solution procedure and the use of this theorem with examples, we make the following remarks regarding the solution of second-order differential equations with variable coefficients about a regular singular point:

1. The form of the first solution is the same for all cases. The three cases differ in the form of the second solution only. For all cases, both solutions involve infinite series with different sets of coefficients a_n and b_n.
2. The coefficients a_0 and b_0 are arbitrary nonzero constants, and can be assigned any suitable values. It is common practice to take $a_0 = 1$ and $b_0 = 1$ for simplicity with no loss in generality.
3. The solutions given are restricted to $x > 0$ to avoid using absolute value signs. This restriction can be lifted by replacing x^{r_1} and x^{r_2} in the solutions by $|x|^{r_1}$ and $|x|^{r_2}$, respectively. A more practical way is to substitute $t = -x$ in the differential equation, and then to solve the resulting equation for $t > 0$.
4. The solutions will converge anywhere both $xP(x)$ and $x^2Q(x)$ are analytic, except possibly at $x = 0$. A solution will diverge at $x = 0$ if it contains $\ln x$ or x^r where $r < 0$. If the point $x = 0$ is the only singular point of the differential equation, then the solution will converge everywhere except maybe the origin. That is, the radius of convergence of the solution in this case will be infinity. If the differential equation

has more singular points, then the radius of convergence of the solution is at least as large as the smaller of the radii of convergence of the coefficient functions $p(x)$ and $q(x)$.

5. The solutions given in Theorem 5–3 are applicable to regular singular points at $x_0 = 0$. Solutions in the neighborhood of regular singular points $x_0 \neq 0$ are easily obtained by changing the independent variable through $t = x - x_0$, and then solving the resulting equation about the point $t = 0$ (Figure 5–38).

6. The determination of the first linearly independent solution y_1 is similar to the determination of the solution about an ordinary point, except now the solution involves x^{n+r_1} instead of x^n. Again, y_1' and y_1'' are obtained by termwise differentiation, substituted into the original differential equation, and the coefficients a_n determined in a usual manner from the requirement that the coefficient of each power of x be equal to zero. The term that corresponds to $n = 0$ is always of the form $f(r_1)a_0x^r$, where $f(r)$ is the indicial equation and thus we will always have $f(r_1) = 0$. This is the direct way of obtaining the indicial equation of the given differential equation.

Note that unless $r = 0$, the summations in y_1' and y_1'' start with $n = 0$ instead of $n = 1$ or $n = 2$, which was the case with power series since the coefficients of the first one or two terms are no longer zero.

7. The second solution for Case 1 ($r_1 = r_2 + \lambda$, λ noninteger) is easily obtained by simply repeating the solution procedure for $x = 0$ using r_2 instead of r_1, and determining the new sets of constants b_n. This approach obviously will not work for Case 2 since $r_1 = r_2$, and it will yield the same solution. As was the case with the Euler equation, the second linearly independent solution in this case involves a logarithmic term $y_1 \ln x$. We can verify this by applying the method of reduction of order. Finally, when r_1 and r_2 differ by an integer (Case 3), it looks like a solution of the form

$$y_2 = x^{r_2} \sum_{n=0}^{\infty} b_n x^n \qquad \text{(5–85)}$$

which will be linearly independent of y_1. Quite often this happens to be the case, but not always. When it is not the case, it becomes necessary to include a logarithmic term to make it linearly independent of y_1. The value of the constant C is determined during solution together with the constants b_n. A finding of $C = 0$ indicates that y_2 does not contain a logarithmic term, and it is of the form of Equation 5–85.

Knowing the general form of y_2, there are several ways to determine it. The obvious one is to perform the indicated derivatives, and to substitute the results into the differential equation, and solve for the unknown coefficients b_n. This procedure is tedious at times, but it is a sound approach and it always works. The presence of logarithmic terms should not be a cause for concern since they always cancel out. An alternative approach would be to ignore the specified y_2 relations, and to apply the method of reduction of order once y_1 is available. Yet another approach when r_1 and r_2 differ by an integer would be to assume, with

---

Given differential equation:

$$y'' + \frac{5x}{x-2}y' + \frac{x+3}{(x-2)^2}y = 0$$

($x = 2$ is the singular point)

Define:

$$t = x - 2$$

Obtain:

$$y'' + \frac{5(t+2)}{t}y' + \frac{t+5}{t^2}y = 0$$

($t = 0$ is the singular point now)

FIGURE 5–38

Shifting the singular point to the origin.

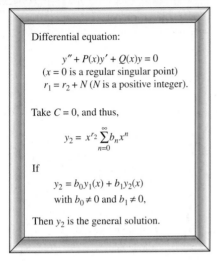

Differential equation:

$$y'' + P(x)y' + Q(x)y = 0$$
($x = 0$ is a regular singular point)
$r_1 = r_2 + N$ (N is a positive integer).

Take $C = 0$, and thus,

$$y_2 = x^{r_2} \sum_{n=0}^{\infty} b_n x^n$$

If

$$y_2 = b_0 y_1(x) + b_1 y_2(x)$$
with $b_0 \neq 0$ and $b_1 \neq 0$,

Then y_2 is the general solution.

FIGURE 5–39

When $r_1 = r_2 + N$ where N is a positive integer, it is advisable to set $C = 0$ and try to determine y_2 first. If the solution obtained involves two arbitrary constant coefficients, then this is usually the general solution.

no justification, that y_2 is of the form of Equation 5–85, and attempt to determine b_n, hoping that this will work. Getting all zeros for b_n indicates that our assumption is incorrect and y_2 contains a logarithmic term. Getting nonzero values for b_n indicates that our assumption is correct. Not only that, the solution obtained usually contains two arbitrary constants b_0 and b_1, and we obtain both linearly independent solutions at once without needing to use the larger root r_1 (Figure 5–39).

8. Once the two linearly independent solutions y_1 and y_2 are available, any other solution of the differential equation can be expressed as a linear combination of these two solutions.

EXAMPLE 5–22   **An Euler Equation**

Solve the second order Euler equation $4x^2y'' + 11xy' - 2y = 0$ using (a) the standard procedure, and (b) the series method about the point $x_0 = 0$.

SOLUTION   (a) Using the solution procedure for Euler equations discussed in Chapter 3, we take the solution to be of the form $y = x^r$. Taking the first and the second derivatives, we have

$$y' = rx^{r-1}$$
$$y'' = r(r-1)x^{r-2}$$

Substituting into the differential equation and dividing out $y = x^r$ yields

$$r^2 + \frac{7}{4}r - \frac{1}{2} = 0 \tag{5–86}$$

The roots of this quadratic equation are $r_1 = 1/4$ and $r_2 = -2$, which are real and distinct. Thus the general solution of this Euler equation is, from Chapter 3,

$$y = C_1 x^{r_1} + C_2 x^{r_2} = C_1 x^{1/4} + C_2 x^{-2} \tag{5–87}$$

This solution is applicable at any point except at $x = 0$ since division by $y = x^r$ is valid only for $x \neq 0$.

(b) Now in complete ignorance of the well-developed solution procedure given previously for Euler equations, we will attempt to solve the given differential equation using the more sophisticated and laborious series method, and hopefully we will obtain the same result.

This is a linear, second-order, homogeneous differential equation with variable coefficients, and it can be put into the standard form by dividing each term by $4x^2$ to obtain

$$y'' + \frac{11}{4x}y' - \frac{1}{2x^2}y = 0$$

Clearly, the point $x = 0$ is a singular point. This is a regular singular point, however, since both $p(x) = xP(x) = 11/4$ and $q(x) = x^2Q(x) = -1/2$ are polynomials (of degree zero), and thus are analytic functions.

From the two relations above we observe that $p_0 = 11/4$ and $q_0 = -1/2$. Substituting these values into the indicial equation $r^2 + (p_0 - 1)r + q_0 = 0$ yields

$$r^2 + \frac{7}{4}r - \frac{1}{2} = 0$$

which is identical to the equation obtained previously by substituting x^r for y in the differential equation (Figure 5–40). This is always the case, and offers an alternative for finding the indicial equation. The roots of this indicial equation are $r_1 = 1/4$ and $r_2 = -1/2$. Note again that we denoted the larger root by r_1.

Considering that the roots are different and differ by a noninteger, according to Theorem 5–3, the given differential equation has two linearly independent solutions both of the form

$$y = x^r \sum_{n=0}^{\infty} a_n x^n = \sum_{n=0}^{\infty} a_n x^{n+r}$$

Differentiating twice, we have

$$y' = \sum_{n=0}^{\infty} (n + r)a_n x^{n+r-1}$$

$$y'' = \sum_{n=0}^{\infty} (n + r)(n + r - 1)a_n x^{n+r-2}$$

Substituting into the given differential equation,

$$4x^2 \sum_{n=0}^{\infty} (n + r)(n + r - 1)a_n x^{n+r-2} + 11x \sum_{n=0}^{\infty} (n + r)a_n x^{n+r-1} - 2\sum_{n=0}^{\infty} a_n x^{n+r} = 0$$

or

$$\sum_{n=0}^{\infty} [4(n + r)(n + r - 1) + 11(n + r) - 2]a_n x^{n+r} = 0$$

This equation will be satisfied for all x if and only if the coefficient of each power of x is zero. This condition gives us an infinite number of equations for the determination of the expansion coefficients a_n:

$$[4(n + r)(n + r - 1) + 11(n + r) - 2]a_n = 0 \quad n = 0, 1, 2, 3, \ldots \quad \textbf{(5–88)}$$

For $n = 0$, the recurrence relation reduces to $[4r(r - 1) + 11r - 2]a_0 = 0$ or $4r(r - 1) + 11r - 2 = 0$, since $a_0 \neq 0$. This equation can be rearranged as

$$r^2 + \frac{7}{4}r - \frac{1}{2} = 0$$

which is the indicial equation, Equation 5–86. Thus we conclude that for $n = 0$, *the recurrence relation always reduces to the indicial equation.*

For $r = r_1 = 1/4$, the recurrence relation (Equation 5–88) reduces to

$$\left[\left(n + \frac{1}{4}\right)\left(n + \frac{1}{4} - 1\right) + \frac{11}{4}\left(n + \frac{1}{4}\right) - \frac{1}{2}\right]a_n = 0$$

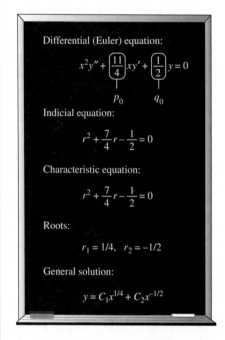

Differential (Euler) equation:

$$x^2 y'' + \left(\frac{11}{4}\right)xy' + \left(\frac{1}{2}\right)y = 0$$

$$\underset{p_0}{\qquad} \underset{q_0}{\qquad}$$

Indicial equation:

$$r^2 + \frac{7}{4}r - \frac{1}{2} = 0$$

Characteristic equation:

$$r^2 + \frac{7}{4}r - \frac{1}{2} = 0$$

Roots:

$$r_1 = 1/4, \quad r_2 = -1/2$$

General solution:

$$y = C_1 x^{1/4} + C_2 x^{-1/2}$$

FIGURE 5–40

The indicial equation of an Euler equation is equivalent to its characteristic equation.

or

$$\left[n\left(n + \frac{9}{4} \right) \right] a_n = 0, \qquad n = 1, 2, 3, \ldots \tag{5–89}$$

Thus,

$$a_n = 0, \qquad n = 1, 2, 3, 4, \ldots$$

since no integer $n \geq 1$ can make the terms in the brackets of Equation 5–89 zero. Then taking $a_0 = 1$, as is customary, the first solution becomes

$$y_1 = x^{r_1} \sum_{n=0}^{\infty} a_n x^{1/4} = a_0 x^{1/4} = x^{1/4} \tag{5–90}$$

The second linearly independent solution is obtained by repeating the procedure for $r = r_2 = -2$. The recurrence relation (Equation 5–88) in this case reduces to

$$\left[(n - 2)(n - 2 - 1) + \frac{11}{4}(n - 2) - \frac{1}{2} \right] b_n = 0$$

or

$$\left[n\left(n - \frac{9}{20} \right) \right] b_n = 0, \qquad n = 1, 2, 3, 4, \ldots \tag{5–91}$$

Thus,

$$b_n = 0, \qquad n = 1, 2, 3, 4, \ldots$$

since no integer $n \geq 1$ can make the terms in the brackets of Equation 5–91 zero. Then taking $b_0 = 1$, as is customary, the second solution becomes

$$y_2 = x^{r_2} \sum_{n=0}^{\infty} b_n x^n = b_0 x^{-2} = x^{-2} \tag{5–92}$$

Thus, the general solution is

$$y = C_1 y_1 + C_2 y_2 = C_1 x^{1/4} + C_2 x^{-2} \tag{5–93}$$

which is the same result obtained in part (a).

EXAMPLE 5–23   Theorem 5–3: Case 1 (r_1 and r_2 Differ by a Non-Integer)

Solve the differential equation $(x - 2)^2 y'' + (x - 2)y' + (x - 4)y = 0$ about the point $x_0 = 2$ for $x > 0$ using the Frobenius method.

SOLUTION This is a linear, second-order homogeneous differential equation with variable coefficients, and we can show that $x = 2$ is a regular singular point. In order to use the solution forms in Theorem 5–3, we first need to shift the singular point to the origin by defining a new variable $t = x - 2$. Then the differential equation becomes

$$t^2\ddot{y} + t\dot{y} + (t - 2)y = 0$$

where the overdot denotes differentiation with respect to t. This equation can be put into the standard form by dividing each term by t^2:

$$\ddot{y} + \frac{1}{t}\dot{y} + \frac{(t - 2)}{t^2}y = 0$$

Clearly, the point $t = 0$ is a singular point. This is a regular singular point: however, since both $p(t) = tP(t) = 1$ and $q(t) = t^2Q(t) = t - 2$ are polynomials and thus are analytic functions.

From the two relations, we observe that $p_0 = 1$ and $q_0 = -2$. Substituting these values into the indicial equation $r^2 + (p_0 - 1)r + q_0 = 0$ yields $r^2 - 2 = 0$.

The roots of this indicial equation are $r_1 = \sqrt{2}$ and $r_2 = -\sqrt{2}$, which differ by a non-integer. Then according to Theorem 5–3, the given differential equation has two linearly independent solutions both of the form

$$y = t^r \sum_{n=0}^{\infty} a_n t^n = \sum_{n=0}^{\infty} a_n t^{n+r}$$

Differentiating twice with respect to t:

$$\dot{y} = \sum_{n=0}^{\infty} (n + r)a_n t^{n+r-1}$$

and

$$\ddot{y} = \sum_{n=0}^{\infty} (n + r)(n + r - 1)a_n t^{n+r-2}$$

Substituting into the differential equation, we obtain

$$\sum_{n=0}^{\infty} (n + r)(n + r - 1)a_n t^{n+r} + \sum_{n=0}^{\infty} (n + r)a_n t^{n+r} + \sum_{n=0}^{\infty} a_n t^{n+r+1} - 2\sum_{n=0}^{\infty} a_n t^{n+r} = 0$$

To equate the exponent of t in all summations, we shift the index of the third summation by 1 by replacing n with $n - 1$. It yields

$$\sum_{n=0}^{\infty} (n + r)(n + r - 1)a_n t^{n+r} + \sum_{n=0}^{\infty} (n + r)a_n t^{n+r} + \sum_{n=1}^{\infty} a_{n-1} t^{n+r} - 2\sum_{n=0}^{\infty} a_n t^{n+r} = 0$$

Now the powers of t in all summations are the same, but the third summation starts with $n = 1$. To make all the summations start with $n = 1$, we write out all the terms that correspond to $n = 0$ and combine the summations, giving

$$[r(r - 1) + r - 2]a_0 t^r + \sum_{n=1}^{\infty} \{[(n + r)(n + r - 1) + (n + r) - 2]a_n + a_{n-1}\}t^{n+r} = 0$$

This equation will be satisfied for all x if and only if the coefficient of each power of t is zero. This condition for the lowest power of t, which is t^r and the requirement that $a_0 \neq 0$ gives us again the indicial equation (Figure 5–41), $r(r - 1) + r - 2 = 0$, which is satisfied only with the two r values determined earlier. (This is the direct way of obtaining the indicial equation). The requirement for the coefficients of all remaining powers of t to vanish gives

$$[(n + r)(n + r - 1) + (n + r) - 2]a_n + a_{n-1} = 0$$

$$[(n + r)^2 - 2]a_n + a_{n-1} = 0$$

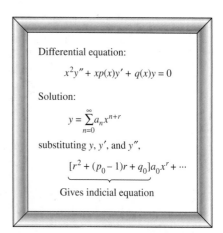

Differential equation:

$$x^2 y'' + xp(x)y' + q(x)y = 0$$

Solution:

$$y = \sum_{n=0}^{\infty} a_n x^{n+r}$$

substituting y, y', and y'',

$$\underbrace{[r^2 + (p_0 - 1)r + q_0]a_0 x^r + \cdots}$$

Gives indicial equation

FIGURE 5–41

With the Frobenius method, the cofficient of a_0 always resembles the indical equation, which becomes zero when $r = r_1$ or $r = r_2$.

or

$$a_n = -\frac{a_{n-1}}{(n+r)^2 - 2}, \qquad n = 1, 2, 3, \ldots \tag{5-94}$$

which is the recurrence relation for the unknown coefficients a_n.

For $r = r_1 = \sqrt{2}$ the recurrence relation becomes

$$a_n = -\frac{a_{n-1}}{(n+\sqrt{2})^2 - 2} = -\frac{a_{n-1}}{n^2 + 2n\sqrt{2} + 2 - 2} = -\frac{a_{n-1}}{n(n+2\sqrt{2})}$$

Therefore,

$$a_1 = -\frac{a_0}{1(1 + 2\sqrt{2})}$$

$$a_2 = -\frac{a_1}{2(2 + 2\sqrt{2})} = \frac{a_0}{1 \cdot 2(1 + 2\sqrt{2})(2 + 2\sqrt{2})}$$

and

$$a_3 = -\frac{a_2}{3(3 + 2\sqrt{2})} = -\frac{a_0}{1 \cdot 2 \cdot 3(1 + 2\sqrt{2})(2 + 2\sqrt{2})(3 + 2\sqrt{2})}$$

Generalizing, we have

$$a_n = \frac{(-1)^n a_0}{n!(1 + 2\sqrt{2})(2 + 2\sqrt{2}) \cdots (n + 2\sqrt{2})}$$

Taking $a_0 = 1$, as is customary, the first solution becomes

$$y_1 = \sum_{n=0}^{\infty} \frac{(-1)^n t^{n+\sqrt{2}}}{n!(1 + 2\sqrt{2})(2 + 2\sqrt{2}) \cdots (n + 2\sqrt{2})} \tag{5-95}$$

The second linearly independent solution is obtained by repeating the procedure for $r = r_2 = -\sqrt{2}$. Denoting the coefficients by b_n, the recurrence relation (Equation 5-94) in this case reduces to

$$b_n = -\frac{b_{n-1}}{(n-\sqrt{2})^2 - 2} = \frac{b_{n-1}}{n^2 - 2n\sqrt{2} + 2 - 2} = \frac{b_{n-1}}{n(n - 2\sqrt{2})}$$

This relation differs from the corresponding a_n relation by a minus sign before $2\sqrt{2}$. Therefore, the coefficients b_n will be just like the coefficients a_n, except the sign of $2\sqrt{2}$ will be different.

$$b_n = \frac{(-1)^n b_0}{n!(1 - 2\sqrt{2})(2 - 2\sqrt{2}) \cdots (n - 2\sqrt{2})}$$

Taking $b_0 = 1$, as is customary, the second linearly independent solution becomes

$$y_2 = \sum_{n=0}^{\infty} \frac{(-1)^n t^{n-\sqrt{2}}}{n!(1 - 2\sqrt{2})(2 - 2\sqrt{2}) \cdots (n - 2\sqrt{2})} \tag{5-96}$$

Thus the general solution is $y = C_1 y_1 + C_2 y_2$. Replacing t with $x - 2$ and substituting for y_1 and y_2, the general solution can also be expressed as

$$y(x) = C_1 \sum_{n=0}^{\infty} \frac{(-1)^n (x - 2)^{n+\sqrt{2}}}{n!(1 + 2\sqrt{2})(2 + 2\sqrt{2}) \cdots (n + 2\sqrt{2})}$$

$$+ C_2 \sum_{n=0}^{\infty} \frac{(-1)^n (x - 2)^{n-\sqrt{2}}}{n!(1 - 2\sqrt{2})(2 - 2\sqrt{2}) \cdots (n - 2\sqrt{2})} \tag{5–97}$$

This solution will converge for any positive x value except $x = 2$.

EXAMPLE 5–24   Theorem 5–3: Case 2 ($r_1 = r_2$)

Solve the differential equation $x^2 y'' + x(x^2 - 3)y' + 4y = 0$ about the point $x_0 = 0$ for $x > 0$ using the Frobenius method.

SOLUTION   This is a linear, second-order, homogeneous differential equation with variable coefficients, and it can be put into the standard form by dividing each term by x^2:

$$y'' + \frac{x^2 - 3}{x} y' + \frac{4}{x^2} y = 0$$

Clearly, the point $x = 0$ is a singular point since at least one coefficient function diverges at this point. This is a regular singular point, however, since both $p(x) = xP(x) = x^2 - 3$ and $q(x) = x^2 Q(x) = 4$ are polynomials (of zeroth order), and thus are analytic functions.

From the two relations above we observe that $p_0 = -3$ and $q_0 = 4$. Substituting these values into the indicial equation $r^2 + (p_0 - 1)r + q_0 = 0$ yields $r^2 - 4r + 4 = 0$ or $(r - 2)^2 = 0$. The roots of this indicial equation are $r_1 = r_2 = r = 2$, which are identical. Then according to Theorem 5–3, the given differential equation has two linearly independent solutions: the second one will contain a logarithmic term and the first one is of the form:

$$y = x^r \sum_{n=0}^{\infty} a_n x^n = \sum_{n=0}^{\infty} a_n x^{n+r}$$

Differentiating twice with respect to x, we have

$$y' = \sum_{n=0}^{\infty} (n + r)a_n x^{n+r-1}$$

and

$$y'' = \sum_{n=0}^{\infty} (n + r)(n + r - 1)a_n x^{n+r-2}$$

Substituting into the differential equation, we have

$$\sum_{n=0}^{\infty} (n + r)(n + r - 1)a_n x^{n+r} + \sum_{n=0}^{\infty} (n + r)a_n x^{n+r+2} - 3\sum_{n=0}^{\infty} (n + r)a_n x^{n+r} + 4\sum_{n=0}^{\infty} a_n x^{n+r} = 0$$

To equate the exponent of x in all summations, we shift the indexes of the second summation by 2 by replacing n by $n - 2$. It yields

$$\sum_{n=0}^{\infty}(n + r)(n + r - 1)a_n x^{n+r} + \sum_{n=0}^{\infty}(n + r - 2)a_{n-2}x^{n+r}$$

$$- 3\sum_{n=0}^{\infty}(n + r)a_n x^{n+r} + 4\sum_{n=0}^{\infty}a_n x^{n+r} = 0$$

Now the powers of x in all summations are the same but the second summation starts with $n = 2$. To make the other summations start with $n = 2$ also, we write out the terms that correspond to $n = 0$ and $n = 1$, and combine the summations,

$$[r(r - 1) - 3r + 4]a_0 x^r + [r(1 + r) - 3(1 + r) + 4]a_1 x^{r+1}$$

$$+ \sum_{n=2}^{\infty}\{[(n + r)(n + r + 1) - 3(n + r) + 4]a_n + a_{n-2}\}x^{n+r} = 0$$

This equation will be satisfied for all x if and only if the coefficient of each power of x is zero. This condition for the lowest power of x, which is x^r, and the requirement that $a_0 \neq 0$ gives us one more time the indicial equation, $r^2 - 4r + 4 = 0$, which is satisfied only with the r values determined earlier. The requirement for the coefficients of all remaining powers of x to vanish gives $[r(1 + r) - 3(1 + r) + 4]a_1 = 0$ and

$$[(n + r)(n + r - 1) - 3(n + r) + 4]a_n + (n + r - 2)a_{n-2} = 0 \qquad n = 2, 3, 4, \ldots$$

For $r = 2$ the first relation yields $a_1 = 0$, and the second relation yields the recurrence relation:

$$a_n = \frac{a_{n-2}}{n}, \qquad n = 2, 3, 4, \ldots \tag{5-98}$$

which expresses a coefficient in terms of the second preceding coefficient. Therefore, all coefficients with an even index will be expressed in terms of a_0, and all coefficients with an odd index in terms of a_1, which is determined to be zero. Thus we conclude that $a_1 = a_3 = a_5 = \cdots = 0$. The even indexed coefficients can be expressed as

$$a_2 = -\frac{a_0}{2} = -\frac{a_0}{2^1 1!}$$

$$a_4 = -\frac{a_2}{4} = \frac{a_0}{2^2 2!}$$

$$a_6 = -\frac{a_4}{6} = -\frac{a_0}{2^3 3!}$$

Generalizing, we have

$$a_{2n} = \frac{(-1)^n a_0}{2^n n!}$$

Taking $a_0 = 1$, as is customary, the first solution becomes

$$y_1 = \sum_{n=0}^{\infty}\frac{(-1)^n x^{2n+2}}{2^n n!} \tag{5-99}$$

The second linearly independent solution is determined in a similar manner by taking y_2, in accordance with Theorem 5-3, to be

$$y_2 = y_1 \ln x + \sum_{n-1}^{\infty} b_n x^{n+r}$$

Differentiating twice with respect to x, we have

$$y_2' = y_1' \ln x + \frac{1}{x}(\ln x)y_1 + \sum_{n=1}^{\infty}(n + r)b_n x^{n+r-1}$$

$$y_2'' = y_1'' \ln x + \frac{1}{x}y_1' + \frac{1}{x}y_1' - \frac{1}{x^2}y_1 + \sum_{n=1}^{\infty}(n + r)(n + r - 1)a_n x^{n+r-2}$$

Substituting into the differential equation and combining the logarithmic terms, we obtain

$$[x^2 y_1'' + x(x^2 - 3)y_1' + 4y_1]\ln x + 2xy_1' + (x^2 - 4)y_1$$
$$+ \sum_{n=1}^{\infty}(n + r)(n + r - 1)b_n x^{n+r} + \sum_{n=1}^{\infty}(n + r)b_n x^{n+r+2} - 3\sum_{n=1}^{\infty}(n + r)b_n x^{n+r}$$
$$+ 4\sum_{n=1}^{\infty}b_n x^{n+r} = 0$$

The logarithmic term drops out since its coefficient is the left-hand side of the differential equation and y_1 is a solution. This is always the case (Figure 5–42). Also, using the y_1 expression in Equation 5–99, the terms involving y_1 can be expressed as

$$2xy_1' + (x^2 - 4)y_1 = 2x\sum_{n=0}^{\infty}\frac{(-1)^n(2n + 2)x^{2n+1}}{2^n n!} + x^2\sum_{n=0}^{\infty}\frac{(-1)^n x^{2n+2}}{2^n n!}$$
$$- 4\sum_{n=0}^{\infty}\frac{(-1)^n x^{2n+2}}{2^n n!} = \sum_{n=1}^{\infty}\frac{(-1)^n 2n x^{2n+2}}{2^n n!}$$

after some manipulations. Note that the terms involving y_1 contribute only even powers of x. Substituting $r = 2$ and combining the three summations with the same power of x in their general terms yields

$$\sum_{n=1}^{\infty}\frac{(-1)^n 2n x^{2n+2}}{2^n n!} + \sum_{n=1}^{\infty}n^2 b_n x^{n+2} + \sum_{n=1}^{\infty}(n + 2)b_n x^{n+4} = 0$$

Again, to equate the exponent of x in all summations, we shift the index of the last summation by 2 by replacing n by $n - 2$. This will cause the last summation to start with $n = 3$. To make the second summation start with $n = 3$ also, we write out the terms that correspond to $n = 1$ and $n = 2$, and combine the summations. We also write out the first terms of the first summation so that no summation contains a term with x^4 or a lower power,

$$- x^4 + \sum_{n=2}^{\infty}\frac{(-1)^n 2n x^{2n+2}}{2^n n!} + b_1 x^3 + 4b_2 x^4 + \sum_{n=3}^{\infty}n^2 b_n x^{n+2} + \sum_{n=3}^{\infty}nb_{n-2}x^{n+2} = 0$$

or

$$b_1 x^3 + (4b_2 - 1)x^4 + \sum_{n=2}^{\infty}\frac{(-1)^n 2n x^{2n+2}}{2^n n!} + \sum_{n=3}^{\infty}[n^2 b_n + nb_{n-2}]x^{n+2} = 0$$

This equation will be satisfied for all x if and only if the coefficient of each power of x is zero. Applying this condition to the first two terms yields $b_1 = 0$ and $b_2 = 1/4$. Considering that any terms with odd powers of x come from the second summation only, and they correspond to the odd values of n, we must have $n^2 b_n + n_{n-2} = 0$ for odd n's but $b_1 = 0$, and thus $b_n = 0$ for all odd n's. That is, $b_1 = b_3 = b_5 = \cdots = 0$. Then the second sum can be modified to

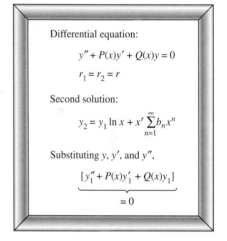

Differential equation:
$$y'' + P(x)y' + Q(x)y = 0$$
$$r_1 = r_2 = r$$

Second solution:
$$y_2 = y_1 \ln x + x^r \sum_{n=1}^{\infty}b_n x^n$$

Substituting y, y', and y'',
$$\underbrace{[y_1'' + P(x)y_1' + Q(x)y_1]}$$
$$= 0$$

FIGURE 5–42

When $r = r_1 = r_2$, the second linearly independent solution always involves a logarithmic term. But all the logarithmic terms cancel out when y_2 and its derivatives are substituted into the differential equation.

exclude all terms with odd powers of x by replacing all occurrences of n by $2n$. It yields

$$\sum_{n=2}^{\infty} \frac{(-1)^n 2nx^{2n+2}}{2^n n!} + \sum_{n=2}^{\infty} [(2n)^2 b_{2n} + 2nb_{2n-2}]x^{2n+2} = 0$$

or

$$\sum_{n=2}^{\infty} \left[\frac{(-1)^n 2n}{2^n n!} + 4n^2 b_{2n} + 2nb_{2n-2} \right]x^{2n+2} = 0$$

The requirement that the terms in the brackets vanish for all $n \geq 2$ yields the recurrence relation:

$$b_{2n} = -\frac{b_{2n-2}}{2n} - \frac{(-1)^n}{2^n n!} = 0, \qquad n = 2, 3, 4, \dots \qquad \text{(5–100)}$$

Remembering that $b_2 = 1/4$, we have

$$b_2 = \frac{1}{4} = \frac{1}{2^2 1!}$$

$$b_4 = -\frac{b_2}{4} - \frac{1}{2^2 2!} = -\frac{3}{2^3 3!}$$

$$b_6 = -\frac{b_4}{6} + \frac{1}{2^3 3!} = \frac{7}{2^4 3!}$$

Generalizing, we have

$$b_{2n} = \frac{(-1)^{n+1}(2n-1)}{2^{n+1} n!}, \qquad n = 1, 2, 3, 4, \dots$$

Therefore,

$$y_2 = y_1 \ln x + \sum_{n=1}^{\infty} \frac{(-1)^{n+1}(2n-1)x^{2n+2}}{2^{n+1} n!} \qquad \text{(5–101)}$$

Then the general solution can be expressed as $y = C_1 y_1 + C_2 y_2$. This solution will converge for any positive x value except $x = 0$.

EXAMPLE 5–25   Theorem 5–3: Case 3 (r_1 and r_2 Differ by an Integer)

Solve the differential equation $x^2 y'' + 2xy' - x^2 y = 0$ about the point $x_0 = 0$ for $x > 0$ using the Frobenius method.

SOLUTION This is a linear, second-order, homogeneous differential equation with variable coefficients, and it can be put into the standard form by dividing each term by x^2:

$$y'' + \frac{2}{x}y' - y = 0$$

Clearly, the point $x = 0$ is a singular point since at least one coefficient function diverges at this point. This is a regular singular point, however, since both $p(x) = xP(x) = 2$ and $q(x) = x^2 Q(x) = -x^2$ are polynomials, and thus analytic functions.

From the two relations above we observe that $p_0 = 2$ and $q_0 = 0$. Substituting these values into the indicial equation $r^2 + (p_0 - 1)r + q_0 = 0$ yields $r^2 + r = 0$ or $r(r + 1)$.

The roots of this indicial equation are $r_1 = 0$ and $r_2 = -1$, which differ by an integer. Then according to Theorem 5–3, the given differential equation has two linearly independent solutions: the second one may contain a logarithmic term. Considering that there is a good chance that $C = 0$ and thus the second solution does not contain a logarithmic term, the best way to approach this problem is to assume this to be the case, and to attempt to determine the series solution corresponding to the smaller r, which is $r = r_2 = -1$. Obtaining zeros for the coefficients will indicate that our assumption is wrong. Obtaining a solution with two arbitrary constants will indicate that we determined both linearly independent solutions, and thus the solution obtained is the general solution (Figure 5–43). We now assume a series solution of the form

$$y = x^r \sum_{n=0}^{\infty} b_n x^n = \sum_{n=0}^{\infty} b_n x^{n+r}$$

Differentiating twice with respect to x, we have

$$y' = \sum_{n=0}^{\infty} (n + r) b_n x^{n+r-1}$$

and

$$y'' = \sum_{n=0}^{\infty} (n + r)(n + r - 1) b_n x^{n+r-2}$$

Substituting into the differential equation, we have

$$\sum_{n=0}^{\infty} (n + r)(n + r - 1) b_n x^{n+r} + 2\sum_{n=0}^{\infty} (n + r) b_n x^{n+r} - \sum_{n=0}^{\infty} b_n x^{n+r+2} = 0$$

To equate the exponent of x in all summations, we shift the index of the last summation by 2 by replacing n with $n - 2$. This yields

$$\sum_{n=0}^{\infty} (n + r)(n + r - 1) b_a x^{n+r} + 2\sum_{n=2}^{\infty} (n + r) b_a x^{n+r} - \sum_{n=2}^{\infty} b_{n-2} x^{n+r} = 0$$

Now the powers of x in all summations are the same but the second summation starts with $n = 2$. To make the other summations start with $n = 2$ also, we write out the terms that correspond to $n = 0$ and $n = 1$, and combine the summations,

$$[r(r - 1) + 2r]b_0 x^r + [r(1 + r) + 2(1 + r)]b_1 x^{r+1}$$

$$+ \sum_{n=2}^{\infty} \{[(n + r)(n + r - 1) + 2(n + r)]b_n - b_{n-2}\} x^{n+r} = 0$$

This equation will be satisfied for all x if and only if the coefficient of each power of x is zero. This condition for the lowest power of x (which is x^r) and the requirement that $b_0 \neq 0$ again gives us the indicial equation ($r^2 + r = 0$), which is satisfied only with the two r values determined earlier. The requirement for the coefficients of all remaining powers of x to vanish gives

$$[r(1 + r) + 2(1 + r)]b_1 = 0$$

$$[(n + r)(n + r - 1) + 2(n + r)]b_n - b_{n-2} = 0 \qquad n = 2, 3, 4, \ldots$$

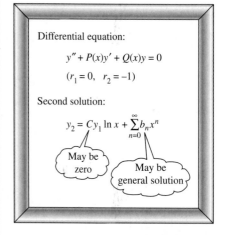

Differential equation:

$$y'' + P(x)y' + Q(x)y = 0$$

$$(r_1 = 0, \quad r_2 = -1)$$

Second solution:

$$y_2 = Cy_1 \ln x + \sum_{n=0}^{\infty} b_n x^n$$

May be zero

May be general solution

FIGURE 5–43

When the roots of the indicial equation differ by an integer, the second solution may contain a logarithmic term. But if it does not ($C = 0$), it usually yields the general solution directly.

For $r = r_2 = -1$, the first relation yields $0 \cdot b_1 = 0$, which indicates that b_1 is arbitrary just like b_0. The second relation yields the recurrence relation:

$$b_n = \frac{b_{n-2}}{(n-1)n}, \qquad n = 2, 3, 4, \ldots \tag{5-102}$$

which expresses a coefficient in terms of the second preceding coefficient. Therefore, all coefficients with even index will be expressed in terms of b_0, and all coefficients with an odd index in terms of b_1. The coefficients corresponding to the even values of n can be expressed as

$$b_2 = \frac{b_0}{1 \cdot 2} = \frac{b_0}{2!}$$

$$b_4 = \frac{b_2}{3 \cdot 4} = \frac{b_0}{4!}$$

$$b_6 = \frac{b_4}{5 \cdot 6} = \frac{b_0}{6!}$$

Generalizing, we have

$$b_{2n} = \frac{b_0}{(2n)!}, \qquad n = 1, 2, 3, \ldots$$

The coefficients corresponding to the odd values of n can be expressed as

$$b_3 = \frac{b_1}{2 \cdot 3} = \frac{b_1}{3!}$$

$$b_5 = \frac{b_3}{4 \cdot 5} = \frac{b_1}{5!}$$

$$b_7 = \frac{b_5}{6 \cdot 7} = \frac{b_1}{7!}$$

Generalizing, we have

$$b_{2n+1} = \frac{b_1}{(2n+1)!}, \qquad n = 1, 2, 3, \ldots$$

Substituting, we obtain

$$y = x^{r_2} \sum_{n=0}^{\infty} b_n x^n = \frac{1}{x} \sum_{n=0}^{\infty} b_n x^n$$

$$= \frac{b_0}{x} \left(1 + \frac{x^2}{2!} + \frac{x^4}{4!} + \cdots \right) + \frac{b_1}{x} \left(x + \frac{x^3}{3!} + \frac{x^5}{5!} \cdots \right)$$

$$= b_0 \sum_{n=0}^{\infty} \frac{x^{2n-1}}{(2n)!} + b_1 \sum_{n=0}^{\infty} \frac{x^{2n}}{(2n+1)!} \tag{5-103}$$

It is easy to see that the two solutions here are linearly independent (their ratio is not a constant). Therefore, not only does the solution not contain a logarithmic term, but also the solution contains both linearly independent solutions with arbitrary constants b_0 and b_1. Thus we conclude that this is the general solution of the given differential equation.

If we repeat the analysis using $r = r_1 = 0$, we will obtain as the first linearly independent solution

$$y_1 = \sum_{n=0}^{\infty} \frac{x^{2n}}{(2n+1)!}$$

which is one of the solutions in Equation 5–103. If we continued with $r = r_1 = -1$ taking Equation 5–83b as the second solution that contains a logarithmic term, we would see that $C = 0$. Thus, the second solution would not involve a logarithmic term, and we would end up with Equation 5–103 as the second linearly independent solution.

This solution will converge for any positive x value except $x = 0$.

Section Review

5–21C How does the method of Frobenius differ from the power series method in solving linear homogeneous equations with variable coefficients?

5–22C What is the indicial equation? What is the use of the roots of the indicial equation of a given differential equation?

5–23 Show that the point $x = 0$ is a regular singular point of the following differential equations and determine the roots of the indicial equation r_1 and r_2.

$$\text{(a) } x^2 y'' - xy' + 3y = 0 \qquad \text{(b) } xy'' - \frac{2}{x(x+1)}y = 0$$

(*Answers*: (a) The roots are $r_1 = 1 + \sqrt{2}i$ and $r_2 = 1 - \sqrt{2}i$. (b) The roots are $r_1 = 2$ and $r_2 = -1$.)

5–24 Determine the form of the two linearly independent solutions of the following linear, second-order differential equations about the regular singular point $x_0 = 0$ without solving them. Also determine the range of x values over which these solutions will converge.

$$\text{(a) } x^2 y'' - xy' - 3y = 0 \qquad \text{(b) } xy'' - \frac{2}{x(x+1)}y = 0$$

(*Answers*: (a) $y_1(x) = x^{r_1} \sum\limits_{n=0}^{\infty} a_n x^n$ and $y_2(x) = Cy_1(x) \ln x + x^{r_2} \sum\limits_{n=0}^{\infty} b_n x^n$ where $a_0 \neq 0$ and $b_0 \neq 0$, but the constant C may be zero. The series solution converges for all $x > 0$. (b) $y_1(x) = x^{r_1} \sum\limits_{n=0}^{\infty} a_n x^n$ and $y_2(x) = Cy_1(x) \ln x + x^{r_2} \sum\limits_{n=0}^{\infty} b_n x^n$ where $a_0 \neq 0$ and $b_0 \neq 0$, but the constant C may be zero. The series solution will converge for any $x > 0$.)

5–25 Determine the general solutions of the following linear, second-order differential equations about the regular singular point $x_0 = 0$.

$$\text{(a) } x^2 y'' - xy' - 3y = 0 \qquad \text{(b) } xy'' - \frac{2}{x(x+1)}y = 0$$

(*Answers*: (a) $y(x) = C_1 x^3 + C_2 x^{-1}$ and

$$\text{(b) } y(x) = C_1\left(x^2 - \frac{1}{2}x^3 + \frac{3}{10}x^4 - \frac{1}{5}x^5 + \frac{1}{7}x^6 - \frac{3}{28}x^7 + \cdots \right) + C_2\left(\frac{x+1}{x} \right))$$

5–26 Determine the general solutions of the following second-order Euler differential equations using (a) the standard method and (b) the method of Frobenius about the regular singular point $x_0 = 0$.

$$\text{(a) } x^2 y'' + xy' - y = 0 \qquad \text{(b) } 2x^2 y'' - xy' - 9y = 0$$

(*Answers*: (a) $y(x) = C_1 x + C_2 x^{-1}$ (b) $y(x) = C_1 x^3 + Cx^{-3/2}$)

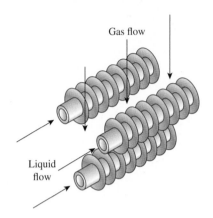

FIGURE 5–44

Circular fins of uniform thickness t placed around pipes to increase heat transfer.

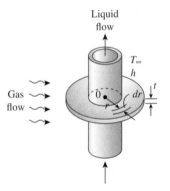

FIGURE 5–45

A differential ring element of the circular fin and its energy interactions.

5–7 · BESSEL'S EQUATION AND BESSEL FUNCTIONS

One of the most important second-order differential equations with variable coefficients is Bessel's equation of order v:

$$x^2 y'' + x y' + (x^2 - v^2)y = 0 \qquad (5\text{–}104)$$

Bessel's equation is named after the German mathematician and astronomer Friedrich W. Bessel (1784–1846) because of his systematic studies of this equation. It arises in a variety of problems in physics and engineering, and its solution is expressed in terms of the Bessel functions, which probably are the best known functions after the elementary functions. Before we discuss the solutions of Bessel's equation, we illustrate one origin of Bessel's equation with an example.

EXAMPLE 5–26 **Origin of Bessel's Equation**

Extended surfaces called *fins* are frequently used in compact heat exchangers to enhance heat transfer by increasing the heat transfer surface area. One type of fin that is frequently used around pipes is the circular fin of uniform thickness t, as shown in Figure 5–44. Because of circular symmetry and high thermal conductivity k of the fin material, the temperature T in a circular fin varies in the radial direction only. Heat is transferred to the surrounding air from both sides of the fin according to Newton's law of cooling (see Chapter 1).

Taking the surrounding air temperature to be zero, obtain the differential equation that describes the variation of fin temperature with r at steady state. Assume the heat transfer coefficient h between the fin and the surrounding air remains constant. Use the conservation of energy principle and Fourier's law of heat conduction.

SOLUTION To derive the differential equation, we need to choose a suitable differential volume element in the fin, and apply the conservation of energy principle. In this case it is appropriate to choose a ring element of thickness dr at location r within the fin, as shown in Figure 5–45 since the temperature changes in the r direction only, and a ring element can incorporate the changes in that direction. Under steady conditions, the energy content of the ring element will remain constant. Then the conservation of energy principle requires that the heat conducted into the element at location r must be equal the sum of the heat conducted out of the element at $r + dr$ plus the heat transferred to the air from the side surfaces. That is,

$$\begin{pmatrix} \text{Heat conducted} \\ \text{into the element} \\ \text{at location } r \end{pmatrix} = \begin{pmatrix} \text{Heat conducted} \\ \text{out of the element} \\ \text{at location } r + dr \end{pmatrix} + \begin{pmatrix} \text{Heat} \\ \text{transferred} \\ \text{to the air} \end{pmatrix}$$

or

$$Q_r = Q_{r+dr} + Q_{\text{air}}$$

where from Newton's law of cooling, we have

$$Q_{\text{air}} = hS(T - T_{\text{air}}) = 4\pi r \, dr \, hT$$

since $T_{\text{air}} = 0$ and the surface area of both sides of the differential element is $S = 2 \times 2\pi r \, dr = 4\pi r \, dr$.

Substituting into the differential equation, dividing by dr, and rearranging gives

$$\frac{Q_{r+dr} - Q_r}{dr} + 4\pi hrT = 0$$

or

$$\frac{dQ}{dr} + 4\pi hrT = 0$$

where we used the definition of derivative as $dr \rightarrow 0$. From Fourier's law of heat conduction (see Chapter 1), we obtain

$$Q = -kA\frac{dT}{dr} = -k(2\pi rt)\frac{dT}{dr} = -2\pi ktr\frac{dT}{dr}$$

Substituting and dividing by the constant $2\pi kt$, we have

$$\frac{d}{dr}\left(-r\frac{dT}{dr}\right) + \frac{2h}{kt}rT = 0$$

Performing the differentiation and multiplying by r after taking $\lambda^2 = 2h/kt$, we have

$$r^2\frac{d^2T}{dr^2} + r\frac{dT}{dr} - \lambda^2r^2T = 0$$

We can eliminate the parameter λ^2 by defining a new variable x as $x = \lambda r$. Noting that $dx = \lambda dr$, the differential equation becomes (Figure 5–46)

$$x^2\frac{d^2T}{dx^2} + x\frac{dT}{dx} - x^2T = 0 \qquad \textbf{(5–105)}$$

which is the desired equation. A comparison of this differential equation and Equation 5–104 reveals that the two differential equations are identical, except for the sign of the last term and $v = 0$. Equation 5–105 is called the **modified Bessel's equation of order zero**, and its solution gives rise to modified Bessel functions. The general form of modified Bessel's function is given as

$$x^2y'' + xy' - (x^2 - v^2)y = 0 \qquad \textbf{(5–106)}$$

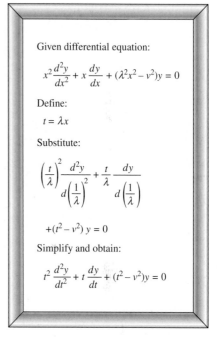

FIGURE 5–46

The parameter λ^2 in Bessel's or the modified Bessel's equation can be eliminated by defining a new variable as $t = \lambda x$.

Now let us examine Bessel's equation more closely. Dividing it by x^2 to make the leading coefficient unity, we observe that

$$P(x) = \frac{1}{x} \qquad \text{and} \qquad Q(x) = \frac{x^2 - v^2}{x^2}$$

Therefore, the origin—and only the origin (the point $x = 0$)—is a singular point of Bessel's equation. It is a regular singular point, since

$$p(x) = xP(x) = 1 \qquad \text{and} \qquad q(x) = x^2Q(x) = x^2 - v^2$$

are polynomials and thus analytic at $x = 0$. From these two relations, we observe that $p_0 = 1$ and $q_0 = -v^2$. Substituting these values into the indicial equation $r^2 + (p_0 - 1)r + q_0 = 0$ yields

$$r^2 - v^2 = 0 \qquad \textbf{(5–107)}$$

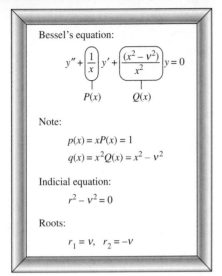

Bessel's equation:

$$y'' + \left(\frac{1}{x}\right)y' + \left(\frac{(x^2 - v^2)}{x^2}\right)y = 0$$

$$\underbrace{\qquad}_{P(x)} \qquad \underbrace{\qquad}_{Q(x)}$$

Note:

$$p(x) = xP(x) = 1$$
$$q(x) = x^2 Q(x) = x^2 - v^2$$

Indicial equation:

$$r^2 - v^2 = 0$$

Roots:

$$r_1 = v, \quad r_2 = -v$$

FIGURE 5–47

The roots of the indicial equation of Bessel's equation are always equal in magnitude and opposite in sign.

whose roots are $r_1 = v$ and $r_2 = -v$ (Figure 5–47). Thus, the two linearly independent solutions of Bessel's equation can be any of the three cases described in Theorem 5–3, depending on the value of v. We now consider these cases separately.

EXAMPLE 5–27   Bessel's Equation of Order Zero ($r_1 = r_1 = 0$)

Determine the general solution of Bessel's equation of order zero:

$$x^2 y'' + xy' + x^2 y = 0 \qquad (5\text{–}108)$$

about the point $x_a = 0$ for $x > 0$ using the Frobenius method.

SOLUTION   In this case, $v = 0$, and the roots of the indicial equation are (from Equation 5–107) $r_1 = r_2 = r = 0$, which are identical. Then according to Theorem 5–3, the given differential equation has two linearly independent solutions: the second one will contain a logarithmic term and the first one is of the form

$$y = x^r \sum_{n=0}^{\infty} a_n x^n = \sum_{n=0}^{\infty} a_n x^n$$

since $r = 0$. Differentiating twice and substituting into the differential equation, we obtain

$$\sum_{n=2}^{\infty} n(n-1)a_n x^n + \sum_{n=1}^{\infty} n a_n x^n + \sum_{n=0}^{\infty} a_n x^{n+2} = 0$$

Now we shift the index of the last summation by 2 by replacing n with $n-2$ and write out the first term of the second summation corresponding to $n = 1$ so that the exponent of x and the lower limits of n in all summations are the same. Then we can combine the summations into one:

$$a_1 x - \sum_{n=2}^{\infty} \{[n(n-1) + n]a_n + a_{n-2}\}x^n = 0$$

This equation will be satisfied for all x if and only if the coefficient of each power of x is zero. Therefore, $a_1 = 0$ and $[n(n-1) + n]a_n + a_{n-2} = 0$. Thus, the recurrence relation is

$$a_n = -\frac{a_{n-2}}{n^2}, \quad n = 2, 3, 4, \ldots \qquad (5\text{–}109)$$

which expresses a coefficient in terms of the second preceding coefficient. Therefore, all coefficients with even indices will be expressed in terms of a_0, and all coefficients with odd indices will be expressed in terms of a_1, which was determined to be zero. Thus, we conclude that $a_1 = a_3 = a_5 = \cdots = 0$. The even indexed coefficients can be expressed as

$$a_2 = -\frac{a_0}{2^2} = -\frac{a_0}{2^2(1!)^2}$$

$$a_4 = -\frac{a_2}{4^2} = \frac{a_0}{2^4(2!)^2}$$

$$a_6 = -\frac{a_4}{6^2} = -\frac{a_0}{2^6(3!)^2}$$

Generalizing, we have

$$a_{2n} = \frac{(-1)^n a_0}{2^{2n}(n!)^2}, \qquad n = 0, 1, 2, 3, 4, \dots$$

Taking $a_0 = 1$ and substituting, the first solution becomes

$$y_1 = \sum_{n=0}^{\infty} \frac{(-1)^n x^{2n}}{2^{2n}(n!)^2}$$

This solution is known as the **Bessel function of the first kind of order zero** and is denoted by $J_0(x)$. Therefore,

$$J_0(x) = \sum_{n=0}^{\infty} \frac{(-1)^n x^{2n}}{2^{2n}(n!)^2} \tag{5–110}$$

Considering that the radius of convergence of Bessel's equation about the origin is infinity, the series represented by $J_0(x)$ converges for all x (including the origin in this case), since $J_0(x)$ is analytic at $x = 0$. Indeed, we can show by direct substitution that $J_0(x) = 1$ at $x = 0$.

A plot of $J_0(x)$ is given in Figure 5–48. Note that $J_0(x)$ is an oscillating function with a decreasing amplitude as x increases, reminding us of the elementary functions $\sin x$ and $\cos x$. These three functions have an infinite number of zeros, but the determination of the zeros of $J_0(x)$ is not easy. The first five zeros of $J_0(x)$ and the interval between them are given in Figure 5–49.

The second linearly independent solution is determined in a similar manner by taking y_2, in accordance with Theorem 5–3, to be

$$y_2 = y_1 \ln x + \sum_{n=1}^{\infty} b_n x^{n+r} = y_1 \ln x + \sum_{n=1}^{\infty} b_n x^n$$

Differentiating twice, substituting into the differential equation, and combining the logarithmic terms, gives

$$[x^2 y_1'' + x y_1' + x^2 y_1] \ln x + 2x y_1' + \sum_{n=2}^{\infty} n(n-1) b_n x^n + \sum_{n=1}^{\infty} n b_n x^n + \sum_{n=1}^{\infty} b_n x^{n+2} = 0$$

Again the logarithmic term drops out—as expected—since y_1 is a solution. Also, using the y_1 expression (Equation 5–110), the term $2x y_1'$ can be expressed as

$$2x y_1' = 2x \sum_{n=1}^{\infty} \frac{(-1)^n (2n) x^{2n-1}}{2^{2n}(n!)^2} = -x^2 + \sum_{n=2}^{\infty} (-1)^n (4n) \frac{x^{2n}}{2^{2n}(n!)^2}$$

Now manipulating the summations exactly as we did in the first part of the solution, writing out the first few terms, and substituting, we have

$$-x^2 + \sum_{n=2}^{\infty} (-1)^n (4n) \frac{x^{2n}}{2^{2n}(n!)^2} + b_1 x + 4 b_2 x^2 + \sum_{n=3}^{\infty} (n^2 b_n + b_{n-2}) x^n = 0$$

This equation will be satisfied for all x if and only if the coefficient of each power of x is zero. Applying this condition to the first two powers of x yields $b_1 = 0$ and $b_2 = 1/4$. Noting that terms with odd powers of x come from the second summation only and that they correspond to the odd values of n, we must have $n^2 b_n + b_{n-2} = 0$ for odd n's. But $b_1 = 0$, and thus $b_n = 0$ for all odd n's. That is, $b_1 = b_3 = b_5 = \cdots = 0$. Then the second sum can be modified to exclude all terms with odd powers of x by replacing all occurrences of n by $2n$. It yields

$$\sum_{n=2}^{\infty} (-1)^n (4n) \frac{x^{2n}}{2^{2n}(n!)^2} + \sum_{n=2}^{\infty} [(2n)^2 b_{2n} + b_{2n-2}] x^{2n} = 0$$

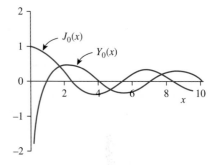

FIGURE 5–48

Bessel function of the first and second kinds of order zero.

Zeros of $J_0(x)$	Interval between zeros
2.4048	
5.5201	3.1153
8.6537	3.1336
11.7915	3.1378
14.9309	3.1394
—	—
—	—
—	π

FIGURE 5–49

The first five zeros of $J_0(x)$ and the distance between them.

or

$$\sum_{n=2}^{\infty} \left[(-1)^n (4n) \frac{x^{2n}}{2^{2n}(n!)^2} + 4n^2 b_{2n} + b_{2n-2} \right] x^{2n} = 0$$

The requirement that the terms in the brackets vanish for all $n \geq 2$ yields the recurrence relation:

$$b_{2n} = -\frac{b_{2n-2}}{4n^2} - \frac{(-1)^n}{2^{2n}(n!)^2 n}, \qquad n = 2, 3, 4, \ldots \tag{5-111}$$

Remembering that $b_2 = 1/4$, we have

$$b_4 = -\frac{b_2}{4 \cdot 2^2} - \frac{1}{2^4(2!)^2 2} = -\frac{1}{2^4(2!)^2}\left(1 + \frac{1}{2} \right)$$

$$b_6 = -\frac{b_4}{4 \cdot 3^2} + \frac{1}{2^6(3!)^2 3} = \frac{1}{2^6(3!)^2}\left(1 + \frac{1}{2} + \frac{1}{3} \right)$$

Generalizing, we have

$$b_{2n} = \frac{(-1)^{n+1} S_n}{2^{2n}(n!)^2}, \qquad n = 1, 2, 3, 4, \ldots$$

where we have defined a new function S_n as

$$S_n = 1 + \frac{1}{2} + \frac{1}{3} + \cdots + \frac{1}{n} = \sum_{j=1}^{n} \frac{1}{j} \tag{5-112}$$

Therefore,

$$y_2 = y_1 \ln x + \sum_{n=1}^{\infty} \frac{(-1)^{n+1} S_n x^{2n}}{2^{2n}(n!)^2}$$

This second linearly independent solution will converge for all x, except for $x = 0$, because of the logarithmic term.

Knowing y_1 and y_2, we could express the general solution of Bessel's equation of order zero as a linear combination of these two. However, it is common practice to express the second solution as

$$Y_0 = \frac{2}{\pi}\left[\left(\gamma - \ln \frac{x}{2} \right) J_0 + y_2 \right]$$

$$Y_0 = \frac{2}{\pi}\left[\left(\gamma + \ln \frac{x}{2} \right) J_0(x) + \sum_{n=1}^{\infty} \frac{(-1)^{n+1} S_n x^{2n}}{2^{2n}(n!)^2} \right] \tag{5-113}$$

because of the more desirable characteristics of $Y_0(x)$ as $x \to \infty$. Here the constant γ is the *Euler's constant* whose value is determined from

$$\gamma = \lim_{n \to \infty}\left(1 + \frac{1}{2} + \frac{1}{3} + \cdots + \frac{1}{n} - \ln n \right) \cong 0.577215665 \tag{5-114}$$

The function $Y_0(x)$ is known as the **Bessel function of the second kind of order zero**. Then the general solution of Bessel's equation of order zero for $x > 0$ can be expressed as

$$y(x) = C_1 J_0(x) + C_2 Y_0(x) \tag{5-115}$$

where the constants C_1 and C_2 are to be determined from the initial or boundary conditions.

A plot of $Y_0(x)$ is also given in Figure 5–48. Note that $Y_0(x)$ oscillates with decreasing amplitude as x increases and it also has infinite number of zeros. But unlike $J_0(x)$, the function $Y_0(x) \to -\infty$ as $x \to 0$. Therefore, if the solution is to remain finite at $x = 0$, which is often the case, then we must choose $C_2 = 0$ to discard $Y_0(x)$ from the solution. For example, when we determine the temperature distribution in a *hollow* cylinder, the solution may involve $Y_0(x)$ since the medium does not contain the point $x = 0$. But the solution for a *solid* cylinder may not contain the function $Y_0(x)$ since the medium contains the point $x = 0$ in this case, and the temperature there cannot be infinite. This fact is commonly used as one of the boundary conditions and expressed as $C_2 = 0$.

EXAMPLE 5–28   **Bessel's Equation of Order One-Half**
$(r_1 = 1/2, r_2 = 1/2)$

Determine the general solution of Bessel's equation of order one-half:

$$x^2 y'' + xy' + \left(x^2 - \frac{1}{4}\right)y = 0 \qquad (5\text{–}116)$$

about the point $x_0 = 0$ for $x_0 > 0$ using the Frobenius method.

SOLUTION   In this case, $\nu_0 = 1/2$, and the roots of the indicial equation are (from Equation 5–107) $r_1 = 1/2$ and $r_2 = -1/2$, which differ by an integer. Then according to Theorem 5–3, the given differential equation has two linearly independent solutions; the second one *may* contain a logarithmic term. Considering that there is a good chance that $C = 0$ and thus the second solution does not contain a logarithmic term, the best way to approach this problem is to assume this to be the case, and to attempt to determine the series solution corresponding to the smaller r, which is $r = r_2 = -1/2$. Obtaining zeros for coefficients will indicate that our assumption is wrong. Obtaining a solution with two arbitrary constants will indicate that we determined *both* linearly independent solutions, and thus the solution obtained is the general solution. We now assume a series solution of the form

$$y = x^r \sum_{n=0}^{\infty} b_n x^n = \sum_{n=0}^{\infty} b_n x^{n+r}$$

Differentiating twice with respect to x and substituting into the differential equation, we have

$$\sum_{n=0}^{\infty} (n + r)(n + r - 1) b_n x^{n+r} + \sum_{n=0}^{\infty} (n + r) b_n x^{n+r}$$

$$+ \sum_{n=0}^{\infty} (n + r) b_n x^{n+r+2} - \frac{1}{4} \sum_{n=0}^{\infty} b_n x^{n+r} = 0$$

To equate the exponent of x in all summations, we shift the index of the third summation by 2 by replacing n by $n - 2$. This process will equate the powers of x in all summations, but the third summation will start with $n = 2$. To make the other summations, start with $n = 2$. Also, we now write out the terms that correspond to $n = 0$ and $n = 1$, and combine the summations.

$$\left[r(r-1) + r - \frac{1}{4} \right] b_0 x^r + \left[r(r+1) + (1+r) - \frac{1}{4} \right] b_1 x^{r+1}$$

$$+ \sum_{n=2}^{\infty} \left\{ \left[(n+r)(n+r-1) + (n+r) - \frac{1}{4} \right] b_n + b_{n-2} \right\} x^{n+r} = 0$$

This equation will be satisfied for all x if and only if the coefficient of each power of x is zero. Substituting $r = r_2 = -1/2$ yields (after simplifications)

$$0 \cdot b_0 = 0$$

$$0 \cdot b_1 = 0$$

$$n(n-1)b_n + b_{n-2} = 0, \quad n = 2, 3, 4, \ldots$$

The first two relations indicate that the first two coefficients b_0 and b_1 are arbitrary. The last relation yields the recurrence relation:

$$b_n = -\frac{b_{b-2}}{(n-1)n}, \qquad n = 2, 3, 4, \ldots \tag{5-117}$$

which expresses a coefficient in terms of the second preceding coefficient. Therefore, all coefficients with an even index will be expressed in terms of b_0, and all coefficients with an odd index in terms of b_1. The coefficients corresponding to the even values of n can be expressed as

$$b_2 = -\frac{b_0}{1 \cdot 2} = -\frac{b_0}{2!}$$

$$b_4 = -\frac{b_2}{3 \cdot 4} = \frac{b_0}{4!}$$

$$b_6 = -\frac{b_4}{5 \cdot 6} = -\frac{b_0}{6!}$$

Generalizing, we have

$$b_{2n} = \frac{(-1)^n b_0}{(2n)!}, \qquad n = 0, 1, 2, 3, \ldots$$

The coefficients corresponding to the odd values of n can be expressed as

$$b_3 = -\frac{b_1}{2 \cdot 3} = -\frac{b_1}{3!}$$

$$b_5 = -\frac{b_3}{4 \cdot 5} = \frac{b_1}{5!}$$

$$b_7 = -\frac{b_5}{6 \cdot 7} = -\frac{b_1}{7!}$$

Generalizing, we have

$$b_{2n+1} = \frac{(-1)^n b_1}{(2n+1)!}, \qquad n = 1, 2, 3, \ldots$$

Substituting, we obtain

$$y = x^{r_2}\sum_{n=0}^{\infty} b_n x^n = \frac{1}{\sqrt{x}}\sum_{n=0}^{\infty} b_n x^n$$

$$= \frac{1}{\sqrt{x}}\left[b_0\left(1 - \frac{x^2}{2!} + \frac{x^4}{4!} + \cdots \right) + b_1\left(x - \frac{x^3}{3!} + \frac{x^5}{5!} + \cdots \right) \right]$$

$$= \frac{1}{\sqrt{x}}\left[b_0\sum_{n=0}^{\infty} \frac{(-1)^n x^{2n}}{(2n)!} + b_1\sum_{n=0}^{\infty} \frac{(-1)^n x^{2n+1}}{(2n+1)!} \right]$$

$$= \frac{1}{\sqrt{x}}(b_0 \cos x + b_1 \sin x) \qquad (5\text{--}118)$$

It is easy to see that the two solutions above are linearly independent (the ratio of $\sin x$ and $\cos x$ is $\tan x$, which is not a constant). Therefore, not only does the solution not contain a logarithmic term, but the solution also contains both linearly independent solutions with arbitrary constants b_0 and b_1. Thus, we conclude that this is the general solution of Bessel's equation of order one-half.

If we repeat the analysis using $r = r_1 = -1/2$, we will obtain as the first linearly independent solution

$$y_1 = \frac{a_0}{\sqrt{x}}\sin x$$

which is one of the solutions in Equation 5–118, differing only by a constant. If we continued with $r = r_1 = -1/2$ taking Equation 5–83b as the second solution that contains a logarithmic term, we would see that $C = 0$ and thus the second solution would not involve a logarithmic term, and we would end up with Equation 5–118 as the second linearly independent solution.

It is customary to express this solution in terms of the **Bessel functions of order one-half** as (Figure 5–50)

$$y = C_1 J_{1/2}(x) + C_2 J_{-1/2}(x) \qquad (5\text{--}119)$$

where

$$J_{1/2}(x) = \sqrt{\frac{2}{\pi x}}\sin x \quad \text{and} \quad J_{-1/2}(x) = \sqrt{\frac{2}{\pi x}}\cos x \qquad (5\text{--}120)$$

Again, the arbitrary constants C_1 and C_2 (or b_0 and b_1) are to be determined from the boundary or initial conditions. Note also that the Bessel functions of order one-half oscillate just like the trigonometric functions $\sin x$ and $\cos x$, but their amplitude decreases with increasing x because of the factor $\sqrt{x}$ in the denominator.

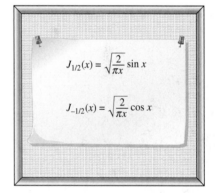

$$J_{1/2}(x) = \sqrt{\frac{2}{\pi x}}\sin x$$

$$J_{-1/2}(x) = \sqrt{\frac{2}{\pi x}}\cos x$$

FIGURE 5–50

Bessel functions of order one-half are related to the trigonometric functions $\sin x$ and $\cos x$.

EXAMPLE 5–29 **Bessel's Equation of Order ν**
(where ν is a Positive Integer)

Determine the general solution of Bessel's equation of order ν

$$x^2 y'' + xy' + (x^2 - \nu^2)y = 0 \qquad (5\text{--}121)$$

where ν is a positive integer, about the point $x_0 = 0$ for $x_0 > 0$ using the Frobenius method.

SOLUTION In this case, the roots of the indicial equation are (from Equation 5–107) $r_1 = \nu$ and $r_2 = -\nu$, which differ by an integer. Then according to Theorem 5–3, the given differential equation has two linearly independent solutions: the second one *may* contain a logarithmic term and the first one is of the form

$$y_1 = x^{r_1} \sum_{n=0}^{\infty} a_n x^n = \sum_{n=0}^{\infty} a_n x^{n+\nu}$$

Differentiating twice and substituting into the differential equation, we have

$$\sum_{n=0}^{\infty} (n + \nu)(n + \nu - 1)a_n x^{n+\nu} + \sum_{n=0}^{\infty} (n + \nu)a_n x^{n+\nu} + \sum_{n=0}^{\infty} a_n x^{n+\nu+2} - \nu^2 \sum_{n=0}^{\infty} a_n x^{n+\nu} = 0$$

We now shift the index of the third summation by 2 by replacing n with $n - 2$ and write out the first two terms of the other summations corresponding to $n = 0$ and $n = 1$ so that the exponent of x and the lower limit of n in all summations are the same. Then we can combine the summations into one:

$$[\nu(\nu - 1) + \nu - \nu^2]a_0 x^\nu + [\nu(\nu + 1) + (\nu + 1) - \nu^2]a_1 x^{\nu+1}$$
$$+ \sum_{n=2}^{\infty} \{[(n + \nu)(n + \nu - 1) + (n + \nu) - \nu^2]a_n + a_{n-2}\}x^{n+\nu} = 0$$

or

$$(2\nu + 1)a_1 x^{\nu+1} + \sum_{n=2}^{\infty} \{n(n + 2\nu)a_n + a_{n-2}\}x^{n+\nu} = 0$$

This equation will be satisfied for all x if and only if the coefficient of each power of x is zero. Therefore,

$$a_1 = 0$$
$$n(n + 2\nu)a_n + a_{n-2} = 0$$

Thus, the recurrence relation is

$$a_n = -\frac{a_{n-2}}{n(n + 2\nu)} \qquad n = 2, 3, 4, \ldots \tag{5–122}$$

which expresses a coefficient in terms of the second preceding coefficient. Therefore, all coefficients with even index will be expressed in terms of a_0, and all coefficients with an odd index in terms of a_1, which must be zero since $2\nu + 1$ cannot be zero when ν is a positive integer. Thus we conclude that $a_1 = a_3 = a_5 = \cdots = 0$. The even indexed coefficients can be expressed as

$$a_2 = -\frac{a_0}{2(2 + 2\nu)} = -\frac{a_0}{2^2(1 + \nu)}$$

$$a_4 = -\frac{a_2}{4(4 + 2\nu)} = \frac{a_0}{2^4 2!(1 + \nu)(2 + \nu)}$$

$$a_6 = -\frac{a_4}{6(6 + 2\nu)} = -\frac{a_0}{2^6 3!(1 + \nu)(2 + \nu)(3 + \nu)}$$

Generalizing, we have

$$a_{2n} = \frac{(-1)^n a_0}{2^{2n} n!(1 + \nu)(2 + \nu) \cdots (n + \nu)} \tag{5–123}$$

or

$$a_{2n} = \frac{(-1)^n a_0 \nu!}{2^{2n} n!(n + \nu)!}, \qquad n = 1, 2, 3, 4, \ldots \qquad (5\text{--}124)$$

since ν is a positive integer. Substituting, the first solution becomes

$$y_1 = \sum_{n=0}^{\infty} \frac{(-1)^n a_0 \nu! x^{2n+\nu}}{2^{2n} n!(n + \nu)!}$$

The constant a_0 can be chosen to be any suitable value as long as it is non-zero. In this case, it is customary to take $a_0 = 1/(\nu! 2^\nu)$. Substituting, we obtain

$$J_\nu(x) = \sum_{n=0}^{\infty} \frac{(-1)^n x^{2n+\nu}}{2^{2n+\nu} n!(n + \nu)!} \qquad (5\text{--}125)$$

This function is known as the **Bessel function of the first kind of order** ν, and is commonly taken as the first solution of Bessel's equation of order ν, where ν is a positive integer. When $\nu = 0$, the $J_\nu(x)$ relation reduces to $J_0(x)$ expression (Equation 5–110), as expected.

The second linearly independent solution of Bessel's equation of order ν is determined following the procedure used in determining $Y_0(x)$.

$$Y_\nu(x) = \frac{2}{\pi} \left[\left(\gamma + \ln \frac{x}{2} \right) J_\nu(x) - \frac{1}{2} \sum_{n=0}^{\nu-1} \frac{(\nu - n - 1)! x^{2n-\nu}}{2^{2n-\nu} n!} \right.$$
$$\left. + \frac{1}{2} \sum_{n=0}^{\infty} \frac{(-1)^{n+1}(S_n + S_{n+\nu}) x^{2n+\nu}}{2^{2n+\nu} n!(n + \nu)!} \right] \qquad (5\text{--}126)$$

The function $Y_\nu(x)$ is called the **Bessel function of the second kind of order** ν. The first few of $J_\nu(x)$ and $Y_\nu(x)$ are plotted in Figures 5–51 and 5–52. Note that the functions $J_\nu(x)$ behave very much like $J_0(x)$. This is also true for the functions $Y_\nu(x)$ and $Y_0(x)$.

The general solution of Bessel's equation of order ν for $\nu > 0$ can be expressed as

$$y(x) = C_1 J_\nu(x) + C_2 Y_\nu(x) \qquad (5\text{--}127)$$

where the constants C_1 and C_2 are to be determined from the initial or boundary conditions.

The functions $J_\nu(x)$ and $Y_\nu(x)$ oscillate with decreasing amplitude as x increases and they have infinite number of zeros. But unlike $J_\nu(x)$, the functions $Y_\nu(x) \to \infty$ as $x \to 0$. Therefore, if the solution is to remain finite at $x = 0$, which is often the case, then we must choose $C_2 = 0$ to discard $Y_\nu(x)$ from the solution.

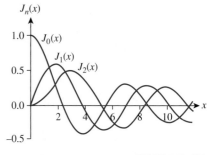

FIGURE 5–51

Bessel functions of the first kind.

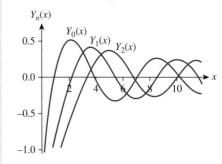

FIGURE 5–52

Bessel functions of the second kind.

Gamma Function

When v is not an integer, the solution of Bessel's equation of order v involves the factorial of nonintegers, which are best represented by the **Gamma function** $\Gamma(v)$, which is defined for all $v > 0$ by the improper integral

$$\Gamma(v) = \int_0^{\infty} t^{v-1} e^{-t} dt \qquad (5\text{--}128)$$

Replacing by v by $v + 1$ and integrating by parts yields

$$\Gamma(v + 1) = v\Gamma(v) \tag{5–129}$$

Also note that for $v = 1$,

$$\Gamma(1) = \int_0^\infty -e^{-t}dt = \left.e^{-t}\right|_0^\infty = 1 \tag{5–130}$$

Thus for integer values of v, we have

$$\Gamma(2) = 1\Gamma(1) = 1$$

$$\Gamma(3) = 2\Gamma(2) = 2(1) = 2!$$

$$\Gamma(4) = 3\Gamma(3) = 3(2!) = 3!$$

and

$$\Gamma(n) = (n - 1)! \qquad n = 1, 2, 3, \ldots \tag{5–131}$$

Note that $0! = 1$ by definition. Therefore, the factorial function can be viewed as a special case of the Gamma function with integer arguments. For noninteger values of v, the application of Equation 5–129 to $\Gamma(n + v + 1)$ several times yields

$$(1 + v)(2 + v) \cdots (n + v) = \frac{\Gamma(n + v + 1)}{\Gamma(v + 1)} \tag{5–132}$$

When v is an odd multiple of 1/2 (such as 1/2, 3/2, 5/2, etc.), then we can show that (Figure 5–53)

$$\Gamma\left(\frac{1}{2}\right) = \sqrt{\pi} \tag{5–133}$$

and

$$\Gamma\left(n + \frac{1}{2}\right) = \frac{(2n - 1)!\sqrt{\pi}}{2^{2n-1}(n - 1)!} \tag{5–134}$$

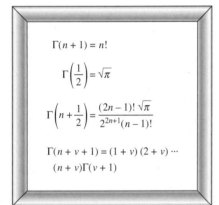

$$\Gamma(n + 1) = n!$$

$$\Gamma\left(\frac{1}{2}\right) = \sqrt{\pi}$$

$$\Gamma\left(n + \frac{1}{2}\right) = \frac{(2n - 1)! \sqrt{\pi}}{2^{2n+1}(n - 1)!}$$

$$\Gamma(n + v + 1) = (1 + v)(2 + v) \cdots$$
$$(n + v)\Gamma(v + 1)$$

FIGURE 5–53

Some special values of the Gamma function ($n = 0, 1, 2, 3 \ldots$).

EXAMPLE 5–30   **Bessel's Equation of Order v (where v is a Positive Noninteger)**

Determine the general solution of Bessel's equation of order v

$$x^2y'' + xy' + (x^2 - v^2)y = 0$$

where v is a positive noninteger, about the point $x_0 = 0$ for $x > 0$ using the Frobenius method.

SOLUTION In this case, the roots of the indicial equation still are (from Equation 5–107) $r_1 = v$ and $r_2 = -v$, but this time they do not differ by an integer. Then according to Theorem 5–3, the given differential equation has two linearly independent solutions, both of the form

$$y_1 = x^r \sum_{n=0}^\infty a_n x^n = \sum_{n=0}^\infty a_n x^{n+r}$$

For $r_1 = v$, the solution procedure for the first solution y_1 is exactly as given in the previous example, except now the factor $[(1 + v)(2 + v) \cdots (n + v)]$

needs to be expressed in terms of the gamma functions (Equation 5–131) instead of factorials. The first linearly independent solution of Bessel's equation in this case is obtained easily by replacing $(n + v)!$ in Equation 5–125 by $\Gamma(n + v + 1)$, which is its equivalent in terms of Gamma functions,

$$J_v(x) = \sum_{n=0}^{\infty} \frac{(-1)^n x^{2n+v}}{2^{2n+v} n! \Gamma(n + v + 1)} \tag{5–135}$$

This function again is the Bessel function of the first kind of order v, which reduces to Equation 5–125 when v is an integer.

The second linearly independent solution y_2 is determined easily from the first solution (Equation 5–132) by replacing all occurrences of v by $-v$. The resulting function is called the *Bessel function of the first kind or order* $-v$ and is given by

$$J_{-v}(x) = \sum_{n=0}^{\infty} \frac{(-1)^n x^{2n-v}}{2^{2n-v} n! \Gamma(n - v + 1)} \tag{5–136}$$

Then the general solution of Bessel's equation of order v with v a noninteger for $x > 0$ can be expressed as

$$y(x) = C_1 J_v(x) + C_2 J_{-v}(x), \quad v \text{ noninteger} \tag{5–137}$$

where the constants C_1 and C_2 are to be determined from the initial or boundary conditions.

The function $J_v(x)$ is analytic for all x, but the function $J_{-v}(x)$ diverges at $x = 0$. Also, the argument of the Gamma function in $J_{-v}(x)$ can be negative. The Gamma function for such cases is still defined so long as its argument is not equal to a negative integer, as shown in Figure 5–54.

A Special Case: $\qquad v = \dfrac{1}{2}, \dfrac{3}{2}, \dfrac{5}{2}, \cdots, n + \dfrac{1}{2}, \qquad n = 0, 1, 2, 3, 4 \ldots$

When v is an odd multiple of 1/2, then the roots of the indicial equation differ by $v - (-v) = 2v$, which is an integer. Therefore, ordinarily we would expect the second linearly independent solution to contain a logarithmic term $C \ln x J_v(x)$. However, the functions $J_v(x)$ and $J_{-v}(-x)$ happen to be linearly independent in this case, and consequently the constant C is zero. Therefore, the solution obtained above for noninteger v is also applicable to this case. In addition, the Gamma function in the denominator can be determined easily in this case using Equations 5–133 and 5–134.

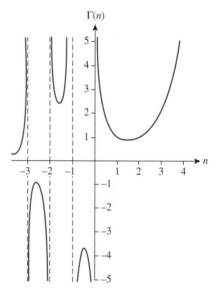

$\Gamma(n)$

FIGURE 5–54

A plot of the Gamma function.

Properties of Bessel Functions

Having obtained the series expansions of $J_v(x)$, $J_{-v}(x)$ and $Y_v(x)$, it is left as an exercise to the student to show that the following relations involving Bessel functions and their derivatives apply:

1. When v is an integer, the functions $J_v(x)$ and $J_{-v}(x)$ are dependent, and are related to each other by (Figure 5–55)

$$J_v(x) = (-1)^n J_{-v}(x), \quad n = 0, 1, 2, 3, 4, \ldots \tag{5–138}$$

2. Recurrence relations:

$$J_{v+1}(x) = \frac{2v}{x} J_v(x) - J_{v-1}(x) \tag{5–139}$$

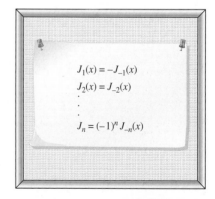

$J_1(x) = -J_{-1}(x)$

$J_2(x) = J_{-2}(x)$

$\vdots$

$J_n = (-1)^n J_{-n}(x)$

FIGURE 5–55

When v is an integer, the functions $J_v(x)$ and $J_{-v}(x)$ become dependent.

and

$$J_{v+1}(x) = -2\frac{dJ_v(x)}{dx} + J_{v-1}(x) \tag{5-140}$$

3. Derivatives:

$$\frac{d}{dx}[x^v J_v(x)] = x^v J_{v-1}(x) \tag{5-141}$$

$$\frac{d}{dx}[x^{-v} J_v(x)] = -x^{-v} J_{v+1}(x) \tag{5-142}$$

$$\frac{d}{dx}[x^v J_v(kx)] = kx^v J_{v-1}(kx) \tag{5-143}$$

$$\frac{d}{dx}[x^{-v} J_v(kx)] = -kx^{-v} J_{v+1}(kx) \tag{5-144}$$

Derivatives involving the Bessel function of the second kind are obtained by replacing J_v in the above relations by Y_v.

4. Integrals:

$$\int x^v J_{v-1}(x)\,dx = x^v J_v(x) + C \tag{5-145}$$

$$\int x^{-v} J_{v+1}(x)\,dx = -x^{-v} J_v(x) + C \tag{5-146}$$

$$\int [J_{v-1}^2(x) - J_{v+1}^2(x)]\,x\,dx = 2v J_v^2(x) + C \tag{5-147}$$

$$\int J_{v+1}(x)\,dx = \int J_{v-1}(x)\,dx - 2J_v(x) \tag{5-148}$$

EXAMPLE 5–31   **Integrals of the Bessel Functions**

Using the integral relations (Equations 5–145 and 5–146), show that

(a) $\displaystyle\int x J_0(x)\,dx = x J_1(x) + C$

(b) $\displaystyle\int J_1(x)\,dx = -J_0(x) + C$

(c) $\displaystyle\int J_3(x)\,dx = -J_2(x) - \frac{2}{x}J_1(x) + C$

SOLUTION (a) This integral is obtained directly from Equation 5–145 by substituting $v = 1$.

(b) This integral is obtained directly from Equation 5–146 by substituting $v = 0$.

(c) This integral is not in the form of any of the given integrals, but can be put into the form of Equation 5–146 by multiplying and dividing the integrand by x^2:

$$I = \int J_3(x)\,dx = \int x^2 [x^{-2} J_3(x)]\,dx$$

Integrating by parts by taking $u = x^2$ and $dv = x^{-2}J_3(x)dx$ yields

$$I = -J_2(x) + 2\int x^{-1}J_2(x)dx$$

This integral can be determined from Equation 5–146, and we obtain the desired result:

$$I = -J_2v(x) - \frac{2}{x}J_1(x) + C$$

Modified Bessel Functions

When the last term is negative, Bessel's equation is called the modified Bessel's equation, and is expressed as

$$x^2y'' + xy' - (x^2 + v^2)y = 0 \tag{5–149}$$

The solution of this equation is expressed in terms of the **modified Bessel functions** I_v and K_v, which are related to ordinary Bessel functions for $v \geq 0$ by

$$I_v(x) = (i)^{-v}J_v(ix) \tag{5–150}$$

$$I_{-v}(x) = (i)^{v}J_{-v}(ix) \tag{5–151}$$

$$K_v(x) = (-1)^{v+1}\left[\gamma + \ln\frac{x}{2}\right]I_v(x) + \frac{1}{2}\sum_{n=0}^{v-1}\frac{(-1)^n(v-n-1)!x^{2n-v}}{2^{2n-v}}$$

$$+ \frac{1}{2}(-1)^v\sum_{n=0}^{\infty}\frac{(S_n + S_{n+v})x^{2n+v}}{2^{2n+v}n!(n+v)!} \tag{5–152}$$

where $i = \sqrt{-1}$ and in the last relation v is an integer. Then the general solution of the modified Bessel's equation is expressed as

$$y = C_1I_v(x) + C_2I_{-v}(x), (v \text{ noninteger}) \tag{5–153}$$

or

$$y = C_1I_v(x) + C_2K_v(x), (v \text{ integer}) \tag{5–154}$$

The first few modified Bessel functions of the first and the second kind are plotted in Figures 5–56 and 5–57. Note that the function $I_v(x)$ is finite at $v = 0$ but increases quickly as x increases. The function $K_v(x)$—on the other hand—is unbounded at $x = 0$ but vanishes quickly as x increases. For large values of x, these two functions do not depend on v and are approximated as

$$I_v(x) \cong \frac{e^x}{\sqrt{2x\pi}} \quad \text{and} \quad K_v(x) \cong \sqrt{\frac{\pi}{2x}}e^{-x} \tag{5–155}$$

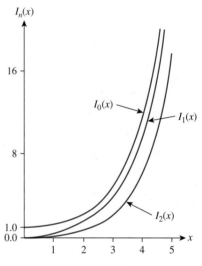

FIGURE 5–56

Modified Bessel functions of the first kind.

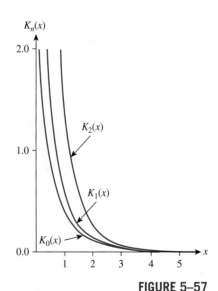

FIGURE 5–57

Modified Bessel functions of the second kind.

Section Review

5–27C How does modified Bessel's equation of order v differ from Bessel's equation?

5–28C For which values of v will the roots of the indicial equation of Bessel's equation of order v differ by an integer?

5–29C In what ways are the functions $J_0(x)$ and $\cos x$ similar and in what ways are they different?

5–30 Using the method of Frobenius, determine the first linearly independent solution of Bessel's equation of order 1. Compare it with $J_1(x)$.

(*Answers:* $y_1(x) = \dfrac{1}{2}x - \dfrac{1}{16}x^3 + \dfrac{1}{384}x^5 - \dfrac{1}{18\,432}x^7 + \cdots$

whereas $J_1(x) = \displaystyle\sum_{n=0}^{\infty} \dfrac{(-1)^n}{2^{2n+1}\,n!(n+1)!}x^{2n+1}$

whose first four terms agree with $y_1(x)$.)

5–31 Determine the following integrals involving Bessel functions.

(a) $\displaystyle\int x^2 J_1(x)\,dx$ (b) $\displaystyle\int \dfrac{1}{x^2}J_3(x)\,dx$

(*Answers:* (a) $x^2 J_2(x) + C$ and (b) $-\dfrac{J_2(x)}{x^2} + C$)

5–8 ▪ COMPUTER METHODS

Software packages sometimes give solutions to differential equations in terms of **special functions**. Legendre and Hermite polynomials, and Bessel functions are examples of special functions we have already seen. Other examples are the Airy functions $Ai(x)$ and $Bi(x)$, which are the two independent solutions to Airy's equation $y'' - xy = 0$. The special functions may be given different names in different packages. For example, in MuPAD, the Airy functions are functions of two variables and are named `airyAi(x,n)` and `airyBi(x,n)`, where n indicates the nth derivative of the Airy function. Thus `airyAi(x,0)` and `airyBi(x,0)` give the Airy functions introduced in Section 5–4. In Maple and Mathematica they are functions of x only and are capitalized as `AiryAi` and `AiryBi`. Table 5–1 lists some of the special functions available in the various software packages.

TABLE 5–1

Special Function Calls by Language

Name and Symbol	MuPAD	Maple	Mathematica
Airy, $Ai(x)$	`airyAi(x)`	`AiryAi(x)`	`AiryAi[x]`
Airy, $Bi(x)$	`airyBi(x)`	`AiryBi(x)`	`AiryBi[x]`
Chebyshev 1st Kind, $T(n, x)$	`chebyshev1(n,x)`	`ChebyshevT(n,x)`	`ChebyshevT[n,x]`
Gamma, $\Gamma(x)$	`gamma(x)`	`GAMMA(x)`	`Gamma[x]`
Hermite, $H_n(x)$	`hermite(n,x)`	`HermiteH(n,x)`	`HermiteH[n,x]`
Bessel I, $I_n(x)$	`besselI(n,x)`	`BesselI(n,x)`	`BesselI[n,x]`
Bessel J, $J_n(x)$	`besselJ(n,x)`	`BesselJ(n,x)`	`BesselJ[n,x]`
Bessel K, $K_n(x)$	`besselK(n,x)`	`BesselK(n,x)`	`BesselK[n,x]`
Laguerre, $L(n, a, x)$	`laguerreL(n,a,x)`	`L(n,ax)`	`LaguerreL[n,a,x]`
Legendre, $P_n(x)$	`legendre(n,x)`	`LegendreP(n,x)`	`LegendreP[n,x]`
Bessel Y, $Y_n(x)$	`besselY(n,x)`	`BesselY(n,x)`	`BesselY[n,x]`

Solutions with MuPAD

Consider Legendre's equation with $\alpha = 2$: $(1 - x^2)y'' - 2xy' + 6y = 0$ with the initial conditions $y(0) = 1$, $y'(0) = 0$. It has an ordinary singular point and can be solved in MuPAD with the following session:

```
[eqn1:=ode({(1-x^2)*y"(x)-2*x*y'(x)+6*y(x)=0,
  y(0)=1,y'(0)=0},y(x)):
```

```
[solve(eqn1)
```

$$\{1 - 3x^2\}$$

The result is a finite polynomial of degree 2.

Airy's equation $y'' - xy = 0$ with the same initial conditions can be solved with the following session:

```
[eqn2:=ode({y"(x)-x*y(x)=0,y(0)=1,y'(0)=0},y(x)):
```

```
[solve(eqn2)
```

$$\left\{ \frac{3^{2/3}\Gamma\left(\frac{2}{3}\right)\text{airyAi}(x, 0)}{2} + \frac{3^{1/6}\Gamma\left(\frac{2}{3}\right)\text{airyBi}(x, 0)}{2} \right\}$$

where $\Gamma(x)$ is another special function called the *Gamma function*. Table 5–1 lists some of the special functions available in MuPAD. The Gamma function is evaluated by selecting the Greek symbol from the Greek palette or by typing gamma(x). Table 5–2 shows that the float function is used to evaluate special functions numerically. For example,

```
[float(gamma(2/3))
```

$$1.354117939$$

```
[float(airyAi(2,0))
```

$$0.03492413042$$

If an explicit series solution is preferred, you can use the **series** option as follows. Using Legendre's equation with $\alpha = 3$ as an example and solving it with the **solve** function (even with simple initial conditions like $y(0) = 1$ and $y'(0) = 0$), results in a complicated expression that is too detailed to

TABLE 5–2

Evaluation of Special Functions by Language

Result	MuPAD	Maple	Mathematica
Symbolic finite series	orthpoly::	simplify	Series
Symbolic finite series	series	series	Series
Numeric result	float	evalf	//N

display here (try it). However, even with arbitrary initial conditions, the series solution is not very complicated. The session is

```
[eqn3:=(1-x^2)*y"(x)-2*x*y'(x)+12*y(x)=0:
[ode::series({y(0)=a,y'(0)=b,eqn3},y(x),x=0)
```

$$\left\{ a + bx - 6ax^2 - \frac{5b}{3}x^3 + 3ax^4 + O(x^6) \right\}$$

To evaluate a special function symbolically as a *finite* series, that is, as a polynomial, use either the `orthpoly::` option or the `series` function. The `orthpoly` package provides some standard orthogonal polynomials. Call the package functions by using the package name `orthpoly` and the name of the function. For example, the fifth order Legendre polynomial is obtained as follows:

```
[orthpoly::legendre(5,x)
```

$$\left\{ \text{poly}\left(\frac{63x^5}{8} - \frac{35x^3}{4} + \frac{15x}{8}, [x] \right) \right\}$$

```
[orthpoly::legendre(5,2)
```

$$\frac{743}{4}$$

```
[float(orthpoly::legendre(5,2))
```

$$185.75$$

To symbolically evaluate a special function that consists of an *infinite* series, use the `series` function. For example,

```
[series(besselJ(0,x),x)
```

$$1 - \frac{x^2}{4} + \frac{x^4}{64} + O(x^6)$$

You can plot special functions just as any other function. For example,

```
[plot(airyAi(x),x=0..5)
```

You can plot the solution of a differential equation by following this example based on Airy's equation.

```
[eqn4:=ode({y"(x)=x*y(x),y(0)=1,y'(0)=-0.1},y(x)):
[solve(eqn4)
[Y4:=op(%)
[plotfunc2d(Y4,x=0..1)
```

The `op` function removes the braces surrounding the solution obtained by the `solve` function.

Solutions with Maple

When solving differential equations in Maple, it is good practice to load the `DEtools` package and also the `plots` package if you will be making plots. If you will be obtaining series solutions, you also should load the `powseries` package.

Consider Legendre's equation with $\alpha = 2$: $(1 - x^2)y'' - 2xy' + 6y = 0$. It has an ordinary singular point and can be solved in Maple with the following session:

```
>  eqn1:=(1-x^2)*y"(x)-2*x*y'(x)+6*y(x)=0:

>  dsolve({eqn1,y(0)=1,y'(0)=0},y(x))
```

$$y(x) = 1 - 3x^2$$

The result is a finite polynomial of degree 2.

Table 5–1 lists some of the special functions available in Maple. Table 5–2 shows how to evaluate the special functions. Legendre polynomials are obtained by typing `simplify(LegendreP(n,x))`. For example,

```
>  simplify(LegendreP(5,x))
```

$$\frac{63x^5}{8} - \frac{35x^3}{4} + \frac{15x}{8}$$

Use the `evalf` function to obtain a numerical evaluation. For example,

```
>  evalf(LegendreP(5,2))
```

$$185.7500000$$

Airy's equation can be solved with the following session:

```
>  eqn2:=y"(x)-x*y(x)=0:
>  dsolve({eqn2,y(0)=1,  y'(0)=0},y(x))
```

$$y(x) = \frac{1}{2}3^{2/3}\Gamma\left(\frac{2}{3}\right)\text{AiryAi}(x) + \frac{1}{2}3^{1/6}\Gamma\left(\frac{2}{3}\right)\text{AiryBi}(x)$$

where $\Gamma(x)$ is the special function called the *Gamma function*. The Gamma function is evaluated by selecting the Greek symbol from the Greek palette or by typing `GAMMA(x)`.

If an explicit series solution is preferred, you can use the `series` option as follows. Using the Airy's equation `eqn2` as an example (with arbitrary initial conditions), the session is

```
>  dsolve({eqn2,y(0)=a,y'(0)=b},y(x),series)
```

$$y(x) = a + bx + \frac{1}{6}ax^3 + \frac{1}{12}bx^4 + 0(x^6)$$

The `series` function also can be used to obtain a series representation of a special function. For example,

```
>  series(BesselJ(0,x),x)
```

$$1 - \frac{1}{4}x^2 + \frac{1}{64}x^4 + 0(x^6)$$

Maple can find the recursion relation when `dsolve` does not give the solution in a convenient form. For example, the solution of the equation $y'' + 2xy' + 5y = 0$ given by `dsolve` is a complicated expression consisting of several Bessel functions and is too detailed to display here (try it). In such cases, we can use the `powseries` package and the functions `powsolve` and `tpsform` to obtain the recursion relation. The Maple session follows, using the initial conditions $y(0) = 1$, $y'(0) = 0$ and displaying the result up to order 8. Recall that the default value of `Order` is 6, which is overridden here by the `tpsform` function, which gives an answer as a truncated power series form. The `powsolve` function in the `powseries` package solves a linear differential equation as a power series.

```
> eqn3 := y"(x)+2*x*y'(x)+5*y(x) = 0
```

$$eqn3 := \frac{d^2}{dx^2}y(x) + 2x\frac{d}{dx}y(x) + 5y(x) = 0$$

```
> initial:=y(0)=1,y'(0)=0:
```

```
> IVP:={eqn3,initial}:
```

```
> sol:=powsolve(IVP):
```

```
> Sol:=tpsform(sol,x,8)
```

$$Sol := 1 - \frac{5}{2}x^2 + \frac{15}{8}x^4 - \frac{13}{16}x^6 + 0(x^8)$$

```
> RecursionRelation:=a(\_n)=subs(\_k=n,sol(\_k))
```

$$Recursion\ relation := a(\_n) = -\frac{(1 + 2n)a(n - 2)}{n(n - 1)}$$

Be sure to type the backslash before typing the underscore! From the initial conditions, we note that $a_0 = 1$ and $a_1 = 0$, so that $a_n = 0$ for n odd, $a_2 = -(5/2)a_0 = -5/2$, $a_4 = -(9/12)a_2 = (15/8)a_0 = 15/8$, and $a_6 = -(13/30)a_4 = -13/16$. These agree with the series displayed for *Sol*.

You can plot the solution of a differential equation by following this example based on Airy's equation. The `unapply` function returns an operator from an expression. The `rhs` function selects the right-hand side of the equation.

```
> with(plots),with(DEtools):
```

```
> eqn:=y"(x)-x*y(x)=0:
```

```
> sol1:=dsolve({eqn, y(0)=1,y'(0)=0},y(x)):
```

```
> y1:=unapply(rhs(sol1),x):
```

```
> plot(y1(x),x=0..2)
```

Solutions with Mathematica

Consider Legendre's equation $\alpha = 2$: $(1 - x^2)y'' - 2xy' + 6y = 0$. It has an ordinary singular point and can be solved in Mathematica with the following session:

```
> eqn1=(1-x^2)*y"[x]-2*x*y'[x]+6*y[x]==0;
```

```
> DSolve[{eqn1,y[0]==1,y'[0]==0},y[x],x]
```

$$\{\{y[x] \to 1 - 3x^2\}\}$$

The result is a finite polynomial of degree 2.

Table 5–1 lists the function names in Mathematica. Table 5–2 shows how to evaluate the special functions. Legendre polynomials are obtained by typing `LegendreP[n,x]`. For example,

```
> LegendreP[5,x]
```

$$\frac{1}{8}(15x - 70x^3 + 63x^5)$$

Use the `//N` function to obtain a numerical evaluation. For example,

```
> LegendreP(5,2)//N
```

$$185.75$$

Airy's equation $y'' - xy = 0$ with the initial conditions $y(0) = 1$, $y'(0) = 0$ can be solved with the following session:

```
> eqn2=y"[x]-x*y[x]==0;
```

```
> DSolve[{eqn2,y[0]==1,y'[0]==0},y[x],x]
```

$$\{\{y[x] \to 1/2(3^{(2/3)}\text{AiryAi}[x]\text{Gamma}[2/3] + 3^{(1/6)}\text{AiryBi}[x]\text{Gamma}[2/3])\}\}$$

where $\Gamma(x)$ is the special function called the *Gamma function*. The Gamma function is evaluated by selecting the Greek symbol from the Greek palette or by typing `Gamma[x]//N`. For example,

```
> Gamma[2/3]//N
```

$$1.35412$$

```
> AiryAi[2]//N
```

$$0.0349241$$

If an explicit series solution is preferred, you can use the `series` option as follows. Using the Airy's equation as an example, with the initial conditions $y(0) = 1$, $y'(0) = 0$, the session is

```
> odeseries=Series[y"[x]-x*y[x],{x,0,6}];
```

```
> coeffs=Solve[{odeseries==0,y[0]==1,y'[0]==0}]
```

> ```
> seriessol=Series[y[x],{x,0,6}]/.First[coeffs]
> ```

$$1 + \frac{x^3}{6} + \frac{x^6}{180} + O[x^7]$$

Here is the solution for Bessel's equation with $n = 4$. Note that the solution is given in terms of Bessel functions of the first kind, `BesselJ`, as well as those of the second kind, `BesselY`.

> ```
> DSolve[x^2*y"[x]+x*y'[x]+(x^2-16)*y[x]==0,y[x],x]
> ```

$$\{\{y[x] \rightarrow BesselJ[4, x]C[1] + BesselY[4, x]C[2]\}\}$$

You can plot the special functions as any other function. For example, to plot the `BesselJ(n,x)` function for $n = 1,3$ and $0 \le x \le 20$, you enter

> ```
> Plot[{BesselJ[1,x],BesselJ[3,x]},{x,0,20}]
> ```

You can plot the solution of a differential equation by modifying this example as,

> ```
> DSolve[{x^2*y''[x]+x*y'[x]+(x^2-16)*y[x]==0,
>   y[0]==0,y[10]==1},y[x],x]
> ```

$$\left\{\left\{y[x] \rightarrow \frac{BesselJ[4, x]}{BesselJ[4, 10]}\right\}\right\}$$

> ```
> Plot[y[x]/.%,{x,0,10}]
> ```

The ReplaceAll command (`/.`) is used in the `Plot` command to substitute the solution for $y[x]$.

5–9 · SUMMARY

Linear differential equations with variable coefficients usually must be solved in terms of infinite series.

Power Series An infinite series whose terms involve the powers of the variable x in the form x^n, where n is integer is called a *power series* and is expressed as

$$f(x) = \sum_{n=0}^{\infty} C_n x^n = C_0 + C_1 x + C_2 x^2 + C_3 x^3 + \cdots \quad \text{(5–1)}$$

Two power series are *identical* if they represent the same function. Therefore, if $\Sigma_{n=0}^{\infty} C_n x^n = 0$ for all x in some interval, then $C_n = 0$ for all $n = 0, 1, 2, 3, \ldots$.

Manipulation of Series A series expression can manipulated just like a definite integral. Any quantity that does not depend on the index of summation can be moved into or out of the summation sign, just like a quantity that does not depend on the integration variable can be moved in or out of the integral sign. Often it is necessary to shift the index of summation to combine series whose general terms are not of the same power. This is done by replacing all occurrences of the index n by $n + k$, where k can be any integer. A relation that relates two or more coefficients of the power series to each other is called a *recurrence relation*.

Series Convergence Test A power series of the form $\Sigma_{n=0}^{\infty} C_n x^n$ is said to *converge* on an interval I if the limit $\lim_{n \to \infty} \Sigma_{n=0}^{\infty} C_n x^n$ exists for all x in that interval. Convergence can be checked by applying the *ratio test*,

$$L = \lim_{n \to \infty} \left| \frac{(n+1)\text{th term}}{n\text{th term}} \right| = \lim_{n \to \infty} \left| \frac{C_{n+1} x^{n+1}}{C_n x^n} \right| = |x| \lim_{n \to \infty} \left| \frac{C_{n+1}}{C_n} \right| \quad \text{(5–22)}$$

The power series converges for a given x value if $L < 1$ and diverges if $L > 1$.

Interval of Convergence On the x-axis, the open interval in which a power series converges is called the *interval of convergence*, which can be determined from the ratio test. The interval of convergence often is described in terms of the *radius of convergence ρ*, which is the distance from the center of the series to the closest singular point. The interval of convergence of a power series of center x_0 is usually described in terms of the radius of convergence as $|x - x_0| < \rho$, where

$$\rho = \lim_{n \to \infty} \left| \frac{C_n}{C_{n+1}} \right| \tag{5-24}$$

If two power series converge in the interval I, then their sum, difference, and product also will converge in that interval. However, the quotient of these two series (in general) will have a smaller radius of convergence than either series, since their ratio may diverge at the zeros of the denominator.

Taylor Series The Taylor series expansion of the function $f(x)$ about the point x_0 is given by

$$f(x) = \sum_{n=0}^{\infty} \frac{f^{(n)}(x_0)}{n!} (x - x_0)^n$$

Thus, if a function is infinitely differentiable at a point x_0, its Taylor series exists at that point. A function $f(x)$ whose Taylor series expansion at a point x_0 and its immediate vicinity exists is said to be analytic at that point. Therefore, any function that is analytic at x_0 can be expressed as a power series of center x_0 with a nonzero radius of convergence. Polynomials, as well as their sums, differences, products, and quotients (except at the zeros of the denominator) are analytic everywhere.

Solutions About a Point When solving linear differential equations with variable coefficients, we have to talk about solutions about a point. This refers to a solution in an interval that contains that point, since the interval in which the solution is applicable will rarely be the entire x-axis because of singularities. The solution of the equation around a point depends not only on the point itself but also on the nature of the point.

Ordinary Points and Singular Points The point x_0 of the differential equation

$$y'' + P(x)y' + Q(x)y = 0 \tag{5-47}$$

is called an ordinary point if both of the functions $P(x)$ and $Q(x)$ are analytic at that point. The point x_0 is called a singular point of the differential equation if one or both of the functions $P(x)$ and $Q(x)$ are not analytic at that point. A singular point of a differential equation is further classified as follows. A singular point x_0 is called a regular singular point of the differential equation if both of the functions

$$(x - x_0)P(x) \quad \text{and} \quad (x - x_0)^2 Q(x) \tag{5-48}$$

are analytic at that point. Otherwise, the point x_0 is called an irregular singular point of the differential equation.

When the functions $P(x)$ and $Q(x)$ are polynomials, all points are ordinary points of the differential equation. When the functions $P(x)$ and $Q(x)$ are ratios of polynomials, the points at which the denominators of $P(x)$ or $Q(x)$ vanish are the singular points, and all other points are ordinary points of the differential equation.

Radius of Convergence The radius of convergence of the series solution of a differential equation is related to the radius of convergence of the functions $P(x)$ and $Q(x)$, and is expressed by the following theorem:

THEOREM 5–1

If x_0 is an ordinary point of the differential equation
$$y'' + P(x)y' + Q(x)y = 0$$
then the infinite series in the general solution of this differential equation has a radius of convergence that is at least as large as the smaller of the radii of convergence of the functions $P(x)$ and $Q(x)$.

Existence and Uniqueness of Solutions The existence and uniqueness of solutions about ordinary points is addressed by the following theorem.

THEOREM 5–2

If x_0 is an ordinary point of the differential equation
$$y'' + P(x)y' + Q(x)y = 0$$
then this differential equation has two linearly independent solutions y_1 and y_2, each of the form $\sum_{n=0}^{\infty} C_n(x - x_0)^n$. The general solution of this differential equation is

$$y = \sum_{n=0}^{\infty} C_n(x - x_0)^n = C_0 y_1(x) + C_1 y_2(x) \tag{5-50}$$

where C_0 and C_1 are two arbitrary constants that are determined from the initial or boundary conditions. The remaining coefficients in the series solution are determined by substituting the series solution into the differential equation. Furthermore, the radius of convergence of the series solution is at least as large as the distance from x_0 to the nearest real or complex singular point.

Legendre's Equation The differential equation

$$(1 - x^2)y'' - 2xy' + \alpha(\alpha + 1)y = 0 \tag{5-57}$$

where α is a constant is known as Legendre's differential equation, and any series solution of this equation is called a Legendre function of order α. When α is a non-negative integer, some Legendre functions reduce to polynomials, which are called Legendre polynomials. The Legendre polynomial of order n is expressed as

$$P_n(x) = \sum_{k=0}^{N} \frac{(-1)^k (2n-2k)!}{2^n k! (n-k)! (n-2k)!} x^{n-2k}, \qquad \text{(5–62)}$$

$$n = 0, 1, 2, 3, \dots$$

where N is the greatest integer less than or equal to $n/2$. Unlike the Legendre functions, the Legendre polynomials converge at the end points $x = \pm 1$ as well as the interval in between. The Legendre polynomials can be generated in a systematic manner from the relation:

$$P_n(x) = \frac{1}{2^n n!} \frac{d^n}{dx^n} (x^2 - 1)^n, \qquad n = 0, 1, 2, 3, \dots \quad \text{(5–63)}$$

which is known as Rodrigues formula. Knowing that $P_0(x) = 1$ and $P_1(x) = x$, all of the remaining Legendre polynomials can be determined using the recurrence relation:

$$P_n = \frac{(2n-1)x P_{n-1} - (n-1) P_{n-2}}{n} \qquad \text{(5–67)}$$

Method of Frobenius   The solution of a second-order linear differential equation with variable coefficients in the neighborhood of a regular singular point that is taken to be at the origin is obtained by the method of Frobenius. This is described by the following theorem.

THEOREM 5–3

Let the point $x = 0$ be a regular point of the differential equation

$$y'' + P(x)y' + Q(x)y = 0$$

and ρ be the smaller radius of convergence of the two functions $p(x) = xP(x)$ and $q(x) = x^2 Q(x)$. Let r_1 and r_2 be the roots of the indicial equation

$$r^2 + (p_0 - 1)r + q_0 = 0 \qquad \text{(5–75)}$$

where

$$p_0 = \lim_{x \to 0} xP(x) \quad and \quad q_0 = \lim_{x \to 0} x^2 Q(x)$$

Let $r_1 > r_2$ when the roots are real and unequal, then two linearly independent solutions $y_1(x)$ and $y_2(x)$ to this differential equation exist with a radius of convergence of ρ, and if $x > 0$ they are one of the following forms.

CASE 1: $r_1 = r_2 + \lambda$ (λ is a positive noninteger)

$$y_1 = x^{r_1} \sum_{n=0}^{\infty} a_n x^n \qquad (a_0 \neq 0) \qquad \text{(5–81a)}$$

$$y_2 = x^{r_2} \sum_{n=0}^{\infty} b_n x^n \qquad (b_0 \neq 0) \qquad \text{(5–81b)}$$

CASE 2: $r_1 = r_2 = r$

$$y_1 = x^r \sum_{n=0}^{\infty} a_n x^n \quad (a_0 \neq 0) \qquad \text{(5–82a)}$$

$$y_2 = y_1 \ln x + x^r \sum_{n=1}^{\infty} b_n x^n \qquad \text{(5–82b)}$$

CASE 3: $r_1 = r_2 + N$ (N is a positive integer)

$$y_1 = x^{r_1} \sum_{n=0}^{\infty} a_n x^n \qquad (a_0 \neq 0) \qquad \text{(5–83a)}$$

$$y_2 = C y_1 \ln x + x^{r_2} \sum_{n=0}^{\infty} b_n x^n \quad (b_0 \neq 0) \quad \text{(5–83b)}$$

where C is a constant which may be zero. Then the general solution of the differential equation for all three cases is expressed as

$$y = C_1 y_1(x) + C_2 y_2(x) \qquad \text{(5–84)}$$

where the arbitrary constants C_1 and C_2 are determined from the initial or boundary conditions.

The form of the first solution is the same for all cases. The three cases differ in the form of the second solution only. Also, the coefficients a_0 and b_0 are arbitrary nonzero constants and can be assigned any suitable values. It is common practice to take $a_0 = 1$ and $b_0 = 1$ for simplicity with no loss in generality. The restriction $x > 0$ can be lifted by replacing x^{r_1} and x^{r_2} in the solutions by $|x|^{r_1}$ and $|x|^{r_2}$, respectively. A more practical way is to substitute $t = -x$ in the differential equation and then solve the resulting equation for $t > 0$. The determination of the first linearly independent solution y_1 is similar to the determination of the solution about an ordinary point, except now the solution involves x^{n+r_1} instead of x^n. The second linearly independent solution in Case 2 always involves a logarithmic term. However, in Case 3, the logarithmic term *may* be zero. Once the two linearly independent solutions y_1 and y_2 are available, any other solution of the differential equation can be expressed as a linear combination of these two solutions.

Bessel's Equation   One of the most important second-order differential equations with variable coefficients is *Bessel's equation of order v* expressed as

$$x^2 y'' + xy' + (x^2 - v^2)y = 0 \qquad \text{(5–104)}$$

Its solutions are expressed in terms of the *Bessel functions*. The origin (the point $x = 0$) is the only singular point of Bessel's equation, and it is a regular singular point. The indicial equation is $r^2 - v^2 = 0$, whose roots are $r_1 = v$ and

$r_2 = -v$. The two linearly independent solutions of Bessel's equation of order zero are

$$J_0(x) = \sum_{n=0}^{\infty} \frac{(-1)^n x^{2n}}{2^{2n}(n!)^2} \quad (5\text{-}110)$$

and

$$Y_0 = \frac{2}{\pi}\left[\left(\gamma + \ln\frac{x}{2}\right)J_0(x) + \sum_{n=1}^{\infty}\frac{(-1)^{n+1}S_n x^{2n}}{2^{2n}(n!)^2}\right] \quad (5\text{-}113)$$

which are called *Bessel functions of the first and second kind of order zero,* respectively. Here

$$S_n = 1 + \frac{1}{2} + \frac{1}{3} + \cdots + \frac{1}{n} = \sum_{j=1}^{n}\frac{1}{j} \quad (5\text{-}112)$$

The two linearly independent solutions of Bessel's equation of order one-half are related to the trigonometric functions $\sin x$ and $\cos x$, and are expressed as

$$J_{1/2}(x) = \sqrt{\frac{2}{\pi x}}\sin x \quad \text{and} \quad J_{-1/2}(x) = \sqrt{\frac{2}{\pi x}}\cos x \quad (5\text{-}120)$$

When v is a positive integer, the two linearly independent solutions of Bessel's equation of order v are expressed as

$$J_v(x) = \sum_{n=0}^{\infty}\frac{(-1)^n x^{2n+v}}{2^{2n+v}n!(n+v)!} \quad (5\text{-}125)$$

and

$$Y_v(x) = \frac{2}{\pi}\left[\left(\gamma + \ln\frac{x}{2}\right)J_v(x) - \frac{1}{2}\sum_{n=0}^{v-1}\frac{(v-n-1)!x^{2n-v}}{2^{2n-v}n!}\right.$$
$$\left. + \frac{1}{2}\sum_{n=0}^{\infty}\frac{(-1)^{n+1}(S_n + S_{n+v})x^{2n+v}}{2^{2n+v}n!(n+v)!}\right] \quad (5\text{-}126)$$

When v is not an integer, the two linearly independent solutions of Bessel's equation of order v are $J_v(x)$ and $J_{-v}(x)$, which are expressed as

$$J_v(x) = \sum_{n=0}^{\infty}\frac{(-1)^n x^{2n+v}}{2^{2n+v}n!\Gamma(n+v+1)!} \quad (5\text{-}135)$$

and

$$J_{-v}(x) = \sum_{n=0}^{\infty}\frac{(-1)^n x^{2n-v}}{2^{2n-v}n!\Gamma(n-v+1)!} \quad (5\text{-}136)$$

where the Gamma function is defined as

$$\Gamma(v) = \int_0^{\infty}t^{v-1}e^{-t}dt \quad (5\text{-}128)$$

Some properties of Bessel functions can be summarized as

$$J_v(x) = (-1)^n J_{-v}(x) \qquad n = 0, 1, 2, 3, 4, ... \quad (5\text{-}138)$$

$$J_{v+1}(x) = \frac{2v}{x}J_v(x) - J_{v-1}(x) \quad (5\text{-}139)$$

$$J_{v+1}(x) = -2\frac{dJ_v(x)}{dx} + J_{v-1}(x) \quad (5\text{-}140)$$

$$\frac{d}{dx}[x^v J_v(kx)] = kx^v J_{v-1}(kx) \quad (5\text{-}143)$$

$$\frac{d}{dx}[x^{-v}J_v(kx)] = -kx^{-v}J_{v+1}(kx) \quad (5\text{-}144)$$

$$\int x^v J_{v-1}(x)dx = x^v J_v(x) + C \quad (5\text{-}145)$$

$$\int x^{-v}J_{v+1}(x)dx = -x^{-v}J_v(x) + C \quad (5\text{-}146)$$

The solution of the modified Bessel's equation, which is expressed in terms of *modified Bessel functions* I_v and K_v.

$$x^2 y'' + xy' - (x^2 + v^2) = 0 \quad (5\text{-}149)$$

Historical Notes

George Biddell Airy (1801–1892) British astronomer. The Airy equation and its solution, the Airy function, are named for him. He developed this equation during his studies of light rays reflected or refracted by a curved surface.

Friedrich Wilhelm Bessel (1784–1846) German mathematician and astronomer. He generalized the Bessel functions (which were first developed by Daniel Bernoulli) as a result of his studies in the dynamics of many-body gravitational systems. He was the first to use parallax in calculating the distance to a star.

Pafnuty Lvovich Chebyshev (1821–1894) Russian mathematician. His name has been translated from Russian variously as Chebychev, Chebyshov, Tchebycheff, and Tschebyscheff. Considered the father of Russian mathematics, he made numerous contributions in probability, statistics, and number theory. Although named for Charles Hermite, the Hermite polynomials were actually developed by Chebyshev.

Ferdinand Georg Frobenius (1849–1917) German mathematician known for his contributions to the theory of differential equations, group theory, and the first complete proof of the Cayley–Hamilton theorem of matrix analysis.

Johann Carl Friedrich (1777–1855) German mathematician and scientist. He contributed significantly to number theory, geometry, geophysics, magnetism, astronomy, and optics, among other fields. He developed the prime number theorem and proved the fundamental theorem of algebra. Gauss was the first to give a full systematic treatment of the hypergeometric equation.

Charles Hermite (1822–1901) French mathematician. He did research on number theory, orthogonal polynomials, elliptic functions, and algebra, and he was the first to prove that e (the base of natural logarithms) is a transcendental number.

Edmond Nicolas Laguerre (1834–1886) French mathematician. His primary contributions were in geometry and complex analysis. He developed Laguerre's method for finding the roots of polynomials. He developed Laguerre's polynomials to solve the differential equation named for him. These polynomials also are used for Gaussian quadrature to numerically compute integrals whose integrands have the form $f(x)e^{-x}$.

Adrien-Marie Legendre, (1752–1833) French mathematician. He made significant contributions to statistics, number theory, and algebra. Much of his work was completed and generalized by others. The Legendre polynomials are the solution to Legendre's equation, which results when solving Laplace's partial differential equation for the gravitational potential function in spherical coordinates.

Olinde Rodrigues (1795–1851) French mathematician. He did research in vector analysis, orthogonal polynomials, and the mathematical representation of rotation in three dimensions. He developed the formula for generating the Legendre polynomials.

PROBLEMS

5–1   Review of Power Series

5–32C   Why do we sometimes shift the index of a summation?

5–33C   Explain how we can shift the index of a summation forward by k?

5–34C   What is a recurrence relation?

5–35C   Under what conditions will a power series be identically equal to zero?

5–36C   Why are we concerned with the convergence of series in the method of series solution of differential equations?

5–37C   How is the convergence of power series checked with the ratio test ? What is this test based on?

5–38C   Define the interval of convergence and the radius of convergence of a power series.

5–39C   If two power series converge in an interval, what can you say about the convergence of their sum, difference, product, and quotient in the same interval?

5–40C   When is a function said to be analytic in the vicinity of a specified point? Give examples of functions that are analytic everywhere.

Write out the first three terms of the following series while keeping the rest of the terms under the summation.

5–41   (a) $5x\sum_{n=1}^{\infty}(n+1)^2 x^{n+3}$ (b) $\sum_{n=2}^{\infty}\dfrac{n+5}{n+3}C_{2n+1}x^{2n+1}$

5–42   (a) $x^2\sum_{n=0}^{\infty}(-1)^n 2^n x^{n-1}$ (b) $\sum_{n=1}^{\infty}(n+1)^2 C_{2n}x^{2n}$

Shift the index of the following summations such that the power of x in each of them is n.

5–43   (a) $\sum_{n=1}^{\infty}(n-1)^2 2^n x^{n+3}$ (b) $\sum_{n=3}^{\infty}C_n x^{n+1}$

Shift the index of the following summations such that the power of x in each of them is n − 1.

5–44   (a) $\sum_{n=0}^{\infty}(n+4)x^n$ (b) $\sum_{n=2}^{\infty}(n+1)^3 2^n x^{n+3}$

5–45   (a) $\sum_{n=0}^{\infty}(n+3)x^n$ (b) $\sum_{n=4}^{\infty}C_n x^{n-2}$

Shift the index of the following summations such that the power of x in each of them is n + 1.

5–46   (a) $\sum_{n=2}^{\infty}(n-1)3^n x^n$ (b) $\sum_{n=2}^{\infty}(n-5)^2 x^n$

5–47   (a) $\sum_{n=4}^{\infty}C_n x^{n+2}$ (b) $\sum_{n=3}^{\infty}(n+1)^2 2^{n-1}x^{n-1}$

Combine the three series in the following questions into a single summation in x^n by shifting the index of summation whenever necessary and performing the indicated additions and subtractions. (Write out some of the terms individually when they cannot be combined into the summation.)

5–48 $\sum_{n=0}^{\infty}nC_n x^n - 2\sum_{n=0}^{\infty}(n+1)C_n x^{n+2} + x\sum_{n=0}^{\infty}n2^n x^{n+1} = 0$

5–49 $\sum_{n=1}^{\infty}n^2 x^{n-1} - 5x\sum_{n=0}^{\infty}(n-3)C_n x^{n-2} + x^2\sum_{n=0}^{\infty}\dfrac{n-1}{n+1}x^{n-4} = 0$

5–50 $\sum_{n=0}^{\infty}(-1)^n(n+2)C_n x^{n+1} + 2\sum_{n=1}^{\infty}n^3 x^{n+2} - 3x^2\sum_{n=0}^{\infty}nx^n = 0$

Determine if the following equalities are correct.

5–51 $3\sum_{n=0}^{\infty}nx^n = \sum_{n=2}^{\infty}3(n-2)x^{n-2}$

5–52 $\sum_{n=1}^{\infty}n^2 C_n x^n = C_1 x + \sum_{j=2}^{\infty}j^2 C_j x^j$

5–53 $3x^2\sum_{n=1}^{\infty}(n+2)^2 x^{n-1} = \sum_{n=1}^{\infty}3(n+2)^2 x^{n+1}$

5–54 $\sum_{n=0}^{\infty}(n+5)C_n x^{n+1} = \sum_{n=1}^{\infty}(n+4)C_{n-1}x^n$

5–55 $\sum_{n=0}^{\infty}2n^2 x^n = 2\sum_{n=2}^{\infty}(n^2-2)x^{n-2}$

Determine the interval of convergence and the radius of convergence of the following power series.

5–56 (a) $\sum_{n=0}^{\infty} \frac{n-1}{n!}(x-1)^n$ (b) $\sum_{n=1}^{\infty} \frac{(-1)^n}{n+5}x^{n+2}$

5–57 (a) $\sum_{n=0}^{\infty} 3^{n+1}x^n$ (b) $\sum_{n=2}^{\infty} \frac{2^n}{n}(x-1)^n$

5–58 (a) $\sum_{n=0}^{\infty} \frac{1}{(2n)!}x^{2n}$ (b) $\sum_{n=1}^{\infty} n!x^n$

Taking $y = \sum_{n=0}^{\infty} C_n x^n$, determine y' and y'' and substitute into the following differential equations. Then obtain the recurrence relation for the unknown coefficients C_n for each case:

5–59 (a) $y'' - 3y = 0$

(b) $(x+2)y'' - xy' + 2y = 0$

5–60 (a) $y'' - 2xy' + 3y = 0$

(b) $y'' + x^2y' - 4y = 0$

5–61 (a) $y'' + y' - 2y = 0$

(b) $(x^2 - 1)y'' + 3xy' = 0$

5–2   Introduction to Power Series Solutions

5–62C When solving a linear second-order differential equation with the method of power series, is it possible to determine all the unknown coefficients C_n? Explain.

Solve the following differential equations using two different methods, one being the method of power series. Show that the two solutions are identical.

5–63 (a) $y'' - y = 0$ (b) $y' - 4y = 0$

5–64 (a) $y'' + 2y' = 0$ (b) $y' - 2xy = 0$

5–65 $y'' + 4y' - 12y = 0$

5–3   Ordinary versus Singular Points

5–66C Why do we distinguish between regular and irregular singular points?

5–67C Consider a linear second-order differential equation whose leading coefficient is one and the other two coefficients are polynomials. What can you say about the ordinary and singular points of this differential equation?

5–68C Describe two ways of determining the radius of convergence of the power series solution of a linear second-order differential equation about an ordinary point.

Identify the ordinary and singular points of the following differential equations. Also, determine whether the singular points are regular or irregular.

5–69 (a) $y'' + 2x^2y' - 5xy = 0$

(b) $(x^2 - 4)y'' + (x-1)y' + xy = 0$

5–70 (a) $y'' + \frac{1}{x}y' + 3y = 0$

(b) $x^2y'' - y' + 3y = 0$

5–71 (a) $(x^2 - 1)y'' - xy' + 2y = 0$

(b) $y'' - (x+2)y' + (2x^2 - 1)y = 0$

5–72 (a) $y'' + y = 0$

(b) $xy'' + \frac{1}{(x+1)^2}y' + \frac{1}{x}y = 0$

Determine the radius of convergence of the series solution of the following differential equations about the specified ordinary point.

5–73 $(x^2 - 4)y'' - x^2y' + y = 0, x_0 = 1$

5–74 $(x^2 + 4)y'' + \frac{1}{x-2}y' + xy = 0, x_0 = 0$

5–75 $x^3y'' + \frac{1}{x^2+1}y' - 2xy = 0, x_0 = 4$

5–76 $(x^2 - 2x + 4)y'' - x^2y = 0, x_0 = 0$

5–77 $(x^2 + 1)y'' + \frac{1}{x}y' - \frac{1}{x-2}y = 0, x_0 = 3$

5–4   Power Series Solutions About an Ordinary Point

5–78C Express the existence and uniqueness theorem for the general solution of a linear, homogeneous, second-order differential equation with variable coefficients about an ordinary point.

Solve the following linear, second-order differential equations about the specified ordinary point using the power series method. Also determine the interval of convergence of the solution.

5–79 $(x^2 - 1)y'' - y = 0, x_0 = 0$

5–80 $(x^2 + 1)y'' + 2xy' - xy = 0, x_0 = 0$

5–81 $y'' - 6xy = 0, x_0 = 1$

5–82 $(1 - x^2)y'' + 4y = 0, x_0 = 0$

5–83 $y'' - \frac{1}{(x-1)^2}y = 0, x_0 = 0$

5–84 $xy'' + 2y = 0, x_0 = 2$

5–85 $xy'' + (1-x)y' + y = 0, x_0 = 1$

5–86 $y'' - 4xy = 0, x_0 = 0$

5–87 $(x-1)^2y'' + (x-1)y' + y = 0, x_0 = 0$

5–88 $y'' + \frac{4x}{x+2}y = 0, x_0 = 0$

5–89 $y'' + y' - 2xy = 0, x_0 = 0$

Solve the following linear, second-order initial-value problems about the ordinary point $x_0 = 0$ using the power series method.

5–90 $y'' - \dfrac{1}{x^2 - 1}y = 0$, $y(0) = 0$, $y'(0) = 0$

5–91 $y'' - 4xy = 0$, $y(0) = 1$, $y'(0) = 0$

5–92 $(x^2 - 1)y'' + xy' - 2y = 0$, $y(0) = 2$, $y'(0) = 2$

5–5 Legendre's Equation and Legendre Polynomials

5–93C What is the relation that enables one to obtain the Legendre polynomials by successive differentiation?

5–94C Knowing the first two Legendre polynomials $P_0(x) = 1$ and $P_1(x) = x$, how can we obtain the remaining Legendre polynomials?

5–95 Show that $P_n(1) = 1$ and $P_n(-1) = (-1)^n$.

5–96 For $m \neq n$, show that

$$\int_{-1}^{1} P_m(x)P_n(x)\,dx = 0$$

This relation is called the orthogonality property of the Legendre polynomials.

5–97 Solve Legendre's equation for $\alpha = 2$, and determine the interval of convergence of this solution.

5–98 Determine the Legendre polynomial $P_4(x)$ using (a) the series expansion, (b) Rodrigues formula, and (c) the recurrence relation.

5–99 Determine the Legendre polynomial $P_5(x)$ using (a) the series expansion, (b) Rodrigues formula, and (c) the recurrence relation.

5–6 Series Solution About a Regular Singular Point

5–100C When does the second linearly independent solution of a linear, homogeneous, second-order equation about a regular singular point involve a logarithmic term?

5–101C When the roots of the indicial equation of a linear, homogeneous, second-order differential equation with variable coefficients differ by an integer, what will happen if we assume the solution corresponding to the smaller root does not involve a logarithmic term (i.e., $C = 0$)?

5–102C Describe two ways of obtaining the indicial equation of a linear, second-order differential equation.

5–103C Explain how we can shift a singular point x_0 of a differential equation to the origin.

Show that the point $x = 0$ is a regular singular point of the following differential equations and determine the roots of their indicial equations r_1 and r_2.

5–104 (a) $y'' - \dfrac{4}{x}y' + \dfrac{1}{x^2}y = 0$

   (b) $x(1 - x)y'' + (1 + x)y' - 3xy = 0$

5–105 (a) $xy'' + (x^2 - 1)y' - \dfrac{2}{x}y = 0$

   (b) $x(x^2 - 1)y'' + y' + \dfrac{2}{x}y = 0$

5–106 (a) $x^2y'' + y = 0$

   (b) $y'' + \dfrac{x - 1}{x}y' - y = 0$

5–107 (a) $xy'' - 3xy' + \dfrac{4}{x}y = 0$

   (b) $x^2y'' + 2xy' + y = 0$

5–108 (a) $2x^2y'' - 3xy' - y = 0$

   (b) $(x^2 - 1)y'' - 4y' + \dfrac{1}{x^2}y = 0$

Determine the form of the two linearly independent solutions of the following linear, second-order differential equations about the regular singular point $x_0 = 0$ without solving for them. Also, determine the range of x values over which these solutions will converge.

5–109 (a) $y'' - \dfrac{3}{x}y' + \dfrac{1}{x^2}y = 0$

   (b) $x(1 - x)y'' + (1 + x)y' - 3xy = 0$

5–110 (a) $xy'' - (x^2 - 1)y' - \dfrac{2}{x}y = 0$

   (b) $x(x^2 - 1)y'' + y' - \dfrac{1}{x}y = 0$

5–111 (a) $x^2y'' - 6y = 0$

   (b) $y'' + \dfrac{x - 1}{x}y' - y = 0$

5–112 (a) $xy'' - 3xy' - \dfrac{4}{x}y = 0$

   (b) $x^2y'' - 2xy' + 2y = 0$

5–113 (a) $2x^2y'' - 3xy' - y = 0$

   (b) $(x^2 - 4)y'' - 4y' + \dfrac{3}{x^2}y = 0$

Determine the general solutions of the following linear, second-order differential equations about the regular singular point $x_0 = 0$.

5–114 (a) $y'' - \dfrac{3}{x}y' + \dfrac{1}{x^2}y = 0$

   (b) $x(1 - x)y'' + (1 + x)y' - 3xy = 0$

5–115 (a) $xy'' + (x^2 - 1)y' - \dfrac{2}{x}y = 0$

   (b) $x(x^2 - 1)y'' + y' - \dfrac{1}{x}y = 0$

5–116 (a) $xy'' - 3xy' - \dfrac{4}{x}y = 0$

(b) $x^2y'' - 2xy' + 2y = 0$

5–117 (a) $2x^2y'' - 3xy' - y = 0$

(b) $(x^2 - 4)y'' - 4y' + \dfrac{3}{x^2}y = 0$

Determine the general solutions of the following second-order Euler differential equations using (a) the standard method and (b) the method of Frobenius about the regular singular point $x_0 = 0$.

5–118 (a) $2x^2y'' + 6xy' - y = 0$

(b) $y'' - \dfrac{12}{x^2}y = 0$

5–119 (a) $x^2y'' + 5xy' + 4y = 0$

(b) $3x^2y'' + 2xy' - 4y = 0$

5–120 (a) $x^2y'' - 2xy' - 10y = 0$

(b) $x^2y'' - \dfrac{3}{4}y = 0$

5–7 Bessel's Equation and Bessel Functions

5–121C In what ways do the Bessel functions of the first and the second kind differ?

5–122C How is the Bessel function of order one-half related to sin x? How do they differ?

5–123C How is the Gamma function defined? How is the factorial function related to the Gamma function?

5–124C How does the general behavior of modified Bessel functions differ from the behavior of Bessel functions of the same kind and order?

5–125 Using the method of Frobenius, determine the first linearly independent solution of Bessel's equation of order 2. Compare it with $J_2(x)$.

5–126 Using the method of Frobenius, determine the general solution of Bessel's equation of order three-halves.

5–127 For positive integer values of v, show that $J_v(x) = (-1)^n J_{-v}(x)$.

5–128 Using the method of Frobenius, determine the general solution of modified Bessel's equation of order zero.

Determine the following integrals involving Bessel functions.

5–129 (a) $\displaystyle\int xJ_1(x)\,dx$ (b) $\displaystyle\int \dfrac{1}{x^3}J_4(x)\,dx$

5–130 (a) $\displaystyle\int xJ_4(x)\,dx$ (b) $\displaystyle\int J_1^2(x)\,dx$

5–8 Computer Methods

Solve the following problems, using the software of your choice.

5–131 Problem 5–63

5–132 Problem 5–64

5–133 Problem 5–65

5–134 Problem 5–79

5–135 Problem 5–80

5–136 Problem 5–81

5–137 Problem 5–82

5–138 Problem 5–83

5–139 Problem 5–84

5–140 Problem 5–85

5–141 Problem 5–86

5–142 Problem 5–87

5–143 Problem 5–88

5–144 Problem 5–89

5–145 Problem 5–90

5–146 Problem 5–91

5–147 Problem 5–92

5–148 Problem 5–114

5–149 Problem 5–115

5–150 Problem 5–116

5–151 Problem 5–117

5–152 Problem 5–118

5–153 Problem 5–119

5–154 Problem 5–120

6

SYSTEMS OF LINEAR DIFFERENTIAL EQUATIONS: SCALAR APPROACH

So far, we have considered *single* differential equations in a *single* dependent variable. Although many problems encountered in sciences and engineering involve only one dependent variable, many others involve two or more dependent variables, each a function of a single independent variable. Such problems result in a *system* of ordinary differential equations. Here, a **system** means a set of two or more *coupled* differential equations. The term *coupled* means that the equations cannot be solved separately; they must be solved simultaneously. The independent variable is usually time, and it is denoted by t. The dependent variables are customarily denoted by $x, y, z, \ldots$ or $x_1, x_2, x_3, \ldots, x_n$. Primes as well as overdots are used to denote differentiation with respect to t.

In this chapter, we will focus on systems of *linear* differential equations with *constant coefficients*, since solutions for such systems always can be found in terms of elementary functions. Also, we will usually consider a system of two first-order differential equations in two dependent variables throughout the discussions to keep complexities to a minimum. But the methods presented can be extended to a system with any number of equations of any order, since the same principles apply to systems with more equations and any nth-order differential equation can be expressed as a system of n first-order differential equations.

We will start this chapter with an overview of systems of differential equations and demonstrate how such systems arise in practice. This is followed by the *method of elimination*, which is a way of converting a system of n first-order differential equations into a single nth-order equation that can be solved using the techniques discussed in the previous chapters. Then we will present the *method of eigenvalues*, which is a systematic way of solving linear differential equations with constant coefficients. It closely resembles the solution of a single differential equation with constant coefficients in which the characteristic equation and its characteristic roots play a major role. We will see that eigenvalues are the same as the characteristic roots.

6–1 · AN OVERVIEW OF SYSTEMS OF DIFFERENTIAL EQUATIONS

You are probably familiar with systems of equations from algebra. But the ones you have seen did not involve any differential quantities or derivatives. That is, they were a system of *algebraic equations* such as

$$x + y = 5$$
$$3x - 5y = -7$$
(6–1)

Systems of *differential equations*, on the other hand, involve the derivatives of two or more dependent variables with respect to a single independent variable, usually time t (Figure 6–1).

A system of three differential equations in three unknown functions x, y, and z with t as the independent variable:

$$x' = 2x - 3y + z + t^3$$
$$y' = x + tz + 1$$
$$z' = 4x - 3xy - t^3z$$

FIGURE 6–1

A system of differential equations involves the derivatives of two or more dependent variables.

EXAMPLE 6–1   A System of Equations Describing a Mixing Process

Consider two brine tanks each containing 1000 L(liters) of brine connected as shown in Figure 6–2. At any time t, the first and the second tank contain $x_1(t)$ and $x_2(t)$ kg of salt, respectively. The brine concentration in each tank is kept uniform by continuous stirring. Brine containing 0.1 kg of salt per liter is entering the first tank at a rate of 15 L/min, and fresh water is entering the second tank at a rate of 5 L/min. Brine is pumped from the first tank to the second one at a rate of 50 L/min and from the second tank to the first one at a rate of 35 L/min. Brine is discharged from the second tank at a rate of 20 L/min. Obtain the differential equations, in terms of x_1 and x_2, that govern the salt content in each tank as a function of time.

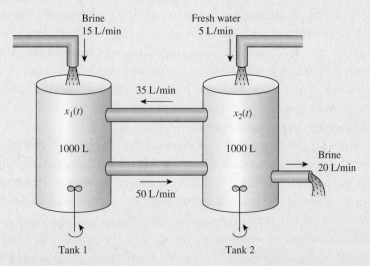

FIGURE 6–2

Mixing in two brine tanks.

SOLUTION We assume that the liquid volume does not change when the salt is dissolved in it. We also observe that the total volume of the brine in each tank remains constant at 1000 L since the incoming and the outgoing volume flow rates for each tank are equal. Therefore, each liter of brine in the first tank contains $x_1/1000$ kg of salt, and salt leaves the first tank at a rate of $50(x_1/1000)$ kg/min.

Considering that each liter of brine in the second tank contains $x_2/1000$ kg of salt, the rate at which salt leaves the second tank and enters the first one is $35(x_2/1000)$ kg/min. In addition, new brine enters the first tank at a rate of 1.5 kg/min, since each liter of the new brine contains 0.1 kg of salt. A similar argument can be given for the second tank. Then the rates of change of the salt content of each tank (in kg/min) can be expressed as.

$$\frac{dx_1}{dt} = 1.5 - 50\frac{x_1}{1000} + 35\frac{x_2}{1000} \tag{6-2a}$$

$$\frac{dx_2}{dt} = 0 - 50\frac{x_1}{1000} - 55\frac{x_2}{1000} \tag{6-2b}$$

This is a system of two first-order differential equations in two unknowns $x_1(t)$ and $x_2(t)$. They are coupled and thus need to be solved simultaneously, since each equation contains both unknowns.

Systems Containing Higher-Order Derivatives

In Example 6–1, application of the appropriate physical principle (conservation of mass) resulted in a system of first-order equations. However, other physical principles can result in a system of higher-order equations. For example, Newton's laws of motion can produce systems containing second-order derivatives. For example, the equations

$$\begin{align}
x'' &= 2y' - 3x - 2x' + y + 5e^t \\
y'' &= 3x' + x - y' + 6y + 2
\end{align} \tag{6-3}$$

form a system of two second-order differential equations in two unknown functions $x(t)$ and $y(t)$. Note that each equation involves both unknowns, and thus, we need to solve both equations simultaneously (just as we need to solve the algebraic equations in Equation 6–1 simultaneously) to determine the unknown functions. The solutions obtained must satisfy both equations over the specified interval of t.

The differential equations that make up a system may be of different orders. For example, all the equations in a system may be of second-order, as in Equations 6–3, or some of them may be first-order while the rest are second or higher-order.

There are two approaches to dealing with systems of equations. The preferred method depends on the specific application and on what we need to find. In some cases it is easier to obtain the solution by reducing the system to a single, higher-order equation, and then use the methods of the previous chapters to solve the equation. This is the method of elimination, which is discussed in Section 6–3. The disadvantage of this method is that it cannot be generalized.

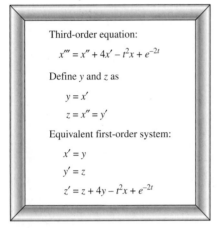

Third-order equation:

$$x''' = x'' + 4x' - t^2x + e^{-2t}$$

Define y and z as

$$y = x'$$
$$z = x'' = y'$$

Equivalent first-order system:

$$x' = y$$
$$y' = z$$
$$z' = z + 4y - t^2x + e^{-2t}$$

FIGURE 6–3

A higher-order differential equation always can be transformed into a system of first-order equations by defining each order of the derivatives (except the highest order) as new variables.

The other method is to expand the system to a set of first-order equations. The advantage of this approach is that it leads to a general method that is applicable to any number of equations. This enables it to be used as the basis for numerical solution methods, which will be covered in Chapter 9. We introduce this method (called the method of eigenvalues) in Section 6–4 and then expand on it in Chapter 7, using matrix methods to exploit the general nature of the method.

Any nth-order differential equation always can be transformed into a system of n first-order differential equations (Figure 6–3). To demonstrate how this transformation is done, consider the third-order differential equation

$$x''' = 2x'' - 3x' + 5x + 7t^2 \tag{6-4}$$

which is to be converted to a system of three first-order equations. To accomplish this, we define three new variables as

$$\begin{align} x_1 &= x \\ x_2 &= x' = x_1' \\ x_3 &= x'' = x_2' \end{align} \tag{6-5}$$

That is, we define the unknown function and each of its derivatives (except the one of the highest order) as new variables. Noting that $x_3' = x'''$, the substitution of these definitions into the original differential equation (Equation 6–4) gives $x_3' = 2x_3 - 3x_2 + 5x_1 + 7t^2$, which is a first-order differential equation in three unknown functions. This equation, together with the definitions of x_2 and x_3, form a system of three first-order equations:

$$\begin{align} x_1' &= x_2 \\ x_2' &= x_3 \\ x_3' &= 2x_3 - 3x_2 + 5x_1 + 7t^2 \end{align} \tag{6-6}$$

This system of three first-order equations in three unknowns is equivalent to the original third-order equation in one unknown. The procedure just described is quite general and can be applied to any differential equation of any order. The form obtained this way is known as the *Cauchy* or *state variable* form.

As we will see, defining new variables according to the scheme in Equation 6–5 is not the only way to define a new set of variables, but it is perhaps the most straightforward way.

EXAMPLE 6–2   **Converting Higher-Order Systems to a First-Order System**

Convert the following system of equations with the specified initial conditions into an equivalent first-order system.

$$\begin{align} x'' &= 2x - 3y + x' + f(t), & x(0) = 0, \; x'(0) = 1 \\ y'' &= -x + y + 2x' + g(t), & y(0) = 0, \; y'(0) = 2 \end{align}$$

SOLUTION This is a system of two second-order equations in two unknowns. We expect the equivalent first-order system to consist of four equations in four unknowns, since each second-order equation reduces to a system of two first-order equations. First we define the new four dependent variables as

$$x_1 = x$$
$$x_2 = x' = x_1'$$
$$x_3 = y$$
$$x_4 = y' = x_3'$$

Substituting these definitions into the given differential equations yields

$$x_1' = x_2, \qquad\qquad x_1(0) = 0$$
$$x_2' = 2x_1 - 3x_3 + x_2 + f(t), \qquad x_2(0) = 1$$
$$x_3' = x_4, \qquad\qquad x_3(0) = 0$$
$$x_4' = -x_1 + x_3 + 2x_2 + g(t), \qquad x_4(0) = 2$$

This is a system of four first-order equations in four unknowns and is equivalent to the original given system. Note that the sum of the order of the equations in both systems is equal to four. Note also that the original and transformed equations are of the same type. Since the equations in the original system are linear with constant coefficients, so are the equations in the transformed system.

Be aware that it may not be necessary to transform a single higher-order equation into a first-order system if it can be solved readily by any of the available methods. However, many higher-order differential equations encountered in practice are nonlinear; some of these only can be solved approximately by numerical methods. As you will see in Chapter 9, it is standard procedure to convert the given higher-order equations into a system of first-order equations.

Classification of Systems of Equations

Most definitions associated with a single differential equation can be extended to a system of differential equations. There is also a close parallel between the systems of algebraic equations and systems of differential equations. For example, a system of algebraic equations is linear if every equation in the system is linear. Therefore, the equations

$$x + 2y = 5$$
$$2x - 3y^2 = -10 \tag{6-7}$$

form a nonlinear system of algebraic equations, since the second equation is nonlinear.

A system of differential equations is said to be **linear** if every single equation in the system is linear. A system is said to be **nonlinear** even if only one equation involves a single nonlinear term (Figure 6–4). That is, a system of linear equations cannot involve any nonlinear functions of any of the dependent variables. A linear system of differential equations is said to be **homogeneous** if *every* single equation in the system is homogeneous. The system is said to be nonhomogeneous even if only one equation involves a nonhomogeneous term (Figure 6–5).

$$x' = 2x - y + z + t^3 \quad \text{(linear)}$$
$$y' = x + z + 1 \quad \text{(linear)}$$
$$z' = 4x \boxed{- 3xy} - t^2 z \quad \text{(nonlinear)}$$

Nonlinear term

FIGURE 6–4

A system is said to be *nonlinear* even if a single equation involves a single nonlinear term.

$$x' = 2x - y + z \quad \text{(homogeneous)}$$
$$y' = x + t^2 y + z \quad \text{(homogeneous)}$$
$$z' = -3x - y \boxed{+ 3t} \quad \text{(nonhomogeneous)}$$

Nonhomogeneous term

FIGURE 6–5

A system is said to be *nonhomogeneous* even if a single equation involves a single nonhomogeneous term.

A *linear* system of two equations can be expressed in the general form as

$$x' = P_1(t)x + Q_1(t)y + R_1(t)$$
$$y' = P_2(t)x + Q_2(t)y + R_2(t)$$

(6–8)

where $R_1(t)$ and $R_2(t)$ are the nonhomogeneous terms. A *linear homogeneous* system of two equations can be expressed in the general form as

$$x' = P_1(t)x + Q_1(t)y$$
$$y' = P_2(t)x + Q_2(t)y$$

(6–9)

Note that a linear system does not involve any nonlinear functions (powers, products, or transcendental functions) of the dependent variables or their derivatives (such as x^2, xy, xx', or $\sin y$). A homogeneous system contains only homogeneous equations.

Finally, a system of differential equations is said to have **constant coefficients** if every equation in the system in the standard form has constant coefficients. The system is said to have **variable coefficients** even if only one equation involves a variable coefficient (a function of the independent variable), as shown in Figure 6–6.

A linear system of two equations with constant coefficients can be expressed in the general form as

$$x' = a_1x + b_1y + R_1(t)$$
$$y' = a_2x + b_2y + R_2(t)$$

(6–10)

where a_1, a_2, b_1, and b_2 are constants. Note that the nonhomogeneous terms may still be a function of the independent variable.

You may be tempted to say that the general form of the equation for x' in Equation 6–10 should also include a term in y', and the general form of the equation for y' should also include a term in x'. That is, the general form of a linear system of two equations with constant coefficients should be

$$x' = a_1x + b_1y + c_1y' + R_1(t)$$
$$y' = a_2x + b_2y + c_2x' + R_2(t)$$

(6–11)

But we can easily eliminate the c_1y' term in the first equation by using the y' expression in the second equation. Likewise, we can eliminate the c_2x' term in the second equation by using the x' expression in the first equation. After rearranging, the system will resemble Equations 6–10. Therefore, there is no need to include the derivatives of the dependent variables on the right side of the equations in a first-order system. Doing so would only complicate things unnecessarily.

In algebra, you probably ignored systems of nonlinear equations and concentrated on linear systems only. You did this not because nonlinear systems are not important, but because such systems are often impossible to solve analytically. Of course they can be solved numerically with a computer by using a suitable numerical solution technique, but it would require a certain level of sophistication in numerical methods.

This is also the case with systems of differential equations. Systems of *linear* differential equations can be solved using a systematic procedure, but no such procedure exists for systems of *nonlinear* equations. Even linear

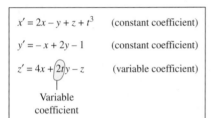

$x' = 2x - y + z + t^3$ (constant coefficient)

$y' = -x + 2y - 1$ (constant coefficient)

$z' = 4x + 2ty - z$ (variable coefficient)

Variable
coefficient

FIGURE 6–6

A system is said to have variable coefficients even if a single equation involves a single term with a variable coefficient.

systems will cause considerable difficulty if they involve variable coefficients since the solutions in such cases typically involve infinite series. Therefore, the emphasis in this chapter will be on *linear* systems of differential equations with *constant* coefficients.

Section Review

Problems Denoted with a C are Conceptual Problems for Discussion

6–1C When is a system of differential equations linear, and when is it nonlinear?

6–2C When is a system of linear differential equations homogeneous, and when is it nonhomogeneous?

6–3 Reduce the following single differential equations to a system of first-order equations (x is the dependent variable and t is the independent variable).

(a) $x''' + 3xx' = 6t^2$ (b) $x''' - 3x = e^{2t}$

(*Answers*: (a) Defining $x_1 = x, x_2 = x' = x_1'$ and $x_3 = x'' = x_2'$ gives $x_1' = x_2$, $x_2' = x_3$, and $x_3' = -3x_1x_2 + 6t^2$, respectively.

(b) Defining $x_1 = x, x_2 = x' = x_1'$, and $x_3 = x'' = x_2'$ gives $x_1' = x_2, x_2' = x_3$, and $x_3' = 3x_1 + e^{2t}$, respectively.)

6–4 Reduce the following system of differential equations to a system of first-order equations (t is the independent variable).

$$x''' = 3y' + \cos t, x(\pi) = 0, x'(\pi) = 4, x''(\pi) = -2$$
$$y'' = 2ty' - x + e^t, y(0) = 2, y'(0) = 1$$

(*Answers*: Defining $x_1 = x, x_2 = x' = x_1', x_3 = x'' = x_2', x_4 = y$, and $x_5 = y' = x_4'$, gives $x_1' = x_2, \ x_2' = x_3, \ x_3' = 3x_5 + \cos t, \ x_4' = x_5$, and $x_5' = 2tx_5 - x_1 + e^t$, respectively, with initial conditions $x_1(\pi) = 0, \ x_2(\pi) = 4, \ x_3(\pi) = -2$, $x_4(0) = 2$, and $x_5(0) = 1$.)

6–5 Determine if the following system of differential equations is (a) linear or nonlinear, (b) homogeneous or nonhomogeneous, and (c) whether it has constant or variable coefficients.

$$x''' = 2xy - y' + \cos t$$
$$y'' = 2ty' - x + e^t$$

(*Answer*: The system is nonlinear due to the term $2xy$, nonhomogeneous due to either $\cos t$ or e^t, and has variable coefficients due to the term $2ty'$.)

6–2 ▪ ORIGIN OF SYSTEMS OF DIFFERENTIAL EQUATIONS

Systems of differential equations arise naturally in the analysis of many practical problems that involve two or more physically coupled systems instead of a simple single system. The dependent variables in such systems are interdependent (they depend on each other as well as on the independent variable), and they need to be determined simultaneously. But before we discuss the theory and solution techniques associated with the systems of differential equations, we will demonstrate how such equations arise with a few examples.

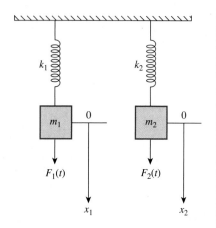

FIGURE 6–7

Two uncoupled masses.

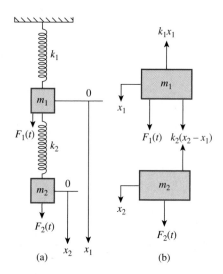

FIGURE 6–8

(a) Two coupled masses. (b) Free-body diagrams for the case where $x_1 > 0$, $x_2 > 0$, and $x_2 > x_1$.

EXAMPLE 6–3   Uncoupled Mechanical Vibrations

Two masses m_1 and m_2 are suspended by two linear springs whose spring constants are k_1, and k_2. The masses are subjected to external forces $F_1(t)$ and $F_2(t)$, as shown in Figure 6–7. Letting $x_1(t)$ and $x_2(t)$ denote the positions of the two masses at any time relative to their equilibrium positions (the position they assume under the influence of their own weight with no external force applied) and neglecting any damping and friction, obtain the differential equations that govern the motion of the two masses.

SOLUTION   The mechanical vibrations of a single mass were discussed in detail in Chapter 3 under various conditions. Considering that there is no damping and taking the downward direction as the positive direction for both x_1 and x_2, the differential equation for the motion of each mass can be expressed as (see Equation 3–92)

$$m_1 \frac{d^2 x_1}{dt^2} + k_1 x_1 = F_1(t) \tag{6–12a}$$

and

$$m_2 \frac{d^2 x_2}{dt^2} + k_2 x_2 = F_2(t) \tag{6–12b}$$

where x_1 and x_2 are the two unknown functions (the dependent variables) and t is time (the independent variable).

Equations 6–12 form a system of two equations with two unknowns. More precisely, they are two equations each of which contain a single unknown. Therefore, these two equations are independent, and they can be solved independently of each other. That is, the first equation can be solved for x_1 and the second one for x_2—like two unrelated equations. This is not surprising, since the motions of the two masses are completely independent and the motion of one mass in no way affects the motion of the other. Equations 6–12 are said to be *uncoupled*, since each unknown function appears in one equation only. Obviously, we are not interested in such systems in this chapter, since no new information is needed to solve systems of uncoupled equations.

EXAMPLE 6–4   Coupled Mechanical Vibrations

Reconsider the two spring-mass systems discussed in the previous example, but this time let them be attached to each other in series, as shown in Figure 6–8. Neglecting any friction, obtain the differential equations that govern the motion of the two masses.

SOLUTION   Again, let x_1 and x_2 denote the positions of the masses m_1 and m_2 relative to their equilibrium positions (the position they assume under the influence of their own weight with no external force applied). We also take the downward direction as the positive direction for both x_1, and x_2. Remembering that the force applied by a linear spring is proportional to the distance it is stretched (or compressed) from its equilibrium position, we have

$$F_{\text{spring 1}} = k_1 x_1 \tag{6–13a}$$

$$F_{\text{spring 2}} = k_2 (x_2 - x_1) \tag{6–13b}$$

The second spring will be stretched (or compressed) by an amount equal to the distance, the second mass is displaced relative to the first mass. Note that if both m_1 and m_2 move by the same amount in the same direction, then $x_1 = x_2$ and thus $F_{spring\,2} = 0$, since the second spring will not be stretched (or compressed) at all. If the first mass remains stationary ($x_1 = 0$), then $F_{spring\,2} = k_2 x_2$, as expected.

It is important to note that the weight mg of each mass cancels the spring forces that exist in the springs when the two masses are in equilibrium. Thus, these forces and the weights do not appear in the equations of motion. This is true only if the displacements x_1 and x_2 are measured from the equilibrium positions.

The free-body diagrams are shown in Figure 6–8b under the assumptions that $x_1 > 0$, $x_2 > 0$, and $x_2 > x_1$. Applying Newton's second law of motion to each of the masses gives the following equations of motion:

$$m_1 \frac{d^2 x_1}{dt^2} + k_1 x_1 = k_2(x_2 - x_1) + F_1(t) \tag{6-14}$$

and

$$m_2 \frac{d^2 x_2}{dt^2} + k_2(x_2 - x_1) = F_2(t) \tag{6-15}$$

Any attempt to solve the first equation alone for $x_1(t)$ would fail, since that equation now involves another unknown function $x_2(t)$. Likewise, we cannot solve the second equation for $x_2(t)$ either, because it involves another unknown function $x_1(t)$. We can, however, solve these two equations simultaneously for the two unknowns $x_1(t)$ and $x_2(t)$, as you will see later in this chapter. Equations 6–14 and 6–15 are said to be *coupled*, since each equation involves more than one unknown function. These are the kind of equations we will learn how to solve in this chapter.

EXAMPLE 6–5   **An Electrical Circuit**

Consider the electrical circuit shown in Figure 6–9, which consists of two closed loops. Obtain the differential equations that govern the currents I_1 and I_2 flowing through the inductors L_1 and L_2, respectively.

SOLUTION   When analyzing electrical circuits with several loops, it is difficult to know ahead of time the actual direction of current flowing through the various components. Therefore, it is often necessary to assume the current to flow in a certain direction before the analysis. A negative value obtained for the current indicates that the actual direction of current is the opposite of the assumed direction.

We assume the currents I_1 and I_2 flow in the indicated directions. Then the current through the resistor R becomes the difference $I_1 - I_2$ or $I_2 - I_1$, depending on the loop analyzed. You will recall from Chapter 3 that the sum of the voltage drops in any loop is equal to the applied voltage in the loop.

Applying this principle to the first and the second loops gives the following differential equations for the two unknown functions I_1 and I_2:

$$L_1 \frac{dI_1}{dt} + R(I_1 - I_2) = E(t) \tag{6-16a}$$

$$L_2 \frac{dI_2}{dt} + R(I_2 - I_1) = 0 \tag{6-16b}$$

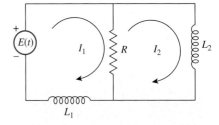

FIGURE 6–9

An *RL* circuit with two coupled loops.

or after rearranging,

$$L_1\frac{dI_1}{dt} + RI_1 = RI_2 + E(t) \tag{6–17a}$$

$$L_2\frac{dI_2}{dt} + RI_2 = RI_1 \tag{6–17b}$$

This is a system of two first-order differential equations in two unknowns. Note that since each equation contains both unknowns, they are coupled and thus need to be solved simultaneously.

Next, we discuss the methods of solving linear systems. First we will introduce the method of elimination, which is a way of converting a system of n first-order differential equations into a single nth-order equation that can be solved using the techniques discussed in the previous chapters. Then we will present the method of eigenvalues, which is a systematic way of solving linear differential equations with constant coefficients. It closely resembles the solution of a single differential equation with constant coefficients.

Section Review

6–6 Figure 6–8b shows the free-body diagrams for the case where $x_1 > 0$, $x_2 > 0$, and $x_2 > x_1$. Draw the free-body diagrams for the case where $x_1 > 0$, $x_2 > 0$, but $x_2 < x_1$. Show that the corresponding equations of motion are identical to Equations 6–14 and 6–15.

6–7 Refer to the circuit shown in Figure 6–9. Let the current through R be denoted I_a, the current through L_1 be denoted I_b, and the current through L_2 be denoted I_c. Apply Kirchhoff's circuit laws to derive the circuit equations and show that they reduce to Equations 6–17.

6–3 · METHOD OF ELIMINATION

The **method of elimination** is the simplest and the most elementary method for solving systems of differential equations. It is based on converting a system of differential equations into a single higher-order equation in a *single* dependent variable by eliminating all other dependent variables one by one.

This method is analogous to solving a system of algebraic equations by eliminating all of the unknowns until there remains a single unknown in a single equation. For example, the algebraic system

$$3x + 2y = 7$$
$$5x - y = 3 \tag{6–18}$$

can be reduced to a single equation in x by solving the second equation for y which yields $y = 5x - 3$ and substituting this into the first equation to eliminate y. It gives (see Figure 6–10)

$$3x + 2(5x - 3) = 7 \tag{6–19}$$

which readily can be solved for x to yield $x = 1$. Once x is available, the other unknown y can be determined by substituting the value of x into either equation and solving it for y to obtain $y = 2$.

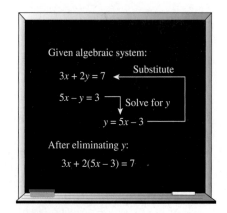

FIGURE 6–10

Application of the method of elimination to an algebraic system.

Now consider a system of two first-order linear differential equations with constant coefficients in the dependent variables x and y,

$$x' = a_1x + b_1y + R_1(t) \tag{6-20a}$$

$$y' = a_2x + b_2y + R_2(t) \tag{6-20b}$$

Solving the first equation for y and differentiating it with respect to the independent variable t yields

$$y = \frac{1}{b_1}[x' - a_1x - R_1(t)], \tag{6-21}$$

and

$$y' = \frac{1}{b_1}[x'' - a_1x' - R_1'(t)] \tag{6-22}$$

Now substituting these relations for y and y' into the second differential equation (Equation 6–20b) and rearranging gives

$$x'' - (a_1 + b_2)x' + (a_1b_2 - a_2b_1)x = R_1'(t) - b_2R_1(t) + b_1R_2(t) \tag{6-23}$$

which is a second-order linear equation with constant coefficients. This equation can be solved using the procedures described in Chapter 3. The characteristic equation of the related homogeneous equation is

$$\lambda^2 - (a_1 + b_2)\lambda + a_1b_2 - a_2b_1 = 0 \tag{6-24}$$

The homogeneous solution is constructed using the two roots of this equation. The general solution for x is determined by combining this homogeneous solution with a particular solution which satisfies the nonhomogeneous equation.

Once $x(t)$ is available, the other unknown function $y(t)$ can be determined by substituting the $x(t)$ and $x'(t)$ expressions into the y relation in Equation 6–21. We now demonstrate the procedure just described with an example.

EXAMPLE 6–6   Method of Elimination

Use the method of elimination to solve the following system of two first-order differential equations with the specified initial conditions.

$$x' = 4x + 6y, \quad x(0) = 1$$
$$y' = -3x - 5y, \quad y(0) = 0 \tag{6-25}$$

SOLUTION This is a system of two linear, homogeneous first-order equations with constant coefficients. To find its equivalent second-order linear, homogeneous equation with constant coefficients in a single unknown function, we solve the first equation for y and differentiate it with respect to t as

$$y = \frac{1}{6}x' - \frac{4}{6}x \tag{6-26}$$

and

$$y' = \frac{1}{6}x'' - \frac{4}{6}x' \tag{6-27}$$

We now substitute these relations into the second differential equation to eliminate y and y'. We obtain

$$\frac{1}{6}x'' - \frac{4}{6}x' = -3x - 5\left(\frac{1}{6}x' - \frac{4}{6}x\right)$$

or

$$x'' + x' - 2x = 0 \qquad \text{(6–28)}$$

which is a second-order, linear, homogeneous equation with constant coefficients (Figure 6–11). Its characteristic equation is $\lambda^2 + \lambda - 2 = 0$ whose roots are $\lambda_1 = 1$ and $\lambda_2 = -2$, which are real and distinct. Thus, the general solution of Equation 6–28 is $x = C_1 e^t + C_2 e^{-2t}$. The other unknown function y is determined by substituting the x and x' expressions into Equation 6–26 to obtain

$$
\begin{aligned}
y &= \frac{1}{6}x' - \frac{4}{6}x \\
&= \frac{1}{6}(C_1 e^t - 2C_2 e^{-2t}) - \frac{4}{6}(C_1 e^t + C_2 e^{-2t}) \\
&= -\frac{1}{2}C_1 e^t - C_2 e^{-2t}
\end{aligned}
$$

Therefore, the general solution of the given system of two first-order equations is

$$x = C_1 e^t + C_2 e^{-2t}$$
$$y = -\frac{1}{2}C_1 e^t - C_2 e^{-2t}$$

The arbitrary constants C_1 and C_2 are determined by applying the initial conditions:

$$x(0) = 1 \rightarrow C_1 + C_2 = 1$$
$$y(0) = 0 \rightarrow -\frac{1}{2}C_1 - C_2 = 0$$

They give $C_1 = 2$ and $C_2 = -1$, and the solutions of the given system of two first-order initial-value problems are determined to be

$$x = 2e^t - e^{-2t}$$
$$y = -e^t + e^{-2t}$$

We can check by direct substitution that these solutions satisfy both differential equations and the initial conditions. Also, we could have solved this problem by eliminating the variable x instead of y.

Note that if all of the equations in a system have constant coefficients, then the single higher-order equation obtained by the method of elimination also will have constant coefficients (Figure 6–12).

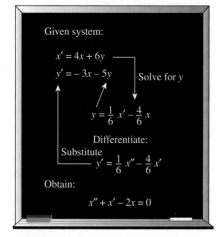

FIGURE 6–11

Transforming a system of two first-order equations into a simple second-order equation by the method of elimination.

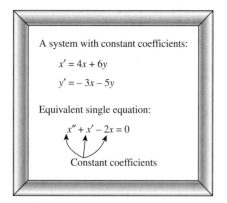

FIGURE 6–12

An example illustrating that, if all the equations in a system have constant coefficients, the single higher-order equation obtained by the method of elimination also will have constant coefficients.

EXAMPLE 6–7   Two Connected Tanks

The cylindrical tanks shown in Figure 6–13 have bottom areas A_1 and A_2. The mass inflow rate $q_{mi}(t)$ from the flow source is a given function of time. The outlet discharges to atmospheric pressure. The pipes are modeled as linear resistances. This means that the mass flow rate through the pipe is proportional to the pressure difference across the ends of the pipe and inversely proportional to the resistance R. The value of the resistance R depends partly on the properties of the fluid and the length and diameter of the pipe. Methods for calculating R can be found in texts on fluid mechanics.

Develop a second-order model of the liquid height h_1 for the case where the pipes are identical so that $R_1 = R_2 = R$ and where the second tank has three times the bottom area, so $A_1 = A$ and $A_2 = 3A$. If the inflow rate is shut off, how long will it take for the tanks to empty? Will the heights oscillate?

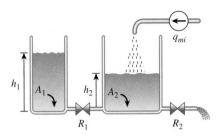

FIGURE 6–13

Two connected tanks.

SOLUTION   The pressure due to a column of liquid of height h is $\rho g h$, where ρ is the liquid mass density, which we take to be constant. Conservation of mass applied to tank 1 gives

$$\frac{d}{dt}(\rho A_1 h_1) = \rho A_1 \frac{dh_1}{dt} = -\frac{\rho g}{R_1}(h_1 - h_2)$$

For tank 2,

$$\frac{d}{dt}(\rho A_2 h_2) = \rho A_2 \frac{dh_2}{dt} = q_{mi} + \frac{\rho g}{R_1}(h_1 - h_2) - \frac{\rho g}{R_2}h_2$$

Substituting $R_1 = R_2 = R$, $A_1 = A$, and $A_2 = 3A$ into the two equations and defining $B = g/RA$ gives

$$\frac{dh_1}{dt} = -B(h_1 - h_2) \tag{a}$$

$$3\frac{dh_2}{dt} = \frac{q_{mi}}{\rho A} + Bh_1 - 2Bh_2 \tag{b}$$

These can be combined into a single equation in terms of h_1 as follows. Comparing these equations with Equation 6–20 and using Equation 6–23, we obtain

$$3\frac{d^2 h_1}{dt^2} + 5B\frac{h_1}{dt} + B^2 h_1 = B\frac{q_{mi}}{\rho A}$$

From Equation 6–24, the characteristic equation is

$$3\lambda^2 + 5B\lambda + B^2 = 0$$

The roots are $\lambda = -1.43B$ and $\lambda = -0.232B$. The homogeneous solution is

$$h_1(t) = C_1 e^{-1.43Bt} + C_2 e^{-0.232Bt}$$

The two constants can be evaluated from the initial conditions $h_1(0)$ and $\dot{h}_1(0)$, which can be found from Equation (a) if $h_2(0)$ is known. Because the roots are real, the liquid heights will not oscillate if the inflow rate q_{mi} is zero or a constant, for example. The term $C_1 e^{-1.43Bt}$ will decay faster than the second term. Because $e^{-t/\tau} \leq 0.02$ for $t \geq 4\tau$, we can predict that, if q_{mi} is zero, the tanks will be almost empty for $t > 4(1/0.232B) = 17.241/B = 17.241RA/g$. Thus, the larger the tank area A or the resistance R, the longer it will take for the tanks to empty.

We make the following important observations from these examples.

1. A system of two linear, homogeneous first-order equations with constant coefficients in two dependent variables can be expressed as a second-order, linear, homogeneous equation with constant coefficients in either variable.

   In general, a system of n first-order linear, homogeneous equations with constant coefficients in n dependent variables can be expressed as an nth-order, linear, homogeneous equation with constant coefficients in one of the dependent variables.

2. The general solution of a single first-order linear equation in one dependent variable involves one arbitrary constant and one function. But the general solution of a system of two first-order linear equations in two dependent variables involves two arbitrary constants and two linearly independent functions.

   In general, the general solution of a system of n first-order linear equations in n dependent variables will involve n arbitrary constants and n linearly independent functions.

3. *The general solution of each unknown function involves the same arbitrary constants C_1 and C_2, whose values are determined from the initial conditions.*

4. The second-order equation arising from two first-order equations might contain the first derivative of one of the nonhomogeneous terms (R_1' in Equation 6–23). This requires R_1 to be sufficiently well behaved in order to solve the second-order equation. If instead we had obtained the equation in terms of y instead of x, then the term R_2' would appear in the equation.

   In general, reducing n first-order equations to a single nth-order equation could result in the (n − 1)th derivative of a nonhomogeneous term to appear in the equation.

A system of n linear first-order equations always can be expressed as a single nth-order linear differential equation and then solved. Therefore, the theory of a system of n linear first-order equations closely parallels the theory of nth-order linear differential equations discussed in Chapter 4.

The method of elimination is simple and easy to track, but it is not practical for systems with more than two or three equations. It becomes extremely tedious and complicated as the number of equations in the system increases. The eigenvalue method discussed later in this chapter requires a little background in linear algebra, but it yields the same characteristic equation in a systematic manner without requiring any elimination or lengthy manipulations—regardless of the number of equations in the system. It is limited, however, to linear equations.

Method of Elimination for Nonhomogeneous Systems

The method of elimination also can be applied to nonhomogeneous systems. In such cases, the equivalent higher-order equation will also be nonhomogeneous, and thus, we will need to find a particular solution to construct the general solution.

EXAMPLE 6–8   **Method of Elimination: Nonhomogeneous Systems**

Use the method of elimination to solve the following system of two first-order differential equations with the specified initial conditions:

$$x' = 4x + 6y + 1, \qquad x(0) = 1$$
$$y' = -3x - 5y + t, \qquad y(0) = 0$$

SOLUTION   This is a system of two linear, nonhomogeneous first-order equations with constant coefficients. To find its equivalent second-order linear equation with constant coefficients in a single unknown function, we solve the first equation for y and differentiate it with respect to t as

$$y = \frac{1}{6}x' - \frac{4}{6}x - \frac{1}{6} \tag{6-29}$$

and

$$y' = \frac{1}{6}x'' - \frac{4}{6}x' \tag{6-30}$$

We now substitute these relations into the second differential equation to eliminate y and y' from that equation. We obtain

$$\frac{1}{6}x'' - \frac{4}{6}x' = -3x - 5\left(\frac{1}{6}x' - \frac{4}{6}x - \frac{1}{6}\right) + t$$

or

$$x'' + x' - 2x = 6t + 5 \tag{6-31}$$

which is a second-order, linear, nonhomogeneous equation with constant coefficients. Its related homogeneous equation is $x'' + x' - 2x = 0$, whose solution was determined in the previous example to be

$$x = C_1 e^t + C_2 e^{-2t}$$

When using the method of undetermined coefficients, the general form of the particular solution corresponding to the nonhomogeneous terms is $x = At + B$. Substituting this into the differential equation (Equation 6–31) and equating the coefficients of each power of t on each side, we obtain $A = -3$ and $B = -4$. Therefore, the particular solution is $x_p = -3t - 4$. Then the general solution of Equation 6–31 becomes

$$x = C_1 e^t + C_2 e^{-2t} - 3t - 4$$

The other unknown function y is determined by substituting the x and x' expressions into Equation 6–29:

$$y = \frac{1}{6}x' - \frac{4}{6}x - \frac{1}{6}$$

$$= \frac{1}{6}(C_1 e^t - 2C_2 e^{-2t} - 3) - \frac{4}{6}(C_1 e^t + C_2 e^{-2t} - 3t - 4) - \frac{1}{6}$$

$$= -\frac{1}{2}C_1 e^t - C_2 e^{-2t} + 2t + 2$$

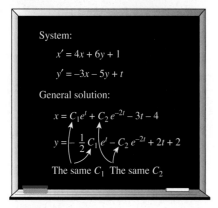

System:

$$x' = 4x + 6y + 1$$

$$y' = -3x - 5y + t$$

General solution:

$$x = C_1 e^t + C_2 e^{-2t} - 3t - 4$$

$$y = \left(-\frac{1}{2}C_1\right)e^t - C_2 e^{-2t} + 2t + 2$$

The same C_1 The same C_2

FIGURE 6–14

The general solution of each unknown function in a system of n first-order linear equations involves the same n arbitrary constants.

Therefore, the general solution of the given system of two first-order equations is (Figure 6–14)

$$x = C_1 e^t + C_2 e^{-2t} - 3t - 4$$

$$y = -\frac{1}{2}C_1 e^t - C_2 e^{-2t} + 2t + 2$$

The arbitrary constants C_1 and C_2 are determined by applying the initial conditions:

$$x(0) = 1 \rightarrow C_1 + C_2 - 4 = 1$$

$$y(0) = 0 \rightarrow -\frac{1}{2}C_1 - C_2 + 2 = 0$$

They give $C_1 = 6$ and $C_2 = -1$. Substituting, the solution of the given system of two first-order, initial-value problems is determined to be

$$x = 6e^t - e^{-2t} - 3t - 4$$

$$y = -3e^t + e^{-2t} + 2t + 2$$

We can check by direct substitution that these solutions satisfy both differential equations as well as the initial conditions.

This method (in principle) also can be applied to nonlinear systems. However, it will rarely result in a closed-form solution for such a system.

Combining equations in this way to obtain a single, higher-order equation can be cumbersome. In such cases, the method based on the Laplace transform (covered in Chapter 8) is easier to use.

Section Review

6–8C What is the method of elimination based on? What are its advantages and disadvantages?

6–9 What is the major limitation of the method of elimination? Is it applicable to nonhomogeneous systems? Is it applicable to nonlinear systems? Is it applicable to systems with variable coefficients?

6–10 Use the method of elimination to determine the general solution of the following system of first-order differential equations.

$$x' = -3x + 2y$$

$$y' = 2x - 6y$$

(*Answer*: $x(t) = C_1 e^{-2t} + C_2 e^{-7t}$, $y(t) = \frac{1}{2}C_1 e^{-2t} - 2C_2 e^{-7t}$)

6–11 Use the method of elimination to determine the general solution of the following system of first-order differential equations.

$$x' = -3x + 2y + 5$$

$$y' = 2x - 6y$$

(*Answer*: $x(t) = C_1 e^{-2t} + C_2 e^{-7t} + \frac{15}{7}$, $y(t) = \frac{1}{2}C_1 e^{-2t} - 2C_2 e^{-7t} + \frac{5}{7}$)

6–12 Use the method of elimination to determine the solution of the following system of first-order differential equations with the specified initial conditions.

$$x' = -3x + 2y + 5, \qquad x(0) = 3$$
$$y' = 2x - 6y, \qquad\qquad y(0) = 0$$

(*Answer:* $x(t) = \dfrac{2}{5}e^{-2t} + \dfrac{16}{35}e^{-7t} + \dfrac{15}{7}$, $y(t) = \dfrac{1}{5}e^{-2t} - \dfrac{32}{35}e^{-7t} + \dfrac{5}{7}$)

6–4 ▪ THE METHOD OF EIGENVALUES

An alternative to the method of elimination just described is the **method of eigenvalues** (also called method of determinants), which provides an easy and systematic way of obtaining the characteristic equation. This method also serves as an excellent way to introduce the basic concepts associated with the powerful matrix method (or the method of eigenvectors) discussed in the next chapter. The use of this method also is limited to linear systems with two or three first-order equations with constant coefficients. Linear systems with a larger number of equations can be solved most efficiently and systematically with the matrix method.

Consider the system of two linear, homogeneous, first-order differential equations with constant coefficients:

$$x' = a_1x + b_1y \qquad \text{(6–32a)}$$
$$y' = a_2x + b_2y \qquad \text{(6–32b)}$$

where a_1, b_1, a_2, and b_2 are real constants. Following the discussion in Section 3–5 regarding the form of the solution of linear differential equations with constant coefficients, we assume the solution functions x and y to be of the form (Figure 6–15):

$$x = k_1e^{\lambda t} \qquad \text{(6–33a)}$$
$$y = k_2e^{\lambda t} \qquad \text{(6–33b)}$$

where k_1, k_2, and λ are constants whose values are to be determined from the requirement that the assumed solutions satisfy the given system of differential equations. Substituting Equations 6–33 into Equations 6–32 gives

$$k_1\lambda e^{\lambda t} = a_1k_1e^{\lambda t} + b_1k_2e^{\lambda t} \qquad \text{(6–34a)}$$
$$k_2\lambda e^{\lambda t} = a_2k_1e^{\lambda t} + b_2k_2e^{\lambda t} \qquad \text{(6–34b)}$$

Dividing both equations by $e^{\lambda t}$ and rearranging, we obtain

$$(a_1 - \lambda)k_1 + b_1k_2 = 0 \qquad \text{(6–35a)}$$
$$a_2k_1 + (b_2 - \lambda)k_2 = 0 \qquad \text{(6–35b)}$$

which can be viewed as a system of two linear, homogeneous *algebraic* equations for the unknown coefficients k_1 and k_2. One obvious solution of this system is $k_1 = k_2 = 0$. But we discard this solution as the *trivial* solution, since it yields $x = y = 0$ (in which we have no interest).

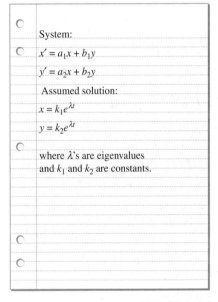

System:

$$x' = a_1x + b_1y$$
$$y' = a_2x + b_2y$$

Assumed solution:

$$x = k_1e^{\lambda t}$$
$$y = k_2e^{\lambda t}$$

where λ's are eigenvalues and k_1 and k_2 are constants.

FIGURE 6–15

The method of eigenvalues is based on assuming the solution of the unknown functions to be of the form of an exponential function ($k_ne^{\lambda t}$), and then determining the required values of λ, which are the eigenvalues.

As you may recall from the theory of linear systems in algebra, this linear, homogeneous system of algebraic equations will have a nontrivial solution if and only if its determinant is equal to zero. That is,

$$\begin{vmatrix} (a_1 - \lambda) & b_1 \\ a_2 & (b_2 - \lambda) \end{vmatrix} = (a_1 - \lambda)(b_2 - \lambda) - a_2 b_1 = 0 \qquad (6\text{-}36)$$

or

$$\lambda^2 - (a_1 + b_2)\lambda + a_1 b_2 - a_2 b_1 = 0 \qquad (6\text{-}37)$$

This quadratic equation in the unknown λ is called the **characteristic equation** of the linear system (Equations 6–32). The two roots λ_1 and λ_2 of this equation are called the **characteristic roots** or **eigenvalues** of the given system of equations. (The word *eigen* means *characteristic* in German.)

Note that the characteristic equation is exactly the same as the characteristic equation (Equation 6–24) obtained with the method of elimination—which involves considerable algebraic manipulations. A careful examination of the determinant in Equation 6–36 reveals a shortcut for the determination of the characteristic equation. You subtract λ from the elements on the main diagonal of the coefficient determinant:

$$A = \begin{vmatrix} a_1 & b_1 \\ a_2 & b_2 \end{vmatrix}$$

and set it equal to zero (Figure 6–16). This is analogous to obtaining the characteristic equation of a single second-order, linear equation directly by replacing y'' by λ^2, y' by λ, y by 1.

Recall from Chapter 3 that the general solution of a second-order, linear, homogeneous equation with constant coefficients depends on whether the two characteristic roots λ_1 and λ_2 are real and distinct, real and equal, or complex. This is also the case for systems of linear equations, since a system of two first-order linear equations can be expressed as a single, second-order linear equation in either dependent variable. Once the characteristic roots are available, the general solution for x can be determined in an analogous manner as

If $\lambda_1 \neq \lambda_2$ and both are real, then $\qquad x(t) = C_1 e^{\lambda_1 t} + C_2 e^{\lambda_2 t}$ $\qquad (6\text{-}38)$

If $\lambda_1 = \lambda_2$, then $\qquad\qquad x(t) = (C_1 + C_2 t)e^{\lambda_1 t}$ $\qquad (6\text{-}39)$

If $\lambda_{1,2} = \alpha \pm i\beta$, then $\qquad x(t) = e^{\alpha t}(C_1 \sin \beta t + C_2 \cos \beta t)$ $\qquad (6\text{-}40)$

where C_1 and C_2 are arbitrary constants. The other unknown function y can be determined by solving the first equation for y and substituting the x and x' expressions obtained from Equations 6–38, 6–39, or 6–40 into it. Note that the general solution for y will involve the same two arbitrary constants C_1 and C_2. The solution procedure is now illustrated with an example.

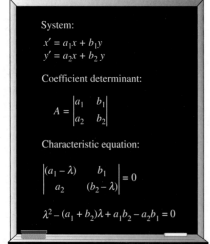

FIGURE 6–16

The characteristic equation of a system is obtained by subtracting λ from the elements on the main diagonal of the coefficient determinant and setting it equal to zero.

EXAMPLE 6–9   The Method of Eigenvalues

Use the method of eigenvalues to solve the following system of two first-order differential equations with the specified initial conditions.

$$x' = 4x + 6y, \qquad x(0) = 1$$
$$y' = -3x - 5y, \quad y(0) = 0$$

SOLUTION   This is the system considered in Example 6–6, and its coefficient determinant is

$$A = \begin{vmatrix} 4 & 6 \\ -3 & -5 \end{vmatrix}$$

The characteristic equation is determined by subtracting λ from the elements on the main diagonal of this determinant and then setting its determinant equal to zero:

$$\begin{vmatrix} (4 - \lambda) & 6 \\ -3 & (-5 - \lambda) \end{vmatrix} = (4 - \lambda)(-5 - \lambda) - 6(-3) = 0$$

or $\lambda^2 + \lambda - 2 = 0$, which is equivalent to the characteristic equation obtained in Example 6–6 with the method of elimination. The roots of this equation are $\lambda = 1$ and $\lambda = -2$, which are real and distinct. Thus, the general solution (from Equation 6–38) of x is

$$x = C_1 e^t + C_2 e^{-2t}$$

To determine the other unknown function y, we solve the first differential equation for y and substitute the x and x' expressions obtained from the previous relation into the expression for y:

$$y = \frac{1}{6}x' - \frac{4}{6}x$$

$$= \frac{1}{6}(C_1 e^t - 2C_2 e^{-2t}) - \frac{4}{6}(C_1 e^t + C_2 e^{-2t})$$

$$= -\frac{1}{2}C_1 e^t - C_2 e^{-2t}$$

Therefore, the general solution of the given system of two first-order equations is

$$x = C_1 e^t + C_2 e^{-2t}$$

$$y = -\frac{1}{2}C_1 e^t - C_2 e^{-2t}$$

which is the same result obtained in Example 6–6.

The arbitrary constants C_1 and C_2 were determined in Example 6–6 to be $C_1 = 2$ and $C_2 = -1$, and thus, the solutions of the given system of two first-order initial-value problems are determined to be

$$x = 2e^t - e^{-2t}$$

$$y = -e^t + e^{-2t}$$

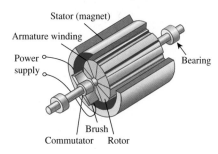

FIGURE 6–17

Cutaway view of a permanent magnet motor.

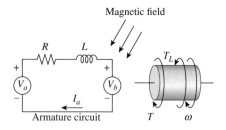

FIGURE 6–18

Circuit diagram of a permanent magnet motor.

EXAMPLE 6–10   A Permanent Magnet Motor

Develop a model for the permanent magnet motor whose cutaway view is shown in Figure 6–17. The voltage applied to the armature circuit is V_a, the armature current is I_a, and the motor speed is ω (Figure 6–18). The armature circuit shown in the figure has a resistance R and an inductance L. In a permanent magnet motor, the magnetic field is produced by the magnet. The mechanical subsystem consists of the inertia I, which consists of the armature inertia as well as the inertia of whatever device is being rotated by the motor, (such as with a fan or pump).

The external torque T_L represents an additional torque acting on the load. For example, if the motor drives the wheel of a vehicle, T_L would be the torque produced by gravity as the vehicle ascends a hill.

The motor produces a torque T that can be shown from electromagnetic theory to be proportional to the armature current (I_a) as $T = K_T I_a$, where K_T is the motor's *torque constant*. The motion of a current-carrying conductor in a field produces a voltage in the conductor that opposes the current. This voltage in the armature is called the *back emf* (for *electromotive force*—an older term for voltage). Its magnitude is proportional to the speed as $V_b = K_b \omega$, where K_b is the motor's *back emf constant*. The back emf is a voltage drop in the armature circuit. (a) Derive the differential equation model. (b) Obtain the characteristic equation. (c) Suppose the applied voltage V_a is a constant. Determine the range of parameter values such that the speed will not oscillate.

SOLUTION   (a) Kirchhoff's voltage law gives

$$V_a - RI_a - L\frac{dI_a}{dt} - V_b = 0$$

or

$$V_a - RI_a - L\frac{dI_a}{dt} - K_b\omega = 0$$

From the angular impulse-momentum principle applied to the inertia I, we have

(*Mass moment of inertia about a fixed rotation axis*) × (*angular acceleration*)
    = *sum of the moments about the fixed rotation axis*

This gives

$$I\frac{d\omega}{dt} = T - T_L = K_T I_a - T_L$$

These equations constitute the system model. To put them in standard form, divide by L and I, respectively. This gives

$$\frac{dI_a}{dt} = \frac{V_a}{L} - \frac{R}{L}I_a - \frac{K_b}{L}\omega \qquad \textbf{(6–41)}$$

$$\frac{d\omega}{dt} = -\frac{T_L}{I} + \frac{K_T}{I}I_a \qquad \textbf{(6–42)}$$

(b) The coefficient determinant is

$$A = \begin{vmatrix} -R/L & -K_b/L \\ K_T/I & 0 \end{vmatrix}$$

The characteristic equation is

$$\begin{vmatrix} (-R/L - \lambda) & -K_b/L \\ K_T/I & -\lambda \end{vmatrix} = 0$$

which gives

$$-\lambda(-R/L - \lambda) + K_T K_b/LI = 0$$

or

$$\lambda^2 + \frac{R}{L}\lambda + K_T K_b/LI = 0$$

Multiplying by LI gives $LI\lambda^2 + RI\lambda + K_T K_b = 0$.

(c) The characteristic roots are found from the quadratic formula:

$$\lambda = \frac{-RI \pm \sqrt{(RI)^2 - 4LIK_T K_b}}{2LI} \tag{6-43}$$

If the applied voltage V_a is a constant, the solution for the speed ω will consist of a constant plus terms that depend on the nature of the characteristic roots. So if these two roots are real, these two terms will be exponentials, and thus, the speed will not oscillate. The roots will be real if the term beneath the square root in Equation 6–43 is nonnegative. This will be true if

$$(RI)^2 - 4LIK_T K_b \geq 0$$

Since $I > 0$, this reduces to

$$IR^2 - 4LK_T K_b \geq 0$$

The motor speed will not oscillate if this inequality is satisfied.

The method of eigenvalues also can be applied to systems of linear, nonhomogeneous equations with constant coefficients. The solution procedure for nonhomogeneous systems closely parallels the solution of a single, linear, nonhomogeneous equation. Again the first step is to ignore all of the nonhomogeneous terms and to determine the homogeneous solution as just described. The next step is to determine a particular solution almost exactly as we did in Chapter 3 for linear second-order equations. The final step is to construct the general solution by combining the homogeneous and particular solutions by superposition.

Both the method of undetermined coefficients and the method of variation of parameters can be used for the determination of the particular solution. The method of undetermined coefficients is simple and easy to apply, but it is limited to nonhomogeneous terms involving products of polynomials, exponential functions, and sine or cosine functions. The selection of the general form of the particular solutions for the case of linear systems differs from the case of single equations in that we must now consider the nonhomogeneous terms in all of the equations in the system rather than the nonhomogeneous term in just one equation (Figure 6–19).

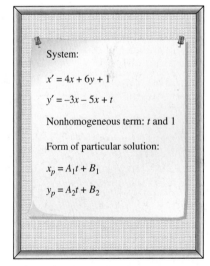

FIGURE 6–19

When applying the method of undetermined coefficients to *systems* to determine the particular solution, we must consider *all* the nonhomogeneous terms in *all* equations.

EXAMPLE 6–11 **Method of Eigenvalues: Nonhomogeneous Systems**

Use the method of eigenvalues to solve the following system of two first-order differential equations with the specified initial conditions.

$$x' = 4x + 6y + 1, \quad x(0) = 1$$

$$y' = -3x - 5y + t, \quad y(0) = 0$$

SOLUTION   This is a system of two linear, nonhomogeneous, first-order equations with constant coefficients. Its related homogeneous system is

$$x' = 4x + 6y$$
$$y' = -3x - 5y$$

whose general solution was determined in the previous example to be

$$x_h = C_1 e^t + C_2 e^{-2t}$$

$$y_h = -\frac{1}{2}C_1 e^t - C_2 e^{-2t}$$

The nonhomogeneous terms in the system are t and 1, and the general form of the particular solution corresponding to these nonhomogeneous terms is

$$x_p = A_1 t + B_1, \quad y_p = A_2 t + B_2$$

Substituting these into the given differential equations, we have

$$A_1 = 4(A_1 t + B_1) + 6(A_2 t + B_2) + 1$$

and

$$A_2 = -3(A_1 t + B_1) - 5(A_2 t + B_2) + t$$

Equating the coefficients of each power of t on each side gives us four equations for the undetermined coefficients:

$$4A_1 + 6A_2 = 0$$

$$A_1 - 4B_1 - 6B_2 = 1$$

$$3A_1 + 5A_2 = 1$$

$$A_2 + 3B_1 + 5B_2 = 0$$

The first and the third equations involve two unknowns A_1 and A_2 only, and the solution of these two equations is $A_1 = -3$ and $A_2 = 2$. Then the remaining two equations are solved to give $B_1 = -4$ and $B_2 = 2$. Therefore, the particular solutions are

$$x_p = -3t - 4$$

$$y_p = 2t + 2$$

Then the general solution of the given system of two first-order equations becomes

$$x = C_1 e^t + C_2 e^{-2t} - 3t - 4$$

and

$$y = -\frac{1}{2}C_1 e^t - C_2 e^{-2t} + 2t + 2$$

The arbitrary constants are determined by applying the initial conditions to be $C_1 = 6$ and $C_2 = -1$. Substituting, the solution of the given system of two first-order, initial-value problems are determined to be

$$x = 6e^t - e^{-2t} - 3t - 4$$

and

$$y = -3e^t + e^{-2t} + 2t + 2$$

which is identical to the result obtained in Example 6–8 by the method of elimination.

You will note from this example that the general form of the particular solution for both unknown functions is the same. They differ in the values of the constant coefficients only.

Nonhomogeneous Terms That Are Solutions of the Related Homogeneous Equation

When a nonhomogeneous term happens to be one of the homogeneous solutions, the assumed form of the particular solution for a system of equations will be different than what it would be for a single equation. You will recall that for single equations we would take the particular solution to be of the form $t^k x_p$ in such cases where x_p is the normal form of the particular solution (i.e., the form of the particular solution corresponding to that nonhomogeneous term if it were not a homogeneous solution) and k is the smallest positive integer that eliminates any duplication between the homogeneous and particular solutions.

When dealing with a system of equations, multiplying the particular solutions by t^k is not enough. Instead, we need to multiply them by a polynomial:

$$P_k(t) = A_0 t^k + A_1 t^{k-1} + \cdots + A_0 \tag{6–44}$$

where the A's are constants (Figure 6–20). The only exception is the particular solution of the dependent variable, whose general homogeneous solution is taken as a base with arbitrary constants C_1 and C_2. They can absorb any additional homogeneous solutions that arise as part of the particular solution. But the homogeneous solutions for all other dependent variables involve fixed multiples of the arbitrary constants. Thus, they cannot be modified to absorb the homogeneous solutions that arise as part of their particular solutions. Therefore, we need to account for them separately. Of course, we can combine them later with the homogeneous solutions. This is now illustrated with an example.

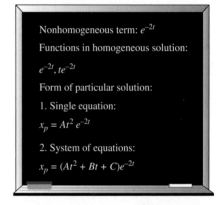

Nonhomogeneous term: e^{-2t}

Functions in homogeneous solution:

e^{-2t}, te^{-2t}

Form of particular solution:

1. Single equation:

$x_p = At^2 e^{-2t}$

2. System of equations:

$x_p = (At^2 + Bt + C)e^{-2t}$

FIGURE 6–20

When a nonhomogeneous term appears in the homogeneous solution of a *system* of equations, the basic form of the particular solution corresponding to that term should be multiplied by a polynomial of degree k, where k is the smallest positive integer that eliminates the duplication between the homogeneous and particular solutions.

EXAMPLE 6–12 **Method of Eigenvalues: Systems with Related Nonhomogeneous Terms**

Use the method of eigenvalues to solve the system of two first-order differential equations.

$$x' = 4x + 6y + 1$$
$$y' = -3x - 5y - e^{-2t}$$

SOLUTION This is a system of two linear, nonhomogeneous, first-order equations with constant coefficients. Its related homogeneous system is

$$x' = 4x + 6y$$
$$y' = -3x - 5y$$

whose general solution was determined in the previous example to be

$$x_h = C_1 e^t + C_2 e^{-2t}$$

$$y_h = -\frac{1}{2}C_1 e^t - C_2 e^{-2t}$$

The nonhomogeneous terms in the system are e^{-2t} and 1. The particular solution corresponding to the constant 1 is simply a constant. However, the particular solution corresponding to e^{-2t} would be a constant multiple of te^{-2t}, since e^{-2t} is a homogeneous solution. For systems, however, we also must include a constant multiple of e^{-2t} as part of the particular solution. Therefore, the proper forms of the particular solutions in this case are

$$x_p = A_1 e^{-2t} + B_1 te^{-2t} + D_1$$

and

$$y_p = A_2 e^{-2t} + B_2 te^{-2t} + D_2$$

However, we can take $A_1 = 0$ in x_p with no loss in generality, since the homogeneous solution x_h is taken to be the base solution (the solution with completely arbitrary coefficients), and the arbitrary constants in the x_h relation can absorb any additional e^{-2t} terms that may arise as part of the particular solution.[1] Therefore, we take the particular solutions to be

$$x_p = B_1 te^{-2t} + D_1$$

and

$$y_p = A_2 e^{-2t} + B_2 te^{-2t} + D_2$$

Substituting these into given differential equations, we obtain

$$B_1 e^{-2t} - 2B_1 te^{-2t} = 4(B_1 te^{-2t} + D_1) + 6(A_2 e^{-2t} + B_2 te^{-2t} + D_2) + 1$$

$$-2A_2 e^{-2t} + B_2 e^{-2t} - 2B_2 te^{-2t} = -3(B_1 te^{-2t} + D_1)$$

$$-5(A_2 e^{-2t} + B_2 te^{-2t} + D_2) - e^{-2t}$$

Equating the coefficients of like terms on each side gives us the following six equations for the determination of the five undetermined coefficients:

$$4D_1 + 6D_2 + 1 = 0$$
$$-3D_1 - 5D_2 = 0$$
$$B_1 = 6A_2$$
$$-2A_2 + B_2 = -5A_2 - 1$$
$$-2B_1 = 4B_1 + 6B_2$$
$$-2B_2 = -3B_1 - 5B_2$$

You easily can verify that last two equations are identical. The first two equations involve two of the unknowns (D_1 and D_2 only), and the solution of these two equations is $D_1 = -2.5$ and $D_2 = 1.5$. Then the remaining equations are solved to give $A_2 = 1/3$, $B_1 = 2$, and $B_2 = -2$. Therefore, the particular solutions are

$$x_p = 2te^{-2t} - \frac{5}{2}$$

---

[1]We cannot take *both* A_1 and A_2 to be zero however, because the term e^{-2t} must be retained in one of the particular solutions, either x_p or y_p. Try setting both $A_1 = A_2 = 0$ and see what happens.

and

$$y_p = -\frac{1}{3}e^{-2t} - 2te^{-2t} + \frac{3}{2}$$

Then the general solution of the given system of two first equations becomes

$$x = C_1e^t + C_2e^{-2t} + 2te^{-2t} - \frac{5}{2}$$

and

$$y = -\frac{1}{2}C_1e^t - C_2e^{-2t} + \frac{1}{3}e^{-2t} - 2te^{-2t} + \frac{3}{2}$$

$$= -\frac{1}{2}C_1e^t - \left(C_2 + \frac{1}{3}\right)e^{-2t} - 2te^{-2t} + \frac{3}{2}$$

These solutions can be checked by substituting them directly into each of the equations of the given system.

Modes

Systems having multiple degrees of freedom (such as multiple masses connected by elastic or damping elements) can exhibit complicated behavior. Their free response is the sum of certain behavior patterns called **modes**. Knowledge of these modes enables us to understand better the response of such systems.

EXAMPLE 6–13   **Modes of a Non-Vibrating System**

Determine the modes of the system:

$$x' = 4x + 6y$$
$$y' = -3x - 5y$$

SOLUTION   Generalizing the results of Example 6–6, the solution can be expressed as

$$x(t) = C_1e^t + C_2e^{-2t} = \frac{2}{3}[x(0) + y(0)]e^t + \left[\frac{1}{3}x(0) - \frac{2}{3}y(0)\right]e^{-2t}$$

and

$$y(t) = \frac{1}{2}C_1e^t - C_2e^{-2t} = \frac{1}{3}[x(0) + y(0)]e^t - \left[\frac{1}{3}x(0) - \frac{2}{3}y(0)\right]e^{-2t}$$

Thus, we can see that if the initial conditions are such that $C_1 = 0$ (that is, if $x(0) = -y(0)$), then the e^t term will not appear in the solution, and $x(t) = -y(t) = C_2e^{-2t}$ is the solution. This solution is called a *mode* of the system of equations. Note that it approaches zero as $t \to \infty$.

Similarly, if the initial conditions are such that $C_2 = 0$ (that is, if $x(0) = 2y(0)$), then the e^{-2t} term will not appear in the solution, and $x(t) = 2y(t) = C_1e^t$ is the solution. This solution is also a mode of the system of equations. Note that it approaches infinity as $t \to \infty$.

Thus, the general solution consists of the sum of two terms: the modes. If the initial conditions are just right, then only one mode will appear in the solution. For example, the mode corresponding to e^t is an unstable mode, because it will become infinite. So if we are looking for a set of initial conditions that guarantees that the solution will remain finite, any set of initial conditions such that $x(0) = -y(0)$ will give a finite solution. The solution will become infinite for any other set of initial conditions.

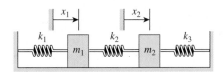

FIGURE 6–21

An undamped two-mass system.

Modes are very useful when analyzing vibratory systems. We will show that these modes are found more easily if we use the original second-order equations rather than converting them into a set of first-order equations.

Consider an undamped two-mass system like that shown in Figure 6–21, where x_1 and x_2 are the displacements of the masses. If we neglect any friction between the masses and the surface, the equations of motions for the system are

$$m_1\ddot{x}_1 = -k_1x_1 - k_2(x_1 - x_2)$$

and

$$m_1\ddot{x}_2 = -k_3x_2 + k_2(x_1 - x_2)$$

We could convert this system of second-order equations into an equivalent system of four first-order equations. Then, using the method of eigenvalues, we could substitute $x_1(t) = A_1e^{\lambda t}$ and $x_2(t) = A_2e^{\lambda t}$ into the four equations. The resulting determinant would be 4×4, which would be tedious to reduce to obtain the characteristic equation.

Instead, substitute $x_1(t) = A_1e^{\lambda t}$ and $x_2(t) = A_2e^{\lambda t}$ into the preceding differential equations, and cancel the exponential terms to obtain

$$m_1\lambda^2A_1 = -k_1A_1 - k_2(A_1 - A_2)$$

and

$$m_2\lambda^2A_2 = -k_3A_2 + k_2(A_1 - A_2)$$

Collect the coefficients of A_1 and A_2:

$$(m_1\lambda^2 + k_1 + k_2)A_1 - k_2A_2 = 0 \tag{6-45}$$

and

$$-k_2A_1 + (m_2\lambda^2 + k_2 + k_3)A_2 = 0 \tag{6-46}$$

To have nonzero solutions for A_1 and A_2, the determinant of these equations must be zero. Thus,

$$\begin{vmatrix} (m_1\lambda^2 + k_1 + k_2) & -k_2 \\ -k_2 & (m_2\lambda^2 + k_2 + k_3) \end{vmatrix} = 0$$

Expanding this determinant gives

$$(m_1\lambda^2 + k_1 + k_2)(m_2\lambda^2 + k_2 + k_3) + k_2^2 = 0 \tag{6-47}$$

When dealing with models of vibratory systems that do not contain damping forces, it can be shown that the characteristic roots are always purely imaginary with no real part. Thus, the characteristic roots will have the form

$\lambda = \pm ib_1$ and $\lambda = \pm ib_2$, where b_1 and b_2 are the radian frequencies of oscillation. The homogeneous solution for x_1 has the form

$$x_1(t) = A_{11}e^{ib_1 t} + A_{12}e^{-ib_1 t} + A_{13}e^{ib_2 t} + A_{14}e^{-ib_2 t}$$

where A_{11} and A_{12} are complex conjugates, as are A_{13} and A_{14}. Thus, the imaginary parts in the expression for $x_1(t)$ will cancel, leaving $x_1(t)$ to be real. This expression can be put into the form

$$x_1(t) = B_1 \sin(b_1 t + \varphi_1) + B_2 \sin(b_2 t + \varphi_2) \tag{6-48}$$

Similarly, the response of x_2 has the form

$$x_2(t) = r_1 B_1 \sin(b_1 t + \varphi_3) + r_2 B_2 \sin(b_2 t + \varphi_4) \tag{6-49}$$

where r_1 and r_2 are called the **mode ratios** for the first and second modes. The first mode is a motion in which $x_2(t) = r_1 x_1(t)$. In the second mode, $x_2(t) = r_2 x_1(t)$. The displacement in each mode is sinusoidal with a fixed amplitude. From Equation 6–48 and Equation 6–49, we see that the complete motion in general is a linear combination of the two modes.

The velocity in each mode is cosinusoidal and easily found from the displacements. For example, if the velocity of the first mass is $v_1 = x_1'$, then from Equation 6–48,

$$v_1 = b_1 B_1 \cos(b_1 t + \varphi_1) + b_2 B_2 \cos(b_2 t + \varphi_2)$$

Even though this is a fourth-order system, we need to be concerned with only two modes—the modes dealing with displacements. The other two modes describe the velocities, which in an undamped vibrating system are easily found, as already shown.

When there is no damping in the model, it is easier to perform the modal analysis using the second-order reduced model for each mass in the system. The undamped model can be arranged so that the mode ratios are real, are ratios of displacements only, and thus are easier to interpret. This is one reason why damping is often neglected when making a modal analysis of a vibratory system. If the damping is slight, the characteristic roots and modes will be almost the same as those of the undamped model. Even if the damping is not small, the insight gained from the undamped analysis is often quite useful for design purposes. If damping is to be accounted for in the modal analysis, the state variable form is easier to use.

EXAMPLE 6–14   Modes of Two Masses in Translation

Find and interpret the mode ratios for the system shown in Figure 6–21 for the case $m_1 = m_2 = m$, $k_1 = k_3 = k$, and $k_2 = 2k$.

SOLUTION Using $m_1 = m_2 = m$, $k_1 = k_3 = k$, and $k_2 = 2k$, we obtain from Equations 6–45, 6–46, and 6–47:

$$(m\lambda^2 + 2k)A_1 - kA_2 = 0 \tag{6-50}$$

$$-kA_1 + (m\lambda^2 + 2k)A_2 = 0 \tag{6-51}$$

and $(m\lambda^2 + 3k)^2 - 4k^2 = 0$. This can be simplified to $m\lambda^4 + 6km\lambda^2 + 5k^2 = 0$ or $\lambda^4 + 6\alpha\lambda^2 + 5\alpha^2 = 0$, where $\alpha = k/m$.

This polynomial has four roots, because it is of fourth-order. We can solve it for λ^2 using the quadratic formula, because it is quadratic in λ^2 (there is no λ term or λ^3 term). To see why this is true, let $u = \lambda^2$. Then the preceding equation becomes $u^2 + 6\alpha u + 5\alpha^2 = 0$ which has the solutions $u = -\alpha$ and $u = -5\alpha$. Thus, $\lambda = \pm i\sqrt{\alpha}$ and $\lambda = \pm i\sqrt{5\alpha}$. The two modal frequencies are thus $\omega_1 = \sqrt{\alpha}$ and $\omega_2 = \sqrt{5\alpha}$.

The mode ratio can be found from either Equation 6–50 or Equation 6–51. Choosing the former, we obtain

$$\frac{A_1}{A_2} = \frac{2\alpha}{\lambda^2 + 3\alpha} \qquad (6\text{–}52)$$

The mode ratio A_1/A_2 can be thought of as the ratio of the amplitudes of x_1 and x_2 in that mode.

For the first mode, the mode ratio can be found by substituting $\lambda^2 = -\alpha$ to obtain $A_1/A_2 = 1$. Thus, in mode 1, the masses move in the same direction with the same amplitude. This oscillation has a frequency of $\omega_1 = \sqrt{\alpha} = \sqrt{k/m}$.

For the second mode, substitute $\lambda^2 = -5\alpha$ into Equation 6–52 to obtain $A_1/A_2 = -1$. Thus, in mode 2, the masses move in *opposite* directions but with the same amplitude. This oscillation has a higher frequency of $\omega_2 = \sqrt{5\alpha} = \sqrt{5k/m}$.

The specific motion depends on the initial conditions, which in general are a combination of both modes. If the masses are initially displaced an equal distance in the same direction and then released, only the first mode will be stimulated. Only the second mode will be stimulated if the masses are initially displaced an equal distance but in opposite directions.

For the system treated in Example 6–14, the modes were *symmetric* because the system is symmetric about its middle; that is, the masses are equal and the stiffnesses are equal. In general, this is not the case.

EXAMPLE 6–15   Nonsymmetric Modes

Find and interpret the mode ratios for the system shown in Figure 6–21 for the case $m_1 = m$, $m_2 = 3m$, $k_1 = k$, and $k_2 = k_3 = 2k$.

SOLUTION For this case, Equation 6–47 becomes $3u^2 + 13\alpha u + 8\alpha^2 = 0$ where $u = \lambda^2$ and $\alpha = k/m$. From the quadratic formula, we obtain $u = \lambda^2 = -0.743\alpha$ and $u = \lambda^2 = -3.591\alpha$. Thus, the two modal frequencies are $\omega_1 = \sqrt{0.743\alpha} = 0.862\sqrt{k/m}$, and $\omega_2 = \sqrt{3.591\alpha} = 1.89\sqrt{k/m}$. From Equation 6–45, the mode ratio for mode 1 is computed by substituting $\lambda^2 = -0.743\alpha$ as

$$\frac{A_1}{A_2} = \frac{2\alpha}{\lambda^2 + 3\alpha} = 0.866$$

Thus, in mode 1, the masses move in the same direction with the amplitude of mass m_1 equal to 0.886 times the amplitude of mass m_2. This oscillation has a radian frequency of $\omega_1 = 0.862\sqrt{k/m}$. Substituting $\lambda^2 = -3.591\alpha$ into

Equation 6–52 gives $A_1/A_2 = -3.39$. Thus, in mode 2, the masses move in the *opposite* direction with the amplitude of mass m_1 equal to 3.39 times the amplitude of mass m_2. This oscillation has a higher frequency of $\omega_2 = 1.89\sqrt{k/m}$.

To stimulate the first mode, displace mass m_1 0.866 times the initial displacement of mass m_2, in the same direction. To stimulate the second mode, displace mass m_1 3.39 times the initial displacement of mass m_2, but in the opposite direction.

The mode ratios are important in building design, for example, because they indicate the amount of relative motion of the floors and thus the amount of stress on the supporting columns. Data on ground motion during an earthquake can be analyzed to determine if the motion contains frequencies near the modal frequencies of a building. If so, the building may experience large motions during an earthquake. So it is important to be able to calculate the modal frequencies as the building is being designed.

Section Review

6–13C How does the method of eigenvalues compare to the method of elimination? What are the advantages and the disadvantages of each method?

6–14C What is the main limitation of the method of eigenvalues? Is it applicable to nonhomogeneous systems? Is it applicable to nonlinear systems? Is it applicable to systems with variable coefficients?

6–15 Use the method of eigenvalues to determine the general solution of the following systems of first-order differential equations.

(a) $x' = 3x - y$ (b) $x' = 3x - y + t$

   $y' = x + y$ $y' = x + y - 2$

(*Answers:* (a) $x(t) = C_1e^{2t} + C_2te^{2t}$ and $y(t) = C_1e^{2t} + C_2(t-1)e^{2t}$

(b) $x(t) = C_1e^{2t} + C_2te^{2t} - \frac{1}{4}t + \frac{1}{2}$ and $y(t) = C_1e^{2t} + C_2(t-1)e^{2t} + \frac{1}{4}t + \frac{7}{4}$)

6–16 Use the method of eigenvalues to determine the solution of the following system of first-order differential equations with the specified initial conditions.

$x' = 2x - 6y + 1,\ x(0) = 1$

$y' = 4x + 2y + t,\ y(0) = 0$

(*Answers:* $x(t) = \frac{33\sqrt{6}}{192}e^{2t}\sin 2\sqrt{6}t + \frac{54}{49}e^{2t}\cos 2\sqrt{6}t - \frac{3}{14}t - \frac{5}{49}$ and

   $y(t) = -\frac{33}{196}e^{2t}\cos 2\sqrt{6}t + \frac{18\sqrt{6}}{49}e^{2t}\sin 2\sqrt{6}t - \frac{1}{14}t + \frac{33}{196}$)

6–5 ▪ COMPUTER METHODS

Computers can make the methods of this chapter easy to apply.

Method of Eigenvalues   One advantage of the method of eigenvalues is that the characteristic equation is obtained along with the solution. As we have seen in several examples in previous chapters, this equation can

TABLE 6-1

Computer Solution for the System

$$x' = 4x + 6y + 1, y' = -3x - 5y - e^{-2t}$$

MATLAB Symbolic Math Toolbox
`[x,y]=dsolve('Dx=4*x+6*y+1','Dy=-3*x-5*y-exp(-2*t)')`
MuPAD
`eqns:={x'(t)=4*x(t)+6*y(t)+1,y'(t)=-3*x(t)-5*y(t)-exp(-2*t)}` `ode::solve(eqns, {x(t),y(t)})`
Maple
`eqns:=x'(t)=4*x(t)+6*y(t)+1,y'(t)=-3*x(t)-5*y(t)-exp(-2*t)` `dsolve([eqns])`
Mathematica
`DSolve[{z'[x] == 4*z[x]+6*y[x]+1,` `y'[x] == -3*z[x]-5*y[x] - Exp[-2*x]},{z,y},x]`

quickly give useful information about the solution without actually obtaining the solution. The method of eigenvalues requires that a determinant be evaluated symbolically. This can be done on a computer using the determinant methods described in Chapter 4, Section 4–9.

Direct Solution of Systems of Equations If you require the solution, many systems of equations can be solved in closed form on a computer. For example, consider the system given in Example 6–13.

$$x' = 4x + 6y + 1, y' = -3x - 5y - e^{-2t}$$

where t is the independent variable. The solution for arbitrary initial conditions is

$$x = C_1 e^t + C_2 e^{-2t} + 2te^{-2t} - 2.5$$

and

$$y = -\frac{1}{2}C_1 e^t - C_2 e^{-2t} + \frac{2}{3}e^{-2t} - 2te^{-2t} + 1.5$$

Table 6–1 shows how to obtain this solution using various programs. If you use two or more different programs to solve these equations, you will notice that they may arrange the two undetermined coefficients differently.

Table 6–2 shows how to obtain the solution for the initial conditions $x(0) = 1$, $y(0) = 0$. The solution is

$$x(t) = \frac{10}{3}e^t + \frac{1}{6}e^{-2t} - \frac{5}{2} + 2te^{-2t}$$

and

$$y(t) = -\frac{5}{3}e^t + \frac{1}{6}e^{-2t} + \frac{3}{2} - 2te^{-2t}$$

TABLE 6-2

Computer Solution for the System

$$x' = 4x + 6y + 1, \, y' = -3x - 5y - e^{-2t}$$
$$x(0) = 1, \, y(0) = 0$$

MATLAB

```
[x,y]=dsolve('Dx=4*x+6*y+1','Dy=-3*x-5*y-exp(-2*t)',
 'x(0)=1','y(0)=0')
```

MuPAD

```
eqns:={x'(t)=4*x(t)+6*y(t)+1,y'(t)=-3*x(t)-5*y(t)
 -exp(-2*t),x(0)=1,y(0)=0}
ode::solve(eqns, {x(t),y(t)})
```

Maple

```
eqn:= x'(t)=4*x(t)+6*y(t)+1,y'(t)=-3*x(t)-5*y(t)-exp(-2*t)
ics:= x(0)=1, y(0)=0
dsolve([eqn,ics])
```

Mathematica

```
DSolve[{z'[x]==4*z[x]+6*y[x]+1,z[0]==1,
y'[x]==-3*z[x]-5*y[x]-Exp[-2*x],y[0]==0},{z,y},x]
```

6-6 · SUMMARY

Systems of differential equations arise naturally in the analysis of many practical problems that involve two or more physically coupled systems. The dependent variables in such systems are interdependent, and they need to be determined simultaneously. Systems of differential equations involve the derivatives of two or more dependent variables with respect to a single independent variable, usually time t.

Standard Form   The differential equations that make up a system may be of different orders. But to bring uniformity to the treatment of systems of differential equations, it is common practice to transform such systems into an equivalent system of first-order equations. Any nth-order differential equation always can be transformed into a system of n first-order differential equations.

Classification of Systems   A system of differential equations is said to be *linear* if every single equation in the system is linear. A system is said to be *nonlinear* even if only one equation involves a single nonlinear term. A linear system of differential equations is said to be *homogeneous* if every single equation in the system is homogeneous. A system is said to be *nonhomogeneous* even if only one equation involves a single nonhomogeneous term.

A system of differential equations is said to have *constant coefficients* if every equation in the system in the standard form has constant coefficients. A system is said to have *variable coefficients* even if only one equation involves a variable coefficient (a function of the independent variable).

Solution Procedures for Linear Systems   Systems of linear differential equations can be solved using a systematic procedure, but even linear systems will cause considerable difficulty in solution if they involve variable coefficients, since the solutions in such cases typically involve infinite series. Therefore, the emphasis in this chapter has been on linear systems of differential equations with constant coefficients.

The Method of Elimination   There are several methods available for solving linear systems. The *method of elimination* is the simplest and the most elementary method for solving systems of differential equations. It is based on converting a system of n first-order equations into a single nth-order equation in a *single* dependent variable by eliminating all other dependent variables one by one. The nth-order equation is then solved using the techniques discussed in the previous chapters. This method is analogous to solving a system of algebraic equations by eliminating all the unknowns but one.

The Method of Eigenvalues   An alternative to the method of elimination is the *method of eigenvalues* (also called the *method of determinants*), which provides an easy and systematic way of obtaining the characteristic equation of linear systems with constant coefficients. In this method, the characteristic equation is obtained by subtracting λ from the elements on the main diagonal of the coefficient determinant and then setting the determinant equal to zero. The roots of this equation are called the *characteristic roots* or the *eigenvalues*. This method yields the same characteristic equation in a systematic manner without requiring any elimination or lengthy manipulations regardless of the number of equations in the system. It closely resembles the solution of a single differential equation with constant coefficients.

System Modes The method of eigenvalues can be used to illustrate the concept of modes, which are the basic solution forms of a set of equations. A set of two equations will have two modes, and so on. For a specific set of initial conditions, only one mode will appear in the solution. For sets having real eigenvalues, all of the modes will have exponential behavior. For sets having at least some complex eigenvalues, at least some of the modes will be oscillatory.

Both the method of elimination and the method of eigenvalues are simple and easy to track, but they are not practical for systems with more than two or three equations. They become tedious and complicated as the number of equations in the system increases. Such large systems can be solved most efficiently and systematically with the *method of eigenvectors*, to be presented in Chapter 7.

PROBLEMS

6–1   An Overview of Systems of Differential Equations

6–17C   How do systems of differential equations differ from the systems of algebraic equations?

6–18C   Under what conditions can an nth-order differential equation be transformed into a system of n first-order equations? What is the procedure for expressing an nth-order differential equation as a system of n first-order equations?

6–19C   How does a system of linear differential equations with constant coefficients differ from a system with variable coefficients?

Reduce the following single differential equations to a system of first-order equations (x is the dependent variable and t is the independent variable).

6–20   (a) $t^3 x''' + tx' + x = 0$
    (b) $x''' + tx' - 3x = \sin 2t$

6–21   (a) $x''' + 2t^2 x' + 2x = te^{-3t}$
    (b) $x'' + 5x' - kx = 0$

6–22   (a) $x''' - 3x' + tx = 0$
    (b) $x''' + x' = t^2 \cos t$

6–23   (a) $x^{(iv)} - 5x' + \cos x = t + 1$
    (b) $x^{(iv)} = 0$

6–24   (a) $x^{(iv)} + 2t^2 x' + 5x = 0$
    (b) $x^{(iv)} + e^t x = \dfrac{1}{t}$

6–25   (a) $x'' + e^x x' - 2x = 6$
    (b) $x''' - 2x' + x = t^3 \cos 2t$

6–26   (a) $x^{(v)} + \dfrac{1}{x} = 1$
    (b) $x^{(iv)} - 8x' - e^{\ln x} = 0$

Reduce the following systems of differential equations to systems of first-order equations (t is the independent variable).

6–27 $x''' = xy$
    $(t - 1)^3 y'' = 2txy' - y + e^{-t}$

6–28 $x''' = ty' - 3y + x^2 e^{3t}, x(-1) = 1, x'(-1) = 0,$
    and $x''(-1) = 4$
    $y'' = 6xy - 2, y(-1) = -2, y'(-1) = 0$

6–29 $x''' = x + y' + z'' - 3t, y'' = t^2 y - xz,$ and
    $z'' = xy - yz - 1$

6–30 $x'' = 4(y - z) + tz' - \cos 2t,$
    $x(0) = 0,$ and $x'(0) = -1$
    $y'' = -3xy' - tz, y(0) = 0,$ and $y'(0) = 7$
    $z'' = x^2 - 3xz, z(0) = 0,$ and $z'(0) = 2$

Determine if the following systems of differential equations are (a) linear or nonlinear, (b) homogeneous or nonhomogeneous, and (c) whether they have constant or variable coefficients.

6–31 $x''' = x + y$
    $y'' = 2txy' - y + e^{-t} - 1$

6–32 $x^{(iv)} = 2(x - y) + y' - 3x'$
    $y'' = x + y$

6–33 $x''' = x + y' + z''$
    $y'' = t^2 y - xz$
    $z'' = xy - yz - 1$

6–34 $x'' = 4(y - x) + z'$
    $y'' = -3x + y' - z$
    $z'' x + y + z$

6–35 $x''' = 4(y - x) + z'$
$y' = 3x + y - z + 3$
$z'' = 2x - 3z$

6–36 $x' = 2(x + z) - 3xy + e^t$
$y' = -x + y - z$
$z' = x - 3z + 1$

6–37 $x' = 3x - z$
$y' = tx + y - 3z$
$z' = t^2(x - z) + 1$

6–2 Origin of Systems of Differential Equations

6–38 Consider the two masses m_1 and m_2 and three linear springs with spring constants k_1, k_2, and k_3 connected in series, as shown in Figure P6–38. Initially, both masses are motionless, and they are at their equilibrium positions. Consequently, the springs are neither stretched nor compressed at $t = 0$. Now a periodic force $F(t)$ is applied to m_2, causing both masses to undergo a motion. Letting $x_1(t)$ and $x_2(t)$ denote the positions of the two masses relative to their equilibrium positions, and neglecting any friction, obtain the differential equations that govern the motion of the two masses.

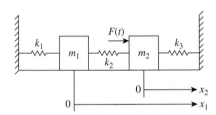

FIGURE P6–38

6–39 Consider the three masses m_1, m_2, and m_3 and three linear springs with spring constants k_1, k_2, and k_3 connected in series, as shown in Figure P6–39. Initially, all three masses are motionless, and they are at their equilibrium positions. Consequently, the springs are neither stretched nor compressed at $t = 0$. Now a periodic force $F(t)$ is applied to m_3, causing all three masses to undergo a motion. Letting $x_1(t)$, $x_2(t)$, and $x_3(t)$ denote the positions of the masses relative to their equilibrium positions and neglecting any friction, obtain the differential equations that govern the motion of the masses.

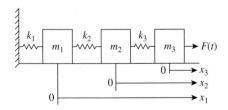

FIGURE P6–39

6–40 Consider the two masses m_1 and m_2 and two linear springs with spring constants k_1 and k_2 connected in series, as shown in Figure P6–40. The second mass is also connected to a dashpot whose damping coefficient is c. Initially, both masses are motionless, and they are at their equilibrium positions. Consequently, the springs are neither stretched nor compressed at $t = 0$. Now a periodic force $F(t)$ is applied to m_1, causing both masses to undergo a motion. Letting $x_1(t)$ and $x_2(t)$ denote the positions of the two masses relative to their equilibrium positions, obtain the differential equations that govern the motion of the two masses.

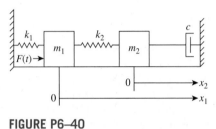

FIGURE P6–40

6–41 Consider the electrical circuit shown in Figure P6–41. It consists of two closed loops. Taking the indicated directions of the currents to be positive, obtain the differential equations that govern the currents I_1 and I_2 flowing through the resistor R and the inductor L, respectively.

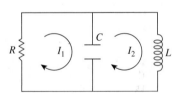

FIGURE P6–41

6–42 The electrical circuit shown in Figure P6–42 consists of two closed loops. Taking the indicated directions of the currents to be positive, obtain the differential equations that govern the currents I_1 and I_2 flowing through the capacitor C and the inductor I_2, respectively.

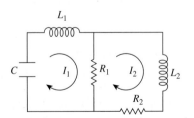

FIGURE P6–42

6–43 The electrical circuit shown in Figure P6–43 consists of three closed loops. Taking the indicated directions of the currents to be positive, obtain the differential equations that govern the currents I_1, I_2, and I_3 flowing through the resistors R_1, R_2, and R_3, respectively.

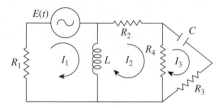

FIGURE P6–43

6–44 Two brine tanks each containing 1000 L (liters) of brine are connected, as shown in Figure P6–44. At any time t, the first and the second tank contain $x_1(t)$ and $x_2(t)$ kg of salt, respectively. The brine concentration in each tank is kept uniform by continuous stirring. Fresh water is entering the first tank at a rate of 50 L/min, brine is discharged from the second tank at the same rate. Brine is pumped from the first tank to the second one at a rate of 100 L/min and from the second tank to the first one at a rate of 50 L/min. Obtain the differential equations that govern the salt content in each tank as a function of time: $x_1(t)$ and $x_2(t)$.

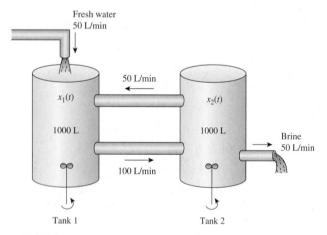

FIGURE P6–44

6–45 Repeat Problem 6–44 assuming that, instead of fresh water, brine containing 0.05 kg of salt per liter enters the first tank at a rate of 50 L/min.

6–3 The Method of Elimination

6–46C Consider a system of three first-order linear, homogeneous equations with constant coefficients. Is the equivalent single third-order differential equation obtained by the method of elimination necessarily linear and homogeneous with constant coefficients?

Use the method of elimination to determine the general solution of the following systems of first-order differential equations.

6–47 (a) $x' = x - y$ (b) $x' = x - y - t + 1$
  $y' = -x + 4y$ $y' = -x + 4y + te^t$

6–48 (a) $x' = x - y$ (b) $x' = x - y - t^2 - 1$
  $y' = -3x - 2y$ $y' = -3x - 2y + 3t$

6–49 (a) $x' = 2x + 4y$ (b) $x' = 2x + 4y - 5t^2 e^{3t}$
  $y' = -x + 2y$ $y' = -x + 2y$

6–50 (a) $x' = 7x + y$ (b) $x' = 7x + y - 1$
  $y' = -x - 3y$ $y' = -x - 3y + 1$

6–51 (a) $x' = 2x + y$ (b) $x' = 2x + y + 1$
  $y' = x - 2y$ $y' = x - 2y + 3t^2$

6–52 (a) $x' = -x + 2y$ (b) $x' = -x + 2y + 3\sin 2t$
  $y' = 3x + y$ $y' = 3x + y - 2$

6–53 (a) $x' = 4x - 2y$ (b) $x' = 4x - 2y + t^2 - 3$
  $y' = 2x - 4y$ $y' = 2x - 4y - 5t$

6–54 (a) $x' = 5x - y$ (b) $x' = 5x - y + te^{2t}$
  $y' = x + 2y$ $y' = x + 2y - 1$

6–55 (a) $x' = x - 5y$ (b) $x' = x - 5y + 3$
  $y' = x + y$ $y' = x + y - 3$

6–56 (a) $x' = -5x + 6y$ (b) $x' = -5x + 6y + 1$
  $y' = 2x + 7y$ $y' = 2x + 7y + t^2$

6–57 (a) $x' = 4y$ (b) $x' = 4y + 1$
  $y' = x$ $y' = x - 3 + e^t$

6–58 (a) $x' = x - 3y$ (b) $x' = x - 3y$
  $y' = -z + 2y$ $y' = -z + 2y - 2e^t$
  $z' = x - y$ $z' = x - y - 1$

6–59 (a) $x' = -3x + y - 2z$
  $y' = x - z + 2y$
  $z' = y + 3z$
  (b) $x' = -3x + y - 2z + t^2$
  $y' = x - z + 2y - 3t$
  $z' = y + 3z + 2$

Use the method of elimination to determine the general solution of the following systems of first-order differential equations.

6–60 (a) $x' = -\dfrac{3}{t}x + \dfrac{8}{t^2}y - 5$ (b) $x' = \dfrac{2}{t^2}y + \dfrac{1}{t}$
  $y' = x + \ln t$ $y' = x + t^2$

6–61 (a) $x' = \dfrac{6}{t^2}y$ (b) $x' = -\dfrac{2}{t^2}x + 4$
  $y' = -3x + 5$ $y' = x + 1$

6–62 (a) $x' = \dfrac{4}{t}x + \dfrac{3}{t^3}y$ (b) $x' = -\dfrac{2}{t}x - \dfrac{1}{t^3}y + \dfrac{4}{t^2}z$

$\qquad\qquad y' = 2z \qquad\qquad\qquad y' = 2z + 1$

$\qquad\qquad z' = 3x + \dfrac{\ln t}{t} \qquad\qquad z' = 3x - t + 1$

Use the method of elimination to determine the solution of the following systems of first-order differential equations with the specified initial conditions.

6–63 $x' = 2x - y + t,\ x(0) = 1$
$\qquad y' = -x + 4y,\ y(0) = 1$

6–64 $x' = 2x - y - t,\ x(0) = 1$
$\qquad y' = -x + 4y,\ y(0) = 1$

6–65 $x' = x - 4y + 1,\ x(0) = 2$
$\qquad y' = 5x - 2y,\ y(0) = -3$

6–66 $x' = 2x + 4y + t,\ x(1) = 0$
$\qquad y' = x - 3y - 1,\ y(0) = 2$

6–67 $x' = x + y,\ x(2) = 0$
$\qquad y' = -2x - 2y,\ y(2) = 0$

6–68 Consider the system of two first-order equations that describes the two connected tanks treated in Example 6–7. Suppose the resistances are unequal: $R_1 = R$, $R_2 = 2R$, and the areas are equal: $A_1 = A_2 = A$. Obtain the single second-order equation in terms of the height $h_1(t)$. If the inflow rate is shut off, estimate how long it will take for the tanks to empty. Will the heights oscillate?

6–69 Consider the system of two first-order equations that describes the two connected tanks treated in Example 6–7. Obtain the single second-order equation in terms of the height $h_2(t)$. Discuss the solution of this equation if the inflow rate q_{mi} is discontinuous. This would be the case in the situation where the flow rate is suddenly turned off.

6–4 The Method of Eigenvalues

6–70C In the method of eigenvalues, how are the eigenvalues of a given system determined? In this method, how is the particular solution corresponding to nonhomogeneous terms determined?

6–71C In the method of eigenvalues, how is the particular solution corresponding to a nonhomogeneous term determined when the nonhomogeneous term appears in the solution of the related homogeneous equation?

Use the method of eigenvalues to determine the general solution of the following systems of first-order differential equations.

6–72 (a) $x' = 2x - y$ (b) $x' = 2x - y - t + 1$
$\qquad\quad y' = -x + 4y \qquad y' = -x + 4y + te^t$

6–73 (a) $x' = x - y$ (b) $x' = x - y + t^2 - 1$
$\qquad\quad y' = -3x - y \qquad y' = -3x - y + 3t$

6–74 (a) $x' = 2x + 4y$ (b) $x' = 2x + 4y - 5t^2 e^{3t}$
$\qquad\quad y' = -x + 2y \qquad\quad y' = -x + 2y$

6–75 (a) $x' = 7x + y$ (b) $x' = 7x + y - 1$
$\qquad\quad y' = -x - 3y \qquad y' = -x - 3y + 1$

6–76 (a) $x' = 2x + y$ (b) $x' = 2x + y + 1$
$\qquad\quad y' = x - 2y \qquad y' = x - 2y + 3t^2$

6–77 (a) $x' = -x + 2y$ (b) $x' = -x + 2y + 3\sin 2t$
$\qquad\quad y' = 3x + y \qquad y' = 3x + y - 2$

6–78 (a) $x' = 4x - 2y$ (b) $x' = 4x - 2y + t^2 - 3$
$\qquad\quad y' = 2x - 4y \qquad y' = 2x - 4y - 5t$

6–79 (a) $x' = 6x - y$ (b) $x' = 6x - y + te^{2t}$
$\qquad\quad y' = x + 2y \qquad y' = x + 2y - 1$

6–80 (a) $x' = x - 5y$ (b) $x' = x - 5y + 3$
$\qquad\quad y' = x + y \qquad y' = x + y - 3$

6–81 (a) $x' = -5x + 6y$ (b) $x' = -5x + 6y + 1$
$\qquad\quad y' = 2x + 7y \qquad y' = 2x + 7y + t^2$

6–82 (a) $x' = 4y$ (b) $x' = 4y + 1$
$\qquad\quad y' = x \qquad\qquad y' = x - 3 + e^t$

Use the method of eigenvalues to determine the solution of the following systems of first-order differential equations with the specified initial conditions.

6–83 $x' = 2x - y + t,\ x(0) = 1$
$\qquad y' = -x + 4y,\ y(0) = 1$

6–84 $x' = 2x - 4y + 1,\ x(0) = 2$
$\qquad y' = 5x - 2y,\ y(0) = -3$

6–85 $x' = 2x + 4y + t,\ x(1) = 0$
$\qquad y' = x - y - 1,\ y(0) = 2$

6–86 $x' = 3x + y - 1,\ x(0) = 0$
$\qquad y' = -4x - y + 3e^{2t},\ y(0) = 1$

6–87 For the dc motor model developed in Example 6–10, obtain the single second-order differential equation for (a) the speed ω and (b) the current I_a.

6–88 For the dc motor model developed in Example 6–10, use the following parameter values and solve the system of equations simultaneously for both the speed $\omega(t)$ and the current $I_a(t)$. Assume the initial conditions are zero.

$K_T = K_b = 0.05\ \text{N·m/A} \qquad R = 0.5\Omega \qquad L = 2 \times 10^{-3}\,\text{H}$

$I = 9 \times 10^{-5}\ \text{kg·m}^2 \qquad V_a = 10\,V$

6–89 For the two-mass system shown in Figure 6–21, suppose there is an external force $F_1(t)$ applied to mass 1 and $F_2(t)$ applied to mass 2. How do these forces affect the modal frequencies and mode ratios?

6–90 For the two-mass system shown in Figure 6–21, find the modal frequencies and mode ratios for the case where $m_1 = m_2 = m$, $k_1 = k_3 = k$, and $k_2 = 4k$.

6–91 For the two-mass system shown in Figure 6–21, find the modal frequencies and mode ratios for the case where $m_1 = m$, $m_2 = 3m$, and $k_1 = k_2 = k_3 = k$.

6–92 The equations of motion of the two-story building model shown in Figure P6–92 were derived in Chapter 4. They are

$$m_1 \ddot{x}_1 = -k_2(x_1 - x_2) + k_1(y - x_1)$$

$$m_2 \ddot{x}_2 = -k_2(x_1 - x_2)$$

Data on ground motion during an earthquake can be analyzed to determine if the motion contains frequencies near the modal frequencies of a building. If so, the building may experience large motions during an earthquake. So it is important to be able to calculate the modal frequencies as the building is being designed. The mode ratios are also important because they indicate the amount of relative motion of the floors and thus the amount of stress on the supporting columns.

Obtain the modal frequencies and the mode ratios for the case where $m_1 = m_2 = m$ and $k_1 = k_2 = k$.

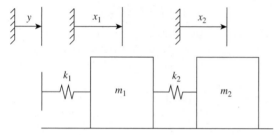

FIGURE P6–92

6–4 Computer Methods

6–93 Use a computer to obtain the symbolic solution of the following set of equations, which are the equations for brine mixing obtained in Example 6–1, for arbitrary initial conditions.

$$\frac{dx_1}{dt} = 1.5 - 50\frac{x_1}{1000} + 35\frac{x_2}{1000} \qquad \text{(6–18a)}$$

$$\frac{dx_2}{dt} = -50\frac{x_1}{1000} - 55\frac{x_2}{1000} \qquad \text{(6–18b)}$$

Use a computer to obtain the symbolic solution of the following problems.

6–94 (a) $x' = 3x - y$ (b) $x' = 3x - y + t$
           $y' = x + y$ $y' = x + y - 2$

6–95 (a) $x' = x - y$ (b) $x' = x - y - t + 1$
           $y' = -x + 4y$ $y' = -x + 4y + te^t$

6–96 (a) $x' = x - y$ (b) $x' = x - y + t^2 - 1$
           $y' = -3x - 2y$ $y' = -3x - 2y + 3t$

Use a computer to obtain the symbolic solution of the following problems for the specified initial conditions.

6–97 $x' = x - 6y + 1$, $x(0) = 1$
       $y' = 4x + 2y + t$, $y(0) = 0$

6–97 $x' = 2x - y + t$, $x(0) = 1$
       $y' = -x + 4y$, $y(0) = 1$

6–98 $x' = x - 4y + 1$, $x(0) = 2$
       $y' = 5x - 2y$, $y(0) = -3$

6–99 $x' = 3x + y - 1$, $x(0) = 0$
       $y' = -4x - y + 3e^{2t}$, $y(0) = 1$

Review Problems

For the following problems, use the method of your choice to obtain the analytical solution for arbitrary initial conditions.

6–100 $x' = 5x - 3y$
        $y' = 2y - z$
        $z' = x - y$

6–101 $x' = 5x - 3y$
        $y' = 2y - z - 2e^t$
        $z' = x - y - 1$

6–102 $x' = -3x + y - 2z$
        $y' = x + 2y + 9z$
        $z' = -3y + 3z$

6–103 $x' = -3x + y - 2z + t$
        $y' = x + 2y + 9z - 3t$
        $z' = -3y + 3z + 2$

SYSTEMS OF LINEAR DIFFERENTIAL EQUATIONS: MATRIX APPROACH

Following reviews of the basic properties of matrices and some important topics from linear algebra, we introduce the *matrix method* (or the *method of eigenvectors*), which is the most general and systematic solution procedure for solving systems of linear differential equations. Two other solution methods (the *Laplace transform method* and the *numerical methods*) are discussed in the following chapters.

We then show how models of physical systems can be expressed in standard matrix form. The basic theory of the matrix method is then presented applied to linear, homogeneous equations and next to linear, nonhomogeneous equations. We then discuss special matrix forms, called the canonical forms and the transition matrix. These are useful for understanding the dynamics of processes. Finally, we illustrate the powerful computer methods available to implement the methods discussed in this chapter.

■ ■ ■ ■ ■ ■ ■

Objectives

When you have finished this chapter, you should be able to:

1. perform basic matrix operations,

2. transform an nth-order differential equation into a set of n first-order equations,

3. express a set of n linear, first-order constant coefficient equations in matrix form,

4. solve a set of n first-order constant-coefficient equations in matrix form using the method of eigenvectors,

5. express a set of n linear, first-order constant coefficient equations in the Jordan canonical form, given the system eigenvalues and eigenvectors, and

6. use a computer package to obtain eigenvalues and eigenvectors, and the numerical solution of a set of n first-order constant coefficient equations.

A system of algebraic equations:

$$2x_1 - 3x_2 + 3x_3 = 5$$

$$5x_1 + 4x_2 - 6x_3 = -5$$

$$x_1 + 7x_2 - x_3 = 12$$

The system in matrix form:

$$\begin{pmatrix} 2 & -3 & 3 \\ 5 & 4 & -6 \\ 1 & 7 & -1 \end{pmatrix} \begin{pmatrix} x_1 \\ x_2 \\ x_3 \end{pmatrix} = \begin{pmatrix} 5 \\ -5 \\ 12 \end{pmatrix}$$

or $\mathbf{Ax} = \mathbf{b}$

FIGURE 7–1

Large systems of algebraic equations are best represented in matrix form.

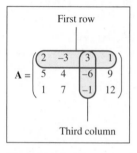

FIGURE 7–2

A 3 × 4 matrix.

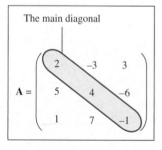

FIGURE 7–3

A 3 × 3 square matrix and its main diagonal.

7–1 ▪ REVIEW OF MATRICES*

Either the method of elimination or the method of eigenvalues discussed in Chapter 6 is sufficient for solving small linear systems with two or three differential equations, but these methods become rather awkward and impractical for larger systems. Large systems of differential equations are best studied and most conveniently described in matrix notation. You may recall from algebra that this is also the case for systems of algebraic equations (Figure 7–1). Therefore, in this section, we will review matrices briefly and discuss their properties to the extent necessary for our study of linear systems in a systematic manner.

Not only does the matrix representation allow general theorems to be developed that are valid for any number of equations, but the matrix notation is used to communicate with powerful computer programs that can solve equations of any order. We will introduce these methods in this chapter.

An $m \times n$ **matrix** (read as m by n matrix) is defined as a rectangular array of numbers or elements arranged in m rows and n columns, such as (Figure 7–2)

$$\mathbf{A} = \begin{pmatrix} a_{11} & a_{12} & \dots & a_{1n} \\ a_{21} & a_{22} & \dots & a_{2n} \\ \vdots & \vdots & & \vdots \\ a_{m1} & a_{m2} & \dots & a_{mn} \end{pmatrix} \qquad (7\text{–}1)$$

Matrices are denoted by bold-faced capital letters, such as **A**. The elements of a matrix can be real constants (scalars), complex numbers, or even functions. The element of an $m \times n$ matrix **A** on the ith row and the jth column is denoted by a_{ij}, where $i = 1, 2, \dots, m$ and $j = 1, 2, \dots, n$. Note that the first subscript indicates the row number and the second subscript the column number of the element. For example, a_{32} represents the element of the matrix on the third row and second column. It sometimes is convenient to represent the matrix **A** as $\mathbf{A} = (a_{ij})$ when manipulating its elements.

In this chapter, we will mostly deal with the following special kinds of matrices.

1. **Square Matrix** A matrix that has the same number of rows and columns is called a **square matrix**. A square matrix that has n rows and n columns is referred to as a *square matrix of order n* or an $n \times n$ matrix. The imaginary line that passes through the elements $a_{11}, a_{22}, \dots, a_{nn}$ is called the **main diagonal** of a square matrix (Figure 7–3).

2. **Vector** A matrix that consists of only one column is called a **column vector** or just a **vector**. Thus, the number of elements of a vector is equal to its number of rows. Vectors are usually denoted by bold-face lowercase letters, such as **b**. A vector of order n can be viewed as an $n \times 1$ matrix that has n rows and a single column and can be expressed as

$$\mathbf{b} = \begin{pmatrix} b_1 \\ b_2 \\ \vdots \\ b_n \end{pmatrix} \qquad (7\text{–}2)$$

---

*This section is included to refresh the reader's memory. It may be skipped if desired.

Likewise, a matrix that consists of only one row is called a **row vector**. A row vector can be viewed as a $1 \times n$ matrix.

An $m \times n$ matrix can be viewed as n column vectors of order m (or as m row vectors of order n) stacked together. Note that a vector is a special case of a matrix (Figure 7–4).

3. **Zero Matrix** A matrix is called a **zero matrix** if each of its elements is zero. It is denoted by boldface **0** and is expressed as

$$\mathbf{0} = \begin{pmatrix} 0 & 0 & \cdots & 0 \\ 0 & 0 & \cdots & 0 \\ \vdots & \vdots & & \vdots \\ 0 & 0 & \cdots & 0 \end{pmatrix} \tag{7–3}$$

4. **Symmetric Matrix** A square matrix that possesses symmetry about its main diagonal is called a **symmetric matrix**. Therefore, $a_{ij} = a_{ji}$ for symmetric matrices. For example,

$$\mathbf{A} = \begin{pmatrix} 1 & 5 & -9 \\ 5 & 3 & 4 \\ -9 & 4 & 2 \end{pmatrix} \tag{7–4}$$

is a 3×3 symmetric matrix.

5. **Upper or Lower Triangular Matrix** A matrix that has all zero elements below its main diagonal is called an **upper triangular matrix**. Likewise, a matrix that has all zero elements above its main diagonal is called a **lower triangular matrix**. For example,

$$\mathbf{U} = \begin{pmatrix} 1 & 6 & 7 \\ 0 & -2 & 3 \\ 0 & 0 & 5 \end{pmatrix} \quad \text{and} \quad \mathbf{L} = \begin{pmatrix} 3 & 0 & 0 \\ -1 & 6 & 0 \\ 5 & 0 & -4 \end{pmatrix} \tag{7–5}$$

are 3×3 upper and lower triangular matrices, respectively.

6. **Diagonal Matrix** A square matrix that has all zero elements below and above the main diagonal is called a **diagonal matrix**. Therefore, $a_{ij} = 0$ whenever $i \neq j$ for diagonal matrices. For example,

$$\mathbf{D} = \begin{pmatrix} 2 & 0 & 0 \\ 0 & -7 & 0 \\ 0 & 0 & -4 \end{pmatrix}$$

is a 3×3 diagonal matrix. It is sometimes convenient to represent a diagonal matrix by listing only its diagonal elements as $\mathbf{D} = \text{diag}\,(2, -7, -4)$. Note that the diagonal matrix is a special case of the symmetric matrix.

7. **Identity Matrix** A diagonal matrix with all 1's on the main diagonal is called an **identity matrix** and is denoted by **I**. In other words, an identity matrix of order n is an $n \times n$ square matrix whose elements are 1 on the main diagonal and zero everywhere else. For example,

$$\mathbf{I} = \begin{pmatrix} 1 & 0 & 0 \\ 0 & 1 & 0 \\ 0 & 0 & 1 \end{pmatrix}$$

Three 3×1 vectors:

$$v_1 = \begin{pmatrix} 2 \\ 5 \\ 1 \end{pmatrix}, \ v_2 = \begin{pmatrix} -3 \\ 4 \\ 7 \end{pmatrix}, \ v_3 = \begin{pmatrix} 3 \\ -6 \\ -1 \end{pmatrix}$$

The 3×3 matrix they form:

$$\mathbf{A} = (v_1 \ v_2 \ v_3) = \begin{pmatrix} 2 & -3 & 3 \\ 5 & 4 & -6 \\ 1 & 7 & -1 \end{pmatrix}$$

FIGURE 7–4

A 3×3 matrix can be viewed as three vectors of the third order stacked side by side.

is a 3×3 identity matrix. The identity matrix is the matrix equivalent of the number 1, since the product of a matrix with the identity matrix yields itself.

Properties of Matrices

The matrix notation enables us to represent a large number of entries by a single symbol, and thus, it is a great convenience in representing large systems algebraic or differential equations in a very compact form. A large system of equations can be manipulated easily in a systematic manner when expressed in the matrix form. Definite rules exist for the manipulation of matrices, and we now state the most fundamental ones.

Equality   Two matrices are said to be of the same **size** if they have the same number of rows *and* the same number of columns. For example, any two 3×5 matrices are of the same size. Two matrices **A** and **B** of the same size are said to be equal to each other if

$$a_{ij} = b_{ij} \tag{7-6}$$

for each i and j (Figure 7–5). This is expressed as $\mathbf{A} = \mathbf{B}$. For example, if

$$\mathbf{A} = \begin{pmatrix} a_{11} & a_{12} \\ a_{21} & a_{22} \end{pmatrix} \quad \text{and} \quad \mathbf{B} = \begin{pmatrix} 3 & 0 \\ -1 & 6 \end{pmatrix}$$

then $\mathbf{A} = \mathbf{B}$ only if $a_{11} = 3$, $a_{12} = 0$, $a_{21} = -1$, and $a_{22} = 6$. Therefore, for example, a matrix equation involving two 5×6 matrices is equivalent to 30 scalar equations. Note that we cannot talk about the equality of two matrices if they are not of the same size (that is, if they have different numbers of rows or columns). For example, the matrices

$$\mathbf{A} = \begin{pmatrix} 1 & 2 \\ 3 & 4 \end{pmatrix} \quad \text{and} \quad \mathbf{B} = \begin{pmatrix} 1 & 2 & 0 \\ 3 & 4 & 0 \end{pmatrix}$$

are not equal, since they have the same number of rows but different number of columns (even though the differing elements are zero).

Addition   Two $m \times n$ matrices are added by adding their respective elements, as

$$\mathbf{A} + \mathbf{B} = (a_{ij}) + (b_{ij}) = (a_{ij} + b_{ij}) \tag{7-7}$$

For example,

$$\begin{pmatrix} 2 & 4 \\ -1 & 6 \end{pmatrix} + \begin{pmatrix} -3 & 8 \\ 2 & 0 \end{pmatrix} = \begin{pmatrix} 2 + (-3) & 4 + 8 \\ -1 + 2 & 6 + 0 \end{pmatrix} = \begin{pmatrix} -1 & 12 \\ 1 & 6 \end{pmatrix}$$

Note that two matrices must be of the same size to be added. Also note that the sum of two $m \times n$ matrices is also an $m \times n$ matrix.

It can be verified easily that matrix addition is commutative and associative. That is,

$$\mathbf{A} + \mathbf{B} = \mathbf{B} + \mathbf{A} \tag{7-8a}$$

and

$$\mathbf{A} + (\mathbf{B} + \mathbf{C}) = (\mathbf{A} + \mathbf{B}) + \mathbf{C} \tag{7-8b}$$

Also, the addition of any matrix **A** with the zero matrix of the same size is equivalent to the matrix itself. That is, $\mathbf{A} + \mathbf{0} = \mathbf{A}$.

A 2×3 matrix:

$$\mathbf{A} = \begin{pmatrix} 2 & -3 & 3 \\ 5 & 4 & -6 \end{pmatrix}$$

Another 2×3 matrix:

$$\mathbf{B} = \begin{pmatrix} 2 & -3 & 3 \\ 5 & 7 & -6 \end{pmatrix}$$

FIGURE 7–5

Two matrices that are of the same size but unequal.

Multiplication by a Scalar   A matrix **A** is multiplied by a scalar k by multiplying *each* of its elements by that scalar (Figure 7–6), as

$$k\mathbf{A} = k(a_{ij}) = (ka_{ij}) \tag{7–9}$$

For example,

$$3\begin{pmatrix} 2 & -1 \\ 4 & 7 \end{pmatrix} = \begin{pmatrix} 3 \times 2 & 3 \times (-1) \\ 3 \times 4 & 3 \times 7 \end{pmatrix} = \begin{pmatrix} 6 & -3 \\ 12 & 21 \end{pmatrix}$$

Note that the size of the matrix does not change as a result of multiplication by a scalar. It can be verified easily that this process is commutative and distributive. That is,

$$k\mathbf{A} = \mathbf{A}k \tag{7–10a}$$

and

$$k(\mathbf{A} + \mathbf{B}) = k\mathbf{A} + k\mathbf{B} \tag{7–10b}$$

$$(k_1 + k_2)\mathbf{A} = k_1\mathbf{A} + k_2\mathbf{B} \tag{7–10c}$$

Also, the product of any $m \times n$ matrix **A** by zero is an $m \times n$ zero matrix. That is, $0 \cdot \mathbf{A} = \mathbf{0}$.

Subtraction   The difference $\mathbf{A} - \mathbf{B}$ of two $m \times n$ matrices **A** and **B** is defined as the addition of the matrix **A** with the negative of the matrix **B**. That is,

$$\mathbf{A} - \mathbf{B} = \mathbf{A} + (-\mathbf{B}) \tag{7–11}$$

or $(a_{ij}) - (b_{ij}) = (a_{ij} - b_{ij})$. For example,

$$\begin{pmatrix} 4 & 2 \\ -3 & 6 \end{pmatrix} - \begin{pmatrix} 3 & 6 \\ 0 & -2 \end{pmatrix} = \begin{pmatrix} 4 - 3 & 2 - 6 \\ -3 - 0 & 6 - (-2) \end{pmatrix} = \begin{pmatrix} 1 & -4 \\ -3 & 8 \end{pmatrix}$$

Matrix Multiplication   The product of an $m \times n$ matrix **A** with an $n \times r$ matrix **B** is an $m \times r$ matrix **C**, whose elements are determined from

$$c_{ij} = \sum_{k=1}^{n} a_{ik}b_{kj} = a_{i1}b_{1j} + a_{i2}b_{2j} + \cdots + a_{in}b_{1n} \tag{7–12}$$

for any i and j. That is, the elements of the matrix **C** in the ith row and the jth column is determined by multiplying each element of **A** on the ith row by the corresponding element of **B** on the jth column and adding the results of those products, as illustrated in Figure 7–7. Thus, the multiplication of the two matrices **A** and **B** is quite a lengthy process, since the determination of each element of the resulting matrix **C** requires n products and $n - 1$ additions.

For example, consider a 3×3 matrix **A** and a matrix (a column vector) **x** given as

$$\mathbf{A} = \begin{pmatrix} 3 & 5 & -2 \\ 4 & 9 & 7 \\ 3 & 6 & 8 \end{pmatrix} \quad \text{and} \quad \mathbf{x} = \begin{pmatrix} x_1 \\ x_2 \\ x_3 \end{pmatrix}$$

$$\mathbf{A} = \begin{pmatrix} 2 & 0 \\ 14 & -6 \end{pmatrix}$$

$$= 2\begin{pmatrix} 1 & 0 \\ 7 & -3 \end{pmatrix}$$

FIGURE 7–6

A scalar factor that is common to all elements of a matrix can be taken out as a scalar factor to that matrix.

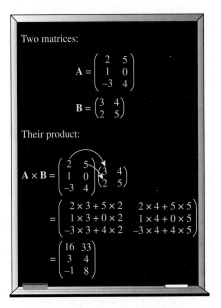

FIGURE 7–7

Multiplication of a 3×2 matrix by a 2×2 matrix.

The product $\mathbf{Ax}$ of these two matrices is

$$\mathbf{Ax} = \begin{pmatrix} 3 & 5 & -2 \\ 4 & 9 & 7 \\ 3 & 6 & 8 \end{pmatrix} \begin{pmatrix} x_1 \\ x_2 \\ x_3 \end{pmatrix} = \begin{pmatrix} 3x_1 + 5x_2 - 2x_3 \\ 4x_1 + 9x_2 + 7x_3 \\ 3x_1 + 6x_2 + 8x_3 \end{pmatrix}$$

which is a 3×1 matrix, as expected. This example shows that the definition of matrix multiplication is motivated from the desire to represent the left side of a system of equations as the product of a matrix whose elements are the coefficients of the unknowns and a vector whose elements are the unknowns. For $\mathbf{A}$ and $\mathbf{x}$ given previously, the simple matrix equation $\mathbf{Ax} = \mathbf{0}$ is equivalent to the system:

$$3x_1 + 5x_2 - 2x_3 = 0$$
$$4x_1 + 9x_2 + 7x_3 = 0$$
$$3x_1 + 6x_2 + 8x_3 = 0$$

Therefore, systems of algebraic equations can conveniently be expressed and studied using matrix notation and matrix multiplication, as previously defined.

It can be shown that matrix multiplication is associative and distributive, but it is not always commutative. That is,

$$(\mathbf{AB})\mathbf{C} = \mathbf{A}(\mathbf{BC}) \tag{7-13a}$$

$$\mathbf{A}(\mathbf{B} + \mathbf{C}) = \mathbf{AB} + \mathbf{AC} \tag{7-13b}$$

but

$$\mathbf{AB} \neq \mathbf{BA} \tag{7-13c}$$

Here is an easy way to check the validity of matrix multiplication. Suppose that $\mathbf{A}$ is $n \times m$ and $\mathbf{B}$ is $p \times q$. Then the product $\mathbf{AB}$ is $(n \times m)(p \times q) = n \times q$ only if $m = p$. So the two inner dimensions (here m and p) must be equal. The size of the result is given by the product of the two outer dimensions, here $n \times q$.

Similarly, the product $\mathbf{BA}$ is $(p \times q)(n \times m) = p \times m$ only if $q = n$. So the two inner dimensions (here q and n) must be equal. The size of the result is given by the product of the two outer dimensions, here $p \times m$. The result of this analysis shows that the products $\mathbf{AB}$ and $\mathbf{BA}$ exist if and only if $\mathbf{A}$ is $n \times m$ and $\mathbf{B}$ is $m \times n$. The product $\mathbf{AB}$ is square and is $n \times n$; the product $\mathbf{BA}$ is also square but of a different size, $m \times m$.

EXAMPLE 7-1 Matrix Multiplication

Determine the products $\mathbf{AB}$ and $\mathbf{BA}$ for the two 3×3 matrices:

$$\mathbf{A} = \begin{pmatrix} 1 & 0 & -3 \\ 2 & -6 & 1 \\ 0 & 4 & 2 \end{pmatrix} \quad \text{and} \quad \mathbf{B} = \begin{pmatrix} 2 & -1 & 4 \\ 0 & -1 & 5 \\ 6 & 3 & 0 \end{pmatrix}$$

SOLUTION Both $\mathbf{A}$ and $\mathbf{B}$ are 3×3 matrices. Thus, their products $\mathbf{AB}$ and $\mathbf{BA}$ will also be 3×3 matrices. From the definition of matrix multiplication, we have

$$\mathbf{AB} = \begin{pmatrix} 2+0-18 & -1+0-9 & 4+0+0 \\ 4+0+6 & -2+6+3 & 8-30+0 \\ 0+0+12 & 0-18+0 & -18+3+0 \end{pmatrix} = \begin{pmatrix} -16 & -10 & 4 \\ 10 & 7 & -22 \\ 12 & 2 & 20 \end{pmatrix}$$

and

$$\mathbf{BA} = \begin{pmatrix} 2-2+0 & 0+6+16 & -6-1+8 \\ 0-2+0 & 0+6+20 & 0-1+10 \\ 6+6+0 & 0-18+0 & -18+3+0 \end{pmatrix} = \begin{pmatrix} 0 & 22 & 2 \\ -2 & 26 & 9 \\ 12 & -18 & -15 \end{pmatrix}$$

Note that $\mathbf{AB} \neq \mathbf{BA}$.

It easily can be verified that if $\mathbf{A}$ is a square matrix of order n and $\mathbf{I}$ is an identity matrix, then (Figure 7–8)

$$\mathbf{AI} = \mathbf{IA} = \mathbf{A} \qquad (7\text{--}14)$$

In matrix manipulations, the identity matrix $\mathbf{I}$ is always assumed to be of the same order as the matrix $\mathbf{A}$.

Transpose The transpose of an $m \times n$ matrix $\mathbf{A}$ is the $n \times m$ matrix denoted by the special symbol $\mathbf{A}^T$, where the transposed matrix is obtained from $\mathbf{A}$ by interchanging its rows and columns. Therefore, if $\mathbf{A} = (a_{ij})$, then

$$\mathbf{A}^T = (a_{ji}) \qquad (7\text{--}15)$$

For example, if

$$\mathbf{A} = \begin{pmatrix} 1 & 2 & 9 \\ 4 & 5 & 6 \\ 7 & 8 & 9 \end{pmatrix}$$

then

$$\mathbf{A}^T = \begin{pmatrix} 1 & 4 & 7 \\ 2 & 5 & 8 \\ 9 & 6 & 9 \end{pmatrix}$$

Note that the elements on the main diagonal of the matrix (1, 5, and 9 in this case) remain unchanged during the transposing process. The transpose of a square matrix can be obtained by imagining that there is a double sided mirror on the main diagonal and moving the elements to the location of their images.

A 2×2 matrix:

$$\mathbf{A} = \begin{pmatrix} a & b \\ c & d \end{pmatrix}$$

An identity matrix:

$$\mathbf{I} = \begin{pmatrix} 1 & 0 \\ 0 & 1 \end{pmatrix}$$

Their product:

$$\mathbf{A} \times \mathbf{I} = \begin{pmatrix} a & b \\ c & d \end{pmatrix} \begin{pmatrix} 1 & 0 \\ 0 & 1 \end{pmatrix}$$

$$= \begin{pmatrix} a \times 1 + b \times 0 & a \times 0 + b \times 1 \\ c \times 1 + d \times 0 & c \times 0 + d \times 1 \end{pmatrix}$$

$$= \begin{pmatrix} a & b \\ c & d \end{pmatrix}$$

$$= \mathbf{A}$$

FIGURE 7–8

Demonstrating that the product of a square matrix with the identity matrix is equal to the matrix itself.

The transpose concept also enables us to represent column vectors conveniently as row vectors and thus to save space. For example, the vector

$$\mathbf{a} = \begin{pmatrix} 1 \\ 2 \\ 3 \end{pmatrix}$$

is equivalent to $\mathbf{b} = (1 \quad 2 \quad 3)^T$. That is, an $n \times 1$ column vector can be represented as the transpose of a $1 \times n$ row vector.

Scalar Product of Vectors   The **scalar product** $\mathbf{a} \cdot \mathbf{b}$ (also called the dot product or inner product) of a row vector $\mathbf{a}$ and a column vector $\mathbf{b}$, having the same number of elements, is a scalar number whose value is determined from

$$\mathbf{a} \cdot \mathbf{b} = (a_1 \quad a_2 \ldots a_n)(b_1 \quad b_2 \ldots b_n)^T = a_1 b_1 + a_2 b_2 + \cdots + a_n b_n \qquad \text{(7–16)}$$

For example, if $\mathbf{a} = (1 \quad -2 \quad 5)$ and $\mathbf{b}^T = (2 \quad 0 \quad 6)$, then

$$\mathbf{a} \cdot \mathbf{b} = (1 \quad -2 \quad 5)(2 \quad 0 \quad 6)^T = 2 + 0 + 30 = 32$$

which is a scalar quantity. Notice that the scalar product $\mathbf{a} \cdot \mathbf{b}$ is equivalent to the scalar product of two vectors $\mathbf{a}$ and $\mathbf{b}$ in an n dimensional domain.

Determinants   The determinant of an $n \times n$ square matrix $\mathbf{A}$ is an $n \times n$ determinant denoted by $|\mathbf{A}|$ or $\det \mathbf{A}$, whose elements are identical to the corresponding elements of the matrix $\mathbf{A}$. Unlike matrices, the determinants can be represented by a number whose value is evaluated by reducing the order of the determinant by expanding it along its rows or columns. The determinant of a 2×2 matrix $\mathbf{A}$ is

$$\det \mathbf{A} = \begin{vmatrix} a_{11} & a_{12} \\ a_{21} & a_{22} \end{vmatrix} = a_{11}a_{22} - a_{21}a_{12} \qquad \text{(7–17)}$$

For example, if

$$\mathbf{A} = \begin{pmatrix} 2 & 6 \\ -1 & 5 \end{pmatrix}$$

then

$$\det \mathbf{A} = \begin{vmatrix} 2 & 6 \\ -1 & 5 \end{vmatrix} = 2 \times 5 - 6 \times (-1) = 16$$

Therefore, the value of the determinant of the given matrix $\mathbf{A}$ is 16.

The determinant of a 3×3 matrix can be evaluated by expanding its determinant along its first row:

$$
\begin{aligned}
\det \mathbf{A} &= \begin{vmatrix} a_{11} & a_{12} & a_{13} \\ a_{21} & a_{22} & a_{23} \\ a_{31} & a_{32} & a_{33} \end{vmatrix} \\
&= a_{11}\begin{vmatrix} a_{22} & a_{23} \\ a_{32} & a_{33} \end{vmatrix} - a_{12}\begin{vmatrix} a_{21} & a_{23} \\ a_{31} & a_{33} \end{vmatrix} + a_{13}\begin{vmatrix} a_{21} & a_{22} \\ a_{31} & a_{32} \end{vmatrix} \\
&= a_{11}a_{22}a_{33} + a_{12}a_{23}a_{31} + a_{13}a_{21}a_{32} \\
&\quad - a_{31}a_{22}a_{13} - a_{32}a_{23}a_{11} - a_{33}a_{21}a_{12}
\end{aligned}
\qquad \text{(7–18)}
$$

Higher-order determinants can be evaluated by extending this procedure. Note that the expansion of a determinant of order n gives n determinants of order $n - 1$. The expansion process can be done along any of the rows or columns of the determinant. For example, if M_{ij} represent the $(n - 1) \times (n - 1)$ determinant obtained by deleting its ith row and jth column, the expansion of the determinant along its ith row can be expressed as

$$\det \mathbf{A} = \sum_{j=1}^{n} (-1)^{i+j} a_{ij} M_{ij} \tag{7-19}$$

This process can be continued until all M_{ij}'s become determinants of the second order, whose values can be calculated easily from Equation 7–18.

A shortcut for evaluating the determinant of a 3×3 matrix is to write the first two columns of the matrix to the right of the matrix and to draw three solid and three dashed lines in diagonal directions so that each is passing through three elements, as shown in Figure 7–9. Then $\det \mathbf{A}$ is determined by adding the products of the elements on the solid lines and subtracting those on the dashed lines, which yields Equation 7–19 directly.

The determinant of a matrix can be evaluated with minimal effort by performing the expansion process along a row or column that contains the largest number of zero elements. For example, the easiest way to evaluate the following determinant

$$\det \mathbf{A} = \begin{vmatrix} 1 & 2 & 1 \\ 0 & 0 & 3 \\ 7 & 5 & 0 \end{vmatrix}$$

is to expand it along the second row to yield

$$\det \mathbf{A} = -0 \begin{vmatrix} 2 & 1 \\ 5 & 0 \end{vmatrix} + 0 \begin{vmatrix} 1 & 1 \\ 7 & 0 \end{vmatrix} - 3 \begin{vmatrix} 1 & 2 \\ 7 & 5 \end{vmatrix}$$

$$= -0 + 0 - 3(1 \times 5 - 2 \times 7) = 27$$

Note that $\det \mathbf{A} = 0$ if the matrix $\mathbf{A}$ has a row or column with all zero elements.

The Inverse of a Matrix   The $n \times n$ square matrix that (when multiplied by a given $n \times n$ square matrix $\mathbf{A}$) gives the identity matrix $\mathbf{I}$ is called the **inverse** of $\mathbf{A}$ and is denoted by $\mathbf{A}^{-1}$. It can be shown that this multiplication process is commutative and can be expressed as

$$\mathbf{A}\mathbf{A}^{-1} = \mathbf{A}^{-1}\mathbf{A} = \mathbf{I} \tag{7-20}$$

The inverse of a matrix is analogous to the reciprocal of a number, except that the inverse of a matrix $\mathbf{A}$ may or may not exist. If $\mathbf{A}^{-1}$ exists, then the matrix $\mathbf{A}$ is said to be **nonsingular**. Otherwise, the matrix $\mathbf{A}$ is said to be **singular**. It can be shown that the inverse $\mathbf{A}^{-1}$ exists if and only if the determinant of $\mathbf{A}$ is nonzero. Therefore, the matrix $\mathbf{A}$ is nonsingular if $\det \mathbf{A} \neq 0$

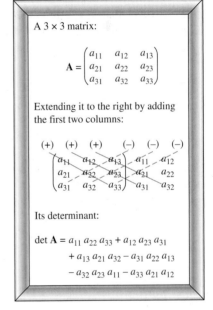

A 3×3 matrix:

$$\mathbf{A} = \begin{pmatrix} a_{11} & a_{12} & a_{13} \\ a_{21} & a_{22} & a_{23} \\ a_{31} & a_{32} & a_{33} \end{pmatrix}$$

Extending it to the right by adding the first two columns:

Its determinant:

$$\det \mathbf{A} = a_{11}\,a_{22}\,a_{33} + a_{12}\,a_{23}\,a_{31}$$
$$+ a_{13}\,a_{21}\,a_{32} - a_{31}\,a_{22}\,a_{13}$$
$$- a_{32}\,a_{23}\,a_{11} - a_{33}\,a_{21}\,a_{12}$$

FIGURE 7–9

A shortcut for evaluating the determinant of a 3×3 matrix.

(a) A singular matrix:

(A^{-1} does not exist)

$$A = \begin{pmatrix} 3 & 6 \\ 2 & 4 \end{pmatrix}$$

$$\det A = \begin{vmatrix} 3 & 6 \\ 2 & 4 \end{vmatrix} = 12 - 12 = 0$$

(b) A nonsingular matrix:

(A^{-1} exists)

$$A = \begin{pmatrix} 5 & 7 \\ 2 & 6 \end{pmatrix}$$

$$\det A = \begin{vmatrix} 5 & 7 \\ 2 & 6 \end{vmatrix} = 30 - 14 = 16 \neq 0$$

FIGURE 7–10

A matrix is singular if its determinant is zero, and it is nonsingular otherwise.

and is singular otherwise (Figure 7–10). A practical procedure for the determination of the inverse of a matrix is described in Section 7–3.

Matrix Functions A matrix whose elements are functions of a variable (say t) is called a **matrix function**. This is in contrast to constant matrices—all of whose elements are constants. As a special case, a matrix function that consists of a single column is called a **vector function**. For example, a general 3×3 matrix function can be expressed as

$$A(t) = \begin{pmatrix} a_{11}(t) & a_{12}(t) & a_{13}(t) \\ a_{21}(t) & a_{22}(t) & a_{23}(t) \\ a_{31}(t) & a_{32}(t) & a_{33}(t) \end{pmatrix} \tag{7–21}$$

A matrix function $A(t)$ is said to be continuous at a point $t = t_0$ if every element of it is continuous at that point. Likewise, a matrix function $A(t)$ is said to be continuous on an interval $t_1 < t < t_2$ if each of its elements is continuous on that interval. For example, the matrix function

$$A(t) = \begin{pmatrix} t^2 & \sin t \\ e^{-3t} & 5 \end{pmatrix}$$

is continuous over the entire t-axis, since each of the four elements is continuous for all t.

Derivatives of Matrix Functions The derivative $A'(t)$ of a differentiable matrix function $A(t)$ is defined as the matrix whose elements are the derivatives of the corresponding elements of $A(t)$ and can be expressed as

$$A'(t) = \frac{dA(t)}{dt} = \left(\frac{da_{ij}(t)}{dt} \right) = (a'_{ij}(t)) \tag{7–22}$$

Therefore, the derivative of the 3×3 matrix function in Equation 7–21 is

$$A'(t) = \begin{pmatrix} a'_{11}(t) & a'_{12}(t) & a'_{13}(t) \\ a'_{21}(t) & a'_{22}(t) & a'_{23}(t) \\ a'_{31}(t) & a'_{32}(t) & a'_{33}(t) \end{pmatrix} \tag{7–23}$$

For example, if

$$A(t) = \begin{pmatrix} t^2 & \sin t \\ e^{-3t} & 5 \end{pmatrix}$$

then

$$A'(t) = \begin{pmatrix} 2t & \cos t \\ -3e^{-3t} & 0 \end{pmatrix}$$

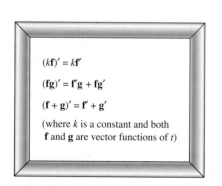

$(k\mathbf{f})' = k\mathbf{f}'$

$(\mathbf{fg})' = \mathbf{f}'\mathbf{g} + \mathbf{fg}'$

$(\mathbf{f} + \mathbf{g})' = \mathbf{f}' + \mathbf{g}'$

(where k is a constant and both $\mathbf{f}$ and $\mathbf{g}$ are vector functions of t)

FIGURE 7–11

The rules for the derivatives of real-valued functions are also applicable to matrix functions.

Many of the rules for the derivatives of real-valued functions in elementary calculus readily can be extended to matrix functions (Figure 7–11). If c is a real, constant number and C is a constant matrix, we have

$$\frac{d}{dt}(c\mathbf{A}) = c\frac{d\mathbf{A}}{dt} \tag{7–24a}$$

$$\frac{d}{dt}(\mathbf{CA}) = \mathbf{C}\frac{d\mathbf{A}}{dt} \tag{7–24b}$$

$$\frac{d}{dt}(\mathbf{AC}) = \frac{d\mathbf{A}}{dt}\mathbf{C} \tag{7–24c}$$

$$\frac{d}{dt}(\mathbf{A} + \mathbf{B}) = \frac{d\mathbf{A}}{dt} + \frac{d\mathbf{B}}{dt} \tag{7–24d}$$

$$\frac{d}{dt}(\mathbf{AB}) = \mathbf{A}\frac{d\mathbf{B}}{dt} + \frac{d\mathbf{A}}{dt}\mathbf{B} \tag{7–24e}$$

When taking the derivative of the product of two matrices, it should be kept in mind that matrix multiplication is not commutative. For example, $(\mathbf{AB})' = \mathbf{AB}' + \mathbf{A}'\mathbf{B}$, not $\mathbf{B}'\mathbf{A} + \mathbf{BA}'$.

Integrals of Matrix Functions The integral $\int \mathbf{A}(t)dt$ of a matrix function $\mathbf{A}(t)$ is defined as the matrix whose elements are the integrals of the corresponding elements of $\mathbf{A}(t)$ and can be expressed as (Figure 7–12)

$$\int \mathbf{A}(t)dt = \left(\int a_{ij}(t)dt\right) \tag{7–25}$$

Therefore, the integral of the 3×3 matrix function in Equation 7–22 is

$$\int \mathbf{A}(t)dt = \begin{pmatrix} \int a_{11}(t)dt & \int a_{12}(t)dt & \int a_{13}(t)dt \\ \int a_{21}(t)dt & \int a_{22}(t)dt & \int a_{23}(t)dt \\ \int a_{31}(t)dt & \int a_{32}(t)dt & \int a_{33}(t)dt \end{pmatrix} \tag{7–26}$$

For example, if

$$\mathbf{A}(t) = \begin{pmatrix} t^2 & \sin t \\ e^{-3t} & 5 \end{pmatrix}$$

then

$$\int_0^t \mathbf{A}(t)dt = \begin{pmatrix} \int_0^t t^2 dt & \int_0^t \sin t\, dt \\ \int_0^t e^{-3t}dt & \int_0^t 5dt \end{pmatrix} = \begin{pmatrix} \frac{1}{3}t^3 & 1 - \cos t \\ -\frac{1}{3}(e^{-3t} - 1) & 5t \end{pmatrix}$$

Many of the rules for the integrals of real-valued functions in elementary calculus readily can be extended to matrix functions. If c is a real, constant number and $\mathbf{C}$ is a constant matrix, then

$$\int c\mathbf{A}dt = c\int \mathbf{A}dt \tag{7–27a}$$

$$\int \mathbf{CA}dt = \mathbf{C}\int \mathbf{A}dt \tag{7–27b}$$

$$\int (\mathbf{A} + \mathbf{B})dt = \int \mathbf{A}dt + \int \mathbf{B}dt \tag{7–27c}$$

A given matrix:

$$\mathbf{A}(t) = \begin{pmatrix} 2t & \cos t \\ -3e^{-3t} & 0 \end{pmatrix}$$

Its integral:

$$\int \mathbf{A}(t)dt = \begin{pmatrix} \int 2tdt & \int \cos t\, dt \\ \int -3e^{-3t}dt & \int 0dt \end{pmatrix}$$
$$= \begin{pmatrix} t^2 + c_1 & \sin t + c_2 \\ e^{-3t} + c_3 & 0 + c_4 \end{pmatrix}$$
$$= \begin{pmatrix} t^2 & \sin t \\ e^{-3t} & 0 \end{pmatrix} + \begin{pmatrix} c_1 & c_2 \\ c_3 & c_4 \end{pmatrix}$$

FIGURE 7–12

A matrix is integrated by integrating each of its elements.

Note that integration or differentiation has no effect on the size of a matrix function.

Section Review

Problems Denoted with a C are Conceptual Problems for Discussion

7–1C What is a square matrix? When is a square matrix symmetric? Is the identity matrix a symmetric matrix? What kind of matrix is called a vector?

7–2C When are two matrices of the same size? When are they equal?

7–3C How is an $n \times n$ matrix multiplied by a constant k? How is an $n \times n$ determinant multiplied by a constant k?

7–4 Show that $(c\mathbf{A})' = c\mathbf{A}'$ and $\int(\mathbf{A} + \mathbf{B})dt = \int\mathbf{A}dt + \int\mathbf{B}dt$.

7–5 If

$$\mathbf{A} = \begin{pmatrix} 1 & -4 \\ -2 & 2 \end{pmatrix} \quad \text{and} \quad \mathbf{B} = \begin{pmatrix} 0 & -6 \\ 5 & 3 \end{pmatrix}$$

verify that (a) $\mathbf{A} + \mathbf{B} = \mathbf{B} + \mathbf{A}$, (b) $4(\mathbf{A} + \mathbf{B}) = 4\mathbf{A} + 4\mathbf{B}$, and (c) $\mathbf{AB} \neq \mathbf{BA}$.

7–2 · MODELS IN MATRIX FORM

In the previous section, we considered the set of linear algebraic equations:

$$2x_1 - 3x_2 + 3x_3 = 5$$
$$5x_1 + 4x_2 - 6x_3 = -5$$
$$x_1 + 7x_2 - x_3 \quad = 12$$

which can be expressed in matrix form as

$$\begin{pmatrix} 2 & -3 & 3 \\ 5 & 4 & -6 \\ 1 & 7 & -1 \end{pmatrix} \begin{pmatrix} x_1 \\ x_2 \\ x_3 \end{pmatrix} = \begin{pmatrix} 5 \\ -5 \\ 12 \end{pmatrix}$$

or in the compact form $\mathbf{Ax} = \mathbf{b}$. A similar approach can be used to represent a system of linear differential equations. For example, consider the system

$$x_1' = -x_1 + x_2 + r_1(t)$$
$$x_2' = x_1 - 2x_2 + x_3 + r_2(t)$$
$$x_3' = x_2 - 2x_3 + r_3(t)$$

These can be represented in matrix form as

$$\begin{pmatrix} x_1' \\ x_2' \\ x_3' \end{pmatrix} = \begin{pmatrix} -1 & 1 & 0 \\ 1 & -2 & 1 \\ 0 & 1 & -2 \end{pmatrix} \begin{pmatrix} x_1 \\ x_2 \\ x_3 \end{pmatrix} + \begin{pmatrix} r_1(t) \\ r_2(t) \\ r_3(t) \end{pmatrix}$$

or $\mathbf{x}' = \mathbf{Ax} + \mathbf{r}(t)$. We call the vector $\mathbf{x}$ the **state vector**, whose components are the **state variables**. This terminology signifies that these variables completely describe the condition (or state) of the system at any time. Therefore, the matrix $\mathbf{A}$ is sometimes called the **state matrix**. In general, our equations will have forcing functions (also called the **inputs**) which appear in vector form as $\mathbf{r}(t)$. As a consequence, the state variables are sometimes called the **outputs**. Sometimes it is more convenient to express the forcing function vector $\mathbf{r}(t)$ as a matrix $\mathbf{B}$ times another function of time, $\mathbf{f}(t)$. The equation set is expressed as

$$\mathbf{x}' = \mathbf{A}\mathbf{x} + \mathbf{B}\mathbf{f}(t)$$

where the matrix $\mathbf{B}$ is called the **input matrix**. The examples in this section illustrate the use of this form. Note that these standard forms require that the coefficients of all the derivatives be 1.

The basic principles of conservation of mass, charge, and heat energy often result in models of physical processes and devices that are a set of coupled first-order equations easily expressible in matrix form. On the other hand, Newton's laws of motion usually result in coupled second-order equations. In these cases, we must define a set of variables—often the displacement and velocity of each mass—in order to write the equations as a set of first-order equations suitable for expressing in matrix form. We now present some engineering examples to illustrate these concepts.

EXAMPLE 7–2   Three Coupled Storage Tanks

Figure 7–13 shows three identical tanks for storing liquid, while various chemical processing occurs in each tank. Liquid flows into the system at the volume flow rate $q_i(\text{m}^3/\text{s})$. Pipes connecting the tanks resist the flow such that the pipe flow is proportional to the liquid height difference across the ends of the pipe. The proportionality constant is $1/R$, where R is called the fluid resistance. The bottom area of each tank is A. Develop a vector–matrix model of the three liquid heights.

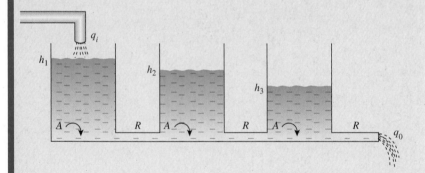

FIGURE 7–13

Three storage tanks.

SOLUTION   Applying conservation of liquid volume to each tank gives

$$(Ah_1)' = Ah_1' = q_i - \frac{h_1 - h_2}{R} = q_i - \frac{1}{R}h_1 + \frac{1}{R}h_2$$

$$(Ah_2)' = Ah_2' = \frac{h_1 - h_2}{R} - \frac{h_2 - h_3}{R} = \frac{1}{R}h_1 - \frac{2}{R}h_2 + \frac{1}{R}h_3$$

$$(Ah_3)' = Ah_3' = \frac{h_2 - h_3}{R} - \frac{1}{R}h_3 = \frac{1}{R}h_2 - \frac{2}{R}h_3$$

From these equations, we can easily determine the matrix elements as follows:

$$\begin{pmatrix} h_1' \\ h_2' \\ h_3' \end{pmatrix} = \frac{1}{RA} \begin{pmatrix} -1 & 1 & 0 \\ 1 & -2 & 1 \\ 0 & 1 & -2 \end{pmatrix} \begin{pmatrix} h_1 \\ h_2 \\ h_3 \end{pmatrix} + \frac{1}{A} \begin{pmatrix} 1 \\ 0 \\ 0 \end{pmatrix} q_i$$

In abbreviated form, we have

$$\mathbf{h}' = \mathbf{A}\mathbf{h} + \mathbf{B}q_i$$

where

$$\mathbf{A} = \frac{1}{RA} \begin{pmatrix} -1 & 1 & 0 \\ 1 & -2 & 1 \\ 0 & 1 & -2 \end{pmatrix} \quad \text{and} \quad \mathbf{B} = \frac{1}{A} \begin{pmatrix} 1 \\ 0 \\ 0 \end{pmatrix}$$

EXAMPLE 7–3   A Circuit with Three *RC* Loops

Figure 7–14 shows a circuit having three *RC* loops and a current supply i_s. Develop a vector–matrix model of the circuit.

SOLUTION   Using the currents i_1, i_2, and i_3 and the voltages v_1, v_2, and v_3 marked on the circuit diagram, we have

$$v_1 = \frac{1}{C}\int i_1 \, dt = \frac{1}{C}\int \left(i_s - \frac{v_1 - v_2}{R} \right) dt$$

$$v_2 = \frac{1}{C}\int i_2 \, dt = \frac{1}{C}\int \left(\frac{v_1 - v_2}{R} - \frac{v_2 - v_3}{R} \right) dt$$

$$v_3 = \frac{1}{C}\int i_3 \, dt = \frac{1}{C}\int \left(\frac{v_2 - v_3}{R} - \frac{v_3}{R} \right) dt$$

Differentiating each equation and collecting terms gives

$$v_1' = \frac{1}{C}\left(i_s - \frac{v_1 - v_2}{R} \right) = \frac{1}{C}i_s - \frac{1}{RC}v_1 + \frac{1}{RC}v_2$$

$$v_2' = \frac{1}{C}\left(\frac{v_1 - v_2}{R} - \frac{v_2 - v_3}{R} \right) = \frac{1}{RC}v_1 - \frac{2}{RC}v_2 + \frac{1}{RC}v_3$$

$$v_3' = \frac{1}{C}\left(\frac{v_2 - v_3}{R} - \frac{v_3}{R} \right) = \frac{1}{RC}v_2 - \frac{2}{RC}v_3$$

From these, we can easily determine the matrix elements:

$$\begin{pmatrix} v_1' \\ v_2' \\ v_3' \end{pmatrix} = \frac{1}{RC} \begin{pmatrix} -1 & 1 & 0 \\ 1 & -2 & 1 \\ 0 & 1 & -2 \end{pmatrix} \begin{pmatrix} v_1 \\ v_2 \\ v_3 \end{pmatrix} + \frac{1}{C} \begin{pmatrix} 1 \\ 0 \\ 0 \end{pmatrix} i_s$$

In abbreviated form, we have

$$\mathbf{v}' = \mathbf{A}\mathbf{v} + \mathbf{B}i_s$$

where

$$\mathbf{A} = \frac{1}{RC} \begin{pmatrix} -1 & 1 & 0 \\ 1 & -2 & 1 \\ 0 & 1 & -2 \end{pmatrix} \quad \text{and} \quad \mathbf{B} = \frac{1}{C} \begin{pmatrix} 1 \\ 0 \\ 0 \end{pmatrix}$$

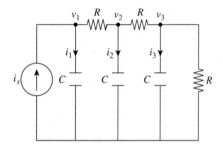

FIGURE 7–14

A circuit with three *RC* loops.

Analogous Systems   Note that the equations in Example 7–3 are identical to those describing the three connected storage tanks covered in Example 7–2, with C replacing A, i_s replacing q_i, and v_1, v_2, and v_3 replacing h_1, h_2, and h_3, respectively. The pipe resistances act like resistors, and the tanks store liquid as a capacitor stores charge. Liquid flow is analogous to charge flow, which is current. Liquid height, which produces pressure that drives liquid flow, is analogous to voltage, which drives current flow. Thus, these two physical systems are said to be *analogous*. Use of such analogies often helps engineers to understand different types of systems. For example, an engineer who is more comfortable with analyzing electric circuits may be helped in analyzing liquid systems using this analogy. Another useful analogy is the one between electric circuits and heat transfer, in which temperature is analogous to voltage and heat-flow rate is analogous to current. This analogy is explored in the chapter problems.

EXAMPLE 7–4   Mass–Damper–Spring Model in Matrix Form

In Chapter 4, we saw that the equation of motion for a mass–damper–spring is

$$mx'' + cx' + kx = f(t)$$

where $f(t)$ is an external force applied to the mass. Develop two vector-matrix representations of this equation.

SOLUTION   An equation always can be converted to the standard vector–matrix form $\mathbf{x}' = \mathbf{A}\mathbf{x} + \mathbf{B}u$ by choosing the state variables to be the basic variable (here, x) and successive derivatives of that variable, until the number of required variables (equal to the order of the equation) is obtained. Since this is a second-order equation, we need only two state variables. So we choose them to be $x_1 = x$ and $x_2 = x'$. Thus,

$$x'_1 = x' = x_2$$

and

$$x'_2 = x'' = \frac{1}{m}\left[-kx - c\frac{dx}{dt} + f(t)\right] = -\frac{k}{m}x_1 - \frac{c}{m}x_2 + \frac{1}{m}f(t)$$

We can write this in the vector–matrix form as $\mathbf{x}' = \mathbf{A}\mathbf{x} + \mathbf{B}f(t)$ as

$$\begin{pmatrix} x'_1 \\ x'_2 \end{pmatrix} = \begin{pmatrix} 0 & 1 \\ -\dfrac{k}{m} & -\dfrac{c}{m} \end{pmatrix}\begin{pmatrix} x_1 \\ x_2 \end{pmatrix} + \begin{pmatrix} 0 \\ \dfrac{1}{m} \end{pmatrix}f(t)$$

where

$$\mathbf{A} = \begin{pmatrix} 0 & 1 \\ -\dfrac{k}{m} & -\dfrac{c}{m} \end{pmatrix}, \quad \mathbf{B} = \begin{pmatrix} 0 \\ \dfrac{1}{m} \end{pmatrix},$$

and

$$\mathbf{x} = \begin{pmatrix} x_1 \\ x_2 \end{pmatrix}$$

The choice for state variables is not unique. For example, we could choose $x_1 = x + x'$ and $x_2 = x - x'$. If $m = c = k = 1$, the system in terms of these new variables would be

$$\begin{pmatrix} x_1' \\ x_2' \end{pmatrix} = \begin{pmatrix} -\dfrac{1}{2} & -\dfrac{1}{2} \\ \dfrac{3}{2} & -\dfrac{1}{2} \end{pmatrix} \begin{pmatrix} x_1 \\ x_2 \end{pmatrix} + \begin{pmatrix} 1 \\ 1 \end{pmatrix} f(t)$$

Although not the case here, sometimes the choice of state variables is made to yield a more convenient form for the matrix $\mathbf{A}$.

EXAMPLE 7–5   Model of a Two-Story Building

The model of a two-story building subjected to the effects of ground motion was developed in Example 4–7 in Chapter 4. Figure 4–7 is repeated here as Figure 7–15. The equations of motion are

$$m_1 x_1'' = -k_2(x_1 - x_2) + k_1(y - x_1)$$

$$m_2 x_2'' = k_2(x_1 - x_2)$$

Develop a vector–matrix model from these equations.

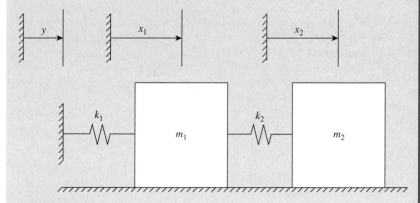

FIGURE 7–15

Model of vibration of a two-story building.

SOLUTION   To convert this equation set, which is of the fourth order, to a set of four first-order equations, we need two additional variables. We may choose these to be the velocities x_1' and x_2', so that the two new variables are $x_3 = x_1'$ and $x_4 = x_2'$. Thus, the four equations are

$$x_1' = x_3$$

$$x_2' = x_4$$

$$m_1 x_3' = -k_2(x_1 - x_2) + k_1(y - x_1)$$

$$m_2 x_4' = k_2(x_1 - x_2)$$

From these equations, we can easily determine the matrix elements.

$$\begin{pmatrix} x_1' \\ x_2' \\ x_3' \\ x_4' \end{pmatrix} = \begin{pmatrix} 0 & 0 & 1 & 0 \\ 0 & 0 & 0 & 1 \\ -\dfrac{k_1 + k_2}{m_1} & \dfrac{k_2}{m_1} & 0 & 0 \\ \dfrac{k_2}{m_2} & -\dfrac{k_2}{m_2} & 0 & 0 \end{pmatrix} \begin{pmatrix} x_1 \\ x_2 \\ x_3 \\ x_4 \end{pmatrix} + \begin{pmatrix} 0 \\ 0 \\ \dfrac{k_1}{m_1} \\ 0 \end{pmatrix} y$$

In abbreviated form, we have

$$\mathbf{x}' = \mathbf{A}\mathbf{x} + \mathbf{B}y$$

where

$$\mathbf{A} = \begin{pmatrix} 0 & 0 & 1 & 0 \\ 0 & 0 & 0 & 1 \\ -\dfrac{k_1 + k_2}{m_1} & \dfrac{k_2}{m_1} & 0 & 0 \\ \dfrac{k_2}{m_2} & -\dfrac{k_2}{m_2} & 0 & 0 \end{pmatrix}$$

and

$$\mathbf{B} = \begin{pmatrix} 0 \\ 0 \\ \dfrac{k_1}{m_1} \\ 0 \end{pmatrix}$$

7–3 ▪ EIGENVALUES AND EIGENVECTORS

Matrix notation offers great convenience when solving large systems of algebraic or differential equations. The important concepts of matrix algebra are best studied in conjunction with the systems of algebraic equations, since the reader is already familiar with such systems. These concepts then can be extended directly to systems of differential equations, which we will do in the following sections.

Consider the following system of three linear, algebraic equations in three unknowns:

$$\begin{aligned} x_1 - 2x_2 + x_3 &= 14 \\ -x_1 + 4x_2 + 2x_3 &= 1 \\ 3x_1 + x_2 - x_3 &= -7 \end{aligned} \qquad \textbf{(7–28)}$$

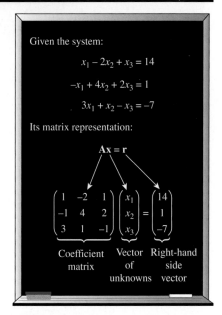

FIGURE 7–16

The matrix representation of a system of algebraic equations.

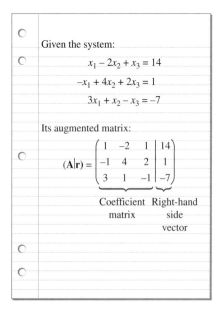

FIGURE 7–17

A system of algebraic equations and its augmented matrix.

This system can be expressed in the matrix notation as

$$\begin{pmatrix} 1 & -2 & 1 \\ -1 & 4 & 2 \\ 3 & 1 & -1 \end{pmatrix} \begin{pmatrix} x_1 \\ x_2 \\ x_3 \end{pmatrix} = \begin{pmatrix} 14 \\ 1 \\ -7 \end{pmatrix} \qquad (7\text{–}29)$$

or

$$\mathbf{Ax} = \mathbf{r} \qquad (7\text{–}30)$$

where

$$\mathbf{A} = \begin{pmatrix} 1 & -2 & 1 \\ -1 & 4 & 2 \\ 3 & 1 & -1 \end{pmatrix}, \quad \mathbf{x} = \begin{pmatrix} x_1 \\ x_2 \\ x_3 \end{pmatrix}, \quad \text{and} \quad \mathbf{r} = \begin{pmatrix} 14 \\ 1 \\ -7 \end{pmatrix}$$

Here the matrix **A** contains all of the coefficients of the unknowns and is called the **coefficient matrix**. The vector **x** contains all of the unknowns and is called the **unknown vector**. The vector **r** contains all of the terms in the right-hand side and is called the **right-hand side vector**. (See Figure 7–16.)

Notice that the vector **r** contains the nonhomogeneous terms. If $\mathbf{r} = \mathbf{0}$, the system of equations is said to be **homogeneous**. Otherwise, it is said to be **nonhomogeneous**. For example, Equations 7–28 form a nonhomogeneous system. The determinant of the coefficient matrix of this system is

$$\det \mathbf{A} = \begin{vmatrix} 1 & -2 & 1 \\ -1 & 4 & 2 \\ 3 & 1 & -1 \end{vmatrix} = -29 \neq 0$$

The coefficient matrix is nonsingular, since $\det \mathbf{A} \neq 0$. Thus, this system of equations has a unique solution. Next, we will discuss how to solve systems of algebraic equations in a systematic manner.

Row Operations

We know that any two equations in a system of algebraic equations can be interchanged; an equation can be multiplied by a nonzero constant, and any two equations can be added to yield another equation that can be used in place of one of those equations. The system will appear quite different after such manipulations, called row operations, but it still remains equivalent to the original system. That is, both the modified and the original systems have the same solution.

These simple manipulations can be used to solve a system of linear algebraic equations simultaneously. Consider that only the coefficients and the right-hand sides are affected by such operations. We first combine the coefficient matrix **A** and the right-hand side vector **r** into a single matrix, called the **augmented matrix**, by attaching **r** to **A** as an additional column separated by a vertical line. For the system in Equations 7–28, the augmented matrix is expressed as (Figure 7–17)

$$(\mathbf{A}|\mathbf{r}) = \begin{pmatrix} 1 & -2 & 1 & | & 14 \\ -1 & 4 & 2 & | & 1 \\ 3 & 1 & -1 & | & -7 \end{pmatrix} \qquad (7\text{-}31)$$

The vertical line in the augmented matrix serves merely as a visual aid to show the partition between the coefficient matrix and the right-hand side vector $\mathbf{r}$. We now apply the row operations on both the system of equations (Equations 7–28) and the augmented matrix (Equation 7–31) for comparison and obtain the solution.

1. Add the first row to the second one and (-3) times the first row to the third one to make the off-diagonal positions of the first column zero. This gives

$$\begin{aligned} x_1 - 2x_2 + x_3 &= 14 \\ 2x_2 + 3x_3 &= 15 \\ 7x_2 - 4x_3 &= -49 \end{aligned} \qquad \begin{pmatrix} 1 & -2 & 1 & | & 14 \\ 0 & 2 & 3 & | & 15 \\ 0 & 7 & -4 & | & -49 \end{pmatrix}$$

This is equivalent to replacing the second equation with the equation obtained by adding the first equation to the second one, and replacing the third equation with the equation obtained by adding (-3) times the first to the third equation. This process eliminates x_1 from the second and third equations.

2. Divide the second row by 2 to obtain a 1 in the diagonal position:

$$\begin{aligned} x_1 - 2x_2 + x_3 &= 14 \\ x_2 + \frac{3}{2}x_3 &= \frac{15}{2} \\ 7x_2 - 4x_3 &= -49 \end{aligned} \qquad \begin{pmatrix} 1 & -2 & 1 & | & 14 \\ 0 & 1 & \frac{3}{2} & | & \frac{15}{2} \\ 0 & 7 & 3 & | & -49 \end{pmatrix}$$

This is equivalent to replacing the second equation with the equation obtained by dividing it by 2. As a rule, we would like to have 1's in all diagonal positions because of the convenience it offers in row operations.

3. Add 2 times the second row to the first one and (-7) times the second row to the third one to make the off-diagonal positions of the second column zero. This gives

$$\begin{aligned} x_1 + 0x_2 + 4x_3 &= 29 \\ x_2 + \frac{3}{2}x_3 &= \frac{15}{2} \\ -\frac{29}{2}x_3 &= -\frac{203}{2} \end{aligned} \qquad \begin{pmatrix} 1 & 0 & 14 & | & 14 \\ 0 & 1 & \frac{3}{2} & | & \frac{15}{2} \\ 0 & 0 & -\frac{29}{2} & | & -\frac{203}{2} \end{pmatrix}$$

This is equivalent to replacing the first equation with the equation obtained by adding 2 times the second equation to the first one, and replacing the third equation with the equation obtained by adding (-7) times the second one to the third one. This process eliminates x_2 from the first and third equations.

4. Divide the last row by $(-29/2)$ to obtain a 1 in the diagonal position:

$$x_1 + 0x_2 + 4x_3 = 29$$
$$x_2 + \frac{3}{2}x_3 = \frac{15}{2}$$
$$x_3 = 7$$

$$\begin{pmatrix} 1 & 0 & 14 & | & 14 \\ 0 & 1 & \frac{3}{2} & | & \frac{15}{2} \\ 0 & 0 & 1 & | & 7 \end{pmatrix}$$

Thus, one of the unknowns is determined to be $x_3 = 7$. Substituting this value of x_3 into the second equation gives $x_2 = -3$, and then substituting it into the first equation gives $x_1 = 1$.

Therefore, once the coefficient matrix is put into the form of an upper triangular matrix by row operations, the unknowns can be determined one by one in reverse order by back substitution. These operations also can be performed systematically on the augmented matrix, as follows. Add $(-3/2)$ times the last row to the second one and (-4) times the last row to the first one to make the off-diagonal positions of the third column zero. We obtain (Figure 7–18)

$$x_1 = 1$$
$$x_2 = -3$$
$$x_3 = 7$$

$$\begin{pmatrix} 1 & 0 & 0 & | & 1 \\ 0 & 1 & 0 & | & -3 \\ 0 & 0 & 1 & | & 7 \end{pmatrix}$$

which is equivalent to

$$\begin{pmatrix} 1 & 0 & 0 \\ 0 & 1 & 0 \\ 0 & 0 & 1 \end{pmatrix} \begin{pmatrix} x_1 \\ x_2 \\ x_3 \end{pmatrix} = \begin{pmatrix} 1 \\ -3 \\ 7 \end{pmatrix}$$

The first matrix on the left is the identity matrix, and the product of any matrix with the identity matrix is equal to itself. Therefore,

$$\begin{pmatrix} x_1 \\ x_2 \\ x_3 \end{pmatrix} = \begin{pmatrix} 1 \\ -3 \\ 7 \end{pmatrix}$$

which again yields $x_1 = 1$, $x_2 = -3$ and, $x_3 = 7$. Therefore, when the coefficient matrix reduces to the identity matrix by row operations, the right-hand side vector reduces to the solution vector.

Row reduction provides a systematic approach for solving systems of linear algebraic equations, and it is very suitable for computer applications. The row operations can be summarized as follows.

1. Any two rows can be interchanged.
2. Any row can be multiplied by a nonzero constant.
3. Any multiple of one row can be added to another row.

These elementary operations correspond to legitimate manipulations of the equations in the system. Note that the ultimate goal in row reduction is to reduce the coefficient matrix to an identity matrix, which is a diagonal matrix with 1's on the main diagonal and zeros everywhere else. If the coefficient matrix does not have a 1 in the upper-left corner ($a_n \neq 1$) to start with, the

The reduced form of the augmented matrix:

$$\begin{pmatrix} 1 & 0 & 0 & | & 1 \\ 0 & 1 & 0 & | & -3 \\ 0 & 0 & 1 & | & 7 \end{pmatrix}$$

Corresponding system:
$$x_1 = 1$$
$$x_2 = -3$$
$$x_3 = 7$$

FIGURE 7–18

When the coefficient matrix of the augmented matrix reduces to an identity matrix, the right-hand column reduces to the solution of the system.

first thing we need to do is to divide the first row by a_{11} to produce a 1 in that position. If $a_{11} = 0$, then we need to interchange the first row with a row whose first element is not zero (Figure 7–19).

A less efficient way of solving the system of linear algebraic equations:

$$\mathbf{A}\mathbf{x} = \mathbf{r}$$

is to evaluate the inverse of the coefficient matrix $\mathbf{A}$. Multiplying the equation by $\mathbf{A}^{-1}$ from the left yields $\mathbf{A}^{-1}\mathbf{A}\mathbf{x} = \mathbf{A}^{-1}\mathbf{r}$ or

$$\mathbf{x} = \mathbf{A}^{-1}\mathbf{r} \qquad (7\text{–}32)$$

since $\mathbf{A}^{-1}\mathbf{A} = \mathbf{I}$ and $\mathbf{I}\mathbf{x} = \mathbf{x}$. Therefore, once $\mathbf{A}^{-1}$ is available, the solution of the given system can be determined by multiplying $\mathbf{A}^{-1}$ by the right-hand side vector $\mathbf{r}$ (Figure 7–20).

Consider a general 2×2 nonsingular matrix:

$$\mathbf{A} = \begin{pmatrix} a & b \\ c & d \end{pmatrix}$$

We can also show by row reduction that the inverse of this 2×2 matrix is

$$\mathbf{A}^{-1} = \frac{1}{\det \mathbf{A}} \begin{pmatrix} d & -b \\ -c & a \end{pmatrix}$$

where $\det \mathbf{A} = ad - cb$.

The inverse of a matrix $\mathbf{A}$ can be determined by taking $\mathbf{A}^{-1}$ in the equation $\mathbf{A}\mathbf{A}^{-1} = \mathbf{I}$ to be the matrix of unknowns, and the identity matrix $\mathbf{I}$ to be the right-hand side matrix. Then $\mathbf{A}^{-1}$ is obtained by transforming the augmented matrix $(\mathbf{A}|\mathbf{I})$ into $(\mathbf{I}|\mathbf{B})$ where the matrix $\mathbf{B}$ is equivalent to $\mathbf{A}^{-1}$. The procedure is now illustrated with an example.

EXAMPLE 7–6   Matrix Inversion By Row Reduction

Solve the following system of three algebraic equations by finding the inverse of its coefficient matrix:

$$x_1 - 2x_2 + x_3 = 14$$
$$-x_1 + 4x_2 + 2x_3 = 1$$
$$3x_1 + x_2 - x_3 = -7$$

SOLUTION This is the system solved earlier by row reduction. Again, we first express the system in the matrix form as $\mathbf{A}\mathbf{x} = \mathbf{r}$, where

$$\mathbf{A} = \begin{pmatrix} 1 & -2 & 1 \\ -1 & 4 & 2 \\ 3 & 1 & -1 \end{pmatrix}, \mathbf{x} = \begin{pmatrix} x_1 \\ x_2 \\ x_3 \end{pmatrix}, \text{ and } \mathbf{r} = \begin{pmatrix} 14 \\ 1 \\ -7 \end{pmatrix}$$

To determine $\mathbf{A}^{-1}$ (assuming it exists), we form the augmented matrix $(\mathbf{A}|\mathbf{I})$.

$$(\mathbf{A}|\mathbf{I}) = \begin{pmatrix} 1 & -2 & 1 & | & 1 & 0 & 0 \\ -1 & 4 & 2 & | & 0 & 1 & 0 \\ 3 & 1 & -1 & | & 0 & 0 & 1 \end{pmatrix}$$

(It is left as an exercise to the student to show that this augmented matrix reduces to the following matrix by applying the row operations until we obtain an identity matrix on the left of the partition.)

Given the system and its augmented matrix:

$$x_2 + 3x_3 = 5$$
$$x_1 - 4x_2 + 2x_3 = 7$$
$$2x_1 + x_2 - 5x_3 = -8$$

$$(\mathbf{A}|\mathbf{r}) = \begin{pmatrix} 0 & 1 & 3 & | & 5 \\ 1 & -4 & 2 & | & 7 \\ 2 & 1 & -5 & | & -8 \end{pmatrix}$$

the equivalent system is obtained by interchanging the first and the second equations:

$$x_1 - 4x_2 + 2x_3 = 7$$
$$x_2 + 3x_3 = 5$$
$$2x_1 + x_2 - 5x_3 = -8$$

$$(\mathbf{A}|\mathbf{r}) = \begin{pmatrix} 1 & -4 & 2 & | & 7 \\ 0 & 1 & 3 & | & 5 \\ 2 & 1 & -5 & | & -8 \end{pmatrix}$$

FIGURE 7–19

Interchanging two rows in the augmented matrix corresponds to interchanging two equations in the corresponding system.

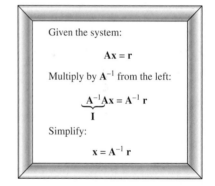

Given the system:

$$\mathbf{A}\mathbf{x} = \mathbf{r}$$

Multiply by $\mathbf{A}^{-1}$ from the left:

$$\underbrace{\mathbf{A}^{-1}\mathbf{A}}_{\mathbf{I}}\mathbf{x} = \mathbf{A}^{-1}\mathbf{r}$$

Simplify:

$$\mathbf{x} = \mathbf{A}^{-1}\mathbf{r}$$

FIGURE 7–20

Solving a system of linear algebraic equations using the inverse of the coefficient matrix.

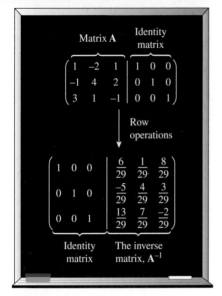

FIGURE 7–21

When the coefficient matrix **A** in the augmented matrix $(\mathbf{A}|\mathbf{I})$ is reduced to the identity matrix, the identity matrix reduces to the inverse matrix.

Given system: $\mathbf{Ax} = \mathbf{r}$

(1) det $\mathbf{A} \neq 0$: The system has a unique solution.

(2) det $\mathbf{A} = 0$: the system has either no solution or multiple solutions.

FIGURE 7–22

A linear, nonhomogeneous system of algebraic equations has a unique solution only when the determinant of its coefficient matrix is not zero, so det $\mathbf{A} \neq 0$.

The reduced matrix is

$$\left(\begin{array}{ccc|ccc} 1 & 0 & 0 & \dfrac{6}{29} & \dfrac{1}{29} & \dfrac{8}{29} \\[2mm] 0 & 1 & 0 & \dfrac{-5}{29} & \dfrac{4}{29} & \dfrac{3}{29} \\[2mm] 0 & 0 & 1 & \dfrac{13}{29} & \dfrac{7}{29} & \dfrac{-2}{29} \end{array} \right)$$

Therefore, the inverse of the coefficient matrix **A** is (Figure 7–21)

$$\mathbf{A}^{-1} = \left(\begin{array}{ccc} \dfrac{6}{29} & \dfrac{1}{29} & \dfrac{8}{29} \\[2mm] \dfrac{-5}{29} & \dfrac{4}{29} & \dfrac{3}{29} \\[2mm] \dfrac{13}{29} & \dfrac{7}{29} & -2 \end{array} \right) = \dfrac{1}{29} \left(\begin{array}{ccc} 6 & 1 & 8 \\ -5 & 4 & 3 \\ 13 & 7 & -2 \end{array} \right)$$

Then the solution of the given system can be determined from Equation 7–32 to be

$$\mathbf{x} = \mathbf{A}^{-1}\mathbf{r} = \dfrac{1}{29} \left(\begin{array}{ccc} 6 & 1 & 8 \\ -5 & 4 & 3 \\ 13 & 7 & -2 \end{array} \right) \left(\begin{array}{c} 14 \\ 1 \\ -7 \end{array} \right) = \left(\begin{array}{c} 1 \\ -3 \\ 7 \end{array} \right)$$

which is the same result obtained earlier by row reduction.

The previous examples show that when the coefficient matrix **A** of a nonhomogeneous system of n linear algebraic equations in n unknowns is nonsingular, det $\mathbf{A} \neq 0$, and a unique solution exists. But when the coefficient matrix **A** is singular, det $\mathbf{A} = 0$, and the system $\mathbf{Ax} = \mathbf{r}$ has either no solution or multiple solutions, as illustrated in the following two examples (Figure 7–22).

EXAMPLE 7–7   **System of Equations with No Solutions**

Solve the following system of three algebraic equations.

$$\begin{aligned} x_1 + x_2 - 2x_3 &= 1 \\ 3x_1 - 2x_2 + x_3 &= -15 \\ 2x_1 - 3x_2 + 3x_3 &= 2 \end{aligned}$$

SOLUTION   This system can be expressed in the matrix notation as $\mathbf{Ax} = \mathbf{r}$, where

$$\mathbf{A} = \left(\begin{array}{ccc} 1 & 1 & -2 \\ 3 & -2 & 1 \\ 2 & -3 & 3 \end{array} \right), \mathbf{x} = \left(\begin{array}{c} x_1 \\ x_2 \\ x_3 \end{array} \right), \text{ and } \mathbf{r} = \left(\begin{array}{c} 1 \\ -15 \\ 2 \end{array} \right)$$

The determinant of the coefficient matrix is

$$\det \mathbf{A} = \left| \begin{array}{ccc} 1 & 1 & -2 \\ 3 & -2 & 1 \\ 2 & -3 & 3 \end{array} \right| = -6 + 2 + 18 - 8 - (-3) - 9 = 0$$

Thus, the coefficient matrix is singular, and the given system has either no solution or multiple solutions. The augmented matrix of this system is

$$(\mathbf{A}|\mathbf{r}) = \begin{pmatrix} 1 & 1 & -2 & 1 \\ 3 & -2 & 1 & -15 \\ 2 & -3 & 3 & 2 \end{pmatrix}$$

It reduces by row operations to

$$\begin{pmatrix} 1 & 0 & -\dfrac{3}{5} & -\dfrac{13}{5} \\ 0 & 1 & -\dfrac{7}{5} & \dfrac{18}{5} \\ 0 & 0 & 0 & 18 \end{pmatrix}$$

The last row is equivalent to the equation

$$0 \cdot x_1 + 0 \cdot x_2 + 0 \cdot x_3 = 18$$

which cannot be satisfied by any set of values for x_1, x_2, and x_3. Thus, we conclude that the given system has *no* solution.

EXAMPLE 7–8   System of Equations with Multiple Solutions

Solve the following system of three algebraic equations.

$$x_1 + x_2 - 2x_3 = 1$$
$$3x_1 - 2x_2 + x_3 = -15$$
$$2x_1 - 3x_2 + 3x_3 = -16$$

SOLUTION   This is the system considered in the last example, except the right side of the last equation is –16 instead of 2. It can be expressed in the matrix notation as $\mathbf{Ax} = \mathbf{r}$, where

$$\mathbf{A} = \begin{pmatrix} 1 & 1 & -2 \\ 3 & -2 & 1 \\ 2 & -3 & 3 \end{pmatrix}, \mathbf{x} = \begin{pmatrix} x_1 \\ x_2 \\ x_3 \end{pmatrix}, \text{ and } \mathbf{r} = \begin{pmatrix} 1 \\ -15 \\ -16 \end{pmatrix}$$

We notice that the coefficient matrix $\mathbf{A}$ remains the same, and its determinant was determined in the previous example to be zero. Therefore, the coefficient matrix is singular, and the given system again has either no solution or multiple solutions. The augmented matrix of this system is

$$(\mathbf{A}|\mathbf{r}) = \begin{pmatrix} 1 & 1 & -2 & 1 \\ 3 & -2 & 1 & -15 \\ 2 & -3 & 3 & -16 \end{pmatrix}$$

It reduces by row operations to

$$\begin{pmatrix} 1 & 0 & -\dfrac{3}{5} & -\dfrac{13}{5} \\ 0 & 1 & -\dfrac{7}{5} & \dfrac{18}{5} \\ 0 & 0 & 0 & 0 \end{pmatrix}$$

which is equivalent to

$$x_1 - \frac{3}{5}x_3 = -\frac{13}{5} \quad \text{and} \quad x_2 - \frac{7}{5}x_3 = \frac{18}{5}$$

This is a system of two equations in three unknowns. Such systems always have infinite sets of solutions, since one of the unknowns can be assigned any arbitrary value. If we take $x_3 = \alpha$ (where α is arbitrary), the solution of the given system can be expressed as

$$x_1 = \frac{3}{5}\alpha - \frac{13}{5}, \ x_2 = \frac{7}{5}\alpha + \frac{18}{5}, \ \text{and} \ x_3 = \alpha$$

or in the vector form

$$\mathbf{x} = \begin{pmatrix} x_1 \\ x_2 \\ x_3 \end{pmatrix} = \alpha \begin{pmatrix} \dfrac{3}{5} \\ \dfrac{7}{5} \\ 1 \end{pmatrix} + \begin{pmatrix} -\dfrac{13}{5} \\ \dfrac{18}{5} \\ 0 \end{pmatrix} \tag{7-33}$$

Therefore, the system will have different solutions corresponding to the different values of α. The solution of the given system also can be expressed as

$$x = x_h + x_p \tag{7-34}$$

where

$$\mathbf{x}_n = \alpha \begin{pmatrix} \dfrac{3}{5} \\ \dfrac{7}{5} \\ 1 \end{pmatrix} \quad \text{and} \quad \mathbf{x}_p = \begin{pmatrix} -\dfrac{13}{5} \\ \dfrac{18}{5} \\ 0 \end{pmatrix} \tag{7-35}$$

It can be checked by direct substitution that the *homogeneous solution* $\mathbf{x}_h$ satisfies the homogeneous part of the system, and the *particular solution* $\mathbf{x}_p$ satisfies the entire (nonhomogeneous) system.

Homogeneous Systems

A system of n linear, homogeneous algebraic equations in n unknowns can be expressed as

$$a_{11}x_1 + a_{12}x_2 + \cdots + a_{1n}x_n = 0$$
$$a_{21}x_1 + a_{22}x_2 + \cdots + a_{2n}x_n = 0$$
$$\vdots \qquad\qquad\qquad \vdots$$
$$a_{n1}x_1 + a_{n2}x_2 + \cdots + a_{nn}x_n = 0$$

or in the matrix notation, as

$$\mathbf{Ax = 0} \tag{7-36}$$

where $\mathbf{A}$ is the coefficient matrix, $\mathbf{x}$ is the vector of unknowns, and $\mathbf{0}$ is the zero vector.

We mentioned earlier that a nonhomogeneous system of n algebraic equations in n unknowns has a unique solution only when the determinant of the coefficient matrix is nonzero: det $\mathbf{A} \neq 0$. This is also the case for homogeneous systems, except the unique solution in this case is the trivial solution $\mathbf{x} = \mathbf{0}$, in which we normally have no interest. Therefore, a homogeneous system will have meaningful (nontrivial) solutions only when the coefficient matrix is singular and thus det $\mathbf{A} = 0$. In this case, the homogeneous system $\mathbf{Ax} = \mathbf{0}$ will have an infinite number of solutions—the trivial solution being just one of them. Therefore, disregarding the trivial solution, we say that a homogeneous system has either an infinite number of solutions or no solutions at all (Figure 7–23).

Given system: $\mathbf{Ax} = \mathbf{0}$

(1) det $\mathbf{A} \neq 0$: The system has no
   (nontrivial) solution.

(2) det $\mathbf{A} = 0$: the system has an
   infinite number of solutions.

FIGURE 7–23

A linear, *homogeneous* system of algebraic equations has nontrivial solutions only when the determinant of its coefficient matrix is zero: det $\mathbf{A} = 0$.

EXAMPLE 7–9   Homogeneous Systems of Equations

Solve the following system of three algebraic equations.

$$x_1 + x_2 - 2x_3 = 0$$
$$3x_1 - 2x_2 + x_3 = 0$$
$$2x_1 - 3x_2 + 3x_3 = 0$$

SOLUTION This is a homogeneous system, since all of the right-hand sides are zero, and it is equivalent to the homogeneous part of the system considered in Example 7–8. It can be expressed in the matrix notation as $\mathbf{Ax} = \mathbf{0}$, where

$$\mathbf{A} = \begin{pmatrix} 1 & 1 & -2 \\ 3 & -2 & 1 \\ 2 & -3 & 3 \end{pmatrix}, \mathbf{x} = \begin{pmatrix} x_1 \\ x_2 \\ x_3 \end{pmatrix}, \text{ and } \mathbf{0} = \begin{pmatrix} 0 \\ 0 \\ 0 \end{pmatrix}$$

We notice that the coefficient matrix $\mathbf{A}$ is identical to the one in the previous example, and its determinant was determined to be zero. Therefore, the coefficient matrix is singular, and the given system has an infinite number of solutions.

The augmented matrix of this system is

$$(\mathbf{A}|\mathbf{0}) = \begin{pmatrix} 1 & 1 & -2 & | & 0 \\ 3 & -2 & 1 & | & 0 \\ 2 & -3 & 3 & | & 0 \end{pmatrix}$$

It reduces by row operations to

$$\begin{pmatrix} 1 & 0 & -\dfrac{3}{5} & | & 0 \\ 0 & 1 & -\dfrac{7}{5} & | & 0 \\ 0 & 0 & 0 & | & 0 \end{pmatrix}$$

which is equivalent to

$$x_1 - \frac{3}{5}x_3 = 0 \quad \text{and} \quad x_2 - \frac{7}{5}x_3 = 0$$

This is a system of two equations in three unknowns. Such systems always have infinite sets of solutions, since one of the unknowns can be assigned any arbitrary value. If we take $x_3 = \alpha$, (where α is arbitrary), the solution of given system can be expressed as

$$x_1 = \frac{3}{5}\alpha, \quad x_2 = \frac{7}{5}\alpha, \quad \text{and} \quad x_3 = \alpha$$

or in the vector form, as

$$\mathbf{x} = \begin{pmatrix} x_1 \\ x_2 \\ x_3 \end{pmatrix} = \alpha \begin{pmatrix} \dfrac{3}{5} \\ \dfrac{7}{5} \\ 1 \end{pmatrix} \tag{7-37}$$

which is identical to the homogeneous solution $\mathbf{x}_h$ of the system in Example 7–8. This is not surprising, since the system of equations in this example is identical to the homogeneous part of the system considered in the previous example. Again, the system will have different solutions corresponding to the different values of α.

The two given vectors:

$$\mathbf{v}_1 = \begin{pmatrix} 2 \\ -4 \\ 1 \end{pmatrix} \text{ and } \mathbf{v}_2 = \begin{pmatrix} 6 \\ -12 \\ 3 \end{pmatrix}$$

are linearly dependent, since

$$\mathbf{v}_2 = \begin{pmatrix} 6 \\ -12 \\ 3 \end{pmatrix} = 3 \begin{pmatrix} 2 \\ -4 \\ 1 \end{pmatrix} = 3\mathbf{v}_1$$

FIGURE 7–24

Two vectors are linearly dependent if one is a constant multiple of the other.

Linear Independence of Vectors

The concept of linear independence of vectors closely parallels the linear independence of functions. Two vectors are said to be **linearly independent** if one vector is not a constant multiple of the other. Geometrically, this corresponds to two vectors that are not parallel to each other (Figure 7–24).

Generalizing, n vectors $\mathbf{v}_1, \mathbf{v}_2, \mathbf{v}_3, \ldots, \mathbf{v}_n$ are said to be **linearly independent** if the equation

$$C_1\mathbf{v}_1 + C_2\mathbf{v}_2 + C_3\mathbf{v}_3 + \cdots + C_n\mathbf{v}_n = 0 \tag{7-38}$$

where $C_1, C_2, \ldots, C_n$ are constants is satisfied only when $C_1 = C_2 = \cdots = C_n = 0$. Otherwise, they are linearly dependent.

The solution of a system of n first-order linear differential equations in n unknown functions involves n vectors (each with n elements), and it is often necessary to determine whether these solution vectors are linearly dependent or independent. Therefore, we will limit the following discussion to the linear independence of n vectors (each with n elements). Consider the system:

$$a_1C_1 + b_1C_2 + c_1C_3 = 0$$
$$a_2C_1 + b_2C_2 + c_2C_3 = 0$$
$$a_3C_1 + b_3C_2 + c_3C_3 = 0$$

which is the system of three homogeneous equations in the three unknowns C_1, C_2, and C_3. This system can be expressed in matrix from as $\mathbf{Ax} = \mathbf{0}$, where

$$\mathbf{A} = \begin{pmatrix} a_1 & b_1 & c_1 \\ a_2 & b_2 & c_3 \\ a_3 & b_3 & c_3 \end{pmatrix}, \quad \mathbf{x} = \begin{pmatrix} C_1 \\ C_2 \\ C_3 \end{pmatrix}, \text{ and } \mathbf{0} = \begin{pmatrix} 0 \\ 0 \\ 0 \end{pmatrix}$$

This system will have the trivial solution $\mathbf{x} = \mathbf{0}$ or $C_1 = C_2 = C_3 = 0$ if and only if the determinant of the coefficient matrix is not zero:

$$\det \mathbf{A} = \begin{vmatrix} a_1 & b_1 & c_1 \\ a_2 & b_2 & c_2 \\ a_3 & b_3 & c_3 \end{vmatrix} \neq 0$$

Thus, we conclude that n vectors (each containing n elements) are linearly independent if and only if the determinant of the $n \times n$ matrix whose columns consist of these vectors is nonzero.

EXAMPLE 7–10   Linear Independence of Constant Vectors

Determine if the following three vectors are linearly independent.

$$\mathbf{v}_1 = \begin{pmatrix} 2 \\ 0 \\ 1 \end{pmatrix}, \mathbf{v}_2 = \begin{pmatrix} 1 \\ 1 \\ -1 \end{pmatrix}, \text{ and } \mathbf{v}_3 = \begin{pmatrix} 2 \\ 1 \\ -3 \end{pmatrix}$$

SOLUTION   These three vectors each containing three elements. We first form the linear combination of these vectors using the constants C_1, C_2, and C_3 and setting it equal to zero, as

$$C_1\mathbf{v}_1 + C_2\mathbf{v}_2 + C_3\mathbf{v}_3 = 0$$

or

$$C_1 \begin{pmatrix} 2 \\ 0 \\ 1 \end{pmatrix} + C_2 \begin{pmatrix} 1 \\ 1 \\ -1 \end{pmatrix} + C_3 \begin{pmatrix} 2 \\ 1 \\ -3 \end{pmatrix} = \begin{pmatrix} 0 \\ 0 \\ 0 \end{pmatrix}$$

This matrix equation is equivalent to the following system of three linear homogeneous algebraic equations:

$$2C_1 + C_2 + 2C_3 = 0$$
$$C_2 + C_3 = 0$$
$$C_1 - C_2 - 3C_3 = 0$$

or

$$\begin{pmatrix} 2 & 1 & 2 \\ 0 & 1 & 1 \\ 1 & -1 & -3 \end{pmatrix} \begin{pmatrix} C_1 \\ C_2 \\ C_3 \end{pmatrix} = \begin{pmatrix} 0 \\ 0 \\ 0 \end{pmatrix}$$

The determinant of the coefficient matrix is

$$\begin{vmatrix} 2 & 1 & 2 \\ 0 & 1 & 1 \\ 1 & -1 & -3 \end{vmatrix} = -5$$

which is nonzero. Therefore, the only solution of this homogeneous system is the trivial solution $C_1 = C_2 = C_3 = 0$. Thus, we conclude that the given vectors are linearly independent (Figure 7–25).

Three given vectors:

$$\mathbf{v}_1 = \begin{pmatrix} 2 \\ 0 \\ 1 \end{pmatrix}, \mathbf{v}_2 = \begin{pmatrix} 1 \\ 1 \\ -1 \end{pmatrix}, \text{ and } \mathbf{v}_3 = \begin{pmatrix} 2 \\ 1 \\ -3 \end{pmatrix}$$

are linearly independent, since the determinant of the matrix they form is not zero:

$$\begin{vmatrix} 2 & 1 & 2 \\ 0 & 1 & 1 \\ 1 & -1 & -3 \end{vmatrix} = -5 \neq 0$$

FIGURE 7–25

Three 3×1 vectors are linearly independent if the determinant of the 3×3 matrix whose columns are these vectors is not zero.

When determining the linear independence of vectors, we can skip the intermediate steps, directly examine the matrix whose columns are the given vectors, and evaluate its determinant. The vectors are linearly independent if this determinant is nonzero, and they are linearly dependent otherwise.

The concepts of linear dependence and independence are also applicable to vector functions. The n vectors $\mathbf{v}_1(t)$, $\mathbf{v}_2(t)$, ..., $\mathbf{v}_n(t)$ are said to be linearly dependent in an interval $t_1 < t < t_2$ if there exist n constants $C_1, C_2, \dots, C_n$, where at least one is nonzero, such that the equation

$$C_1\mathbf{v}_1(t) + C_2\mathbf{v}_2(t) + C_3\mathbf{v}_3(t) + \cdots + C_n\mathbf{v}_n(t) = 0 \qquad (7\text{–}39)$$

is satisfied for all t in that interval. Otherwise, they are linearly independent.

A quantity that is very useful in determining the linear independence of n solution vectors of a system of n linear, first-order differential equations with constant coefficients is the *Wronskian* $W(t)$, which was introduced in Chapter 3 for single equations.

The Wronskian of the n vector functions each containing n elements:

$$\mathbf{v}_1(t) = \begin{pmatrix} v_{11}(t) \\ v_{21}(t) \\ \vdots \\ v_{n1}(t) \end{pmatrix}, \mathbf{v}_2(t) = \begin{pmatrix} v_{12}(t) \\ v_{22}(t) \\ \vdots \\ v_{n2}(t) \end{pmatrix}, \mathbf{v}_n(t) = \begin{pmatrix} v_{1n}(t) \\ v_{2n}(t) \\ \vdots \\ v_{nn}(t) \end{pmatrix}$$

is defined as the $n \times n$ determinant whose columns are these vectors. That is,

$$W(t) = \begin{vmatrix} v_{11}(t) & v_{12}(t) & . & . & v_{1n}(t) \\ v_{21}(t) & v_{22}(t) & . & . & v_{2n}(t) \\ \vdots & \vdots & \vdots & \vdots & \vdots \\ v_{n1}(t) & v_{n2}(t) & . & . & v_{nn}(t) \end{vmatrix} \qquad (7\text{-}40)$$

These vectors are linearly dependent in an interval if their Wronskian is identically zero for all t in that interval. Otherwise, they are linearly independent (Figure 7–26).

Three given vector functions

$$\mathbf{v}_1 = \begin{pmatrix} v_{11}(t) \\ v_{21}(t) \\ v_{31}(t) \end{pmatrix}, \mathbf{v}_2 = \begin{pmatrix} v_{12}(t) \\ v_{22}(t) \\ v_{32}(t) \end{pmatrix}, \mathbf{v}_3 = \begin{pmatrix} v_{13}(t) \\ v_{23}(t) \\ v_{33}(t) \end{pmatrix}$$

are linearly dependent in $t_1 < t < t_2$ if

$$W(t) = \begin{vmatrix} v_{11}(t) & v_{12}(t) & v_{13}(t) \\ v_{21}(t) & v_{22}(t) & v_{23}(t) \\ v_{31}(t) & v_{32}(t) & v_{33}(t) \end{vmatrix} = 0$$

for all t in $t_1 < t < t_2$.

FIGURE 7–26

Three (or more) vector functions are linearly dependent in an interval if their Wronskian is identically equal to zero in that interval.

EXAMPLE 7–11   Linear Independence of Vector Functions

Determine if the following three vector functions are linearly independent in the interval $0 < t < \infty$.

$$\mathbf{v}_1(t) = \begin{pmatrix} e^t \\ -e^{2t} \\ e^{-2t} \end{pmatrix}, \mathbf{v}_2(t) = \begin{pmatrix} 0 \\ 2e^{2t} \\ -e^{-2t} \end{pmatrix}, \text{ and } \mathbf{v}_3(t) = \begin{pmatrix} -2e^t \\ e^{2t} \\ 3e^{-2t} \end{pmatrix}$$

SOLUTION   These are three vector functions each containing three elements. We now evaluate the Wronskian of these vectors by first forming the determinant whose columns are the given vectors, as

$$W(t) = \begin{vmatrix} e^t & 0 & -2e^t \\ -e^{2t} & 2e^{2t} & e^{2t} \\ e^{-2t} & -e^{-2t} & 3e^{-2t} \end{vmatrix} = 9e^t$$

which is never zero in the interval $0 < t < \infty$. Therefore, these three vectors are linearly independent in that interval.

The evaluation of the Wronskian of vector functions can be simplified somewhat by factoring out the common functions from the rows or the columns of the determinant, as shown in Figure 7–27. In doing that, we should keep in mind that multiplying a determinant by a factor is equivalent to multiplying *any* one of its rows or columns by that factor. This is in contrast to matrices, since multiplying a matrix by a factor is equivalent to multiplying *all* of its elements by that factor.

The systematic solution of a system of linear differential equations of the form

$$\mathbf{x}' = \mathbf{A}\mathbf{x} \qquad (7\text{-}41)$$

where $\mathbf{A}$ is the coefficient matrix, involves the use of eigenvalues and the corresponding eigenvectors of the matrix $\mathbf{A}$. Therefore, we devote the rest of

$$W(t) = \begin{vmatrix} e^t & 0 & -2e^t \\ -e^{2t} & 2e^{2t} & e^{2t} \\ e^{-2t} & -e^{-2t} & 3e^{-2t} \end{vmatrix}$$

$$= e^t \begin{vmatrix} 1 & 0 & -2 \\ -e^{2t} & 2e^{2t} & e^{2t} \\ e^{-2t} & -e^{-2t} & 3e^{-2t} \end{vmatrix}$$

$$= e^t e^{2t} \begin{vmatrix} 1 & 0 & -2 \\ -1 & 2 & 1 \\ e^{-2t} & -e^{-2t} & 3e^{-2t} \end{vmatrix}$$

$$= e^t e^{2t} e^{-2t} \begin{vmatrix} 1 & 0 & -2 \\ -1 & 2 & 1 \\ 1 & -1 & 3 \end{vmatrix}$$

$$= 9e^t$$

FIGURE 7–27

Factoring out the common functions from the rows (or columns) of a determinant to simplify its evaluation.

this section to the determination of eigenvalues and eigenvectors associated with an $n \times n$ square matrix $\mathbf{A}$ whose elements are real constants.

If we attempt a solution to Equation 7–41 of the form $\mathbf{x} = \mathbf{C}e^{\lambda t}$, where $\mathbf{C}$ is a vector of constants, then $\mathbf{x}' = \mathbf{C}\lambda e^{\lambda t}$, and Equation 7–41 gives $\mathbf{x}' = \mathbf{C}\lambda e^{\lambda t} = \mathbf{A}\mathbf{C}e^{\lambda t}$. Dividing out $e^{\lambda t}$ and rearranging gives

$$\mathbf{AC} - \lambda\mathbf{C} = \mathbf{AC} - \lambda\mathbf{IC} = (\mathbf{A} - \lambda\mathbf{I})\mathbf{C} = 0$$

Since the right-hand side is zero, a meaningful solution to Equation 7–41 is possible only if the vector $\mathbf{C}$ is nonzero, and this is possible only if $\det(\mathbf{A} - \lambda\mathbf{I}) = 0$.

Eigenvalues and Eigenvectors

Consider an $n \times n$ matrix $\mathbf{A}$ expressed as

$$\mathbf{A} = \begin{pmatrix} a_{11} & a_{12} & . & . & a_{1n} \\ a_{21} & a_{22} & . & . & a_{2n} \\ \vdots & \vdots & \vdots & \vdots & \vdots \\ a_{n1} & a_{n2} & . & . & a_{nn} \end{pmatrix} \qquad (7\text{–}42)$$

The real or complex values of λ that satisfy the equation

$$\det(\mathbf{A} - \lambda\mathbf{I}) = 0 \qquad (7\text{–}43)$$

are called **eigenvalues** (or characteristic values) of the matrix $\mathbf{A}$. The nonzero vector $\mathbf{v}$ that satisfies the equation

$$(\mathbf{A} - \lambda\mathbf{I})\mathbf{v} = \mathbf{0} \qquad (7\text{–}44)$$

is called an **eigenvector** (or characteristic vector) associated with the eigenvalue λ of the matrix $\mathbf{A}$ (Figure 7–28).

The matrix $\mathbf{A} - \lambda\mathbf{I}$ can be expressed as

$$\mathbf{A} - \lambda\mathbf{I} = \begin{pmatrix} a_{11} & a_{12} & . & . & a_{1n} \\ a_{21} & a_{22} & . & . & a_{2n} \\ \vdots & \vdots & \vdots & \vdots & \vdots \\ a_{n1} & a_{n2} & . & . & a_{nn} \end{pmatrix} - \begin{pmatrix} \lambda & 0 & . & . & 0 \\ 0 & \lambda & . & . & 0 \\ \vdots & \vdots & \vdots & \vdots & \vdots \\ 0 & 0 & . & . & \lambda \end{pmatrix}$$

$$= \begin{pmatrix} a_{11}-\lambda & a_{12} & . & . & a_{1n} \\ a_{21} & a_{22}-\lambda & . & . & a_{2n} \\ \vdots & \vdots & \vdots & \vdots & \vdots \\ a_{n1} & a_{n2} & . & . & a_{nn}-\lambda \end{pmatrix}$$

which is equivalent to the matrix obtained by subtracting λ from the elements on the main diagonal of the matrix $\mathbf{A}$. Then Equation 7–43 becomes

$$\det(\mathbf{A} - \lambda\mathbf{I}) = \begin{vmatrix} a_{11}-\lambda & a_{12} & . & . & a_{1n} \\ a_{21} & a_{22}-\lambda & . & . & a_{2n} \\ \vdots & \vdots & \vdots & \vdots & \vdots \\ a_{n1} & a_{n2} & . & . & a_{nn}-\lambda \end{vmatrix} = 0 \qquad (7\text{–}45)$$

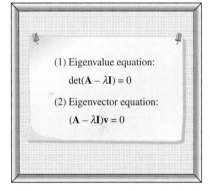

(1) Eigenvalue equation:

$$\det(\mathbf{A} - \lambda\mathbf{I}) = 0$$

(2) Eigenvector equation:

$$(\mathbf{A} - \lambda\mathbf{I})\mathbf{v} = 0$$

FIGURE 7–28

The equations that give the eigenvalues λ and the eigenvectors $\mathbf{v}$ of a matrix $\mathbf{A}$.

Expanding this determinant gives

$$\lambda^n + b_1\lambda^{n-1} + b_2\lambda^{n-2} + \cdots + b_n = 0 \qquad \textbf{(7–46)}$$

which is an nth-degree polynomial equation in λ called the **characteristic equation of the matrix A**. By the fundamental theorem of algebra, this equation has n roots—some of which may be repeated or complex. Therefore, an $n \times n$ matrix has n eigenvalues, which are not necessarily real and distinct (Figure 7–29).

A root that is repeated k times is called a **k-fold root** or a **root of multiplicity k**. A root that has a multiplicity 1 is called a **simple root**. A root that has a multiplicity 2 or higher is called a repeated root. When all of the elements of the matrix $\mathbf{A}$ are real, all of the coefficients of the polynomial equation (Equation 7–46) become real, and any complex roots in this case must appear in conjugate pairs.

Note that the zero vector $\mathbf{v} = \mathbf{0}$ always satisfies the eigenvector equation $(\mathbf{A} - \lambda\mathbf{I})\mathbf{v} = \mathbf{0}$. But we always disregard it as the trivial case and look for an eigenvector that has at least one nonzero element.

Also, note that if $\mathbf{v}$ is an eigenvector, a constant multiple of it, $k\mathbf{v}$, is also an eigenvector. This is because if $(\mathbf{A} - \lambda\mathbf{I})\mathbf{v} = \mathbf{0}$ then $(\mathbf{A} - \lambda\mathbf{I})k\mathbf{v} = k(\mathbf{A} - \lambda\mathbf{I})\mathbf{v} = k \times \mathbf{0} = \mathbf{0}$

Therefore, an eigenvector only can be determined to within an arbitrary multiplicative constant. The value of this constant is of no consequence, and we can choose it to be any convenient number except zero. It is usually convenient to specify an eigenvector by setting one of its elements equal to 0 or 1. The eigenvector thus represents a geometric vector whose direction is important but not its length.

There is only one linearly independent eigenvector corresponding to a simple eigenvalue of a matrix $\mathbf{A}$. One would think that there will be k linearly independent eigenvectors corresponding to an eigenvalue of multiplicity k, but this is not necessarily the case. An eigenvalue of multiplicity k may have m eigenvectors corresponding to it, where $1 \le m \le k$. The case $m < k$ causes some difficulty in the solution of systems of differential equations, as you will see later in this chapter. The reader should also bear in mind that some of the eigenvalues and their corresponding eigenvectors may be complex even if every element of the matrix $\mathbf{A}$ is real.

It can be proved that eigenvectors corresponding to different eigenvalues of a matrix $\mathbf{A}$ are linearly independent. If the matrix $\mathbf{A}$ is an $n \times n$ matrix having n distinct eigenvalues, the n eigenvectors corresponding to them are linearly independent. But if the $n \times n$ matrix has one or more repeated eigenvalues, the number of linearly independent eigenvectors of $\mathbf{A}$ may be less than n. The only exception to this rule is the *real symmetric* matrix, which is a matrix whose elements are all real and whose transpose is equal to itself.

If $\mathbf{A}$ is an $n \times n$ real symmetric matrix, then there are n linearly independent eigenvectors of $\mathbf{A}$—even if one or more eigenvalues of $\mathbf{A}$ are repeated. Also, all of the eigenvalues are real in this case, and there are m linearly independent eigenvectors corresponding to an eigenvalue of multiplicity m. The evaluation of eigenvalues and eigenvectors for different cases is now illustrated with examples.

The eigenvalues of an $n \times n$ matrix $\mathbf{A}$ are the roots of the equation:

$$\det(\mathbf{A} - \lambda\mathbf{I}) = 0$$

which reduces to an nth-degree polynomial equation:

$$\lambda^n + b_1\lambda^{n-1} + b_2\lambda^{n-2} + \ldots + b_n = 0$$

FIGURE 7–29

A square real matrix of order n always has n eigenvalues, which are not necessarily real and distinct.

EXAMPLE 7–12   Real and Distinct Eigenvalues

Find the eigenvalues and eigenvectors of the matrix

$$\mathbf{A} = \begin{pmatrix} 5 & 4 \\ 3 & 1 \end{pmatrix}$$

SOLUTION   This is a 2×2 matrix, and its eigenvalues are the roots of the equation $\det(\mathbf{A} - \lambda\mathbf{I}) = 0$

$$\det(\mathbf{A} - \lambda\mathbf{I}) = \begin{vmatrix} 5 - \lambda & 4 \\ 3 & 1 - \lambda \end{vmatrix} = (5 - \lambda)(1 - \lambda) - 12$$

$$= \lambda^2 - 6\lambda - 7 = 0$$

whose roots are 7 and -1. Therefore, eigenvalues of the given matrix are $\lambda_1 = 7$ and $\lambda_2 = -1$, which are real and distinct. Therefore, we expect to obtain two linearly independent eigenvectors of $\mathbf{A}$. These eigenvectors are determined from the equation $(\mathbf{A} - \lambda\mathbf{I})\mathbf{v} = \mathbf{0}$, which in this case becomes

$$\begin{pmatrix} 5 - \lambda & 4 \\ 3 & 1 - \lambda \end{pmatrix}\begin{pmatrix} x_1 \\ x_2 \end{pmatrix} = \begin{pmatrix} 0 \\ 0 \end{pmatrix} \tag{7–47}$$

The eigenvector corresponding to the first eigenvalue $\lambda = \lambda_1 = 7$ is obtained by substituting this value of λ into Equation (7–47) to obtain

$$\begin{pmatrix} -2 & 4 \\ 3 & -6 \end{pmatrix}\begin{pmatrix} x_1 \\ x_2 \end{pmatrix} = \begin{pmatrix} 0 \\ 0 \end{pmatrix}$$

which is equivalent to the system of equations:

$$-2x_1 + 4x_2 = 0$$

$$3x_1 - 6x_2 = 0$$

These two equations are identical, since multiplying the first one by $-3/2$ gives the second one. Thus, either equation can be used to determine the relationship between the two unknowns. This allows us to choose any convenient value (except zero) for one of the unknowns. Taking $x_2 = 1$ for simplicity, we obtain $x_1 = 2$. Thus, the eigenvector corresponding to the eigenvalue $\lambda_1 = 7$ is

$$\mathbf{v}_1 = \begin{pmatrix} 2 \\ 1 \end{pmatrix}$$

Note that, if we had taken $x_2 = c$ where c is an arbitrary constant, we would obtain $x_1 = 2c$, and the eigenvector corresponding to the eigenvalue $\lambda_1 = 7$ would be

$$\mathbf{v}_1 = \begin{pmatrix} 2c \\ c \end{pmatrix} = c\begin{pmatrix} 2 \\ 1 \end{pmatrix}$$

which is a constant multiple of the eigenvector obtained earlier. The arbitrary constant c is of no consequence in eigenvector calculation, and we will always disregard it. (It determines the length of the vector.) But we will keep in mind that any constant multiple of an eigenvector is also an eigenvector. (Figure 7–30)

If the vector

$$\mathbf{v}_1 = \begin{pmatrix} 2 \\ 1 \end{pmatrix}$$

is an eigenvector of a matrix $\mathbf{A}$ corresponding to an eigenvalue λ_1, so are the vectors:

$$\mathbf{v}_2 = 2\mathbf{v}_1 = \begin{pmatrix} 4 \\ 2 \end{pmatrix}$$

$$\mathbf{v}_3 = -5\mathbf{v}_1 = \begin{pmatrix} -10 \\ -5 \end{pmatrix}$$

$$\mathbf{v}_4 = \frac{1}{3}\mathbf{v}_1 = \begin{pmatrix} 2/3 \\ 1/3 \end{pmatrix}$$

$$\mathbf{v}_n = c\mathbf{v}_1\begin{pmatrix} 2c \\ c \end{pmatrix}$$

where c is a constant.

FIGURE 7–30

Any constant multiple of an eigenvector is also an eigenvector (but no two such eigenvectors are linearly independent).

The second eigenvector is determined by substituting $\lambda = \lambda_2 = -1$ into Equation 7–47. It yields

$$\begin{pmatrix} 6 & 4 \\ 3 & 2 \end{pmatrix} \begin{pmatrix} x_1 \\ x_2 \end{pmatrix} = \begin{pmatrix} 0 \\ 0 \end{pmatrix}$$

which is equivalent to the system of equations:

$$6x_1 + 4x_2 = 0$$

$$3x_1 + 2x_2 = 0$$

These two equations are identical, since multiplying the second one by 2 gives the first one, and either equation can be expressed as

$$3x_1 + 2x_2 = 0$$

Again we have only one equation for the determination of two unknowns. Taking $x_2 = 3$ to avoid fractions, we obtain $x_1 = -2$. Thus, the eigenvector corresponding to the eigenvalue $\lambda_2 = -1$ is

$$\mathbf{v}_2 = \begin{pmatrix} -2 \\ 3 \end{pmatrix}$$

Note that the eigenvectors $\mathbf{v}_1$ and $\mathbf{v}_2$ are linearly independent, as expected.

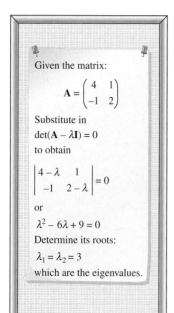

FIGURE 7–31

A systematic procedure to determine the eigenvalues of a given matrix.

EXAMPLE 7–13   **Repeated Eigenvalues**

Find the eigenvalues and eigenvectors of the matrix:

$$\mathbf{A} = \begin{pmatrix} 4 & 1 \\ -1 & 2 \end{pmatrix}$$

SOLUTION   This is a 2 × 2 matrix, and its eigenvalues are the roots of the equation $\det(\mathbf{A} - \lambda\mathbf{I}) = 0$ (see Figure 7–31), as

$$\begin{vmatrix} 4-\lambda & 1 \\ -1 & 2-\lambda \end{vmatrix} = (4-\lambda)(2-\lambda) + 1$$

$$= \lambda^2 - 6\lambda + 9 = 0$$

The roots of this equation (and thus the eigenvalues of the given matrix) are $\lambda_1 = \lambda_2 = 3$ (Figure 7–31). Therefore, $\lambda = 3$ is a double eigenvalue.

The eigenvectors of the matrix $\mathbf{A}$ are determined from the equation $(\mathbf{A} - \lambda\mathbf{I})\mathbf{v} = \mathbf{0}$, which in this case becomes

$$\begin{pmatrix} 4-\lambda & 1 \\ -1 & 2-\lambda \end{pmatrix} \begin{pmatrix} x_1 \\ x_2 \end{pmatrix} = \begin{pmatrix} 0 \\ 0 \end{pmatrix} \tag{7–48}$$

Substituting $\lambda = 3$ into Equation 7–48 gives

$$\begin{pmatrix} 1 & 1 \\ -1 & -1 \end{pmatrix} \begin{pmatrix} x_1 \\ x_2 \end{pmatrix} = \begin{pmatrix} 0 \\ 0 \end{pmatrix}$$

which is equivalent to the system of equations:

$$x_1 + x_2 = 0$$

$$-x_1 - x_2 = 0$$

These two equations are identical, since multiplying the first one by -1 gives the second one, and either equation can be expressed as $x_1 + x_2 = 0$. Again we have only one equation for the determination of two unknowns. Taking $x_1 = 1$, we obtain $x_2 = -1$. Thus, the eigenvector of the given matrix $\mathbf{A}$ corresponding to the eigenvalue $\lambda_1 = 3$ is

$$v_1 = \begin{pmatrix} 1 \\ -1 \end{pmatrix}$$

This is the only linearly independent eigenvector of $\mathbf{A}$, since λ cannot have any value other than 3. This is typical for 2×2 matrices that have double eigenvalues. Thus, we conclude that there is only one linearly independent eigenvector corresponding to an eigenvalue of multiplicity 2 associated with a 2×2 matrix. For 3×3 or larger matrices, there may be two linearly independent eigenvectors corresponding to an eigenvalue of multiplicity 2, as shown in the following example.

EXAMPLE 7–14   Real, Symmetric Matrices

Find the eigenvalues and eigenvectors of the matrix:

$$\mathbf{A} = \begin{pmatrix} 0 & 3 & 3 \\ 3 & 0 & 3 \\ 3 & 3 & 0 \end{pmatrix}$$

SOLUTION   This is a real and symmetric 3×3 matrix, and its eigenvalues are the roots of the equation

$$\det(\mathbf{A} - \lambda\mathbf{I}) = \begin{vmatrix} 0-\lambda & 3 & 3 \\ 3 & 0-\lambda & 3 \\ 3 & 3 & 0-\lambda \end{vmatrix} = -\lambda(\lambda^2 - 9) - 3(-3\lambda - 9) + 3(9 + 3\lambda)$$

$$= -(\lambda + 3)(\lambda + 3)(\lambda - 6) = 0$$

whose roots are -3, -3, and 6. Therefore, the eigenvalues of the given matrix are $\lambda_1 = 6$ and $\lambda_2 = \lambda_3 = -3$. Thus, we have a distinct eigenvalue of 6 and a double eigenvalue of -3. The matrix $\mathbf{A}$ is real and symmetric. Therefore, we expect to obtain three linearly independent eigenvectors for $\mathbf{A}$.

The eigenvectors of the matrix $\mathbf{A}$ are determined from the equation $(\mathbf{A} - \lambda\mathbf{I})\,\mathbf{v} = 0$, which in this case becomes

$$\begin{pmatrix} -\lambda & 3 & 3 \\ 3 & -\lambda & 3 \\ 3 & 3 & -\lambda \end{pmatrix}\begin{pmatrix} x_1 \\ x_2 \\ x_3 \end{pmatrix} = \begin{pmatrix} 0 \\ 0 \\ 0 \end{pmatrix} \tag{7-49}$$

The eigenvector corresponding to the first eigenvalue $\lambda = \lambda_1 = 6$ is obtained by substituting this value of λ into Equation 7–49 to obtain

$$\begin{pmatrix} -6 & 3 & 3 \\ 3 & -6 & 3 \\ 3 & 3 & -6 \end{pmatrix}\begin{pmatrix} x_1 \\ x_2 \\ x_3 \end{pmatrix} = \begin{pmatrix} 0 \\ 0 \\ 0 \end{pmatrix}$$

The augmented matrix of the matrix equation is

$$\left(\begin{array}{ccc|c} -6 & 3 & 3 & 0 \\ 3 & -6 & 3 & 0 \\ 3 & 3 & -6 & 0 \end{array} \right)$$

which reduces by row operations to

$$\left(\begin{array}{ccc|c} 1 & 0 & -1 & 0 \\ 0 & 1 & -1 & 0 \\ 0 & 0 & 0 & 0 \end{array} \right)$$

It is equivalent to the system of equations:

$$x_1 - x_3 = 0$$
$$x_2 - x_3 = 0$$

Thus, we have only two equations for the determination of three unknowns. This allows us to choose any convenient value for one of the unknowns and to determine the other two in terms of this one. Taking $x_3 = 1$ for simplicity, we obtain $x_1 = 1$ and $x_2 = 1$.

Thus, the eigenvector corresponding to the eigenvalue $\lambda_1 = 6$ is

$$\mathbf{v}_1 = \left(\begin{array}{c} 1 \\ 1 \\ 1 \end{array} \right)$$

The second eigenvector is determined by substituting $\lambda_2 = \lambda_3 = -3$ into Equation 7–49. It yields

$$\left(\begin{array}{ccc} 3 & 3 & 3 \\ 3 & 3 & 3 \\ 3 & 3 & 3 \end{array} \right) \left(\begin{array}{c} x_1 \\ x_2 \\ x_3 \end{array} \right) = \left(\begin{array}{c} 0 \\ 0 \\ 0 \end{array} \right)$$

which is equivalent to the single equation $3x_1 + 3x_2 + 3x_3 = 0$ or $x_1 + x_2 + x_3 = 0$.

This time we have one equation for the determination of three unknowns. Thus, we can assign arbitrary values to any two of the unknowns and solve for the third one. Taking $x_1 = 1$ and $x_2 = 0$ gives $x_3 = -1$. The eigenvector corresponding to the eigenvalue $\lambda_2 = -3$ for these choices is

$$\mathbf{v}_2 = \left(\begin{array}{c} 1 \\ 0 \\ -1 \end{array} \right)$$

An eigenvalue that is linearly independent of v_2 is obtained by making another choice for x_1 and x_2. Taking $x_1 = 0$ and $x_2 = 1$ again gives $x_3 = 1$. The eigenvector corresponding to the eigenvalue $\lambda_2 = -3$ for these choices is

$$\mathbf{v}_3 = \left(\begin{array}{c} 0 \\ 1 \\ -1 \end{array} \right)$$

The eigenvectors $\mathbf{v}_2$ and $\mathbf{v}_3$ are linearly independent—even though they correspond to the same eigenvalue—since one is not a constant multiple of the other.

To show that there are no other linearly independent eigenvectors corresponding to the double eigenvalue $\lambda_2 = -3$, we take $x_1 = c_1$ and $x_2 = c_2$, which gives $x_3 = -c_1 - c_2$. The eigenvector corresponding to the eigenvalue -3 for these choices is

$$\mathbf{v} = \begin{pmatrix} c_1 \\ c_2 \\ -c_1 - c_2 \end{pmatrix} = \begin{pmatrix} c_1 \\ 0 \\ -c_1 \end{pmatrix} + \begin{pmatrix} 0 \\ c_2 \\ -c_2 \end{pmatrix} = c_1 \begin{pmatrix} 1 \\ 0 \\ -1 \end{pmatrix} + c_2 \begin{pmatrix} 0 \\ 1 \\ -1 \end{pmatrix} = c_1 \mathbf{v}_2 + c_2 \mathbf{v}_3$$

which is a linear combination of the two eigenvectors determined earlier. Therefore, there are only two linearly independent eigenvectors corresponding to the double eigenvalue.

EXAMPLE 7–15   Complex Eigenvalues

Find the eigenvalues and eigenvectors of the matrix:

$$\mathbf{A} = \begin{pmatrix} 1 & 2 \\ -1 & 1 \end{pmatrix} \tag{7–50}$$

SOLUTION   This is a 2×2 matrix, and its eigenvalues are the roots of the equation $\det(\mathbf{A} - \lambda\mathbf{I}) = 0$. Thus,

$$\det(\mathbf{A} - \lambda\mathbf{I}) = \begin{vmatrix} 1 - \lambda & 2 \\ -1 & 1 - \lambda \end{vmatrix} = (1 - \lambda)(1 - \lambda) + 2 = \lambda^2 - 2\lambda + 3 = 0$$

The roots of this equation (and thus the eigenvalues of the given matrix) are $\lambda_{1,2} = 1 \pm \sqrt{2}i$, which are complex conjugates. Therefore, both eigenvalues are complex in this case.

The eigenvectors of the matrix $\mathbf{A}$ are determined from the equation $(\mathbf{A} - \lambda\mathbf{I})\mathbf{v} = \mathbf{0}$, which in this case becomes

$$\begin{pmatrix} 1 - \lambda & 2 \\ -1 & 1 - \lambda \end{pmatrix} \begin{pmatrix} x_1 \\ x_2 \end{pmatrix} = \begin{pmatrix} 0 \\ 0 \end{pmatrix}$$

Substituting $\lambda = \lambda_1 = 1 + \sqrt{2}i$ into this equation gives

$$\begin{pmatrix} -\sqrt{2}i & 2 \\ -1 & -\sqrt{2}i \end{pmatrix} \begin{pmatrix} x_1 \\ x_2 \end{pmatrix} = \begin{pmatrix} 0 \\ 0 \end{pmatrix}$$

which is equivalent to the system of equations:

$$-\sqrt{2}ix_1 + 2x_2 = 0$$

$$-x_1 + \sqrt{2}ix_2 = 0$$

These two equations are identical, since multiplying the second one by $\sqrt{2}i$ gives the first one. Either equation can be expressed as $x_1 - \sqrt{2}ix_2 = 0$.

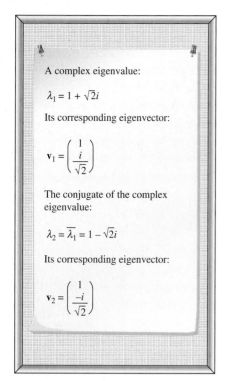

FIGURE 7–32

The eigenvector that corresponds to the conjugate of a complex eigenvalue is identical to the conjugate of the eigenvector that corresponds to that eigenvalue.

Again, we have only one equation for the determination of two unknowns. Taking $x_1 = 1$ gives $x_2 = i/\sqrt{2}$. Thus, the eigenvector of the given matrix **A** corresponding to the eigenvalue $\lambda_1 = 1 + \sqrt{2}i$ is

$$\mathbf{v}_1 = \begin{pmatrix} 1 \\ i \\ \sqrt{2} \end{pmatrix}$$

If we repeat the eigenvector calculations with the second eigenvalue $\lambda_2 = 1 - \sqrt{2}i$, which is the complex conjugate of λ_1, we would obtain

$$\mathbf{v}_2 = \begin{pmatrix} 1 \\ -i \\ \sqrt{2} \end{pmatrix}$$

which is the complex conjugate of $\mathbf{v}_1$; that is, $\mathbf{v}_2 = \overline{\mathbf{v}_1}$ where the overbar denotes the complex conjugate. Therefore, if the eigenvector corresponding to λ_1 is $\mathbf{v}_1$, the eigenvector corresponding to the complex conjugate of λ_1 is the complex conjugate of $\mathbf{v}_1$. That is, if $\lambda_2 = \overline{\lambda_1}$, then $\mathbf{v}_2 = \overline{\mathbf{v}_1}$. Note that the conjugate of a complex number or vector is obtained by replacing all occurrences of i by $-i$. Also note that the eigenvectors corresponding to complex eigenvalues are obtained in exactly the same manner as the eigenvectors corresponding to real eigenvalues (Figure 7–32).

Special Case: Matrix A Containing a Common Factor

Sometimes all of the elements of the matrix **A** are multiplied by a common scalar variable. In such cases, that variable can be factored out of the matrix, leaving only numerical values for the matrix elements. Examples 7–2 and 7–3 contain such matrices. From Example 7–3, we have

$$\mathbf{A} = \frac{1}{RC}\begin{pmatrix} -1 & 1 & 0 \\ 1 & -2 & 1 \\ 0 & 1 & -2 \end{pmatrix} = \frac{1}{RC}\mathbf{A}_1$$

where we have defined $\mathbf{A}_1$ as

$$\mathbf{A}_1 = \begin{pmatrix} -1 & 1 & 0 \\ 1 & -2 & 1 \\ 0 & 1 & -2 \end{pmatrix}$$

Here the common factor is $1/RC$.

In general, if a term α can be factored out of the matrix **A**, leaving the matrix $\mathbf{A}_1$, we now show that the eigenvalues of **A** are α times the eigenvalues of $\mathbf{A}_1$. In addition, the eigenvectors of **A** are the same as the eigenvectors of $\mathbf{A}_1$. From the basic equations, we have

$$(\mathbf{A} - \lambda\mathbf{I})\mathbf{v} = \mathbf{0}$$

$$\det(\mathbf{A} - \lambda\mathbf{I}) = 0$$

If we replace $\mathbf{A}$ with $\alpha\mathbf{A}_1$, we have

$$(\alpha\mathbf{A}_1 - \lambda\mathbf{I})\mathbf{v} = 0$$

$$\det(\alpha\mathbf{A}_1 - \lambda\mathbf{I}) = 0$$

If we divide both equations by the scalar α, we obtain

$$\left(\mathbf{A}_1 - \frac{\lambda}{\alpha}\mathbf{I}\right)\mathbf{v} = \mathbf{0}$$

$$\det\left(\mathbf{A}_1 - \frac{\lambda}{\alpha}\mathbf{I}\right) = 0$$

From this, we see that $\lambda_1 = \lambda/\alpha$ are the eigenvalues of $\mathbf{A}_1$. Thus, the eigenvalues of $\mathbf{A}$ are $\lambda = \alpha\lambda_1$. Since $\mathbf{v}$ is unchanged by the division, we also see that the eigenvectors are unchanged.

The significance of this result is that if we need to determine the eigenvalues and eigenvectors by a numerical method (which is usually true for systems of three or more equations), we can apply the numerical method to the matrix $\mathbf{A}_1$ without needing to know the value of α. For example, the $\mathbf{A}_1$ matrix given previously for Example 7–3 has the following eigenvalues and eigenvectors, which were obtained by computer.

$$\lambda_1 = -3.2470, -1.5550, -0.1981$$

and

$$\mathbf{v} = \begin{pmatrix} 1 \\ -2.2469 \\ 1.8019 \end{pmatrix}, \begin{pmatrix} -1.8019 \\ 1 \\ 2.2469 \end{pmatrix}, \begin{pmatrix} 2.2469 \\ 1.8019 \\ 1 \end{pmatrix}$$

Thus, the eigenvalues for the circuit model are $\lambda = -3.2470/RC$, $-1.5550/RC$, $-0.1981/RC$. Therefore, the time constants of the circuit are

$$\tau = RC/3.2470, RC/1.5550, RC/0.1981$$

$$= 0.3080RC, 0.6431RC, 5.0480RC$$

The dominant time constant is $5.0480RC$, and four times this value gives an estimate of the response time of the circuit. In the free response, the currents will not oscillate because all of the eigenvalues are real.

Section Review

7–6C How do you decide if a given system of linear algebraic equations is homogeneous or nonhomogeneous?

7–7C How is the augmented matrix of a system of algebraic equations formed?

7–8C How do you decide if a given system of linear algebraic equations is homogeneous or nonhomogeneous?

7–9C How is the augmented matrix of a system of algebraic equations formed?

7–10C What can you say about the solution of a linear system of (a) homogeneous and (b) nonhomogeneous algebraic equations if the coefficient matrix of the system is singular?

7–11C Consider n vector functions of order n. How would you determine if these n vectors are linearly dependent or independent over a specified interval?

7–12C Consider a constant square matrix of order n. How many eigenvalues will this matrix have? How are they determined?

7–13 First determine if the inverse of the following matrices exists, and obtain it if it does exist.

(a) $\mathbf{A} = \begin{pmatrix} 2 & 0 \\ -7 & 5 \end{pmatrix}$
(b) $\mathbf{B} = \begin{pmatrix} 4 & -2 & 3 \\ -1 & 0 & 3 \\ -3 & 0 & 2 \end{pmatrix}$

(*Answers*: (a) $\det \mathbf{A} = \begin{vmatrix} 2 & 0 \\ -7 & 5 \end{vmatrix} = 10 \neq 0$

$$\mathbf{A}^{-1} = \begin{pmatrix} \dfrac{1}{2} & 0 \\ \dfrac{7}{10} & \dfrac{1}{5} \end{pmatrix}$$

(b) $\det \mathbf{B} = 14 \neq 0$, $\mathbf{B}^{-1} = \dfrac{1}{14} \begin{bmatrix} 0 & 4 & -6 \\ -7 & 17 & -15 \\ 0 & 6 & -2 \end{bmatrix}$)

7–14 First determine if the following systems of algebraic equations have solutions, and find all the solutions when they do.

(a) $x_1 + 2x_2 + x_3 = 5$
$\quad -2x_1 + 4x_2 - x_3 = 0$
$\quad 2x_1 + x_2 - x_3 = 1$

(b) $x_1 + 2x_2 + x_3 = 0$
$\quad -2x_1 + 4x_2 - x_3 = 0$
$\quad 2x_1 + x_2 - x_3 = 0$

(c) $x_1 + 2x_2 + x_3 = 5$
$\quad -2x_1 + 4x_2 - x_3 = 0$
$\quad -x_1 + 6x_2 = 5$

(d) $x_1 + 2x_2 + x_3 = 5$
$\quad -2x_1 + 4x_2 - x_3 = -2$
$\quad 2x_1 + x_2 - x_3 = 1$

(*Answers*: (a) Unique solution: $\mathbf{x} = \begin{pmatrix} x_1 \\ x_2 \\ x_3 \end{pmatrix} = \begin{pmatrix} 1 \\ 1 \\ 2 \end{pmatrix}$

(b) Trivial solution: $\mathbf{x} = \begin{pmatrix} x_1 \\ x_2 \\ x_3 \end{pmatrix} = \begin{pmatrix} 0 \\ 0 \\ 0 \end{pmatrix}$

(c) No unique solution; α is an arbitrary constant:

$$\mathbf{x} = \begin{pmatrix} x_1 \\ x_2 \\ x_3 \end{pmatrix} = \alpha \begin{pmatrix} -\dfrac{3}{4} \\ -\dfrac{1}{8} \\ 1 \end{pmatrix} + \begin{pmatrix} \dfrac{5}{2} \\ \dfrac{5}{4} \\ 0 \end{pmatrix}$$

(d) $\mathbf{x} = \begin{pmatrix} x_1 \\ x_2 \\ x_3 \end{pmatrix} = \begin{pmatrix} \dfrac{9}{7} \\ \dfrac{5}{7} \\ \dfrac{16}{7} \end{pmatrix}$)

7–15 Determine if the following vectors are linearly dependent or independent.

$$\mathbf{v}_1 = \begin{pmatrix} 1 \\ 0 \\ 1 \end{pmatrix}, \mathbf{v}_2 = \begin{pmatrix} 1 \\ 2 \\ -1 \end{pmatrix}, \quad \text{and} \quad \mathbf{v}_3 = \begin{pmatrix} 0 \\ 1 \\ -4 \end{pmatrix}$$

(*Answer*: Linearly independent.)

7–16 Determine if the following vectors are linearly dependent or independent for $-\infty < t < \infty$.

$$\mathbf{v}_1(t) = \begin{pmatrix} 2e^t \\ -3e^{2t} \\ e^{-2t} \end{pmatrix}, \mathbf{v}_2(t) = \begin{pmatrix} e^{2t} \\ 0 \\ -2e^{-2t} \end{pmatrix}, \quad \text{and} \quad \mathbf{v}_3(t) = \begin{pmatrix} t^2 \\ t \\ 1 \end{pmatrix}$$

(*Answer*: Linearly independent.)

7–17 Determine all of the eigenvalues and eigenvectors of the following matrices.

(a) $\mathbf{A} = \begin{pmatrix} 2 & 0 \\ -7 & 5 \end{pmatrix}$ (b) $\mathbf{A} = \begin{pmatrix} 4 & -2 & 3 \\ -1 & 0 & 3 \\ -3 & 0 & 2 \end{pmatrix}$

(*Answers*: (a) $\mathbf{v}_1 = \begin{pmatrix} 0 \\ 1 \end{pmatrix}$ $\mathbf{v}_2 = \begin{pmatrix} \dfrac{3}{7} \\ 1 \end{pmatrix}$

$\lambda_1 = 5$ $\lambda_2 = 2$

(b) $\mathbf{v}_1 = \begin{pmatrix} 0 \\ \dfrac{3}{2} \\ 1 \end{pmatrix}$ $\mathbf{v}_2 = \begin{pmatrix} -\dfrac{1}{\sqrt{3}}i \\ 1 - \dfrac{1}{\sqrt{3}}i \\ 1 \end{pmatrix}$ $\mathbf{v}_3 = \begin{pmatrix} \dfrac{1}{\sqrt{3}}i \\ 1 + \dfrac{1}{\sqrt{3}}i \\ 1 \end{pmatrix}$

$\lambda_1 = 2$ $\lambda_2 = 2 + \sqrt{3}$ $\lambda_3 = 2 - \sqrt{3}$)

7–18 In Example 7–2, let $R = A = 1$. Find the eigenvalues and eigenvectors of the matrix **A** given in that example.

7–19 In Example 7–4, let $m = c = k = 1$. Find the eigenvalues and eigenvectors of the matrix **A** given in that example.

7–4 ▪ THE THEORY OF SYSTEMS OF LINEAR DIFFERENTIAL EQUATIONS

You will recall that a system of n linear, first-order differential equations always can be expressed as a single nth-order linear equation. Therefore, it is natural to expect close parallels between the theory of a single nth-order linear equation and a system of n first-order linear equations. In this section, we will briefly present the key theorems that pertain to linear systems. The reader may refer to the relevant theorems in Chapters 3 and 4 for more indepth discussions that pertain to equivalent higher-order, single linear equations.

Consider a system of n first-order linear equations of the form

$$x_1' = a_{11}(t)x_1 + a_{12}(t)x_2 + \cdots + a_{1n}(t)x_n + r_1(t)$$

$$x_2' = a_{21}(t)x_1 + a_{22}(t)x_2 + \cdots + a_{2n}(t)x_n + r_2(t)$$

$$\vdots$$

$$x_n' = a_{n1}(t)x_1 + a_{n2}(t)x_2 + \cdots + a_{2n}(t)x_n + r_n(t) \qquad \text{(7–51)}$$

This system also can be expressed compactly in the matrix form as

$$\mathbf{x}' = \mathbf{A}(t)\mathbf{x} + \mathbf{r}(t) \qquad \text{(7–52)}$$

where

$$\mathbf{A}(t) = \begin{pmatrix} a_{11}(t) & a_{12}(t) & \cdots & a_{1n}(t) \\ a_{21}(t) & a_{22}(t) & \cdots & a_{2n}(t) \\ \vdots & \vdots & \cdots & \vdots \\ a_{n1}(t) & a_{n2}(t) & \cdots & a_{nn}(t) \end{pmatrix}, \quad \mathbf{x} = \begin{pmatrix} x_1 \\ x_2 \\ \vdots \\ x_n \end{pmatrix}$$

$$\text{and} \quad \mathbf{r}(t) = \begin{pmatrix} r_1(t) \\ r_2(t) \\ \cdot \\ \cdot \\ r_n(t) \end{pmatrix} \qquad \text{(7–53)}$$

Consider also the set of n initial conditions:

$$x_1(t_0) = x_{10}, \quad x_2(t_0) = x_{20}, \dots, x_n(t_0) = x_{n0} \qquad \text{(7–54)}$$

The system of equations (Equations 7–51) together with the initial conditions (Equations 7–54) form a system of n initial-value problems, and the existence and uniqueness theorem for such systems can be expressed as follows.

THEOREM 7–1 Existence and Uniqueness for Linear Systems

If the coefficients a_{11}, a_{12}, ..., a_{nn} and the nonhomogeneous functions $r_1, r_2, \dots, r_n$ are continuous in an interval $t_1 < t < t_2$ that contains the point t_0, the system of n first-order linear equations has a unique solution that satisfies the n initial conditions:

$$x_1(t_0) = x_{10}, \quad x_2(t_0) = x_{20}, \dots, x_n(t_0) = x_{n0}$$

This solution is valid over the entire interval $t_1 < t < t_2$.

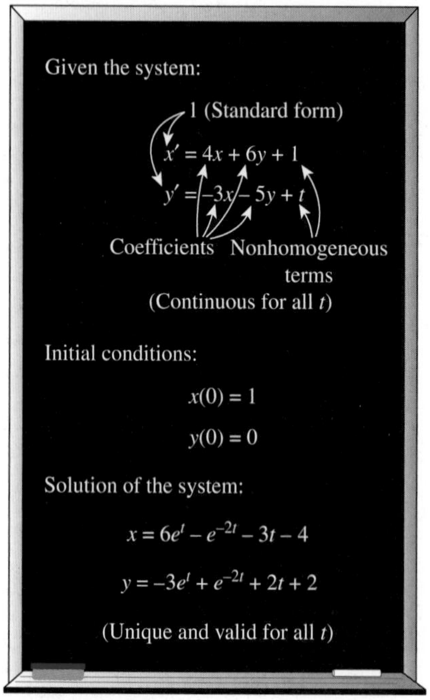

The analogy between this theorem and Theorems 2–1, 3–1, and 4–1 is quite obvious. All four theorems state that, if the coefficients and the nonhomogeneous terms of the differential equations in the standard form are continuous in an interval, a linear equation has one and only one solution satisfying the given initial conditions (Figure 7–33).

Given the system:

1 (Standard form)

$$x' = 4x + 6y + 1$$

$$y' = -3x - 5y + t$$

Coefficients Nonhomogeneous terms
(Continuous for all t)

Initial conditions:

$$x(0) = 1$$

$$y(0) = 0$$

Solution of the system:

$$x = 6e^t - e^{-2t} - 3t - 4$$

$$y = -3e^t + e^{-2t} + 2t + 2$$

(Unique and valid for all t)

FIGURE 7–33

A system in standard form (whose coefficients and nonhomogeneous terms are continuous in the interval $\infty < t < \infty$) has a unique solution that satisfies a given set of initial conditions, and that solution is valid for all t.

Considering that a system of n first-order, linear differential equations is equivalent to an nth-order linear equation, we expect the general solution of such a system to involve n arbitrary constants. Thus, it is no surprise that initial conditions are needed to uniquely determine these n arbitrary constants and to obtain an unique solution.

The solutions of systems of equations are expressed in terms of vectors. A vector is said to be solution of a system of equations if its components satisfy every equation in the system. The solution vectors are expressed as

$$\mathbf{x}_1 = \begin{pmatrix} x_{11} \\ x_{21} \\ \vdots \\ x_{n1} \end{pmatrix}, \mathbf{x}_2 = \begin{pmatrix} x_{12} \\ x_{22} \\ \vdots \\ x_{n2} \end{pmatrix}, \ldots, \mathbf{x}_n = \begin{pmatrix} x_{1n} \\ x_{2n} \\ \vdots \\ x_{nn} \end{pmatrix}$$

where the individual solutions x_{ij} represent the jth solution of the ith unknown function. Note that boldface $\mathbf{x}_k$ represents the kth solution vector; whereas, x_k represents the kth unknown function.

Throughout the following discussions, we will assume the coefficient matrix $\mathbf{A}$ (and thus each of its elements $a_{11}, a_{12}, \ldots, a_{nn}$) and the nonhomogeneous vector $\mathbf{r}$ (and thus the functions $r_1, r_2, \ldots, r_n$) to be continuous in the interval of interest to guarantee the existence of a solution in that interval. We first discuss homogeneous linear systems and then nonhomogeneous linear systems.

Theory of Linear, Homogeneous Systems

Consider the linear, homogeneous system of differential equations expressed as

$$\mathbf{x}' = \mathbf{A}(t)\mathbf{x} \tag{7–55}$$

which is obtained from Equation 7–52 by setting the nonhomogeneous vector equal to zero, $\mathbf{r}(t) = \mathbf{0}$. If vectors $\mathbf{x}_1, \mathbf{x}_2, \mathbf{x}_3, \mathbf{x}_4, \ldots, \mathbf{x}_n$ satisfy the given linear, homogeneous system, any linear combination of the vectors as expressed by the following theorem also will satisfy the system (see also Figure 7–34).

THEOREM 7–2   Superposition Principle

If the vector functions $\mathbf{x}_1, \mathbf{x}_2, \ldots, \mathbf{x}_n$ are solutions of the linear homogeneous system:

$$\mathbf{x}' = \mathbf{A}(t)\mathbf{x} \tag{7–56}$$

then the linear combination

$$\mathbf{x} = c_1\mathbf{x}_1 + c_2\mathbf{x}_2 + c_3\mathbf{x}_3 + \cdots + c_n\mathbf{x}_n \tag{7–57}$$

is also a solution of this system, where $c_1, c_2, \ldots, c_n$ are arbitrary constants.

---

(1) **Constant multiple of solutions:**

If a vector function $\mathbf{x}_1$ is a solution of the system $\mathbf{x}' = \mathbf{A}\mathbf{x}$, then $c\mathbf{x}_1$ also is a solution, where c is any constant.

(2) **Sum of solutions:**

If the vector functions $\mathbf{x}_1$ and $\mathbf{x}_2$ are solutions of the system $\mathbf{x}' = \mathbf{A}\mathbf{x}$, then $\mathbf{x}_1 + \mathbf{x}_2$ also is a solution.

(3) **General solution:**

If the vector functions $\mathbf{x}_1$ and $\mathbf{x}_2$ are solutions of the system $\mathbf{x}' = \mathbf{A}\mathbf{x}$, then $c_1\mathbf{x}_1 + c_2\mathbf{x}_2$ also is a solution, where c_1 and c_2 are arbitrary constants.

FIGURE 7–34

The superposition principle for linear, homogeneous systems.

Proof This theorem can be proved in a straightforward manner by differentiating Equation 7–57 and substituting the result into Equation 7–56:

$$\mathbf{x}' = c_1\mathbf{x}'_1 + c_2\mathbf{x}'_2 + c_3\mathbf{x}'_3 + \cdots + c_n\mathbf{x}'_n = c_1\mathbf{A}\mathbf{x}'_1 + c_2\mathbf{A}\mathbf{x}'_2 + c_3\mathbf{A}\mathbf{x}'_3$$

$$+ \cdots + c_n\mathbf{A}\mathbf{x}'_n = \mathbf{A}(c_1\mathbf{x}_1 + c_2\mathbf{x}_2 + c_3\mathbf{x}_3 + \cdots + c_n\mathbf{x}_n) = \mathbf{A}\mathbf{x}$$

Therefore, Equation 7–57 satisfies the system (Equation 7–56). This completes the proof.

EXAMPLE 7–16   Superposition Principle for Systems

Verify that the vectors $\mathbf{x}_1$ and $\mathbf{x}_2$ are solutions of the system $\mathbf{x}' = \mathbf{A}\mathbf{x}$, where

$$\mathbf{x}_1 = \begin{pmatrix} 2e^t \\ -e^t \end{pmatrix}, \mathbf{x}_2 = \begin{pmatrix} -e^{-2t} \\ e^{-2t} \end{pmatrix}, \text{ and } \mathbf{A} = \begin{pmatrix} 4 & 6 \\ -3 & -5 \end{pmatrix}$$

Show that $2\mathbf{x}_1 - 8\mathbf{x}_2$ is also a solution of this system.

SOLUTION The given vectors are solutions of the system $\mathbf{x}' = \mathbf{A}\mathbf{x}$ if they result in identical left and right-hand sides when substituted into that system. Substituting $\mathbf{x}_1$ into the system yields

$$\mathbf{x}'_1 = \begin{pmatrix} 2e^t \\ -e^t \end{pmatrix}$$

and

$$\mathbf{A}\mathbf{x}_1 = \begin{pmatrix} 4 & 6 \\ -3 & -5 \end{pmatrix}\begin{pmatrix} 2e^t \\ -e^t \end{pmatrix} = \begin{pmatrix} 8e^t - 6e^t \\ -6e^t + 5e^t \end{pmatrix} = \begin{pmatrix} 2e^t \\ -e^t \end{pmatrix}$$

Thus, the vector $\mathbf{x}_1$ satisfies the given system, and it is a solution. Substituting $\mathbf{x}_2$ into the system yields

$$\mathbf{x}'_2 = \begin{pmatrix} 2e^{-2t} \\ -2e^{-2t} \end{pmatrix}$$

and

$$\mathbf{A}\mathbf{x}_2 = \begin{pmatrix} 4 & 6 \\ -3 & -5 \end{pmatrix}\begin{pmatrix} -e^{-2t} \\ e^{-2t} \end{pmatrix} = \begin{pmatrix} 2e^{-2t} \\ -2e^{-2t} \end{pmatrix}$$

So,

$$\mathbf{A}\mathbf{x}_2 = \begin{pmatrix} 4 & 6 \\ -3 & -5 \end{pmatrix}\begin{pmatrix} -e^{2t} \\ e^{2t} \end{pmatrix} = \begin{pmatrix} -4e^{-2t} + 6e^{-2t} \\ 3e^{-2t} - 5e^{-2t} \end{pmatrix} = \begin{pmatrix} 2e^{-2t} \\ -2e^{-2t} \end{pmatrix}$$

Thus, the vector $\mathbf{x}_2$ also satisfies the given system. Substituting $\mathbf{x} = 2\mathbf{x}_1 - 8\mathbf{x}_2$ into the system yields

$$\mathbf{x}' = 2\mathbf{x}'_1 - 8\mathbf{x}'_2 = \mathbf{A}(2\mathbf{x}_1 - 8\mathbf{x}_2) = 2\mathbf{A}\mathbf{x}_1 - 8\mathbf{A}\mathbf{x}_2$$

or $\mathbf{x}'_1 = \mathbf{A}\mathbf{x}_1$ and $\mathbf{x}'_2 = \mathbf{A}\mathbf{x}_2$, which is true because both $\mathbf{x}_1$ and $\mathbf{x}_2$ are solutions of the equation $\mathbf{x}' = \mathbf{A}\mathbf{x}$.

The reader is again cautioned that the superposition principle is applicable to linear homogeneous systems only. It is not applicable nonhomogeneous systems—even if they are linear.

You will recall that an nth-order linear, homogeneous equation has n linearly independent solutions in an interval in which its coefficients are continuous. Thus, it will come as no surprise that a system of n first-order linear, homogeneous equations have n linearly independent solutions, called a **fundamental set of solutions**, as expressed in the following theorem (Figure 7–35).

THEOREM 7–3 General Solution of Homogeneous Systems

The system of n first-order linear, homogeneous differential equation set:

$$\mathbf{x}' = \mathbf{A}(t)\mathbf{x}$$

always possesses n linearly independent solutions $\mathbf{x}_1, \mathbf{x}_2, \ldots, \mathbf{x}_n$ in an interval $t_1 < t < t_2$ in which the elements of the coefficient matrix $\mathbf{A}$ are continuous. Furthermore, the general solution of this system in that interval can be expressed as a linear combination of these n solutions as

$$\mathbf{x} = c_1\mathbf{x}_1 + c_2\mathbf{x}_2 + c_3\mathbf{x}_3 + \cdots + c_n\mathbf{x}_n$$

where $c_1, c_2, \ldots, c_n$ are arbitrary constants. Any solution of this system in that interval can be obtained from the general solution by assigning suitable values to the arbitrary constants.

This theorem is analogous to Theorem 3–4, which was proved in Chapter 3.

It was demonstrated in the previous section that the linear independence of n solution vectors can be determined with the help of the Wronskian $W(t)$, which is the determinant of the matrix whose columns are the solution vectors $\mathbf{x}_1, \mathbf{x}_2, \ldots, \mathbf{x}_n$. Thus, the Wronskian of n solutions can be expressed as

$$W(t) = \begin{vmatrix} x_{11}(t) & x_{12}(t) & . & . & x_{1n}(t) \\ x_{21}(t) & x_{22}(t) & . & . & x_{2n}(t) \\ . & & . & . & . \\ . & & . & . & . \\ x_{n1}(t) & x_{n2}(t) & . & . & x_{nn}(t) \end{vmatrix} \qquad \textbf{(7–58)}$$

which is an $n \times n$ determinant. These n solutions are linearly dependent in an interval if their Wronskian is identically zero in that interval. Otherwise, they are linearly independent (Figure 7–36).

The Wronskian of n solutions of a given system is either always zero or never zero in an interval in which the coefficients of the equations are continuous, as stated in the following theorem.

Given system:

$$\mathbf{x}' = \mathbf{Ax} \text{ where } \mathbf{A} = \begin{pmatrix} 4 & 6 \\ -3 & -5 \end{pmatrix}$$

Two linearly independent solutions of the system are

$$\mathbf{x}_1 = \begin{pmatrix} 2e^t \\ -e^t \end{pmatrix} \text{ and } \mathbf{x}_2 = \begin{pmatrix} -e^{-2t} \\ e^{-2t} \end{pmatrix}$$

Then the general solution of the given system is

$$\mathbf{x} = c_1\mathbf{x}_1 + c_2\mathbf{x}_2$$

FIGURE 7–35

A system of two first-order linear, homogeneous equations with constant coefficients has two solutions whose linear combination forms the general solution of the system valid for all t.

Given system:

$$\mathbf{x}' = \mathbf{Ax} \text{ where } \mathbf{A} = \begin{pmatrix} 4 & 6 \\ -3 & -5 \end{pmatrix}$$

Two solutions:

$$\mathbf{x}_1 = \begin{pmatrix} 2e^t \\ -e^t \end{pmatrix} \text{ and } \mathbf{x}_2 = \begin{pmatrix} -6e^t \\ 3e^t \end{pmatrix}$$

The Wronskian of these solutions:

$$W(t) = |\mathbf{x}_1\ \mathbf{x}_2| = \begin{vmatrix} 2e^t & -6e^t \\ -e^t & 3e^t \end{vmatrix} = 0$$

Therefore the solutions are linearly dependent.

FIGURE 7–36

Any n solution vectors of a system of n first-order linear, homogeneous equations are linearly dependent in an interval if their Wronskian is identically zero in that interval.

THEOREM 7–4   Abel's Theorem for Systems

If $\mathbf{x}_1, \mathbf{x}_2, \ldots, \mathbf{x}_n$ are solutions of the system n first-order linear, homogeneous differential equations $\mathbf{x}' = \mathbf{A}\mathbf{x}$ in an interval $t_1 < t < t_2$ in which the elements of the coefficient matrix $\mathbf{A}$ are continuous, then the Wronskian of $\mathbf{x}_1, \mathbf{x}_2, \ldots, \mathbf{x}_n$ is either always zero (indicating these n solutions are linearly dependent) or never zero (indicating these n solutions are linearly independent) in that interval.

The proof of this theorem is outlined in Problem 7–104C for a system of two equations in two unknowns. This theorem indicates that the Wronskian of n solutions cannot be zero for some t and nonzero for other t values in an interval in which all coefficients of the differential equations in the system are continuous. Therefore, when determining the linear independence of n solutions in a specified interval, it is sufficient to evaluate the Wronskian of these solutions *at any convenient point* t_0 in that interval, since if the Wronskian is zero at $t = t_0$, it is zero for all t in that interval. Likewise, if the Wronskian is nonzero at $t = t_0$, then it is nonzero for all t in that interval; thus, the n solutions $\mathbf{x}_1, \mathbf{x}_2, \ldots, \mathbf{x}_n$ are linearly independent.

EXAMPLE 7–17   Linear Independence of Solutions

It can be verified by direct substitution that the vectors $\mathbf{x}_1$ and $\mathbf{x}_2$ are solutions of the system $\mathbf{x}' = \mathbf{A}(t)\mathbf{x}$ where

$$\mathbf{A} = \begin{pmatrix} 4 & 6 \\ -3 & -5 \end{pmatrix}$$

$$\mathbf{x}_1 = \begin{pmatrix} 2e^t \\ -e^t \end{pmatrix}$$

$$\mathbf{x}_2 = \begin{pmatrix} -e^{-2t} \\ e^{-2t} \end{pmatrix}$$

Determine if these two solutions are linearly independent in the interval $-\infty < t < \infty$.

SOLUTION   The Wronskian of these two solution vectors is

$$W(t) = |\mathbf{x}_1 \ \mathbf{x}_2| = \begin{vmatrix} 2e^t & -e^{-2t} \\ -e^t & e^{-2t} \end{vmatrix}$$

We now take advantage of Theorem 7–4 to simplify the calculations and evaluate the determinant at a convenient point in the specified interval. We choose $t_0 = 0$ for convenience, since $e^0 = 1$. Substituting $t = 0$ into the determinant yields

$$W(0) = \begin{vmatrix} 2 & -1 \\ -1 & 1 \end{vmatrix} = 2 - 1 = 1$$

which is nonzero. Therefore, these two solutions are linearly independent, and they form a fundamental set of solutions for the given system of two equations in two unknowns. Note that, in the light of Theorem 7–4, we would obtain $W(t_0) \neq 0$ no matter what we choose for t_0. This is verified by noting that $W(t) = 2e^{-t} - e^{-t} = e^{-t} \neq 0$.

EXAMPLE 7–18   General Solution of Linear Systems

It can be verified by direct substitution that the vectors $\mathbf{x}_1$ and $\mathbf{x}_2$ are solutions of system $\mathbf{x}' = \mathbf{A}(t)\mathbf{x}$, where

$$\mathbf{A} = \begin{pmatrix} 4 & 6 \\ -3 & -5 \end{pmatrix}$$

$$\mathbf{x}_1 = \begin{pmatrix} 2e^t \\ -e^t \end{pmatrix}$$

$$\mathbf{x}_2 = \begin{pmatrix} -e^{-2t} \\ e^{-2t} \end{pmatrix}$$

Determine the general solution of this system in the interval $-\infty < t < \infty$.

SOLUTION   This is a system of two first-order linear, homogeneous equations in two unknowns, and according to Theorem 7–3, it has two linearly independent solution vectors. In the previous example, it was shown that the given solution vectors $\mathbf{x}_1$ and $\mathbf{x}_2$ are linearly independent in the specified interval. Therefore, the general solution of the given system in the specified interval is

$$\mathbf{x} = c_1\mathbf{x}_1 + c_2\mathbf{x}_2 = c_1\begin{pmatrix} 2e^t \\ -e^t \end{pmatrix} + c_2\begin{pmatrix} -e^{-2t} \\ e^{-2t} \end{pmatrix}$$

This solution also can be expressed in scalar form as

$$x_1 = 2c_1e^t - c_2e^{-2t}$$

$$x_2 = -c_1e^t + c_2e^{-2t}$$

Theory of Linear, Nonhomogeneous Systems

We now consider the linear, nonhomogeneous system of differential equations expressed as

$$\mathbf{x}' = \mathbf{A}(t)\mathbf{x} + \mathbf{r}(t) \tag{7–59}$$

where the vector $\mathbf{r}(t)$ contains the nonhomogeneous terms. The first step in the solution of nonhomogeneous systems is to obtain the homogeneous solution $\mathbf{x}_h$ by solving the related system $\mathbf{x}' = \mathbf{A}(t)\mathbf{x}$. The next step is to determine the particular solution $\mathbf{x}_p$ that corresponds to the homogeneous vector $\mathbf{r}(t)$ by applying the method of undetermined coefficients or the method variation of parameters. The general solution of the nonhomogeneous system is obtained by combining the homogeneous and the particular solutions according to the following theorem, which closely resembles Theorem 4–6 for single equations.

> **THEOREM 7–5   General Solution of Nonhomogeneous Systems**
>
> *If x_p is a particular solution of the linear, nonhomogeneous system*
>
> $$\mathbf{x}' = \mathbf{A}\mathbf{x} + \mathbf{r}(t)$$
>
> *and $\mathbf{x}_h$ is the general solution of its related homogeneous system $\mathbf{x}' = \mathbf{A}\mathbf{x}$ in an interval $t_1 < t < t_2$ in which elements of the coefficient matrix $\mathbf{A}$ and the vector $\mathbf{r}$ are continuous, the general solution of this nonhomogeneous system in that interval is*
>
> $$\mathbf{x} = \mathbf{x}_h + \mathbf{x}_p$$
> $$= c_1\mathbf{x}_1 + c_2\mathbf{x}_2 + \cdots + c_n\mathbf{x}_n + \mathbf{x}_p \qquad \text{(7–60)}$$
>
> *where $c_1, c_2 \ldots, c_n$ are arbitrary constants and $\mathbf{x}_1, \mathbf{x}_2, \ldots, \mathbf{x}_n$ are n linearly independent solutions. Any solution of this nonhomogeneous system in that interval can be obtained from the general solution by assigning suitable values to the arbitrary constants.*

Given the system:

$$\mathbf{x}' = \mathbf{A}\mathbf{x} + \mathbf{r}$$

where

$$\mathbf{A} = \begin{pmatrix} 4 & 6 \\ -3 & -5 \end{pmatrix} \text{ and } \mathbf{r} = \begin{pmatrix} 1 \\ t \end{pmatrix}$$

Homogeneous solution:

$$\mathbf{x}_h = c_1 \begin{pmatrix} 2e^t \\ -e^t \end{pmatrix} + c_2 \begin{pmatrix} -e^{-2t} \\ e^{-2t} \end{pmatrix}$$

Particular solution:

$$\mathbf{x}_p = \begin{pmatrix} -3t - 4 \\ 2t + 2 \end{pmatrix}$$

Then the general solution of the given system is

$$\mathbf{x} = c_1 \begin{pmatrix} 2e^t \\ -e^t \end{pmatrix} + c_2 \begin{pmatrix} -e^{-2t} \\ e^{-2t} \end{pmatrix} + \begin{pmatrix} -3t - 4 \\ 2t + 2 \end{pmatrix}$$

FIGURE 7–37

The general solution of a nonhomogeneous system is obtained by adding a particular solution to the general solution of the related homogeneous system.

Therefore, once the general solution of the related homogeneous system is available, all we need to do is to determine a particular solution $\mathbf{x}_p$ that satisfies the given nonhomogeneous system. Then the sum $\mathbf{x} = \mathbf{x}_h + \mathbf{x}_p$ will be the general solution of the nonhomogeneous system (Figure 7–37). We can apply the superposition principle to particular solutions if the nonhomogeneous term $\mathbf{r}(t)$ involves several terms, as shown in Section 3–6.

Section Review

7–20C If a vector function $\mathbf{x}$ of order n is a solution of a system of n first-order equations in n unknown functions, under what conditions is a constant multiple of $\mathbf{x}$ also a solution of that system?

7–21C If two vector functions $\mathbf{x}_1$ and $\mathbf{x}_2$ of order n are solutions of a system of n first-order equations in n unknown functions, under what conditions is $3\mathbf{x}_1 - 5\mathbf{x}_2$ also a solution of that system?

7–22C Consider a system of n first-order linear, homogeneous equations with constant coefficients. How many solution vectors can this system have? How many of these solutions can be linearly independent?

7–23 Verify that the given vectors are the solution of the given system, and determine if the solution vectors are linearly independent. If they are, obtain the general solution of the given system on $-\infty < t < \infty$.

$$\mathbf{x}' = \begin{pmatrix} 18 & 10 \\ -30 & -17 \end{pmatrix}\mathbf{x}, \quad \mathbf{x}_1 = \begin{pmatrix} 2e^{3t} \\ -3e^{3t} \end{pmatrix}, \quad \mathbf{x}_2 = \begin{pmatrix} e^{-2t} \\ -2e^{-2t} \end{pmatrix}$$

(*Answer:* The vectors $\mathbf{x}_1$ and $\mathbf{x}_2$ are solutions and are linearly independent and the general solution is $x_1(t) = 2C_1e^{3t} + C_2e^{-2t}$, $x_2(t) = -3C_1e^{3t} - 2C_2e^{-2t}$)

7–24 Verify that the given particular solution vector is the solution of the given system.

$$\mathbf{x}' = \begin{pmatrix} 18 & 10 \\ -30 & -17 \end{pmatrix}\mathbf{x} + \begin{pmatrix} 1 \\ 0 \end{pmatrix}; \quad \mathbf{x}_p = \frac{1}{6}\begin{pmatrix} -17 \\ 30 \end{pmatrix}$$

(*Answer:* The vector $\mathbf{x}_p$ satisfies the given system, and it is a solution).

7–5 ▪ LINEAR HOMOGENEOUS SYSTEMS WITH CONSTANT COEFFICIENTS

In the previous chapter, we introduced the method of elimination and the method of eigenvalues for solving systems of linear differential equations. We pointed out that these methods are elementary in nature and are not practical for systems with more than three equations. In this section, we introduce the powerful **matrix method** or **the method of eigenvectors** for solving linear systems of equations. This method is an extension of the method of eigenvalues and is based on matrix operations and linear algebra that we reviewed earlier in this chapter.

Consider a system of n first-order linear, homogeneous equations with constant coefficients in n unknowns expressed as

$$\begin{aligned}
x_1' &= a_{11}x_1 + a_{12}x_2 + \cdots + a_{1n}x_n \\
x_2' &= a_{21}x_1 + a_{22}x_2 + \cdots + a_{2n}x_n \\
&\vdots \\
x_n' &= a_{n1}x_1 + a_{n2}x_2 + \cdots + a_{nn}x_n
\end{aligned} \tag{7–61}$$

This system also can be expressed compactly in the matrix form as

$$\mathbf{x}' = \mathbf{A}\mathbf{x} \tag{7–62}$$

where

$$\mathbf{A}(t) = \begin{pmatrix} a_{11} & a_{12} & . & . & a_{1n} \\ a_{21} & a_{22} & . & . & a_{21} \\ . & . & . & . & . \\ . & . & . & . & . \\ a_{n1} & a_{n2} & . & . & a_{nn} \end{pmatrix} \quad \text{and} \quad \mathbf{x} = \begin{pmatrix} x_1 \\ x_2 \\ . \\ . \\ x_n \end{pmatrix} \tag{7–63}$$

Theorem 7–3 states that the linear homogeneous system (Equation 7–63) has n linearly independent solution vectors $\mathbf{x}_1, \mathbf{x}_2, \ldots, \mathbf{x}_n$ whose linear combination gives the general solution

$$\mathbf{x} = c_1\mathbf{x}_1 + c_2\mathbf{x}_2 + \cdots + c_n\mathbf{x}_n \tag{7–64}$$

Therefore, *finding the general solution of a linear homogeneous system of n equations is equivalent to determining its n linearly independent solution vectors* (Figure 7–38).

Following the discussions in Section 7–3 for solving single linear homogeneous equations and the discussion in Section 7–4 for solving a system of

---

Given the system:

$$\mathbf{x}' = \mathbf{A}\mathbf{x} \text{ where } \mathbf{A} = \begin{pmatrix} 4 & 6 \\ -3 & -5 \end{pmatrix}$$

Two linearly independent solutions are:

$$\mathbf{x}_1 = \begin{pmatrix} 2e^t \\ -e^t \end{pmatrix} \text{ and } \mathbf{x}_2 = \begin{pmatrix} -e^{-2t} \\ e^{-2t} \end{pmatrix}$$

Then the general solution of the given system is

$$\mathbf{x} = c_1\mathbf{x}_1 + c_2\mathbf{x}_2$$

$$= c_1\begin{pmatrix} 2e^t \\ -e^t \end{pmatrix} + c_2\begin{pmatrix} -e^{-2t} \\ e^{-2t} \end{pmatrix}$$

FIGURE 7–38

Finding the general solution of a linear, homogeneous system of n equations is equivalent to determining its n linearly independent solution vectors.

two linear homogeneous equations with constant coefficients, we seek solutions for the system $\mathbf{x}' = \mathbf{A}\mathbf{x}$ in the form

$$\mathbf{x} = \begin{pmatrix} x_1 \\ x_2 \\ \vdots \\ x_n \end{pmatrix} = \begin{pmatrix} v_1 e^{\lambda t} \\ v_2 e^{\lambda t} \\ \vdots \\ v_n e^{\lambda t} \end{pmatrix} = \begin{pmatrix} v_1 \\ v_2 \\ \vdots \\ v_n \end{pmatrix} e^{\lambda t} = \mathbf{v} e^{\lambda t} \qquad (7\text{--}65)$$

where λ and $v_1, v_2, \ldots, v_n$ are constants (real or complex). To determine the values of λ and the constant vector $\mathbf{v}$, we substitute the assumed form of solution $\mathbf{x} = \mathbf{v}e^{\lambda t}$ and its derivative $\mathbf{x}' = \lambda \mathbf{v}e^{\lambda t}$ into the system $\mathbf{x}' = \mathbf{A}\mathbf{x}$. We obtain

$$\lambda \mathbf{v} e^{\lambda t} = \mathbf{A}\mathbf{v}e^{\lambda t}$$

or

$$\mathbf{A}\mathbf{v} = \lambda \mathbf{v} \qquad (7\text{--}66)$$

since the scalar factor $e^{\lambda t}$ is never zero and thus can be divided out. Therefore, $\mathbf{x} = \mathbf{v}e^{\lambda t}$ will be a solution of the given system if the values of the λ, and the elements of the constant vector $\mathbf{v}$ are such that Equation 7–66 is satisfied. Note that the coefficient matrix $\mathbf{A}$ transforms the vector $\mathbf{v}$ into a constant multiple of itself.

To determine the values of λ and $\mathbf{v}$ that satisfy Equation 7–66, we rewrite this equation in the equivalent form

$$(\mathbf{A} - \lambda \mathbf{I})\mathbf{v} = \mathbf{0} \qquad (7\text{--}67)$$

where $\mathbf{I}$ is the identity matrix. But this is exactly the equation that gives the eigenvectors of the matrix $\mathbf{A}$ corresponding to the eigenvalues λ_i. Thus, we conclude the following (Figure 7–39):

The vector $\mathbf{x} = \mathbf{v}e^{\lambda t}$ is a solution of the linear homogeneous system $\mathbf{x}' = \mathbf{A}\mathbf{x}$, provided that λ is an eigenvalue of the coefficient matrix $\mathbf{A}$ and $\mathbf{v}$ is the eigenvector associated with λ.

Recall from Section 7–3 that an $n \times n$ matrix $\mathbf{A}$ has n eigenvalues λ, which are the roots of the equation $\det(\mathbf{A} - \lambda \mathbf{I}) = \mathbf{0}$. Some of these eigenvalues may be repeated while others may be complex. The n eigenvalues of the coefficient matrix $\mathbf{A}$ can always be found, though not necessarily easily. Thus, all we need for constructing the general solution of a given system of n equations is to determine the n linearly independent eigenvectors associated with these eigenvalues. If the n eigenvalues are real and distinct, the eigenvectors corresponding to them are also real and linearly independent. This is also the case when some of the eigenvalues are complex but still distinct. The only time we may not be able to obtain n linearly independent eigenvectors is when some of the eigenvalues are repeated. In such cases, it may be necessary to find the remaining linearly independent solutions by other methods.

But before we discuss the solution of homogeneous systems, we will introduce the concept of fundamental matrix $\mathbf{F}$, which is very useful when determining the arbitrary constants $c_1, c_2, \ldots, c_n$, corresponding to a given set of initial values and when determining the particular solution of nonhomogeneous systems by the method of variation of parameters.

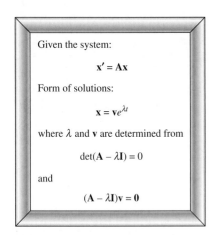

Given the system:

$$\mathbf{x}' = \mathbf{A}\mathbf{x}$$

Form of solutions:

$$\mathbf{x} = \mathbf{v}e^{\lambda t}$$

where λ and $\mathbf{v}$ are determined from

$$\det(\mathbf{A} - \lambda \mathbf{I}) = 0$$

and

$$(\mathbf{A} - \lambda \mathbf{I})\mathbf{v} = \mathbf{0}$$

FIGURE 7–39

The vector $\mathbf{x} = \mathbf{v}e^{\lambda t}$ where λ is an eigenvalue of the coefficient matrix $\mathbf{A}$ and $\mathbf{v}$ is the eigenvector associated with it is a solution of the system $\mathbf{x}' = \mathbf{A}\mathbf{x}$ with constant coefficients.

The $n \times n$ matrix whose columns are n linearly independent solution vectors $\mathbf{x}_1, \mathbf{x}_2, \ldots, \mathbf{x}_n$ of a system in an interval is called the **fundamental matrix** of that system in that interval and is expressed as (Figure 7–40)

$$\mathbf{F}(t) = \begin{pmatrix} x_{11}(t) & x_{12}(t) & . & . & x_{1n}(t) \\ x_{21}(t) & x_{22}(t) & . & . & x_{2n}(t) \\ . & . & . & . & . \\ . & . & . & . & . \\ x_{n1}(t) & x_{n2}(t) & . & . & x_{nn}(t) \end{pmatrix} \tag{7-68}$$

Then the general solution of a system of n equations can be expressed as

$$\mathbf{x}(t) = \mathbf{F}(t)\mathbf{c} \tag{7-69}$$

where

$$\mathbf{c} = \begin{pmatrix} c_1 \\ c_2 \\ \vdots \\ c_n \end{pmatrix} \tag{7-70}$$

is the vector of arbitrary constants. The values of these arbitrary constants corresponding to a set of initial conditions $\mathbf{x}(t_0) = \mathbf{x}_0$ can be determined by applying these conditions to Equation 7–69. It yields

$$\mathbf{F}(t_0)\mathbf{c} = \mathbf{x}_0 \tag{7-71}$$

since $\mathbf{x}(t_0) = \mathbf{F}(t_0)\mathbf{c}$. Multiplying both sides of Equation 7–71 from the left by $\mathbf{F}^{-1}(t_0)$ yields

$$\mathbf{c} = \mathbf{F}^{-1}(t_0)\mathbf{x}_0 \tag{7-72}$$

since $\mathbf{F}^{-1}(t_0)\mathbf{F}(t_0) = \mathbf{I}$ and $\mathbf{Ic} = \mathbf{c}$ (Figure 7–41). Thus the arbitrary constants can be determined by finding the inverse of the fundamental matrix at the specified point, and multiplying it by the vector that contains the initial values. Note that the inverse $\mathbf{F}^{-1}(t_0)$ always exists, since the columns of $\mathbf{F}(t)$ are linearly independent vectors. Also note that once $\mathbf{F}^{-1}(t_0)$ is available, it can be used repeatedly to solve the given system for different sets of initial conditions at the point t_0.

A convenient alternative to the procedure just described is to solve Equation 7–71 for $\mathbf{c}$ by row reduction. It should be kept in mind that the solution of linear homogeneous systems with constant coefficients is valid over the entire real axis $-\infty < t < \infty$; thus, there is no need to talk about the interval of the solution.

Next, we discuss the solution of homogeneous systems with constant coefficients for the cases of real and distinct eigenvalues, complex eigenvalues, and repeated eigenvalues.

Case 1 Real and Distinct Eigenvalues

When the n eigenvalues $\lambda_1, \lambda_2, \ldots, \lambda_n$ of the $n \times n$ matrix $\mathbf{A}$ are real and distinct, then the n associated eigenvectors $\mathbf{v}_1, \mathbf{v}_2, \ldots, \mathbf{v}_n$ are always real and linearly independent. Therefore, the solution vectors $\mathbf{v}_1 e^{\lambda_1 t}, \mathbf{v}_2 e^{\lambda_2 t}, \ldots, \mathbf{v}_n e^{\lambda_n t}$

Given the system:

$$\mathbf{x}' = \mathbf{Ax} \text{ where } \mathbf{A} = \begin{pmatrix} 4 & 6 \\ -3 & -5 \end{pmatrix}$$

Two linearly independent solutions:

$$\mathbf{x}_1 = \begin{pmatrix} 2e^t \\ -e^t \end{pmatrix} \text{ and } \mathbf{x}_2 = \begin{pmatrix} -e^{-2t} \\ e^{-2t} \end{pmatrix}$$

Then the fundamental matrix of the given system is

$$\mathbf{F}(t) = \begin{pmatrix} 2e^t & -e^{-2t} \\ -e^t & e^{-2t} \end{pmatrix}$$

FIGURE 7–40

The fundamental matrix of a system of n first-order linear, homogeneous equations is the matrix whose columns are n linearly independent solution vectors of that system.

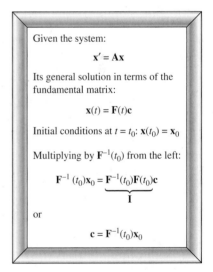

Given the system:

$$\mathbf{x}' = \mathbf{Ax}$$

Its general solution in terms of the fundamental matrix:

$$\mathbf{x}(t) = \mathbf{F}(t)\mathbf{c}$$

Initial conditions at $t = t_0$: $\mathbf{x}(t_0) = \mathbf{x}_0$

Multiplying by $\mathbf{F}^{-1}(t_0)$ from the left:

$$\mathbf{F}^{-1}(t_0)\mathbf{x}_0 = \underbrace{\mathbf{F}^{-1}(t_0)\mathbf{F}(t_0)}_{\mathbf{I}}\mathbf{c}$$

or

$$\mathbf{c} = \mathbf{F}^{-1}(t_0)\mathbf{x}_0$$

FIGURE 7–41

The arbitrary constants in the general solution of a linear, homogeneous system can be expressed in terms of the inverse of the fundamental matrix evaluated at $t = t_0$ and the vector that contains the initial values.

Given the system:

$$\mathbf{x}' = \mathbf{A}\mathbf{x} \text{ where } \mathbf{A} = \begin{pmatrix} 4 & 6 \\ -3 & -5 \end{pmatrix}$$

The eigenvalues of $\mathbf{A}$ are $\lambda_1 = 1$ and $\lambda_2 = -2$ which are real and distinct. The eigenvectors associated with λ_1 and λ_2 are

$$\mathbf{v}_1 = \begin{pmatrix} 2 \\ -1 \end{pmatrix} \text{ and } \mathbf{v}_2 = \begin{pmatrix} -1 \\ 1 \end{pmatrix}$$

Then the general solution of the given system is

$$\mathbf{x} = C_1 \, \mathbf{v}_1 e^{\lambda_1 t} + C_2 \, \mathbf{v}_2 e^{\lambda_2 t}$$

$$= C_1 \begin{pmatrix} 2 \\ -1 \end{pmatrix} e^t + C_2 \begin{pmatrix} -1 \\ 1 \end{pmatrix} e^{-2t}$$

FIGURE 7–42

When the n eigenvalues of the coefficient matrix $\mathbf{A}$ of a system of n first-order linear, homogeneous equations are real and distinct, the general solution of that system is simply the linear combination of the solution vectors $\mathbf{v}e^{\lambda t}$.

are also linearly independent, and the general solution of the given system of n equations in this case can be expressed as (Figure 7–42)

$$\mathbf{x} = c_1\mathbf{v}_1 e^{\lambda_1 t} + c_2\mathbf{v}_2 e^{\lambda_2 t} + \cdots + c_n\mathbf{v}_n e^{\lambda_n t} \qquad \text{(7–73)}$$

The linear independence of the solution vectors $\mathbf{v}_1 e^{\lambda_1 t}, \mathbf{v}_2 e^{\lambda_2 t}, \ldots, \mathbf{v}_n e^{\lambda_n t}$ can be verified by showing that their Wronskian is never zero in the interval of interest.

EXAMPLE 7–19 **Homogeneous System with Real and Distinct Eigenvalues and Arbitrary Initial Conditions**

Determine the general solution of the system:

$$x_1' = 4x_1 + 6x_2$$
$$x_2' = -3x_1 - 5x_2$$

SOLUTION This is a system of two first-order linear, homogeneous equations with constant coefficients in two unknowns, and it can be expressed in matrix form as $\mathbf{x}' = \mathbf{A}\mathbf{x}$, where

$$\mathbf{A} = \begin{pmatrix} 4 & 6 \\ -3 & -5 \end{pmatrix} \text{ and } \mathbf{x} = \begin{pmatrix} x_1 \\ x_2 \end{pmatrix}$$

We first determine the eigenvalues of $\mathbf{A}$, which are the roots of the equation $\det(\mathbf{A} - \lambda \mathbf{I}) = 0$, as

$$\det(\mathbf{A} - \lambda \mathbf{I}) = \begin{vmatrix} 4 - \lambda & 6 \\ -3 & -5 - \lambda \end{vmatrix}$$

$$= (4 - \lambda)(-5 - \lambda) + 18$$

$$= \lambda^2 + \lambda - 2 = 0$$

whose roots are 1 and -2. Therefore, the eigenvalues of the given matrix are $\lambda_1 = 1$ and $\lambda_2 = -2$, which are real and distinct.

The eigenvectors of the matrix $\mathbf{A}$ are determined from the equation $(\mathbf{A} - \lambda \mathbf{I})\mathbf{v} = \mathbf{0}$, which in this case becomes

$$\begin{pmatrix} 4 - \lambda & 6 \\ -3 & -5 - \lambda \end{pmatrix} \begin{pmatrix} v_1 \\ v_2 \end{pmatrix} = \begin{pmatrix} 0 \\ 0 \end{pmatrix} \qquad \text{(7–74)}$$

For $\lambda = \lambda_1 = 1$, it gives

$$\begin{pmatrix} 3 & 6 \\ -3 & -6 \end{pmatrix} \begin{pmatrix} v_1 \\ v_2 \end{pmatrix} = \begin{pmatrix} 0 \\ 0 \end{pmatrix}$$

which is equivalent to the single equation $3v_1 + 6v_2 = 0$. Taking $v_2 = -1$ gives $v_1 = 2$, and the eigenvector corresponding to $\lambda_1 = 1$ becomes

$$\mathbf{v}_1 = \begin{pmatrix} 2 \\ -1 \end{pmatrix}$$

For $\lambda = \lambda_2 = -2$, Equation 7–74 becomes

$$\begin{pmatrix} 6 & 6 \\ -3 & -3 \end{pmatrix} \begin{pmatrix} v_1 \\ v_2 \end{pmatrix} = \begin{pmatrix} 0 \\ 0 \end{pmatrix}$$

which is equivalent to the single equation $6v_1 + 6v_2 = 0$. Taking $v_1 = -1$ gives $v_2 = 1$, and the eigenvector corresponding to $\lambda_2 = -2$ becomes

$$\mathbf{v}_2 = \begin{pmatrix} -1 \\ 1 \end{pmatrix}$$

Therefore, two linearly independent solution vectors of the given system are

$$\mathbf{x}_1 = \mathbf{v}_1 e^{\lambda_1 t} = \begin{pmatrix} 2 \\ -1 \end{pmatrix} e^t = \begin{pmatrix} 2e^t \\ -e^t \end{pmatrix}$$

$$\mathbf{x}_2 = \mathbf{v}_2 e^{\lambda_2 t} = \begin{pmatrix} -1 \\ 1 \end{pmatrix} e^{-2t} = \begin{pmatrix} -e^{-2t} \\ e^{-2t} \end{pmatrix}$$

These two solutions are linearly independent, since their Wronskian is

$$\mathbf{W}(t) = |\mathbf{x}_1 \quad \mathbf{x}_2| = \begin{vmatrix} 2e^t & -e^{-2t} \\ -e^t & e^{-2t} \end{vmatrix} = -e^{-t}$$

which is never zero. Therefore, the solution vectors $\mathbf{x}_1$ and $\mathbf{x}_2$ form a fundamental set of solutions, and the general solution of the given system is

$$\mathbf{x} = c_1 \mathbf{x}_1 + c_2 \mathbf{x}_2 = c_1 \begin{pmatrix} 2 \\ -1 \end{pmatrix} e^t + c_2 \begin{pmatrix} -1 \\ 1 \end{pmatrix} e^{-2t} = \begin{pmatrix} 2c_1 e^t - c_2 e^{-2t} \\ -c_1 e^t + c_2 e^{-2t} \end{pmatrix}$$

The solution can also be expressed in the scalar (nonvector) form as

$$x_1 = 2c_1 e^t - c_2 e^{-2t}$$
$$x_2 = -c_1 e^t + c_2 e^{-2t}$$

These solutions easily can be verified by substituting them into the given system of equations and showing that they satisfy every equation in the system.

EXAMPLE 7–20   Homogeneous System with Real and Distinct Eigenvalues and Specified Initial Conditions

Determine the general solution of the system of initial-value problems:

$$x_1' = 4x_1 + 6x_2, \ x_1(0) = 1$$
$$x_2' = -3x_1 - 5x_2, \ x_2(0) = 0$$

SOLUTION   The general solution of this system of differential equations was determined in the previous example to be

$$\mathbf{x} = c_1 \begin{pmatrix} 2e^t \\ -e^t \end{pmatrix} + c_2 \begin{pmatrix} -e^{-2t} \\ e^{-2t} \end{pmatrix}$$

Thus, the fundamental matrix of the given system of equations is

$$\mathbf{F}(t) = \begin{pmatrix} 2e^t & -e^{-2t} \\ -e^t & e^{-2t} \end{pmatrix}$$

The arbitrary constants can be determined from $\mathbf{c} = \mathbf{F}^{-1}(t_0)\mathbf{x}_0$ (Equation 7–72), where

$$\mathbf{F}(t_0) = \mathbf{F}(0) = \begin{pmatrix} 2 & -1 \\ -1 & 1 \end{pmatrix}$$

The inverse of this 2×2 matrix is

$$\mathbf{F}^{-1}(0) = \begin{pmatrix} 1 & 1 \\ 1 & 2 \end{pmatrix}$$

Substituting this into Equation 7–72 yields

$$\mathbf{c} = \begin{pmatrix} c_1 \\ c_2 \end{pmatrix} = \mathbf{F}^{-1}(0)\mathbf{x}_0 = \begin{pmatrix} 1 & 1 \\ 1 & 2 \end{pmatrix}\begin{pmatrix} 1 \\ 0 \end{pmatrix} = \begin{pmatrix} 1 \\ 1 \end{pmatrix}$$

Therefore, $c_1 = 1$, $c_2 = 1$, and the solution of this system of initial-value problems is

$$\mathbf{x} = \begin{pmatrix} x_1 \\ x_2 \end{pmatrix} = \begin{pmatrix} 2 \\ -1 \end{pmatrix}e^t + \begin{pmatrix} -1 \\ 1 \end{pmatrix}e^{-2t}$$

This solution also can be expressed in the scalar (nonvector) form as

$$x_1 = 2e^t - e^{-2t}$$
$$x_2 = -e^t + e^{-2t}$$

For small systems such as this one, the unknown constants c_1 and c_2 can be determined easily by applying the initial conditions directly to the general solution. The purpose of this example was to demonstrate the general procedure for determining the arbitrary constants corresponding to a set of initial conditions using the fundamental matrix approach.

Case 2 Complex Eigenvalues

We have seen that the matrix method gives n linearly independent solutions directly when the eigenvalues are real and distinct. This is also the case when some or all of the eigenvalues are complex so long as they are distinct. The eigenvectors (and the solution vectors) corresponding to complex eigenvalues are normally complex valued. But if the coefficient matrix $\mathbf{A}$ is real, then all the coefficients of the characteristic equation will be real, and any complex eigenvalues and their corresponding eigenvectors must occur in complex conjugate pairs. In such cases, we can always obtain two linearly independent real-valued solution vectors corresponding to a pair of complex conjugate eigenvalues.

If $\mathbf{v} = \mathbf{a} + i\mathbf{b}$ is the eigenvector corresponding to the eigenvalue $\lambda = \alpha + i\beta$ where $\mathbf{a}, \mathbf{b}, \alpha$, and β are real, then the solution corresponding to this eigenvalue can be expressed as

$$
\begin{aligned}
\mathbf{x} &= \mathbf{v}e^{\lambda t} \\
&= (\mathbf{a} + i\mathbf{b})e^{(\alpha+i\beta)t} \\
&= (\mathbf{a} + i\mathbf{b})e^{\alpha t}(\cos\beta t + i\sin\beta t) \\
&= e^{\alpha t}(\mathbf{a}\cos\beta t - \mathbf{b}\sin\beta t) + ie^{\alpha t}(\mathbf{a}\sin\beta t + \mathbf{b}\cos\beta t) \\
&= \mathbf{x}_1(t) + i\mathbf{x}_2(t) \tag{7-75}
\end{aligned}
$$

where

$$\mathbf{x}_1(t) = e^{\alpha t}(\mathbf{a}\cos\beta t - \mathbf{b}\sin\beta t) \tag{7-76a}$$

and

$$\mathbf{x}_2(t) = e^{\alpha t}(\mathbf{a}\sin\beta t + \mathbf{b}\cos\beta t) \tag{7-76b}$$

which are two real-valued vector solutions (Figure 7–43). It can be shown that these two solutions are linearly independent, and that we would obtain

---

Given the system:

$$\mathbf{x}' = \mathbf{A}\mathbf{x}$$

A pair of complex conjugate eigenvalues of $\mathbf{A}$:

$$\lambda_1 = \alpha + i\beta$$
$$\lambda_2 = \alpha - i\beta$$

Corresponding eigenvectors:

$$\mathbf{v}_1 = \mathbf{a} + i\mathbf{b}$$
$$\mathbf{v}_2 = \mathbf{a} - i\mathbf{b}$$

Two linearly independent solutions corresponding to them:

$$\mathbf{x}_1(t) = e^{\alpha t}(\mathbf{a}\cos\beta t - \mathbf{b}\sin\beta t)$$

$$\mathbf{x}_2(t) = e^{\alpha t}(\mathbf{a}\sin\beta t + \mathbf{b}\cos\beta t)$$

FIGURE 7–43

Determination of two real-valued linearly independent solution vectors of a system corresponding to a pair of complex conjugate eigenvalues of the coefficient matrix.

the same two solutions corresponding to the complex conjugate eigenvalue $\lambda = \alpha - i\beta$. Therefore, we can determine the two linearly independent real-valued solutions corresponding to a complex conjugate pair by working with one of the complex eigenvalues and its corresponding eigenvector and ignoring their complex conjugates. Once we know the complex eigenvalue λ and its corresponding eigenvector $\mathbf{v}$, it is more practical to manipulate the solution $\mathbf{x} = \mathbf{v}e^{\lambda t}$, as shown previously, and take the real and imaginary parts of the solution as the two linearly independent real-valued solutions instead of memorizing Equations 7–76.

EXAMPLE 7–21   **Homogeneous System with Complex Eigenvalues**

Determine the general solution of the system

$$x_1' = x_1 + 2x_2$$
$$x_2' = -x_1 + x_2$$

SOLUTION   This is a system of two first-order linear homogeneous equations with constant coefficients in two unknowns, and it can be expressed in matrix form as $\mathbf{x}' = \mathbf{Ax}$, where

$$\mathbf{A} = \begin{pmatrix} 1 & 2 \\ -1 & 1 \end{pmatrix} \quad \text{and} \quad \mathbf{x} = \begin{pmatrix} x_1 \\ x_2 \end{pmatrix}$$

The eigenvalues of $\mathbf{A}$ were determined in Example 7–15 to be $\lambda_{1,2} = 1 \pm \sqrt{2}i$, which are complex conjugates of each other. The eigenvector corresponding to $\lambda_1 = 1 + \sqrt{2}i$ was also determined in that example to be

$$\mathbf{V_1} = \begin{pmatrix} 1 \\ \dfrac{i}{\sqrt{2}} \end{pmatrix}$$

Thus, the solution corresponding to λ_1 can be expressed as (Figure 7–44)

$$\mathbf{x} = \mathbf{v}_1 e^{\lambda_1 t}$$

$$= \begin{pmatrix} 1 \\ \dfrac{i}{\sqrt{2}} \end{pmatrix} e^{(1+i\sqrt{2})t}$$

$$= \begin{pmatrix} 1 \\ \dfrac{i}{\sqrt{2}} \end{pmatrix} e^t (\cos \sqrt{2}t + i \sin \sqrt{2}t)$$

$$= \begin{pmatrix} e^t \cos \sqrt{2}t + ie^t \sin \sqrt{2}t \\ \dfrac{i}{\sqrt{2}} e^t \cos \sqrt{2}t - \dfrac{1}{\sqrt{2}} e^t \sin \sqrt{2}t \end{pmatrix}$$

$$= \begin{pmatrix} e^t \cos \sqrt{2}t \\ -\dfrac{1}{\sqrt{2}} e^t \sin \sqrt{2}t \end{pmatrix} + i \begin{pmatrix} e^t \sin \sqrt{2}t \\ \dfrac{1}{\sqrt{2}} e^t \cos \sqrt{2}t \end{pmatrix}$$

Given the system:

$$\mathbf{x}' = \mathbf{Ax} \text{ where } \mathbf{A} = \begin{pmatrix} 1 & 2 \\ -1 & 1 \end{pmatrix}$$

Eigenvalues of $\mathbf{A}$:

$$\lambda_1 = 1 + \sqrt{2}i$$
$$\lambda_2 = 1 - \sqrt{2}i$$

Corresponding eigenvectors:

$$\mathbf{v}_1 = \begin{pmatrix} 1 \\ \dfrac{i}{\sqrt{2}} \end{pmatrix}$$

$$\mathbf{v}_2 = \begin{pmatrix} 1 \\ \dfrac{-i}{\sqrt{2}} \end{pmatrix}$$

Solution vector:

$$\mathbf{x} = \mathbf{v}_1 e^{\lambda_1 t}$$

$$= \begin{pmatrix} e^t \cos \sqrt{2}t \\ -\dfrac{1}{\sqrt{2}} e^t \sin \sqrt{2}t \end{pmatrix} + i \begin{pmatrix} e^t \sin \sqrt{2}t \\ \dfrac{1}{\sqrt{2}} e^t \cos \sqrt{2}t \end{pmatrix}$$

Two linearly independent solutions:

$$\mathbf{x}_1(t) = Re(\mathbf{x}) = \begin{pmatrix} e^t \cos \sqrt{2}t \\ -\dfrac{1}{\sqrt{2}} e^t \sin \sqrt{2}t \end{pmatrix}$$

$$\mathbf{x}_2(t) = Im(\mathbf{x}) = \begin{pmatrix} e^t \sin \sqrt{2}t \\ \dfrac{1}{\sqrt{2}} e^t \cos \sqrt{2}t \end{pmatrix}$$

FIGURE 7–44

Two linearly independent solutions corresponding to a pair of complex conjugate eigenvalues can be determined by working with only one of the eigenvalues and its corresponding eigenvector, and ignoring their conjugates.

Therefore, two linearly independent solutions are

$$\mathbf{x}_1(t) = Re(\mathbf{x}) = \begin{pmatrix} e^t \cos\sqrt{2}t \\ -\dfrac{1}{\sqrt{2}} e^t \sin\sqrt{2}t \end{pmatrix}$$

and

$$\mathbf{x}_2(t) = Im(\mathbf{x}) = \begin{pmatrix} e^t \sin\sqrt{2}t \\ \dfrac{1}{\sqrt{2}} e^t \cos\sqrt{2}t \end{pmatrix}$$

Then the general solution can be expressed as

$$\mathbf{x}(t) = c_1\mathbf{x}_1(t) + c_2\mathbf{x}_2(t) = c_1\begin{pmatrix} e^t \cos\sqrt{2}t \\ -\dfrac{1}{\sqrt{2}} e^t \sin\sqrt{2}t \end{pmatrix} + c_2\begin{pmatrix} e^t \sin\sqrt{2}t \\ \dfrac{1}{\sqrt{2}} e^t \cos\sqrt{2}t \end{pmatrix}$$

The solution can also be expressed in the scalar form as

$$x_1(t) = e^t(c_1\cos\sqrt{2}t + c_2\sin\sqrt{2}t)$$

$$x_2(t) = e^t\left(-\dfrac{1}{\sqrt{2}} c_1\sin\sqrt{2}t + \dfrac{1}{\sqrt{2}} c_2\cos\sqrt{2}t\right)$$

These solutions easily can be verified by substituting them into the given system of equations and showing that they satisfy every equation in the system.

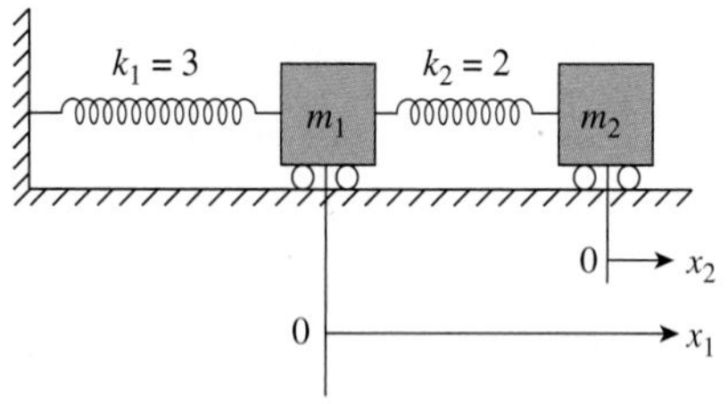

FIGURE 7–45

The coupled mass-spring system discussed in Example 7–22.

EXAMPLE 7–22   Coupled Mechanical Systems: Free Vibrations

Consider a mass–spring system that consists of two masses $m_1 = 1$ and $m_2 = 1$ and two linear springs whose spring constants are $k_1 = 3$ and $k_2 = 2$ in proper units, connected as shown in Figure 7–45. At $t = 0$, the first mass is pulled to a location $x_1(0) = 1$, and the second mass to a location $x_2(0) = 5$ relative to their equilibrium positions. Both masses are released with zero velocities.

Letting $x_1(t)$ and $x_2(t)$ denote the positions of the two masses at any time t relative to their equilibrium positions (the positions they assume when no external force is applied) and neglecting any friction, determine the position of each mass relative to their respective equilibrium positions as a function of time.

SOLUTION   The governing equations for this coupled mechanical system were derived in Example 6–4 under the influence of external forces. In our case, there are no external forces. Thus, the differential equations governing the motion of each mass in this case (from Equations 6–14) are

$$x_1'' = -\left(\dfrac{k_1}{m_1} + \dfrac{k_2}{m_2}\right)x_1 + \dfrac{k_2}{m_1}x_2, \quad x_1(0) = x_{01}, \quad x_1'(0) = v_{01}$$

$$x_2'' = \dfrac{k_2}{m_2}x_1 - \dfrac{k_2}{m_2}x_2, \quad x_2(0) = x_{02}, \quad x_2'(0) = v_{02}$$

This is a system of two linear, homogeneous second-order equations in two unknown functions with specified initial conditions. The first thing we need to do is to reduce this system into a system of first-order equations by defining two new variables as $x_3 = x_1'$ and $x_4 = x_2'$. With these definitions, the system can be expressed as

$$
\begin{aligned}
x_1' &= x_3, & x_1(0) &= x_{01} \\
x_2' &= x_4, & x_2(0) &= x_{02} \\
x_3' &= -\left(\frac{k_1}{m_1} + \frac{k_2}{m_1}\right)x_1 + \frac{k_2}{m_1}x_2, & x_3(0) &= x_1'(0) = v_{01} \\
x_4' &= \frac{k_2}{m_2}x_1 - \frac{k_2}{m_2}x_2, & x_4(0) &= x_2'(0) = v_{02}
\end{aligned}
$$

Note that physically, x_3 and x_4 represent the velocities of the masses m_1 and m_2, respectively.

We now simplify the system by substituting $m_1 = m_2 = 1$, $k_1 = 3$, $k_2 = 2$, and $x_1(0) = 1$, $x_2(0) = 5$, and $v_{01} = v_{02} = 0$, which gives

$$
\begin{aligned}
x_1' &= x_3, & x_1(0) &= 1 \\
x_2' &= x_4, & x_2(0) &= 5 \\
x_3' &= -5x_1 + 2x_2, & x_3(0) &= x_1'(0) = 0 \\
x_4' &= 2x_1 - 2x_2, & x_4(0) &= x_2'(0) = 0
\end{aligned}
$$

This system can be expressed in the matrix form as $\mathbf{x}' = \mathbf{A}\mathbf{x}$, where

$$
\mathbf{A} = \begin{pmatrix} 0 & 0 & 1 & 0 \\ 0 & 0 & 0 & 1 \\ -5 & 2 & 0 & 0 \\ 2 & -2 & 0 & 0 \end{pmatrix} \quad \text{and} \quad \mathbf{x} = \begin{pmatrix} x_1 \\ x_2 \\ x_3 \\ x_4 \end{pmatrix}
$$

The eigenvalues of the coefficient matrix $\mathbf{A}$ are determined from $\det(\mathbf{A} - \lambda\mathbf{I}) = 0$, as

$$
\det(\mathbf{A} - \lambda\mathbf{I}) = \begin{vmatrix} -\lambda & 0 & 1 & 0 \\ 0 & -\lambda & 0 & 1 \\ -5 & 2 & -\lambda & 0 \\ 2 & -2 & 0 & -\lambda \end{vmatrix} = -\lambda \begin{vmatrix} -\lambda & 0 & 1 \\ 2 & -\lambda & 0 \\ -2 & 0 & -\lambda \end{vmatrix}
$$

$$
+ \begin{vmatrix} 0 & -\lambda & 1 \\ -5 & 2 & 0 \\ 2 & -2 & -\lambda \end{vmatrix}
$$

$$
= -\lambda(-\lambda^3 - 2\lambda) + (10 - 4 + 5\lambda^2)
$$

$$
= \lambda^4 + 7\lambda^2 + 6 = (\lambda^2 + 1)(\lambda^2 + 6) = 0
$$

whose roots are $\pm i$ and $\pm\sqrt{6}i$. Therefore, the eigenvalues of the coefficient matrix are $\lambda_{1,2} = \pm i$ and $\lambda_{3,4} = \pm\sqrt{6}i$, which are two pairs of complex conjugate numbers. We need to determine only two eigenvectors in this case using $\lambda_1 = i$ and $\lambda_3 = \sqrt{6}i$, since the eigenvectors corresponding to the complex conjugate eigenvalues are simply the complex conjugates of the eigenvectors determined. Besides, the two eigenvectors are sufficient to determine four linearly independent solution vectors for the given system.

The eigenvector corresponding to the first eigenvalue $\lambda_1 = i$ is determined from the equation $(\mathbf{A} - \lambda \mathbf{I})\mathbf{v}_1 = \mathbf{0}$, which in this case becomes

$$\begin{pmatrix} -i & 0 & 1 & 0 \\ 0 & -i & 0 & 1 \\ -5 & 2 & -i & 0 \\ 2 & -2 & 0 & -i \end{pmatrix} \begin{pmatrix} v_1 \\ v_2 \\ v_3 \\ v_4 \end{pmatrix} = \begin{pmatrix} 0 \\ 0 \\ 0 \\ 0 \end{pmatrix}$$

This system reduces by row operations to

$$\begin{pmatrix} 1 & 0 & 0 & 0.5i \\ 0 & 1 & 0 & \\ 0 & 0 & 1 & -0.5 \\ 0 & 0 & 0 & 0 \end{pmatrix} \begin{pmatrix} v_1 \\ v_2 \\ v_3 \\ v_4 \end{pmatrix} = \begin{pmatrix} 0 \\ 0 \\ 0 \\ 0 \end{pmatrix}$$

which is equivalent to the system

$$v_1 + 0.5iv_4 = 0$$
$$v_2 + iv_4 = 0$$
$$v_3 - 0.5v_4 = 0$$

Taking $v_4 = 2$, we obtain $v_3 = 1$, $v_2 = -2i$, and $v_1 = -i$. Therefore, the eigenvector corresponding to the eigenvalue $\lambda_1 = i$ is

$$\mathbf{v}_1 = \begin{pmatrix} -i \\ -2i \\ 1 \\ 2 \end{pmatrix}$$

The eigenvector corresponding to the eigenvalue $\lambda_3 = \sqrt{6}i$ is determined in the same manner to be

$$\mathbf{v}_3 = \begin{pmatrix} \dfrac{\sqrt{6}}{3}i \\ -\dfrac{\sqrt{6}}{6}i \\ -2 \\ 1 \end{pmatrix}$$

The solution corresponding to $\lambda_1 = i$ can be expressed as

$$\mathbf{x} = \mathbf{v}_1 e^{\lambda_1 t} = \begin{pmatrix} -i \\ -2i \\ 1 \\ 2 \end{pmatrix} e^{it} = \begin{pmatrix} -i \\ -2i \\ 1 \\ 2 \end{pmatrix}(\cos t + i \sin t)$$

$$= \begin{pmatrix} -i\cos t + \sin t \\ -2i\cos t + 2\sin t \\ \cos t + i\sin t \\ 2\cos t + 2i\sin t \end{pmatrix} = \begin{pmatrix} \sin t \\ 2\sin t \\ \cos t \\ 2\cos t \end{pmatrix} + i \begin{pmatrix} -\cos t \\ -2\cos t \\ \sin t \\ 2\sin t \end{pmatrix}$$

Thus, the two linearly independent solution vectors are

$$\mathbf{x}_1(t) = Re(\mathbf{x}) = \begin{pmatrix} \sin t \\ 2\sin t \\ \cos t \\ 2\cos t \end{pmatrix} \quad \text{and} \quad \mathbf{x}_2(t) = Im(\mathbf{x}) = \begin{pmatrix} -\cos t \\ -2\cos t \\ \sin t \\ 2\sin t \end{pmatrix}$$

The other two linearly independent solution vectors are determined in a similar manner using $\lambda_3 = \sqrt{6}i$ and the eigenvector $\mathbf{v}_2$ to be

$$\mathbf{x}_3(t) = \begin{pmatrix} \dfrac{-\sqrt{6}}{3}\sin\sqrt{6}t \\ \dfrac{\sqrt{6}}{6}\sin\sqrt{6}t \\ -2\cos\sqrt{6}t \\ \cos\sqrt{6}t \end{pmatrix} \quad \text{and} \quad \mathbf{x}_4(t) = \begin{pmatrix} \dfrac{\sqrt{6}}{3}\cos\sqrt{6}t \\ \dfrac{-\sqrt{6}}{6}\cos\sqrt{6}t \\ -2\sin\sqrt{6}t \\ \sin\sqrt{6}t \end{pmatrix}$$

Then the general solution of the given system can be expressed as

$$\mathbf{x}(t) = c_1\mathbf{x}_1(t) + c_2\mathbf{x}_2(t) + c_3\mathbf{x}_3(t) + c_4\mathbf{x}_4(t)$$

$$= c_1\begin{pmatrix} \sin t \\ 2\sin t \\ \cos t \\ 2\cos t \end{pmatrix} + c_2\begin{pmatrix} -\cos t \\ -2\cos t \\ \sin t \\ 2\sin t \end{pmatrix} + c_3\begin{pmatrix} \dfrac{-\sqrt{6}}{3}\sin\sqrt{6}t \\ \dfrac{\sqrt{6}}{6}\sin\sqrt{6}t \\ -2\cos\sqrt{6}t \\ \cos\sqrt{6}t \end{pmatrix} + c_4\begin{pmatrix} \dfrac{\sqrt{6}}{3}\cos\sqrt{6}t \\ \dfrac{-\sqrt{6}}{6}\cos\sqrt{6}t \\ -2\sin\sqrt{6}t \\ \sin\sqrt{6}t \end{pmatrix}$$

The solution also can be expressed in the scalar (nonvector) form as

$$x_1(t) = c_1\sin t - c_2\cos t - \frac{\sqrt{6}}{3}c_3\sin\sqrt{6}t + \frac{\sqrt{6}}{3}c_4\cos\sqrt{6}t$$

$$x_2(t) = 2c_1\sin t - 2c_2\cos t + \frac{\sqrt{6}}{6}c_3\sin\sqrt{6}t - \frac{\sqrt{6}}{6}c_4\cos\sqrt{6}t$$

$$x_3(t) = c_1\cos t + c_2\sin t - 2c_3\cos\sqrt{6}t + c_4\sin\sqrt{6}t$$

$$x_4(t) = 2c_1\cos t + 2c_2\sin t + c_3\cos\sqrt{6}t + c_4\sin\sqrt{6}t$$

Applying the four initial conditions gives the following four equations for the determination of the arbitrary constants, after noting that $x_3(0) = x_4(0) = 0$:

$$-c_2 + \frac{\sqrt{6}}{3}c_4 = 1$$

$$-2c_2 - \frac{\sqrt{6}}{6}c_4 = 5$$

$$c_1 - 2c_3 = 0$$

$$2c_1 + c_3 = 0$$

The first two equations give $c_2 = -11/5$ and $c_4 = -3\sqrt{6}/5$; whereas, the last two simply give $c_1 = c_3 = 0$. Substituting these into the general solutions of x_1 and x_2 gives the motions of the two masses to be

$$x_1(t) = \frac{11}{5}\cos t - \frac{6}{5}\cos\sqrt{6}t$$

$$x_2(t) = \frac{22}{5}\cos t + \frac{3}{5}\cos\sqrt{6}t$$

Observe that the motion of both masses is the superposition of two modes of oscillations with natural frequencies of $\omega_1 = 1$ and $\omega_2 = \sqrt{6}$. In the first mode ($\omega_1 = 1$), the two masses move in synchrony in the same direction at the same frequency but with different amplitudes. The amplitude of the motion of m_1 is half that of m_2 in the first mode. In the second mode ($\omega_2 = \sqrt{6}$), the masses move in opposite directions. The amplitude of m_1 is twice that of m_2.

Case 3 Repeated Eigenvalues

We now consider an eigenvalue λ of multiplicity k, which is a k-fold root of the characteristic equation of the system. Such an eigenvalue may still have k linearly independent eigenvectors $\mathbf{v}$ associated with it, and thus there are k linearly independent solution vectors. This is always the case with the systems of equations whose coefficient matrix $\mathbf{A}$ is *symmetric*, and a repeated eigenvalue causes no problem in such cases. When an eigenvalue of multiplicity k has *fewer* than k linearly independent eigenvectors associated with it, there are *fewer* than k linearly independent solution vectors of the form $\mathbf{v}e^{\lambda t}$ associated with that eigenvalue. This means that some of the solutions associated with that eigenvalue are *not* of the form $\mathbf{v}e^{\lambda t}$, and we must seek solutions in other forms to make up the deficit in the number of linearly independent solutions associated with λ.

You will recall from Chapters 3 and 4 that the linearly independent solutions corresponding to a repeated characteristic root λ of a single differential equation are obtained by multiplying the solution $e^{\lambda t}$ by the powers of the independent variable. For example, three linearly independent solutions associated with the three-fold characteristic root λ are $e^{\lambda t}$, $te^{\lambda t}$, and $t^2 e^{\lambda t}$. The close analogy between a single nth-order linear equation and a system of n first-order linear equations suggests that we seek additional solution vectors in the same manner by multiplying the solution $\mathbf{v}e^{\lambda t}$ by the powers of the independent variable. But as explained here, this turns out to be inadequate for systems of equations, and it becomes necessary to multiply the basic solution by *polynomials* of t instead of *powers* of t to obtain other linearly independent solutions associated with the repeated eigenvalue λ (Figure 7–46).

Consider an eigenvalue λ of multiplicity two ($k = 2$), which has only one linearly independent eigenvector $\mathbf{v}$ associated with it. We need to find two linearly independent solution vectors corresponding to λ. One of these solutions is

$$\mathbf{x}_1(t) = \mathbf{v}e^{\lambda t} \tag{7–77}$$

In the light of this discussion, we choose the second solution of the form

$$\mathbf{x}_2(t) = \mathbf{v}te^{\lambda t} + \mathbf{u}e^{\lambda t} \tag{7–78}$$

where $\mathbf{u}$ is a constant vector that is to be determined from the requirement that $\mathbf{x}_2$ satisfy the differential equation $\mathbf{x}' = \mathbf{Ax}$. Substituting Equation 7–78 into $\mathbf{x}' = \mathbf{Ax}$ yields

$$\mathbf{v}e^{\lambda t} + \lambda \mathbf{v}te^{\lambda t} + \lambda \mathbf{u}e^{\lambda t} = \mathbf{Av}te^{\lambda t} + \mathbf{Au}e^{\lambda t} \tag{7–79}$$

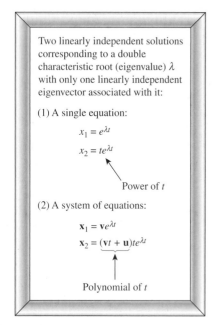

Two linearly independent solutions corresponding to a double characteristic root (eigenvalue) λ with only one linearly independent eigenvector associated with it:

(1) A single equation:

$$x_1 = e^{\lambda t}$$
$$x_2 = te^{\lambda t}$$

Power of t

(2) A system of equations:

$$\mathbf{x}_1 = \mathbf{v}e^{\lambda t}$$
$$\mathbf{x}_2 = \underbrace{(\mathbf{v}t + \mathbf{u})}te^{\lambda t}$$

Polynomial of t

FIGURE 7–46

When there is only one linearly independent eigenvector $\mathbf{v}$ associated with an eigenvalue λ of multiplicity k, the remaining $k - 1$ linearly independent solutions associated with λ are obtained by multiplying the basic solution $\mathbf{v}e^{\lambda t}$ by polynomials of $\mathbf{v}$ with constant vector coefficients.

Equating the coefficients of $e^{\lambda t}$ and $te^{\lambda t}$ gives

$$(\mathbf{A} - \lambda\mathbf{I})\mathbf{v} = \mathbf{0} \qquad\qquad (7\text{-}80\text{a})$$

and

$$(\mathbf{A} - \lambda\mathbf{I})\mathbf{u} = \mathbf{v} \qquad\qquad (7\text{-}80\text{b})$$

The first of these equations simply reaffirms that $\mathbf{v}$ is an eigenvector associated with λ. The second equation always can be solved for the unknown constant vector $\mathbf{u}$.

The difference between the treatment of the second solution associated with a repeated characteristic root λ for a single second-order equation and a system of two first-order equations can be explained as follows.

For a single equation, a constant multiple of the first solution $e^{\lambda t}$ is fundamentally not any different than $e^{\lambda t}$, and there is no need to include it in the second solution. That is, the solutions $x = c_1 e^{\lambda t} + c_2 te^{\lambda t}$ and

$$x = c_1 e^{\lambda t} + (c_2 te^{\lambda t} + c_3 e^{\lambda t}) = (c_1 + c_3)e^{\lambda t} + c_2 te^{\lambda t}$$

are equivalent, since the sum of two arbitrary constants is still an arbitrary constant.

But for a system of two first-order equations, the solution $\mathbf{u}e^{\lambda t}$ is not necessarily a constant multiple of the first solution $\mathbf{v}e^{\lambda t}$, since $\mathbf{u}$ and $\mathbf{v}$ are vectors. For example, the solution

$$\mathbf{x}_2(t) = \begin{pmatrix} 2 \\ 1 \end{pmatrix} e^{\lambda t} \qquad\qquad (7\text{-}81)$$

cannot be obtained by multiplying the solution

$$\mathbf{x}_1(t) = \begin{pmatrix} 1 \\ 1 \end{pmatrix} e^{\lambda t} \qquad\qquad (7\text{-}82)$$

by a constant. In fact, $\mathbf{x}_2(t)$ may not even be a solution even when $\mathbf{x}_1(t)$ is. This is in contrast to single linear, homogeneous equations where if $2e^{\lambda t}$ is a solution, so is $3e^{\lambda t}$ or $-5e^{\lambda t}$. Thus, the difference lies the fact that two constant scalars are always a constant multiple of each other, but two constant vectors are not necessarily a constant multiple of each other (Figure 7–47). This is now illustrated with examples.

(1) Two scalars:
$$a = 2$$
$$b = 8$$
($b = ka$ where $k = 4$)

(2) Two vectors:
$$\mathbf{a} = \begin{pmatrix} 2 \\ 1 \end{pmatrix}$$
$$\mathbf{b} = \begin{pmatrix} 8 \\ 1 \end{pmatrix}$$
($\mathbf{b} \neq k\mathbf{a}$)

FIGURE 7–47

Two constant *scalars* are always a constant multiple of each other, but this is not the case for two constant *vectors*.

EXAMPLE 7–23 **Homogeneous System with Repeated (Double) Eigenvalues**

Determine the general solution of the system:

$$x_1' = 4x_1 + x_2$$

$$x_2' = -x_1 + 2x_2$$

SOLUTION This is a system of two first-order linear, homogeneous equations with constant coefficients in two unknowns, and it can be expressed in matrix form as $\mathbf{x}' = \mathbf{A}\mathbf{x}$, where

$$\mathbf{A} = \begin{pmatrix} 4 & 1 \\ -1 & 2 \end{pmatrix} \quad \text{and} \quad \mathbf{x} = \begin{pmatrix} x_1 \\ x_2 \end{pmatrix}$$

The eigenvalues of the coefficient matrix $\mathbf{A}$ were determined in Example 7–13 to be $\lambda_1 = \lambda_2 = 3$. That is, the system has a single eigenvalue of multiplicity 2. It was also determined that there is only one linearly independent eigenvector associated with this eigenvalue, and it was

$$\mathbf{v} = \begin{pmatrix} -1 \\ 1 \end{pmatrix}$$

Therefore, one solution of the given system is

$$\mathbf{x}_1(t) = \mathbf{v}e^{\lambda t} = \begin{pmatrix} -1 \\ 1 \end{pmatrix} e^{3t}$$

The second linearly independent solution is taken to be (Equation 7–78)

$$\mathbf{x}_2(t) = (\mathbf{u} + \mathbf{v}t)e^{\lambda t}$$

where the constant vector $\mathbf{u}$ is determined from Equation 7–80,

$$(\mathbf{A} - \lambda\,\mathbf{I})\mathbf{u} = \mathbf{v}$$

Substituting, we have

$$\begin{pmatrix} 1 & 1 \\ -1 & -1 \end{pmatrix} \begin{pmatrix} u_1 \\ u_2 \end{pmatrix} = \begin{pmatrix} -1 \\ 1 \end{pmatrix}$$

which is equivalent to the single equation

$$u_1 + u_2 = -1$$

This is a nonhomogeneous equation. Thus, we can choose one of the unknowns to be zero and still obtain a nontrivial solution. Taking $u_1 = 0$ gives $u_2 = -1$, and

$$\mathbf{u} = \begin{pmatrix} 0 \\ -1 \end{pmatrix}$$

Then the second linearly independent solution becomes

$$\mathbf{x}_2(t) = (\mathbf{u} + \mathbf{v}t)e^{\lambda t} = \left[\begin{pmatrix} 0 \\ -1 \end{pmatrix} + \begin{pmatrix} -1 \\ 1 \end{pmatrix} t \right] e^{3t} = \begin{pmatrix} -t \\ -1 + t \end{pmatrix} e^{3t}$$

It can be shown that the Wronskian of $\mathbf{x}_1(t)$ and $\mathbf{x}_2(t)$ is not zero, and thus, these two solutions are linearly independent. Therefore, the solutions $\mathbf{x}_1$ and $\mathbf{x}_2$ form a fundamental set of solutions, and the general solution of the given system is

$$\mathbf{x} = c_1\mathbf{x}_1 + c_2\mathbf{x}_2 = c_1 \begin{pmatrix} -1 \\ 1 \end{pmatrix} e^{3t} + c_2 \begin{pmatrix} -t \\ t - 1 \end{pmatrix} e^{3t}$$

$$= \begin{pmatrix} -c_1 - c_2 t \\ c_1 + c_2(t - 1) \end{pmatrix} e^{3t}$$

The solution also can be expressed in the scalar (nonvector) form as

$$x_1(t) = -(c_1 + c_2 t)e^{3t}$$

$$x_2(t) = [c_1 + c_2(t - 1)]e^{3t}$$

These solutions easily can be verified by substituting them into the given system of equations, and showing that they satisfy every equation in the system.

Discussion

Let us see what happens if we choose the second linearly independent solution to be of the form

$$\mathbf{x}_2(t) = \mathbf{u}\, te^{\lambda t}$$

where $\mathbf{u}$ is again a constant vector, which is to be determined. Substituting this into the equation $\mathbf{x}' = \mathbf{A}\mathbf{x}$ gives

$$\mathbf{u}e^{\lambda t} + \lambda\, \mathbf{u}te^{\lambda t} = \mathbf{A}\mathbf{u}te^{\lambda t}$$

Equating the coefficients of $e^{\lambda t}$ and $te^{\lambda t}$ on both sides gives $\mathbf{u} = \mathbf{0}$ and $(\mathbf{A} - \lambda\,\mathbf{I})\mathbf{u} = \mathbf{0}$, which requires that $\mathbf{u} = \mathbf{0}$. Thus, we conclude that we cannot have a nontrivial solution of the form $\mathbf{x}_2(t) = \mathbf{u}te^{\lambda t}$, and we must take the second linearly independent solution to be of the form $\mathbf{x}_2(t) = (\mathbf{u} + \mathbf{v}t)^{\lambda t}$.

The situation becomes even more complex as the degree of multiplicity increases. For example, there are three possibilities associated with an eigenvalue λ with a multiplicity of three: (1) there are three linearly independent eigenvectors associated with λ, and thus, three linearly independent solutions; (2) there are two linearly independent eigenvectors associated with λ, and thus, we need to find one additional linearly independent solution; and (3) there is a single linearly independent eigenvector associated with λ, and thus, we need to find two additional linearly independent solutions. Each case needs to be treated differently, and there is no general procedure for handling eigenvalues with a multiplicity of three.

Case 3a *The triple eigenvalue λ has three linearly independent eigenvectors* $\mathbf{v}_1$, $\mathbf{v}_2$, *and* $\mathbf{v}_3$ *associated with it.* In this case, the three linearly independent solutions are simply (Figure 7–48).

$$\mathbf{x}_1 = \mathbf{v}_1 e^{\lambda t} \tag{7–83a}$$

$$\mathbf{x}_2 = \mathbf{v}_2 e^{\lambda t} \tag{7–83b}$$

$$\mathbf{x}_3 = \mathbf{v}_3 e^{\lambda t} \tag{7–83c}$$

Case 3b *The triple eigenvalue λ has two linearly independent eigenvectors* $\mathbf{v}_1$ *and* $\mathbf{v}_2$ *associated with it.* In this case, the first two linearly independent solutions are

$$\mathbf{x}_1 = \mathbf{v}_1 e^{\lambda t} \tag{7–84a}$$

$$\mathbf{x}_2 = \mathbf{v}_2 e^{\lambda t} \tag{7–84b}$$

and the third linearly independent solution is determined from

$$\mathbf{x}_3 = \mathbf{v}te^{\lambda t} + \mathbf{u}e^{\lambda t} \tag{7–85}$$

Again, the constant vector $\mathbf{u}$ is determined from Equation 7–80b,

$$(\mathbf{A} - \lambda\,\mathbf{I})\mathbf{u} = \mathbf{v}$$

There is the question of whether to use $\mathbf{v}_1$ or $\mathbf{v}_2$ for $\mathbf{v}$ in this relation in order to obtain a nontrivial solution for $\mathbf{u}$. In general, neither choice will work,

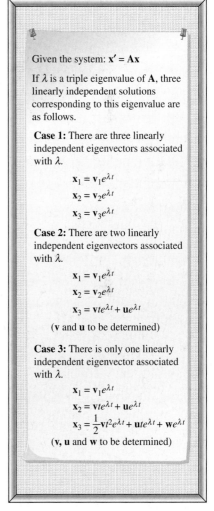

Given the system: $\mathbf{x}' = \mathbf{A}\mathbf{x}$

If λ is a triple eigenvalue of $\mathbf{A}$, three linearly independent solutions corresponding to this eigenvalue are as follows.

Case 1: There are three linearly independent eigenvectors associated with λ.

$$\mathbf{x}_1 = \mathbf{v}_1 e^{\lambda t}$$
$$\mathbf{x}_2 = \mathbf{v}_2 e^{\lambda t}$$
$$\mathbf{x}_3 = \mathbf{v}_3 e^{\lambda t}$$

Case 2: There are two linearly independent eigenvectors associated with λ.

$$\mathbf{x}_1 = \mathbf{v}_1 e^{\lambda t}$$
$$\mathbf{x}_2 = \mathbf{v}_2 e^{\lambda t}$$
$$\mathbf{x}_3 = \mathbf{v}te^{\lambda t} + \mathbf{u}e^{\lambda t}$$

($\mathbf{v}$ and $\mathbf{u}$ to be determined)

Case 3: There is only one linearly independent eigenvector associated with λ.

$$\mathbf{x}_1 = \mathbf{v}_1 e^{\lambda t}$$
$$\mathbf{x}_2 = \mathbf{v}te^{\lambda t} + \mathbf{u}e^{\lambda t}$$
$$\mathbf{x}_3 = \frac{1}{2}\mathbf{v}t^2 e^{\lambda t} + \mathbf{u}te^{\lambda t} + \mathbf{w}e^{\lambda t}$$

($\mathbf{v}$, $\mathbf{u}$ and $\mathbf{w}$ to be determined)

FIGURE 7–48

Determination of three linearly independent solutions of a system associated with a triple eigenvalue λ of the coefficient matrix for three different cases.

and we must use their linear combination $k_1\mathbf{v}_1 + k_2\mathbf{v}_2$ for $\mathbf{v}$. Then the equation for the determination of $\mathbf{u}$ can be expressed as

$$(\mathbf{A} - \lambda \mathbf{I})\mathbf{u} = k_1\mathbf{v}_1 + k_2\mathbf{v}_2 \tag{7-86}$$

where the constants k_1 and k_2 must be chosen such that this equation has a nontrivial solution for $\mathbf{u}$. Once the constant vectors $\mathbf{v}$ and $\mathbf{u}$ are available, the third linearly independent solution can be obtained from Equation 7–85.

Case 3c *The triple eigenvalue has only one linearly independent eigenvector v associated with it.* In this case, the first linearly independent solution is

$$\mathbf{x}_1 = \mathbf{v}e^{\lambda t} \tag{7-87}$$

and the other two linearly independent solutions are determined from

$$\mathbf{x}_2 = \mathbf{v}te^{\lambda t} + \mathbf{u}e^{\lambda t} \tag{7-88a}$$

$$\mathbf{x}_3 = \frac{1}{2}\mathbf{v}t^2e^{\lambda t} + \mathbf{u}e^{\lambda t} + \mathbf{w}e^{\lambda t} \tag{7-88b}$$

where the constant vectors $\mathbf{u}$ and $\mathbf{w}$ are determined from

$$(\mathbf{A} - \lambda \mathbf{I})\mathbf{u} = \mathbf{v} \quad \text{and} \quad (\mathbf{A} - \lambda \mathbf{I})\mathbf{w} = \mathbf{u} \tag{7-89}$$

Note that the second solution is determined the same way it is determined in the double eigenvalue case.

The solutions corresponding to the triple eigenvalue λ obtained as just described are linearly independent for all three cases. This always can be checked easily by determining the Wronskian of the solutions.

These procedures just described for triple eigenvalues can be extended to eigenvalues with a multiplicity of four or higher, but the process is very tedious. It is possible to solve linear systems with any number of repeated eigenvalues in a systematic manner; however, the use of such methods require a certain level of sophistication in linear algebra. Therefore, we will limit our consideration of linear systems to those that do not involve eigenvalues of multiplicity greater than three.

EXAMPLE 7–24   **Homogeneous Systems with Repeated (Triple) Eigenvalues**

Determine the general solution of the system

$$x_1' = 3x_1 + x_2$$
$$x_2' = 2x_1 + 3x_2 - x_3$$
$$x_3' = 2x_2 + 3x_3$$

SOLUTION   This is a system of three first-order linear, homogeneous equations with constant coefficients in three unknowns, and it can be expressed in matrix form as $\mathbf{x}' = \mathbf{A}\mathbf{x}$, where

$$\mathbf{A} = \begin{pmatrix} 3 & 1 & 0 \\ 2 & 3 & -1 \\ 0 & 2 & 3 \end{pmatrix} \quad \text{and} \quad \mathbf{x} = \begin{pmatrix} x_1 \\ x_2 \\ x_3 \end{pmatrix}$$

The eigenvalues of the coefficient matrix $\mathbf{A}$ are determined from $\det(\mathbf{A} - \lambda\, \mathbf{I}) = 0$, as

$$\det(\mathbf{A} - \lambda\mathbf{I}) = \begin{vmatrix} 3-\lambda & 1 & 0 \\ 2 & 3-\lambda & -1 \\ 0 & 2 & 3-\lambda \end{vmatrix}$$

$$= (3 - \lambda)^3 + 2(3 - \lambda) - 2(3 - \lambda)$$

$$= (3 - \lambda)^3 = 0$$

whose roots are 3, 3, and 3. Therefore, the coefficient matrix has an eigenvalue $\lambda = 3$ with a multiplicity of three.

The eigenvector corresponding to this eigenvalue is determined from the equation $(\mathbf{A} - \lambda\mathbf{I})\mathbf{v} = \mathbf{0}$, which in this case becomes

$$\begin{pmatrix} 0 & 1 & 0 \\ 2 & 0 & -1 \\ 0 & 2 & 0 \end{pmatrix} \begin{pmatrix} v_1 \\ v_2 \\ v_3 \end{pmatrix} = \begin{pmatrix} 0 \\ 0 \\ 0 \end{pmatrix}$$

By matrix multiplication, we can show easily that this equation is equivalent to the system of equations

$$v_2 = 0$$
$$2v_1 - v_3 = 0$$
$$2v_2 = 0$$

or

$$v_2 = 0$$
$$v_3 = 2v_1$$

Taking $v_1 = 1$ for simplicity, we obtain $v_3 = 2$ from the last equation. Therefore, one eigenvector corresponding to the triple eigenvalue $\lambda = 3$ is

$$\mathbf{v} = \begin{pmatrix} 1 \\ 0 \\ 2 \end{pmatrix}$$

This is the only linearly independent eigenvector associated with the eigenvalue $\lambda = 3$, since choosing another value for v_1 will simply give a vector that is a constant multiple of $\mathbf{v}$. Therefore, this is a special case of Case 3, and the three linearly independent solutions of the given system will be determined from Equations 7–87 and 7–88. But first we need to determine the constant vectors $\mathbf{u}$ and $\mathbf{w}$ from Equations 7–89.

Substituting the eigenvector $\mathbf{v}$ into the equation $(\mathbf{A} - \lambda\mathbf{I})\mathbf{u} = \mathbf{v}$ gives

$$\begin{pmatrix} 0 & 1 & 0 \\ 2 & 0 & -1 \\ 0 & 2 & 0 \end{pmatrix} \begin{pmatrix} u_1 \\ u_2 \\ u_3 \end{pmatrix} = \begin{pmatrix} 1 \\ 0 \\ 2 \end{pmatrix}$$

By matrix multiplication, we can show that this equation is equivalent to the system of equations

$$u_2 = 1$$
$$2u_1 - u_3 = 0$$
$$2u_2 = 2$$

or

$$u_2 = 1$$
$$u_3 = 2u_1$$

Taking $u_1 = 1$ for simplicity, we obtain $u_3 = 2$ from the last equation. Therefore, the vector $\mathbf{u}$ is

$$\mathbf{u} = \begin{pmatrix} 1 \\ 1 \\ 2 \end{pmatrix}$$

Now substituting the vector $\mathbf{u}$ into the equation $(\mathbf{A} - \lambda\mathbf{I})\mathbf{w} = \mathbf{u}$ gives

$$\begin{pmatrix} 0 & 1 & 0 \\ 2 & 0 & -1 \\ 0 & 2 & 0 \end{pmatrix} \begin{pmatrix} w_1 \\ w_2 \\ w_3 \end{pmatrix} = \begin{pmatrix} 1 \\ 1 \\ 2 \end{pmatrix}$$

Again, performing the matrix multiplication on the left gives

$$w_2 = 1$$
$$2w_1 - w_3 = 1$$
$$2w_2 = 2$$

or

$$w_2 = 1$$
$$2w_1 - w_3 = 1$$

Taking $w_1 = 1$ for simplicity, the last equation gives $w_3 = 1$. Therefore, the vector $\mathbf{w}$ is

$$\mathbf{w} = \begin{pmatrix} 1 \\ 1 \\ 1 \end{pmatrix}$$

Then the three linearly independent solutions of the given system are determined from Equations 7–87 and 7–88 to be

$$\mathbf{x}_1 = \mathbf{v}e^{\lambda t} = \begin{pmatrix} 1 \\ 0 \\ 2 \end{pmatrix} e^{3t}$$

$$\mathbf{x}_2 = \mathbf{v}te^{\lambda t} + \mathbf{u}e^{\lambda t} = \begin{pmatrix} 1 \\ 0 \\ 2 \end{pmatrix} te^{3t} + \begin{pmatrix} 1 \\ 1 \\ 2 \end{pmatrix} e^{3t} = \begin{pmatrix} t+1 \\ 1 \\ 2t+2 \end{pmatrix} e^{3t}$$

$$\mathbf{x}_3 = \frac{1}{2}\mathbf{v}t^2 e^{\lambda t} + \mathbf{u}te^{\lambda t} + \mathbf{w}e^{\lambda t} = \frac{1}{2}\begin{pmatrix} 1 \\ 0 \\ 2 \end{pmatrix} t^2 e^{3t} + \begin{pmatrix} 1 \\ 1 \\ 2 \end{pmatrix} te^{3t} + \begin{pmatrix} 1 \\ 1 \\ 1 \end{pmatrix} e^{3t}$$

$$= \begin{pmatrix} 0.5t^2 + t + 1 \\ t + 1 \\ t^2 + 2t + 1 \end{pmatrix} e^{3t}$$

It can be shown that the Wronskian of $\mathbf{x}_1$, $\mathbf{x}_2$, and $\mathbf{x}_3$ is not zero, and thus these three solutions are linearly independent. Therefore, the solutions $\mathbf{x}_1$, $\mathbf{x}_2$, and $\mathbf{x}_3$ form a fundamental set of solutions, and the general solution of the given system is

$$\mathbf{x} = c_1\mathbf{x}_1 + c_2\mathbf{x}_2 + c_3\mathbf{x}_3$$

$$= c_1\begin{pmatrix} 1 \\ 0 \\ 2 \end{pmatrix}e^{3t} + c_2\begin{pmatrix} t+1 \\ 1 \\ 2t+2 \end{pmatrix}e^{3t} + c_3\begin{pmatrix} 0.5t^2 + t + 1 \\ t+1 \\ t^2 + 2t + 1 \end{pmatrix}e^{3t}$$

The solution also can be expressed in the scalar (nonvector) form as

$$x_1 = [c_1 + c_2(t+1) + c_3(0.5t^2 + t + 1)]e^{3t}$$

$$x_2 = [c_2 + c_3(t+1)]e^{3t}$$

$$x_3 = [2c_1 + 2c_2(t+1) + c_3(t^2 + 2t + 1)]e^{3t}$$

These solutions easily can be verified by substituting them into the given system of equations, and showing that they satisfy every equation in the system.

Section Review

7–25 Under what conditions is the vector $\mathbf{u}e^{kt}$ a solution of a linear, homogeneous system $\mathbf{x}'(t) = \mathbf{A}\mathbf{x}(t)$ with constant coefficients?

7–26 Consider a system of n linear, homogeneous equations with constant coefficients expressed as $\mathbf{x}'(t) = \mathbf{A}\mathbf{x}(t)$. How many linearly independent solution vectors will the general solution of this system involve? How many arbitrary constants will it involve? For what values of the independent variable t is this general solution valid?

7–27 Consider a system of n linear, homogeneous equations with constant coefficients expressed as $\mathbf{x}'(t) = \mathbf{A}\mathbf{x}(t)$. How would you express the general solution of this system if the coefficient matrix $\mathbf{A}$ has n real and distinct eigenvalues?

7–28 Using the matrix method, determine the general solution of the following system of first-order differential equations.

$$\mathbf{x}' = \begin{pmatrix} 3 & -1 \\ -1 & 1 \end{pmatrix}\mathbf{x}$$

(*Answer:* $\mathbf{x} = C_1\mathbf{x}_1 + C_2\mathbf{x}_2 = C_1\begin{pmatrix} 1 \\ 1 - \sqrt{2} \\ 1 \end{pmatrix}e^{(2+\sqrt{2})t} + C_2\begin{pmatrix} 1 \\ 1 + \sqrt{2} \\ 1 \end{pmatrix}e^{(2-\sqrt{2})t}$)

7–29 Using the matrix method, determine the solution of the following systems of first-order differential equations with the specified initial conditions.

$$\mathbf{x}' = \begin{pmatrix} 1 & -6 \\ 4 & 1 \end{pmatrix}\mathbf{x}, \qquad \mathbf{x}(0) = \begin{pmatrix} 1 \\ 0 \end{pmatrix}$$

(*Answer:* $\mathbf{x} = \begin{pmatrix} x_1 \\ x_2 \end{pmatrix} = \begin{pmatrix} e^t \cos 2\sqrt{6}t \\ \dfrac{\sqrt{6}}{3}e^t \sin 2\sqrt{6}t \end{pmatrix}$)

7–6 · LINEAR NONHOMOGENEOUS SYSTEMS

We now consider the nonhomogeneous system

$$\mathbf{x}' = \mathbf{A}(t)\mathbf{x} + \mathbf{r}(t) \tag{7-90}$$

where all elements of the coefficient matrix $\mathbf{A}(t)$ and the nonhomogeneous vector $\mathbf{r}(t)$ are continuous in an interval $t_1 < t < t_2$. In analogy with single nonhomogeneous equations, the general solution of this nonhomogeneous system is expressed as (see Theorem 7–5)

$$\mathbf{x} = \mathbf{x}_h + \mathbf{x}_p \tag{7-91}$$

where $\mathbf{x}_h$ is the general solution of the related homogeneous system $\mathbf{x}' = \mathbf{A}(t)\mathbf{x}$, and $\mathbf{x}_p$ is the particular solution of the given nonhomogeneous system.

In the preceding section, we learned how to obtain the homogeneous solution $\mathbf{x}_h$. In this section, we will learn how to determine the particular solution $\mathbf{x}_p$. The method of *undetermined coefficients* and the method of *variation of parameters* introduced in Chapter 3 for single equations are also applicable to systems with some modifications. We now discuss both methods.

The Method of Undetermined Coefficients

The method of undetermined coefficients is essentially identical for both single equations and systems of equations. As you may recall, it is based on making an intelligent guess for the general form of the particular solution $\mathbf{x}_p$ and then determining the unknown coefficients from the requirement that $\mathbf{x}_p$ satisfy the nonhomogeneous system.

Table 3–2 still can be used to determine the proper form of the particular solution corresponding to the nonhomogeneous terms. But in the case of systems, the coefficients are taken to be constant *vectors* instead of constant *scalars*. As a result, the general form of the particular solution is the same for each unknown function in the system no matter what the nonhomogeneous terms of the individual equations are (Figure 7–49). When deciding the general form of the particular solution of a nonhomogeneous system, it is helpful to express the nonhomogeneous terms uniformly as a sum of functions with constant vector coefficients. For example, the nonhomogeneous terms of the system

$$x_1' = 2x_1 - 3x_3 + 5t - 5$$
$$x_2' = x_1 + x_2 - x_3 + 3te^{-2t} + 1$$
$$x_3' = -x_1 + 5x_3$$

can be expressed as

$$\mathbf{r}(t) = \begin{pmatrix} 0 \\ 3 \\ 0 \end{pmatrix} te^{-2t} + \begin{pmatrix} 5 \\ 0 \\ 0 \end{pmatrix} t + \begin{pmatrix} -5 \\ 1 \\ 0 \end{pmatrix}$$

Given the nonhomogeneous system:

$$x_1' = 4x_1 + 6x_2 + 3\sin 2t$$
$$x_2' = -3x_1 - 5x_2 - 4$$

Nonhomogeneous terms

The proper form of the particular solution (assuming no duplication between the homogeneous solution and the nonhomogeneous terms):

$$\mathbf{x}_p = \mathbf{a} + \mathbf{b}\cos 2t + \mathbf{c}\sin 2t$$

$$= \begin{pmatrix} a_1 \\ a_2 \end{pmatrix} + \begin{pmatrix} b_1 \\ b_2 \end{pmatrix}\cos 2t + \begin{pmatrix} c_1 \\ c_2 \end{pmatrix}\sin 2t$$

FIGURE 7–49

When determining the proper form of the particular solution with the method of undetermined coefficients, we must consider *all* of the nonhomogeneous terms in *all* equations.

The proper form of the particular solution in this case (assuming no duplication between the homogeneous solution and the nonhomogeneous terms) is

$$x_p = (\mathbf{a}t + \mathbf{b})e^{-2t} + \mathbf{c}t + \mathbf{d} = \begin{pmatrix} a_1 \\ a_2 \\ a_3 \end{pmatrix} te^{-2t} + \begin{pmatrix} b_1 \\ b_2 \\ b_3 \end{pmatrix} e^{-2t} + \begin{pmatrix} c_1 \\ c_2 \\ c_3 \end{pmatrix} t + \begin{pmatrix} d_1 \\ d_2 \\ d_3 \end{pmatrix}$$

which involves twelve undetermined coefficients. Note that the general form of the particular solution involves all of the nonhomogeneous terms in the given system.

Nonhomogeneous terms that are solutions of the related homogeneous equations are handled differently in systems. You will recall that for single equations, we multiply the basic form of the particular solution by t^k, where t is the independent variable and k is the smallest integer that totally removes any duplication between the homogeneous solution and the particular solution. For systems, however, we multiply the basic form of the particular solution not only by t^k but also by all of the lower powers of t, including its zeroth power. That is, in systems, we multiply the basic form of the particular solution by a kth-degree polynomial in t instead of the kth power of t. For example, if e^{-2t} is a homogeneous solution, then the correct form of the particular solution corresponding to a nonhomogeneous term of the form e^{-2t} is $\mathbf{x}_p = \mathbf{a}te^{-2t} + \mathbf{b}e^{-2t}$ instead of just $\mathbf{x}_p = \mathbf{a}te^{-2t}$.

The reader is again reminded that the method of undetermined coefficients is practical only when all the equations in the system have constant coefficients, and the nonhomogeneous terms involve only polynomials, exponential functions, and sine or cosine functions as factors.

EXAMPLE 7–25　The Method of Undetermined Coefficients

Using the method of undetermined coefficients for the particular solution, determine the general solution of the system

$$x_1' = 4x_1 + 6x_2 + 1$$
$$x_2' = -3x_1 - 5x_2 + e^t$$

SOLUTION　This is a system of two first-order linear, nonhomogeneous equations with constant coefficients in two unknowns, and it can be expressed in matrix form as $\mathbf{x}' = \mathbf{Ax} + \mathbf{r}$, where

$$\mathbf{A} = \begin{pmatrix} 4 & 6 \\ -3 & -5 \end{pmatrix}, \quad \mathbf{x} = \begin{pmatrix} x_1 \\ x_2 \end{pmatrix}, \quad \text{and} \quad \mathbf{r} = \begin{pmatrix} 1 \\ e^t \end{pmatrix} = \begin{pmatrix} 0 \\ 1 \end{pmatrix}e^t + \begin{pmatrix} 1 \\ 0 \end{pmatrix}$$

The general solution of the related homogeneous system $\mathbf{x}' = \mathbf{Ax}$ was determined in Example 7–18 to be

$$\mathbf{x}_h = c_1 \begin{pmatrix} 2 \\ -1 \end{pmatrix}e^t + c_2 \begin{pmatrix} -1 \\ 1 \end{pmatrix}e^{-2t}$$

Comparing the nonhomogeneous terms e^t and 1 to the homogeneous solution, we notice that the function e^t also appears in the homogeneous solution.

Therefore, we choose the particular solution corresponding to this term as $\mathbf{a}te^t + \mathbf{b}e^t$ (instead of just $\mathbf{a}te^t$, as we would with a single equation). Also, we take the particular solution corresponding to the constant 1 to be of the form of a constant vector $\mathbf{c}$. Thus, the proper form of the particular solution is

$$\mathbf{x}_p = \mathbf{a}te^t + \mathbf{b}e^t + \mathbf{c}$$

whose derivative is

$$\mathbf{x'}_p = \mathbf{a}e^t + \mathbf{a}te^t + \mathbf{b}e^t$$

Here $\mathbf{a}$, $\mathbf{b}$, and $\mathbf{c}$ are 2×1 constant vectors:

$$\mathbf{a} = \begin{pmatrix} a_1 \\ a_2 \end{pmatrix}, \quad \mathbf{b} = \begin{pmatrix} b_1 \\ b_2 \end{pmatrix}, \quad \text{and} \quad \mathbf{c} = \begin{pmatrix} c_1 \\ c_2 \end{pmatrix}$$

Substituting these relations for the particular solution and its derivative into the system gives

$$\mathbf{a}e^t + \mathbf{a}te^t + \mathbf{b}e^t = \mathbf{A}(\mathbf{a}te^t + \mathbf{b}e^t + \mathbf{c}) + \begin{pmatrix} 0 \\ 1 \end{pmatrix}e^t + \begin{pmatrix} 1 \\ 0 \end{pmatrix}$$

Equating the constant terms and the coefficients of te^t and e^t on both sides of the equation, we obtain the three matrix equations:

$$\mathbf{A}\mathbf{c} + \begin{pmatrix} 1 \\ 0 \end{pmatrix} = 0$$

$$\mathbf{a} = \mathbf{A}\mathbf{a}$$

$$\mathbf{a} + \mathbf{b} = \mathbf{A}\mathbf{b} + \begin{pmatrix} 0 \\ 1 \end{pmatrix}$$

The first equation easily can be solved for $\mathbf{c}$ by multiplying it by $\mathbf{A}^{-1}$ from the left:

$$\mathbf{c} = -\mathbf{A}^{-1}\begin{pmatrix} 1 \\ 0 \end{pmatrix} = -\begin{pmatrix} 4 & 6 \\ -3 & -5 \end{pmatrix}^{-1}\begin{pmatrix} 1 \\ 0 \end{pmatrix} = -\frac{1}{-2}\begin{pmatrix} -5 & -6 \\ 3 & 4 \end{pmatrix}\begin{pmatrix} 1 \\ 0 \end{pmatrix} = \frac{1}{2}\begin{pmatrix} -5 \\ 3 \end{pmatrix}$$

The second equation can be expressed as $(\mathbf{A} - \mathbf{I})\mathbf{a} = 0$, which is the equation for the eigenvector of $\mathbf{A}$ corresponding to the eigenvalue $\lambda = 1$. It was determined in Example 7–16 to be

$$\mathbf{a} = \mathbf{v}_1 = \begin{pmatrix} 2 \\ -1 \end{pmatrix}$$

It is left as an exercise to the student to show that the third matrix equation reduces to a single scalar equation:

$$3b_1 + 6b_2 = 2$$

Taking $b_1 = 0$ for simplicity, this equation gives $b_2 = 1/3$. With these choices, the particular solution can be expressed as

$$\mathbf{x}_p = \begin{pmatrix} 2 \\ -1 \end{pmatrix}te^t + \frac{1}{3}\begin{pmatrix} 0 \\ 1 \end{pmatrix}e^t + \frac{1}{2}\begin{pmatrix} -5 \\ 3 \end{pmatrix}$$

Then the general solution of the given system is determined by adding the particular solution to the homogeneous solution, giving

$$\mathbf{x} = c_1 \begin{pmatrix} 2 \\ -1 \end{pmatrix} e^t + c_2 \begin{pmatrix} -1 \\ 1 \end{pmatrix} e^{-2t} + \begin{pmatrix} 2 \\ -1 \end{pmatrix} te^t + \frac{1}{3} \begin{pmatrix} 0 \\ 1 \end{pmatrix} e^t + \frac{1}{2} \begin{pmatrix} -5 \\ 3 \end{pmatrix}$$

The solution can also be expressed in the scalar (nonvector) form as

$$x_1 = 2(c_1 + t)e^t - c_2 e^{-2t} - \frac{5}{2}$$

$$x_2 = \left(-c_1 + \frac{1}{3} - t \right) e^t + c_2 e^{-2t} + \frac{3}{2}$$

These solutions easily can be verified by substituting them into the given system of equations and showing that they satisfy every equation in the system.

Variation of Parameters

When the elements of the coefficient matrix $\mathbf{A}(t)$ of the linear nonhomogeneous system

$$\mathbf{x}' = \mathbf{A}(t)\mathbf{x} + \mathbf{r}(t)$$

are not constant or the nonhomogeneous vector $\mathbf{r}(t)$ involves functions other than polynomials, exponentials, and sinusoidal functions, the method of undetermined coefficients just discussed becomes impractical. In such cases, we must use the method of variation of parameters, which is the general method for determining particular solutions. If you are expecting to see some very lengthy derivations and complex formulations associated with the method of variation of parameters since it is the general method, you are in for a pleasant surprise because the method turns out to be very natural for systems, and it results in a relatively simple formulation, as shown in the following.

The first step in the solution is to consider the related homogeneous system $\mathbf{x}' = \mathbf{A}(t)\mathbf{x}$, and determine its general solution $\mathbf{x}_h$, which involves n linearly independent solution vectors and n arbitrary constants:

$$\mathbf{x}_h = c_1 \mathbf{x}_1 + c_2 \mathbf{x}_2 + \cdots + c_n \mathbf{x}_n \qquad (7\text{-}92)$$

The homogeneous solution also can be expressed in terms of the fundamental matrix $\mathbf{F}$ (the $n \times n$ matrix whose columns are n linearly independent solution vectors $\mathbf{x}_1, \mathbf{x}_2, \ldots, \mathbf{x}_n$) as

$$\mathbf{x}_h = \mathbf{F}(t)\mathbf{c} \qquad (7\text{-}93)$$

The method of variation of parameters is based on the assumption that the particular solution is of the form of the homogeneous solution, except that the constant vector $\mathbf{c}$ is replaced by a vector function $\mathbf{u}(t)$, which is to be determined. That is,

$$\mathbf{x}_p = \mathbf{F}(t)\mathbf{u} \qquad (7\text{-}94)$$

where the vector $\mathbf{u}(t)$ is to be determined from the requirement that $\mathbf{x}_p$ satisfy the nonhomogeneous system, as illustrated in the following.

Differentiating the $\mathbf{x}_p$ expression (Equation 7–94) and substituting into $\mathbf{x}' = \mathbf{A}(t)\mathbf{x} + \mathbf{r}(t)$ gives

$$\mathbf{F}'(t)\mathbf{u}(t) + \mathbf{F}(t)\mathbf{u}'(t) = \mathbf{A}(t)\mathbf{F}(t)\mathbf{u}(t) + \mathbf{r}(t) \tag{7–95}$$

But $\mathbf{F}'(t) = \mathbf{A}(t)\mathbf{F}(t)$, since $\mathbf{F}(t)$ satisfies the related homogeneous system, and the equation reduces to

$$\mathbf{F}(t)\mathbf{u}'(t) = \mathbf{r}(t) \tag{7–96}$$

$\mathbf{F}(t)$ is a nonsingular matrix on any interval in which $\mathbf{A}(t)$ is continuous. Thus, its inverse $\mathbf{F}^{-1}(t)$ exists. Multiplying both sides of the equation by $\mathbf{F}^{-1}(t)$ from the left gives

$$\mathbf{u}'(t) = \mathbf{F}^{-1}(t)\mathbf{r}(t) \tag{7–97}$$

Then the vector $\mathbf{u}(t)$ can be determined within an arbitrary constant vector $\mathbf{k}$ by integration to be

$$\mathbf{u}(t) = \int \mathbf{F}^{-1}(t)\mathbf{r}(t)\,dt + \mathbf{k} \tag{7–98}$$

Substituting into Equation 7–94, the particular solution is determined to be (Figure 7–50)

$$\mathbf{x}_p = \mathbf{F}(t)\int \mathbf{F}^{-1}(t)\mathbf{r}(t)\,dt + \mathbf{F}(t)\mathbf{k} \tag{7–99}$$

Then the general solution of the nonhomogeneous system is obtained by adding the particular solution to the homogeneous solution (Equation 7–93), giving

$$\mathbf{x} = \mathbf{F}(t)\mathbf{c} + \mathbf{F}(t)\int \mathbf{F}^{-1}(t)\mathbf{r}(t)\,dt + \mathbf{F}(t)\mathbf{k} \tag{7–100}$$

or

$$\boxed{\mathbf{x} = \mathbf{F}(t)\mathbf{c} + \mathbf{F}(t)\int \mathbf{F}^{-1}(t)\mathbf{r}(t)\,dt} \tag{7–101}$$

since the two arbitrary constant vectors $\mathbf{c}$ and $\mathbf{k}$ can be combined into a single arbitrary constant vector $\mathbf{c}$ with no loss in generality. In other words, we can choose $\mathbf{k}$ to be zero or any other convenient constant vector with no loss in generality. The use of Equation 7–101 in the solution of linear nonhomogeneous systems is now illustrated with examples.

Given the system:

$$\mathbf{x}' = \mathbf{A}(t)\mathbf{x} + \mathbf{r}(t)$$

Its homogeneous solution:

$$\mathbf{x}_h = c_1\mathbf{x}_1 + c_2\mathbf{x}_2 + \ldots + c_n\mathbf{x}_n$$

Fundamental matrix:

$$\mathbf{F}(t) = (\mathbf{x}_1\ \mathbf{x}_2\ \ldots\ \mathbf{x}_n)$$

Particular solution:

$$\mathbf{x}_p = \mathbf{F}(t)\int \mathbf{F}^{-1}(t)\mathbf{r}(t)\,dt$$

where $\mathbf{F}^{-1}(t)$ is the inverse of the fundamental matrix.

FIGURE 7–50

Once the homogeneous solution $\mathbf{x}_h$ (and thus the fundamental matrix $\mathbf{F}(t)$ is available), the method of variation of parameters yields the particular solution of a nonhomogeneous system in a straightforward manner.

EXAMPLE 7–26   **The Method of Variation of Parameters**

Using the method of variation of parameters for the particular solution, determine the general solution of the system

$$x_1' = 4x_1 + 6x_2 + 1$$
$$x_2' = -3x_1 - 5x_2 + e^t$$

SOLUTION This is the system we considered in Example 7–25. We again express it in matrix form as $\mathbf{x}' = \mathbf{A}\mathbf{x} + \mathbf{r}$, where

$$\mathbf{A} = \begin{pmatrix} 4 & 6 \\ -3 & -5 \end{pmatrix},\ \mathbf{x} = \begin{pmatrix} x_1 \\ x_2 \end{pmatrix},\ \text{and } \mathbf{r} = \begin{pmatrix} 1 \\ e^t \end{pmatrix}$$

Two linearly independent solution vectors of the related homogeneous system $\mathbf{x}' = \mathbf{A}\mathbf{x}$ were determined in Example 7–16 to be

$$\mathbf{x}_1 = \begin{pmatrix} 2e^t \\ -e^t \end{pmatrix} \quad \text{and} \quad \mathbf{x}_2 = \begin{pmatrix} -e^{-2t} \\ e^{-2t} \end{pmatrix}$$

Therefore, the fundamental matrix of the related homogeneous system is

$$\mathbf{F}(t) = \begin{pmatrix} 2e^t & -e^{-2t} \\ -e^t & e^{-2t} \end{pmatrix}$$

whose determinant is

$$\det \mathbf{F} = \begin{vmatrix} 2e^t & -e^{-2t} \\ -e^t & e^{-2t} \end{vmatrix} = 2e^{-t} - e^{-t} = e^{-t}$$

Then the inverse of this 2×2 fundamental matrix is

$$\mathbf{F}^{-1}(t) = \frac{1}{e^{-t}} \begin{pmatrix} e^{-2t} & e^{-2t} \\ e^t & 2e^t \end{pmatrix} = \begin{pmatrix} e^{-t} & e^{-t} \\ e^{2t} & 2e^{2t} \end{pmatrix}$$

Now we can determine the particular solution using the method of variation of parameters from Equation 7–99. Disregarding the integration constant, we obtain

$$\mathbf{x}_p = \mathbf{F}(t) \int \mathbf{F}^{-1}(t)\mathbf{r}(t)\,dt$$

where

$$\int \mathbf{F}^{-1}(t)\mathbf{r}(t)\,dt = \int \begin{pmatrix} e^{-t} & e^{-t} \\ e^{2t} & 2e^{2t} \end{pmatrix} \begin{pmatrix} 1 \\ e^t \end{pmatrix} dt$$

$$= \int \begin{pmatrix} e^{-t} + 1 \\ e^{2t} + 2e^{3t} \end{pmatrix} dt = \begin{pmatrix} -e^{-t} + t \\ \frac{1}{2}e^{2t} + \frac{2}{3}e^{3t} \end{pmatrix}$$

Substituting, the particular solution is determined to be

$$\mathbf{x}_p = \mathbf{F}(t) \int \mathbf{F}^{-1}(t)\mathbf{r}(t)\,dt = \begin{pmatrix} 2e^t & -e^{-2t} \\ -e^t & e^{-2t} \end{pmatrix} \begin{pmatrix} -e^{-t} + t \\ \frac{1}{2}e^{2t} + \frac{2}{3}e^{3t} \end{pmatrix}$$

$$= \begin{pmatrix} -2 + 2te^t - \dfrac{1}{2} - \dfrac{2}{3}e^t \\ 1 - te^t + \dfrac{1}{2} + \dfrac{2}{3}e^t \end{pmatrix} = \begin{pmatrix} 2te^t - \dfrac{2}{3}e^t - \dfrac{5}{2} \\ -te^t + \dfrac{2}{3}e^t + \dfrac{3}{2} \end{pmatrix}$$

$$= \begin{pmatrix} 2 \\ -1 \end{pmatrix} te^t + \frac{2}{3} \begin{pmatrix} -1 \\ 1 \end{pmatrix} e^t + \frac{1}{2} \begin{pmatrix} -5 \\ 3 \end{pmatrix}$$

Then the general solution of the given system is determined by adding the particular solution to the homogeneous solution determined in Example 7–13, as

$$\mathbf{x} = d_1\mathbf{x}_1 + d_2\mathbf{x}_2 + \mathbf{x}_p$$

$$= d_1 \begin{pmatrix} 2 \\ -1 \end{pmatrix} e^t + d_2 \begin{pmatrix} -1 \\ 1 \end{pmatrix} e^{-2t} + \begin{pmatrix} 2 \\ -1 \end{pmatrix} te^t + \frac{2}{3} \begin{pmatrix} -1 \\ 1 \end{pmatrix} e^t + \frac{1}{2} \begin{pmatrix} -5 \\ 3 \end{pmatrix}$$

The solution can also be expressed in the scalar (nonvector) form as

$$x_1 = 2\left(d_1 - \frac{1}{3} + t\right)e^t - d_2 e^{-2t} - \frac{5}{2}$$

$$x_2 = \left(-d_1 + \frac{2}{3} - t\right)e^t + d_2 e^{-2t} + \frac{3}{2}$$

These solutions easily can be verified by substituting them into the given system of equations and showing that they satisfy every equation in the system.

Notice that the method of variation of parameters gives the particular solution in a more systematic and straightforward manner. The general solution just obtained is identical to the one obtained by the method of undetermined coefficients, except the arbitrary constants c_1 and d_1 in the two solutions differ by the constant 1/3; that is, $c_1 = d_1 - 1/3$. This is of no consequence.

Systems of Nonhomogeneous Initial-Value Problems

The method of variation of parameters is very suitable for solving systems of linear, nonhomogeneous, initial-value problems, since it can incorporate the initial conditions directly.

We have seen in the last section that the general solution of *homogeneous* systems can be expressed in terms of the fundamental matrix $\mathbf{F}(t)$ as

$$\mathbf{x}_h(t) = \mathbf{F}(t)\mathbf{c} \tag{7-102}$$

where $\mathbf{c}$ is the vector containing the arbitrary constants. By multiplying the equation by $\mathbf{F}^{-1}(t)$ from the left and evaluating it at $t = t_0$, the vector $\mathbf{c}$ was determined to be

$$\mathbf{c} = \mathbf{F}^{-1}(t_0)\mathbf{x}_0 \tag{7-103}$$

where $\mathbf{x}_0 = \mathbf{x}(t_0)$ is the specified set of initial conditions. Substituting this into Equation 7–102, the general solution of *homogeneous* systems of initial-value problems is expressed as

$$\mathbf{x}_h(t) = \mathbf{F}(t)\mathbf{F}^{-1}(t_0)\mathbf{x}_0 \tag{7-104}$$

The relation $\mathbf{c} = \mathbf{F}^{-1}(t_0)\mathbf{x}_0$ is very appealing, but it is not applicable to nonhomogeneous systems, since the arbitrary constants must be determined by applying the initial conditions to the *entire* solution (homogeneous plus particular) instead of just the homogeneous solution. Unless of course, the particular solution is zero at the point $t = t_0$. This suggests that we may be able to use this relation for the determination of the arbitrary constants even for nonhomogeneous systems if, somehow, we can express the particular solution such that it is always zero at $t = t_0$.

Recall that the relation we obtained for the particular solution using the method of variation of parameters (Equation 7–99) involves an indefinite integral with an arbitrary constant vector $\mathbf{k}$. It was shown that $\mathbf{k}$ can be chosen to be zero or any convenient constant vector without any loss in generality. When solving systems of *differential equations,* it is convenient to choose $\mathbf{k}$ to be zero (or simply to ignore it). But when solving systems of *initial-value problems*, it is more convenient to choose **k** so that it will make the particular solution zero at $t = t_0$. This goal is easily accomplished by expressing the indefinite integral in Equation 7–99 as a definite integral between the limits t_0 and t as

$$\mathbf{x}_p = \mathbf{F}(t)\int_{t_0}^{t}\mathbf{F}^{-1}(t)\mathbf{r}(t)dt \qquad (7\text{–}105)$$

This will ensure that $\mathbf{x}_p = 0$ at $t = t_0$ since any definite integral with identical lower and upper limits is zero. Finally, combining the homogeneous and particular solutions from Equations 7–104 and 7–105, the solution of a nonhomogeneous system of initial-value problems can be expressed as (Figure 7–51)

$$\mathbf{x}(t) = \mathbf{F}(t)\left[\mathbf{F}^{-1}(t)\mathbf{x}_0 + \int_{t_0}^{t}\mathbf{F}^{-1}(t)\mathbf{r}(t)dt\right] \qquad (7\text{–}106)$$

Therefore, once the fundamental matrix $\mathbf{F}(t)$ of the related homogeneous system is available, Equation 7–106 can be used to determine the solution of a system of nonhomogeneous equations subject to the initial conditions $\mathbf{x}(t_0) = \mathbf{x}_0$.

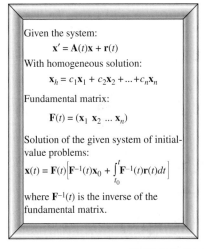

Given the system:
$$\mathbf{x}' = \mathbf{A}(t)\mathbf{x} + \mathbf{r}(t)$$
With homogeneous solution:
$$\mathbf{x}_h = c_1\mathbf{x}_1 + c_2\mathbf{x}_2 + ... + c_n\mathbf{x}_n$$
Fundamental matrix:
$$\mathbf{F}(t) = (\mathbf{x}_1 \ \mathbf{x}_2 \ ... \ \mathbf{x}_n)$$
Solution of the given system of initial-value problems:
$$\mathbf{x}(t) = \mathbf{F}(t)\left[\mathbf{F}^{-1}(t)\mathbf{x}_0 + \int_{t_0}^{t}\mathbf{F}^{-1}(t)\mathbf{r}(t)dt\right]$$
where $\mathbf{F}^{-1}(t)$ is the inverse of the fundamental matrix.

FIGURE 7–51

Once the homogeneous solution $\mathbf{x}_h$ (and thus the fundamental matrix $\mathbf{F}(t)$ is available), the method of variation of parameters yields the solution of a nonhomogeneous system of initial-value problems directly.

EXAMPLE 7–27   **Systems of Nonhomogeneous Initial-Value Problems**

Determine the solution of the following two nonhomogeneous equations with the specified initial conditions,

$$x_1' = 4x_1 + 6x_2 + 1, \qquad x_1(0) = 1$$
$$x_2' = -3x_1 - 5x_2 + e^t, \qquad x_2(0) = 0$$

SOLUTION   This is the nonhomogeneous system we solved in Example 7–25. The solution that satisfies the specified initial conditions can be determined by applying the initial conditions to the general solution obtained earlier and solving for the arbitrary constants c_1, and c_2. This will give $c_1 = 5/3$ and $c_2 = -1/6$. Then the solution of the given system of initial-value problems becomes

$$x_1 = \left(2t + \frac{10}{3}\right)e^t + \frac{1}{6}e^{-2t} - \frac{5}{2}$$

$$x_2 = -\left(t + \frac{4}{3}\right)e^t - \frac{1}{6}e^{-2t} + \frac{3}{2}$$

Now we will show that the same result can be obtained directly from Equation 7–106—without a need to determine the particular solution first—once the fundamental matrix $\mathbf{F}(t)$ of the related homogeneous system is available. From Example 7–26, we have

$$\mathbf{F}(t) = \begin{pmatrix} 2e^t & -e^{-2t} \\ -e^t & e^{-2t} \end{pmatrix}, \mathbf{F}^{-1}(t) = \begin{pmatrix} e^{-t} & e^{-t} \\ e^{2t} & 2e^{2t} \end{pmatrix}, \text{ and } \mathbf{F}^{-1}(0) = \begin{pmatrix} 1 & 1 \\ 1 & 2 \end{pmatrix}$$

Also, the initial conditions and the nonhomogeneous terms can be expressed in the matrix form as

$$\mathbf{x}_0 = \begin{pmatrix} 1 \\ 0 \end{pmatrix} \quad \text{and} \quad \mathbf{r} = \begin{pmatrix} 1 \\ e^t \end{pmatrix}$$

Substituting these into Equation 7–101, and letting $t_0 = 0$, the solution of the given system is determined to be

$$\mathbf{x}(t) = \mathbf{F}(t) \left[\mathbf{F}^{-1}(t)\mathbf{x}_0 + \int_{t_0}^{t} \mathbf{F}^{-1}(t)\mathbf{r}(t)\,dt \right]$$

$$= \mathbf{F}(t) \left[\begin{pmatrix} 1 & 1 \\ 1 & 2 \end{pmatrix}\begin{pmatrix} 1 \\ 0 \end{pmatrix} + \int_{t_0}^{t} \begin{pmatrix} e^{-t} & e^{-t} \\ e^{2t} & 2e^{2t} \end{pmatrix}\begin{pmatrix} 1 \\ e^t \end{pmatrix}dt \right]$$

$$= \mathbf{F}(t) \left[\begin{pmatrix} 1 \\ 1 \end{pmatrix} + \int_{t_0}^{t} \begin{pmatrix} e^{-t} + 1 \\ e^{2t} + 2e^{3t} \end{pmatrix}dt \right]$$

$$= \mathbf{F}(t) \left[\begin{pmatrix} 1 \\ 1 \end{pmatrix} + \begin{pmatrix} -e^{-t} + t + 1 \\ \dfrac{1}{2}e^{2t} + \dfrac{2}{3}e^{3t} - \dfrac{7}{6} \end{pmatrix} \right]$$

Substituting $\mathbf{F}(t)$, this becomes

$$\mathbf{x}(t) = \begin{pmatrix} 2e^t & -e^{-2t} \\ -e^t & e^{-2t} \end{pmatrix}\begin{pmatrix} -e^{-t} + t + 2 \\ \dfrac{1}{2}e^{2t} + \dfrac{2}{3}e^{3t} - \dfrac{1}{6} \end{pmatrix}$$

$$= \begin{pmatrix} \left(2t + \dfrac{10}{3}\right)e^t + \dfrac{1}{6}e^{-2t} - \dfrac{5}{2} \\ -\left(t + \dfrac{4}{3}\right)e^t - \dfrac{1}{6}e^{-2t} + \dfrac{3}{2} \end{pmatrix}$$

or in the scalar form, it is

$$x_1 = \left(2t + \dfrac{10}{3}\right)e^t + \dfrac{1}{6}e^{-2t} - \dfrac{5}{2}$$

$$x_2 = -\left(t + \dfrac{4}{3}\right)e^t - \dfrac{1}{6}e^{-2t} + \dfrac{3}{2}$$

Note that, in this approach, the particular solution is automatically accounted for, and the initial conditions are automatically incorporated into the solution.

Note that the method of variation of parameters fits naturally into the solution of nonhomogeneous systems of differential equations, and it enables us to determine the solution of nonhomogeneous systems with a set of initial conditions directly in a systematic manner.

Section Review

7–30 How does the method of undetermined coefficients differ when it is applied to systems instead of to single equations?

7–31 Which method is easier to apply to linear, nonhomogeneous systems to determine the particular solution: the method of undetermined coefficients or the method of variation of parameters?

7–32 Use (a) the method of undetermined coefficients and (b) the method of variation of parameters to determine the general solution of the following system of first-order differential equations. (Use the matrix method to obtain the homogeneous solution.)

$$\mathbf{x}' = \begin{pmatrix} 3 & -1 \\ 1 & 1 \end{pmatrix} \mathbf{x} + \begin{pmatrix} -5e^{2t} \\ 0 \end{pmatrix}$$

(*Answer:* $\mathbf{x} = C_1 \begin{pmatrix} 1 \\ 1 \end{pmatrix} e^{2t} + C_2 \begin{pmatrix} 1+t \\ t \end{pmatrix} e^{2t} + \begin{pmatrix} -\frac{5}{2} \\ -\frac{5}{2} \end{pmatrix} t^2 e^{2t} + \begin{pmatrix} -5 \\ 0 \end{pmatrix} t e^{2t}$)

7–33 Repeat Problem 7–32 using the following equation set.

$$\mathbf{x}' = \begin{pmatrix} 1 & -6 \\ 4 & 1 \end{pmatrix} \mathbf{x} + \begin{pmatrix} 0 \\ -2\cos 2t \end{pmatrix}, \quad x(0) = \begin{pmatrix} 1 \\ 0 \end{pmatrix}$$

(*Answer:* $x_1(t) = \dfrac{29\sqrt{6}}{457} e^t \sin 2\sqrt{6}t + \dfrac{205}{457} e^t \cos 2\sqrt{6}t - \dfrac{48}{457}\sin 2t + \dfrac{252}{457}\cos 2t$

$x_2(t) = \dfrac{205\sqrt{6}}{1371} e^t \sin 2\sqrt{6}t - \dfrac{58}{457} e^t \cos 2\sqrt{6}t + \dfrac{76}{457}\sin 2t + \dfrac{58}{457}\cos 2t$)

7–7 ▪ CANONICAL FORMS AND THE TRANSITION MATRIX

Consider the results of Example 7–18, in which the eigenvectors and eigenmodes corresponding to the system

$$\mathbf{x}' = \begin{pmatrix} 4 & 6 \\ -3 & -5 \end{pmatrix} \mathbf{x}$$

are

$$\mathbf{v}_1 = \begin{pmatrix} 2 \\ -1 \end{pmatrix} \qquad \mathbf{v}_2 = \begin{pmatrix} 1 \\ -1 \end{pmatrix}$$

$$\mathbf{x}_1(t) = \begin{pmatrix} 2 \\ -1 \end{pmatrix} e^t \quad \mathbf{x}_2(t) = \begin{pmatrix} 1 \\ -1 \end{pmatrix} e^{-2t}$$

We have seen that we can obtain other eigenvectors by simply multiplying any of the eigenvectors by a constant. This process merely changes the length of the vector but not its direction. For example, arbitrarily choosing to make the first component of each vector 1, a set of eigenvectors can be derived from the eigenvectors by dividing the first vector by 2.

$$\mathbf{w}_1 = \begin{pmatrix} 1 \\ -1/2 \end{pmatrix} \qquad \mathbf{w}_2 = \begin{pmatrix} 1 \\ -1 \end{pmatrix}$$

We can create eigenvectors that are *unit vectors* (having a length of 1) by dividing each vector by its length, which is computed by taking the square root of the sum of the squares of each vector component. The lengths of the vectors are $\sqrt{1^2 + (-1/2)^2} = \sqrt{5}/2$ and $\sqrt{1^2 + (-1)^2} = \sqrt{2}$. Thus, a set of eigenvectors that is also a set of unit vectors is

$$\hat{\mathbf{e}}_1 = \frac{2}{\sqrt{5}}\mathbf{w}_1 = \frac{2}{\sqrt{5}}\begin{pmatrix} 1 \\ -1/2 \end{pmatrix} \qquad \hat{\mathbf{e}}_2 = \frac{2}{\sqrt{5}}\mathbf{w}_2 = \frac{1}{\sqrt{5}}\begin{pmatrix} 1 \\ -1 \end{pmatrix}$$

We will show that eigenvectors that are also unit vectors are useful for solving sets of equations.

Diagonalization

We can think of the state variables x_1 and x_2 as being two coordinates in a coordinate system having two axes. The coordinate system in which the coordinates are the state variables is called the *state space*. This concept can be generalized to any number of state variables, although it loses its geometric meaning when there are more than three state variables.

Consider two-dimensional eigenvectors $\mathbf{v}_1$ and $\mathbf{v}_2$ normalized so that their first component is 1:

$$\mathbf{v}_1 = \begin{pmatrix} 1 \\ m_1 \end{pmatrix} \quad \text{and} \quad \mathbf{v}_2 = \begin{pmatrix} 1 \\ m_2 \end{pmatrix}$$

These eigenvectors can be represented by arrows in the state space. The system's behavior is due to the vector combination of the motion of each eigenmode along its eigenvector. These motions take place at different rates, with each rate determined by the time constant of the eigenmode. The projection of the initial condition vector $\mathbf{x}(0)$ onto each eigenvector determines the initial magnitude associated with the eigenmode. If the vector $\mathbf{x}(0)$ lies exactly on one of the eigenvectors, only that eigenmode will appear in the motion.

If the eigenvectors are linearly independent, they can be used to form a new set of coordinate axes. Let the new coordinates be z_1 and z_2, and let the unit-length basis vectors in this system be denoted $\hat{\mathbf{e}}_1$ and $\hat{\mathbf{e}}_2$. If the basis vectors lie along the eigenvectors $\mathbf{v}_1$ and $\mathbf{v}_2$, they are eigenvectors also. They are found by normalizing the vectors $\mathbf{v}_1$ and $\mathbf{v}_2$ by dividing by their lengths. That is,

$$\hat{\mathbf{e}}_1 = \frac{1}{\sqrt{1 + m_1^2}}\begin{pmatrix} 1 \\ m_1 \end{pmatrix} \quad \text{and} \quad \hat{\mathbf{e}}_2 = \frac{1}{\sqrt{1 + m_2^2}}\begin{pmatrix} 1 \\ m_2 \end{pmatrix}$$

The solution vector $\mathbf{x}$ expressed in these coordinates is

$$\mathbf{x} = z_1\hat{\mathbf{e}}_1 + z_2\hat{\mathbf{e}}_2$$

and its derivative is

$$\mathbf{x}' = z_1'\,\hat{\mathbf{e}}_1 + z_2'\hat{\mathbf{e}}_2$$

The free response satisfies $\mathbf{x}' = \mathbf{A}\mathbf{x}$; therefore,

$$z_1'\,\hat{\mathbf{e}}_1 + z_2'\,\hat{\mathbf{e}}_2 = \mathbf{A}(z_1\,\hat{\mathbf{e}}_1 + z_2\,\hat{\mathbf{e}}_2) = z_1\,\mathbf{A}\hat{\mathbf{e}}_1 + z_2\,\mathbf{A}\hat{\mathbf{e}}_2$$

because z_1 and z_2 are scalars. From the definition of the eigenvectors, $\hat{\mathbf{e}}_1$ and $\hat{\mathbf{e}}_2$ must satisfy

$$\mathbf{A}\hat{\mathbf{e}}_1 = \lambda_1\hat{\mathbf{e}}_1$$

$$\mathbf{A}\hat{\mathbf{e}}_2 = \lambda_2\hat{\mathbf{e}}_2$$

Thus,

$$z_1'\hat{\mathbf{e}}_1 + z_2'\hat{\mathbf{e}}_2 = \lambda_1 z_1\hat{\mathbf{e}}_1 + \lambda_2 z_2\hat{\mathbf{e}}_2$$

Comparing components we see that

$$z_1' = \lambda_1 z_1 \qquad (7\text{-}107)$$

$$z_2' = \lambda_2 z_2 \qquad (7\text{-}108)$$

This shows that the homogeneous differential equations become uncoupled when expressed in coordinate axes along the eigenvector directions. It can be shown by analytic geometry in the two-dimensional case or by linear algebra in general, that the transformation matrix between the $\mathbf{x}$ and the $\mathbf{z}$ coordinate systems is the **modal matrix M**, whose columns are the eigenvectors.

For the two-dimensional case, we have

$$\mathbf{M} = (\mathbf{v}_1, \mathbf{v}_2)$$

where $\mathbf{x} = \mathbf{M}\mathbf{z}$. This implies that $\mathbf{x}' = \mathbf{M}\mathbf{z}'$. From the differential equation set $\mathbf{x}' = \mathbf{A}\mathbf{x} + \mathbf{r}(t)$, we obtain

$$\mathbf{M}\mathbf{z}' = \mathbf{A}\mathbf{M}\mathbf{z} + \mathbf{r}(t)$$

It can be shown that $\mathbf{M}^{-1}$ exists for the distinct eigenvalues case. Thus,

$$\mathbf{z}' = \mathbf{M}^{-1}\mathbf{A}\mathbf{M}\mathbf{z} + \mathbf{M}^{-1}\mathbf{r}(t) \qquad (7\text{-}109)$$

Comparison with Equations 7–107 and 7–108 for $\mathbf{f}(t) = 0$ shows that

$$\mathbf{M}^{-1}\mathbf{A}\mathbf{M} = \begin{pmatrix} \lambda_1 & 0 \\ 0 & \lambda_2 \end{pmatrix} \qquad (7\text{-}110)$$

This property also holds for the general vector case, if the eigenvalues of $\mathbf{A}$ are distinct; that is,

$$\mathbf{M}^{-1}\mathbf{A}\mathbf{M} = \Lambda \qquad (7\text{-}111)$$

where Λ is a diagonal matrix whose elements are the system's eigenvalues. The equation set in terms of the vector $\mathbf{z}$ is then

$$\mathbf{z}' = \Lambda\mathbf{z} + \mathbf{M}^{-1}\mathbf{r}(t) \qquad (7\text{-}112)$$

For the nth-order case, the modal matrix has the form

$$\mathbf{M} = (\mathbf{v}_1, \mathbf{v}_2, \ldots, \mathbf{v}_n) \qquad (7\text{-}113)$$

The matrix Λ is called the *decoupling matrix* because the resulting differential equations in terms of the variables in the vector $\mathbf{z}$ are decoupled, or independent, equations, if the eigenvalues are distinct. Since decoupled equations are easier to solve, we first solve for the $\mathbf{z}$ variables and then use the transformation $\mathbf{x} = \mathbf{M}\mathbf{z}$ to obtain the solutions for the original variables (Figure 7–52).

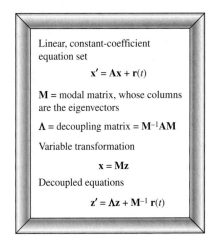

Linear, constant-coefficient equation set

$$\mathbf{x}' = \mathbf{A}\mathbf{x} + \mathbf{r}(t)$$

$\mathbf{M}$ = modal matrix, whose columns are the eigenvectors

Λ = decoupling matrix = $\mathbf{M}^{-1}\mathbf{A}\mathbf{M}$

Variable transformation

$$\mathbf{x} = \mathbf{M}\mathbf{z}$$

Decoupled equations

$$\mathbf{z}' = \Lambda\mathbf{z} + \mathbf{M}^{-1}\mathbf{r}(t)$$

FIGURE 7–52

Use of the modal matrix to decouple sets of differential equations.

EXAMPLE 7–28   **Decoupling Equations with Distinct, Real Eigenvalues**

Obtain the solution of the set

$$x_1' = 4x_1 + 6x_2 + 1$$
$$x_2' = -3x_1 - 5x_2 + e^t$$

by decoupling them with a new set of variables, z_1 and z_2.

SOLUTION   The eigenvalues and eigenvectors of this set were obtained in Example 7–19, and $\lambda_1 = 1$, $\lambda_2 = -2$, and

$$\mathbf{v}_1 = \begin{pmatrix} 2 \\ -1 \end{pmatrix} \qquad \mathbf{v}_2 = \begin{pmatrix} -1 \\ 1 \end{pmatrix}$$

Thus, the modal matrix and its inverse are

$$\mathbf{M} = \begin{pmatrix} 2 & -1 \\ -1 & 1 \end{pmatrix} \qquad \mathbf{M}^{-1} = \begin{pmatrix} 1 & 1 \\ 1 & 2 \end{pmatrix}$$

The decoupling matrix is

$$\mathbf{\Lambda} = \begin{pmatrix} 1 & 0 \\ 0 & -2 \end{pmatrix}$$

Using the variable transformation $\mathbf{x} = \mathbf{Mz}$, we obtain the decoupled equations

$$\mathbf{z}' = \mathbf{\Lambda z} + \mathbf{M}^{-1}\mathbf{r}(t) = \begin{pmatrix} 1 & 0 \\ 0 & -2 \end{pmatrix}\begin{pmatrix} z_1 \\ z_2 \end{pmatrix} + \begin{pmatrix} 1 & 1 \\ 1 & 2 \end{pmatrix}\begin{pmatrix} 1 \\ e^t \end{pmatrix}$$

These give the following decoupled equations.

$$z_1' = z_1 + 1 + e^t$$
$$z_2' = -2z_2 + 1 + 2e^t$$

These are two independent first-order equations. Thus, they can be solved using the methods of Chapter 2. The solutions are

$$z_1 = C_1 e^t + t e^t - 1$$
$$z_2 = \frac{2}{3} e^t + C_2 e^{-2t} + \frac{1}{2}$$

To obtain the solution for the original variables, we use the transformation $\mathbf{x} = \mathbf{Mz}$. This gives

$$\begin{pmatrix} x_1 \\ x_2 \end{pmatrix} = \begin{pmatrix} 2 & -1 \\ -1 & 1 \end{pmatrix}\begin{pmatrix} z_1 \\ z_2 \end{pmatrix} = \begin{pmatrix} 2z_1 - z_2 \\ -z_1 + z_2 \end{pmatrix}$$

or

$$x_1 = \left(2c_1 - \frac{2}{3} + 2t \right)e^t - c_2 e^{-2t} - \frac{5}{2}$$

$$x_2 = \left(-c_1 + \frac{2}{3} - t \right)e^t + c_2 e^{-2t} + \frac{3}{2}$$

Eigenmodes for Repeated Eigenvalues If the eigenvalues are repeated, linearly independent eigenvectors may not exist, and if so, the matrix Λ will not be diagonal. For a second-order system having the eigenvalue λ_1 repeated twice, we can show that the matrix has the form:

$$\Lambda_R = \begin{pmatrix} \lambda_1 & 1 \\ 0 & \lambda_1 \end{pmatrix} \tag{7-114}$$

where we have used the subscript R to distinguish Λ_R from the Λ matrix used for the distinct eigenvalues case. Direct extension to the third-order case where the eigenvalue λ_1 repeated three times gives

$$\Lambda_R = \begin{pmatrix} \lambda_1 & 1 & 0 \\ 0 & \lambda_1 & 1 \\ 0 & 0 & \lambda_1 \end{pmatrix} \tag{7-115}$$

For the third-order case where the eigenvalue λ_1 is repeated twice and the third eigenvalue is λ_2, we have

$$\Lambda = \begin{pmatrix} \Lambda_R & \mathbf{0} \\ \mathbf{0} & \lambda_2 \end{pmatrix} = \begin{pmatrix} \lambda_1 & 1 & 0 \\ 0 & \lambda_1 & 0 \\ 0 & 0 & \lambda_2 \end{pmatrix} \tag{7-116}$$

EXAMPLE 7–29   Decoupling Equations with Repeated Eigenvalues

Obtain the solution of the set

$$x_1' = 4x_1 + x_2$$
$$x_2' = -x_1 + 2x_2$$

by decoupling them with a new set of variables, z_1 and z_2.

SOLUTION   The eigenvalues and eigenvectors of this set were obtained in Example 7–23, and are $\lambda_1 = 3$, $\lambda_2 = 3$, and

$$\mathbf{v} = \begin{pmatrix} -1 \\ 1 \end{pmatrix} \qquad \mathbf{u} = \begin{pmatrix} 0 \\ -1 \end{pmatrix}$$

Thus, the modal matrix and its inverse are

$$\mathbf{M} = \begin{pmatrix} -1 & 0 \\ 1 & -1 \end{pmatrix} \qquad \mathbf{M}^{-1} = \begin{pmatrix} 1 & 1 \\ 1 & 2 \end{pmatrix}$$

The decoupling matrix is

$$\Lambda = \begin{pmatrix} 3 & 1 \\ 0 & 3 \end{pmatrix}$$

Using the variable transformation $\mathbf{x} = \mathbf{Mz}$, we obtain the decoupled equations

$$\mathbf{z}' = \Lambda \mathbf{z} = \begin{pmatrix} 3 & 1 \\ 0 & 3 \end{pmatrix} \begin{pmatrix} z_1 \\ z_2 \end{pmatrix}$$

These give the following decoupled equations.

$$z_1' = 3z_1 + z_2$$
$$z_2' = 3z_2$$

The second equation is an independent first-order equation. Thus, it can be solved using the methods of Chapter 2. The solution is

$$z_2 = C_2 e^{3t}$$

The first equation is dependent on the second equation, but is also a first-order equation. Thus, it can be solved using the methods of Chapter 2. The solution is

$$z_1 = C_1 e^{3t} + C_2 t e^{3t}$$

To obtain the solution for the original variables, we use the transformation $\mathbf{x} = \mathbf{Mz}$. This gives

$$\begin{pmatrix} x_1 \\ x_2 \end{pmatrix} = \begin{pmatrix} -1 & 0 \\ 1 & -1 \end{pmatrix} \begin{pmatrix} z_1 \\ z_2 \end{pmatrix} = \begin{pmatrix} -z_1 \\ z_1 - z_2 \end{pmatrix}$$

or

$$x_1 = -C_1 e^{3t} - C_2 t e^{3t}$$
$$x_2 = C_1 e^{3t} + C_2 t e^{3t} - C_2 e^{3t}$$

Eigenmodes for Complex Eigenvalues The occurrence of complex eigenvalues is included in the distinct-eigenvalues case. However, the eigenvectors and the diagonal elements of the matrix Λ will be complex. In this case, the physical interpretation of the eigenmodes is difficult. For example, the eigenvectors are no longer coordinate axes in the real plane containing the state variables. Also, for some computational purposes, it is desirable to avoid complex quantities. Therefore, we now discuss the complex-roots case from a slightly different viewpoint.

Consider the second-order case where the matrix $\mathbf{A}$ has the eigenvalues $\lambda = -a \pm ib$, $b > 0$. It is easily shown that the eigenvectors $\mathbf{v}_1$ and $\mathbf{v}_2$ are complex conjugates such that

$$\mathbf{v}_1 = \mathbf{q} + i\mathbf{r}$$
$$\mathbf{v}_2 = \mathbf{q} - i\mathbf{r}$$

In place of the modal matrix $\mathbf{M}$, defined by Equation 7–113, use instead the matrix

$$\mathbf{M}_C = [\mathbf{q}, \mathbf{r}]$$

Note that $\mathbf{M}_C$ has real elements. To derive the properties of $\mathbf{M}_C$, we use the definition of the eigenvector $\mathbf{v}_1$. It must satisfy

$$\mathbf{A}\mathbf{v}_1 = (-a + ib)\mathbf{v}_1$$

or

$$\mathbf{A}(\mathbf{q} + i\mathbf{r}) = (-a + ib)(\mathbf{q} + i\mathbf{r}) = (-a\mathbf{q} - b\mathbf{r}) + i(b\mathbf{q} - a\mathbf{r})$$

Thus,

$$\mathbf{Aq} = -a\mathbf{q} - b\mathbf{r}$$
$$\mathbf{Ar} = b\mathbf{q} - a\mathbf{r}$$

Rearranging into matrix form, we get

$$\mathbf{A}\,[\mathbf{q},\mathbf{r}] = [\mathbf{q},\mathbf{r}] \begin{bmatrix} -a & b \\ -b & -a \end{bmatrix}$$

or

$$\mathbf{AM}_C = \mathbf{M}_C \mathbf{\Lambda}_C$$

where

$$\mathbf{\Lambda}_C = \begin{bmatrix} -a & b \\ -b & -a \end{bmatrix} \qquad (7\text{--}117)$$

With the transformation $\mathbf{x} = \mathbf{M}_C\mathbf{z}$, the state equation $\mathbf{x}' = \mathbf{Ax} + \mathbf{Bf}$ becomes (for the second-order case)

$$\mathbf{z}' = \mathbf{\Lambda}_C \mathbf{z} + \mathbf{M}_C^{-1}\mathbf{Bf}$$

The different forms for the distinct, repeated, and complex eigenvalue cases are summarized in Figure 7–53.

Jordan Canonical Form We have seen that for distinct eigenvalues it is always possible to transform the state model to obtain a diagonal matrix in the form of Equation 7–110. If any of the eigenvalues are repeated, this diagonalization is usually not possible, and the form Equation 7–114 results. These forms are the *canonical forms* of the state equation. Their usefulness will become apparent shortly. For a higher-order system we can state that it is always possible to find a transformation matrix $\mathbf{M}$ to obtain the following **Jordan canonical form**:

$$\mathbf{\Lambda} = \mathbf{M}^{-1}\mathbf{AM} = \begin{bmatrix} \lambda_1 & \alpha_1 & 0 & 0 & 0 & \ldots & 0 \\ 0 & \lambda_2 & \alpha_2 & 0 & 0 & \ldots & 0 \\ \cdot & \cdot & \cdot & \cdot & \cdot & \ldots & \cdot \\ 0 & \cdot & \cdot & \cdot & 0 & s_{n-1} & \alpha_{n-1} \\ 0 & \cdot & \cdot & \cdot & 0 & 0 & s_n \end{bmatrix}$$

where the α_i, $i = 1, \ldots, n - 1$ can be either zero or one. For example, we have seen that a third-order system with two repeated roots λ_1 and one distinct root λ_2 give the form:

$$\mathbf{\Lambda} = \begin{bmatrix} & & & | & 0 \\ & \mathbf{\Lambda}_R & & | & \\ & & & | & 0 \\ - & - & - & - & - \\ 0 & 0 & | & \mathbf{\Lambda}_D \end{bmatrix}$$

where $\mathbf{\Lambda}_D = \lambda_2$ and

$$\mathbf{\Lambda}_R = \begin{bmatrix} \lambda_1 & 1 \\ 0 & \lambda_2 \end{bmatrix}$$

In general, $\mathbf{\Lambda}$ will consist of blocks of submatrices corresponding to the canonical matrix $\mathbf{\Lambda}_i$ for each system mode set. Two repeated roots correspond to one set of two modes that are usually coupled, and $\mathbf{\Lambda}_R$ is a (2×2) matrix.

Linear, constant-coefficient equation set ($\mathbf{A}$ is 2×2)

$$\mathbf{x}' = \mathbf{Ax} + \mathbf{r}(t)$$

$\mathbf{M} =$ modal matrix, whose columns are the eigenvectors

$\mathbf{\Lambda} =$ decoupling matrix $= \mathbf{M}^{-1}\mathbf{AM}$

Two distinct, real eigenvalues:

$$\mathbf{\Lambda} = \begin{pmatrix} \lambda_1 & 0 \\ 0 & \lambda_2 \end{pmatrix}$$

Two repeated eigenvalues:

$$\mathbf{\Lambda} = \mathbf{\Lambda}_R = \begin{pmatrix} \lambda_1 & 1 \\ 0 & \lambda_1 \end{pmatrix}$$

Complex conjugate eigenvalues, $-a \pm ib$:

$$\mathbf{\Lambda} = \mathbf{\Lambda}_C = \begin{bmatrix} -a & b \\ -b & -a \end{bmatrix}$$

FIGURE 7–53

Forms of the decoupling matrix for a set of two equations.

For three repeated roots, Λ_i is (3×3), and so forth. For each distinct root, $\Lambda_i = \lambda_i$.

When complex roots occur, the Jordan form will have complex entries; therefore, it is sometimes rewritten using the form Λ_C given by Equation 7–117. For example, consider a sixth-order system model with two repeated roots λ_1, two complex roots $-a \pm ib$, and two distinct roots λ_5 and λ_6. If the eigenvectors corresponding to λ_1 are dependent, the modified Jordan form is

$$\Lambda = \begin{bmatrix} \lambda_1 & 1 & 0 & 0 & 0 & 0 \\ 0 & \lambda_1 & 0 & 0 & 0 & 0 \\ 0 & 0 & -a & b & 0 & 0 \\ 0 & 0 & -b & -a & 0 & 0 \\ 0 & 0 & 0 & 0 & \lambda_5 & 0 \\ 0 & 0 & 0 & 0 & 0 & \lambda_6 \end{bmatrix}$$

An Application of the Canonical Form   In many engineering applications, we must design a controller to provide a force, torque, voltage, or pressure to drive the system so that the output is a specified function of time. An example is the shoulder joint of a robot arm driven by an electric motor. The input is the motor voltage and the output is the angle of the shoulder. It is desirable to be able to predict whether or not the output can be driven to some desired value. This requires an understanding of the *controllability* of the system. A state $\mathbf{x}_1 = \mathbf{x}(t_1)$ of a system is controllable if it is possible for the input vector to transfer any state $\mathbf{x}_0 = \mathbf{x}(t_0)$ at any previous time to the state $\mathbf{x}_1$ in a finite amount of time. If all states $\mathbf{x}_1$ of the system are controllable, the system is controllable. The canonical matrix is very useful in assessing controllability.

The first-order model $x' = ax + bf(t)$ is controllable if $b \neq 0$. To show this, use the general solution:

$$x(t) = e^{at}x(t_0) + e^{at}\int_{t_0}^{t} e^{-a\tau}bf(\tau)d\tau.$$

Controllability requires that any desired value of $x(t)$ at any desired time t can be attained, for arbitrary values of $x(t_0)$ and t_0. A constant input f can accomplish this task if no constraints are put on its magnitude. To see this, carry out the integration for arbitrary but constant f, and solve for f.

When considering higher-order systems, the controllability properties are not always so apparent. Consider the second-order system:

$$x_1' = -2x_1 + f(t)$$
$$x_2' = x_1 - x_2 - f(t)$$

From the previous results, we can see that the state x_1 is controllable because its equation does not depend on x_2, but the situation for x_2 is not as clear. The answer is found by recalling that the modes of a model form the structure of its dynamic behavior. In order to control the system's behavior, we must be able to influence each of its modes separately. Therefore, let us examine the modal composition of the model. The eigenvalues are $\lambda = -1$, -2, and the eigenvectors are

$$\mathbf{v}_1 = \begin{bmatrix} 0 \\ 1 \end{bmatrix} \qquad \mathbf{v}_2 = \begin{bmatrix} 1 \\ -1 \end{bmatrix}$$

The modal transformation matrix $\mathbf{M}$ and its inverse are

$$\mathbf{M} = \begin{bmatrix} 0 & 1 \\ 1 & -1 \end{bmatrix} \qquad \mathbf{M}^{-1} = \begin{bmatrix} 1 & 1 \\ 1 & 0 \end{bmatrix}$$

The modes are $\mathbf{z} = \mathbf{M}^{-1}\mathbf{x}$, or

$$z_1 = x_1 + x_2$$

$$z_2 = x_1$$

The modal equations are

$$\dot{\mathbf{z}} = \Lambda\mathbf{z} + \mathbf{M}^{-1}\mathbf{B}f(t) = \begin{bmatrix} -1 & 0 \\ 0 & -2 \end{bmatrix}\mathbf{z} + \begin{bmatrix} 0 \\ 1 \end{bmatrix}f(t)$$

or

$$\dot{z}_1 = -z_1$$
$$\dot{z}_2 = -2z_2 + f(t)$$

Because neither $f(t)$ nor z_2 appears in the first modal equation, the mode z_1 is uncontrollable. Therefore, the system is uncontrollable. We can control x_2 but not the sum $x_1 + x_2$, which means we cannot control x_1.

The Transition Matrix

Recall that the columns of the *fundamental matrix* $\mathbf{F}(t)$ are the linearly independent solution vectors $\mathbf{x}_1, \mathbf{x}_2, \dots, \mathbf{x}_n$ of a system. The free response can be expressed as

$$\mathbf{x}(t) = \mathbf{F}(t)\mathbf{F}^{-1}(t)\mathbf{x}(0)$$

We define a new matrix, called the **transition matrix**, as

$$\boldsymbol{\varphi}(t) = \mathbf{F}(t)\mathbf{F}^{-1}(t) \tag{7--118}$$

Thus,

$$\mathbf{x}(t) = \boldsymbol{\varphi}(t)\mathbf{x}(0) \tag{7--119}$$

Instead of using Equation 7–118 to compute $\boldsymbol{\varphi}(t)$, let us develop an alternate method.

Solution from the Eigenmodes Consider the diagonal form of Equation 7–112 for distinct eigenvalues. With $\mathbf{r}(t) = 0$, the equation for each modal coordinate $\mathbf{z}_i$ is

$$z_i' = \lambda_i z_i$$

The free response is easily shown to be

$$z_i(t) = z_i(0)e^{\lambda_i t}$$

or in matrix form

$$\mathbf{z}(t) = \begin{bmatrix} e^{\lambda_1 t} & 0 & 0 & \cdots & . & 0 \\ 0 & e^{\lambda_2 t} & 0 & \cdots & . & 0 \\ . & . & . & \cdots & . & . \\ 0 & . & . & \cdots & 0 & e^{\lambda_n t} \end{bmatrix} \mathbf{z}(0) \tag{7--120}$$

Let the matrix of exponentials in Equation 7–120 be denoted $\varphi_M(t)$. Then

$$\mathbf{z}(t) = \varphi_M(t)\mathbf{z}(0) \tag{7–121}$$

The matrix $\varphi_M(t)$ is the **modal transition matrix**. It describes the transition of each modal coordinate from one point in time to another. The diagonal form was obtained by the transformation $\mathbf{x}(t) = \mathbf{M}\mathbf{z}(t)$. Thus, $\mathbf{z}(0) = \mathbf{M}^{-1}\mathbf{x}(0)$, and from Equation 7–121,

$$\mathbf{M}\mathbf{z}(t) = \mathbf{M}\varphi_M(t)\mathbf{z}(0)$$

or

$$\mathbf{x}(t) = \mathbf{M}\varphi_M(t)\mathbf{M}^{-1}\mathbf{x}(0) \tag{7–122}$$

We have now recovered the free response of the equation $\mathbf{x}' = \mathbf{A}\mathbf{x} + \mathbf{r}(t)$ in terms of the original state variables. In analogy with the first-order case, we write Equation 7–122 as $\mathbf{x}(t) = \varphi(t)\mathbf{x}(0)$ where the **state transition matrix** is given by:

$$\varphi(t) = \mathbf{M}\varphi_M(t)\mathbf{M}^{-1} \tag{7–123}$$

This equation describes another way to obtain the state transition matrix, which is analogous to the function e^{at} for the first-order equation $x' = ax$. If $\mathbf{A}$ is an $n \times n$ matrix, so is $\varphi(t)$.

Properties of the State Transition Matrix   Some useful properties of the state transition matrix can be derived from Equations 7–119 and 7–123. Set $t = 0$ in Equation 7–119 to show that

$$\varphi(0) = \mathbf{I} \tag{7–124}$$

If $\mathbf{r}(t) = \mathbf{0}$, $\mathbf{x}' = \mathbf{A}\mathbf{x}$. Use this with the derivative of Equation 7–119 to obtain

$$\mathbf{x}' = \varphi'(t)\mathbf{x}(0) = \mathbf{A}\mathbf{x}(t) = \mathbf{A}\varphi(t)\mathbf{x}(0)$$

or

$$\varphi'(t) = \mathbf{A}\varphi(t) \tag{7–125}$$

Thus, $\varphi(t)$ is the solution of the differential equation Equation 7–125 with the initial condition Equation 7–124. Solve Equation 7–123 for $\varphi_M(t)$.

$$\varphi_M(t) = \mathbf{M}^{-1}\varphi(t)\mathbf{M} \tag{7–126}$$

The inverse of a diagonal matrix is found by simply inverting the diagonal elements. Thus, since $\varphi_M(t)$ is diagonal if the eigenvalues are distinct, $\varphi_M^{-1}(t) = \varphi_M(-t)$. It follows that

$$\varphi^{-1}(t) = \varphi(-t) \tag{7–127}$$

This property avoids the need to perform the usually tedious calculations in finding the matrix inverse.

Equation 7–119 relates $\mathbf{x}(t)$ to the initial state at $t = 0$. However, because we are dealing with the free response of a constant coefficient equation, we could also write the solution in terms of the state at any time, say t_1, as

$$\mathbf{x}(t + t_1) = \varphi(t)\mathbf{x}(t_1) \tag{7–128}$$

But $\mathbf{x}(t_1) = \varphi(t_1)\mathbf{x}(0)$, and thus,

$$\mathbf{x}(t + t_1) = \varphi(t)\varphi(t_1)\mathbf{x}(0)$$

If we had used Equation 7–128 immediately, we would have obtained

$$\mathbf{x}(t + t_1) = \varphi(t + t_1)\mathbf{x}(0)$$

Comparison of the last two equations shows that

$$\varphi(t + t_1) = \varphi(t)\varphi(t_1) \tag{7-129}$$

for any t and t_1. Also, since $\varphi(t + t_1) = \varphi(t_1 + t)$, the commutative property holds. Thus,

$$\varphi(t)\varphi(t_1) = \varphi(t_1)\varphi(t) \tag{7-130}$$

Finally, if we let $t = t_1 = \Delta$ in Equation 7–129, we see that

$$\varphi(2\Delta) = \varphi(\Delta)\varphi(\Delta) = \varphi^2(\Delta)$$

or in general,

$$\varphi(n\Delta) = \varphi^n(\Delta) \tag{7-131}$$

This property is especially useful for numerical solutions since computers can easily multiply matrices.

EXAMPLE 7–30   Transition Matrix for a Mass–Spring–Damper System

(a) Find the transition matrix for a mass–spring–damper system with $m = 1$, $c = 7$, and $k = 10$. The differential equation is

$$m\ddot{x} + c\dot{x} + kx = 0$$

(b) Find the displacement $x_1 = x$ and the velocity $x_2 = \dot{x}$ of the mass at the times $t = 0.1$ and $t = 0.2$ if the initial displacement is $x_1(0) = 3$ and the initial velocity is $x_2(0) = 0$.

(c) If the displacement and velocity at $t = 0.1$ are measured to be $x_1(0.1) = 0.5013$ and $x_2(0.1) = -0.2141$, what initial conditions produced this motion?

SOLUTION (a) The characteristic equation is $m\lambda^2 + c\lambda + k = \lambda^2 + 7\lambda + 10 = 0$. The eigenvalues are $\lambda = -2$ and -5. The eigenvectors can be normalized as

$$\mathbf{v}_1 = \begin{pmatrix} 1 \\ -2 \end{pmatrix} \qquad \mathbf{v}_2 = \begin{pmatrix} 1 \\ -5 \end{pmatrix}$$

and the modal transformation matrix with its inverse are

$$\mathbf{M} = \begin{pmatrix} 1 & 1 \\ -2 & -5 \end{pmatrix} \qquad \mathbf{M}^{-1} = \frac{1}{3}\begin{pmatrix} 5 & 1 \\ -2 & -1 \end{pmatrix}$$

The modal transition matrix is

$$\varphi_M(t) = \begin{pmatrix} e^{-2t} & 0 \\ 0 & e^{-5t} \end{pmatrix}$$

The state transition matrix is found from Equation 7–123.

$$\varphi(t) = \mathbf{M}\varphi_M(t)\mathbf{M}^{-1} = \frac{1}{3}\begin{pmatrix} (5e^{-2t}-2e^{-5t}) & (e^{-2t}-e^{-5t}) \\ (10e^{-2t}+10e^{-5t}) & (-2e^{-2t}+5e^{-5t}) \end{pmatrix}$$

(b) Here the evaluation times $t = 0.1, 0.2$ are separated by the same interval, so we can evaluate $\varphi(t)$ once for $t = 0.1$ and use Equation 7–128.

$$\varphi(0.1) = \frac{1}{3}\begin{pmatrix} 2.8806 & 0.21220 \\ -2.1220 & 1.3952 \end{pmatrix}$$

Thus

$$\mathbf{x}(0.1) = \varphi(0.1)\mathbf{x}(0) = \varphi(0.1)\begin{pmatrix} 3 \\ 0 \end{pmatrix} = \begin{pmatrix} 2.8806 \\ -2.1220 \end{pmatrix}$$

Also,

$$\mathbf{x}(0.2) = \varphi(0.1)\mathbf{x}(0.1) = \begin{pmatrix} 2.6159 \\ -3.0244 \end{pmatrix}$$

(c) Given $\mathbf{x}(0.1)$, we use the property given by Equation 7–127 to obtain $\mathbf{x}(0)$.

$$\mathbf{x}(0) = \varphi^{-1}(0.1)\mathbf{x}(0.1) = \varphi(-0.1)\mathbf{x}(0.1)$$

This gives

$$\mathbf{x}(0) = \frac{1}{3}\begin{pmatrix} 2.8806 & -0.4273 \\ 4.273 & 5.8008 \end{pmatrix}\begin{pmatrix} 0.5013 \\ -0.2141 \end{pmatrix} = \begin{pmatrix} 0.5 \\ 0.3 \end{pmatrix}$$

Series Solution for The Transition Matrix The scalar form of the vector equation $\mathbf{x}' = \mathbf{A}\mathbf{x}$ is $x' = ax$, and its solution is $x(t) = e^{at}x(0)$. But we can represent e^{at} as the series:

$$e^{at} = 1 + at + \frac{(at)^2}{2!} + \cdots + \frac{(at)^k}{k!} + \cdots$$

Therefore, it makes sense to try the following series solution for $\varphi(t)$, which is the solution of $\mathbf{x}' = \mathbf{A}\mathbf{x}$:

$$\varphi(t) = \mathbf{I} + \mathbf{A}t + \frac{(\mathbf{A}t)^2}{2!} + \cdots + \frac{(\mathbf{A}t)^k}{k!} + \cdots \qquad \text{(7–132)}$$

You can prove that this is the solution of $\mathbf{x}' = \mathbf{A}\mathbf{x}$ by differentiating the series term by term (see Problem 7–168). Because of its similarity to the series expression for the scalar exponential e^{at}, the transition matrix $\varphi(t)$ is sometimes called the **matrix exponential** and is denoted by $e^{\mathbf{A}t}$. The series representation is particularly well suited for calculating the transition matrix for a particular value of t with a computer, because it merely requires repeated multiplication of the matrix $\mathbf{A}$.

Section Review

In each of the following problems, find the eigenvectors, the modal matrix, and the Jordan canonical form for the equation $\mathbf{x}' = \mathbf{A}\mathbf{x}$ whose matrix $\mathbf{A}$

is given. Determine whether or not the eigenvectors are linearly independent. Obtain the solutions by decoupling the equations.

7–34
$$A = \begin{pmatrix} -4 & 4 \\ 1 & -4 \end{pmatrix}$$

(*Answer:* $\lambda = -2, -6$; $M = \begin{pmatrix} 1 & 1 \\ \frac{1}{2} & -\frac{1}{2} \end{pmatrix}$; $\Lambda = \begin{pmatrix} -2 & 0 \\ 0 & -6 \end{pmatrix}$; and linearly independent. $x_1 = 2c_1 e^{-2t} - 2c_2 e^{-6t}$, $x_2 = c_1 e^{-2t} + c_2 e^{-6t}$)

7–35
$$A = \begin{pmatrix} 1 & -1 \\ 1 & 3 \end{pmatrix}$$

(*Answer:* $\lambda = 2, 2$ $v_1 = v_2 = \begin{pmatrix} 1 \\ -1 \end{pmatrix}$; $\Lambda = \begin{pmatrix} 2 & 1 \\ 0 & 2 \end{pmatrix}$; linearly dependent. $x_1 = c_1 e^{2t} - c_2 e^{2t} - c_1 t e^{2t}$, $x_2 = c_2 e^{2t} + c_1 t e^{2t}$

7–8 ▪ COMPUTER METHODS

Commonly available computer packages can find eigenvalues, eigenvectors, and the transition matrix (the matrix exponential) in both symbolic and numeric form (with the exception of MATLAB, which has numerical capability only in the absence of the add-ons MuPAD and the Symbolic Math Toolbox). However, for large matrices, a symbolic solution may not be obtainable, and even if it is, it could be too cumbersome to be useful. Since there is no formula available for the roots of a polynomial higher than the fourth degree, you can expect this to be the limit for symbolic results. The advantage of matrix methods is that they can handle systems with a large number of equations, and this requires a numerical solution for the eigenvalues and eigenvectors.

These packages also can solve large sets of equations numerically without requiring much programming. Their ease of use derives partly from their use of the standard state variable matrix form. These methods are covered later in this section.

Eigenvalues and Eigenvectors We will use the following as our test case.

$$A = \begin{pmatrix} -1 & 1 \\ 1 & -2 \end{pmatrix}$$

The eigenvalues to four decimal places are -2.6180, -0.3820, and the eigenvectors are

$$\begin{pmatrix} -0.5257 \\ 0.8507 \end{pmatrix} \quad \text{and} \quad \begin{pmatrix} 0.8507 \\ 0.5257 \end{pmatrix}$$

Different programs will normalize the eigenvectors in different ways. A common way is to adjust the components of the vector so that its magnitude (its geometric length) is 1. This is the case here, because $\sqrt{(-0.5257)^2 + (0.8507)^2} = 1$. Eigenvector results may also be normalized so that one of the components in each eigenvector is 1. The commands shown in Table 7–1 display a list with the eigenvalues listed first, followed by the eigenvectors. An exception is MATLAB, which displays the eigenvectors

TABLE 7–1

Eigenvalues and Eigenvectors of the Matrix

$$\mathbf{A} = \begin{pmatrix} -1 & 1 \\ 1 & -2 \end{pmatrix}$$

MATLAB

```
A = [-1,1;1,-2];
[v, Lambda] = eig(A)
```

Symbolic Math Toolbox

```
A = [-1,1;1,-2];
[v, Lambda] = eig(A)
```

MuPAD

For symbolic results:
```
A := matrix([[-1,1],[1,-2]])
linalg::eigenvectors(A)
```

For numeric results:
```
A := matrix([[-1,1],[1,-2]])
numeric::eigenvectors(A)
```

Maple

```
with(LinearAlgebra)
A := matrix([[-1,1;1,-2]]);
Eigenvectors(A)
```

Mathematica

```
A = {{-1,1},{1,-2}}
Eigensystem[A]
```

in the variable v and the eigenvalues as the diagonal elements of the matrix Lambda. MATLAB can also compute the Jordan canonical form by typing `[v,J] = jordan(A)`. The matrix v contains the eigenvectors, and the matrix J is the Jordan matrix. For the matrix **A** given previously, we obtain

$$\mathbf{J} = \begin{pmatrix} -2.6180 & 0 \\ 0 & -0.3820 \end{pmatrix}$$

Transition Matrix (Matrix Exponential)   For our test case we use the following matrix:

$$\mathbf{A} = \begin{pmatrix} 0 & 1 \\ -1 & 0 \end{pmatrix}$$

Its transition matrix is

$$\boldsymbol{\varphi}(t) = \begin{pmatrix} \cos t & \sin t \\ -\sin t & \cos t \end{pmatrix}$$

Table 7–2 shows how to obtain this matrix. Note that the MATLAB function `expm(A)` computes e^A numerically and thus does *not* compute the matrix exponential e^{At}.

TABLE 7–2

Transition Matrix for

$$\mathbf{A} = \begin{pmatrix} 1 & 1 \\ -1 & 0 \end{pmatrix}$$

Symbolic Math Toolbox

```
syms t
A = [0 1; -1 0];
expm(A*t);
simplify(ans)
```

Maple

```
with(LinearAlgebra)
A := Matrix([[0,1],[-1,0]])
MatrixExponential(A)
```

Mathematica

```
A = {{0,1},{-1,0}}
MatrixExp[A t]
```

Standard State-Variable Form Higher-order sets of differential equations do not have simple (easy to use) solutions, so they must be solved numerically. Although the numerical solution methods covered in Chapter 9 can solve any differential equation or sets of equations, MATLAB and other commercial programs take advantage of the fact that the *form* of the solutions of *linear* equations can always be determined at least in part, especially when the coefficients are constants. This is because the characteristic roots can always be obtained numerically, and these roots determine part of the solution form. Because of this, MATLAB and other programs contain functions that are specifically designed to solve linear equations. The advantage is that these functions are more efficient and easier to use than the more general methods covered in Chapter 9.

Since the state-variable matrix form

$$\mathbf{x}' = \mathbf{A}\mathbf{x} + \mathbf{B}\mathbf{u} \tag{7–133}$$

can represent *any* set of linear equations, it forms the basis for specifying such equations for computer solution. We may use any symbols we choose for the state variables and the input or forcing functions, but a common choice is x_i for the state variables and u_i for the input functions. Let the number of state variables be n and the number of inputs be m. So the vector and matrix dimensions are as follows.

- The *state vector* $\mathbf{x}$ is a column vector having n rows.
- The *system matrix* $\mathbf{A}$ is a square matrix having n rows and n columns.
- The *input vector* $\mathbf{u}$ is a column vector having m rows.
- The *control* or *input matrix* $\mathbf{B}$ has n rows and m columns.

Sometimes, however, we do not want to plot all the variables in the solution, and so we need a way to specify which variables are to be plotted.

Some software packages and some design methods require you to define an *output vector*, usually denoted by **y**. The output vector contains the variables that are of interest for the particular problem at hand. These variables are not necessarily the state variables, but might be some combination of the state variables and the inputs. For example, in the mass-spring-damper model, we might be interested in the total force $f - kx - cx'$ acting on the mass, and in the momentum mx'. In this case, the output vector has two elements. If the state variables are $x_1 = x$ and $x_2 = x'$ and the input vector **u** is the scalar force f, the output vector is

$$\mathbf{y} = \begin{pmatrix} y_1 \\ y_2 \end{pmatrix} = \begin{pmatrix} f - kx - cx' \\ mx' \end{pmatrix} = \begin{pmatrix} f - kx_1 - cx_2 \\ mx_2 \end{pmatrix}$$

$$= \begin{pmatrix} -k & -c \\ 0 & m \end{pmatrix} \begin{pmatrix} x_1 \\ x_2 \end{pmatrix} + \begin{pmatrix} 1 \\ 0 \end{pmatrix} f = \mathbf{Cx} + \mathbf{Du}$$

where

$$\mathbf{C} = \begin{pmatrix} -k & -c \\ 0 & m \end{pmatrix} \quad \text{and} \quad \mathbf{D} = \begin{pmatrix} 1 \\ 0 \end{pmatrix}$$

This is an example of the general form:

$$\mathbf{y} = \mathbf{Cx} + \mathbf{Du} \tag{7-134}$$

This is the standard vector-matrix form of the output equation, where the number of outputs is p, the number of state variables is n, and the number of inputs is m. The dimensions are as follows:

- The *output vector* **y** is a column vector having p rows.
- The *state output matrix* **C** has p rows and n columns.
- The *control output matrix* **D** has p rows and m columns.

The matrices **C** and **D** can always be found whenever the chosen output vector **y** is a linear combination of the state variables and the inputs. However, if the output is a nonlinear function, then the standard form (Equation 7–134) does not apply. This would be the case, for example, if the output is chosen to be the system's kinetic energy: $m(x')^2/2$.

We now illustrate these methods using MATLAB but the state variable form is the universally-used notation for programs dealing with linear systems. When the coefficient matrices **A** and **B** are constant, the equation set is called a *linear time-invariant* (*LTI*) object. To create an LTI object from a state model, you use the ss(A,B,C,D) function, where ss stands for *state space*, and the matrix arguments of the function are the matrices in the standard form of a state model given by Equations 7–133 and 7–134.

For example, to create an LTI object in state-model form for the system described by

$$x_1' = x_2$$
$$x_2' = -4x_1 - 7x_2 + 5f(t)$$

where x_1 is the desired output, the MATLAB code is

```
A = [0, 1; -4, -7];
B = [0; 5];
C = [1, 0];
D = 0;
sys1 = ss(A,B,C,D);
```

where `sys1` is an arbitrarily chosen name for the LTI object created by the `ss` function.

The MATLAB Control System Toolbox provides several solvers for linear models expressed in state variable form. These solvers are categorized by the type of input function they can accept: zero input, impulse input, step input, and a general input function. The `initial` function computes and plots the free response of a state model. This response is sometimes called the *initial condition response* or the *undriven response* in the MATLAB documentation. The basic syntax is `initial(sys,x0)`, where sys is the LTI object in state variable form, and x0 is the initial condition vector. The time span and number of solution points are chosen automatically. This is a very useful feature.

EXAMPLE 7–31   Free Response of a Two-Mass Model

The equations of motion for the two-mass system shown in Figure 7–52 reduce to the following equations for the specific coefficient values: $m_1 = 5$, $m_2 = 3$, $c_1 = 4$, $c_2 = 8$, $k_1 = 1$, and $k_2 = 4$.

$$5x_1'' + 12x_1' + 5x_1 - 8x_2' - 4x_2 = 0$$
$$3x_2'' + 8x_2' + 4x_2 - 8x_1' - 4x_1 = f(t)$$

Plot the free response $x_1(t)$ and $x_1'(t)$ for the initial conditions $x_1(0) = 5$, $x_1'(0) = -3$, $x_2(0) = 4$, and $x_2'(0) = 2$.

SOLUTION   Choosing the state variables to be x_1, x_2, $x_3 = x_1'$, $x_4 = x_2'$, the state equations are

$$x_1' = x_3 \quad x_2' = x_4$$

$$x_3' = \frac{1}{5}(-5x_1 + 4x_2 - 12x_3 + 8x_4)$$

$$x_4' = \frac{1}{3}(4x_1 - 4x_2 + 8x_3 - 8x_4) + \frac{1}{3}f(t)$$

The system and input matrices are

$$\mathbf{A} = \begin{pmatrix} 0 & 0 & 1 & 0 \\ 0 & 0 & 0 & 1 \\ -1 & \dfrac{4}{5} & -\dfrac{12}{5} & \dfrac{8}{5} \\ \dfrac{4}{3} & -\dfrac{4}{3} & \dfrac{8}{3} & -\dfrac{8}{3} \end{pmatrix} \quad \mathbf{B} = \begin{pmatrix} 0 \\ 0 \\ 0 \\ \dfrac{1}{3} \end{pmatrix}$$

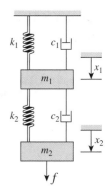

FIGURE 7–52

Model of a two-mass system with an applied force $f(t)$.

We must relate the initial conditions given in terms of the original variables to the state variables. We see easily that $x_3(0) = x'_1(0) = -3$ and $x_4(0) = x'_2(0) = 2$. Next we must select the output matrices appropriately. Since we are told to plot $x_1(t)$ and $x_3(t)$, the output vector y is $(x_1, x_3)^T$. Since the input is a scalar, $u = f(t)$, the output equation is

$$y = \mathbf{Cx} + \mathbf{Du} = \begin{pmatrix} x_1 \\ x_2 \end{pmatrix} = \begin{pmatrix} 1 & 0 & 0 & 0 \\ 0 & 0 & 1 & 0 \end{pmatrix} \begin{pmatrix} x_1 \\ x_2 \\ x_3 \\ x_4 \end{pmatrix} + \begin{pmatrix} 0 \\ 0 \end{pmatrix} f(t)$$

Thus,

$$\mathbf{C} = \begin{pmatrix} 1 & 0 & 0 & 0 \\ 0 & 0 & 1 & 0 \end{pmatrix} \quad \mathbf{D} = \begin{pmatrix} 0 \\ 0 \end{pmatrix}$$

The MATLAB program is as follows.

```
A = [0, 0, 1, 0; 0,0,0,1;-1,4/5,-12/5,8/5;...
        4/3,-4/3,8/3,-8/3];
B = [0; 0; 0; 1/3];
C = [1, 0, 0, 0;0,0,1,0]; D = [0;0];
sys2 = ss(A, B, C, D);
initial(sys2, [5, 4, -3, 2])
```

The plot of $x_1(t)$ and $x_3(t)$ will be displayed on the screen using standard axis labels and title, as shown in Figure 7–53. The first output (x_1) is displayed in the top graph and the second output (x_3) is displayed in the bottom graph. Note that the time span is chosen automatically by an algorithm based on the characteristic roots, which determine the response time. The steady-state responses are displayed by dashed lines.

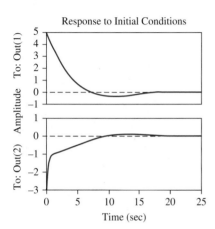

FIGURE 7–53

The free response for Example 7–31.

To specify the final time, say `tfinal`, use the syntax `initial(sys, x0, tfinal)`. To specify a vector of times of the form $t = [0: dt:tfinal]$, at which to obtain the solution, use the syntax `initial(sys,x0,t)`. When called with left-hand arguments, as `[y,t] = initial(sys,x0)`, the function returns the output response `y` and the time vector `t` used for the simulation. No plot is drawn. The array `y` is $(q \times p \times m)$, where q is `length(t)`, p is the number of outputs, and m is the number of inputs.

MATLAB provides the `impulse`, `step`, and `lsim` functions to use with state-variable models. An impulse input is a rapidly applied and rapidly removed input. It is described in Chapter 8. If the area under its curve is unity, then it is called a *unit* impulse. The response to a unit impulse input starting at $t = 0$ is found by typing `impulse(sys)`. If the input has an area A, type `impulse(A*sys)`. The response to a unit step input starting at $t = 0$ is found by typing `step(sys)`. If the step input has a magnitude M, type `step(M*sys)`.

The `lsim` function can be used to plot the solution of an LTI model with any input function u that can be programmed. The syntax is `lsim (sys,u,t,x0)`. The initial condition vector `x0` is needed only if the initial conditions are nonzero. For example, to plot $x_1(t)$ and $x_3(t)$ of the model `sys2` given in Example 7–29 when the input is $f(t) = 4 \sin 7t$, $0 \le t \le 30$ using a step size of 0.01, the MATLAB code is

```
A = [0, 0, 1, 0; 0,0,0,1;-1,4/5,-12/5,8/5;...
     4/3,-4/3,8/3,-8/3];
B = [0; 0; 0; 1/3];
C = [1, 0, 0, 0;0,0,1,0]; D = [0;0];
sys2 = ss(A, B, C, D);
t = 0:0.01:30;
u = 4*sin(7*t);
x0 = [5, 4, -3, 2];
lsim(sys2,u,t,x0)
```

The extended syntax of the `impulse`, `step`, and `lsim` functions with left-hand arguments, as `[y,t]`, is the same as that of the `initial` function.

Maple and Mathematica both have functions for simulating sets of linear, constant coefficient differential equations described in the standard state variable form, Equations 7–133 and 7–134.

Linear Systems Simulation in Maple The DynamicSystems package in Maple is a collection of procedures for creating, manipulating, simulating, and plotting linear systems models that are defined in terms of state space matrices. Input functions such as sine, ramp, and step functions can be created by using the Signal Generation commands, such as `Step(height, t0)`. The standard plotting tools, such as `ResponsePlot(sys,input,opts)`, can be used to plot LTI objects.

Linear Systems Simulation in Mathematica The Mathematica Control System Professional add-on has functions for creating, manipulating, simulating, and plotting linear systems models that are defined in terms of state space matrices. You create an LTI object `sys` with `StateSpace(A,B,C,D)`. Then use `SimulationPlot[sys,u,{t,t,max}]` to plot the state variable responses to the input function `u`.

7–9 ▪ SUMMARY

Systems of differential equations arise naturally in the analysis of many practical problems that involve two or more physically coupled systems. The unknown functions of such systems are interdependent, and they need to be determined simultaneously. Systems of differential equations involve the derivatives of two or more dependent variables with respect to a single independent variable, usually time t. The differential equations that make up a system may be of different orders. However, to bring uniformity to the treatment of systems of differential equations, it is common practice to transform such systems into an equivalent system of first-order equations. Any nth-order differential equation can always be transformed into a system of n first-order differential equations.

Classification A system of differential equations is said to be *linear* if every single equation in the system is linear. A system is said to be *nonlinear* even if only one equation involves a single nonlinear term. A linear system of differential equations is said to be *homogeneous* if every single equation in the system is homogeneous. A system is said to be *nonhomogeneous* even if only one equation involves a single nonhomogeneous term. A system of differential equations is said to have *constant coefficients* if every equation in the system in the standard form has constant coefficients. A system is said to have *variable coefficients* even if only one equation involves a variable coefficient (a function of the independent variable).

Solution Procedures Systems of linear differential equations can be solved using a systematic procedure, but even linear systems can be difficult to solve if they involve variable coefficients, since the solutions in such cases typically involve infinite series. Therefore, the emphasis in this chapter has been on linear systems of differential equations with constant coefficients.

Both the method of elimination and the method of eigenvalues covered in Chapter 6 are simple and easy to track, but they are not practical for systems with more than two or three equations. They become extremely tedious and complicated as the number of equations in the system increases. Such large systems can be solved most efficiently and systematically with the *matrix method*, which is also called the *method of eigenvectors*.

Standard Matrix Form Matrix notation offers great convenience when solving large systems of algebraic or differential equations. The general form of a linear set of equations is $\mathbf{x}' = \mathbf{Ax} + \mathbf{r}(t)$. The matrix $\mathbf{A}$ that contains all the coefficients of the unknowns is called the *coefficient matrix*. The vector $\mathbf{x}$ that contains all the unknowns is called the *unknown vector*. The vector $\mathbf{r}$ that contains all the terms that do not involve any of the unknowns as a factor is called the *right-hand side vector* in systems of algebraic equations, and *nonhomogeneous vector* in systems of differential equations. If $\mathbf{r} = \mathbf{0}$, the system of equations is said to be *homogeneous*. Otherwise, it is said to be *nonhomogeneous*.

Uniqueness and Linearity If the coefficients and the nonhomogeneous terms are continuous in an interval $t_1 < t < t_2$ that contains the point t_0, then the system of n first-order linear equations $\mathbf{x}' = \mathbf{A}(t)\mathbf{x} + \mathbf{r}(t)$ has a *unique solution* in that interval, which satisfies a given set of initial conditions at t_0. If two or more vector functions are solutions of a linear homogeneous system, so is their linear combination.

Linear Independence A system of n first-order linear homogeneous differential equations always possesses n linearly independent solutions $\mathbf{x}_1, \mathbf{x}_2, \ldots, \mathbf{x}_n$ in an interval $t_1 < t < t_2$ in which the elements of the coefficient matrix $\mathbf{A}$ are continuous. Further, the *general solution* of this system in that interval can be expressed as a linear combination of these n solutions as

$$\mathbf{x} = c_1\mathbf{x}_1 + c_2\mathbf{x}_2 + \cdots + c_n\mathbf{x}_n$$

where $c_1, c_2, \ldots, c_n$ are arbitrary constants. Also, if $\mathbf{x}_1, \mathbf{x}_2, \ldots, \mathbf{x}_n$ are solutions of the system n first-order linear homogeneous differential equations in an interval $t_1 < t < t_2$ in which the elements of the coefficient matrix $\mathbf{A}$ are continuous, then the Wronskian of $\mathbf{x}_1, \mathbf{x}_2, \ldots, \mathbf{x}_n$ is either always zero (indicating these n solutions are linearly dependent) or never zero (indicating these n solutions are linearly independent) in that interval. This is known as *Abel's identity*. The general solution of nonhomogeneous systems is obtained by adding a particular solution to the general solution of the related homogeneous system.

Real and Distinct Eigenvalues When the n eigenvalues $\lambda_1, \lambda_2, \ldots, \lambda_n$ of the coefficient matrix $\mathbf{A}$ of a system of n first-order linear homogeneous equations with constant coefficients in n unknowns are real and distinct, then the n associated eigenvectors $\mathbf{v}_1, \mathbf{v}_2, \ldots, \mathbf{v}_n$ are always real and linearly independent.

Then the solution vectors $\mathbf{v}_1 e^{\lambda_1 t}, \mathbf{v}_2 e^{\lambda_2 t}, \ldots, \mathbf{v}_n e^{\lambda_n t}$ are also linearly independent, and the general solution of this system can be expressed as

$$\mathbf{x} = c_1\mathbf{v}_1 e^{\lambda_1 t} + c_2\mathbf{v}_2 e^{\lambda_2 t} + \cdots + c_n\mathbf{v}_n e^{\lambda_n t} \tag{7–73}$$

Complex Eigenvalues When the coefficient matrix $\mathbf{A}$ is real, any complex eigenvalues and their corresponding eigenvectors must occur in complex conjugate pairs. If $\mathbf{v} = \mathbf{a} \pm i\mathbf{b}$ are the eigenvectors corresponding to the eigenvalues $\lambda = \alpha \pm i\beta$, then the two linearly independent real-valued solution vectors corresponding to them can be expressed as

$$\mathbf{x}_1(t) = e^{\alpha t}(\mathbf{a} \cos \beta t - \mathbf{b} \sin \beta t) \tag{7–76a}$$

and

$$\mathbf{x}_2(t) = e^{\alpha t}(\mathbf{a} \sin \beta t + \mathbf{b} \cos \beta t) \tag{7–76b}$$

Repeated Eigenvalues When an eigenvalue of multiplicity k has fewer than k linearly independent eigenvectors associated with it, then there are fewer than k linearly independent solution vectors of the form $\mathbf{v}e^{\lambda t}$ associated with that eigenvalue. In that case we must seek solutions in other forms to make up the deficit in the number of linearly independent solutions associated with that eigenvalue. Two linearly independent solution vectors corresponding to an eigenvalue λ of multiplicity two that has only one linearly independent eigenvector $\mathbf{v}$ associated with it are expressed as

$$\mathbf{x}_1(t) = \mathbf{v}e^{\lambda t} \tag{7–77}$$

and

$$\mathbf{x}_2(t) = \mathbf{v}te^{\lambda t} + \mathbf{u}e^{\lambda t} \tag{7–78}$$

where the constant vector $\mathbf{u}$ is determined from

$$(\mathbf{A} - \lambda\mathbf{I})\mathbf{u} = \mathbf{v} \tag{7–80b}$$

There are three possibilities associated with an eigenvalue λ of multiplicity 3. If the triple eigenvalue λ has three linearly independent eigenvectors $\mathbf{v}_1, \mathbf{v}_2$, and $\mathbf{v}_3$ associated with it, the three linearly independent solutions corresponding to it are simply

$$\mathbf{x}_1 = \mathbf{v}_1 e^{\lambda t}, \quad \mathbf{x}_2 = \mathbf{v}_2 e^{\lambda t}, \quad \text{and} \quad \mathbf{x}_3 = \mathbf{v}_3 e^{\lambda t} \tag{7–83}$$

If the triple eigenvalue λ has two linearly independent eigenvectors $\mathbf{v}_1$ and $\mathbf{v}_2$ associated with it, the three linearly independent solutions corresponding to it become

$$\mathbf{x}_1 = \mathbf{v}_1 e^{\lambda t}, \quad x_2 = \mathbf{v}_2 e^{\lambda t}, \quad \text{and} \quad \mathbf{x}_3 = \mathbf{v}_3 te^{\lambda t} + \mathbf{u}e^{\lambda t}$$

where the constant vector $\mathbf{u}$ is determined from Equation 7–80b by using the linear combination $k_1\mathbf{v}_1 + k_2\mathbf{v}_2$ for $\mathbf{v}$.

If the triple eigenvalue λ has only one linearly independent eigenvector $\mathbf{v}$ associated with it, then the three linearly independent solutions associated with it are

$$\mathbf{x}_1 = \mathbf{v}e^{\lambda t}, \; \mathbf{x}_2 = \mathbf{v}te^{\lambda t} + \mathbf{u}e^{\lambda t}, \text{ and } \mathbf{x}_3 = \frac{1}{2}\mathbf{v}t^2 e^{\lambda t} + \mathbf{u}te^{\lambda t} + \mathbf{w}e^{\lambda t}$$

where the constant vectors $\mathbf{u}$ and $\mathbf{w}$ are determined from

$$(\mathbf{A} - \lambda \mathbf{I})\mathbf{u} = \mathbf{v} \quad \text{and} \quad (\mathbf{A} - \lambda \mathbf{I})\mathbf{w} = \mathbf{u} \qquad \textbf{(7–89)}$$

Particular Solutions The method of undetermined coefficients for the determination of a particular solution is essentially identical for both single nonhomogeneous equations and systems of such equations. But in systems, the coefficients are taken to be constant vectors instead of constant scalars. Also, in single equations, when a nonhomogeneous term is a solution of the related homogeneous equation, the basic form of the particular solution is multiplied by the kth power of t where t is the independent variable and k is the smallest integer that removes any duplication between the homogeneous solution and the particular solution. But in systems, we multiply the basic form of the particular solution by a kth degree polynomial in t instead of just the kth power of t. The method of undetermined coefficients is practical only when all the equations in the system have constant coefficients, and the nonhomogeneous terms may involve only polynomials, exponential functions, and sine or cosine functions as factors.

When the homogeneous solution $\mathbf{x}_h$ and thus the fundamental matrix $\mathbf{F}$ are available, the particular solution of a nonhomogeneous system can be obtained directly with the method of variation of parameters to be

$$\mathbf{x}_p = \mathbf{F}(t) \int \mathbf{F}^{-1}(t)\mathbf{r}(t)\,dt + \mathbf{F}(t)\mathbf{k} \qquad \textbf{(7–99)}$$

where the arbitrary constant vector $\mathbf{k}$ can be taken to be zero or any other convenient constant vector. When a set of initial conditions are specified, the solution of the nonhomogeneous system that satisfies these initial conditions can be determined directly from

$$\mathbf{x}(t) = \mathbf{F}(t)\left[\mathbf{F}^{-1}(t)\mathbf{x}_0 + \int_{t_0}^{t} \mathbf{F}^{-1}(t)\mathbf{r}(t)\,dt\right] \qquad \textbf{(7–106)}$$

where $\mathbf{x}(t_0) = \mathbf{x}_0$ is the specified set of initial conditions at $t = t_0$. Thus, the method of variation of parameters enables us to determine the solution of nonhomogeneous systems with a set of initial conditions directly in a systematic manner.

Modes and Modal Variables The eigenvectors can be used to define a new set of variables, called the modal variables or modes, in which the coefficient matrix is diagonal if the eigenvalues are distinct and almost diagonal if the some of the eigenvalues are repeated. This results in the so-called Jordan canonical form for the coefficient matrix. This representation gives us a better understanding of the overall response of the system. This approach also gives us another way to obtain the transition matrix, which can be used to obtain the free and forced responses of the system in a systematic manner.

Role of Computer Methods The advantage of matrix methods is that they can handle systems with a large number of equations, and this requires a numerical solution for the eigenvalues and eigenvectors. The commonly available computer packages can find eigenvalues, eigenvectors, and the transition matrix (the matrix exponential) in both symbolic and numeric form. However, for large matrices a symbolic solution may not be obtainable, and even if it is, it could be too cumbersome to be useful. Since there is no formula available for the roots of a polynomial higher than 4th degree, you can expect this to be the limit for symbolic results.

PROBLEMS

SECTION 7–1   Review of Matrices

7–36C Do two matrices have to be of the same size to be added? Do they have to be of the same size to be multiplied?

7–37C How is the inverse of a matrix defined? When is a matrix singular? When is it nonsingular?

7–38C How is the derivative of a matrix function defined? How is the integral of a matrix function defined?

7–39 If

$$\mathbf{A} = \begin{pmatrix} 2 & 0 \\ -7 & 5 \end{pmatrix} \quad \text{and} \quad \mathbf{B} = \begin{pmatrix} 1 & -3 \\ 8 & 3 \end{pmatrix}$$

determine (a) $\mathbf{A} + \mathbf{B}$, (b) $2\mathbf{A}$, (c) $3\mathbf{A} - \mathbf{B}$, and (d) $-3\mathbf{AB}$.

7–40 If

$$\mathbf{A} = \begin{pmatrix} 1 & -4 \\ -2 & 2 \end{pmatrix} \quad \text{and} \quad \mathbf{B} = \begin{pmatrix} 0 & -6 \\ 5 & 3 \end{pmatrix}$$

determine (a) $\mathbf{A} - \mathbf{B}$, (b) $-4\mathbf{A}$, (c) $\mathbf{A} - 2\mathbf{B}$, and (d) $2\mathbf{BA}$.

7–41 If

$$\mathbf{A} = \begin{pmatrix} 7 & -3 \\ 6 & 12 \end{pmatrix} \quad \text{and} \quad \mathbf{B} = \begin{pmatrix} 11 & -9 \\ 4 & 1 \end{pmatrix}$$

determine (a) $5\mathbf{A}$, (b) $2\mathbf{A} + 3\mathbf{B}$, (c) $2\mathbf{AB}$, and (d) $\det \mathbf{A}$.

7–42 If

$$\mathbf{A} = \begin{pmatrix} 3 & -1 & 0 \\ -2 & 4 & 3 \\ -1 & 1 & 0 \end{pmatrix} \quad \text{and} \quad \mathbf{B} = \begin{pmatrix} -3 & 1 & -6 \\ 0 & 3 & -2 \\ -1 & 4 & 8 \end{pmatrix}$$

determine (a) $-4\mathbf{A}$, (b) $2\mathbf{A} + 3\mathbf{B}$, (c) $2\mathbf{AB}$, and (d) $\det \mathbf{A}$.

7–43 If

$$\mathbf{A} = \begin{pmatrix} 4 & -2 & 3 \\ -1 & 0 & 3 \\ -3 & 0 & 2 \end{pmatrix} \quad \text{and} \quad \mathbf{B} = \begin{pmatrix} -3 & 4 & -5 \\ 1 & 3 & 0 \\ -3 & 9 & 1 \end{pmatrix}$$

determine (a) $\mathbf{A} - 4\mathbf{B}$, (b) $\mathbf{AB}$, (c) $\mathbf{BA}$, and (d) $\det \mathbf{A}$.

7–44 If

$$\mathbf{A} = \begin{pmatrix} 4 & -2 \\ -1 & 3 \\ -3 & 0 \end{pmatrix} \quad \text{and} \quad \mathbf{B} = \begin{pmatrix} 1 & 3 & 0 \\ -3 & 9 & 1 \end{pmatrix}$$

determine (a) $4\mathbf{A}$, (b) $\mathbf{AB}$, and (c) $\mathbf{A}^T + 2\mathbf{B}$.

7–45 If

$$\mathbf{A} = \begin{pmatrix} 7 & -3 \\ 6 & 12 \end{pmatrix} \quad \text{and} \quad \mathbf{B} = \begin{pmatrix} 11 & -9 \\ 4 & 1 \end{pmatrix}$$

verify that (a) $\mathbf{A} + \mathbf{B} = \mathbf{B} + \mathbf{A}$, (b) $2(\mathbf{A} + \mathbf{B}) = 2\mathbf{A} + 2\mathbf{B}$, and (c) $\mathbf{AB} \neq \mathbf{BA}$

7–46 If

$$\mathbf{A} = \begin{pmatrix} 1 & 0 \\ -2 & 5 \end{pmatrix}, \mathbf{B} = \begin{pmatrix} 0 & -6 \\ 5 & 1 \end{pmatrix}, \quad \text{and} \quad \mathbf{C} = \begin{pmatrix} 3 & -3 \\ 8 & 3 \end{pmatrix}$$

verify that (a) $(\mathbf{A} + \mathbf{B}) + \mathbf{C} = \mathbf{A} + (\mathbf{B} + \mathbf{C})$, (b) $\mathbf{A}(\mathbf{BC}) = (\mathbf{AB})\mathbf{C}$, and (c) $\mathbf{A}(\mathbf{B} + \mathbf{C}) = \mathbf{AB} + \mathbf{AC}$.

7–47 If

$$\mathbf{A} = \begin{pmatrix} 2 & 5 \\ -1 & 3 \end{pmatrix}, \mathbf{B} = \begin{pmatrix} -2 & 7 \\ 5 & 2 \end{pmatrix}, \quad \text{and} \quad \mathbf{C} = \begin{pmatrix} 0 & -4 \\ 7 & 3 \end{pmatrix}$$

verify that (a) $(\mathbf{A} + \mathbf{B}) + \mathbf{C} = \mathbf{A} + (\mathbf{B} + \mathbf{C})$, (b) $\mathbf{A}(\mathbf{BC}) = (\mathbf{AB})\mathbf{C}$, and (c) $\mathbf{A}(\mathbf{B} + \mathbf{C}) = \mathbf{AB} + \mathbf{AC}$.

7–48 If

$$\mathbf{A}(t) = \begin{pmatrix} 2t^2 - 1 & 2\cos 2t \\ e^{-t} & 0 \end{pmatrix}$$

determine (a) $\int_0^t \mathbf{A}(t)\,dt$ and (b) $d\mathbf{A}(t)/dt$.

7–49 If

$$\mathbf{A} = \begin{pmatrix} \dfrac{1}{1 - t} & 3\sin 3t \\ e^{-2t} & t + 1 \end{pmatrix}$$

determine (a) $\int_0^t \mathbf{A}(t)\,dt$ and (b) $d\mathbf{A}(t)/dt$.

7–50 If

$$\mathbf{A}(t) = \begin{pmatrix} t^2 + 2 & e^t \\ e^{-t} & \cos 2t \end{pmatrix} \quad \text{and} \quad \mathbf{B} = \begin{pmatrix} 1 & -2 \\ 0 & 3 \end{pmatrix}$$

determine (a) $\mathbf{B}\int_0^1 \mathbf{A}(t)\,dt$, (b) $\int_0^1 \mathbf{BA}(t)\,dt$, (c) $\mathbf{B}d\mathbf{A}(t)/dt$,

and (d) $d[\mathbf{BA}(t)]/dt$

7–51 If

$$\mathbf{A}(t) = \begin{pmatrix} \sqrt{t} & e^{-t} \\ e^t & \sin 2t \end{pmatrix} \quad \text{and} \quad \mathbf{B} = \begin{pmatrix} 4 & -1 \\ 2 & 7 \end{pmatrix}$$

determine (a) $\mathbf{B}\int_0^1 \mathbf{A}(t)\,dt$, (b) $\int_0^1 \mathbf{BA}(t)\,dt$, (c) $\mathbf{B}d\mathbf{A}(t)/dt$,

and (d) $d[\mathbf{BA}(t)]/dt$

7–52 If

$$\mathbf{A}(t) = \begin{pmatrix} t + 1 & e^{-t} \\ e^t & 2 \end{pmatrix} \quad \text{and} \quad \mathbf{B} = \begin{pmatrix} 0 & e^t \\ t & 1 \end{pmatrix}$$

determine (a)$\mathbf{B}\int_0^1 \mathbf{A}(t)\,dt$, (b) $\int_0^1 \mathbf{B}(t)\mathbf{A}(t)\,dt$, (c) $\mathbf{B}(t)d\mathbf{A}/dt$,

and (d) $d[\mathbf{B}(t)\mathbf{A}(t)]/dt$

SECTION 7–2 Models in Matrix Form

7–53 Consider the system shown in part (a) of Figure P7–53. The free body diagrams are shown in part (b) of the figure. Derive the equations of motion, select a suitable set of state variables $\mathbf{x}$, and find the matrices $\mathbf{A}$ and $\mathbf{B}$ required to put the equations of motion into the form $\mathbf{x}' = \mathbf{Ax} + \mathbf{B}f(t)$.

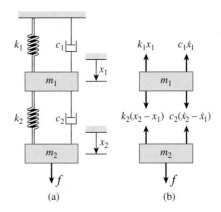

FIGURE P7–53

7–54 Figure P7–54 shows two pendula coupled by a spring. The equations of motion for small angles are

$$m_1 L_1^2 \theta_1'' = -m_1 g_1 L_2 \theta_1 - k L_1(L_1\theta_1 - L_1\theta_2)$$

$$m_2 L_2^2 \theta_2'' = -m_2 g L_2 \theta_2 + k L_1(L_1\theta_1 - L_1\theta_2)$$

Select a suitable set of state variables $\mathbf{x}$, and find the matrices $\mathbf{A}$ and $\mathbf{B}$ required to put the equations of motion into the form $\mathbf{x}' = \mathbf{Ax}$.

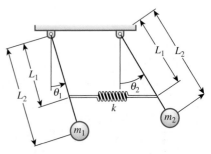

FIGURE P7–54

SECTION 7–3   Eigenvalues and Eigenvectors

7–55C   What operations on the augmented matrix are known as row operations? What do they correspond to in a system of linear algebraic equations? What is the purpose of the row operations on the augmented matrix? Can we have column operations in analogy to row operations?

7–56   How is the inverse of a matrix determined by row reduction?

7–57C   What can you say about the solution of a linear system of (a) homogeneous and (b) nonhomogeneous algebraic equations if the coefficient matrix of the system is nonsingular?

7–58C   Can a system of linear homogeneous algebraic equations have a nontrivial unique solution?

7–59C   Consider two vectors of equal size. How would you determine if these two vectors are linearly dependent or independent? Answer the same question for vector functions in a specified interval.

7–60C   Consider a constant square matrix $\mathbf{A}$ of order n, and a simple eigenvalue λ. How is the eigenvector $\mathbf{v}$ of this matrix corresponding to λ determined? How many eigenvectors corresponding to λ can this matrix have? How many of these eigenvectors can be linearly independent?

7–61C   What is the number of linearly independent eigenvectors of a matrix $\mathbf{A}$ associated with an eigenvalue λ of multiplicity k? Answer the same question for the special case of $\mathbf{A}$ being a real symmetric matrix?

7–62C   Consider two eigenvalues λ_1 and λ_2 that are complex conjugates of each other. If the eigenvector corresponding to λ_1 is $\mathbf{v}_1$, what do you think the eigenvector corresponding to λ_2 will be?

7–63C   Show that n vectors each with m components are linearly dependent if $m < n$.

For the following problems first determine if the inverse of the following matrices exists, and obtain it if it does exist.

7–64   (a) $\mathbf{A} = \begin{pmatrix} 1 & -4 \\ -2 & 2 \end{pmatrix}$

(b) $\mathbf{A} = \begin{pmatrix} -3 & 4 & -5 \\ 1 & 3 & 0 \\ -3 & 9 & 1 \end{pmatrix}$

7–65   (a) $\mathbf{A} = \begin{pmatrix} 7 & -3 \\ 6 & 12 \end{pmatrix}$

(b) $\mathbf{A} = \begin{pmatrix} 3 & -1 & 0 \\ -2 & 4 & 3 \\ -1 & 1 & 0 \end{pmatrix}$

7–66   (a) $\mathbf{A} = \begin{pmatrix} 4 & -2 & 3 \\ -1 & 0 & 3 \\ -3 & 0 & 2 \end{pmatrix}$

(b) $\mathbf{A} = \begin{pmatrix} -3 & 1 & -6 \\ 0 & 3 & -2 \\ -1 & 4 & 8 \end{pmatrix}$

7–67   (a) $\mathbf{A} = \begin{pmatrix} 1 & 0 \\ -2 & 5 \end{pmatrix}$

(b) $\mathbf{A} = \begin{pmatrix} 0 & 1 & 5 & -6 \\ -5 & 3 & -7 & 0 \\ -8 & 0 & 5 & 4 \\ 1 & 2 & 4 & 8 \end{pmatrix}$

7–68   (a) $\mathbf{A} = \begin{pmatrix} 4 & -3 \\ 6 & 12 \end{pmatrix}$

(b) $\mathbf{A} = \begin{pmatrix} -1 & 1 & 4 \\ 0 & -2 & 5 \\ 2 & 5 & 0 \end{pmatrix}$

7–69   (a) $\mathbf{A} = \begin{pmatrix} 11 & -9 \\ 4 & 1 \end{pmatrix}$

(b) $\mathbf{A} = \begin{pmatrix} 2 & 0 & -6 \\ 1 & 1 & -3 \\ 5 & 0 & 2 \end{pmatrix}$

7–70   (a) $\mathbf{A} = \begin{pmatrix} 0 & -6 \\ 5 & 1 \end{pmatrix}$

(b) $\mathbf{A} = \begin{pmatrix} 4 & 1 & 0 \\ 1 & -2 & 3 \\ 0 & 3 & 1 \end{pmatrix}$

7–71   (a) $\mathbf{A} = \begin{pmatrix} 3 & -3 \\ 8 & 3 \end{pmatrix}$

(b) $\mathbf{A} = \begin{pmatrix} 0 & 1 & -4 \\ 1 & 0 & 2 \\ -4 & 2 & 0 \end{pmatrix}$

7–72   (a) $\mathbf{A} = \begin{pmatrix} 2 & 5 \\ -1 & 3 \end{pmatrix}$

(b) $\mathbf{A} = \begin{pmatrix} 1 & 1 & 1 \\ 0 & 2 & -2 \\ -1 & 5 & 1 \end{pmatrix}$

7-73　(a) $\mathbf{A} = \begin{pmatrix} -2 & 7 \\ 5 & 2 \end{pmatrix}$

(b) $\mathbf{A} = \begin{pmatrix} 1 & 1 & 1 \\ 2 & 2 & 2 \\ 1 & 2 & 0 \end{pmatrix}$

7-74　(a) $\mathbf{A} = \begin{pmatrix} 0 & -4 \\ 7 & 3 \end{pmatrix}$

(b) $\mathbf{A} = \begin{pmatrix} -1 & 1 & 5 & -2 \\ 3 & 3 & -5 & 0 \\ -5 & 0 & 5 & 1 \\ -2 & 0 & 3 & 1 \end{pmatrix}$

For the following problems, first determine if the following systems of algebraic equations have solutions, and find all the solutions when they do.

7-75　(a) $x_1 + 2x_2 + x_3 = 5$
$-2x_1 + 4x_2 - x_3 = 0$
$2x_1 + x_2 - x_3 = 1$

(b) $x_1 + 2x_2 + x_3 = 0$
$-2x_1 + 4x_2 - x_3 = 0$
$2x_1 + x_2 - x_3 = 0$

(c) $x_1 + 2x_2 + x_3 = 5$
$-2x_1 + 4x_2 - x_3 = 0$
$-x_1 + 6x_2 = 5$

(d) $x_1 + 2x_2 + x_3 = 5$
$-2x_1 + 4x_2 - x_3 = -2$
$2x_1 + x_2 - x_3 = 1$

7-76　(a) $3x_1 - x_2 - x_3 = 6$
$2x_1 - 6x_2 + 2x_3 = -4$
$-x_1 + x_2 - 4x_3 = 11$

(b) $3x_1 - x_2 - x_3 = 0$
$2x_1 - 6x_2 + 2x_3 = 0$
$-x_1 + x_2 - 4x_3 = 0$

(c) $3x_1 - x_2 - x_3 = 2$
$2x_1 - 6x_2 + 2x_3 = -4$
$-x_1 + x_2 - 4x_3 = 1$

(d) $3x_1 - x_2 - x_3 = 6$
$2x_1 - 6x_2 + 2x_3 = -4$

7-77　(a) $x_1 + x_2 + x_3 = 2$
$-3x_1 + 2x_2 + 4x_3 = -4$
$-x_1 + 4x_2 + 6x_3 = 0$

(b) $x_1 + x_2 + x_3 = 0$
$-3x_1 + 2x_2 + 4x_3 = 0$
$-x_1 + 4x_2 + 6x_3 = 0$

(c) $x_1 + x_2 + x_3 = 2$
$-3x_1 + 2x_2 + 4x_3 = -4$
$-x_1 + 4x_2 + 6x_3 = 8$

(d) $x_1 + x_2 + x_3 = 2$
$-3x_1 + 2x_2 + 4x_3 = -4$
$x_1 + 4x_2 + 6x_3 = 4$

7-78　(a) $4x_1 - 3x_2 + x_3 = -4$
$-x_1 + 4x_2 + 2x_3 = 12$
$2x_1 + 5x_2 + 5x_3 = 10$

(b) $4x_1 - 3x_2 + x_3 = 0$
$-x_1 + 4x_2 + 2x_3 = 0$
$2x_1 + 5x_2 + 5x_3 = 0$

(c) $4x_1 - 3x_2 + x_3 = -4$
$-x_1 + 4x_2 + 2x_3 = 12$
$2x_1 - 5x_3 = 10$

(d) $4x_1 - 3x_2 + x_3 = -4$
$-x_1 + 4x_2 + 2x_3 = 12$
$x_1 + x_3 = 5$

7-79　(a) $x_1 + 2x_2 - x_3 = 7$
$3x_1 - x_2 + 2x_3 = -10$
$2x_1 - 3x_2 + 3x_3 = -17$

(b) $x_1 + 2x_2 - x_3 = 0$
$3x_1 - x_2 + 2x_3 = 0$
$2x_1 - 3x_2 + 3x_3 = 0$

(c) $x_1 + 2x_2 - x_3 = 7$
$3x_1 - x_2 + 2x_3 = -14$
$2x_1 + x_2 + 2x_3 = -17$

(d) $x_1 + 2x_2 - x_3 = 7$
$3x_1 - x_2 + 2x_3 = -14$
$2x_1 + x_2 + 2x_3 = 2$

7-80　(a) $4x_1 - x_2 - 2x_3 = -7$
$-x_1 - x_2 + x_3 = 0$
$3x_2 - 2x_3 = 5$

(b) $4x_1 - x_2 - 2x_3 = 0$
$-x_1 - x_2 + x_3 = 0$
$3x_2 - 2x_3 = 0$

(c) $x_1 + 2x_2 - x_3 = 7$
$3x_1 + 6x_2 - 3x_3 = 21$
$-2x_1 - 4x_2 + 2x_3 = -14$

(b) $4x_1 - x_2 - 2x_3 = -7$
$-x_1 - x_2 + x_3 = 2$
$3x_2 - 2x_3 = 5$

Determine if each of the sets of vectors in the following problems are linearly dependent or independent.

7-81　$\mathbf{v}_1 = \begin{pmatrix} 2 \\ -3 \\ 1 \end{pmatrix}$, $\mathbf{v}_2 = \begin{pmatrix} 3 \\ 2 \\ 1 \end{pmatrix}$, and $\mathbf{v}_3 = \begin{pmatrix} 7 \\ 0 \\ -6 \end{pmatrix}$

7-82　$\mathbf{v}_1 = \begin{pmatrix} 2 \\ -1 \end{pmatrix}$, $\mathbf{v}_2 = \begin{pmatrix} -4 \\ 3 \end{pmatrix}$, and $\mathbf{v}_3 = \begin{pmatrix} 5 \\ 0 \end{pmatrix}$

7-83　$\mathbf{v}_1 = \begin{pmatrix} 0 \\ 1 \\ 0 \end{pmatrix}$, $\mathbf{v}_2 = \begin{pmatrix} 2 \\ 0 \\ 2 \end{pmatrix}$, and $\mathbf{v}_3 = \begin{pmatrix} 4 \\ 0 \\ 0 \end{pmatrix}$

7-84　$\mathbf{v}_1 = \begin{pmatrix} 6 \\ 0 \\ 2 \end{pmatrix}$, $\mathbf{v}_2 = \begin{pmatrix} 1 \\ 0 \\ -3 \end{pmatrix}$, and $\mathbf{v}_3 = \begin{pmatrix} 0 \\ -2 \\ -2 \end{pmatrix}$

7-85　$\mathbf{v}_1 = \begin{pmatrix} -4 \\ 5 \\ 1 \end{pmatrix}$, $\mathbf{v}_2 = \begin{pmatrix} 3 \\ -4 \\ 2 \end{pmatrix}$, and $\mathbf{v}_3 = \begin{pmatrix} -5 \\ 1 \\ 0 \end{pmatrix}$

Determine if each of the sets of vectors in the following problems are linearly dependent or independent for $-\infty < t < \infty$.

7-86　$\mathbf{v}_1(t) = \begin{pmatrix} e^t \\ -2e^t \\ 0 \end{pmatrix}$, $\mathbf{v}_2(t) = \begin{pmatrix} 2e^t \\ 0 \\ -4e^t \end{pmatrix}$, and $\mathbf{v}_3(t) = \begin{pmatrix} -e^t \\ 4e^t \\ e^t \end{pmatrix}$

7-87　$\mathbf{v}_1(t) = \begin{pmatrix} -3e^{-t} \\ 2e^{-t} \\ e^{-t} \end{pmatrix}$, $\mathbf{v}_2(t) = \begin{pmatrix} 0 \\ t \\ 1 \end{pmatrix}$, and $\mathbf{v}_3(t) = \begin{pmatrix} 4e^{-t} \\ e^{-t} \\ 5e^{-t} \end{pmatrix}$

7-88　$\mathbf{v}_1(t) = \begin{pmatrix} t^3 \\ 4t^3 \\ -2t^3 \end{pmatrix}$, $\mathbf{v}_2(t) = \begin{pmatrix} t^2 \\ 4t^2 \\ -2t^2 \end{pmatrix}$, and $\mathbf{v}_3(t) = \begin{pmatrix} t \\ 4t \\ -2t \end{pmatrix}$

7-89　$\mathbf{v}_1(t) = \begin{pmatrix} 0 \\ t \\ e^t \end{pmatrix}$, $\mathbf{v}_2(t) = \begin{pmatrix} e^t \\ 3t \\ -2e^t \end{pmatrix}$, and $\mathbf{v}_3(t) = \begin{pmatrix} e^t \\ 2t \\ -e^t \end{pmatrix}$

Determine all of the eigenvalues and eigenvectors of the following matrices.

7–90 (a) $\mathbf{A} = \begin{pmatrix} 7 & -4 \\ -2 & 5 \end{pmatrix}$

(b) $\mathbf{A} = \begin{pmatrix} -3 & 4 & 0 \\ 1 & 3 & 1 \\ -3 & 9 & 0 \end{pmatrix}$

7–91 (a) $\mathbf{A} = \begin{pmatrix} 7 & -3 \\ 6 & 1 \end{pmatrix}$

(b) $\mathbf{A} = \begin{pmatrix} 3 & -1 & 0 \\ -2 & 4 & 3 \\ 2 & 1 & 0 \end{pmatrix}$

7–92 (a) $\mathbf{A} = \begin{pmatrix} 4 & -2 & 3 \\ -1 & 0 & 3 \\ -3 & 0 & 2 \end{pmatrix}$

(b) $\mathbf{A} = \begin{pmatrix} -3 & 1 & -6 \\ 0 & 3 & -2 \\ 6 & 4 & 8 \end{pmatrix}$

7–93 (a) $\mathbf{A} = \begin{pmatrix} 1 & 0 \\ -2 & 5 \end{pmatrix}$

(b) $\mathbf{A} = \begin{pmatrix} 2 & 2 & 2 & 2 \\ 2 & 2 & 2 & 2 \\ 2 & 2 & 2 & 2 \\ 2 & 2 & 2 & 2 \end{pmatrix}$

7–94 (a) $\mathbf{A} = \begin{pmatrix} 1 & -3 \\ 6 & -7 \end{pmatrix}$

(b) $\mathbf{A} = \begin{pmatrix} -1 & -1 & 4 \\ 0 & -2 & 5 \\ 2 & 4 & 0 \end{pmatrix}$

7–95 (a) $\mathbf{A} = \begin{pmatrix} 1 & -9 \\ 4 & 1 \end{pmatrix}$

(b) $\mathbf{A} = \begin{pmatrix} 2 & 0 & -6 \\ 1 & 1 & -3 \\ -6 & 0 & 2 \end{pmatrix}$

7–96 (a) $\mathbf{A} = \begin{pmatrix} 0 & -6 \\ 5 & 1 \end{pmatrix}$

(b) $\mathbf{A} = \begin{pmatrix} 1 & 1 & 0 \\ 1 & -2 & 3 \\ 0 & 3 & 1 \end{pmatrix}$

7–97 (a) $\mathbf{A} = \begin{pmatrix} 3 & -3 \\ 8 & 3 \end{pmatrix}$

(b) $\mathbf{A} = \begin{pmatrix} 0 & 1 & 4 \\ 1 & 0 & 2 \\ -4 & 2 & 0 \end{pmatrix}$

7–98 (a) $\mathbf{A} = \begin{pmatrix} 2 & 5 \\ 4 & 3 \end{pmatrix}$

(b) $\mathbf{A} = \begin{pmatrix} 1 & 1 & 1 \\ 0 & 2 & -2 \\ -1 & -3 & 1 \end{pmatrix}$

7–99 (a) $\mathbf{A} = \begin{pmatrix} -2 & 7 \\ 3 & 2 \end{pmatrix}$

(b) $\mathbf{A} = \begin{pmatrix} 1 & 1 & -1 \\ -2 & 2 & -3 \\ 1 & 2 & 0 \end{pmatrix}$

7–100 (a) $\mathbf{A} = \begin{pmatrix} 0 & -4 \\ 7 & 3 \end{pmatrix}$

(b) $\mathbf{A} = \begin{pmatrix} -1 & 0 & 0 & -2 \\ 3 & 1 & -5 & 0 \\ -1 & 0 & 1 & 1 \\ -2 & 0 & -1 & -1 \end{pmatrix}$

Section 7–4 The Theory of Systems of Linear Differential Equations

7–101C Given a system of n first-order linear homogeneous equations in n unknown functions with n specified initial conditions, under what conditions is this system guaranteed to have a unique solution on an interval $t_1 < t < t_2$?

7–102C How would you determine the general solution of a system of n first-order linear homogeneous equations on an interval in which the coefficient matrix is continuous? What would your answer be if some of the equations in the system were nonhomogeneous?

7–103C Given n solution vectors of order n of a system of n first-order linear homogeneous equations, how would you determine if these n solutions are linearly dependent or independent?

7–104C Prove Theorem 7–4 (Abel's theorem) for a system of two linear homogeneous equations with constant coefficients equations in two unknowns. *Hint:* Let the system be $\mathbf{x}' = \mathbf{Ax}$ where

$$\mathbf{A} = \begin{pmatrix} a_{11} & a_{12} \\ a_{21} & a_{22} \end{pmatrix}$$

and let $\mathbf{x}_1 = [x_{11} \quad x_{21}]^T$ and $\mathbf{x}_2 = [x_{12} \quad x_{22}]^T$ be two solutions of this system. Show that

$$W' = (x_{11}x_{22} - x_{21}x_{12})' = \begin{vmatrix} \dfrac{dx_{11}}{dt} & \dfrac{dx_{12}}{dt} \\ x_{21} & x_{22} \end{vmatrix} + \begin{vmatrix} x_{11} & x_{12} \\ \dfrac{dx_{21}}{dt} & \dfrac{dx_{22}}{dt} \end{vmatrix}$$

Then substitute $\mathbf{x}_1$ and $\mathbf{x}_2$ into $\mathbf{x}' = \mathbf{Ax}$ to show that $W' = (a_{11} + a_{22})W$, and thus $W = Ke^{(a_{11}+a_{22})t}$.

For the following problems, verify that the given vectors are the solution of the given system, and determine if the solution vectors are linearly independent. If they are, obtain the general solution of the given system on $-\infty < t < \infty$.

7–105 $\mathbf{x}' = \begin{pmatrix} 1 & 0 \\ -3 & 2 \end{pmatrix}\mathbf{x}; \mathbf{x}_1 = \begin{pmatrix} e^t \\ -3e^t \end{pmatrix}, \mathbf{x}_2 = \begin{pmatrix} 0 \\ 2e^{-t} \end{pmatrix}$

7–106 $\mathbf{x}' = \begin{pmatrix} 2 & 1 \\ 1 & 2 \end{pmatrix}\mathbf{x}; \mathbf{x}_1 = \begin{pmatrix} e^t \\ -e^t \end{pmatrix}, \mathbf{x}_2 = \begin{pmatrix} 2e^{3t} \\ 2e^{3t} \end{pmatrix}$

7–107 $\mathbf{x}' = \begin{pmatrix} 4 & 6 \\ -3 & -5 \end{pmatrix}\mathbf{x}; \mathbf{x}_1 = \begin{pmatrix} 4e^t \\ -2e^t \end{pmatrix}, \mathbf{x}_2 = \begin{pmatrix} 6e^t \\ -3e^t \end{pmatrix}$

7–108 $\mathbf{x}' = \begin{pmatrix} 2 & 4 \\ 1 & -1 \end{pmatrix}\mathbf{x}; \mathbf{x}_1 = \begin{pmatrix} 4e^{3t} \\ e^{3t} \end{pmatrix}, \mathbf{x}_2 = \begin{pmatrix} e^{-2t} \\ -e^{-2t} \end{pmatrix}$

7–109 $\mathbf{x}' = \begin{pmatrix} -1 & 2 \\ 2 & -4 \end{pmatrix}\mathbf{x}; \mathbf{x}_1 = \begin{pmatrix} 2 \\ 1 \end{pmatrix}, \mathbf{x}_2 = \begin{pmatrix} e^{-5t} \\ -2e^{-5t} \end{pmatrix}$

7–110 $\mathbf{x}' = \begin{pmatrix} 3 & -1 \\ 1 & 1 \end{pmatrix}\mathbf{x}; \mathbf{x}_1 = \begin{pmatrix} e^{2t} \\ e^{2t} \end{pmatrix}, \mathbf{x}_2 = \begin{pmatrix} 2e^{2t} \\ 2e^{2t} \end{pmatrix}$

7–111 $\mathbf{x}' = \begin{pmatrix} -1 & -1 & 0 \\ 1 & 0 & -1 \\ 3 & 1 & 1 \end{pmatrix}\mathbf{x}; \mathbf{x}_1 = \begin{pmatrix} e^t \\ -2e^t \\ 3e^t \end{pmatrix}$,

$\mathbf{x}_2 = \begin{pmatrix} -2e^t \\ 4e^t \\ -6e^t \end{pmatrix}$, and $\mathbf{x}_3 = \begin{pmatrix} -e^t \\ 2e^t \\ -3e^t \end{pmatrix}$

7–112 $\mathbf{x}' = \begin{pmatrix} 0 & 3 & 3 \\ 3 & 0 & 3 \\ 3 & 3 & 0 \end{pmatrix}\mathbf{x}; \mathbf{x}_1 = \begin{pmatrix} e^{6t} \\ e^{6t} \\ e^{6t} \end{pmatrix}, \mathbf{x}_2 = \begin{pmatrix} -2e^{-3t} \\ 0 \\ -e^{-3t} \end{pmatrix}$,

and $\mathbf{x}_3 = \begin{pmatrix} 0 \\ e^{-3t} \\ -e^{-3t} \end{pmatrix}$

7–113 $\mathbf{x}' = \begin{pmatrix} 0 & 3 & 3 \\ 3 & 0 & 3 \\ 3 & 3 & 0 \end{pmatrix}\mathbf{x}; \mathbf{x}_1 = \begin{pmatrix} 2e^{-3t} \\ 0 \\ -2e^{-3t} \end{pmatrix}, \mathbf{x}_2 = \begin{pmatrix} 0 \\ -3e^{-3t} \\ 3e^{-3t} \end{pmatrix}$,

and $\mathbf{x}_3 = \begin{pmatrix} e^{-3t} \\ e^{-3t} \\ -2e^{-3t} \end{pmatrix}$

7–114 $\mathbf{x}' = \begin{pmatrix} 1 & 0 & 2 \\ 1 & -1 & 0 \\ 1 & -2 & 0 \end{pmatrix}\mathbf{x}; \mathbf{x}_1 = \begin{pmatrix} 2e^t \\ e^t \\ 0 \end{pmatrix}, \mathbf{x}_2 = \begin{pmatrix} -6e^t \\ -3e^t \\ 0 \end{pmatrix}$,

and $\mathbf{x}_3 = \begin{pmatrix} -2e^{-2t} \\ 2e^{-2t} \\ -3e^{-2t} \end{pmatrix}$

Verify that the given particular solution vector is the solution of the given system.

7–115 $\mathbf{x}' = \begin{pmatrix} 2 & 1 \\ 1 & 2 \end{pmatrix}\mathbf{x} + \begin{pmatrix} 4e^{-t} \\ 3 \end{pmatrix}; \mathbf{x}_p = \dfrac{1}{2}\begin{pmatrix} -3e^{-t} + 2 \\ e^{-t} - 4 \end{pmatrix}$

7–116 $\mathbf{x}' = \begin{pmatrix} 2 & 4 \\ 1 & -1 \end{pmatrix}\mathbf{x} + \begin{pmatrix} 6t^2 - 1 \\ t \end{pmatrix}$;

$\mathbf{x}_p = \dfrac{1}{9}\begin{pmatrix} -9t^2 + 21t - 1 \\ -9t^2 - 6t - 7 \end{pmatrix}$

7–117 $\mathbf{x}' = \begin{pmatrix} -1 & 2 \\ 2 & -4 \end{pmatrix}\mathbf{x} + \begin{pmatrix} -3e^{2t} \\ 0 \end{pmatrix}; \mathbf{x}_p = -\dfrac{3}{7}\begin{pmatrix} 3e^{2t} \\ e^{2t} \end{pmatrix}$

7–118 $\mathbf{x}' = \begin{pmatrix} 3 & -1 \\ 1 & 1 \end{pmatrix}\mathbf{x} + \begin{pmatrix} 2t \\ -1 \end{pmatrix}; \mathbf{x}_p = \dfrac{1}{4}\begin{pmatrix} -2t + 1 \\ 2t + 5 \end{pmatrix}$

7–119 $\mathbf{x}' = \begin{pmatrix} 0 & 3 & 3 \\ 3 & 0 & 3 \\ 3 & 3 & 0 \end{pmatrix}\mathbf{x} + \begin{pmatrix} 1 \\ e^{-t} \\ 0 \end{pmatrix}; \mathbf{x}_p = \begin{pmatrix} -e^{-t} \\ -e^{-t} \\ e^{-t} \end{pmatrix}$

7–120 $\mathbf{x}' = \begin{pmatrix} 1 & 0 & 2 \\ 1 & -1 & 0 \\ 1 & -2 & 0 \end{pmatrix}\mathbf{x} + \begin{pmatrix} 1 \\ e^{-t} \\ 0 \end{pmatrix}; \mathbf{x}_p = \begin{pmatrix} -e^{-t} \\ -e^{-t} \\ e^{-t} - 1/2 \end{pmatrix}$

Section 7–5 Linear Homogeneous Systems with Constant Coefficients

7–121 How is the fundamental matrix of a linear homogeneous system $\mathbf{x}'(t) = \mathbf{Ax}(t)$ defined? Can the determinant of the fundamental matrix be negative? Can it be zero? How can the arbitrary constants in the general solution of the system be expressed in terms of the fundamental matrix and the initial conditions?

7–122 Consider a system of n linear, homogeneous equations with constant coefficients expressed as $\mathbf{x}'(t) = \mathbf{Ax}(t)$. How would you determine two linearly independent solution vectors corresponding to a double eigenvalue λ of $\mathbf{A}$ if there is only one linearly independent eigenvector associated with it?

7–123 Consider a system of n linear, homogeneous equations with constant coefficients expressed as $\mathbf{x}'(t) = \mathbf{Ax}(t)$. How would you determine three linearly independent solution vectors corresponding to a triple eigenvalue λ of $\mathbf{A}$ if there is only one linearly independent eigenvector associated with it?

Using the matrix method, determine the general solution of the following systems of first-order differential equations.

7–124 $\mathbf{x}' = \begin{pmatrix} 1 & -4 \\ -1 & 4 \end{pmatrix} \mathbf{x}$

7–125 $\mathbf{x}' = \begin{pmatrix} 1 & -1 \\ -4 & -2 \end{pmatrix} \mathbf{x}$

7–126 $\mathbf{x}' = \begin{pmatrix} 2 & 4 \\ -1 & 2 \end{pmatrix} \mathbf{x}$

7–127 $\mathbf{x}' = \begin{pmatrix} 7 & 1 \\ -1 & -3 \end{pmatrix} \mathbf{x}$

7–128 $\mathbf{x}' = \begin{pmatrix} 2 & 1 \\ 1 & -2 \end{pmatrix} \mathbf{x}$

7–129 $\mathbf{x}' = \begin{pmatrix} -1 & 2 \\ 4 & 1 \end{pmatrix} \mathbf{x}$

7–130 $\mathbf{x}' = \begin{pmatrix} 4 & -2 \\ -2 & -4 \end{pmatrix} \mathbf{x}$

7–131 $\mathbf{x}' = \begin{pmatrix} 4 & -1 \\ 1 & 2 \end{pmatrix} \mathbf{x}$

7–132 $\mathbf{x}' = \begin{pmatrix} 1 & -5 \\ 1 & 1 \end{pmatrix} \mathbf{x}$

7–133 $\mathbf{x}' = \begin{pmatrix} 3 & 6 \\ 2 & 7 \end{pmatrix} \mathbf{x}$

7–134 $\mathbf{x}' = \begin{pmatrix} 0 & 4 \\ 1 & 0 \end{pmatrix} \mathbf{x}$

7–135 $\mathbf{x}' = \begin{pmatrix} 1 & -4 & 0 \\ 0 & 2 & -1 \\ 1 & -1 & 0 \end{pmatrix} \mathbf{x}$

7–136 $\mathbf{x}' = \begin{pmatrix} -3 & 1 & -2 \\ 1 & 1 & 3 \\ 0 & 0 & 3 \end{pmatrix} \mathbf{x}$

Using the matrix method, determine the solution of the following systems of first-order differential equations with the specified initial conditions.

7–137 $\mathbf{x}' = \begin{pmatrix} 2 & -1 \\ -3 & 4 \end{pmatrix} \mathbf{x}, \qquad \mathbf{x}_0(0) = \begin{pmatrix} 1 \\ 1 \end{pmatrix}$

7–138 $\mathbf{x}' = \begin{pmatrix} 1 & -4 \\ 5 & -3 \end{pmatrix} \mathbf{x}, \qquad \mathbf{x}_0(0) = \begin{pmatrix} 2 \\ -3 \end{pmatrix}$

7–139 $\mathbf{x}' = \begin{pmatrix} 2 & 6 \\ 1 & -3 \end{pmatrix} \mathbf{x}, \qquad \mathbf{x}_0(1) = \begin{pmatrix} 0 \\ 2 \end{pmatrix}$

7–140 $\mathbf{x}' = \begin{pmatrix} 3 & 1 \\ -4 & -1 \end{pmatrix} \mathbf{x}, \qquad \mathbf{x}_0(0) = \begin{pmatrix} 0 \\ 1 \end{pmatrix}$

7–141 $\mathbf{x}' = \begin{pmatrix} 1 & 1 \\ -2 & -2 \end{pmatrix} \mathbf{x}, \qquad \mathbf{x}_0(0) = \begin{pmatrix} 0 \\ 0 \end{pmatrix}$

7–142 In Example 7–22, let $m_1 = m_2 = k_1 = k_2 = 1$. Find the eigenvalues and eigenvectors of the matrix A given in that example.

Section 7–6 Linear Nonhomogeneous Systems

7–143C In systems of equations, how is the proper form of the particular solution corresponding to a nonhomogeneous term determined with the method of undetermined coefficients if the nonhomogeneous term appears in the homogeneous solution?

7–144C Once the fundamental matrix is available, how is the particular solution of a linear, nonhomogeneous system determined by the method of variation of parameters?

7–145C Once the fundamental matrix is available, how is the solution of a linear, nonhomogeneous system (which satisfies a given set of initial conditions) determined by the method of variation of parameters?

Using (a) the method of undetermined coefficients and (b) the method of variation of parameters, determine the general solution of the following systems of first-order differential equations. (Use the matrix method to obtain the homogeneous solution.)

7–146 $\mathbf{x}' = \begin{pmatrix} 4 & -1 \\ -1 & 4 \end{pmatrix} \mathbf{x} + \begin{pmatrix} t^2 - 1 \\ 3t + 2 \end{pmatrix}$

7–147 $\mathbf{x}' = \begin{pmatrix} 1 & -1 \\ -4 & 2 \end{pmatrix} \mathbf{x} + \begin{pmatrix} -2 \sin 3t \\ \cos 3t \end{pmatrix}$

7–148 $\mathbf{x}' = \begin{pmatrix} 2 & 4 \\ -1 & 2 \end{pmatrix} \mathbf{x} + \begin{pmatrix} -7 \\ 0 \end{pmatrix}$

7–149 $\mathbf{x}' = \begin{pmatrix} 3 & 1 \\ -1 & -3 \end{pmatrix} \mathbf{x} + \begin{pmatrix} 2te^t \\ -e^t \end{pmatrix}$

7–150 $\mathbf{x}' = \begin{pmatrix} 2 & 1 \\ 1 & -2 \end{pmatrix} \mathbf{x} + \begin{pmatrix} -e^{-2t} \\ 0 \end{pmatrix}$

7–151 $\mathbf{x}' = \begin{pmatrix} -1 & 2 \\ 3 & 4 \end{pmatrix} \mathbf{x} + \begin{pmatrix} t + 2 \\ 3t - 1 \end{pmatrix}$

7–152 $\mathbf{x}' = \begin{pmatrix} 4 & -2 \\ 2 & -1 \end{pmatrix} \mathbf{x} + \begin{pmatrix} -37 \\ 5 \end{pmatrix}$

7–153 $\mathbf{x}' = \begin{pmatrix} 5 & -1 \\ 2 & 2 \end{pmatrix} \mathbf{x} + \begin{pmatrix} 0 \\ -2 \cos 3t \end{pmatrix}$

7–154 $\mathbf{x}' = \begin{pmatrix} 1 & -5 \\ 16/5 & 1 \end{pmatrix} \mathbf{x} + \begin{pmatrix} 3e^{-3t} \\ 2e^{2t} \end{pmatrix}$

7–155 $\mathbf{x}' = \begin{pmatrix} -4 & 6 \\ 2 & 7 \end{pmatrix}\mathbf{x} + \begin{pmatrix} 6 \\ -2 \end{pmatrix}$

7–156 $\mathbf{x}' = \begin{pmatrix} 0 & 4 \\ 1 & 0 \end{pmatrix}\mathbf{x} + \begin{pmatrix} 4t^3 - 14t - 5 \\ 0 \end{pmatrix}$

7–157 $\mathbf{x}' = \begin{pmatrix} 1 & -3 & 0 \\ 1 & 2 & -1 \\ 1 & -1 & 0 \end{pmatrix}\mathbf{x} + \begin{pmatrix} t + 3 \\ 3t - 5 \\ -2 \end{pmatrix}$

7–158 $\mathbf{x}' = \begin{pmatrix} 5 & 1 & -2 \\ 1 & -1 & -1 \\ 0 & 1 & 3 \end{pmatrix}\mathbf{x} + \begin{pmatrix} e^t \\ -5e^t \\ 0 \end{pmatrix}$

Using (a) the method of undetermined coefficients and (b) the method of variation of parameters, determine the solution of the following systems of first-order differential equations with the specified initial conditions. (Use the matrix method to obtain the homogeneous solution.)

7–159 $\mathbf{x}' = \begin{pmatrix} 2 & -1 \\ -3 & 4 \end{pmatrix}\mathbf{x} + \begin{pmatrix} -3 \\ 4e^t \end{pmatrix}; \mathbf{x}_0(0) = \begin{pmatrix} 1 \\ 1 \end{pmatrix}$

7–160 $\mathbf{x}' = \begin{pmatrix} 1 & -4 \\ 5 & -3 \end{pmatrix}\mathbf{x} + \begin{pmatrix} t^2 - 1 \\ -4 \end{pmatrix}; \mathbf{x}_0(0) = \begin{pmatrix} 2 \\ -3 \end{pmatrix}$

7–161 $\mathbf{x}' = \begin{pmatrix} 2 & 6 \\ 1 & -3 \end{pmatrix}\mathbf{x} + \begin{pmatrix} t + 1 \\ 2t - 3 \end{pmatrix}; \mathbf{x}_0(1) = \begin{pmatrix} 0 \\ 2 \end{pmatrix}$

7–162 $\mathbf{x}' = \begin{pmatrix} 3 & 1 \\ -4 & -1 \end{pmatrix}\mathbf{x} + \begin{pmatrix} 3e^{-2t} \\ 0 \end{pmatrix}; \mathbf{x}_0(0) = \begin{pmatrix} 0 \\ 1 \end{pmatrix}$

7–163 $\mathbf{x}' = \begin{pmatrix} 1 & 1 \\ -2 & -2 \end{pmatrix}\mathbf{x} + \begin{pmatrix} -2\sin t \\ 2\cos t \end{pmatrix}; \mathbf{x}_0(0) = \begin{pmatrix} 0 \\ 0 \end{pmatrix}$

Section 7–7 Canonical Forms and the Transition Matrix

7–164 Find the eigenvectors, the modal matrix, and the Jordan canonical form for the equation $\mathbf{x}' = \mathbf{A}\mathbf{x}$ whose matrix **A** is given in each of the following. If complex eigenvalues occur, obtain the modified canonical form instead. Also, determine whether or not the eigenvectors are linearly independent. Obtain the solutions by decoupling the equations,

(a) $\dfrac{1}{3}\begin{pmatrix} -9 & 9 \\ 1 & -9 \end{pmatrix}$

(b) $\begin{pmatrix} 1 & 1 \\ 0 & 1 \end{pmatrix}$

(c) $\begin{pmatrix} 3 & 0 \\ 0 & 3 \end{pmatrix}$

(d) $\begin{pmatrix} 0 & 1 \\ -10 & -2 \end{pmatrix}$

(e) $\begin{pmatrix} 2 & -2 & 3 \\ 1 & 1 & 1 \\ 1 & 3 & -1 \end{pmatrix}$

(f) $\begin{pmatrix} 0 & 6 & -5 \\ 1 & 0 & 2 \\ 3 & 2 & 4 \end{pmatrix}$

(g) $\dfrac{1}{5}\begin{pmatrix} -9 & 2 & -2 \\ 0 & -5 & 0 \\ -2 & 1 & -6 \end{pmatrix}$

(h) $\begin{pmatrix} 0 & 1 & 0 \\ -1 & -2 & 1 \\ -2 & 0 & 0 \end{pmatrix}$

(i) $\begin{pmatrix} 0 & 1 & 0 \\ 0 & 0 & 1 \\ -6 & -11 & -6 \end{pmatrix}$

7–165 The *Cayley-Hamilton theorem* states that every matrix **A** satisfies its own characteristic equation, $|\lambda\mathbf{I} - \mathbf{A}| = 0$. Suppose

$$\mathbf{A} = \begin{pmatrix} 3 & 2 \\ 2 & 3 \end{pmatrix}$$

Then $|\lambda\mathbf{I} - \mathbf{A}| = \lambda^2 - 6\lambda + 5 = 0$, and so $\mathbf{A}^2 - 6\mathbf{A} + 5\mathbf{I} = 0$.

(a) The theorem provides a way of expressing any power of **A** in terms of a linear combination of lower powers of **A**. Use this fact to find $\mathbf{A}^3$.

(b) Use the theorem to find $\mathbf{A}^{-1}$ in terms of **A**.

7–166 Viscous damping limits the amplitude of vibration near the resonant frequencies but often changes the resonant frequencies only slightly from their undamped values. Consider the system shown in part (a) of Figure P7–166. The free-body diagrams are shown in part (b) of the figure. The matrix form of the equations of motion was derived in the solution to Problem 7–53.

Let $k_1 = k_2 = k_3$ and $m_1 = m_2 = 1$.

(a) Let $c_1 = c_2 = 0$. Find the system's eigenvectors and eigenvalues.

(b) Let $c_1 = c_2 = 0.1$. Find the system's eigenvectors and eigenvalues, and compare with those found in part (a). How does the damping affect the resonant frequencies?

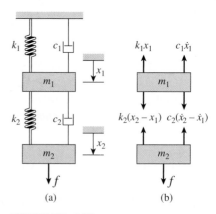

(a)   (b)

FIGURE P7–166

7–167 Determine the controllability of each mode of the system $\mathbf{x}' = \mathbf{A}\mathbf{x} + \mathbf{B}f(t)$ for the case where

$$\mathbf{A} = \frac{1}{3}\begin{pmatrix} -9 & 9 \\ 1 & -9 \end{pmatrix} \quad \mathbf{B} = \begin{pmatrix} -3 & 3 \\ 1 & -1 \end{pmatrix}$$

7–168 Differentiate the series expression for the transition matrix (Equation 7–132) and prove that it is the solution to the equation $\mathbf{x}' = \mathbf{Ax}$.

7–169 Refer to Example 7–28. Use the series expression for the transition matrix (Equation 7–132) to compute the matrix out to the t^2 term. Compare the result here with the exact solution obtained in that example.

Section 7–8 Computer Methods

7–170 Use a computer to obtain the eigenvalues and eigenvectors of the matrices given in Problem 7–164.

7–171 Use a computer to obtain the transition matrix for the matrices given in parts (a), (b), (c), and (d) of Problem 7–164.

7–172 Given the state-variable model:

$$x_1' = -5x_1 + 3x_2 + 2u_1$$
$$x_2' = -4x_2 + 6u_2$$

use a computer package to find the characteristic polynomial and the characteristic roots.

7–173 Use a computer package to create a state-variable model for the following equations. Obtain the expressions for the matrices $\mathbf{A}$, $\mathbf{B}$, $\mathbf{C}$, and $\mathbf{D}$ for the given inputs and outputs.

(a) The outputs are x_1 and x_2. The input is u.

$$x_1' = -5x_1 + 3x_2$$
$$x_2' = x_1 - 4x_2 + 5u$$

(b) The output is x_1. The inputs are u_1 and u_2.

$$x_1' = -5x_1 + 3x_2 + 4u_1$$
$$x_2' = x_1 - 4x_2 + 5u_2$$

7–174 Use a computer package to obtain a state model for the following equations. Obtain the expressions for the matrices $\mathbf{A}$, $\mathbf{B}$, $\mathbf{C}$, and $\mathbf{D}$. In both cases, the input is $f(t)$; the output is y.

(a) $2y''' + 5y'' + 4y' + 7y = f(t)$

(b) $3y'' + 6y' + 10y = 6f(t)$

7–175 For the following model, the output is x_1 and the input is $f(t)$.

$$x_1' = -5x_1 + 3x_2$$
$$x_2' = x_1 - 4x_2 + 5 f(t)$$

(a) Use a computer package to compute and plot the free response for $x_1(0) = 3$ and $x_2(0) = 5$.

(b) Use a computer package to compute and plot the unit-step response for zero initial conditions.

(c) Use a computer package to compute and plot the response for zero initial conditions with the input $f(t) = 3 \sin 10\pi t$, for $0 \le t \le 2$.

7–176 Given the state-variable model:

$$x_1' = -5x_1 + 3x_2 + 2u_1$$
$$x_2' = -4x_2 + 6u_2$$

use a computer package to find the characteristic polynomial and the characteristic roots.

7–177 The equations of motion for the two-mass, quarter-car model of the suspension system shown in Figure P7–177 are

$$m_1x_1'' = c_1(x_2' - x_1) + k_1(x_2 - x_1)$$
$$m_2x_2'' = -c_1(x_2' - x_1) - k_1(x_2 - x_1) + k_2(y - x_2)$$

Suppose the coefficient values are $m_1 = 240$ kg, $m_2 = 36$ kg, $k_1 = 1.6 \times 10^4$ N/m, $k_2 = 1.6 \times 10^5$ N/m, and $c_1 = 98$ N·s/m.

(a) Put the equations into state-variable matrix form. Use a computer package to create a state model. The input is $y(t)$; the outputs are x_1 and x_2.

(b) Use a computer package to find the characteristic polynomial and the characteristic roots.

(c) Use a computer package to compute and plot the response of x_1 and x_2 if the initial conditions are zero and if the input $y(t)$ represents a single bump described as follows. Suppose the vehicle encounters a half-meter high bump about one meter in length while moving at 18 m/s (about 40 mph). The bump profile is given by

$$y(z) = 5.437e^{-4z}$$

where z is the horizontal distance traveled by the vehicle while going over the bump. The displacement $y(t)$ felt by the suspension is related to $y(z)$ through the vehicle speed as follows: $z = vt$, where $v = 18$ m/s. Substitute z into the expression for $y(z)$ to obtain

$$y(t) = 97.858te^{-72t}$$

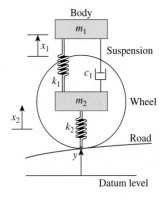

FIGURE P7–177

Two-mass model of a vehicle suspension system.

7–178 Even though a set of equations is linear and second order, they may be difficult to solve if the forcing function is a complicated function. The equations for an armature-controlled dc motor are the following. The motor's current is i and its rotational velocity is ω.

$$L\frac{di}{dt} = -Ri - K_b\omega + v(t)$$

$$I\frac{d\omega}{dt} = K_Ti - c\omega$$

where L, R, and I are the motor's inductance, resistance, and inertia; K_T and K_b are the torque constant and back emf constant; c is a viscous damping constant; and $v(t)$ is the applied voltage. Use the values $R = 0.8\ \Omega$, $L = 0.003$ H, $K_T = 0.05$ N·m/A, $K_b = 0.05$ V·s/rad, $c = 0$, and $I = 8 \times 10^{-5}$ kg·m^2.

(a) Suppose the applied voltage is 20 V. Plot the motor's speed and current versus time. Choose a final time large enough to show the motor's speed becoming constant.

(b) Suppose the applied voltage is trapezoidal and is described by

$$v(t) = \begin{cases} 400t & 0 \leq t < 0.05 \\ 20 & 0.05 \leq t \leq 2 \\ -400(t-0.2)+20 & 0.2 < t \leq 0.25 \\ 0 & t > 0.25 \end{cases}$$

Plot the motor's speed versus time for $0 \leq t \leq 0.3$ s. Also, plot the applied voltage versus time. How well does the motor speed follow a trapezoidal profile?

7–179 Figure P7–179 is a representation of a two-story building. The floor masses are m_1 and m_2. Each floor is supported by six columns. When the ground moves horizontally due to an earthquake, the floors also move horizontally, and the columns act like springs and resist this motion. The total horizontal stiffnesses of each set of six columns are k_1 and k_2. The horizontal ground motion is y. The equations of motion are

$$m_1\frac{d^2x_1}{dt^2} = -k_2(x_1 - x_2) + k_1(y - x_1)$$

$$m_2\frac{d^2x_2}{dt^2} = k_2(x_1 - x_2)$$

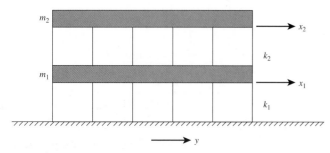

FIGURE P7–179

A two-story building. The floor masses are m_1 and m_2. The horizontal ground motion is y. The total horizontal stiffnesses of each set of six columns are k_1 and k_2.

Consider the case where the masses are identical ($m_1 = m_2 = m$) and the stiffnesses are identical ($k_1 = k_2 = k$). Suppose that $k/m = 4$, and the ground motion is described by $y(t) = \sin 3t$. Plot the response of x_1 and x_2 assuming zero initial conditions.

Review Problems

7–180 A small copper ball at 80°C is dropped into a small tank, which is filled with mercury at 20°C. The combined system is then placed into a very large tank, which is filled with ice water at 0°C, as shown in Figure P7–180. Heat is transferred from the copper ball to the mercury with a heat transfer coefficient of h_1 and from the mercury to the ice water with a heat transfer coefficient of h_2. As a result, the temperature of the ball $T_2(t)$ starts to drop. The temperature of the mercury $T_1(t)$ also changes during this process with time, but remains essentially uniform in space because of the high thermal conductivity of the mercury. Show that the variation of the temperatures of mercury and copper during this cooling process are governed by

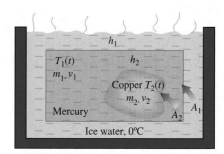

FIGURE P7–180

$$\frac{dT_1}{dt} = -\frac{A_1h_1}{\rho_1c_1V_1}T_1 - \frac{A_2h_2}{\rho_1c_1V_1}(T_1 - T_2)$$

$$\frac{dT_2}{dt} = \frac{A_2h_2}{\rho_2c_2V_2}(T_1 - T_2)$$

where ρ, c, V, and A denote density, specific heat, volume, and surface area, respectively. The subscripts 1 and 2 are used to represent the properties of the mercury and the copper ball, respectively. Also, determine the variation of the temperatures of mercury and copper ball with time, assuming $(A_1h_1)/(\rho_1c_1V_1) = 0.1$, $(A_2h_2)/(\rho_1c_1V_1) = 0.001$, and $(A_2h_2)/(\rho_2c_2V_2) = 1/900$. (*Hint:* See Example 1–3.)

7–181 Consider the two masses m_1 and m_2 and two linear springs with spring constants k_1 and k_2 connected in series, as shown in Figure 7–181. Initially, both masses are motionless, and they are at their equilibrium positions. Consequently, the springs are neither stretched nor compressed at $t = 0$. Now a periodic external force $f(t) = 5\sin 2t$ is applied to m_2, causing both masses to undergo a motion. If we let $x_1(t)$ and $x_2(t)$ denote the positions of the two masses relative to their

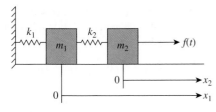

FIGURE P7–181

equilibrium positions, the motions of m_1 and m_2 will be governed by the following system of two differential equations:

$$m_1 x_1'' + k_1 x_1 - k_2(x_2 - x_1) = 0$$
$$m_2 x_2'' + k_2(x_2 - x_1) = f(t)$$

with

$$x_1(0) = x_1'(0) = x_2(0) = x_2'(0)0$$

Taking $m_1 = 2$, $m_2 = 1$, $k_1 = 2$, and $k_2 = 1$ in proper units, the system of two differential equations will reduce to

$$2x_1'' + 2x_1 - (x_2 - x_1) = 0$$
$$x_2'' + (x_2 - x_1) = f(t)$$

or

$$2x_1'' + 3x_1 - x_2 = 0$$
$$x_2'' + x_2 - x_1 = f(t)$$

Determine the motions $x_1(t)$ and $x_2(t)$ by solving this system of two initial-value problems.

Using the matrix method, determine the general solution of the following systems of first-order differential equations for the following problems. Also, determine the arbitrary constants in the general solution when initial conditions are specified.

7–182 $\mathbf{x}' = \begin{pmatrix} -2 & 1 \\ 4 & 1 \end{pmatrix}\mathbf{x} + \begin{pmatrix} 4e^{2t} \\ 3 \end{pmatrix}$

7–183 $\mathbf{x}' = \begin{pmatrix} 2 & -10 \\ 1 & 4 \end{pmatrix}\mathbf{x} + \begin{pmatrix} t^3 \\ t^2 + 5 \end{pmatrix}$

7–184 $\mathbf{x}' = \begin{pmatrix} 6 & -2 \\ -3 & 7 \end{pmatrix}\mathbf{x}\,;\, x_0(0) = \begin{pmatrix} 1 \\ 0 \end{pmatrix}$

7–185 $\mathbf{x}' = \begin{pmatrix} 2 & -1 \\ 5 & 0 \end{pmatrix}\mathbf{x} + \begin{pmatrix} -4\sin t \\ \cos t - 3\sin t \end{pmatrix}$

7–186 $\mathbf{x}' = \begin{pmatrix} 4 & -3 \\ -3 & 4 \end{pmatrix}\mathbf{x}$

7–187 $\mathbf{x}' = \begin{pmatrix} -7 & 2 \\ 1 & -6 \end{pmatrix}\mathbf{x} + \begin{pmatrix} 1 \\ 4e^{-3t} \end{pmatrix};\, x_0(0) = \begin{pmatrix} 1 \\ 1 \end{pmatrix}$

7–188 $\mathbf{x}' = \begin{pmatrix} 4 & 2 \\ -1 & 6 \end{pmatrix}\mathbf{x} + \begin{pmatrix} 4te^t + 3e^t \\ -4e^t \end{pmatrix}$

7–189 $\mathbf{x}' = \begin{pmatrix} 4 & -3 \\ 3 & 4 \end{pmatrix}\mathbf{x}$

7–190 $\mathbf{x}' = \begin{pmatrix} 2 & -4 \\ 1 & -3 \end{pmatrix}\mathbf{x} + \begin{pmatrix} t^3 - 1 \\ 1 \end{pmatrix};\, \mathbf{x}_0(0) = \begin{pmatrix} 2 \\ -3 \end{pmatrix}$

7–191 $\mathbf{x}' = \begin{pmatrix} 2 & -3 \\ 3 & 2 \end{pmatrix}\mathbf{x} + \begin{pmatrix} t^2 + 2 \\ 0 \end{pmatrix}$

7–192 $\mathbf{x}' = \begin{pmatrix} -3 & -2 \\ -1 & -4 \end{pmatrix}\mathbf{x} + \begin{pmatrix} e^{-2t} \\ -2 \end{pmatrix}$

7–193 $\mathbf{x}' = \begin{pmatrix} 7 & -1 \\ 2 & 9 \end{pmatrix}\mathbf{x} + \begin{pmatrix} 2e^{8t}\sin t \\ 0 \end{pmatrix}$

7–194 $\mathbf{x}' = \begin{pmatrix} 5 & -3 \\ -4 & 1 \end{pmatrix}\mathbf{x}$

7–195 $\mathbf{x}' = \begin{pmatrix} -3 & -8 \\ 2 & 5 \end{pmatrix}\mathbf{x};\, \mathbf{x}_0(2) = \begin{pmatrix} 0 \\ 0 \end{pmatrix}$

7–196 $\mathbf{x}' = \begin{pmatrix} -2 & 5 \\ 6 & 0 \end{pmatrix}\mathbf{x} + \begin{pmatrix} -3 \\ 2 \end{pmatrix}$

7–197 $\mathbf{x}' = \begin{pmatrix} -3 & 4 \\ 1 & -3 \end{pmatrix}\mathbf{x} + \begin{pmatrix} -2te^t - 1 \\ -t - 3 \end{pmatrix}$

7–198 $\mathbf{x}' = \begin{pmatrix} -1 & 2 \\ 4 & 1 \end{pmatrix}\mathbf{x};\, \mathbf{x}_0(0) = \begin{pmatrix} 0 \\ 1 \end{pmatrix}$

7–199 $\mathbf{x}' = \begin{pmatrix} -1 & 4 & 0 \\ 1 & 2 & -3 \\ 3 & -2 & 5 \end{pmatrix}\mathbf{x} + \begin{pmatrix} t \\ 3t - 5 \\ 0 \end{pmatrix}$

7–200 $\mathbf{x}' = \begin{pmatrix} 1 & 3 & -2 \\ 1 & 0 & -5 \\ 0 & 1 & -5 \end{pmatrix}\mathbf{x} + \begin{pmatrix} e^t \\ 2t \\ 0 \end{pmatrix}$

7–201 $\mathbf{x}' = \begin{pmatrix} 1 & -3 \\ 0 & -4 \end{pmatrix}\mathbf{x} + \begin{pmatrix} t \\ -t + 1 \end{pmatrix};\, \mathbf{x}_0(0) = \begin{pmatrix} 2 \\ 5 \end{pmatrix}$

7–202 $\mathbf{x}' = \begin{pmatrix} -7 & 1 & 0 & 2 \\ 0 & 1 & -2 & 0 \\ -2 & 2 & 0 & 4 \\ 0 & 0 & 1 & 1 \end{pmatrix}\mathbf{x}$

7–203 The following equations are the model of the roll dynamics of a missile (see Figure P7–203) on the next page:

$$\delta' = u$$
$$\omega' = -\frac{1}{\tau}\omega + \frac{b}{\tau}\delta$$
$$\varphi' = \omega$$

where δ = aileron deflection, b = aileron effectiveness constant, u = command signal to the aileron actuator, φ = roll angle, and ω = roll rate. Using the specific values $b = 10$ s^{-1} and $\tau = 1$ s, (a) obtain the characteristic equation and characteristic roots and (b) solve for the three state variables as functions of time for the case where $u = 1$.

FIGURE P7–203

7–204 Find the natural frequencies and mode ratios, and interpret the mode ratios for the coupled pendulum system shown in Figure P7–204. Use the values $m_1 = 1$, $m_2 = 4$, $L_1 = 2$, $L_2 = 5$, and $k = 2$. The equations of motion for small angles are

$$m_1 L_2^2 \theta_1'' = -m_1 g_1 L_2 \theta_1 - kL_1(L_1\theta_1 - L_1\theta_2)$$
$$m_2 L_2^2 \theta_2'' = -m_2 g L_2 \theta_2 + kL_1(L_1\theta_1 - L_1\theta_2)$$

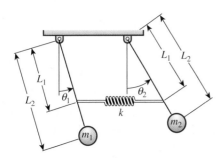

FIGURE P7–204

7–205 For any orthogonal set of body coordinates, the general relation between the angular momentum vector **M** of a rigid body and its angular velocity ω is $\mathbf{M} = \mathbf{I}\omega$, where **I** is the moment of inertia matrix:

$$I = \begin{pmatrix} I_{xx} & I_{xy} & I_{xz} \\ I_{yx} & I_{yy} & I_{yz} \\ I_{zx} & I_{zy} & I_{zz} \end{pmatrix}$$

The element I_{ii} is the moment of inertia about the i-axis, and I_{ij} is the product of inertia about the ij-axes. Use the fact that the matrix I is symmetric, so that $I_{ij} = I_{ji}$. The *principal axes* of a rigid body are a set of axes such that **M** is parallel to ω. Thus, $\mathbf{M} = I_p\omega$ where I_p is a scalar, called the *principal moment of inertia*. The principal axes and principal moments are the eigenvectors and eigenvalues of the matrix **I** and can be found from the eigenvalue problem:

$$\mathbf{I}\omega = \mathbf{I}_p\omega$$

Find the principal moments and principal axes of a uniform square, thin plate of side length b. For the axes shown in Figure P7–205, the matrix **I** is

$$\mathbf{I} = mb^2 \begin{pmatrix} 1/3 & -1/4 & 0 \\ -1/4 & 1/3 & 0 \\ 0 & 0 & 2/3 \end{pmatrix}$$

where m is the plate mass.

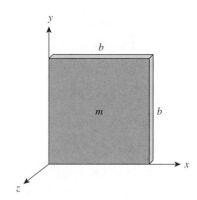

FIGURE P7–205

7–206 Engineers must be able to predict the rate of heat loss through a building wall to determine the heating system's requirements. The wall cross section shown in Figure P7–206a consists of four layers: an inner layer of plaster/lathe 10 mm thick, a layer of fiberglass insulation 125 mm thick, a layer of wood 60 mm thick, and an outer layer of brick 50 mm thick.

We assume that all of the mass in each layer is concentrated at the centerline of its respective layer, and we assign half of the layer's thermal resistance to the heat-flow path on the left and half to the path on the right side of the concentrated mass. The representation is shown in Figure P7–206b. Therefore, let

$$R_a = \frac{R_1}{2} \quad R_b = \frac{R_1}{2} + \frac{R_2}{2}$$
$$R_c = \frac{R_2}{2} + \frac{R_3}{2} \quad R_d = \frac{R_3}{2} + \frac{R_4}{2} \quad R_e = \frac{R_4}{2}$$

An equivalent electrical circuit is shown in Figure 7–206c for those who benefit from such an analogy. For the thermal capacitance C_1, conservation of energy gives

$$C_1 T_1' = \frac{T_i - T_1}{R_a} - \frac{T_1 - T_2}{R_b}$$

For C_2,

$$C_2 T_2' = \frac{T_1 - T_2}{R_b} - \frac{T_2 - T_3}{R_c}$$

For C_3,

$$C_3 T_3' = \frac{T_2 - T_3}{R_c} - \frac{T_3 - T_4}{R_d}$$

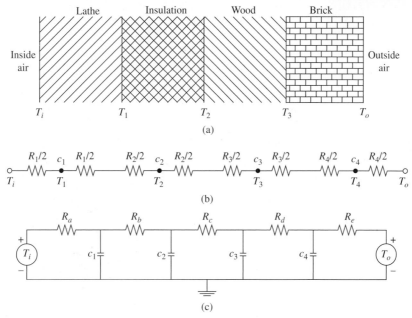

FIGURE P7–206

Finally, for C_4,

$$C_4 T'_4 = \frac{T_3 - T_4}{R_d} - \frac{T_4 - T_O}{R_e}$$

(a) Put these four equations into the state variable form $\mathbf{T}' = \mathbf{AT} + \mathbf{Bu}$ and find the expressions for the matrices $\mathbf{A}$ and $\mathbf{B}$, where

$$\mathbf{T} = \begin{pmatrix} T_1 \\ T_2 \\ T_3 \\ T_4 \end{pmatrix} \qquad \mathbf{u} = \begin{pmatrix} T_i \\ T_o \end{pmatrix}$$

(b) For the given materials, the resistances for a wall area of 1 m^2 are $R_1 = 0.036$, $R_2 = 4.01$, $R_3 = 0.408$, and $R_4 = 0.038°$C/W. The capacitance values are $C_1 = 8720$, $C_2 = 6210$, $C_3 = 6637$, and $C_4 = 2.08 \times 10^4$ J/$°$C. Plot the temperatures versus time for the case where the inside temperature is constant at $T_i = 20°$C and the outside temperature T_o decreases linearly from 5 to $-10°$C in 1 hour. The initial wall temperature is 10$°$C.

LAPLACE TRANSFORMS

8

Differential equations, in general, are much harder to solve than algebraic equations. Therefore, it is natural to wonder if there is a way to transform the differential equations into algebraic equations. It turns out that there is. In fact, there is more than one way to transform a differential equation into an algebraic equation. Such transforms, in general, involve multiplying each term in the differential equations by a suitable function called the *kernel* and integrating each term over the domain of the differential equation with respect to the independent variable. The result is an equation that does not involve any derivatives of the independent variable. The unknown function is then determined by algebraically solving for the transformed function and applying the inverse transformation. All of these transformations involve integrations, and thus, they are called *integral transforms*. Each integral transform has certain limitations associated with it, and each is applicable to certain types of problems.

In this chapter, we will discuss the *Laplace transform*, which is one of the best known integral transforms. It is particularly suited to problems whose independent variable varies from zero to infinity, such as the initial-value problems in time and boundary-value problems in semi-infinite geometries. We will use the Laplace transform to solve linear differential equations with constant coefficients and systems of such equations. You will see that the Laplace transform often provides considerable simplification to the solution of differential equations, especially when they involve nonhomogeneous terms with jump discontinuities. Such problems frequently arise in circuit analysis, mechanical vibrations, and other fields. They are quite awkward to handle by the previous methods as they require piecing together solutions valid in different intervals.

■ ■ ■ ■ ■ ■ ■
Objectives

When you have finished this chapter, you should be able to:

1. obtain the Laplace transform of a given function from a standard table, using the properties of the transform if the function is not given in the table,

2. obtain the inverse Laplace transform of a given function from a standard table, using partial fraction expansion or the convolution theorem if the function is not given in the table,

3. use the Laplace transform to solve an *n*th-order, linear, constant coefficient differential equation,

4. obtain the transfer functions of a given set of linear, constant coefficient differential equations, and

5. use a computer package to obtain Laplace transforms and inverse transforms, and to solve *n*th-order, linear constant coefficient equations.

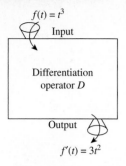

$f(t) = t^3$

Input

Differentiation
operator D

Output

$f'(t) = 3t^2$

FIGURE 8–1

Ordinary differentiation is an operator that converts a function $f(t)$ into its derivative $f'(t)$.

8–1 ▪ LAPLACE TRANSFORMS OF FUNCTIONS

The Laplace transform is named after the French mathematician and physicist P. S. Laplace (1749–1827), who first studied it in 1782. But major credit for the development and application of the method is due to Oliver Heaviside (1850–1925), the English electrical engineer who used it extensively.

You are already familiar with some operators that transform a function into a more desirable form. The ordinary *differentiation*, for example, can be viewed as an operator that transforms a function $f(t)$ into $f'(t)$. If the differentiation operator is represented by D, this transformation can be expressed as (Figure 8–1)

$$D\{f(t)\} = f'(t) \tag{8–1}$$

Another familiar operator is integration, which can be denoted by I and expressed as

$$I\{f(t)\} = \int_0^a f(t)\,dt \tag{8–2}$$

Integration reverses differentiation, and thus can be viewed as the inverse transform of differentiation. Notice the integral transform in Equation 8–2 converts the function $f(t)$, which depends on t, into the function $f(a)$ that depends on the parameter a but is independent of t.

The **Laplace transform** is simply an integral transform with integration limits 0 and ∞ and the kernel e^{-st}. It is denoted by L, and the Laplace transform of a function $f(t)$ is defined as

$$L\{f(t)\} = \int_0^\infty e^{-st} f(t)\,dt \tag{8–3}$$

Notice that the definition of the Laplace transform involves an integral over an *unbounded interval*; thus, it is an *improper integral*. As such, it must be interpreted as

$$L\{f(t)\} = \int_0^\infty e^{-st} f(t)\,dt = \lim_{R \to \infty} \int_0^R e^{-st} f(t)\,dt \tag{8–4}$$

The Laplace transform of a function exists if and only if the improper integral converges for at least some values of s. An improper integral is said to *converge* if the limit as $R \to \infty$ exists (Figure 8–2). Otherwise it is said to *diverge* or to become infinite. The integration variable t is a dummy variable and can be replaced by any other symbol.

Two observations can be made from the definition of the Laplace transform. First, the Laplace transform involves integrations over the entire positive values of the independent variable t, from 0 to ∞. This integration can be performed only if the function $f(t)$ is defined for all positive values of t. If, for example, $f(t)$ is defined in $0 \le t \le 5$ but is not defined in $5 < t < \infty$, then obviously we cannot perform this integration, and thus we cannot talk of the Laplace transform of this function. This observation reaffirms that the only differential equations that can be solved by Laplace transform method are those whose domains include all positive values of the independent variable.

The second observation that can be made from this definition is that the Laplace transform of a function $f(t)$ is no longer a function of the independent

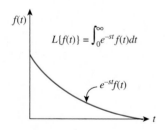

$f(t)$

$L\{f(t)\} = \int_0^\infty e^{-st} f(t)\,dt$

$e^{-st} f(t)$

t

FIGURE 8–2

The Laplace transform of a function.

variable t since neither integration limit is a function of t. However, it will always be a function of s since the integrand $e^{-st}f(t)$ contains the parameter s.

As a convention, wherever possible, we will use lower case letters to represent a given function, and the capital of the same letter to represent its Laplace transform. Curly braces are used to enclose the function of t. For example, the Laplace transform of a function $f(t)$ will be expressed as (Figure 8–3).

$$L\{f(t)\} = F(s) \qquad (8\text{--}5)$$

The determination of Laplace transform is now demonstrated with some examples.

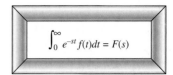

FIGURE 8–3

The Laplace transformation.

EXAMPLE 8–1   Laplace Transforms of Some Common Functions

Determine the Laplace transform of the following functions that are defined for all $t \geq 0$. (a) $f(t) = 1$, (b) $f(t) = t$, (c) $f(t) = e^{at}$, and (d) $f(t) = \cos at$.

SOLUTION All these functions are defined for all positive values of t, and thus their Laplace transforms can be obtained from Equation 8–4 so long as the integral converges. We use standard integral tables whenever necessary, and indicate the range of s for which the integral converges.

(a) $$L\{1\} = \int_0^\infty e^{-st}1\,dt = \lim_{R \to \infty} \int_0^R e^{-st}1\,dt$$

$$= \lim_{R \to \infty}\left[-\frac{e^{-st}}{s}\right]_0^R = \lim_{R \to \infty}\left[-\frac{e^{-sR}}{s}\right] + \frac{1}{s}$$

$$= 0 + \frac{1}{s} = \frac{1}{s}, \text{ for } s > 0 \qquad (8\text{--}6)$$

(b) $$L\{t\} = \int_0^\infty e^{-st}t\,dt = \lim_{R \to \infty} \int_0^R e^{-st}t\,dt$$

$$= \lim_{R \to \infty}\left[-\frac{e^{-st}}{s^2}(st + 1)\right]_0^R$$

$$= \lim_{R \to \infty}\left[-\frac{e^{-sR}}{s^2}(Rs + 1)\right] + \frac{1}{s^2} = 0 + \frac{1}{s^2} = \frac{1}{s^2}, \text{ for } s > 0 \qquad (8\text{--}7)$$

(c) $$L\{e^{at}\} = \int_0^\infty e^{-st}e^{at}\,dt = \lim_{R \to \infty} \int_0^R e^{-(s-a)t}\,dt$$

$$= \lim_{R \to \infty}\left[-\frac{e^{-(s-a)t}}{s - a}\right]_0^R = \lim_{R \to \infty}\left[-\frac{e^{-(s-a)R}}{s - a}\right] + \frac{1}{s - a}$$

$$= 0 + \frac{1}{s - a} = \frac{1}{s - a}, \text{ for } s > a \qquad (8\text{--}8)$$

(d) $$L\{\cos at\} = \int_0^\infty e^{-st} \cos at\,dt = \lim_{R \to 0} \int_0^R e^{-st} \cos at\,dt$$

$$= \lim_{R \to \infty}\left[-\frac{e^{-st}}{s^2 + a^2}(s \cos at + a \sin at)\right]_0^R$$

$$= \lim_{R \to \infty}\left[-\frac{e^{-sR}}{s^2 + a^2}(s \cos aR + a \sin aR)\right] + \frac{s}{s^2 + a^2}$$

$$= 0 + \frac{s}{s^2 + a^2} = \frac{s}{s^2 + a^2}, \text{ for } s > 0 \qquad (8\text{--}9)$$

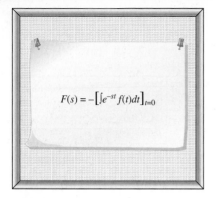

$$F(s) = -\left[\int e^{-st} f(t)dt\right]_{t=0}$$

FIGURE 8–4

The Laplace transform of a continuous function that converges as $t \to \infty$ is simply the negative of the value of the defining integral at $t = \infty$.

Note that all the functions considered in Example 8–1 are continuous in $0 \le t < \infty$, and their Laplace transform integrals vanish at the upper limit. For such functions the Laplace transform simply becomes the negative of the value of the integral at the lower limit, $t = 0$ (Figure 8–4).

It is neither necessary nor practical to resort to the definition of a Laplace transform every time we want to determine the transform of a function. A more practical approach is to determine the transform of frequently encountered functions once, and to list them in a table, such as Table 8–1. Then one can determine the transform of a function by simply looking it up in the

TABLE 8–1

Laplace Transforms

$f(t)$	$F(s) = L\{f(t)\}$
$C_1 f(t) + C_2 g(t)$	$C_1 F(s) + C_2 G(s)$
$e^{kt} f(t)$	$F(s - k)$
$f(kt)$	$\dfrac{1}{k} F\left(\dfrac{s}{k}\right)$
$t f(t)$	$-\dfrac{dF(s)}{ds}$
$t^n f(t)$	$(-1)^n \dfrac{d^n F(s)}{ds^n}$
$\dfrac{1}{t} f(t)$	$\displaystyle\int_s^\infty F(s)\,ds$
$\displaystyle\int_0^t f(t)\,dt$	$\dfrac{1}{s} F(s)$
1	$\dfrac{1}{s}$
$t^a, a > -1$	$\dfrac{\Gamma(a + 1)}{s^{a+1}}$
$t^{-1/2}$	$\sqrt{\dfrac{\pi}{s}}$
t	$\dfrac{1}{s^2}$
t^2	$\dfrac{2}{s^3}$
$t^n, n = 1, 2, 3, \ldots$	$\dfrac{n!}{s^{n+1}}$
e^{at}	$\dfrac{1}{s - a}$
$t^n e^{at}, n = 1, 2, 3, \ldots$	$\dfrac{n!}{(s - a)^{n+1}}$
$\sin at$	$\dfrac{a}{s^2 + a^2}$
$e^{kt} \sin at$	$\dfrac{a}{(s - k)^2 + a^2}$

TABLE 8–1 (Continued)

Laplace Transforms

$f(t)$	$F(s) = L\{f(t)\}$
$t\sin at$	$\dfrac{2as}{(s^2 + a^2)^2}$
$\cos at$	$\dfrac{s}{s^2 + a^2}$
$e^{kt}\cos at$	$\dfrac{s - k}{(s - k)^2 + a^2}$
$t\cos at$	$\dfrac{s^2 - a^2}{(s^2 + a^2)^2}$
$\sinh at$	$\dfrac{a}{s^2 - a^2}$
$\cosh at$	$\dfrac{s}{s^2 - a^2}$
$u(t - t_0)$	$\dfrac{e^{-t_0 s}}{s}$
$u(t - t_0)f(t - t_0)$	$e^{-t_0 s}F(s)$
$\delta(t - t_0)$	$e^{-t_0 s}$
$f(t)$, periodic of period p	$\dfrac{1}{1 - e^{-ps}}\displaystyle\int_0^p e^{-st}f(t)\,dt$
$f'(t)$	$sF(s) - f(0)$
$f''(t)$	$s^2 F(s) - sf(0) - f'(0)$
$f^{(n)}(t)$	$s^n F(s) - s^{n-1}f(0) - \cdots - f^{(n-1)}(0)$
$\displaystyle\int_0^t f(\tau)g(t - \tau)\,d\tau$	$F(s)G(s)$

table, much the same way as looking up an integral from a table of integrals. No table is large enough to contain the transforms of all conceivable functions, and it often becomes necessary to express the function in a form that exists in the table. The properties of the Laplace transform that are discussed later will be very useful in this respect. Some of the transforms in Table 8–1 are treated in detail in the later sections of this chapter.

Section Review

8–1   Determine the Laplace transform of the following functions that are defined for all $t \geq 0$.

(a) $f(t) = 5$,   (b) $f(t) = e^{3t}$ (c) $f(t) = \sinh at$

$\left(\textit{Answers: } \text{(a) } \dfrac{5}{s}\ s > 0,\ \ \text{(b) } \dfrac{1}{s - 3}\ s > 3,\ \text{and (c) } \dfrac{a}{s^2 - a^2},\ s > a\right)$

8–2 ▪ EXISTENCE OF LAPLACE TRANSFORMS

The integral defining the Laplace transform (Equation 8–3) cannot be performed for any function $f(t)$, and thus not all functions possess a Laplace transform. Then one would ask what kinds of functions possess Laplace transforms.

Simply stated, any function for which the integration in Equation 8–3 exists has a Laplace transform. For that integral to exist, (1) the function $f(t)$ must be defined for all $t \geq 0$, (2) the function $f(t)$ must be integrable, and (3) this improper integral must converge.

The first condition is obvious. We wouldn't even attempt to integrate a function if it is not defined over the entire domain of integration. The second condition is satisfied by any continuous function, since all continuous functions are integrable. In fact, to be integrable, it suffices for the function to be only **piecewise continuous** (or sectionally continuous), which is defined as follows.

> *A function $f(t)$ is said to be piecewise continuous on a finite interval $a \leq t \leq b$ if this interval can be subdivided into a finite number of subintervals such that in each subinterval, $f(t)$ is continuous and has finite limits at the endpoints.*

In other words, $f(t)$ must not diverge as t approaches either endpoint of a subinterval from within the subinterval.

Notice that a piecewise-continuous function may contain a finite number of *jump discontinues* as shown in Figure 8–5, but the function is still defined at all points of discontinuity. Also notice that the left- and right-hand limits at any endpoint are finite, but generally, they are not equal. In fact, the value of the function at an endpoint can be different from either limit at that endpoint. Only continuous functions have identical left- and right-hand limits at any point $a \leq t \leq b$ both equal to the value of the function at that point. Thus, a continuous function is a special case of a piecewise-continuous function, and any continuous function in a given interval is necessarily piecewise continuous in that interval. Any piecewise-continuous function in a given interval is integrable in that interval.

The upper limit of the integral is infinity, which suggests that the integral may diverge as t approaches infinity. Therefore, if the Laplace transform is to exist, the integrand $e^{-st} f(t)$ should converge. This limits not only the function $f(t)$, but also the values of the parameter s.

An integration that converges in a finite interval $0 \leq t \leq a$ may diverge when $a \to \infty$. This happens when the value of the integrand increases with increasing t, and diverges as t tends infinity. Thus we need some condition on the rate of growth of the integrand as $t \to \infty$. For an improper integral of this kind to exist, the integrand must be convergent. That is, the limit of the integrand as $t \to \infty$ must be a finite number. This condition sounds too restrictive since many functions of practical interest such as t, t^2, t^n, e^{kt} will diverge as $t \to \infty$, but it is not because the convergence requirement is on the integrand $e^{-st} f(t)$, not $f(t)$ alone. Notice that for positive values of s, the factor e^{-st} will vanish as $t \to \infty$, and will force the entire integrand to converge. However, this will be the case only if $f(t)$ does not diverge faster than e^{-st} converges. Thus the function e^{-st} serves as a damping factor.

For example, the function $f(t) = t$ diverges (i.e., it becomes infinite) as $t \to \infty$. But te^{-st} converges as $t \to \infty$, since, from l'Hôpital's rule, we have

$$\lim_{t \to \infty} te^{-st} = \lim_{t \to \infty} \frac{t}{e^{st}} = \lim_{t \to \infty} \frac{1}{se^{st}} = 0, \quad \text{for} \quad s > 0$$

Notice that a finite limit exists only for positive values of s. (For negative values of s the limit diverges). We can also show that the integrand vanishes for $f(t) = t^n$ for any value of n as $t \to \infty$.

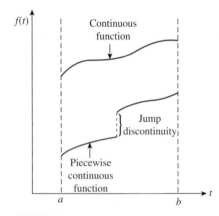

FIGURE 8–5

A continuous and a piecewise-continuous function on a specified interval.

When $f(t)$ is an exponential function such as e^{at}, the integrand becomes $e^{-st} f(t) = e^{-st} e^{at} = e^{-(s-a)t}$, which will vanish as $t \to \infty$ if $s > a$. Then we conclude that a function $f(t)$ will have a Laplace transform if $|f(t)| < e^{at}$, where a is an arbitrary positive number. Such functions are said to be of **exponential order** and are defined here.

> *A function $f(t)$ is said to be of exponential order if there exists a constant a such that $\lim_{t \to \infty} e^{-at} |f(t)| = M$, where M is a finite positive constant or zero, for all t at which $f(t)$ is defined.*

If $f(t)$ is not of exponential order, then this limit will diverge (Figure 8–6).

Note that a function $f(t)$ that is unbounded as $t \to \infty$ may still be of exponential order if it does *not* increase more rapidly than the function Me^{at}. In other words, a function is of exponential order if it grows no more rapidly than the exponential function e^{at}, where a is a constant that can be selected to be as large as one requires.

Any bounded function such as $\sin \omega t$ or $\cos \omega t$ is of exponential order if $a = 0$. Any polynomial $P(t)$ is of exponential order if $a = 1$. Any exponential function with a linear exponent such as e^{-kt} is of exponential order of $a = k$. But an exponential function with a quadratic or higher-order exponent (such as e^{t^2}) is not of exponential order, since the limit in the definition of exponential order diverges in this case, regardless of the value of a.

We can summarize these discussions with the following theorem.

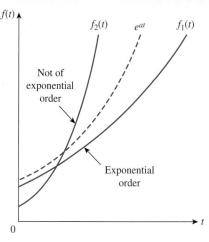

FIGURE 8–6

The function $f_2(t)$ is not of exponential order since it grows more rapidly than the exponential function e^{at}.

THEOREM 8–1   Existence Theorem for Laplace Transforms

If a function $f(t)$ is piecewise continuous for $t \geq 0$ and is of exponential order as $t \to \infty$, then its Laplace transform exists (Figure 8–7).

Note that being piecewise continuous and having exponential order are sufficient conditions for a function $f(t)$ to have a Laplace transform; they are *not* necessary conditions. Some functions that do not satisfy these conditions still possess Laplace transforms. For example, the function $f(t) = t^{-1/2}$ is not piecewise continuous, since it is unbounded as $t \to 0$, but its Laplace transform exists and can be shown to be $\sqrt{\pi/s}$ for $s > 0$.

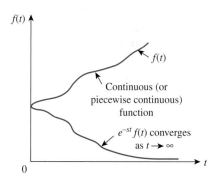

FIGURE 8–7

A function $f(t)$ whose Laplace transform exists.

Section Review

Problems Denoted with a C are Conceptual Problems for Discussion

8–2C   What is the difference between continuous and piecewise-continuous functions?

8–3   Determine if the following functions possess a Laplace transform.

     (a) $f(t) = \dfrac{1}{t}$ (b) $f(t) = e^{-2t^3}$

     (c) $\sinh 5t$ (d) $f(t) = \begin{Bmatrix} 1, & t \leq 3 \\ t^2, & t > 3 \end{Bmatrix}$

(*Answers*: (a) Yes, (b) Yes, (c) Yes, and (d) No.)

8-3 ▪ BASIC PROPERTIES OF THE LAPLACE TRANSFORM

We can obtain the Laplace transform of many functions by repeatedly applying its definition, Equation 8–3, but this would be very tedious and time consuming. It is much more practical to determine the Laplace transform of some basic functions directly and obtain the Laplace transform of other functions using the properties of the Laplace transform. We now discuss some such properties, which are summarized in Table 8–2.

Property 1: The Linearity of Laplace Transform

The Laplace transform is defined as a definite integral, and thus it has the properties of definite integrals. For example, the integral of the sum of two functions is the sum of the integrals of those two functions. That is,

$$\int_a^b [f(t) + g(t)] dt = \int_a^b f(t) dt + \int_a^b g(t) dt$$

Also, the integral of a constant times a function is the constant times the integral of the function. That is,

$$\int_a^b Cf(t) dt = C \int_a^b f(t) dt$$

where C is an arbitrary constant.

Thus integration is a *linear* operator. This is also true for the Laplace transform. The linearity of Laplace transform can be expressed as

$$L\{C_1 f_1(t) + C_2 f_2(t)\} = C_1 L\{f_1(t)\} + C_2 L\{f_2(t)\} \qquad \text{(8–10)}$$

where C_1 and C_2 are any two constants. This is the most significant property of Laplace transform.

TABLE 8–2

The Basic Properties of the Laplace Transform

1	$L\{C_1 f_1(t) + C_2 f_2(t)\} = C_1 L\{f_1(t)\} + C_2 L\{f_2(t)\}$
2	$L\{e^{kt} f(t)\} = F(s - k)$
3	$L\{t^n f(t)\} = (-1)^n \dfrac{d^n F(s)}{ds^n}$
4	$L\left\{\dfrac{1}{t} f(t)\right\} = \displaystyle\int_s^\infty F(s) ds$
5	$L\left\{\displaystyle\int_o^t f(t) dt\right\} = \dfrac{1}{s} F(s)$
6	$L\{f(kt)\} = \dfrac{1}{k} F\left(\dfrac{s}{k}\right)$

EXAMPLE 8–2   **Laplace Transform of sinh kt**

Determine the Laplace transform of sinh kt, where k is a constant.

SOLUTION   In Example 8–1, we determined that $L\{e^{at}\} = 1/(s - a)$. We also know that sinh $at = (e^{at} - e^{-at})/2$. Then from the linearity of the Laplace transform,

$$
\begin{aligned}
L\{\sinh kt\} &= L\left\{\frac{e^{kt} - e^{-kt}}{2}\right\} = \frac{1}{2}L\{e^{kt}\} - \frac{1}{2}L\{e^{-kt}\} \\
&= \frac{1}{2}\left(\frac{1}{s - k}\right) - \frac{1}{2}\left(\frac{1}{s - (-k)}\right) = \frac{1}{2}\left[\frac{(s + k) - (s - k)}{(s - k)(s + k)}\right] \\
&= \frac{k}{s^2 - k^2}, \quad s > k
\end{aligned}
\tag{8–11}
$$

Property 2: The Translation (or Shifting) Property

If the Laplace transform of a function $f(t)$ is known, then the Laplace transform of the function $e^{kt} f(t)$, where k is a constant, is easily determined by the translation property, which can be expressed as

$$
L\{e^{kt}f(t)\} = F(s - k)
\tag{8–12}
$$

Here $F(s)$ is the Laplace transform of $f(t)$, and $F(s - k)$ is obtained by replacing every occurrence of s in $F(s)$ by $s - k$. The proof is straightforward:

$$
L\{e^{kt}f(t)\} = \int_0^\infty e^{-st}e^{kt}f(t)\,dt = \int_0^\infty e^{-(s-k)t}f(t)\,dt = F(s - k)
$$

EXAMPLE 8–3   **Laplace Transform of $e^{3t} \sinh \omega t$**

Determine the Laplace transform of $e^{3t} \sinh \omega t$.

SOLUTION   In Example 8–2, we determined that $L\{\sinh \omega t\} = \omega/(s^2 - \omega^2)$. Then applying the translation property with $k = 3$ yields

$$
L\{e^{3t}\sinh \omega t\} = \frac{\omega}{(s - 3)^2 - \omega^2}, \quad s > \omega + 3
\tag{8–13}
$$

Property 3: The Laplace Transform of $t^n f(t)$

Let us reexamine the defining integral of the Laplace transform, Equation 8–3,

$$
F(s) = \int_0^\infty f(t)e^{-st}dt
$$

Successive differentiation of both sides of this equation with respect to s yields

$$\frac{dF(s)}{ds} = (-1)^1 \int_0^\infty e^{-st} tf(t) \, dt = L\{tf(t)\},$$

$$\frac{d^2F}{ds^2} = (-1)^2 \int_0^\infty e^{-st} t^2 f(t) \, dt,$$

and

$$\frac{d^n F(s)}{ds^n} = (-1)^n \int_0^\infty e^{-st} t^n f(t) \, dt \qquad \text{(8-14)}$$

The last integral on the right-hand side is the Laplace transform of the function $t^n f(t)$. Thus, Equation 8–14 can be expressed as

$$L\{t^n f(t)\} = (-1)^n \frac{d^n F(s)}{ds^n} \qquad \text{(8-15)}$$

where $F(s)$ is the Laplace transform of $f(t)$.

Equation 8–15 is extremely important in the determination of Laplace transforms of functions that involve powers of the independent variable.

EXAMPLE 8–4   Laplace Transform of t^2

Determine the Laplace transform of t^2.

SOLUTION   The given function can be considered as $t^2 f(t)$, where $f(t) = 1$. In Example 8–1, we determined that $F(s) = L\{1\} = 1/s$, Then from Equation 8–15, the Laplace transform of t^2 is determined by taking the second derivative of $F(s)$, as

$$L\{t^2\} = (-1)^2 \frac{d^2 F(s)}{ds^2} = \frac{d^2}{ds^2}\left(\frac{1}{s}\right) = \frac{2}{s^3}, \quad s > 0 \qquad \text{(8-16)}$$

Property 4: The Laplace Transform of $f(t)/t$

Reconsider the defining integral of the Laplace transform (Equation 8–3 as),

$$F(s) = \int_0^\infty e^{-st} f(t) \, dt$$

Integrating both sides of this equation from s to ∞ with respect to s yields

$$\int_s^\infty F(s)\,ds = \int_s^\infty \int_0^\infty e^{-st}f(t)\,dt\,ds$$

$$= \int_0^\infty \left[\int_s^\infty e^{-st}\,ds \right] f(t)\,dt$$

$$= \int_0^\infty e^{-st}\frac{1}{t}f(t)\,dt = L\left\{\frac{1}{t}f(t)\right\}$$

since the order of the double integration can be interchanged. We have also used the fact that

$$\int_s^\infty e^{-st}\,ds = \frac{e^{-st}}{-t}\bigg|_{s=s}^\infty = 0 - \frac{e^{-st}}{-t} = \frac{e^{-st}}{t}$$

Thus we conclude that

$$L\left\{\frac{1}{t}f(t)\right\} = \int_s^\infty F(s)\,ds \qquad\qquad \textbf{(8–17)}$$

where $F(s)$ is the Laplace transform of $f(t)$.

EXAMPLE 8–5   Laplace Transform of 1/t

Determine the Laplace transform of $1/t$.

SOLUTION The given function can be considered as $f(t)/t$, where $f(t) = 1$. In Example 8–1, we determined that $F(s) = L\{1\} = 1/s$. Then from Equation 8–17, the Laplace transform of $1/t$ is determined by integrating $F(s)$ from s to ∞, as

$$L\left\{\frac{1}{t}\right\} = \int_s^\infty F(s)\,ds = \lim_{R\to\infty}\int_s^R \frac{1}{s}\,ds = \lim_{R\to\infty}\big[\ln s\big]_s^R = \lim_{R\to\infty}\ln R - \ln s = \infty$$

Therefore, the Laplace transform of $1/t$ does not exist, since the integral diverges.

Property 5: The Laplace Transform of $\int_0^t f(t)\,dt$

From the definition of the Laplace transform (Equation 8–3), we have,

$$L\left\{\int_0^t f(\tau)\,d\tau\right\} = \int_0^\infty \left[\int_0^t f(\tau)\,d\tau\right]e^{-st}\,dt$$

Taking $u = \int_0^t f(\tau)\,d\tau$ and $dv = e^{-st}dt$ and integrating by parts yields

$$L\left\{\int_0^t f(\tau)\,d\tau\right\} = \left[\frac{e^{-st}}{-s}\int_0^t f(\tau)\,d\tau\right]_0^\infty - \int_0^\infty f(t)\frac{e^{-st}}{-s}\,dt$$

$$= 0 + \frac{1}{s}\int_0^\infty e^{-st}f(t)\,dt = \frac{1}{s}F(s)$$

since the term in brackets vanishes at both $t = 0$ and as $t \to \infty$ (because $f(t)$ is a piecewise-continuous function of exponential order). Thus, we conclude that

$$L\left\{\int_0^t f(t)\,dt\right\} = \frac{1}{s}F(s) \tag{8-18}$$

where $F(s)$ is the Laplace transform of $f(t)$. This result is very useful for solving differential equations that involve integrals.

Property 6: Change of Scale Property

If the Laplace transform of a function $f(kt)$ is known, the Laplace transform of the function $f(kt)$ (where k is a constant) is easily determined by the *change of scale* property, which can be expressed as

$$L\{f(kt)\} = \frac{1}{k}F\left(\frac{s}{k}\right) \tag{8-19}$$

Here $F(s)$ is the Laplace transform of $f(t)$, and $F(s/k)$ is obtained by replacing every occurrence of s in $F(s)$ by s/k. The proof is straightforward:

$$L\{f(kt)\} = \int_0^\infty e^{-st}f(kt)\,dt = \frac{1}{k}\int_0^\infty e^{-sx/k}f(x)\,dx = \frac{1}{k}F\left(\frac{s}{k}\right)$$

where we transformed the integration variable to $x = kt$.

Section Review

8-4   Determine the Laplace transform of the following functions using the basic properties of the transform and Table 8–1.

(a) $f(t) = t^2\sin 2t$ (b) $f(t) = 3t^2 - \sin 3t$

$\left(\text{Answers: (a) } \dfrac{4(3s^2 - 4)}{(s^2 + 4)^3} \text{ and (b) } \dfrac{6}{s^3} - \dfrac{3}{s^2 + 9}\right)$

8–4 ▪ LAPLACE TRANSFORMS OF STEP, PERIODIC, AND IMPULSE FUNCTIONS

Although a function does not need to be continuous to have a Laplace transform, the emphasis so far has been on continuous functions because of their widespread use and simplicity. But some problems of practical interest involve functions that have *jump discontinuities*, rendering them piecewise continuous. Such functions frequently arise in the analysis of certain electric circuits, mechanical systems, and even thermal systems, among other fields (Figure 8–8). Fortunately, the Laplace transform of functions with jump discontinuities (i.e., piecewise-continuous functions) exist, and the Laplace transform technique becomes an invaluable tool for solving differential equations that involve such functions. But first we need to develop the necessary mathematical tools to accurately describe functions with jump discontinuities. For this purpose, we will define *the unit step function $u(t - t_0)$* and *the unit impulse function $\delta(t - t_0)$*. Considering the Laplace transform is defined in the interval $0 \leq t < \infty$, we will limit the discussion to nonnegative values of t.

Unit Step Function

Probably the simplest function that involves a jump discontinuity is the **unit step function** $u(t - t_0)$, also known as *the Heaviside function*, which defined as

$$u(t - t_0) = \begin{cases} 0, & t < t_0 \\ 1, & t \geq t_0 \end{cases} \tag{8-20}$$

where $t = t_0$ is the location of the jump, as shown in Figure 8–9. For the special case of $t_0 = 0$, the unit step function simply becomes $u(t - 0) = 1$ for $t \geq 0$, and its Laplace transform is

$$L\{u(t)\} = L(1) = \frac{1}{s} \tag{8-21}$$

The unit step function $u(t - t_0)$ is merely the translation of $u(t)$ by the amount t_0. Its Laplace transform is easily determined by introducing the dummy variable $x = t - t_0$, as

$$L\{u(t - t_0)\} = \int_{t_0}^{\infty} e^{-st} u(t - t_0) dt = \int_0^{\infty} e^{-s(x + t_0)} u(x) dx$$

$$= e^{-t_0 s} \int_0^{\infty} e^{-sx} u(x) dx = e^{-t_0 s} L\{1\} = \frac{e^{-t_0 s}}{s}$$

Thus,

$$L\{u(t - t_0)\} = \frac{e^{-t_0 s}}{s} \tag{8-22}$$

Now let us see what happens when we multiply a given function $f(t)$ by the unit step function (Figure 8–10). When $t_0 = 0$, we have

$$u(t - t_0)f(t) \equiv f(t) \tag{8-23}$$

since $u(t - 0) = 1$ for $t \geq 0$. Thus, the unit step function has no effect on the function $f(t)$ if $t_0 = 0$. But when $t_0 \neq 0$,

$$u(t - t_0)f(t) = \begin{cases} 0, & t < t_0 \\ f(t), & t \geq t_0 \end{cases} \tag{8-24}$$

That is, multiplying a function $f(t)$ by the unit step function $u(t - t_0)$ causes the part of $f(t)$ in $0 \leq t < t_0$ to vanish, but it has no effect on the remaining part of $f(t)$.

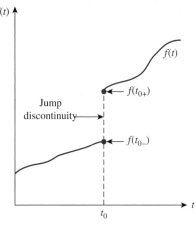

FIGURE 8–8

Many functions of practical interest involve jump discontinuities (abrupt changes in the value of the function at some point).

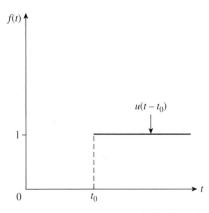

FIGURE 8–9

The unit step function $u(t - t_0)$.

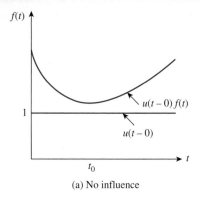

(a) No influence

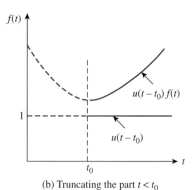

(b) Truncating the part $t < t_0$

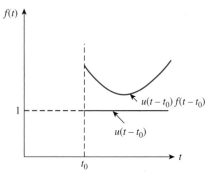

(c) Shifting the start of the function to t_0

FIGURE 8–10

The influence of the unit step function $u(t - t_0)$ on a function $f(t)$.

Now suppose we do not want to suppress that part of $f(t)$ in $0 \leq t < t_0$. Instead, we want to postpone the start of $f(t)$ to $t = t_0$. This is accomplished by shifting $f(t)$ by t_0 units to the right and multiplying it by $u(t - t_0)$ to suppress it for $t < t_0$, as shown in Figure 8–10. Then,

$$u(t - t_0)f(t - t_0) = \begin{cases} 0, & t < t_0 \\ f(t - t_0), & t \geq t_0 \end{cases} \tag{8–25}$$

The unit step function $u(t - t_0)$ can be viewed as a switch that turns the accompanying function "off" until $t = t_0$, and "on" thereafter.

EXAMPLE 8–6   **Laplace Transform of Shifted Functions**

Determine the Laplace transform of the following:

(a) $$f(t) = t^2$$

(b) $$f(t) = \begin{cases} 0, & t < 3 \\ t^2, & t \geq 3 \end{cases}$$

(c) $$f(t) = \begin{cases} 0, & t < 3 \\ (t - 3)^2, & t \geq 3 \end{cases}$$

SOLUTION   All three functions are plotted in Figure 8–11. This example is intended to illustrate the particulars of the Laplace transform of function that are different, but have the same general behavior.

(a) From Table 8–1, we have $L\{f(t)\} = L\{t^2\} = 2/s^3$

(b) Utilizing the unit step function, we see that this function can be expressed as $f(t) = u(t - 3)t^2$. From the definition of the Laplace transform, we have

$$F(s) = L\{u(t - 3)t^2\} = \int_0^\infty e^{-st}u(t - 3)t^2 dt = \int_0^\infty e^{-st}t^2 dt$$

since the function is zero for $t \leq 3$. To restore the lower integration limits back to 0, we define a new variable $x = t - 3$ and substitute:

$$F(s) = \int_0^\infty e^{-s(x+3)}(x + 3)^2 dx = e^{-3s}\int_0^\infty e^{-3x}(x + 3)^2 dx$$

$$= e^{-3s}L\{x^2 + 6x + 9\} = e^{-3s}\left(\frac{2}{s^3} + \frac{6}{s^2} + \frac{9}{s}\right)$$

(c) Utilizing the unit step function, this function can be expressed as $f(t) = u(t - 3)(t - 3)^2$. Then again from the definition of Laplace transform, we obtain

$$F(s) = L\{u(t - 3)(t - 3)^2\} = \int_0^\infty e^{-st}u(t - 3)(t - 3)^2 dt = \int_3^\infty e^{-st}(t - 3)^2 dt$$

since the function is zero for $t \le 3$. To restore the lower integration limit back to 0, we define a new variable $x = t - 3$ and substitute:

$$F(s) = \int_0^\infty e^{-s(x+3)} x^2 dx = e^{-3s} \int_0^\infty e^{-sx} x^2 dx = e^{-3s} L\{x^2\} = \frac{2e^{-3s}}{s^3}$$

In the light of the discussion and the previous example, we conclude the following regarding the Laplace transform of the step functions:

1. $$L\{u(t - 0)\} = \frac{1}{s}$$ (8–21 repeated)

2. $$L\{u(t - t_0)\} = \frac{e^{-t_0 s}}{s}$$ (8–22 repeated)

3. $$L\{u(t - t_0)f(t)\} = e^{-t_0 s} L\{f(t - t_0)\}$$ (8–26)

4. $$L\{u(t - t_0)f(t - t_0)\} = e^{-t_0 s} L\{f(t)\}$$ (8–27)

These relations are summarized in Table 8–3.

EXAMPLE 8–7   Laplace Transform of a Rectangular Pulse

Obtain a mathematical equation for and determine the Laplace transform of the function

$$f(t) = \begin{cases} 0, & t < 3 \\ 1, & 3 \le t \le 5 \\ 0, & t > 5 \end{cases}$$

SOLUTION This function can be considered to be the difference between two unit step functions, as shown in Figure 8–12, and can be expressed as

$$f(t) = u(t - 3) - u(t - 5)$$

The Laplace transform of this function (from Equation 8–22) is

$$F(s) = L\{u(t - 3) - u(t - 5)\} = L\{u(t - 3)\} - L\{(t - 5)\} = \frac{e^{-3s}}{s} - \frac{e^{-5s}}{s}$$

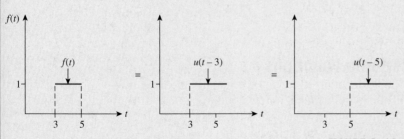

FIGURE 8–12

Forming the functions described in Example 8–7 using unit step functions.

TABLE 8–3

Shifting in the t-Domain with the Laplace Transform

$L\{u(t - 0)\} = \dfrac{1}{s}$
$L\{u(t - t_0)\} = \dfrac{e^{-t_0 s}}{s}$
$L\{u(t - t_0)f(t)\} = e^{-t_0 s} L\{f(t + t_0)\}$
$L\{u(t - t_0)f(t - t_0)\} = e^{-t_0 s} L\{f(t)\}$

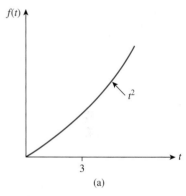

(a)

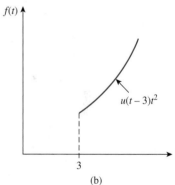

(b)

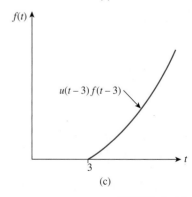

(c)

FIGURE 8–11

The functions described in Example 8–6.

EXAMPLE 8–8   Laplace Transform of a Half-Sine Pulse

Obtain a single equation to describe the following function and determine its Laplace transform.

$$f(t) = \begin{cases} 0, & t < 2\pi \\ \sin t, & 2\pi \le t \le 3\pi \\ 0, & t > 3\pi \end{cases}$$

SOLUTION   This function can be considered to be the product of $\sin t$ and the difference between two unit step functions, as shown in Figure 8–13, and can be expressed as

$$f(t) = \sin t \left[u(t - 2\pi) - u(t - 3\pi) \right]$$

The Laplace transform of this function is, from Equation 8–26,

$$F(s) = L\{\sin t[u(t - 2\pi) - u(t - 3\pi)]\}$$
$$= L\{u(t - 2\pi)\sin t\} - L\{u(t - 3\pi)\sin t\}$$
$$= e^{-2\pi s}L\{\sin(t + 2\pi)\} - e^{-3\pi s}L\{\sin(t + 3\pi)\}$$

But $\sin(t + 2\pi) = \sin t$ and $\sin(t + 3\pi) = \sin(-t) = -\sin t$. Therefore,

$$F(s) = e^{-2\pi s}L\{\sin t\} - e^{-3\pi s}L\{-\sin t\} = (e^{-2\pi s} + e^{-3\pi s})L\{\sin t\}$$
$$= \frac{e^{-2\pi s} + e^{-3\pi s}}{s^2 + 1}$$

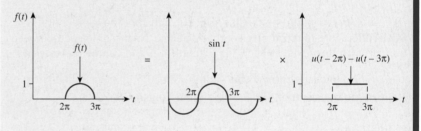

FIGURE 8–13

Forming the function described in Example 8–8 using unit step functions.

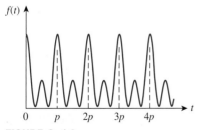

FIGURE 8–14

A periodic function of period p.

Periodic Functions

Periodic functions frequently occur in practice, and thus they deserve special attention. A function $f(t)$ is said to be **periodic** of period p if there exists a positive number p such that $f(t + p) = f(t)$ for every positive value of t, with p being the smallest such number (Figure 8–14). Note that any integer multiples of p such as $2p$, $3p$, and $4p$ will also satisfy the periodicity relation. The well-known trigonometric functions $\sin t$ and $\cos t$, for example, are periodic functions with period 2π.

For the Laplace transform of a periodic function, we have the following theorem.

THEOREM 8–2   Existence of Laplace Transforms of Periodic Functions

If f(t) is a piecewise-continuous periodic function of period p for t ≥ 0, its Laplace transform exists and is determined from

$$F(s) = \frac{1}{1 - e^{-ps}} \int_0^p e^{-st} f(t)\, dt, \; s > 0 \tag{8–28}$$

Proof   This is an important theorem since it enables us to determine the Laplace transform of a periodic function by integrating the function over a single period. We start the proof by breaking the interval of the defining integral of the Laplace transform into segments of length p,

$$F(s) = \int_0^\infty e^{-st} f(t)\, dt$$

$$= \int_0^p e^{-st} f(t)\, dt + \int_p^{2p} e^{-st} f(t)\, dt + \cdots + \int_{np}^{(n+1)p} e^{-st} f(t)\, dt + \cdots$$

$$= \sum_{n=0}^\infty \int_{np}^{(n+1)p} e^{-st} f(t)\, dt$$

We now change the integration variable to $x = t - np$. Substituting, we have

$$F(s) = \sum_{n=0}^\infty \int_0^p e^{-s(x+np)} f(x + np)\, dx = \sum_{n=0}^\infty e^{-nps} \int_0^p e^{-sx} f(x)\, dx$$

$$= (1 + e^{-ps} + e^{-2ps} + e^{-3ps} + \cdots + e^{-nps} + \cdots) \int_0^p e^{-sx} f(x)\, dx$$

$$= \frac{1}{1 - e^{-ps}} \int_0^p e^{-sx} f(x)\, dx$$

since for periodic functions $f(x + np) = f(x)$ and

$$1 + x + x^2 + x^3 + \cdots + x^n + \cdots = \frac{1}{1 - x}$$

for the geometric series with $x = e^{-ps} < 1$. Note that $e^{-ps} < 1$, since both p and s are positive.

EXAMPLE 8–9   Laplace Transform of sin ωt

Determine the Laplace transform of $\sin \omega t$.

SOLUTION   The function $\sin \omega t$ is periodic with period $p = 2\pi/\omega$. Thus, its Laplace transform can be determined from Equation 8–28 with the help of integral tables.

$$F(s) = \frac{1}{1 - e^{-ps}} \int_0^p e^{-st} \sin \omega t \, dt$$

$$= \frac{1}{1 - e^{-ps}} \left[\frac{e^{-st}(-s \sin \omega t - \omega \cos \omega t)}{s^2 + \omega^2} \right]_0^{2\pi/\omega}$$

$$= \frac{1}{1 - e^{-ps}} \frac{\omega(1 - e^{-2\pi/\omega})}{s^2 + \omega^2} = \frac{\omega}{s^2 + \omega^2}$$

which is the same result given in Table 8–1.

EXAMPLE 8–10   Laplace Transform of a Train of Rectangular Pulses

Determine the Laplace transform of the following periodic function of period $p = 6$.

$$f(t) = \begin{cases} 2, & 0 \leq t < 3 \\ -2, & 3 \leq t < 6 \end{cases}$$

SOLUTION   This is a square-wave function with an amplitude of 2 and period of $p = 6$, as shown in Figure 8–15. From Equation 8–28, we have

$$F(s) = \frac{1}{1 - e^{-ps}} \int_0^p e^{-st} f(t) \, dt$$

$$= \frac{1}{1 - e^{-6s}} \left[\int_0^3 e^{-st}(2) \, dt + \int_3^6 e^{-st}(-2) \, dt \right]$$

$$= \frac{1}{1 - e^{-6s}} \left[2 \left| -\frac{e^{-st}}{s} \right|_0^3 - 2 \left| -\frac{e^{-st}}{s} \right|_3^6 \right]$$

$$= \frac{2(1 - 2e^{-3s} + e^{-6s})}{s(1 - e^{-6s})} = \frac{2(1 - e^{-3s})^2}{s(1 - e^{-3s})(1 + e^{-3s})}$$

$$= \frac{2(1 - e^{-3s})}{s(1 + e^{-3s})} = \frac{2}{s} \tanh 3s \qquad \text{(8–29)}$$

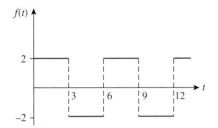

$f(t)$

FIGURE 8–15

The periodic function described in Example 8–10.

Alternative Solution The given square-wave function of amplitude $a = 2$ and period $p = 6$ can be expressed in terms of the unit step functions as

$$f(t) = 2\left[1 + 2\sum_{n=1}^{\infty}(-1)^n u(t - 3n)\right]$$

The Laplace transform of this function is readily determined from

$$F(s) = 2\left[L\{1\} + L\left\{2\sum_{n=1}^{\infty}(-1)^n u(t - 3n)\right\}\right]$$

$$= 2\left[L\{1\} + 2\sum_{n=1}^{\infty}(-1)^n L\{u(t - 3n)\}\right]$$

$$= 2\left[\frac{1}{s} + 2\sum_{n=1}^{\infty}(-1)^n\frac{e^{-3ns}}{s}\right]$$

$$= \frac{2}{s}\left[1 + 2\sum_{n=1}^{\infty}(-1)^n e^{-3ns}\right] \tag{8-30}$$

It is left as an exercise to the reader to show that Equations 8–29 and 8–30 are identical.

In general, for a square-wave function of amplitude a and period p, its Laplace transform can be expressed as (Figure 8–16)

$$f(t) = \begin{cases} a & 0 \le t < p/2 \\ -a & p/2 \le t < p \end{cases} \tag{8-31}$$

and

$$F(s) = \frac{a(1 - e^{-ps/2})}{s(1 + e^{-ps/2})} = \frac{a}{s}\tanh\frac{ps}{2} = \frac{a}{s}\left[1 + 2\sum_{n=1}^{\infty}(-1)^n e^{-pns/2}\right] \tag{8-32}$$

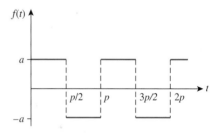

FIGURE 8–16

The general square-wave function amplitude a and period p.

Impulse Functions

Some physical problems involve forcing functions of large magnitude that act over a very short period of time, such as a voltage surge or a striking force on a body. A plot of such functions appears as a highly peaked spurt at some time and zero everywhere else. Because of their unusual nature, such functions need to be treated differently from ordinary functions.

Consider, for example, a player kicking a ball. The player's foot contacts the ball at time t_0, applies a large sudden force $f(t)$ during a very short time period (say ε) and loses contact with the ball. The integral of the force over the time interval ε is called the **impulse** I of the force. This is the same concept as the impulse appearing in the impulse–momentum principle studied in dynamics. This principle states that the change in momentum equals the impulse, which is the area under the force–time curve.

Denoting this force of impulsive nature by $i(t)$, it can be described as (Figure 8–17)

$$i(t) = \begin{cases} 0, & t < t_0 \\ f(t), & t_0 \le t \le t_0 + \varepsilon \\ 0, & t > t_0 + \varepsilon \end{cases} \tag{8-33}$$

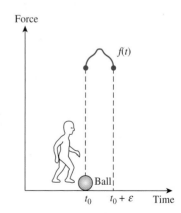

FIGURE 8–17

The time variation of the force applied on a ball when kicked by a football player.

This description is quite accurate and reasonable, except it is not practical. For one thing, it is not easy to measure the time interval ε or the functional form of the force $f(t)$ during ε. However, we need not know the precise value of ε or the exact form of $f(t)$. In most cases, what really matters is the impulse of the force (i.e., the area I under the force–time curve).

$$I = \int_{-\infty}^{\infty} i(t)\,dt = \int_{-\infty}^{t_0} 0\,dt + \int_{t_0}^{t_0+\varepsilon} f(t)\,dt + \int_{t_0+\varepsilon}^{\infty} 0\,dt = \int_{t_0}^{t_0+\varepsilon} f(t)\,dt \quad \textbf{(8–34)}$$

Thus, it is reasonable to assume the entire force to act at the instant t_0 at an intensity that is equal to the impulse I. With this idealization, we will now do what we have done before for step functions in defining the unit step function $u(t - t_0)$. Now we will do it for impulse functions by defining the **unit impulse function** or the **Dirac delta function** $\delta(t - t_0)$. It is described in a rather unconventional way as

$$\delta(t - t_0) = 0, \quad t \neq t_0 \quad \textbf{(8–35a)}$$

$$\int_0^{\infty} \delta(t - t_0)\,dt = 1 \quad \textbf{(8–35b)}$$

The delta function is better understood and makes more sense when studied in conjunction with a function. For example, the impulse $i(t)$ just discussed can be expressed with the help of a delta function as (Figure 8–18).

$$i(t) = I\delta(t - t_0) \quad \textbf{(8–36)}$$

It can be taken to mean the value of $i(t)$ is equal to zero for all t except t_0, where it is equal to I.

The real value of the delta function is realized when it appears under the integral sign. For example, we have

$$\int_0^{\infty} i(t)\delta(t - t_0)\,dt = i(t_0) = I$$

Or, for a general function $f(t)$, as

$$\int_0^{\infty} f(t)\delta(t - t_0)\,dt = f(t_0) \quad \textbf{(8–37)}$$

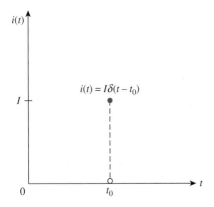

$i(t) = I\delta(t - t_0)$

FIGURE 8–18

The idealized description of a function of impulsive nature in terms of the delta function.

We will use the delta function in this context, and this equation can be taken as the *definition* of the delta function. The integration limits are immaterial as long as the interval includes the point t_0. Note that the delta function is not a function in the ordinary sense. It is more like an *operator* that selects the value of the function at t_0 according to the integral in Equation 8–37.

Noting the similarity of Equation 8–37 to the definition of Laplace transform, the Laplace transform of the delta function is easily determined by replacing $f(t)$ in Equation 8–37 by e^{-st}. We obtain (Figure 8–19).

$$L\{\delta(t - t_0)\} = \int_0^{\infty} e^{-st}\delta(t - t_0)\,dt = e^{-st_0} \quad \textbf{(8–38)}$$

For the special case of $t_0 = 0$, we have

$$L\{\delta(t - 0)\} = e^0 = 1 \quad \textbf{(8–39)}$$

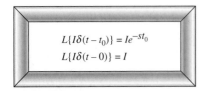

$L\{I\delta(t - t_0)\} = Ie^{-st_0}$
$L\{I\delta(t - 0)\} = I$

FIGURE 8–19

The Laplace transform of an impulse function with an impulse of magnitude I.

We point out that the dependent variable need not be a force and that the independent variable t is not necessarily time. It also can be the space variable. For example, the continuous heat dissipation from a thin resistance wire in the middle of a thick cylinder can be represented by $P\delta(r - 0)$, where r is the space variable in the radial direction and P is the magnitude of the heat dissipated.

EXAMPLE 8–11   Impulse Response of a Circuit

An electric circuit experiences a voltage surge of 20 V at time $t = 5$ s and another surge of 50 V at time $t = 30$ s. Obtain a mathematical equation for the imposed voltage $v(t)$, and determine its Laplace transform.

SOLUTION   The voltage function $v(t)$ can be expressed in stacked form as (Figure 8–20)

$$v(t) = \begin{cases} 0, & t < 5 \\ 20, & t = 5 \\ 0, & 5 < t < 30 \\ 50, & t = 30 \\ 0, & t > 30 \end{cases}$$

Using delta functions, we can also express $v(t)$ in a compact form as

$$v(t) = 20\delta(t - 5) + 50\delta(t - 30)$$

The Laplace transform of this function (from Equation 8–38) is

$$V(s) = L\{[20\delta(t - 5) + 50\delta(t - 30)]\} = 20e^{-5s} + 50e^{-30s}$$

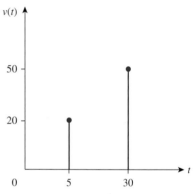

FIGURE 8–20

The voltage function described in Example 8–11.

Section Review

8–5C   Explain how the functions $u(t - t_0)\,f(t)$ and $u(t - t_0)\,f(t - t_0)$ differ from $f(t)$.

8–5 ▪ LAPLACE TRANSFORMS OF DERIVATIVES AND DIFFERENTIAL EQUATIONS

Our main goal in this chapter is to solve differential equations with the Laplace transform. But we cannot attempt to take the Laplace transform of differential equations unless we know the Laplace transform of derivatives.

The Laplace transform of a derivative is obtained by treating the derivative like an ordinary function and applying the definition of the transform. For example, the Laplace transform of the nth derivative of the function $y(t)$ can be determined from

$$L\{f^{(n)}(t)\} = \int_0^\infty e^{-st} f^{(n)}(t)\,dt \tag{8–40}$$

if this integral converges for some values of s. Thus, the derivative function $f^{(n)}(t)$ must satisfy certain requirements if its Laplace transform is to exist.

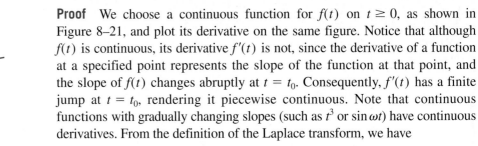

THEOREM 8–3   Laplace Transform of a Derivative

If $f(t)$ is a continuous function of exponential order on $t \geq 0$ and its derivative $f'(t)$ is at least piecewise continuous, then

$$L\{f'(t)\} = sF(s) - f(0) \qquad (8\text{-}41)$$

where $F(s)$ is the Laplace transform of $f(t)$ and $f(0)$ is the value of $f(t)$ at the $t = 0$. (If $f(t)$ is not continuous at $t = 0$, then $f(0) = f(0+)$, where $f(0+)$ is the limit of $f(t)$ as t approaches zero from the right.)

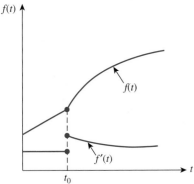

FIGURE 8–21

A continuous function with a
piecewise-continuous derivative.

Proof   We choose a continuous function for $f(t)$ on $t \geq 0$, as shown in Figure 8–21, and plot its derivative on the same figure. Notice that although $f(t)$ is continuous, its derivative $f'(t)$ is not, since the derivative of a function at a specified point represents the slope of the function at that point, and the slope of $f(t)$ changes abruptly at $t = t_0$. Consequently, $f'(t)$ has a finite jump at $t = t_0$, rendering it piecewise continuous. Note that continuous functions with gradually changing slopes (such as t^3 or $\sin \omega t$) have continuous derivatives. From the definition of the Laplace transform, we have

$$L\{f'(t)\} = \int_0^\infty e^{-st} f'(t)\, dt$$

$$= \int_0^{t_0} e^{-st} f'(t)\, dt + \int_{t_0}^\infty e^{-st} f'(t)\, dt$$

The integrands of the two integrals on the right are now continuous; thus, integration by parts is applicable. Taking $u = e^{-st}$ and $dv = f'(t)\, dt$, we have $du = -se^{-st}$ and $v = f(t)$. Then integration by parts yields

$$L\{f'(t)\} = \left[e^{-st}f(t)\,\big|_0^{t_0} - \int_0^{t_0} (-se^{-st})f(t)\, dt \right]$$

$$+ \left[e^{-st}f(t)\,\big|_{t_0}^\infty - \int_{t_0}^\infty (-se^{-st})f(t)\, dt \right]$$

$$= e^{-st_0}f(t_{0-}) - f(0) + \lim_{t \to \infty} e^{-st}f(t) - e^{-st_0}f(t_{0+}) + s\int_0^\infty e^{-st}f(t)\, dt$$

$$= e^{-st_0}\big[f(t_{0-}) - f(t_{0+})\big] - f(0) + sF(s) \qquad (8\text{-}42)$$

$$= sF(s) - f(0)$$

since $f(t_{0-}) = f(t_{0+})$ and $\lim_{t \to \infty} e^{-st} f(t) = 0$. Note that the first condition is true for continuous functions only, and this is the reason we are requiring the function $f(t)$ to be continuous. The second condition is a direct consequence of $f(t)$ being of exponential order. This condition is satisfied by choosing s to be greater than a if $f(t)$ is a function of exponential order a.

There is another observation that can be made from this proof. The function $f(t)$ does not have to be continuous to possess a Laplace transform. It suffices to be only piecewise continuous. But in this case, its Laplace transform will involve the jumps at the points of discontinuity, as given in Equation 8–42 (Figure 8–22).

For simplicity in the proof, we assumed $f'(t)$ to have a single jump discontinuity. We would obtain the same result if we repeated the proof with $f'(t)$ having any number of jump discontinuities.

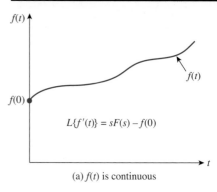

(a) $f(t)$ is continuous

COROLLARY 1 to THEOREM 8–3

If f(t) and f′(t) are continuous functions of exponential order on $t \geq 0$ and f″(t) is at least piecewise continuous, then

$$L\{f''(t)\} = s^2F(s) - sf(0) - f'(0) \qquad \textbf{(8–43)}$$

where F(s) is the Laplace transform of f(t), and f(0) and f′(0) are the values of f(t) and f′(t) at $t = 0$, respectively.

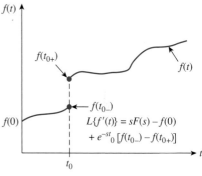

(b) $f(t)$ is piecewise continuous

FIGURE 8–22

The Laplace transform of the first derivative of (a) a continuous function and (b) a piecewise-continuous function.

Proof This is a direct extension of Theorem 8–3 and can be proved easily by defining $g(t) = f'(t)$ and applying Theorem 8–2 twice:

$$\begin{aligned}
L\{f''(t)\} &= L\{g'(t)\} \\
&= sL\{g(t)\} - g(0) \\
&= sL\{f'(t)\} - f'(0) \\
&= s[sF(s) - f(0)] - f'(0) \\
&= s^2F(s) - sf(0) - f'(0)
\end{aligned}$$

COROLLARY 2 to THEOREM 8–3

If f(t), f′(t), f″(t), ..., $f^{(n-1)}(t)$ are continuous functions of exponential order on $t \geq 0$ and $f^{(n)}(t)$ is at least piecewise continuous, then the Laplace transform of $f^{(n)}(t)$ exists and is given by

$$L\{f^{(n)}(t)\} = s^nF(s) - s^{(n-1)}f(0) - s^{(n-2)}f'(0) - \cdots - f^{(n-1)}(0) \quad \textbf{(8–44)}$$

where F(s) is the Laplace transform of f(t), and f(0), f′(0), ..., $f^{(n-1)}(0)$ are the initial values of f(t) and its derivatives.

Proof This corollary can be proved easily by mathematical induction or by successively applying Theorem 8–3 n times as we did in Corollary 1.

The Laplace Transform and Differential Equations

The Laplace transform of a differential equation is obtained by taking the Laplace transform of each term on each side of the equation and applying the linearity of the transform. That is, use the principle that the Laplace transform of a sum is the sum of the Laplace transforms. This is now illustrated with an example.

In Example 8–12, the differential equation was converted into an algebraic equation in $Y(s)$, which is the Laplace transform of the unknown function $y(t)$.

EXAMPLE 8–12   **Laplace Transform of Two Differential Equations**

Determine the Laplace transform of the differential equations
(a) $y'' - 2y' + 3y = 0$ and (b) $y' = te^{3t} + 2$, and solve for $Y(s)$ in each case.

SOLUTION   We assume the derivatives satisfy the conditions of Theorem 2, and thus, their Laplace transform exist. Noting that the Laplace transform of zero is zero and using the Laplace transform relations for derivatives, we obtain the following.

(a) $L\{y'' - 2y' + 3y\} = L\{y''\} - 2L\{y'\} + 3L\{y\}$

$$= [s^2 Y(s) - sy(0) - y'(0)] - 2[sY(s) - y(0)] + 3Y(s)$$

$$= (s^2 - 2s + 3)Y(s) - y'(0) - (s - 2)y(0) = 0$$

Solving for $Y(s)$, we obtain

$$Y(s) = \frac{y'(0) + (s - 2)y(0)}{s^2 - 2s + 3}$$

(b) $L\{y' - te^{3t} - 2\} = L\{y'\} - L\{te^{3t}\} - 2L\{1\}$

$$= [sY(s) - y(0)] - \frac{1}{(s - 3)^2} - \frac{2}{s} = 0$$

Solving for $Y(s)$, we obtain

$$Y(s) = \frac{1}{s(s - 3)^2} + \frac{2}{s^2} + \frac{y(0)}{s}$$

In both solutions, $y(0)$ and $y'(0)$ are the specified initial conditions.

In both cases, we obtained explicit solutions for $Y(s)$. Now the question becomes one of determining the function whose Laplace transform is known—in other words, finding the *inverse Laplace transform* of a function $F(s)$. This is discussed in the next section.

Notice that the function $Y(s)$ already contains the initial conditions. Thus, the inversion give us the solution of the problem directly (Figure 8–23). This is in contrast to the ordinary method of solution that involves obtaining the general solution of a differential equation and then applying the initial or the boundary conditions to obtain the solution for the particular problem on hand.

Differential Equation

$$ay'' + by' + c = 0$$

Laplace Transform

$$Y(s) = \frac{(as + b)y(0) + ay'(0)}{as^2 + bs + c}$$

FIGURE 8–23

The Laplace transform of a differential equation also incorporates the initial conditions.

Section Review

8–6   Determine the Laplace transform of the following differential equations, and obtain a relation for the transform of the unknown function, $Y(s)$.

(a) $y''' - 2y' + 5y = 0$ (b) $y'' = 3te^{2t}$

$$\left(\text{Answers: (a) } Y(s) = \frac{(s^2 - 2)y(0) + sy'(0) + y''(0)}{s^3 - 2s + 5} \text{ and} \right.$$

$$\left. \text{(b) } Y(s) = \frac{(s - 2)^2 y'(0) + s(s - 2)^2 y(0) + 3}{s^2(s - 2)^2} \right)$$

8–6 ▪ INVERSE LAPLACE TRANSFORM

The solution of differential equations using the Laplace transform requires first the determination of the transform of the solution $Y(s)$, which is easy and straightforward, and then the determination of the function $y(t)$ that has $Y(s)$ as its transform, which is much more difficult. Determining the original function from its transform is called *finding the inverse (or inverting) the transformed function*. The **inverse Laplace transform** is denoted by the symbol L^{-1}:

$$L^{-1}\{F(s)\} = f(t) \tag{8–45}$$

The fastest and easiest way of finding the inverse of a transform is to look through a table of Laplace transforms and read the function corresponding to the given transform. Assuming you can find it in the table, of course. Extensive transform tables are available in the literature, but most likely, the transform you have will not be in the table unless it is a very simple or commonly encountered function. It is possible to obtain the inverse function directly, but this involves integration in the complex domain that is not easy to do without a sufficient background on complex variables. Then the only other choice we have left is to use the convolution theorem or to express the given transform as a sum of simple fractions that can be found in the transform tables. Both approaches are discussed in the next sections. But first, we will discuss the properties of the inverse Laplace transform, which are summarized in Table 8–4. They follow directly from the properties of the Laplace transform that were discussed and proved in Section 8–3.

1. $$L^{-1}\{C_1 F_1(s) + C_2 F_2(s)\} = C_1 L^{-1}\{F_1(s)\} + C_2 L^{-1}\{F_2(s)\}$$

    (linearity) **(8–46)**

    That is, the inverse Laplace transform is a linear operator, just like the transform itself. For example,

    $$L^{-1}\left\{\frac{2}{s} - \frac{3}{s+5}\right\} = 2L^{-1}\left\{\frac{1}{s}\right\} - 3L^{-1}\left\{\frac{1}{s+5}\right\} = 2 - 3e^{-5t}$$

2. $$L^{-1}\{F(s-k)\} = e^{kt}L^{-1}\{F(s)\} \quad \text{(shifting property)} \tag{8–47}$$

    That is, the inverse of a Laplace transform in $s - k$ (where k is a constant) can be found by replacing all occurrences of $s - k$ by s, determining the inverse, and multiplying that inverse by e^{kt}. For example,

    $$L^{-1}\left\{\frac{s+3}{(s+3)^2 - w^2}\right\} = e^{-3t}L^{-1}\left\{\frac{s}{s^2 - w^2}\right\} = e^{-3t}\cosh wt$$

3. $$L^{-1}\{sF(s)\} = \frac{d}{dt}L^{-1}\{F(s)\} \tag{8–48}$$

TABLE 8–4

Basic Properties of the Inverse Laplace Transform

1 $L^{-1}\{C_1 F_1(s) + C_2 F_2(s)\} =$ $= C_1 L^{-1}\{F_1(s)\} + C_2 L^{-1}\{F_2(s)\}$
2 $L^{-1}\{F(s-k)\} = e^{kt}L^{-1}\{F(s)\}$
3 $L^{-1}\{sF(s)\} = \dfrac{d}{dt}L^{-1}\{F(s)\}$
4 $L^{-1}\left\{\dfrac{F(s)}{s}\right\} = \displaystyle\int_0^t L^{-1}\{F(s)\}dt$
5 $L^{-1}\left\{\dfrac{d^n F(s)}{ds^n}\right\} = (-t)^n L^{-1}\{F(s)\}$
6 $L^{-1}\{e^{t_0 s}F(s)\} = u(t - t_0)f(t - t_0)$

That is, the inverse of Laplace transform that contains the factors can be found by disregarding the factor s, determining the inverse of the remaining part, and differentiating that inverse with respect to t. For example,

$$L^{-1}\left\{\frac{s}{s^2+9}\right\} = \frac{d}{dt}L^{-1}\left\{\frac{1}{s^2+9}\right\} = \frac{d}{dt}\left(\frac{\sin 3t}{3}\right) = \cos 3t$$

4.
$$L^{-1}\left\{\frac{F(s)}{s}\right\} = \int_0^t L^{-1}\{F(s)\}dt \qquad \text{(8-49)}$$

That is, the inverse of a Laplace transform that contains the factor $1/s$ can be found by disregarding the factor $1/s$, determining the inverse of the remaining part, and integrating that inverse with respect to t from 0 to t. For example,

$$L^{-1}\left\{\frac{6}{s(s-2)}\right\} = \int_0^t L^{-1}\left\{\frac{6}{s-2}\right\}dt = 6\int_0^t e^{2t}dt = 6\frac{e^{2t}}{2}\bigg|_0^t = 3e^{2t} - 3$$

5.
$$L^{-1}\left\{\frac{d^n F(s)}{ds^n}\right\} = (-t)^n L^{-1}\{F(s)\} \qquad \text{(8-50)}$$

That is, the inverse of the nth derivative of a Laplace transform can be found by determining the inverse of the transform and multiplying it with the nth power of $-t$. For example,

$$L^{-1}\left\{\frac{2}{s^3}\right\} = L^{-1}\left\{\frac{d^2\left(\frac{1}{s}\right)}{ds^2}\right\} = (-t)^2 L^{-1}\left\{\frac{1}{s}\right\} = t^2 \times 1 = t^2$$

since $2/s^3$ is the second derivative of $1/s$.

6.
$$L^{-1}\{e^{-t_0 s}F(s)\} = u(t-t_0)f(t-t_0) \qquad \text{(8-51)}$$

That is, the inverse of a Laplace transform that contains the factor $e^{-t_0 s}$ can be found by disregarding the factor $e^{-t_0 s}$, determining the inverse of the remaining part, replacing the variable t by $t - t_0$, and multiplying it by the unit step function $u(t - t_0)$. For example,

$$L^{-1}\left\{\frac{2e^{-3s}}{s^3}\right\} = u(t-3)L^{-1}\left\{\frac{2}{s^3}\right\}\bigg|_{t\to t-3} = u(t-3)(t^2)\big|_{t\to t-3}$$
$$= u(t-3)(t-3)^2$$

7.
$$L^{-1}\{F(ks)\} = \frac{1}{k}f\left(\frac{t}{k}\right) \qquad \text{(scaling property)} \qquad \text{(8-52)}$$

That is, the inverse of a Laplace transform that is a function of ks instead of s can be found by replacing all occurrences of ks by s, determining its inverse replacing all occurrences of t in the inverse by kt, and dividing it by k. For example,

$$L^{-1}\left\{\frac{5s}{25s^2+9}\right\} = \frac{1}{5}\cos\frac{3t}{5}$$

since

$$L^{-1}\left\{\frac{s}{s^2 + 9}\right\} = \cos 3t$$

As an additional basic property, we can mention the *uniqueness* of the inverse transform. The inverse of a given function is a unique continuous function. Therefore, if two continuous functions have the same Laplace transform, they are identical. That is, there is a one-to-one correspondence between continuous functions and their transforms. For functions that are only piecewise continuous, uniqueness still holds over the continuous sections of the functions. Consequently, two piecewise-continuous functions with the same Laplace transform may differ only at their points of discontinuity (Figure 8–24).

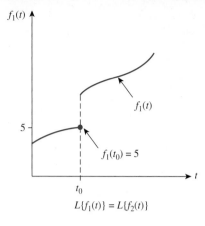

Completing Quadratic Polynomials to Square

When solving differential equations with Laplace transform, we often end up with a quadratic factor in the *denominator*. For example,

$$\frac{1}{s^2 + bs + c}$$

This form does not appear in the Laplace transform Table 8–1. Therefore, it is desirable to express it as

$$\frac{1}{(s + k)^2 + d}$$

which has a known inverse transform. This is easily accomplished by adding and subtracting $(b/2)^2$ as

$$s^2 + bs + c = s^2 + bs + \left(\frac{b}{2}\right)^2 - \left(\frac{b}{2}\right)^2 + c = \left(s + \frac{b}{2}\right)^2 + c - \left(\frac{b}{2}\right)^2$$

Thus, we have the following relation for completing the quadratic polynomials to square:

$$s^2 + bs + c = \left(s + \frac{b}{2}\right)^2 + c - \left(\frac{b}{2}\right)^2 \qquad \text{(8–53)}$$

For example, the inverse Laplace transform of

$$F(s) = \frac{5}{s^2 + 8s + 10}$$

is easily determined by first completing the quadratic polynomial in the denominator to square:

$$F(s) = \frac{5}{s^2 + 8s + 10} = \frac{5}{(s + 4)^2 + 10 - 16} = \frac{5}{(s + 4)^2 - 6}$$

Now the inverse Laplace transform is determined from Table 8–1 to be

$$f(t) = L^{-1}\left\{\frac{5}{(s + 4)^2 - 6}\right\} = 5e^{-4t}L^{-1}\left\{\frac{1}{s^2 - 6}\right\} = \frac{5e^{-4t}\sinh\sqrt{6}t}{\sqrt{6}}$$

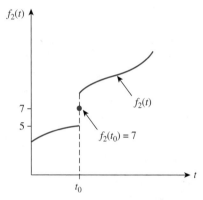

FIGURE 8–24

Two piecewise-continuous functions will have the same Laplace transform if they differ only at their points of discontinuity.

Section Review

8–7   Determine the inverse Laplace transform of the following functions using the basic properties of the inverse Laplace transform and Table 8–1.

$$\text{(a) } F(s) = 5 + \frac{1}{s - 2} \qquad \text{(b) } F(s) = \frac{s}{s^2 - 4} \qquad \text{(c) } F(s) = \frac{3}{s(s^2 + 1)}$$

(*Answers:* (a) $f(t) = 5\delta(t) + e^{2t}$, (b) $f(t) = \cosh 2t$, and (c) $f(t) = 3(1 - \cos t)$)

8–7 ▪ PARTIAL FRACTIONS

When solving differential equations with Laplace transforms, we often end up with a complicated rational fraction for which no inverse Laplace transform can be found in the transform tables. Then it becomes necessary to decompose the complicated rational fraction into simpler fractions that can be found in the tables. This is accomplished with partial fractions.

Partial fractions appear in calculus when determining the integral of complicated rational functions. For example, it is much easier to integrate

$$\frac{1}{x} - \frac{2}{x + 1}$$

than to integrate its equivalent

$$\frac{1 - x}{x(x + 1)}.$$

The method of partial fractions is a systematic approach to express a complicated function as a sum of several simple fractions.

But first some definitions. A function that is expressed as a ratio of two polynomials is called a **rational fraction**. A rational fraction is called a **proper fraction** if the degree of its numerator is lower than the degree of its denominator. Otherwise, it is called an **improper fraction**. We will restrict the discussion to proper fractions only, since the solutions of differential equations typically result in proper fractions. Besides, any improper fraction can be expressed as the sum of a polynomial and a proper fraction by simply dividing its numerator by the denominator.

Now let us consider three simple fractions and add them up.

$$\frac{1}{x} - \frac{2}{x + 2} + \frac{4}{x - 3} = \frac{3x^2 + 13x - 6}{x(x + 2)(x - 3)}$$

where $x(x + 2)(x - 3)$ is the *least common denominator*. Obviously, it is a simple and straightforward matter to obtain a complicated fraction from simple fractions. But how about the reverse process? Can we start with the complicated fraction on the right-hand side and obtain the simple fractions on the left? Well, it turns out that we can, but not so easily. We need to observe some important rules to accomplish it.

Rule 1   *Make sure the given fraction is proper.* That is, visually verify that the degree of the numerator is lower than the degree of the denominator. For example, the fraction

$$\frac{3x^2 + 13x - 6}{x(x + 2)(x - 3)}$$

is a proper fraction, since its numerator is a *second*-degree polynomial, and its denominator is a *third* degree one.

Rule 2 *Don't pay much attention to the numerator.* It has no effect on the selection of partial fractions.

Rule 3 *Make the factors in the denominator as simple as possible.* This will result in simpler partial fractions. For example, of the two equivalent fractions:

$$\frac{x^2 - 3x + 1}{x(x^2 + x - 6)} = \frac{x^2 - 3x + 1}{x(x - 2)(x + 3)}$$

the second one will yield simpler fractions.

Rule 4 *Always keep in mind that the partial fractions of a proper fraction are also proper.* That is, the degree of the numerator of any partial fraction is lower than the degree of its denominator. Therefore, the following complicated fraction can be expressed as

$$\frac{3x^2 + 13x - 6}{x(x + 2)(x - 3)} = \frac{A}{x} + \frac{B}{x + 2} + \frac{C}{x - 3} \tag{8-54}$$

where A, B, and C are unknown constants (i.e., zeroth-order polynomials) since all of the factors in the denominator are first-degree polynomials. The partial fraction corresponding to a linear factor $ax + b$ in the denominator is taken to be $A/(ax + b)$, where A is a constant. The partial fraction corresponding to a quadratic factor $ax^2 + bx + c$ in the denominator is taken to be

$$(Ax + B)/(ax^2 + bx + c)$$

and so on (Table 8–5).

Rule 5 *Treat repeated factors in the denominator as ordinary factors, but include a term for each power of the repeated factor.* For example,

$$\frac{x^3 + 5x^2 - 7}{x^3(x - 5)^2(x^2 + 1)^2} = \left(\frac{A}{x} + \frac{B}{x^2} + \frac{C}{x^3}\right) + \left[\frac{D}{x - 5} + \frac{E}{(x - 5)^2}\right]$$

$$+ \left[\frac{Fx + G}{x^2 + 1} + \frac{Hx + I}{(x^2 + 1)^2}\right]$$

Of course, we could have selected $(Ax + B)/(x - 5)^2$ to correspond to the quadratic factor $(x - 5)^2$, but using a separate term for each power of the repeated term results in simpler partial fractions. These two approaches may appear to be different, but they are identical:

$$\frac{Ax + B}{(x - 5)^2} = \frac{A(x - 5) + (5A + B)}{(x - 5)^2}$$

$$= \frac{A}{(x - 5)} + \frac{5A + B}{(x - 5)^2} = \frac{A}{x - 5} + \frac{C}{(x - 5)^2}$$

These rules clearly state how many constants we need to use when decomposing a complicated fraction, but it is always nice to have some rules to check our work:

Check Rule 1 *The number of unknown constants introduced to correspond to a factor in the denominator is equal to the degree of that factor (Figure 8–25).*

TABLE 8–5

The Selection of Partial Fractions to Correspond to Certain Types of Factors in the Denominator

Factor in Denominator	Corresponding Partial Fraction
x	$\dfrac{A}{x}$
$x - 3$	$\dfrac{A}{x - 3}$
$5x + 7$	$\dfrac{A}{5x + 7}$
$x^2 + 6$	$\dfrac{Ax + B}{x^2 + 6}$
$x^2 - 3x + 5$	$\dfrac{Ax + B}{x^2 - 3x + 5}$
$3x^2 - 7$	$\dfrac{Ax + B}{3x^2 - 7}$
$x^3 - 5$	$\dfrac{Ax^2 + Bx + C}{x^3 - 5}$
$x^3 - 3x^2 + 1$	$\dfrac{Ax^2 + Bx + C}{x^3 - 3x^2 + 1}$
$2x^3 + 5x - 4$	$\dfrac{Ax^2 + Bx + C}{2x^3 + 5x - 4}$
x^3	$\dfrac{A}{x} + \dfrac{B}{x^2} + \dfrac{C}{x^3}$
$(x - 7)^2$	$\dfrac{A}{x - 7} + \dfrac{B}{(x - 7)^2}$
$(x^2 + 3)^2$	$\dfrac{Ax + B}{x^2 + 3} + \dfrac{Cx + D}{(x^2 + 3)^2}$

$$\frac{1}{\cdots(x^2 + 3)\cdots} = \cdots + \frac{Ax + B}{x^2 + 3} + \cdots$$

Degree of the factor: 2 ⟶ Number of constants introduced: 2

FIGURE 8–25

The number of unknown constants introduced to correspond to a factor in the denominator is equal to the degree of that factor (*check rule* 1).

Check Rule 2 *The total number of unknown constants in the partial fractions equals the degree of the entire denominator.*

As an example, consider the following decomposition process:

$$\frac{3x^2 - 6x + 5}{x(x^2 + 3)(x - 5)^2} = \left(\frac{A}{x}\right) + \left(\frac{Bx + C}{x^2 + 3}\right) + \left[\frac{D}{x - 5} + \frac{E}{(x - 5)^2}\right] \quad \text{(8-55)}$$

We can easily verify that this decomposition process satisfies both check rules, since the first factor in the denominator is a first-degree polynomial, and the other two factors are second-degree polynomials. Also, the entire denominator is the product form of a fifth-degree polynomial.

Determination of Unknown Constants

Decomposing a complicated fraction whose denominator is equivalent to an nth-degree polynomial results in n unknown constants. These constants can be determined by any of the several available methods. We now discuss two of them.

Method 1 Multiply each term on both sides of the equation by the denominator of the original fraction, rearrange, equate the coefficients of like powers of x on both sides, and solve the resulting equations for the unknown coefficients.

We now demonstrate this method by applying it to the following problem using Equation 8–54:

$$\frac{3x^2 + 13x - 6}{x(x + 2)(x - 3)} = \frac{A}{x} + \frac{B}{x + 2} + \frac{C}{x - 3}$$

Multiplying each term by $x(x + 2)(x - 3)$ and rearranging, we obtain

$$\begin{aligned}
3x^2 + 13x - 6 &= A(x + 2)(x - 3) + Bx(x - 3) + Cx(x + 2) \\
&= A(x^2 - x - 6) + B(x^2 - 3x) + C(x^2 + 2x) \\
&= (A + B + C)x^2 + (-A - 3B + 2C)x - 6A
\end{aligned}$$

Equating like powers of x, we have

$$\begin{aligned}
3 &= A + B + C \\
13 &= -A - 3B + 2C \\
-6 &= -6A
\end{aligned}$$

Solving these three equations for the three unknowns A, B, and C yields $A = 1$, $B = -2$, and $C = 4$. Substituting, we obtain

$$\frac{3x^2 + 13x - 6}{x(x + 2)(x - 3)} = \frac{1}{x} - \frac{2}{x + 2} + \frac{4}{x - 3} \quad \text{(8-56)}$$

The method just described is the standard method of determining the unknown coefficients, and it always works. However, it is often laborious, since it involves considerable manipulations and requires the simultaneous solution of a system of linear algebraic equations.

Method 2 Multiply each term on both sides of equation by the denominator of the partial fractions, simplify, and replace all the x's by the root of the denominator (Figure 8–26). This process often eliminates all of the unknown constants except one, which is readily evaluated. Repeat the process for other partial fractions.

To demonstrate this method, again consider Equation 8–54, as

$$\frac{3x^2 + 13x - 6}{x(x+2)(x-3)} = \frac{A}{x} + \frac{B}{x+2} + \frac{C}{x-3}$$

Multiplying both sides by the denominator of the first partial fraction x, we have

$$\frac{3x^2 + 13x - 6}{(x+2)(x-3)} = A + \frac{Bx}{x+2} + \frac{Cx}{x-3}$$

Setting $x = 0$ eliminates the last two terms and yields A directly, giving

$$A = \frac{3x^2 + 13x - 6}{(x+2)(x-3)}\bigg|_{x=0} = \frac{-6}{-6} = 1$$

Repeating the process with the denominators of the other two terms, $x + 2$ and $x - 3$, yields

$$B = \frac{3x^2 + 13x - 6}{x(x-3)}\bigg|_{x=-2} = \frac{-20}{10} = -2$$

and

$$C = \frac{3x^2 + 13x - 6}{x(x+2)}\bigg|_{x=3} = \frac{60}{15} = 4$$

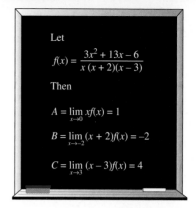

Let

$$f(x) = \frac{3x^2 + 13x - 6}{x(x+2)(x-3)}$$

Then

$$A = \lim_{x \to 0} x f(x) = 1$$

$$B = \lim_{x \to -2} (x+2) f(x) = -2$$

$$C = \lim_{x \to 3} (x-3) f(x) = 4$$

FIGURE 8–26

An alternative way of determining the unknown constants in partial fractions.

This method yields equations with a single unknown, and this makes it very attractive. It is useful for partial fractions with linear denominators, but not as useful for partial fractions with quadratic or higher-order denominators having repeated roots. However, we can always use this method to determine at least some of the unknown coefficients. The necessary equations to determine the remaining coefficients can be determined by applying Method 1 or simply by substituting some x values into both sides of the equation, since the equation holds for any x value. Substitution of an x value will result in an equation for the unknown coefficients. Substitution of another x value will result in another equation. Clever choices of x provide considerable simplifications.

EXAMPLE 8–13   **Partial Fraction Method**

Using the partial fraction method, determine the inverse transform of

$$Y(s) = \frac{s}{(s+1)(s^2+1)}$$

SOLUTION The given function can be expressed in terms of partial fractions as

$$\frac{s}{(s+1)(s^2+1)} = \frac{A}{s+1} + \frac{Bs+C}{s^2+1}$$

Applying Method 1, the unknown constant coefficients are determined to be

$$s = A(s^2 + 1) + (Bs + C)(s + 1) = As^2 + A + Bs^2 + Bs + Cs + C$$
$$= (A + B)s^2 + (B + C)s + (A + C)$$

Equating the coefficients of like power of s on both sides, we have

$$0 = A + B \rightarrow A = -B$$
$$1 = B + C$$
$$0 = A + C \rightarrow A = -C$$

Solving these three equations yields $A = -B = -C = -1/2$. Substituting, we obtain

$$\frac{s}{(s + 1)(s^2 + 1)} = -\frac{1}{2}\frac{1}{s + 1} + \frac{1}{2}\frac{s}{s^2 + 1} + \frac{1}{2}\frac{1}{s^2 + 1}$$

Picking the inverse transforms from Table 8–1, $y(t)$ is determined to be

$$y(t) = \frac{1}{2}(\sin t + \cos t - e^{-t})$$

Section Review

8–8 Determine the inverse Laplace transform of the following functions using the partial fractions method whenever necessary.

(a) $F(s) = \dfrac{3s - 1}{s(s + 1)(s - 3)}$ (b) $F(s) = \dfrac{s + 1}{s^3 - 1}$

$\left(Answers: \text{(a) } f(t) = \dfrac{1}{3} - e^{-t} + \dfrac{2}{3}e^{3t} \text{ and (b) } f(t) = \dfrac{2}{3}\left(e^t - e^{-t/2} \cos \dfrac{\sqrt{3}}{2}t \right) \right)$

8–8 ▪ THE CONVOLUTION THEOREM

When solving differential equations, we frequently end up with an expression for $Y(s)$ that is not the transform of any known function, but can be expressed as the product of two functions of s whose inverses are known. That is, $Y(s)$ can be expressed as $Y(s) = F(s)\,G(s)$, where $F(s)$ and $G(s)$ are the transforms of the known functions $f(t)$ and $g(t)$. In such cases, the inverse transform of $Y(s)$ can be determined from the convolution theorem, which can be expressed as follows.

THEOREM 8–4   Convolution Theorem

The inverse Laplace transform of the product of two functions $F(s)$ and $G(s)$ can be determined from the integral.

$$L^{-1}\{F(s)G(s)\} = \int_0^t f(t - \tau)g(\tau)d\tau = \int_0^t f(\tau)g(t - \tau)d\tau \qquad \textbf{(8–57)}$$

where τ is a dummy variable.

This integral is called *the convolution of f(t) and g(t)* and is sometimes denoted by $f(t)*g(t)$. Note that the variable t appears in both the integrand and the upper limit of the definite integral; thus, this integration will result in a function of t.

Proof   Using the definition of Laplace transform with dummy variables u and τ, we have

$$F(s)G(s) = \int_{u=0}^{\infty} e^{-su}f(u)du \int_{\tau=0}^{\infty} e^{-s\tau}g(\tau)d\tau$$

$$= \int_{\tau=0}^{\infty}\int_{u=0}^{\infty} e^{-s(u+\tau)}f(u)g(\tau)dud\tau$$

since the integrands $e^{-su}f(u)$ and $e^{-s\tau}g(\tau)$ approach zero as $u \to \infty$ and $\tau \to \infty$, and each integrand depends on its own variable only.

We now change the variable of the inner integral from u to $t = u + \tau$ for fixed τ. This change of variable changes the integration domain from a rectangle extending to infinity in both directions in the $u - \tau$ plane to a wedge-shaped region extending to infinity in the $t - \tau$ plane, as shown in Figure 8–27b. Noting that $du = dt$, we have

$$F(s)G(s) = \int_{\tau=0}^{\infty}\int_{t=\tau}^{\infty} e^{-st}f(t - \tau)g(\tau)dtd\tau$$

Finally, we would like to change the order of integration of this double integral. This is not as simple as it sounds, however, since the lower limit of the inner integral contains the variable of the outer integral. So we need to go back to basics. The integrand of the double integral represents a surface in space, and the double integral represents the volume under this surface with integration limits specifying the boundaries of its base (the domain of integration). Therefore, we can change the order and limits of integration so long as we cover the same base. In this case, we can cover the same base by marching in the τ direction first from $\tau = 0$ to $\tau = t$ and then advancing a differential amount dt in the t direction each time from $t = 0$ to infinity, as shown in Figure 8–27c. Thus,

$$F(s)G(s) = \int_{t=0}^{\infty}\int_{\tau=0}^{t} e^{-st}f(t - \tau)g(\tau)d\tau dt$$

$$= \int_{t=0}^{\infty} e^{-st}\left[\int_{\tau=0}^{t} f(t - \tau)g(\tau)d\tau\right]dt$$

$$= L\left\{\int_{0}^{t} f(t - \tau)g(\tau)d\tau\right\}$$

or

$$L^{-1}\{F(s)G(s)\} = \int_{0}^{t} f(t - \tau)g(\tau)d\tau$$

This completes the proof.

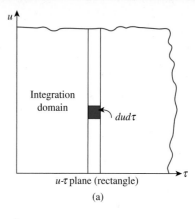

u-τ plane (rectangle)

(a)

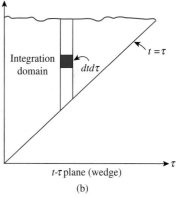

t-τ plane (wedge)

(b)

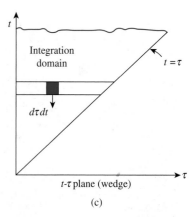

t-τ plane (wedge)

(c)

FIGURE 8–27

Changing the domain and the order of integration in the proof of the convolution theorem.

EXAMPLE 8–14   Application of the Convolution Theorem

Using the convolution theorem, determine the inverse transform of

$$Y(s) = \frac{s}{(s + 1)(s^2 + 1)}$$

SOLUTION   The given function can be treated as a product of $F(s)$ and $G(s)$, where

$$F(s) = \frac{1}{s + 1} \quad \text{and} \quad G(s) = \frac{s}{s^2 + 1}$$

The inverse transforms of these two functions are given in Table 8–1 to be

$$f(t) = e^{-t} \quad \text{and} \quad g(t) = \cos t$$

Thus, from the convolution theorem, we have

$$y(t) = L^{-1}\{Y(s)\} = L^{-1}\{F(s)G(s)\} = \int_0^t f(t - \tau)g(\tau)d\tau$$

$$= \int_0^t e^{-(t-\tau)} \cos \tau d\tau = e^{-t} \int_o^t e^\tau \cos \tau d\tau$$

Using the integral tables, $y(t)$ is determined to be

$$y(t) = \frac{1}{2}(\cos t + \sin t - e^{-t})$$

which is the same result obtained in Example 8–13 using the partial fractions method.

Section Review

8–9   Determine the inverse Laplace transform of the following functions using the convolution theorem.

(a) $F(s) = \dfrac{2}{(s + 1)(s + 2)}$ (b) $Y(s) = \dfrac{5}{s^2(s - 1)^2}$

(*Answers*: (a) $f(t) = -2(e^{-2t} - e^{-t})$ and (b) $f(t) = 5te^t - 10e^t + 5t + 10$)

8–9 ▪ SOLVING DIFFERENTIAL EQUATIONS BY LAPLACE TRANSFORM

The solution of differential equations with constant coefficients by Laplace transform involves three basic steps (Figure 8–28):

Step 1. Apply the Laplace transform to the differential equation. That is, take the Laplace transform of each term in the differential equation. This will result in an algebraic equation in $Y(s)$, which is the transform of the unknown function $y(t)$.

Step 2. Solve for $Y(s)$. This usually results in a fraction in s.

Step 3. Determine the unknown function $y(t)$ by taking the inverse of $Y(s)$. This step usually requires expressing $Y(s)$ in terms of simple fractions and then using the transform tables.

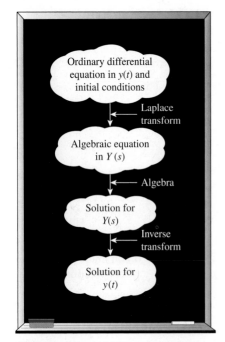

FIGURE 8–28

The basic steps involved in the solution of differential equations by Laplace transform.

Before we illustrate the procedure with several examples, some comments are in order. You will notice that the transformed equation incorporates all the specified conditions at $t = 0$. Therefore, one no longer needs to deal with the unknown coefficients and to apply the boundary conditions to determine those coefficients.

You will also notice that the transformed equation involves specified values of the unknown function and its derivatives at a *fixed point only*, typically at $t = 0$. However, the method can be modified to handle boundary conditions specified at some time other than $t = 0$.

EXAMPLE 8–15   Temperature of a Cooling Copper Ball

A small copper ball at 80°C is dropped into a large tank that is filled with ice water at 0°C, as shown in Figure 8–29. Heat is transferred from the copper ball to the water, and the temperature of the ball starts to drop as a result. The heat transfer coefficient between the ball and the water is such that the variation of the ball temperature with time $T(t)$ is governed by

$$T' + 0.01T = 0$$

with $T(0) = 80$. Determine the temperature distribution $T(t)$ by solving this initial-value problem with the Laplace transform.

SOLUTION   Taking the Laplace transform of the differential equation, we have

$$L\{T'\} + L\{0.01T\} = L\{0\}$$

$$[sT(s) - T(0)] + [0.01T(s)] = 0$$

$$sT(s) - 80 + 0.01T(s) = 0$$

Solving for $T(s)$, we have

$$T(s) = \frac{80}{s + 0.01}$$

Taking the inverse transform, we obtain

$$T(t) = 80e^{-0.01t}$$

which is the desired solution. The temperature of the ball at any time t can be determined by substituting a t value (in seconds) into this equation.

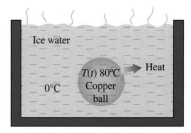

FIGURE 8–29
Schematic for Example 8–15.

You are probably thinking that we could have solved this problem much more easily using any of the standard methods discussed in earlier chapters. So what is the point of solving the same differential equation with a more complicated method? At this stage, we are trying to show that the method works and that it is an alternative to existing methods by applying it to simple problems.

A new method is not worth studying unless it offers some advantages over the existing, well-established methods. As you will see later in this chapter, the Laplace transform method offers considerable simplification on solving initial-value problems with discontinuous forcing functions and systems of such problems. The Laplace transform also is used successfully to reduce certain partial differential equations to ordinary differential equations.

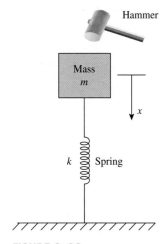

Hammer

Mass
m

x

k Spring

FIGURE 8–30

The mass-spring system for Example 8–16.

EXAMPLE 8–16   Impulse Response of a Mass–Spring

A stationary mass m that is resting on top of a linear spring (whose spring constant is k) is struck by hammer at time $t = 0$ with an impulse I, as shown in Figure 8–30. As a result of this impulse, the mass starts to vibrate up and down. Choosing the x-axis downward with its origin located at the center of gravity of the mass when the mass is in static equilibrium, the mathematical formulation of this problem can be expressed as

$$mx'' + kx = I\delta(t - 0)$$

with $x(0) = x'(0) = 0$.

Determine the motion of the mass $x(t)$ by solving this initial-value problem using the Laplace transform.

SOLUTION   Dividing the differential equation by m and taking its Laplace transform, we obtain

$$L\{x''\} + L\left\{\frac{k}{m}x\right\} = L\left\{\frac{I}{m}\delta(t - 0)\right\}$$

$$\left[s^2X(s) - sx(0) - x'(0)\right] + \left[\frac{k}{m}X(s)\right] = \frac{I}{m} \times 1$$

$$s^2X(s) - 0 - 0 + \frac{k}{m}X(s) = \frac{I}{m}$$

Solving for $X(s)$, we have

$$X(s) = \frac{I}{m}\frac{1}{s^2 + k/m} = \frac{I}{m}\sqrt{\frac{m}{k}}\frac{\sqrt{k/m}}{s^2 + k/m} = \frac{I}{\sqrt{mk}}\frac{\sqrt{k/m}}{s^2 + k/m}$$

Taking the inverse transform, we have

$$x(t) = \frac{I}{\sqrt{mk}}\sin\sqrt{\frac{k}{m}}t$$

which is the desired solution. Thus, the mass will undergo a periodic sinusoidal motion. The maximum displacement is $I/\sqrt{mk}$.

In previous chapters, we urged you to always check your solution to see if the initial conditions are satisfied. If we do that with the solution here, we obtain $x(0) = 0$ as required, but

$$x'(t) = \frac{I}{\sqrt{mk}}\sqrt{\frac{k}{m}}\cos\sqrt{\frac{k}{m}}t = \frac{I}{m}\cos\sqrt{\frac{k}{m}}t$$

Thus, $x'(0) = I/m$, not a zero solution as required. The apparent contradiction can be resolved by noting that the impulse–momentum principle from dynamics states that

$$mx'(0+) - mx'(0) = I$$

where $x'(0+)$ is the velocity just after the impulse disappears. Thus, if $x'(0) = 0$, we have $x'(0+) = I/m$. The impulse disappears so quickly that it does not displace the mass, but it does change the velocity.

When dealing with impulse forcing functions, the solution correctly gives the values of the dependent variables at $t = 0 +$. These are found from the solution by taking the limit as $t \rightarrow 0$. These values may be different than the specified initial values, but they are correct.

EXAMPLE 8–17   Response of an *RLC* Circuit

Consider an *RLC* circuit with inductance $L = 1$, capacitance $C = 0.002$, and resistance $R = 60$ in compatible units, as shown in Figure 8–31. Initially, there is no charge in the capacitor and no current is flowing in the circuit. When the switch is closed, a battery is connected to the circuit, and it supplies a voltage $V_b = 10$ V for 0.2 seconds, at which time the switch is opened again. Obtain the expression for the capacitor voltage $v(t)$.

SOLUTION   The Kirchoff's law requires that the sum of the voltage drops across the components of a circuit be equal to the voltage applied, $V_b(t)$. Denoting the current at time t by $i(t)$, the voltage drop across the three components in this circuit are, $L \, di/dt$, Ri and v where

$$v = \frac{1}{C} \int_0^t i(t)\,dt + Q_0$$

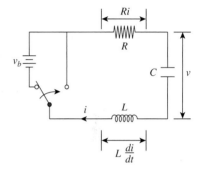

FIGURE 8–31

RLC circuit for Example 8–17.

and Q_0 is the initial charge in the capacitor at time $t = 0$. Then the mathematical formulation of this problem can be expressed as

$$Ri + v + L\frac{di}{dt} = v_b$$

with $i(0) = 0$.

Differentiate the capacitor relation once to obtain

$$\frac{dv}{dt} = \frac{i}{C}$$

which gives $i = C \, dv/dt$. Differentiating again gives

$$\frac{di}{dt} = C\frac{d^2v}{dt^2}$$

Substitute the last two relations in the circuit voltage equation to obtain

$$RC\frac{dv}{dt} + v + LC\frac{d^2v}{dt^2} = v_b$$

Rearranging gives

$$LC\frac{d^2v}{dt^2} + RC\frac{dv}{dt} + v = v_b$$

Dividing by C and substituting the given parameter values, we obtain

$$\frac{d^2v}{dt^2} + 60\frac{dv}{dt} + 500v = 500v_b = 500(10)\left[u(t) - u(t - 0.2)\right]$$

Noting that the initial conditions imply that $v(0) = 0$ and $v'(0) = 0$, and applying the Laplace transform, we have

$$s^2V(s) + 60sV(s) + 500V(s) = 5000\left(\frac{1}{s} - \frac{e^{-0.2s}}{s}\right)$$

Solve for $V(s)$ and factor out the $1/s$ term:

$$V(s) = \frac{5000}{s(s^2 + 60s + 500)}(1 - e^{-0.2s})$$

The roots of $s^2 + 60s + 500 = 0$ are -50 and -10. Therefore, $s^2 + 60s + 500 = (s + 50)(s + 10)$ and, using partial fractions,

$$\frac{5000}{s(s^2 + 60s + 500)} = \frac{1}{s(s + 50)(s + 10)} = \frac{A}{s} + \frac{B}{s + 10} + \frac{C}{s + 50}$$

$$= \frac{10}{s} - \frac{12.5}{s + 10} + \frac{2.5}{s + 50}$$

Substituting,

$$V(s) = \left(\frac{10}{s} - \frac{12.5}{s + 10} + \frac{2.5}{s + 50}\right) - e^{-0.2s}\left(\frac{10}{s} - \frac{12.5}{s + 10} + \frac{2.5}{s + 50}\right)$$

Taking the inverse transform,

$$v(t) = 10 - 12.5e^{-10t} + 2.5^{-50t} - u(t - 0.2)[10 - 12.5e^{-10t} + 2.5e^{-50t}]_{t \to t-2}$$

or,

$$v(t) = \begin{cases} 10 - 12.5e^{-10t} + 2.5^{-50t}, & t < 0.2 \\ -12.5e^{-10t} + 2.5^{-50t} + 12.5^{-10(t-0.2)} - 2.5^{-50(t-0.2)}, & t \geq 0.2 \end{cases}$$

which is the desired solution. This is plotted in Figure 8–32.

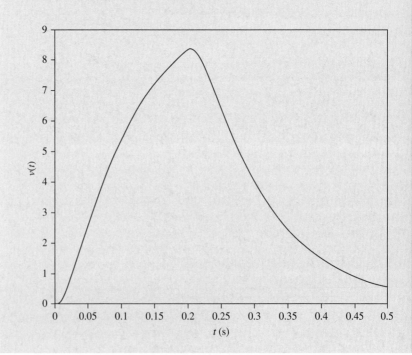

FIGURE 8–32

Plot of voltage versus time.

Solution with General Boundary Conditions

Although the derivative properties of the Laplace transform are stated in terms of conditions at $t = 0$, we can still use the transform to solve equations where the boundary conditions are given at some other value of t, say t_1. Because the transform is used to solve linear differential equations with *constant* coefficients, we can introduce a new time scale that starts at t_1. That is, we replace t with $t + t_1$.

For example, consider the problem

$$x' + 3x = t \quad x(2) = 10$$

Shifting the time axis by $t = t + 2$, we note that x and x' remain the same, and the equation becomes

$$x' + 3x = t + 2 \quad x(0) = 10$$

This is easily solved as

$$sX(s) - x(0) + 3X(s) = \frac{1}{s^2} + \frac{2}{s}$$

or

$$X(s) = \frac{10}{s + 3} + \frac{1}{s^2(s + 3)} + \frac{2}{s(s + 3)}$$

This gives

$$x(t) = \frac{85}{9}e^{-3t} + \frac{1}{3}t + \frac{5}{9}$$

We now replace t with $t - 2$ to obtain the solution.

$$x(t) = \frac{85}{9}e^{-3(t-2)} + \frac{1}{3}(t - 2) + \frac{5}{9}$$

Note that $x(2) = 10$.

Transfer Functions

The complete response of a linear ordinary differential equation is the sum of the free and the forced responses. For zero initial conditions, the free response is zero, and the complete response is the same as the forced response. Thus, we can focus our analysis only on the effects of the input by taking the initial conditions to be zero temporarily. When we have finished analyzing the effects of the input, we can add to the result the free response due to any nonzero initial conditions. The concept of the *transfer function* is useful for analyzing the effects of the input.

Consider the equation $x' + ax = bf(t)$, and assume that $x(0) = 0$. Transforming both sides of the equation gives $sX(s) + aX(s) = bF(s)$. Then solve for the ratio $X(s)/F(s)$ and denote it by $T(s)$:

$$T(s) = \frac{X(s)}{F(s)} = \frac{b}{s + a}$$

The function $T(s)$ is called the **transfer function** of the differential equation. The transfer function is the transform of the forced response divided by the transform of the input. In other words, it is the transform of the complete response divided by the transform of the input under the assumption that the initial conditions are all zero. We sometimes say that the transfer function is the ratio of the transformed output over the transformed input.

The transfer function can be used as a multiplier to obtain the forced response transform from the input transform; that is, $X(s) = T(s)F(s)$. The transfer function is a property of the system model only. The transfer function is independent of the input function and the initial conditions. The transfer function concept is extremely useful for several reasons.

1. *Transfer Functions and Software.* Certain useful features in software packages such as MATLAB do not accept system descriptions expressed as single, higher-order differential equations, but do accept a description based on the transfer function. See Section 8–11 for examples.

2. *Differential Equation Equivalence.* The transfer function is equivalent to the differential equation. It contains the same information, and one can be obtained from the other. If we are given the transfer function, we can reconstruct the corresponding differential equation. For example, the transfer function

$$\frac{X(s)}{F(s)} = \frac{6s + 7}{3s^2 + 5s + 8}$$

corresponds to the equation $3x'' + 5x' + 8x = 6f'(t) + 7f(t)$. Obtaining the transfer function is easily done, because the initial conditions are assumed to be zero when working with transfer functions. From the derivative property, this means that to work with a transfer function you can use the simpler relations $L(x') = sX(s)$, $L(x'') = s^2X(s)$, and so forth.

3. *The Transfer Function and Characteristic Roots.* Note that the denominator of the transfer function is the characteristic polynomial. Thus, the transfer function tells us something about the intrinsic behavior of the model—apart from the effects of the input and specific values of the initial conditions.

Sometimes we encounter models of devices or processes that have more than one input. If so, the transfer function concept is useful in distinguishing between the effects of the various inputs. For example, the following equation has two inputs: $5x'' + 30x' + 40x = 6\,f(t) - 20g(t)$. Using the derivative property with zero initial conditions, we can immediately write the equation as

$$5s^2X(s) + 30sX(s) + 40X(s) = 6F(s) - 20G(s)$$

Solving for $X(s)$, we obtain

$$X(s) = \frac{6}{5s^2 + 30s + 40}F(s) - \frac{20}{5s^2 + 30s + 40}G(s)$$

When there is more than one input, the transfer function for a specific input can be obtained by temporarily setting the other inputs equal to zero (this is another aspect of the superposition property of linear equations). Thus, we obtain

$$\frac{X(s)}{F(s)} = \frac{6}{5s^2 + 30s + 40} \qquad \frac{X(s)}{G(s)} = \frac{-20}{5s^2 + 30s + 40}$$

Note that the denominators of both transfer functions have the same roots: $s = -2$ and $s = -40$. This is not surprising, since the denominator comes from the left-hand side of the differential equation, which determines the characteristic roots.

Section Review

8–10 Solve the following initial-value problem using the Laplace transform method:

$$y' - 4y = e^{3t}, \ y(0) = 0$$

(*Answer*: $y(t) = e^{4t} - e^{3t}$)

8–10 ▪ SOLVING SYSTEMS OF LINEAR DIFFERENTIAL EQUATIONS BY LAPLACE TRANSFORM

Some physical problems encountered in practice involve two or more dependent variables—all functions of a single independent variable. The dependent variables of such problems also depend on each other, and the description of the problem involves a system of differential equations. For example, the following is a system of two first-order linear differential equations:

$$a_1 x'(t) + b_1 y'(t) + c_1 x(t) + d_1 y(t) = f_1(t)$$
$$a_2 x'(t) + b_2 y'(t) + c_2 x(t) + d_2 y(t) = f_2(t)$$

where a_i, b_i, c_i, and d_i are specified constants.

The Laplace transform technique provides considerable simplification in the solution of such systems. The solution procedure for systems of linear differential equations using the Laplace transform is similar to the procedure for a single differential equation (Figure 8–33).

Step 1. Apply the Laplace transform to each of the differential equations. This will result in a linear system of *algebraic equations* in the transforms of the unknown functions.

Step 2. Solve the linear system of algebraic equations to get explicit expressions for each transform.

Step 3. Determine the unknown functions by taking the inverse of the transforms using the transform tables.

The procedure just outlined is now illustrated with an example.

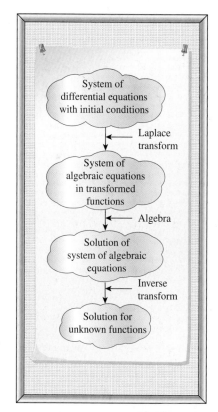

FIGURE 8–33

The basic steps involved in the solution of systems of linear differential equations by Laplace transform.

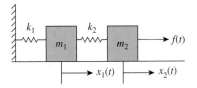

FIGURE 8–34

The mass-spring system considered in Example 8–18.

EXAMPLE 8–18   **Response of Two Coupled Masses**

Consider the two masses m_1 and m_2 and two linear springs with spring constants k_1 and k_2 connected in series, as shown in Figure 8–34. Initially, both masses are motionless, and they are at their equilibrium positions. Consequently, the springs are neither stretched nor compressed at $t = 0$. We are given that $m_1 = 1$, $m_2 = 1$, $k_1 = 2$, and $k_2 = 1$ in compatible units.

A square-wave external force $f(t)$ with an amplitude a and a period p is applied to m_2, causing both masses to undergo a motion. (This wave is shown in Figure 8–16.) If we let $x_1(t)$ and $x_2(t)$ denote the positions of the two masses relative to their equilibrium positions, the motions of m_1 and m_2 will be governed by the following system of two differential equations.

$$m_1 x_1'' + k_1 x_1 - k_2(x_2 - x_1) = 0$$
$$m_2 x_2'' + k_2(x_2 - x_1) = f(t)$$

with

$$x_1(0) = x_1'(0) = x_2(0) = x_2'(0) = 0$$

and

$$f(t) = \begin{cases} a, & 0 \le t < p/2 \\ -a, & p/2 \le t < p \end{cases}$$

The system of two differential equations reduces to

$$x_1'' + 3x_1 - x_2 = 0$$
$$x_2'' + x_2 - x_1 = f(t)$$

Determine the motions $x_1(t)$ and $x_2(t)$ by solving this system of two initial-value problems using the Laplace transform.

SOLUTION   The Laplace transform of the forcing function $f(t)$ (from Equation 8–32) is

$$F(s) = \frac{a}{s}\left[1 + 2\sum_{n=1}^{\infty}(-1)^n e^{-pns/2}\right]$$

We now take the Laplace transform of both differential equations and apply the initial conditions:

$$L\{x_1''\} + L\{3x_1\} - L\{x_2\} = 0$$
$$L\{x_2''\} + L\{x_2\} - L\{x_1\} = L\{f(t)\}$$

Since the initial conditions are zero, we obtain

$$s^2 X_1(s) + 3X_1(s) - X_2(s) = 0$$
$$s^2 X_2(s) + X_2(s) - X_1(s) = F(s)$$

Solving for $X_1(s)$ and $X_2(s)$, we obtain

$$X_1(s) = \frac{F(s)}{s^4 + 4s^2 + 2} = \frac{a}{s(s^4 + 4s^2 + 2)} + 2a\sum_{n=1}^{\infty}(-1)^n\frac{e^{-ps/2}}{s(s^4 + 4s^2 + 2)}$$

$$X_2(s) = \frac{(s^2 + 3)F(s)}{s^4 + 4s^2 + 2} = \frac{a(s^2 + 3)}{s(s^4 + 4s^2 + 2)} + 2a\sum_{n=1}^{\infty}(-1)^n\frac{(s^2 + 3)e^{-ps/2}}{s(s^4 + 4s^2 + 2)}$$

In a more compact form, we have

$$X_1(s) = aG(s) + 2a\sum_{n=1}^{\infty} (-1)^n e^{-ps/2} G(s)$$

$$X_2(s) = aH(s) + 2a\sum_{n=1}^{\infty} (-1)^n e^{-ps/2} H(s)$$

where

$$G(s) = \frac{1}{s(s^4 + 4s^2 + 2)} \quad \text{and} \quad H(s) = \frac{s^2 + 3}{s(s^4 + 4s^2 + 2)}$$

We now express the higher order term in the denominators in a more convenient form as

$$s^4 + 4s^2 + 2 = (s^2 + 2)^2 - 2 = (s^2 + 2 + \sqrt{2})(s^2 + 2 - \sqrt{2})$$

$$\cong (s^2 + 3.414)(s^2 - 0.586)$$

where we have approximated $\sqrt{2}$ to be 1.414. Applying the method of partial fractions, we have

$$G(s) = \frac{1}{s(s^2 + 3.414)(s^2 + 0.586)} = \frac{A}{s} + \frac{Bs + C}{s^2 + 3.414} + \frac{Ds + E}{s^2 + 0.586}$$

$$= \frac{0.5}{s} + \frac{0.104s}{s^2 + 3.414} - \frac{0.604s}{s^2 + 0.586}$$

$$H(s) = \frac{s^2 + 3}{s(s^2 + 3.414)(s^2 + 0.586)} = \frac{A}{s} + \frac{Bs + C}{s^2 + 3.414} + \frac{Ds + E}{s^2 + 0.586}$$

$$= \frac{1.5}{s} - \frac{0.0429s}{s^2 + 3.414} - \frac{1.457s}{s^2 + 0.586}$$

Note that $C = E = 0$ in both cases. The solutions $x_1(t)$ and $x_2(t)$ are obtained by taking the inverse transforms of the $X_1(s)$ and $X_2(s)$ expressions:

$$x_1(t) = ag(t) + 2a\sum_{n=1}^{\infty} (-1)^n u(t - np/2) g(t - np/2)$$

$$x_2(t) = ah(t) + 2a\sum_{n=1}^{\infty} (-1)^n u(t - np/2) h(t - np/2)$$

where $g(t)$ and $h(t)$ are the inverse transforms of $G(s)$ and $H(s)$:

$$g(t) = 0.5 + 0.104 \cos 1.848t - 0.604 \cos 0.765t$$

$$h(t) = 1.5 - 0.0429 \cos 1.848t - 1.457 \cos 0.765t$$

Therefore, the solution of the problem is

$$x_1(t) = a(0.5 + 0.104 \cos 1.848\, t - 0.604 \cos 0.765\, t)$$

$$+ 2a \sum_{n=1}^{\infty} (-1)^n u(t - np/2)\{0.5 + 0.104\cos\left[1.848\,(t - np/2)\right]$$

$$- 0.604\cos\left[0.765(t - np/2)\right]\}$$

$$x_2(t) = a(1.5 - 0.0429 \cos 1.848t - 1.457 \cos 0.765t)$$

$$+ 2a \sum_{n=1}^{\infty} (-1)^n u(t - np/2)\{1.5 - 0.0429\cos\left[1.848(t - np/2)\right]$$

$$- 1.457\cos\left[0.765(t - np/2)\right]\}$$

Transfer Functions of Systems of Equations

We can obtain transfer functions from systems of equations first by transforming the equations using zero initial conditions and then by algebraically eliminating all variables except for the specified input and output. This technique is especially useful when we want to obtain the response of only some of the dependent variables in the system of equations.

EXAMPLE 8–19   Transfer Functions from Two Equations

Consider the following system, which has one input of $f(t)$ and two outputs of $x(t)$ and $y(t)$:

$$x' = -3x + 2y$$

$$y' = -9y - 4x + 3f(t)$$

Obtain the transfer functions $X(s)/F(s)$ and $Y(s)/F(s)$.

SOLUTION   To obtain the transfer functions $X(s)/F(s)$ and $Y(s)/F(s)$, transform both sides of each equation, assuming zero initial conditions:

$$sX(s) = -3\,X(s) + 2Y(s) \tag{a}$$

$$sY(s) = -9Y(s) - 4X(s) + 3F(s) \tag{b}$$

These are two algebraic equations in the two unknowns, $X(s)$ and $Y(s)$. Solve Equation (a) for $Y(s)$:

$$Y(s) = \frac{s + 3}{2}X(s)$$

Substitute this into Equation (b), and solve for $X(s)/F(s)$ to obtain

$$\frac{X(s)}{F(s)} = \frac{6}{s^2 + 12s + 35} \tag{c}$$

Now substitute this into Equation (a) to obtain

$$\frac{Y(s)}{F(s)} = \frac{s+3}{2}\frac{X(s)}{F(s)} = \frac{s+3}{2}\frac{6}{s^2+12s+35}$$

$$= \frac{3(s+3)}{s^2+12s+35} \tag{d}$$

The desired transfer functions are given by Equations (c) and (d). Note that denominators of both transfer functions have the same factors, $s = -5$ and $s = -7$, which are the roots of the characteristic equation: $s^2 + 12s + 35$.

The transfer function enables us to separate out the solution of one or more variables, instead of needing to solve for all the variables simultaneously. Using the Laplace transform in this way avoids solving both *differential* equations simultaneously and converts the problem into one involving the solution of simultaneous *algebraic* equations.

The Transition Matrix

When a system of linear equations is expressed in the following vector–matrix form the Laplace transform can be used to find the transition matrix $\boldsymbol{\phi}(t)$ and the matrix of transfer functions.

$$\mathbf{x}' = \mathbf{A}\mathbf{x} + \mathbf{B}\mathbf{r}(t) \tag{8–58}$$

Transforming Equation 8–58 gives

$$s\mathbf{X}(s) - \mathbf{x}(0) = \mathbf{A}\mathbf{X}(s) + \mathbf{B}\mathbf{R}(s)$$

Since $\mathbf{I}\mathbf{X}(s) = \mathbf{X}(s)$, we have

$$s\mathbf{I}\mathbf{X}(s) - \mathbf{x}(0) = \mathbf{A}\mathbf{X}(s) + \mathbf{B}\mathbf{R}(s)$$

or

$$s\mathbf{I}\mathbf{X}(s) - \mathbf{A}\mathbf{X}(s) = \mathbf{x}(0) + \mathbf{B}\mathbf{R}(s)$$

Factor out $\mathbf{X}(s)$ from the right:

$$(s\mathbf{I} - \mathbf{A})\mathbf{X}(s) = \mathbf{x}(0) + \mathbf{B}\mathbf{R}(s)$$

Solve for $\mathbf{X}(s)$:

$$\mathbf{X}(s) = (s\mathbf{I} - \mathbf{A})^{-1}\mathbf{x}(0) + (s\mathbf{I} - \mathbf{A})^{-1}\mathbf{B}\mathbf{R}(s) \tag{8–59}$$

The first term on the right is the transform of the free response, which is the solution when there are no inputs, so $\mathbf{r}(t) = \mathbf{0}$. In this case, the solution can be expressed as

$$\mathbf{x}(t) = \boldsymbol{\phi}(t)\mathbf{x}(0) \tag{8–60}$$

where $\boldsymbol{\phi}(t)$ is the transition matrix that was introduced in Chapter 7. Thus, $(s\mathbf{I} - \mathbf{A})^{-1}$ is the transform of the transition matrix:

$$\boldsymbol{\Phi}(s) = (s\mathbf{I} - \mathbf{A})^{-1}$$

and

$$\boldsymbol{\phi}(t) = L^{-1}\left[(s\mathbf{I} - \mathbf{A})^{-1}\right] \tag{8–61}$$

This provides a third way to obtain the transition matrix. The other two ways are the modal matrix method and the series expansion method, which were introduced in Chapter 7. Both the modal matrix method and the Laplace transform method require us to solve the characteristic polynomial $|s\mathbf{I} - \mathbf{A}| = 0$. Both also require a matrix inversion to obtain $\mathbf{M}^{-1}$ and $(s\mathbf{I} - \mathbf{A})^{-1}$, respectively. However, the modal matrix consists only of numbers and can be inverted easily by calculator or computer. On the other hand, the matrix $(s\mathbf{I} - \mathbf{A})$ cannot be inverted numerically, because it is a function of the variable s. A fourth-order system requires inversion of a 4×4 matrix containing sixteen elements. After inversion, sixteen partial fraction expansions would be required to find $\phi(t)$. Thus, the Laplace transform method is usually not employed for finding the transition matrix for systems of fourth order or higher.

The Transfer Function Matrix

We are not always interested in all of the dependent variables, so a matrix $\mathbf{C}$, defined from the so-called *output equation* $\mathbf{y} = \mathbf{Cx}$, can be used to indicate which variables in the vector $\mathbf{x}$ are of interest. The vector $\mathbf{y}$ contains the subset of the variables in $\mathbf{x}$ that are of interest to us. For example, consider a system having three dependent variables x_1, x_2, and x_3. Suppose we are interested in just x_1 and x_3. The output equation would be

$$\begin{pmatrix} y_1 \\ y_2 \end{pmatrix} = \begin{pmatrix} x_1 \\ x_3 \end{pmatrix} = \begin{pmatrix} 1 & 0 & 0 \\ 0 & 0 & 1 \end{pmatrix} \begin{pmatrix} x_1 \\ x_2 \\ x_3 \end{pmatrix} = \mathbf{Cx}$$

Thus, the matrix $\mathbf{C}$ is

$$\mathbf{C} = \begin{pmatrix} 1 & 0 & 0 \\ 0 & 0 & 1 \end{pmatrix}$$

The transfer function matrix is found by setting the initial condition vector $\mathbf{x}(0)$ equal to the zero vector in Equation 8–59, as follows. Since $\mathbf{y} = \mathbf{Cx}$,

$$\mathbf{Y}(s) = \mathbf{CX}(s) = \mathbf{C}(s\mathbf{I} - \mathbf{A})^{-1}\mathbf{BR}(s) \qquad \textbf{(8–62)}$$

Thus, the transfer function matrix relating the vector of output variables $\mathbf{Y}(s)$ to the vector of input variables $\mathbf{R}(s)$ is

$$\mathbf{T}(s) = \mathbf{C}(s\mathbf{I} - \mathbf{A})^{-1}\mathbf{B} \qquad \textbf{(8–63)}$$

If there are n dependent variables and m input functions, then $\mathbf{A}$ is $n \times n$, and $\mathbf{B}$ is $n \times m$. Then if there are p output variables, $\mathbf{Y}(s)$ will be $p \times 1$, $\mathbf{C}$ will be $p \times n$, and $\mathbf{T}(s)$ will be $p \times m$. So, for example, if there are three dependent variables, two inputs, and three outputs, the transfer matrix $\mathbf{T}(s)$ will be 2×3, and there will be six transfer functions—one for each input-output pair.

EXAMPLE 8–20   **Obtaining a Transfer Function Matrix**

Consider the following system, which has two inputs, $f_1(t)$ and $f_2(t)$:

$$x_1' = -3x_1 + 2x_2 + f_1(t)$$
$$x_2' = -4x_1 - 9x_2 + f_1(t) + 3f_2(t)$$

Obtain the transfer function matrix for the output x_1.

SOLUTION   The matrices and vectors for this system are

$$\mathbf{A} = \begin{pmatrix} -3 & 2 \\ -4 & -9 \end{pmatrix}, \quad \mathbf{B} = \begin{pmatrix} 1 & 0 \\ 1 & 3 \end{pmatrix}, \quad \text{and} \quad \mathbf{r}(t) = \begin{pmatrix} f_1(t) \\ f_2(t) \end{pmatrix}$$

If the desired output is x_1 we have

$$\mathbf{C} = (1 \quad 0)$$

Then,

$$s\mathbf{I} - \mathbf{A} = \begin{pmatrix} s + 3 & -2 \\ 4 & s + 9 \end{pmatrix}$$

and

$$(s\mathbf{I} - \mathbf{A})^{-1} = \frac{1}{(s + 3)(s + 9) + 8} \begin{pmatrix} s + 9 & 2 \\ 4 & s + 3 \end{pmatrix}$$

From Equation 8–63, we have

$$\mathbf{T}(s) = \frac{1}{s^2 + 12s + 35}(1 \quad 0)\begin{pmatrix} s + 9 & 2 \\ 4 & s + 3 \end{pmatrix}\begin{pmatrix} 1 & 0 \\ 1 & 3 \end{pmatrix}$$

which gives

$$\mathbf{T}(s) = \frac{1}{s^2 + 12s + 35}(s + 11 \quad s + 9)$$

This is the transfer function matrix for the output x_1, which is influenced by both inputs. The two transfer functions are

$$\frac{X_1(s)}{F_1(s)} = \frac{s + 11}{s^2 + 12s + 35} \qquad \frac{X_1(s)}{F_2(s)} = \frac{s + 9}{s^2 + 12s + 35}$$

Note that even though the input $f_2(t)$ does not appear in the x_1' equation, it does influence x_1, as shown by the transfer function $X_1(s)/F_2(s)$.

Matrix Form of the Convolution Theorem

The convolution theorem also applies to the matrix form $\mathbf{x}' = \mathbf{A}\mathbf{x} + \mathbf{B}\mathbf{r}(t)$. Not surprisingly, the transition matrix appears in the convolution integral. In matrix form, the convolution theorem states that

$$L^{-1}[\boldsymbol{\Phi}(s)\mathbf{V}(s)] = \int_0^t \boldsymbol{\phi}(t - \tau)\mathbf{v}(\tau)d\tau \tag{8-64}$$

If we take $\mathbf{v}(t) = \mathbf{B}\mathbf{r}(t)$, we have

$$L^{-1}[\boldsymbol{\Phi}(s)\mathbf{B}\mathbf{R}(s)] = \int_0^t \boldsymbol{\phi}(t - \tau)\mathbf{B}\mathbf{r}(\tau)d\tau \tag{8-65}$$

Since $\boldsymbol{\phi}(t) = L^{-1}[(s\mathbf{I} - \mathbf{A})^{-1}]$, Equation 8–65 must be the forced response. Therefore, the complete response from Equation 8–59 is

$$\mathbf{x}(t) = \boldsymbol{\phi}(t)\mathbf{x}(0) + \int_0^t \boldsymbol{\phi}(t - \tau)\mathbf{B}\mathbf{r}(\tau)d\tau \tag{8-66}$$

The transition matrix $\boldsymbol{\phi}(t)$ used in this equation may be obtained by any of the methods discussed previously: the modal matrix method, the Laplace transform method, or the series expansion method. Problems 8–135 and 8–136 show how to use Equation 8–66 to obtain a general formula for step inputs and ramp inputs.

Transfer Function Form Versus State Variable Form   The transfer function description and the state variable description both contain the same information about the system behavior. However, one form may be easier to use, depending on what information is needed. If the system model consists of a single equation, then the transfer function form is the easiest to use, because the Laplace transform can be immediately applied. However, when the description is given as a *set* of differential equations, the choice is not so clear. In such cases, if we want to obtain the eigenvalues using a computer, converting the equation set to state variable form is the easiest way, because it requires the least amount of algebra.

All of the transfer functions of a given equation will have the same denominators, because the denominator is the characteristic polynomial which contains the free-response characteristics of the equation. The numerators, however, will be different in general. If a numerator contains an s term, its transfer function is said to have *numerator dynamics.* For example, the transfer function $X(s)/R(s) = (4s + 7)/(5s^2 + 4s + 7)$ has numerator dynamics, and corresponds to the equation $5x'' + 4x' + 7x = 4r'(t) + 7r(t)$. So we see that the presence of numerator dynamics indicates that the equation contains one or more derivatives of the forcing function.

There may be situations in which we want to use a general formula that is based on the state variable form. However, in the standard state variable form, $\mathbf{x}' = \mathbf{Ax} + \mathbf{B}r(t)$ there is no derivative of the input $\mathbf{r}(t)$. Thus, when the transfer function model contains numerator dynamics, the state variables are not so easy to identify, and they are not so easily related to the given initial conditions. Consider the transfer function given previously. It represents a mass–spring–damper system with the spring and damper connected between the mass and a displacement input $r(t)$ and with the parameter values $m = 5$, $c = 4$, and $k = 7$. If we choose the first state variable to be x and the second state variable to be the integral of the spring force $k(r - x)$ divided by the mass m, we have

$$x_1 = x$$

$$x_2 = \frac{k(r - x_1)}{m} = \frac{4(r - x_1)}{5}$$

It can be shown that the state variable equations are

$$x_1' = -\frac{4}{5}x_1 + x_2 + \frac{4}{5}r$$

$$x_2' = -\frac{7}{5}x_1 + \frac{7}{5}r$$

which are in the standard form. So now we need to relate the initial conditions $x_1(0)$ and $x_2(0)$ to the given values of $x(0)$ and $x'(0)$. It is easy to see that $x_1(0) = x(0)$. To find $x_2(0)$, solve the first state equation for x_2.

$$x_2 = x_1' + \frac{4}{5}(x_1 - r)$$

Evaluate this at $t = 0$ to obtain the desired result:

$$x_2(0) = x_1'(0) + \frac{4}{5}[x_1(0) - r(0)] = x'(0) + \frac{4}{5}[x(0) - r(0)]$$

We usually cannot depend on intuition to obtain a set of state variables for a transfer function having numerator dynamics. The easiest way is to use a computer package that converts the transfer function description into the standard state variable form. This is discussed in Section 8.11.

Section Review

8–11 Solve the following system of initial-value problems using the Laplace transform method.

$$x' + 2y = e^{-3t}$$

$$y' + 3x = t, \ x(0) = 1, \quad \text{and} \quad y(0) = 2$$

$$\left(\text{Answer: } x(t) = \frac{1}{3}t - e^{-3t} + 2\cosh\sqrt{6}t - \frac{19}{3\sqrt{6}}\sinh\sqrt{6}t \text{ and} \right.$$

$$\left. y(t) = -\frac{1}{6} - e^{-3t} + \frac{19}{6}\cosh\sqrt{6}t - \sqrt{6}\sinh\sqrt{6}t \right)$$

8–12 Find the transfer functions $X(s)/F(s)$ and $Y(s)/F(s)$ for the following set of equations.

$$x' + 2y = f(t)$$

$$y' + 3x = 0$$

$$\left(\text{Answer: } \frac{X(s)}{F(s)} = \frac{s}{s^2 - 6}, \ \frac{Y(s)}{F(s)} = \frac{-3}{s^2 - 6} \right)$$

8–11 ▪ COMPUTER-AIDED LAPLACE TRANSFORM METHODS

The MATLAB Symbolic Math toolbox, MuPad, Maple, and Mathematica all can obtain Laplace transforms and inverse transforms in symbolic form. If you have only MATLAB but not the Symbolic Math toolbox, you can still obtain inverse Laplace transforms by partial fraction expansion, which MATLAB can do because polynomial operations can be done numerically as well as symbolically.

Methods based on transfer functions can be used with these programs only if you have the proper add-on software dealing with control systems. In MATLAB, this is the Control Systems toolbox. In Mathematica, it is the Control Systems Professional. The `DynamicSystems` library implements these methods, and it is built in to Maple.

With each of these packages, we show only the most basic form of the commands. You should access the package's help feature for more information on extended features.

TABLE 8-6

Laplace Transform of $t\sin 2t$

MATLAB Symbolic Math Toolbox
| ```
syms t
laplace(t*sin(2*t),t,s)
``` |

MuPAD
| ```
transform::laplace(t*sin(2*t), t, s)
``` |

Maple
| ```
with(inttrans)
laplace(t*sin(2*t),t,s)
``` |

Mathematica
| ```
LaplaceTransform[t*Sin[2*t],t,s]
``` |

Laplace Transforms   Let us start with obtaining Laplace transforms and inverse transforms in symbolic form, using the following example.

$$L\{t\sin 2t\} = \frac{4s}{\left(4 + s^2\right)^2}$$

Table 8–6 shows how this transform is obtained with the various programs. Note the specific order of t and s.

Table 8–7 shows how the inverse transform is obtained. Note the reversed order of t and s as compared to finding the transform.

These programs can handle the Dirac delta function, including its shifted form. Consider the function

$$f(t) = \delta(t - 3)$$

Its transform is

$$F(s) = e^{-3s}$$

which can be obtained as shown in Table 8–8.

TABLE 8-7

Inverse Laplace Transform of $4s/(4 + s^2)^2$

MATLAB Symbolic Math Toolbox
| ```
syms s
ilaplace(4*s/(s^2+4)^2,s,t)
``` |

MuPAD
| ```
transform::invlaplace(4*s/(s^2+4)^2,s,t)
``` |

Maple
| ```
with(inttrans)
invlaplace(4*s/(4+s^2)^2,s,t)
``` |

Mathematica
| ```
InverseLaplaceTransform[4*s/(4+s^2)^2,s,t]
``` |

TABLE 8–8

Laplace Transform of $\delta(t - 3)$

MATLAB Symbolic Math Toolbox

```
syms s
laplace(dirac(t - 3),t,s)
```

MuPAD

```
transform::laplace(dirac(t - 3),t,s)
```

Maple

```
with(inttrans)
laplace(Dirac(t - 3),t,s)
```

Mathematica

```
LaplaceTransform[DiracDelta[t-3],t,s]
```

The Heaviside function $u(t)$ also can be used to create piecewise functions by shifting. Consider the function from Example 8–8.

$$f(t) = \begin{cases} 0 & t < 2\pi \\ \sin t & 2\pi \le t \le 3\pi \\ 0 & t > 3\pi \end{cases}$$

or

$$f(t) = \sin t\left[u(t - 2\pi) - u(t - 3\pi)\right]$$

Its transform is

$$F(s) = \frac{1}{s^2 + 1}(e^{-2\pi s} + e^{-3\pi s})$$

which can be obtained as shown in Table 8–9. Note that Mathematica has two unit step functions: the `HeavisideTheta[x]` function, which is undefined at $x = 0$, and the `UnitStep[x]` function, which is defined as 1 at $x = 0$.

Partial Fraction Expansion   If you use MATLAB but the Symbolic Math toolbox and MuPad are not available, MATLAB can compute the coefficients in a partial-fraction expansion with the `residue` function. Let $X(s)$ denote the transform. The expansion coefficients are called the *residues* and the factors of the denominator of $X(s)$ are called the *poles*. The poles include the characteristic roots of the model and any denominator roots introduced by the input function. If the order m of the numerator of $X(s)$ is greater than the order n of the denominator, the transform can be represented by a polynomial $K(s)$, called the *direct term*, plus a ratio of two polynomials where the denominator degree is greater than the numerator degree. The syntax of the residue function is

```
[r,p,K] = residue(num,den)
```

where `num` and `den` are arrays containing the coefficients of the numerator and denominator of $X(s)$. The output of the function consists of the array r,

TABLE 8–9

Shifting with the Heaviside Function

MATLAB Symbolic Math Toolbox

```
syms t s
laplace(sin(t)*(heaviside(t-2*pi)-heaviside(t-3*pi)), t,s)
```

MuPAD

```
transform::laplace(sin(t)*(heaviside(t-2*PI)
 -heaviside(t-3*PI)),t,s)
```

Maple

```
with(inttrans)
laplace(sin(t)*(Heaviside(t-2*Pi)-Heaviside(t-3*Pi)), t,s)
```

Mathematica

```
LaplaceTransform[Sin[t]*UnitStep[t-2*Pi]-
 Sin[t]*UnitStep[t-3*Pi],t,s]
```

which contains the residues; the array p, which contains the poles; and the array K, which contains the coefficients of the direct term $K(s)$ in polynomial form.

Consider the equation $x'' + 9x' + 14x = 3f' + 2f$, where $f(t) = 4e^{-7t}$. If the initial conditions are zero, the transform of the forced response is

$$X(s) = \frac{3s + 2}{s^2 + 9s + 14}F(s) = \frac{3s + 2}{s^2 + 9s + 14}\left(\frac{4}{s + 7}\right) = \frac{12s + 8}{(s + 2)(s + 7)^2}$$

$$= \frac{12s + 8}{s^3 + 16s^2 + 77s + 98}$$

The repeated poles are $s = -7, -7$; one of them is a characteristic root and the other is due to the input $f(t)$. To obtain the expansion, type

```
[r,p,K] = residue([12, 8],[1, 16, 77, 98])
```

The answer given by MATLAB is r = [0.64, 15.2, -0.64], p = [-7, -7, -2], and K =[ ] which is an empty array signifying that there is no direct term. This corresponds to the expansion

$$X(s) = 0.64\frac{1}{s + 7} + 15.2\frac{1}{(s + 7)^2} - 0.64\frac{1}{s + 2}$$

Note that for the residues due to repeated poles, the residue corresponding to the *highest* power is displayed as the *last* of those residues. The response here is

$$x(t) = 0.64e^{-7t} + 15.2te^{-7t} - 0.64e^{-2t}$$

Complex poles are handled as follows. Consider the equation

$$x'' + 6x' + 34x = 4g' + g$$

where $g(t)$ is a unit step function and the initial conditions are zero. The transform of the response is

$$X(s) = \frac{4s + 1}{s^2 + 6s + 34} \, G(s) = \frac{4s + 1}{s^2 + 6s + 34} \, \frac{1}{s} = \frac{4s + 1}{s^3 + 6s^2 + 34s}$$

To obtain the expansion, type

```
[r,p,K] = residue([4, 1],[1, 6, 34, 0])
```

Observe that the last coefficient in the denominator is 0. The answer given by MATLAB is $r = [-0.0147-0.3912i, \quad -0.0147+0.3912i, 0.0294]$, $p = [-3+5i,-3-5i,0]$, and $K = [\quad]$. This result corresponds to the expression

$$X(s) = \frac{-0.0147 - 0.3912i}{s + 3 - 5i} + \frac{-0.0147 + 0.3912i}{s + 3 + 5i} + \frac{0.0294}{s}$$

and thus, the response is

$$x(t) = (-0.0147 - 0.3912i)e^{(-3+5i)t}$$
$$+ (-0.0147 + 0.3912i)e^{(-3-5i)t} + 0.0294$$

This form is not very useful because of its complex coefficients, but we can convert it to a more useful form by noting that the first two terms in the expansion have the form

$$\frac{C + iD}{s + a - ib} + \frac{C - iD}{s + a + ib}$$

which corresponds to the time function:

$$(C + iD)e^{(-a+ib)t} + (C - iD)e^{(-a-ib)t}$$

Using Euler's identities: $e^{\pm ibt} = \cos bt \pm i \sin bt$, the previous form can be written as

$$2e^{-at}(C \cos bt - D \sin bt)$$

Using this identity with $C = -0.0147$ and $D = -0.3912$, we can write the response as

$$x(t) = 2e^{-3t}(-0.0147 \cos 5t + 0.3912 \sin 5t) + 0.0294$$

If all you need is a plot of the solution, transfer function methods provide an easy way to obtain the plot.

Transfer Function Methods in MATLAB The MATLAB Control Systems toolbox provides commands for creating transfer functions, converting state variable models into transfer function form, and computing and plotting the response of linear, constant-coefficient equations to step, impulses, and user-defined input functions.

An *LTI object* describes a linear, time-invariant model (i.e., one having constant coefficients). Consider the transfer function:

$$\frac{X(s)}{F(s)} = \frac{4s + 7}{5s^2 + 4s + 7} \tag{8-67}$$

To create its representation in MATLAB, use the $\texttt{tf(num,den)}$ function, where the arrays $\texttt{num}$ and $\texttt{den}$ are the arrays of coefficients of the numerator and denominator of the transfer function arranged in order of descending powers of *s*. For this transfer function, you type sys1 = tf([4,7],[5, 4,7]) to assign the variable name sys1 to the transfer function. If the LTI object already exists, we can extract the coefficients of the numerator and denominator of the transfer function model by using the tfdata function. Its syntax is

```
[num,den] = tfdata(sys).
```

MATLAB provides several solvers for linear equations. These solvers are categorized by the type of input function they can accept: a *step input*, an *impulse input*, and a user-defined input function. In their basic form, each of the functions automatically puts a title and axis labels on the plot. To plot the unit step response or the unit impulse response of the model sys1, type step(sys1) or impulse(sys1).

The lsim function plots the response of the system to a user-defined input. The basic syntax for zero initial conditions is lsim(sys,u,t), where sys is the LTI object, t is an array of values of the independent variable (time, for example) having regular spacing (as t = [t0:dt:t1]), and u is a matrix with as many columns as inputs whose *i*th row specifies the value of the input at time *t(i)*.

For example, to plot the forced response of the model sys1 to the *ramp* input $f(t) = 1.5t$ over the time interval $0 \leq t \leq 2$ with a plot with 300 points, you type

```
t = linspace(0,2,300);
f = 1.5*t;
[y, t] = lsim(sys1,f,t);
plot(t,y,t,f),xlabel('t'),ylabel('x(t) and f(t)')
```

As another example, to find the response to the sinusoidal forcing function $f(t) = 15 \sin(3t)$, replace the second line in the previous program with f= 15*sin(3*t).

You can always create any complicated input function to use with lsim by defining a vector containing the input function's values at specified times, for example, by using for loops and conditional statements. MATLAB provides the gensig function that makes it easy to construct *periodic* input functions. The syntax [u, t] = gensig(type, period) generates a periodic input of a specified type type, having a period period. The following types are available: sine wave (type = 'sin'), square wave (type = 'square'), and narrow-width periodic pulse (type = 'pulse'). The vector t contains the times, and the vector u contains the input values at those times. All generated inputs have unit amplitudes. The syntax

```
[u, t] = gensig(type, period, dur, dt)
```

specifies the time duration dur of the input and the spacing dt between the time instants.

For example, suppose a square wave with a period of 5 is applied to the model:

$$x'' + 2x' + 4x = 4f(t)$$

Its transfer function is

$$\frac{X(s)}{F(s)} = \frac{4}{s^2 + 2s + 4}$$

To find the response for zero initial conditions, over the interval $0 \le t \le 10$ and using a step size of 0.01, enter

```
sys2 = tf(4,[1,2,4]);
[u, t] = gensig('square',5,10,0.01);
[y, t] = lsim (sys2,u,t);plot(t,y,u), . . .
    axis([0 10 -0.5 1.5]), . . .
    xlabel('Time'),ylabel('Response')
```

Converting Between Transfer Function Form and State Variable Form

MATLAB can obtain a transfer function description from the standard-state variable form $\mathbf{x}' = \mathbf{Ax} + \mathbf{B}r(t), \mathbf{y} = \mathbf{Cx} + \mathbf{D}r$ with the `tf` function. Suppose `sys1` is in state variable form, having been created by typing `sys1 = ss(A,B,C,D)`, as discussed in Section 7–8. The transfer function matrix is found by typing `sys2 = tf(sys1)`.

On the other hand, if we already have an LTI object `sys2` created in transfer function form, typing `[A,B,C,D] = ssdata(sys2)` will give the standard matrices for the state variable form. This is an easy way to obtain the state variable description from a transfer function having numerator dynamics.

The `ssdata` function will not always give a set of state variables identical to those obtained in the usual way. For example, the transfer function

$$\frac{X(s)}{R(s)} = \frac{1}{5s^2 + 7s + 4}$$

corresponds to the equation $5x'' + 7x' + 4x = r(t)$, and we would normally choose $x_1 = x$ and $x_2 = x'$ to be the state variables. However, in MATLAB, the commands

```
sys = tf(1,[5,7,4]);
[A,B,C,D] = ssdata(sys)
```

give the following results

$$\mathbf{A} = \begin{pmatrix} -1.4 & -0.8 \\ 1 & 0 \end{pmatrix} \quad \mathbf{B} = \begin{pmatrix} 0.5 \\ 0 \end{pmatrix}$$

$$\mathbf{C} = (0 \quad 0.4) \quad \mathbf{D} = 0$$

These correspond to the state equations:

$$x_1' = -1.4x_1 - 0.8x_2 + 0.5r(t)$$

$$x_2' = x_1$$

and the output equation; $y = 0.4x_2$. Because the output y must be the same as x, we immediately see that $x_2 = y/0.4 = x/0.4 = 2.5x$. The other state variable x_1 is related to x_2 by the second state equation: $x_1 = x_2'$. Thus, $x_1 = 2.5x'$.

TABLE 8–10

LTI Object Functions in MATLAB

Command	Description
`sys = ss(A, B, C, D)`	Creates an LTI object in state-space form, where the matrices A, B, C, and D correspond to those in the model $\dot{\mathbf{x}} = \mathbf{Ax} + \mathbf{Bu}, \mathbf{y} = \mathbf{Cx} + \mathbf{Du}$.
`[A, B, C, D] = ssdata(sys)`	Extracts the matrices A, B, C, and D of the LTI object sys, corresponding to those in the model $\dot{\mathbf{x}} = \mathbf{Ax} + \mathbf{Bu}, \mathbf{y} = \mathbf{Cx} + \mathbf{Du}$.
`sys = tf(num,den)`	Creates an LTI object in transfer function form, where the vector num is the vector of coefficients of the transfer function numerator, arranged in descending order, and den is the vector of coefficients of the denominator, also arranged in descending order.
`sys2=tf(sys1)`	Creates the transfer function model sys2 from the state model sys1.
`sys1=ss(sys2)`	Creates the state model sys1 from the transfer function model sys2.
`[num, den] = tfdata(sys, 'v')`	Extracts the coefficients of the numerator and denominator of the transfer function model sys when the optional parameter 'v' is used. If there is only one transfer function, the coefficients are returned as vectors rather than as cell arrays.

The MATLAB LTI functions are summarized in Table 8–10.

Transfer Function Methods in Maple   Transfer functions can be created in Maple with the `TransferFunction` command. Before using this command, place `with(DynamicSystems)` in the notebook. Using Equation 8–67 as an example, you enter

```
sys3:=TransferFunction((4*s+7)/(5*s^2+4*s+7)):
```

The unit step response always can be obtained by dividing the transfer function by *s* and using the inverse Laplace transform. The unit step response can be plotted as

```
ResponsePlot(sys3,Heaviside(t))
```

The unit impulse response can be obtained as

```
ImpulseResponse(sys3)
```

and it can be plotted as

```
ImpulseResponsePlot(sys3)
```

Here is how to plot the response to a ramp function starting at $t = 0$ and having a slope of 10.

```
ResponsePlot(sys3,Ramp(10))
```

To plot the response to a sinusoidal input of amplitude 10 and radian frequency 5, you enter

```
ResponsePlot(sys3, Sine(10,5))
```

Transfer Function Methods in Mathematica   Transfer functions and their associated methods in Mathematica are in the add-on package Control Systems Professional. Transfer functions can be created in Mathematica with the `TransferFunction` command. Using Equation 8–67 as an example, you enter

```
sys4 = TransferFunction[s, (4*s + 7)/(5*s^2 + 4*s + 7)]
```

The response to a unit impulse can be plotted as follows, using the `SimulationPlot` function.

```
SimulationPlot[sys4,DiracDelta[t]]
```

The response to a unit step can be plotted as

```
SimulationPlot[sys4,UnitStep[t]]
```

As with all packages, we have shown only the most basic form of the commands. You should access the package's help feature for more information.

8–12 ▪ SUMMARY

The *Laplace transform* is an integral transform with integration limits of 0 and ∞ and the kernel e^{-st}. It is denoted by L, and the Laplace transform of a function $f(t)$ is defined as

$$L\{f(t)\} = \int_0^\infty e^{-st}f(t)\,dt = \lim_{R\to\infty}\int_0^R e^{-st}f(t)\,dt \quad \textbf{(8–4)}$$

The Laplace transform of a function exists if and only if the improper integral converges for at least some values of s. As a convention, lowercase letters are used to represent a given function, and the capital of the same letter is used to represent its Laplace transform. The Laplace transforms of commonly encountered functions are given in Table 8–1.

Existence of Laplace Transforms Not all functions possess Laplace transforms. To have a Laplace transform, it is sufficient (but not necessary) for a function $f(t)$ to be piecewise continuous and of exponential order. A function $f(t)$ is said to be piecewise continuous on a finite interval $a \le t \le b$ if this interval can be subdivided into a finite number of subintervals such that in each subinterval $f(t)$ is continuous and has finite limits at the endpoints. A function $f(t)$ is said to be of exponential order if there exists a constant a such that

$$\lim_{t\to\infty} e^{-at}|f(t)| = M$$

where M is a finite positive constant or zero for all t at which $f(t)$ is defined.

Properties of Laplace Transforms The basic properties of Laplace transforms can be summarized as follows.

1. $L\{C_1f_1(t) + C_2f_2(t)\} = C_1L\{f_1(t)\} + C_2L\{f_2(t)\}$ **(8–10)**

2. $L\{e^{kt}f(t)\} = F(s - k)$ **(8–12)**

3. $L\{t^nf(t)\} = (-1)^n\dfrac{d^nF(s)}{ds^n}$ **(8–15)**

4. $L\left\{\dfrac{1}{t}f(t)\right\} = \int_s^\infty F(s)\,ds$ **(8–17)**

5. $L\left\{\int_0^t f(t)\,dt\right\} = \dfrac{1}{s}F(s)$ **(8–18)**

6. $L\{f(kt)\} = \dfrac{1}{k}F\left(\dfrac{s}{k}\right)$ **(8–19)**

The Unit Step Function The unit step function is defined by

$$u(t - t_0) = \begin{cases} 0, & t < t_0 \\ 1, & t \ge t_0 \end{cases} \quad \textbf{(8–20)}$$

The Laplace transform of the unit step function and related functions are listed here.

1. $L\{u(t)\} = \dfrac{1}{s}$ **(8–21)**

2. $L\{u(t - t_0)\} = \dfrac{e^{-t_0s}}{s}$ **(8–22)**

3. $L\{u(t - t_0)f(t)\} = e^{-t_0s}L\{f(t + t_0)\}$ **(8–26)**

4. $L\{u(t - t_0)f(t - t_0)\} = e^{-t_0s}L\{f(t)\}$ **(8–27)**

Laplace Transforms of Periodic Functions A function $f(t)$ is said to be *periodic* of period p if there exists a positive number p such that $f(t + p) = f(t)$ for every positive value of t with p being the smallest period. The Laplace transform of a piecewise-continuous periodic function of period p exists and is determined from

$$F(s) = \frac{1}{1 - e^{-ps}}\int_0^p e^{-st}f(t)\,dt, \quad s > 0 \quad \textbf{(8–28)}$$

Impulsive Forcing Functions Forcing functions of impulsive nature are best described and manipulated with the help of the *unit impulse function* or the *Dirac delta function* $\delta(t - t_0)$. The delta function can be viewed as an operator with the property:

$$\int_0^\infty f(t)\delta(t - t_0)\,dt = f(t_0) \tag{8–37}$$

The Laplace transform of the delta function is

$$L\{\delta(t - t_0)\} = e^{-st_0} \tag{8–38}$$

Laplace Transforms of Derivatives and Differential Equations The Laplace transform of derivatives of a function $f(t)$ exists if $f(t)$ and its derivatives are continuous, and of exponential order. They can be expressed as

$$L\{f'(t)\} = sF(s) - f(0) \tag{8–41}$$

$$L\{f''(t)\} = s^2F(s) - sf(0) - f'(0) \tag{8–43}$$

$$L\{f^{(n)}(t)\} = s^nF(s) - s^{(n-1)}f(0) \\ - s^{(n-2)}f'(0) - \cdots f^{(n-1)}(0) \tag{8–44}$$

where $F(s)$ is the Laplace transform of $f(t)$. Also, $f(0)$, $f'(0), \ldots, f^{(n-1)}(0)$ are the initial values of $f(t)$ and its derivatives.

The Laplace transform of a differential equation is obtained by taking the Laplace transform of each term in the equation and applying the linearity of the transform. The transform of the equation already contains the initial conditions; thus, the inversion will give us directly the solution of our problem.

Inverse Laplace Transforms Determining the original function from its transform is called *finding the inverse* (or inverting) *the transformed function*. The *inverse Laplace transform* is denoted by the symbol L^{-1}. The basic properties of the inverse Laplace transform can be summarized as follows:

1. $L^{-1}\{C_1F_1(s) + C_2F_2(s)\}$
   $= C_1L^{-1}\{F_1(s)\} + C_2L^{-1}\{F_2(s)\}$ (linearity) **(8–46)**

2. $L^{-1}\{F(s - k)\} = e^{kt}L^{-1}\{F(s)\}$ (shifting property) **(8–47)**

3. $L^{-1}\{sF(s)\} = \dfrac{d}{dt}L^{-1}\{F(s)\}$ **(8–48)**

4. $L^{-1}\left\{\dfrac{F(s)}{s}\right\} = \displaystyle\int_0^t L^{-1}\{F(s)\}\,dt$ **(8–49)**

5. $L^{-1}\left\{\dfrac{d^nF(s)}{ds^n}\right\} = (-t)^nL^{-1}\{F(s)\}$ **(8–50)**

6. $L^{-1}\{e^{-t_0s}F(s)\} = u(t - t_0)f(t - t_0)$ **(8–51)**

7. $L^{-1}\{F(ks)\} = \dfrac{1}{k}f\left(\dfrac{t}{k}\right)$ (scaling property) **(8–52)**

The inverse of a given function is a unique continuous function. Therefore, if two continuous functions have the same Laplace transform, they are identical.

Partial Fraction Expansion Solution of differential equations with Laplace transforms often results in a complicated rational fraction for which no inverse Laplace transform can be found in the transform tables. Then it becomes necessary to decompose the complicated rational fraction into simpler fractions through the method of *partial fractions*. By this method, a complicated proper fraction is expressed as a sum of simpler partial fractions that are also proper. That is, the degree of the numerator of any partial fraction is lower than the degree of its denominator.

For repeated factors in the denominators, a separate fraction should be included for each power of the repeated factor. As a check, the number of unknown constants introduced to correspond to a factor in the denominator is equal to the degree of that factor. Also, the total number of unknown constants the partial fractions involve is equal to the degree of the entire denominator.

The Convolution Theorem When solving differential equations, we frequently end up with an expression for $Y(s)$ that can be expressed as the product of two functions of s whose inverses are known. That is, $Y(s)$ can be expressed as $Y(s) = F(s)\,G(s)$, where $F(s)$ and $G(s)$ are the transforms of the known functions $f(t)$ and $g(t)$. In such cases, the inverse transform of $Y(s)$ can be determined from the *convolution theorem*, which can be expressed as

$$L^{-1}\{F(s)G(s)\} = \int_0^t f(t - \tau)g(\tau)\,d\tau \\ = \int_0^t f(t)g(t - \tau)\,d\tau \tag{8–57}$$

where τ is a dummy variable.

Solving Differential Equations The solution of differential equations by Laplace transform involves three basic steps: applying the Laplace transform to the differential equation, solving for the transform of the dependent variable $Y(s)$, and determining the unknown function $y(t)$ by taking the inverse of $Y(s)$. The procedure for solving systems of linear differential equations is similar to the procedure for a single differential equation, except the transform of a system of differential equations results in a system of algebraic equations, which need to be solved simultaneously for the transforms of the unknown functions before the inverse transform can be applied.

Transfer Functions The complete response of a linear ordinary differential equation is the sum of the free and the forced responses. For zero initial conditions, the free response is zero, and the complete response is the same as the forced response. Thus, we can focus our analysis only on the effects of the input by taking the initial conditions to be zero temporarily. When we have finished analyzing the effects of the input, we can add to the result the free response due to any nonzero initial conditions. The concept of the *transfer function* is useful for analyzing the effects of the input.

The transfer function is the transform of the forced response divided by the transform of the input. In other words, it is the transform of the complete response divided by the transform of the input under the assumption that the initial conditions are all zero. The transfer function $T(s)$ can be used as a multiplier to obtain the forced response transform $X(s)$ from the input transform $F(s)$; that is, $X(s) = T(s)F(s)$. The transfer function is a property of the system model only. The transfer function concept is extremely useful for several reasons.

1. *Transfer Functions and Software.* Certain useful features in software packages require a system description based on the transfer function.
2. *Differential Equation Equivalence.* The transfer function is equivalent to the differential equation. It contains the same information, and one can be obtained from the other.
3. *The Transfer Function and Characteristic Roots.* The denominator of the transfer function is the characteristic polynomial. Thus, the transfer function tells us something about the intrinsic behavior of the model, apart from the effects of the input and specific values of the initial conditions.

Laplace Transforms and Computer Software   The MATLAB Symbolic Math toolbox, MuPad, Maple, and Mathematica all can obtain Laplace transforms and inverse transforms in symbolic form. Methods based on transfer functions can be used with these programs only if you have the proper add-on

software dealing with control systems. In MATLAB, this is the Control Systems toolbox. In Mathematica, it is the Control Systems Professional. The DynamicSystems library implements these methods, and it is built in to Maple.

Historical Notes
Pierre-Simon Laplace (1749–1827)   French mathematician and astronomer. He improved the problem-solving capabilities of the classical study of mechanics from one based on geometry to one based on calculus. In addition to the Laplace transform, he developed Laplace's equation, which is a partial differential equation with many applications in physics. The Laplacian differential operator is also named after him. He was one of the first astronomers to conceive of the existence of black holes and the idea of gravitational collapse.

Oliver Heaviside (1850–1925)   Self-taught English electrical engineer, mathematician, and physicist. He applied complex numbers to the analysis of electrical circuits, and solved differential equations using a method later found to be equivalent to Laplace transforms. He also reformulated Maxwell's field equations in terms of electric and magnetic forces and energy flux. The unit step function is also called the Heaviside function in honor of him.

PROBLEMS

8–1   Laplace Transforms of Functions

8–13C   Define the Laplace transform, and explain why it is an attractive method of solving differential equations.

8–14C   Why is the Laplace transform method particularly suitable for initial value problems?

8–15C   Will the Laplace transform of a function $f(t)$ still be a function of t?

Determine the Laplace transform of the following functions that are defined for all $t \geq 0$.

8–16   (a) $f(t) = t^3$ (b) $f(t) = \cosh 2t$

   (c) $f(t) = \begin{cases} t, & t \leq 3 \\ 0, & t > 3 \end{cases}$

8–17   (a) $f(t) = \sin \alpha t$ (b) $f(t) = 5t - 3$ (c) $f(t) = te^{-2t}$

8–18   (a) $f(t) = e^{3t}$ (b) $f(t) = t^2$

   (c) $f(t) = \begin{cases} 1, & t \leq 5 \\ 0, & t > 5 \end{cases}$

8–19   (a) $f(t) = e^{2t-1}$ (b) $f(t) = \cos^2 t$

   (c) $f(t) = \begin{cases} t, & t \leq 1 \\ 2 - t, & 1 < t \leq 1.5 \\ 0.5, & t > 1.5 \end{cases}$

8–2   Existence of Laplace Transforms

8–20   Under what conditions will the Laplace transform of a function exist?

8–21C   What is a jump discontinuity?

8–22C   Under what conditions will the left- and right-hand limits of a function at any point in a specified interval be identical?

8–23C   When is a function of exponential order?

8–24C   Can a function $f(t)$ be of exponential order even if it becomes infinity, as $t \to \infty$?

8–25C   Does a function have to be piecewise continuous and of exponential order in order to possess a Laplace transform?

8–26C   Determine if the following functions are of exponential order.

   (a) $f(t) = 5$ (b) $f(t) = 3t$

   (c) e^{-3t^2} (d) $f(t) = e^{2t}$

8–27   Determine if the following functions are of exponential order.

   (a) $f(t) = 2t^6$ (b) $f(t) = 12 \, e^{30t}$

   (c) $e^{0.001t^2}$ (d) $f(t) = \begin{cases} t, & t \leq 5 \\ e^{2t^2}, & t > 5 \end{cases}$

8–28 Determine if the following functions possess a Laplace transform.

(a) $f(t) = 8t^8$ (b) $f(t) = e^{0.3t^2}$

(c) $\sin t^2$ (d) $f(t) = \begin{Bmatrix} e^{2t}, & t \le 8 \\ t^2, & t > 8 \end{Bmatrix}$

8–3 Basic Properties of the Laplace Transform

8–29 Is it true that $L\{5t^2\sin 3t\} = 5t^2 L\{\sin 3t\}$? How about $L\{5t^2\sin 3t\} = 5L\{t^2\sin 3t\}$?

8–30 Is it true that $L\{t^2 + e^{5t}\} = L\{t^2\} + L\{e^{5t}\}$? How about $L\{t^2 e^{5t}\} = L\{t^2\} \times L\{e^{5t}\}$?

8–31 What is the shifting property of the Laplace transform? How does it differ from the change of scale property?

8–32 Consider two functions $f(t)$ and $g(t)$ and their Laplace transforms $F(s)$ and $G(s)$. If $G(s) = sF(s)$, find a relation between $f(t)$ and $g(t)$.

8–33 Consider two functions $f(t)$ and $g(t)$ and their Laplace transforms $F(s)$ and $G(s)$. If $G(s) = \int_s^\infty F(s)ds$, find a relation between $f(t)$ and $g(t)$.

8–34 Consider two functions $f(t)$ and $g(t)$ and their Laplace transforms $F(s)$ and $G(s)$. If $G(s) = -d^3F(s)/ds^3$ find a relation between $f(t)$ and $g(t)$.

8–35 Is $L\{f(2t)\} = 2L\{f(t)\}$? For what kind of functions will this be the case?

8–36 Show that

$$L\{t^n f(t)\} = (-1)^n \frac{d^n F(s)}{ds^n} \qquad \textbf{(8–15 repeated)}$$

also can be expressed as

$$L\{(-t)^n f(t)\} = \frac{d^n F(s)}{ds^n}$$

Determine the Laplace transform of the following functions using the basic properties of the transform and Table 8–1.

8–37 (a) $f(t) = t^3\cos t$ (b) $f(t) = 2t^5 - 3e^{2t+1}$

(c) $f(t) = \int_0^t e^{3t}dt$

8–38 (a) $f(t) = 3t e^{-2t}\cos \alpha t$ (b) $f(t) = 2t^2 e^{-3t}$

(c) $f(t) = \dfrac{\cos^2 kt}{t}$

8–39 (a) $f(t) = 6t e^{3t}\sin 2t$ (b) $f(t) = 3t \cosh kt$

(c) $f(t) = \sqrt{t} + t^{3/2}$

8–40 (a) $f(t) = t^2 e^{3t+1}\sin \omega t$ (b) $f(t) = te^t$

(c) $f(t) = \int_0^t e^{3t}\sin 2t\,dt$

8–41 (a) $f(t) = 5t^2\sinh 2t$ (b) $f(t) = 2e^{-3t}t^3$

(c) $f(t) = t^2 e^{5t-2}\cos kt$

8–42 (a) $f(t) = t^{5/2}e^{5t}$ (b) $f(t) = t^3\sin 3t\cos 3t$

(c) $f(t) = \int_0^t t\cosh 3t$

8–4 Laplace Transforms of Step, Periodic, and Impulse Functions

8–43C Define the unit step function and explain its value in science and engineering.

8–44C Explain how the functions $u(t - t_0)f(t)$ and $u(t - t_0) f(t - t_0)$ differ from $f(t)$.

8–45C What are the characteristics of a periodic function? Does a periodic function have to be continuous?

8–46C What is the value of the unit impulse function in practice? Give examples of physically meaningful functions that can be described with the help of unit impulse functions.

8–47C Consider two functions $f(t)$ and $g(t)$ whose Laplace transforms are 1 and $1/s$, respectively. Discuss how these two functions differ.

Express the functions in Figures 8–48 through 8–51 in terms of the step and/or delta functions, and determine their Laplace transform.

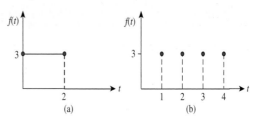

(a) (b)

FIGURE 8–48

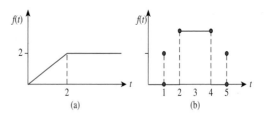

(a) (b)

FIGURE 8–49

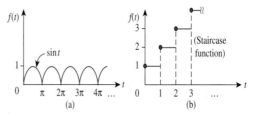

(a) (b)

FIGURE 8–50

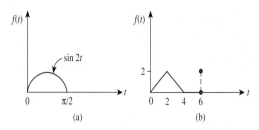

(a)

(b)

FIGURE 8–51

Plot the following functions and determine their Laplace transform.

8–52 (a) $f(t) = \begin{cases} 0, & t < 3\pi \\ \sin t, & t \geq 3\pi \end{cases}$

(b) $f(t) = \begin{cases} t, & t \leq 1 \\ 2 - t, & 1 < t \leq 2 \\ 0, & t > 2 \end{cases}$

8–53 (a) $f(t) = \begin{cases} \cos 2t, & t \leq \pi \\ 0, & t > \pi \end{cases}$

(b) $f(t) = \begin{cases} -1, & t < 1 \\ 0, & 1 \leq t \leq 2 \\ 1, & t > 2 \end{cases}$

8–54 (a) $f(t) = \begin{cases} 0, & t < 2 \\ (t - 2)^2, & t \geq 2 \end{cases}$

(b) $f(t) = \begin{cases} 0, & t < 3\pi/2 \\ 3 \cos t, & 3\pi/2 \leq t \leq 5\pi/2 \\ 0, & t > 5\pi/2 \end{cases}$

8–55 (a) $f(t) = \begin{cases} 0, & t < 3 \\ t^2, & t \geq 3 \end{cases}$ (b) $\begin{cases} 0, & t < 1 \\ 5, & t = 1 \\ 0, & 1 < t < 2 \\ 5, & t = 2 \\ 2, & t > 2 \end{cases}$

Plot the following periodic functions of period p, and determine their Laplace transform:

8–56 $f(t) = \begin{cases} t, & 0 \leq t < 1 \\ 2 - t, & 1 \leq t < 2 \end{cases}$ $(p = 2)$

8–57 $f(t) = \begin{cases} \sin t, & 0 \leq t < \pi \\ -\sin t, & \pi \leq t < 2\pi \end{cases}$ $(p = 2\pi)$

8–58 $f(t) = \begin{cases} 5, & 0 \leq t < 1 \\ -5, & 1 \leq t < 2 \end{cases}$ $(p = 2)$

8–59 $f(t) = \begin{cases} 2, & 0 \leq t < 5 \\ 0, & 5 \leq t < 10 \end{cases}$ $(p = 10)$

Determine the Laplace transform of the periodic functions in Figures 8–60 through 8–62.

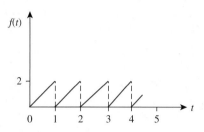

FIGURE 8–60

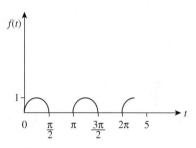

FIGURE 8–61

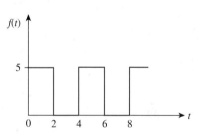

FIGURE 8–62

8–5 Laplace Transform of Derivatives and Differential Equations

8–63C How is the Laplace transform of a differential equation obtained?

8–64C If $f(t)$ is a piecewise-continuous function with a unit jump at $t = 5$, how would you express the Laplace transform of $f'(t)$?

Determine the Laplace transform of the following differential equations, and obtain a relation for the transform of the unknown function, Y(s).

8–65 (a) $y''' - 2y' + 5y = 0$ (b) $y'' = 3te^{2t}$

8–66 (a) $y'' - 2y = \sinh 3t$

(b) $y''' + 3y' + 5y = 3\delta(t - 5) + e^{2t+1}$

8–67 (a) $y'' + 5y = te^{3t} \sin 2t$

$y' + 3y = e^{2t+1} + 3u(t - 0)$

8–6 Inverse Laplace Transform

8–68C What is a practical way of determining the inverse of a Laplace transform that contains the factor s?

8–69C What is a practical way of determining the inverse of a Laplace transform that contains the factor $1/s$?

8–70C What is a practical way of determining the inverse of a Laplace transform that contains the factor e^{-ks}?

Determine the inverse Laplace transform of the following functions using the basic properties of the inverse Laplace transform and Table 8–1. (Do not use the partial fractions method or the convolution theorem.)

8–71 (a) $F(s) = \dfrac{e^{-3s}}{s^2 + 1}$ (b) $F(s) = \dfrac{1}{s + 3} - \dfrac{s}{(s - 3)^4}$

(c) $F(s) = \dfrac{3}{9s^2 + s}$

8–72 (a) $F(s) = \dfrac{s - 3}{s + 3}$ (b) $F(s) = \dfrac{e^{-4s}}{s^2 + 2s + 2}$

(c) $F(s) = \dfrac{s}{(s - 3)^3}$

8–73 (a) $F(s) = \dfrac{s + 3}{s^2 - 1}$ (b) $F(s) = \dfrac{8s}{4s^2 + 3}$

(c) $F(s) = \dfrac{e^{-2}}{s^6}$

8–74 (a) $F(s) = \dfrac{3s}{4s^2 + 4s + 4}$ (b) $F(s) = \dfrac{2s + 1}{(s - 1)^3}$

(c) $F(s) = \dfrac{s + 1}{s - 1}$

8–75 (a) $F(s) = \dfrac{2e^{-2s}}{s^2 - 9}$ (b) $F(s) = \dfrac{2s + 3}{s^2 + 2s + 2}$

(c) $F(s) = \dfrac{s - 2}{s^2 + 1}$

8–76 (a) $F(s) = \dfrac{s}{(s - k)^2 + a^2}$ (b) $F(s) = 3e^{-2s}$

(c) $F(s) = \dfrac{3s + 1}{s - 2}$

8–7 Partial Fractions

8–77C What is the partial fractions method? What is it used for?

8–78C Under what conditions is a rational fraction proper?

8–79C In the partial fractions method, how are the repeated factors handled?

8–80C In the partial fractions method, is there a way to verify that appropriate choices are made for the partial fractions?

Determine the inverse Laplace transform of the following functions using the partial fractions method, whenever necessary.

8–81 (a) $F(s) = \dfrac{2s^2 + 1}{s^2(s - 2)}$ (b) $F(s) = \dfrac{s^2 + 1}{s^2(s^2 + 4s + 8)}$

8–82 (a) $F(s) = \dfrac{1}{(s + 4)(s^2 + 1)}$

(b) $F(s) = \dfrac{s^3 + 5s - 1}{(s + 1)^2(s^2 + 4s + 2)}$

8–83 (a) $F(s) = \dfrac{5s + 1}{s^3(s^2 - 1)}$

(b) $F(s) = \dfrac{s + 1}{s^2(2s^2 + s + 1)}$

8–84 (a) $F(s) = \dfrac{s^2 + 2s - 1}{s(s - 1)^3(s + 3)}$

(b) $F(s) = \dfrac{2s^2 + 1}{s^3(s + 5)}$

8–85 (a) $F(s) = \dfrac{s^2 + s + 2}{s(s^2 + 6s + 5)}$

(b) $F(s) = \dfrac{s^2 + 4}{s^2(s - 1)(s + 4)}$

8–86 (a) $F(s) = \dfrac{4s^2 + 1}{s(s + 4)(s - 5)}$ (b) $F(s) = \dfrac{s^2 - 1}{s(s^2 + 1)}$

8–8 The Convolution Theorem

8–87C What is the importance of the convolution theorem? How is it expressed?

8–88C Is it true that $L^{-1}\{F(s)G(s)\} = f(t)g(t)$? Explain.

8–89C Show that the last two expressions in Equation 8–57 are identical.

Determine the inverse Laplace transform of the following functions using the convolution theorem.

8–90 (a) $Y(s) = \dfrac{e^{-3s}}{s(s^2 + 4s + 3)}$

(b) $Y(s) = \dfrac{s}{(s + 1)(s^2 + 4)}$

8–91 (a) $Y(s) = \dfrac{8}{s^3(s^2 - 1)}$ (b) $Y(s) = \dfrac{1}{s(s + 4)}$

8–92 (a) $Y(s) = \dfrac{s + 1}{s^2(s^2 - 1)}$

(b) $Y(s) = \dfrac{1}{(s + 1)^2(s^2 + 4)}$

8–93 (a) $Y(s) = \dfrac{3e^{-2s}}{(s + 3)(s - 1)^2}$

(b) $Y(s) = \dfrac{4}{s(s^2 + 2s - 3)(s - 3)}$

Determine the inverse Laplace transform of the following functions using both the partial fractions method and the convolution theorem:

8–94 (a) $Y(s) = \dfrac{5}{s^2(s+1)}$

(b) $Y(s) = \dfrac{s+1}{[(s+1)^2 + 4](s-2)}$

8–95 (a) $Y(s) = \dfrac{4}{s(s^4 - 16)}$

(b) $Y(s) = \dfrac{2}{s(s^2 + 2s + 5)}$

8–96 (a) $Y(s) = \dfrac{2e^{-3s}}{s^2(s^2 + 1)}$

(b) $Y(s) = \dfrac{s}{(s-2)^2(s+3)}$

8–97 (a) $Y(s) = \dfrac{2}{s^3(s-1)(s+2)}$

(b) $Y(s) = \dfrac{3}{s(2s^2 + 8)}$

8–98 (a) $Y(s) = \dfrac{6s}{(s+3)(s^2-5)}$ (b) $Y(s) = \dfrac{4s^2}{s^4 - 1}$

8–9 Solving Differential Equations by Laplace Transform

8–99C What are the basic steps involved in solving initial-value problems with the Laplace transform method?

8–100C How are the initial conditions of an initial-value problem incorporated into the solution when using the Laplace transform method?

Solve the following initial-value problems using the Laplace transform method.

8–101 $y' + 3y = \cos t,\ y(0) = -1$

8–102 $y' + 10y = 2\cos t,\ y(0) = 0$

8–103 $y' + 0.001y = e^{-0.02t},\ y(0) = 0$

8–104 $y' + 0.02y = 30,\ y(0) = 80$

8–105 $x'' + 3x' + x = 0,\ x(0) = 0,\ x'(0) = 5$

8–106 $x'' + 4x = [1 - u(t - \pi)]\sin 2t,\ x(0) = 1,\ x'(0) = 2$

8–107 $x'' + x' = e^{-t}\sin t,\ x(0) = 0,\ x'(0) = 1$

8–108 $y'' + 80y = 4[u(t - 1) - u(t - 2)],$
$y(0) = 0,\ y'(0) = 2$

8–109 $y'' + 10y' + 140y = 6\delta(t - 0) + u(t - 1),$
$y(0) = y'(0) = 0$

8–110 $y'' + 2y' + 3y = 3\delta(t) + u(t - 2),\ y(0) = 2,$
$y'(0) = 0$

8–111 $y'' + 3y' - 2y = 0,\ y(2) = 1,\ y'(0) = 0$

8–112 $y'' - 4y = 2\sinh 3t,\ y(0) = y'(0) = 0$

8–113 $y'' - y = 5\delta(t - 0),\ y(0) = y'(0) = 0$

8–114 $y''' - 8y = e^{-2t},\ y(0) = y'(0) = y''(0) = 0$

8–115 $y''' + 3y' + 4y = 2t^2 + 5,\ y(0) = 2,\ y'(0) = 1,$
$y''(0) = 0$

8–116 $y' + y = te^{-t},\ y(1) = 2$

8–117 $y^{iv} = 8,\ y(0) = y'(0) = 0,\ y(1) = 0,\ y'(1) = 2$

8–118 $y'' + y = \sin 2t,\ y(3) = 2,\ y'(3) = 1$

8–119 $y'' + 8y' = e^t \sin t,\ y(\pi) = 1,\ y'(\pi) = 2$

Find the transfer function $Y(s)/F(s)$ for the following equations.

8–120 $y' + 3y = f(t)$ **8–121** $y'' + 3y' + x = f(t)$

8–10 Solving Systems of Linear Differential Equations by Laplace Transform

8–122C What are the basic steps involved in solving a system of linear initial-value problems with the Laplace transform method?

Solve the following systems of initial-value problems using the Laplace transform method:

8–123 $x'' + x - 2y = 3\delta(t),\ y' + 5x = 0,$
$x(0) = x'(0) = 0,\ y(0) = 1$

8–124 $x'' + y' = 5e^{-t},\ y'' - x = \sin t,\ x(0) = 1,$
$x'(0) = 0,\ y(0) = -2,\ y'(0) = 0$

8–125 $x'' + x + y' = \cos t,\ y'' + 2x = e^{-t},\ x(0) = -1,$
$x'(0) = 1,\ y(0) = 0,\ y'(0) = 0$

8–126 $x_1' - 3x_2' + 4x_1 - 5x_2 = 0,\ x_2' - x_1' + 3x_2 = 5,$
$x_1(0) = 0,\ x_2(0) = 0$

8–127 $x' + y + z = e^{-4t},\ y' + x' - x = 0,$
$z' - z + y = \sin t,\ x(0) = y(0) = 0,\ z(0) = 3$

8–128 Find the transfer functions $X(s)/F(s)$ and $Y(s)/F(s)$ for the following set of equations.

$$x'' + x + y = 3f(t),\ y' + x = f(t)$$

Find the transfer functions $X_1(s)/F(s)$ and $X_2(s)/G(s)$ for the following sets of equations.

8–129 $x_1' - 3x_2' + 4x_1 - 5x_2 = f(t) - 4g(t),$
$x_2' - x_1' + 3x_2 = 6f(t)$

8–130 $x' + y + z = 3f(t) + g(t),\ y' + x' - x = f(t),$
$z' - z + y = 10f(t)$

Use the Laplace transform to obtain the transition matrix $\phi(t)$ for each of the following systems, $\mathbf{x}' = \mathbf{A}\mathbf{x}$, where $\mathbf{A}$ is given in the problem.

8–131 $\mathbf{A} = \dfrac{1}{3}\begin{pmatrix} -9 & 9 \\ 1 & -9 \end{pmatrix}$ **8–132** $\mathbf{A} = \begin{pmatrix} 1 & 1 \\ 0 & 1 \end{pmatrix}$

8–133 $\mathbf{A} = \begin{pmatrix} 0 & 1 \\ -10 & -2 \end{pmatrix}$

8–134 Consider the following system, which has two inputs, $f_1(t)$ and $f_2(t)$.

$$x_1' = 5x_1 - 3x_2 + 4f_1(t) - 5f_2(t)$$

$$x_2' = -7x_1 - 3x_2 + f_1(t) - 9f_2(t)$$

Obtain the transfer function matrix for the output x_1.

8–135 Determine the forced response of the system $\mathbf{x}' = \mathbf{Ax} + \mathbf{Br}(t)$ for the case where $\mathbf{r}(t)$ is a vector $\mathbf{p}$ of step functions with different magnitudes, all starting at time $t = 0$. (*Hint*: Use the series expansion for $\boldsymbol{\phi}(t)$, but your answer should not be a series expression.)

$$\boldsymbol{\phi}(t) = \mathbf{I} + \mathbf{A}t + \frac{1}{2!}\mathbf{A}^2 t^2 + \frac{1}{3!}\mathbf{A}^3 t^3 + \cdots$$

8–136 Determine the forced response of the system $\mathbf{x}' = \mathbf{Ax} + \mathbf{Br}(t)$ for the case where $\mathbf{r}(t)$ is a vector of ramp functions all starting at time $t = 0$, so that $\mathbf{r}(t) = \mathbf{q}t$, where the vector $\mathbf{q}$ contains the slopes of the ramps. (*Hint*: Use the series expansion for $\boldsymbol{\phi}(t)$ given in Problem 8–135, but your answer should not be a series expression.)

8–11 Computer-Aided Laplace Transform Methods

8–137 Use a Laplace transform method with a computer to solve for the unit step response of the following models for zero initial conditions:
(a) $3x'' + 21x' + 30x = u(t)$
(b) $5x'' + 20x' + 65x = u(t)$
(c) $4x'' + 32x' + 60x = 3u'(t) + 2u(t)$
(d) $x''' + 10x'' + 31x' + 30x = 3u'(t) + 2u(t)$

8–138 Use the Laplace transform method with a computer to solve for the unit impulse response of the following models for zero initial conditions:
(a) $3x'' + 21x' + 30x = \delta(t)$
(b) $5x'' + 20x' + 65x = \delta(t)$

8–139 Use a Laplace transform method with a computer to solve for the response of the following models for $0 \le t \le 1.5$, where the input is $f(t) = 5t$ and the initial conditions are zero:
(a) $3x'' + 21x' + 30x = f(t)$
(b) $5x'' + 20x' + 65x = f(t)$
(c) $4x'' + 32x' + 60x = 3f'(t) + 2f(t)$
(d) $x''' + 10x'' + 31x' + 30x = 3f'(t) + 2f(t)$

8–140 Use a Laplace transform method with a computer to solve for the response of the following model for a zero initial condition, where the input $f(t)$ is a rectangular pulse of height 3 and duration 5:

$$4x' + x = f(t)$$

8–141 Use a computer to plot the unit-step response of the following models for zero initial conditions:
(a) $3x'' + 21x' + 30x = u(t)$
(b) $5x'' + 20x' + 65x = u(t)$
(c) $4x'' + 32x' + 60x = 3u'(t) + 2u(t)$
(d) $x''' + 10x'' + 31x' + 30x = 3u'(t) + 2u(t)$

8–142 Use a computer to plot the unit-impulse response of the following models for zero initial conditions:
(a) $3x'' + 21x' + 30x = \delta(t)$
(b) $5x'' + 20x' + 65x = \delta(t)$

8–143 Use a computer to plot the response of the following models for $0 \le t \le 1.5$, where the input is $f(t) = 5t$ and the initial conditions are zero:
(a) $3x'' + 21x' + 30x = f(t)$
(b) $5x'' + 20x' + 65x = f(t)$
(c) $4x'' + 32x' + 60x = 3f'(t) + 2f(t)$
(d) $x''' + 10x'' + 31x' + 30x = 3f'(t) + 2f(t)$

8–144 Use a computer to plot the response of the following models for $0 \le t \le 6$, where the input is $f(t) = 6\cos 3t$ and the initial conditions are zero:
(a) $3x'' + 21x' + 30x = f(t)$
(b) $5x'' + 20x' + 65x = f(t)$
(c) $4x'' + 32x' + 60x = 3f'(t) + 2f(t)$
(d) $x''' + 10x'' + 31x' + 30x = 3f'(t) + 2f(t)$

8–145 The equations for an armature-controlled dc motor are the following. The motor's current is i and its rotational velocity is ω.

$$L\frac{di}{dt} = -Ri - K_b\omega + v(t)$$

$$I\frac{d\omega}{dt} = K_T i - c\omega$$

where L, R, and I are the motor's inductance, resistance, and inertia; K_T and K_b are the torque constant and back emf constant; c is a viscous damping constant; and $v(t)$ is the applied voltage. Use the values $R = 0.8\ \Omega$, $L = 4 \times 10^{-3}$ H, $K_T = 0.2$ N·m/A, $K_b = 0.2$ V·s/rad, $c = 5 \times 10^{-4}$, and $I = 5 \times 10^{-4}$ kg·m^2.

(a) Use a computer to obtain the transfer functions $I(s)/V(s)$ and $\Omega(s)/V(s)$.

(b) Suppose the applied voltage is a step function of magnitude 10 V. Plot the motor's speed and current versus time. Determine the peak value of the current from the plot.

(c) Suppose the applied voltage does not increase instantaneously but is given by $v(t) = 10(1 - e^{-100t})$ V. Plot the motor's speed and current versus time. Determine the peak value of the current from the plot. Compare with the peak value found in part b.

Review Problems

8–146 Obtain the Laplace transform of the function plotted in Figure P8–146.

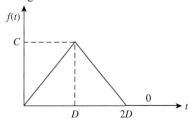

FIGURE P8–146

8–147 Obtain the Laplace transform of the function plotted in Figure P8– 147.

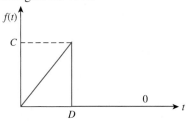

FIGURE P8–147

8–148 Obtain the Laplace transform of the function plotted in Figure P8–148.

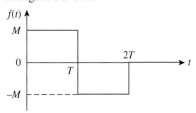

FIGURE P8–148

8–149 Consider the equation

$$x' + x = \tan t$$

This equation cannot be solved by the Laplace transform method, because the transform of $\tan t$ does not exist. An approximate solution of this equation can be obtained by replacing $\tan t$ with a series approximation. The number of terms used in the series determines the accuracy of the resulting solution for $x(t)$. The Taylor series expansion for $\tan t$ is

$$\tan t = t + \frac{t^3}{3} + \frac{2t^5}{15} + \frac{17t^7}{315} + \cdots \; |t| < \frac{\pi}{2}$$

The more terms we retain, the more accurate is the series. Also, the series becomes less accurate as the absolute value of t increases.

Use the Laplace transform with the first three terms in the series to obtain an approximate closed-form solution for $x(t)$ over the interval $0 \leq t \leq 0.5$.

8–150 Obtain the unit impulse response of the equation $x'' = \delta(t)$. The initial conditions are $x(0) = 5$ and $x'(0) = 10$.

8–151 Obtain the unit impulse response of the following equation. The initial conditions are $x(0) = 0$, $x'(0) = 0$.

$$2x'' + 14x' + 20x = \delta(t)$$

8–152 Figure P8–152 shows a circuit representation of a telegraph line. The resistance R is the line resistance and L is the inductance of the solenoid that activates the receiver's clicker. The switch represents the operator's key. Assume that when sending a "dot," the key is closed for 0.1 s. Using the values $R = 20\ \Omega$ and $L = 4$ H, obtain the expression for the current $I(t)$ passing through the solenoid.

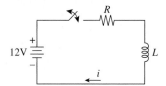

FIGURE P8–152

8–153 Consider the two colliding masses shown in Figure P8–153. Part (a) shows the situation before collision, and part (b) shows the situation after collision.

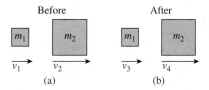

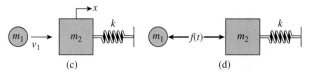

FIGURE P8–153

When the two masses are treated as a single system, no external force is applied to the system, and momentum is conserved. So

$$m_1 v_1 + m_2 v_2 = m_1 v_3 + m_2 v_4$$

If the collision is *perfectly elastic*, kinetic energy is conserved. So

$$\frac{1}{2}m_1 v_1^2 + \frac{1}{2}m_2 v_2^2 = \frac{1}{2}m_1 v_3^2 + \frac{1}{2}m_2 v_4^2$$

The most common application is where we know v_1 and mass m_2 is initially stationary. So $v_2 = 0$. In this case, the equations reduce to

$$v_1 = v_3 + rv_4 \qquad v_1^2 = v_3^2 + rv_4^2$$

where $r = m_2/m_1$. These have the following solution:

$$v_3 = \frac{1-r}{1+r}v_1 \qquad v_4 = \frac{2}{1+r}v_1$$

Consider now the system shown Figure P8–150(b) and (c). Suppose now that the mass $m_1 = m$ moving with a speed v_1 rebounds from the mass $m_2 = 10m$ after striking it. Assume that the collision is perfectly elastic. The impulsive force acting on each mass during the collision is $f(t)$ and is unknown. Determine the expression for the displacement $x(t)$ after the collision.

8–154 Find the forced response of the model $v' = f(t) - 5v$ for the following input function. The initial condition is $v(0) = 0$.

$$f(t) = \begin{cases} 4t, & 0 \leq t \leq 2 \\ -4t + 16, & 2 < t < 4 \\ 0, & t > 4 \end{cases}$$

(*Hint:* Use the ramp response and the shifting theorem.)

8–155 Refer to Figure P8–155. A piston of mass 10 kg and area 2.4×10^{-2} m^2 slides with negligible friction inside a cylinder. At $t = 0$ the air valve is opened and the pressure $p(t)$ decays as follows.

$$p(t) = p_a + p_0 e^{-t/\tau}$$

The initial pressure $p(0)$ is 30 kPa above atmospheric pressure p_a, and at time $t = 0.2$ s, it is 15 kPa above atmospheric pressure. The stiffness is $k = 1000$ N/m. (a) Estimate the values of p_0 and the time constant τ. (b) Obtain the expression for the piston displacement $x(t)$.

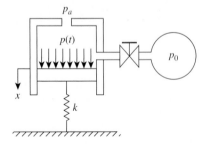

FIGURE P8–155

8–156 Figure P8–156 is a representation of an instrument package of mass m in a space capsule supported by a suspension of stiffness k. When the rocket fires the acceleration y'' increases as $y'' = bt$ where b is a constant. Let $z = x - y$, and assume that $z(0) = z'(0) = 0$. Obtain the expression for the relative displacement $z(t)$ and the acceleration $x''(t)$ felt by the package.

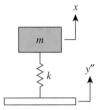

FIGURE P8–156

8–157 Figure P8–156 is a representation of an astronaut and seat in a space capsule. The seat is supported by a suspension of stiffness k. When the final rocket stage fires the acceleration y'' increases as $y'' = ae^{bt}$ where a and b are constants. Let $z = x - y$ and assume that $z(0) = z'(0) = 0$. Obtain the expression for the acceleration $x''(t)$ felt by the astronaut.

8–158 Refer to Figure P8–158. At time $t = 0$, a freight elevator is moving at velocity v_0 and then decelerates to zero velocity at time T with a constant deceleration, so

$$v(t) = v_0\left(1 - \frac{t}{T}\right) \qquad 0 \leq t \leq T$$

$$v(t) = 0 \qquad t > T$$

The elevator contains a package of mass m with cushioning of stiffness k. Obtain the expression for the displacement $x(t)$ for $0 \leq t \leq T$, assuming that $x(0) = x'(0) = 0$.

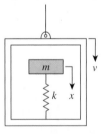

FIGURE P8–158

8–159 Refer to Figure P8–159a, which shows a water tank subjected to a blast force $f(t)$. We will model the tank and its supporting column as the mass–spring system shown in part (b) of the figure. The blast force as a function of time is shown in part (c) of the figure. Assuming zero initial conditions, obtain the expression for $x(t)$ for $0 \leq t \leq T$.

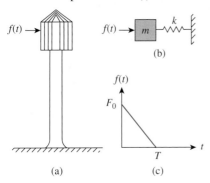

(b)

(a)   (c)

FIGURE P8–159

8–160 Refer to Figure P8–160, which is a simplified representation of a vehicle striking a bump. The vertical displacement x is 0 when the tire first meets the bump. Assuming that the vehicle's horizontal speed v remains constant and that the system is critically damped, obtain the expression for $x(t)$.

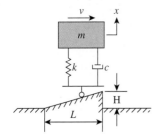

FIGURE P8–160

8–161 A uniform cantilever beam of length L is subjected to a concentrated force f_0 at the middle point, $x = L/2$. See Figure P8–161. The resulting vertical deflection $y(x)$ of the beam is given by

$$EI\frac{d^4y}{dx^4} = f_0\delta\left(x - \frac{L}{2}\right)$$

where E is Young's modulus, which depends on the beam material, and I is the moment of inertia, which depends on the beam geometry. Use the Laplace transform to find the deflection $y(x)$ for the given boundary conditions $y(0) = y'(0) = y''(L) = y'''(L) = 0$.

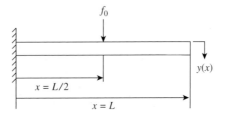

FIGURE P8–161

8–162 A uniform cantilever beam of length L is subjected to a distributed force per unit length $f(x)$ described by

$$f(x) = \frac{2f_0}{L}\left[\frac{L}{2} - x + \left(x - \frac{L}{2}\right)u\left(x - \frac{L}{2}\right)\right]$$

(See Figure P8–162.) The resulting vertical deflection $y(x)$ of the beam is given by

$$EI\frac{d^4y}{dx^4} = f(x)$$

where E is Young's modulus, which depends on the beam material, and I is the moment of inertia, which depends on the beam geometry. Use the Laplace transform to find the deflection $y(x)$ for the given boundary conditions $y(0) = y'(0) = y''(L) = y'''(L) = 0$.

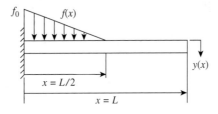

FIGURE P8–162

NUMERICAL SOLUTION OF DIFFERENTIAL EQUATIONS

9

S o far, we have considered differential equations that can be solved analytically using well-developed methods, and we called the solution functions so obtained *analytic* or *closed-form* solutions. The form of these solutions may be *explicit*, which means that the dependent variable is an explicit function of the dependent variable, as in $y = x^2$. Such solutions are very desirable, since they are exact (no approximations are involved in the solution procedure), and the solution at any point can be obtained by simply substituting the value of the independent variable at that point into the explicit function. This is especially true for analytic solutions that are in explicit form. Other analytic solutions may appear in *implicit* form, as in $y + 3xe^{-y} = 5$. Such solutions require a numerical root-finding method to obtain a table or plot of y values versus x values.

It is unfortunate that differential equations for which exact analytic solutions are available are more the exception than the rule. The majority of the nonlinear or variable coefficient differential equations encountered in practice cannot be solved analytically. Unable to obtain exact solutions, we have no choice but to settle for either approximate solutions, such as those obtained by replacing nonlinear terms in the equation with linear approximations, or numerical solutions, in which the solution is obtained in the form of a plot or a table of numbers. In this chapter, we will discuss methods for obtaining numerical solutions.

We will start this chapter with a brief review of *numerical integration*, since it closely parallels the numerical solution of differential equations. After all, solving a differential equation is equivalent (at least in spirit) to integrating it. Of the various numerical methods available for solving ordinary differential equations, we will first consider the *Euler method*, since it is the simplest one—although sometimes not accurate enough. Then we will discuss the *improved Euler method*, since it is more accurate than the Euler method—although a little more involved. Then we will introduce the fourth-order *Runge–Kutta* method, as it is both very accurate and one of the most widely used methods in practice to solve ordinary differential equations. We will also discuss some popular *predictor–corrector* methods and assess the accuracy and complexity of various methods.

Throughout the discussions in this chapter, we will consider first-order initial-value problems or systems of such problems for simplicity. However, the

Objectives

When you have finished this chapter, you should be able to:

1. solve a first-order differential equation whose derivative is a function of the independent variable only, using the rectangular strip method, the trapezoidal rule, and Simpson's rule,

2. solve a first-order differential equation or a system of first-order equations whose derivatives are functions of the independent and dependent variables, using the Euler method and the improved Euler method,

3. discuss the sources of round-off, local discretization, and global discretization errors,

4. write programs that implement the rectangular strip method, the trapezoidal rule, Simpson's rule, the Taylor series method, the classical fourth-order Runge–Kutta method, and the fourth-order Adams–Moulton predictor-corrector method, and

5. use a computer package to obtain numerical solutions of any solvable ordinary differential equation set.

procedures introduced also can be used to solve higher-order differential equations, since any *n*th-order differential equation can be expressed as a system of *n* first-order differential equations. We will also assume that the problems considered satisfy the conditions of existence and uniqueness so that they have a unique solution in the interval of interest. Note that numerical methods do not give a family of solutions with arbitrary constants, and thus, we must always specify enough initial conditions to obtain a unique solution to an *n*th-order differential equation.

Modern commercially available computer packages contain highly developed implementations and extensions of the methods described in this chapter. They are easy to use and powerful enough to handle equations of the type found in this text. We illustrate how to use these tools in Section 9–10.

Although these tools are powerful, easy to use, and widely available, nevertheless, we have included throughout the chapter a number of programs to illustrate the numerical solution methods under discussion. This decision was based on the philosophy that "if you can program a method, then you understand it." Our programs are written in MATLAB, but they do not take advantage of any special features of MATLAB. Because the programs use common structures (like "for" loops), they should be easy to translate into other languages, such as Maple and Mathematica.

For those readers wishing a brief introduction, Sections 9–1 through 9–4 cover the basic concepts of numerical methods, and Section 9–10 may be read as an introduction to the use of commercially available solvers.

9–1 ▪ NUMERICAL INTEGRATION

Solving the first-order initial-value problem

$$\frac{dy}{dx} = f(x), \quad y(0) = 0 \tag{9-1}$$

is equivalent to evaluating the definite integral

$$y(x) = \int_0^x f(x)\,dx \tag{9-2}$$

However, some integrations cannot be performed analytically, and thus, we cannot obtain a closed-form solution. For example, the integral $\int e^{-x^2} dx$ looks very simple, but you will not find it in any integral tables. In such cases, we have no choice but perform the integrations approximately, using a numerical method. Therefore, a good understanding of numerical integration is essential for performing such integrations.

We now introduce some commonly used, simple numerical integration schemes using the function $f(x) = 7x - 6x^2$ as an example throughout the discussions. The integral of this function between the limits of 0 and 1 is

$$I = \int_0^1 f(x)\,dx = \int_0^1 (7x - 6x^2)\,dx = \left| 3.5x^2 - 2x^3 \right|_0^1 = 1.5 \tag{9-3}$$

Noting that analytical integration gives the exact value and that a definite integral of a function represents the area under the curve, we conclude that the area under the curve of the function $f(x) = 7x - 6x^2$ between the limits of 0 and 1 is exactly 1.5, as shown in Figure 9–1. This value will serve as a basis for comparing the approximate values obtained by various methods and thus assessing their accuracy. We keep in mind that the method that predicts the area under the curve more accurately is a more accurate method. Of the various numerical methods available, we now present the strip method, the trapezoidal rule, and Simpson's rule. The reader is referred to any standard numerical methods book for a more in-depth discussion of these and other methods.

Rectangular Strip Method

Before the age of computers, people heavily relied on graphical methods to find the values of integrals, among other things, whenever the analytical methods did not work. For example, the integral of a difficult function was found by plotting the function on a grid and counting the squares under the curve, as shown in Figure 9–2. The product of the number of the squares and the area of each square gave approximately the area under the curve, which corresponds to the value of the integral. The finer the grid, the better the accuracy. This approach often did not even require a calculator.

The **rectangular strip method** is the numerical version of this graphical technique. In this method, the area under the curve is divided into several vertical strips (thin rectangular elements) whose height is equal to the value of the function at the midpoint of the strip. Thus, this method also is called *rectangular integration*. The total area under the curve, which is equivalent to the value of the integral, is determined by calculating the area of each strip and summing them up. The result is approximate, of course since the value of the function at the midpoint of each strip is assumed to represent the average height of that strip.

Consider a function $f(x)$ that is to be integrated by the strip method between the limits of a and b. We now divide this interval into N strips of equal width h where $h = (b - a)/N$. Denote the value of x at any point n by x_n, as shown in Figure 9–3. The average height of a strip between the points n and $n + 1$ can be expressed as

$$\text{Average height} \cong f(x_{\text{average}}) = f\left(\frac{x_n + x_{n+1}}{2}\right)$$

which is the value of a function at the midpoint of a strip. In the strip method, the total area under the curve is determined by multiplying the average height of each strip by its width and summing the results. The area of a general segment between the points x_n and x_{n+1} can be determined from

$$I_n \cong (x_{n+1} - x_n)f\left(\frac{x_{n+1} + x_n}{2}\right), \quad n = 0,1,2,\ldots,N-1 \tag{9-4}$$

where $x_0 = a$ and $x_N = b$. Then the value of a integral I between the limits of a and b can be determined from

$$I = I_0 + I_1 + I_2 + \cdots + I_{N-1} = \sum_{n=0}^{N-1} I_n \tag{9-5}$$

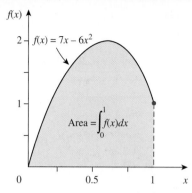

FIGURE 9–1

The area under the curve of a function on the $f(x) - x$ diagram represents the integral of that function.

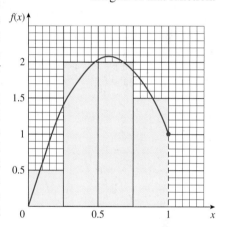

FIGURE 9–2

The graphical determination of a definite integral by plotting the function on a grid and counting the squares under the curve.

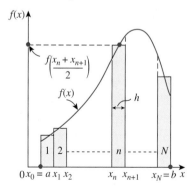

FIGURE 9–3

In the rectangular strip method, the integration interval is divided into N strips of equal width h.

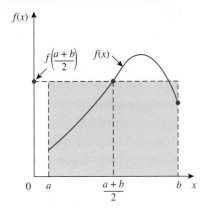

$f(x)$

$f\left(\dfrac{a+b}{2}\right)$ $f(x)$

0 a $\dfrac{a+b}{2}$ b x

FIGURE 9–4

The strip method with one segment (the simplest case).

For $N = 1$, the rectangular strip method involves a single rectangular segment, and this relation simplifies to (Figure 9–4)

$$I \cong (b - a)f\left(\frac{b + a}{2}\right) \tag{9-6}$$

As you would expect, the thinner the strips, the better the accuracy. In other words, as the number of strips increases, the result obtained approaches the exact result.

In general, the value obtained by a numerical method will differ from the exact value, and this difference is called the *error*. Note that the term "error" in this context does not mean a mistake, but rather it is the difference between the correct answer and the approximate answer. The magnitude of the error itself is not a true measure of the accuracy of the result obtained, since a small error is insignificant for a large quantity. Thus, a more realistic measure of the error is the **relative** or **percent error** defined as

$$\text{Relative error} = \left|\frac{\text{exact value} - \text{approximate value}}{\text{exact value}}\right| \times 100\% \tag{9-7}$$

For example, a measurement error of 1 cm corresponds to a percent error of 0.1% for a 10-m long bridge, which is negligible. But a percent error of 20% for a 5-cm long bar is very significant.

EXAMPLE 9–1   **Rectangular Strip Method**

Using the strip method, evaluate the integral

$$I = \int_0^1 (7x - 6x^2)\,dx$$

and compare your result to the exact value of $I = 1.5$. Repeat the calculations for different numbers of strips of equal width.

SOLUTION   In this case, we have $f(x) = 7x - 6x^2$, $a = x_0 = 0$, and $b = x_N = 1$. For $N = 1$, we approximate the entire area under the curve by a single rectangle, as shown in Figure 9–5a. Then from Equation 9–6, we obtain

$$I \cong (b - a)f\left(\frac{b + a}{2}\right) = (1 - 0)f\left(\frac{1 + 0}{2}\right) = f(0.5) = 2$$

which has a relative error of $(2 - 1.5)/1.5 = 33.3\%$.

For $N = 2$, we approximate the entire area under the curve by two rectangles of equal base, as shown in Figure 9–5b. Then $h = (1 - 0)/2 = 0.5$, and from Equations 9–4 and 9–5, we obtain

$$I = I_0 + I_1 = hf\left(\frac{x_0 + x_1}{2}\right) + hf\left(\frac{x_1 + x_2}{2}\right)$$

$$= 0.5\left[f\left(\frac{0 + 0.5}{2}\right) + f\left(\frac{0.5 + 1}{2}\right)\right] = 0.5(1.375 + 1.875) = 1.625$$

which has an error of $(1.625 - 1.5)/1.5 = 8.3\%$. Therefore, dividing the interval into two segments reduced the error from 33.3% to 8.3%.

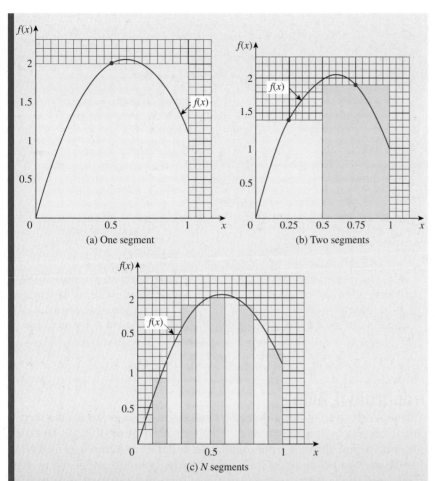

FIGURE 9–5

Graphical representation of the
numerical integration of the function in
Example 9–1. The strip method is
applied by dividing the integration
interval into 1, 2, and N segments.

The results for other values of N's are given in Table 9–1. Note that the percent error decreases gradually as the interval of integration is divided into more and more segments, as expected.

TABLE 9–1

Values of the Integral $\int_0^1 (7x - 6x^2)\,dx$ Obtained with the Strip Method, and the Error Involved for Different Numbers of Segments

Number of Segments	Strip Method	Exact Value	Relative Error
1	2.000000	1.5000	33.33%
2	1.625000	1.5000	8.33%
3	1.555556	1.5000	3.70%
4	1.531250	1.5000	2.08%
5	1.520000	1.5000	1.33%
10	1.505000	1.5000	0.33%
20	1.501250	1.5000	0.08%
30	1.500556	1.5000	0.04%
40	1.500313	1.5000	0.02%
50	1.500200	1.5000	0.01%
100	1.500050	1.5000	0.00%
200	1.500013	1.5000	0.00%

FIGURE 9–6

A MATLAB program for the strip method.

```
lower = 0; upper = 1;
exact = 1.5; m = 1;
f = @(x)7*x-6*x^2;
for nstrip = [1,2,3,4,5,10:10:50,100,200]
    h = (upper-lower)/nstrip;
    x = lower;
    value = 0;
    for n = 1:nstrip
        value = value+h*f(x+h/2);
        x = x+h;
        error(m,:) = [nstrip,value,100*abs(value-exact)/exact];
    end
    m = m+1;
end
error
```

A program written in MATLAB that is used to obtain these results is given in Figure 9–6. The program also can be used for other problems by changing the integration limits `lower` and `upper` in the first two lines, the value of `exact` in the second line, and the definition of the function in the third line.

Trapezoidal Rule

A natural extension of the strip method just discussed is to replace the rectangular elements by trapezoidal ones. The integration method that is based on this principle is called the **trapezoidal rule**. It differs from the strip method in that the average height of each element is taken to be the arithmetic average of the value of the function at the midpoint. Thus, the trapezoidal rule approximates the given function as a series of straight line segments connected to each other at their ends instead of as a staircase function.

To develop the formulation associated with the trapezoidal rule, consider a function $f(x)$ that is to be integrated between the limits of a and b. We now divide this interval into N segments of equal width h where $h = (b - a)/N$ and denote the value of x at any point n by x_n, as shown in Figure 9–7. The average height of a segment between the points n and $n + 1$ can be expressed as

$$\text{Average height} \cong \frac{f(x_n) + f(x_{n+1})}{2} \tag{9–8}$$

which is the average of the values of the function at the end points of the segment. Applying the trapezoidal rule, the total area under the curve is determined by multiplying the average height of each segment by its width and summing them up. The area of a general segment between the points x_n and x_{n+1} can be determined from

$$I_n \cong (x_{n+1} - x_n)\frac{f(x_{n+1}) + f(x_n)}{2}, \quad n = 0, 1, 2, \ldots, N - 1 \tag{9–9}$$

where $x_0 = a$ and $x_N = b$. Then the value of the integral I between the limits of a and b can be determined from Equation 9–5 by summing up the areas

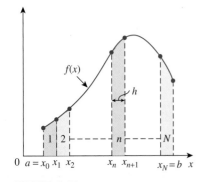

FIGURE 9–7

In the trapezoidal rule, the integration interval is divided into N trapezoids of equal width h.

of the segments. For $N = 1$, the trapezoidal rule involves a single trapezoid, and Equation 9–9 simplifies to (see Figure 9–8)

$$I \cong (b - a)\frac{f(b) + f(a)}{2} \qquad \text{(9–10)}$$

As you would expect, the accuracy will improve as the number of trapezoids used increases.

EXAMPLE 9–2   Trapezoidal Rule

Using the trapezoidal rule, evaluate the integral

$$I = \int_0^1 (7x - 6x^2)\,dx$$

and compare your result to the exact value of $I = 1.5$. Repeat the calculations for different numbers of segments of equal width.

SOLUTION In this case, we have $f(x) = 7x - 6x^2$, $a = x_0 = 0$, and $b = x_N = 1$. For $N = 1$, we approximate the entire area under the curve as a single trapezoid, as shown in Figure 9–9a. Then from Equation 9–10, we obtain

$$I \cong (b - a)\frac{f(b) + f(a)}{2} = (1 - 0) \times \frac{f(1) + f(0)}{2} = 1 \times \frac{1 + 0}{2} = 0.5$$

which has an error of $(1.5 - 0.5)/1.5 = 66.7\%$.

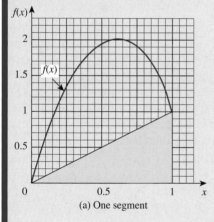

(a) One segment

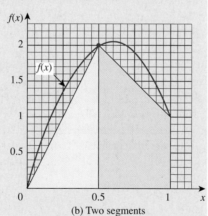

(b) Two segments

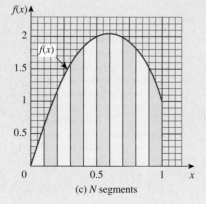

(c) N segments

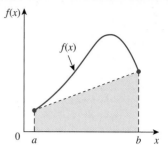

FIGURE 9–8

The trapezoidal rule with one segment (the simplest case).

FIGURE 9–9

Graphical representation of the numerical integration of the function in Example 9–2 with the trapezoidal rule, which is applied by dividing the integration interval into (a) one segment, (b) two segments, and (c) N segments.

For $N = 2$, we have approximated the entire area under the curve as two trapezoids with an equal base, as shown in Figure 9–9b. Then $h = (1 - 0)/2 = 0.5$, and from Equations 9–5 and 9–9, we obtain

$$I \cong I_0 + I_1 = h\frac{f(x_0) + f(x_1)}{2} + h\frac{f(x_1) + f(x_2)}{2}$$

$$= 0.5 \times \left[\frac{f(0) + f(0.5)}{2} + \frac{f(0.5) + f(1)}{2}\right]$$

$$= 0.5 \times \left[\frac{0 + 2}{2} + \frac{2 + 1}{2}\right] = 1.25$$

which has an error of $(1.5 - 1.25)/1.5 = 16.7\%$. Therefore, dividing the interval into two segments reduced the error from 66.7% to 16.7%.

The results for other values of N are given in Table 9–2. Note that for a given value of N, the relative errors involved in the strip method and the trapezoidal rule are of comparable magnitude. This is because the approximations involved in both methods are of the same order. The results of the strip method would be considerably less accurate if the average value of the function in a segment was taken as the value of the function at the left end point instead of at the midpoint of the segment. For linear functions, both methods give the exact result for $N = 1$ or higher.

A program written in MATLAB used to obtain these results is given in Figure 9–10. The program also can be used for other problems by changing the integration limits in the first line, the exact value in the second line, and the function definition in the third line.

TABLE 9–2

Values of the Integral $\int_0^1 (7x - 6x^2)\,dx$ Obtained with the Trapezoidal Rule, and the Error Involved for Different Number of Segments

Number of Segments	Trapezoidal Rule	Exact Value	Relative Error
1	0.500000	1.5000	66.67%
2	1.250000	1.5000	16.67%
3	1.388889	1.5000	7.41%
4	1.437500	1.5000	4.16%
5	1.460000	1.5000	2.67%
10	1.490000	1.5000	0.67%
20	1.497500	1.5000	0.17%
30	1.498889	1.5000	0.07%
40	1.499375	1.5000	0.04%
50	1.499600	1.5000	0.03%
100	1.499900	1.5000	0.01%
200	1.499976	1.5000	0.00%

```
lower = 0; upper = 1;
exact = 1.5;   m = 1;
f = @(x)7*x-6*x^2;
for nstrip = [1,2,3,4,5,10:10:50,100,200]
    h = (upper-lower)/nstrip;
    x = lower; value = 0;
    for n = 1: nstrip
        value = value+h*(f(x)+f(x+h))/2;
        x = x+h;
        error(m,:) = [nstrip,value,100*abs(value-exact)/exact];
    end
    m = m+1;
end
error
```

FIGURE 9–10

A MATLAB program for the trapezoidal rule.

Simpson's Rule

It is clear from the previous discussions that one way of improving the accuracy of numerical integration is to use a greater number of segments. Another way is to use a better approximation in each segment. For example, assuming the value of the function to vary linearly within each segment, the trapezoidal method approximates the function better than by assuming it to be a constant at the value of the function at the left end point, as done with the rectangular strip method.

Now we go one step further and approximate the function within each segment by a second-degree polynomial instead of a first-degree polynomial (a straight line) or a zeroth-degree polynomial (a constant). The numerical integration method that is based on this principle is called **Simpson's 1/3 rule** or just **Simpson's rule**.

The development of the formulation associated with Simpson's rule is more involved, and thus, we present the results only. Again, we consider a function $f(x)$ that is to be integrated between the limits of a and b. We now divide this interval into N segments of equal width and denote the value of x at any point n by x_n.

For $N = 1$ (one segment that covers the entire interval), Simpson's rule is expressed as

$$I \cong \frac{b-a}{3}\left[\frac{f(x_0)}{2} + 2f\left(\frac{x_0 + x_1}{2}\right) + \frac{f(x_1)}{2}\right] \tag{9–11}$$

as shown in Figure 9–11. Note that the average height of the segment this time is determined by adding half the values of the function at the end points to twice its value at the midpoint and dividing it by 3. The name Simpson's 1/3 rule comes from the factor 1/3 in the expression.

The area of a general segment between the points x_n and x_{n+1} can be determined from

$$I_n \cong \frac{x_{n+1} - x_n}{6}\left[f(x_n) + 4f\left(\frac{x_{n+1} + x_n}{2}\right) + f(x_{n+1})\right], n = 0, 1, \dots, N-1 \tag{9–12}$$

where $x_0 = a$ and $x_N = b$. Then the value of the integral I between the limits of a and b can be determined from Equation 9–5 by summing the areas of the segments.

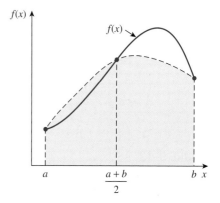

FIGURE 9–11

Simpson's rule with one segment (the simplest case).

If we go another step further and approximate the function within each segment by a *third*-degree polynomial, we will obtain similar but more complicated expressions that will involve the factor 3/8. The numerical integration method that is based on this principle is called **Simpson's 3/8 rule**. Simpson's 1/3 rule is usually preferred, since the 3/8 rule does not offer enough improvement in accuracy over the 1/3 rule to justify the added complexity.

EXAMPLE 9–3   Simpson's Rule

Using Simpson's rule, evaluate the integral

$$I = \int_0^1 (7x - 6x^2)\,dx$$

and compare your result to the exact value of $I = 1.5$. Repeat the calculations for different numbers of segments of equal width.

SOLUTION   In this case, we have $f(x) = 7x - 6x^2$, $a = x_0 = 0$, and $b = x_N = 1$. For $N = 1$, we use Equation 9–11, which is the lowest-order approximation of Simpson's rule. It gives

$$I \cong \frac{b - a}{3}\left[\frac{f(x_0)}{2} + 2f\left(\frac{x_0 + x_1}{2}\right) + \frac{f(x_1)}{2}\right] = \frac{1 - 0}{3}\left[\frac{f(0)}{2} + 2f(0.5) + \frac{f(1)}{2}\right]$$

$$= \frac{1}{3}\left[\frac{0}{2} + 2(2) + \frac{1}{2}\right] = 1.5$$

which is identical to the exact result. This is very impressive but not surprising, since $f(x)$ in this case is a second-degree polynomial. Simpson's rule approximates second-degree polynomials exactly.

We would keep getting the same result if we repeat the calculations by dividing the interval into two or more segments. We do not show the results, because no matter what value of N is used the results will be exact. A program written in MATLAB used to obtain these results is given in Figure 9–12. The program also can be used for other problems by changing the integration limits (the variables `lower` and `upper`), the value of `exact`, and the definition of the function in the third line.

```
lower = 0; upper = 1;
exact = 1.5;m = 1;
f = @(x)7*x-6*x^2;
for nstrip = [1,2,3,4,5,10:10:50,100,200]

    h = (upper-lower)\nstrip;
    x = lower; value = 0;
    for n = 1; nstrip

        value = value+h*(f(x)/2+2*f(x+h/2)+f(x+h)/2)/3;
        x = x+h;
        error(m, :) = [nstrip,value,100*abs(value-exact)/exact];

    end
    m = m+1;

end
error
```

FIGURE 9–12

A MATLAB program for Simpson's rule.

Simpson's rule is a little more complicated than the trapezoidal rule, but it is also much more accurate. Therefore, it is commonly used in practice to obtain accurate results with relatively few calculations.

In practice, we will not know the exact result, and thus, we can not assess the error involved in the numerical integration precisely. Therefore, it is advisable to use a general program that keeps dividing the interval into smaller segments automatically until doing so causes a smaller change in the final answer than a specified value. Once the error criterion is satisfied and the computer returns an answer, we can take it as an indication that our result is sufficiently close to the exact result.

The reader is reminded that there are more sophisticated numerical integration methods (called *adaptive*, such as *Romberg integration* and Gauss *quadrature*) that utilize variable size segments selected in a complex but clever manner. Very accurate results can be obtained by these methods without increasing the number of calculations significantly. However, the simple methods discussed here are adequate for many applications.

Section Review

Problems Denoted with a C are Conceptual Problems for Discussion

9–1C How does the trapezoidal rule differ from Simpson's rule of numerical integration? Which one of them is a more accurate method?

9–2C How can we improve the accuracy of the results obtained by numerical integration?

9–3 Evaluate the following integral using a calculator by dividing the integration interval into (a) one and (b) two segments using the indicated methods. Also, perform the integration analytically, and determine the relative error of the results obtained by numerical integration.

$$\int_0^2 (x - 1)\,dx,\ \text{Rectangular strip method, Trapezoidal rule}$$

(*Answer:* The integral is zero exactly. For both methods, the relative error is 0% for both one and two segments.)

9–2 ▪ NUMERICAL SOLUTION OF DIFFERENTIAL EQUATIONS

Most nonlinear or variable coefficient differential equations encountered in practice do not have a closed-form analytic solution, and it becomes necessary to find an approximate solution using one of the several numerical methods available. Noting that any nth-order differential equation can be expressed as a system of n first-order differential equations, in this chapter, we will concentrate on the solution of the first-order differential equations of the form

$$\frac{dy}{dx} = f(x, y) \tag{9-13}$$

with

$$y(x_0) = y_0 \tag{9-14}$$

Throughout the discussions, we will assume that the function f and its partial derivative $\partial f/\partial y$ are continuous in a region that includes the point

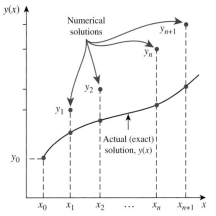

FIGURE 9–13

Numerical methods give the solution of an initial-value problem at distinct points using the initial condition $y(x_0) = y_0$ as the starting point.

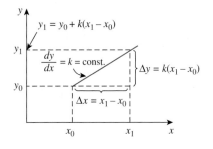

FIGURE 9–14

Graphical representation of the solution of the differential equation $y' = f(x, y) = k$, where k is a constant.

(x_0, y_0), so the initial-value problem has a unique solution in the region of interest.

Note that y_0 is the solution of the differential equation at the point x_0, and our goal is to find the values of the unknown function y at other x values taking the point (x_0, y_0) as the starting point (Figure 9–13).

We now multiply Equation 9–13 by dx and integrate both sides from (x_0, y_0) to (x_1, y_1). We obtain

$$\int_{y_0}^{y_1} dy = \int_{x_0}^{x_1} f(x, y)\,dx$$

or

$$y_1 = y_0 + \int_{x_0}^{x_1} f(x, y)\,dx \tag{9–15}$$

where y_1 is the solution of the differential equation at x_1. The distance $h = x_1 - x_0$ we step over to the solution at the new point x_1 is called the **step size**. Therefore, we can determine y_1 using Equation 9–15, assuming of course that we can somehow perform the integral it involves. If as a special case $f(x, y) = k = $ constant, this integral can be performed easily to yield the solution (Figure 9–14)

$$y_1 = y_0 + k(x_1 - x_0) \tag{9–16}$$

where the point x_1 can be any point in the interval.

With the exception of special cases such as this one, the possibility of performing the integration in Equation 9–15 analytically is not very high. Therefore, we will attempt to get an approximate result using a numerical method. In general, the function f depends on both x and y. However, sometimes it depends on x only, which is easier to deal with. We now discuss both cases.

Case 1: $f = f(x)$

In this case, Equation 9–15 simplifies to

$$y_1 = y_0 + \int_{x_0}^{x_1} f(x)\,dx \tag{9–17}$$

and the determination of the solution y_1 at any point x_1 reduces to performing a numerical integration using any of the methods discussed in the last section. Equation 9–17 can be generalized for any two points n and $n + 1$ as

$$y_{n+1} = y_n + \int_{x_n}^{x_{n+1}} f(x)\,dx \tag{9–18}$$

The use of this relation is now illustrated with an example.

EXAMPLE 9–4   Numerical Solution of a Differential Equation

Using the trapezoidal rule for numerical integration, determine the solution of the initial-value problem

$$\frac{dy}{dx} = f(x) = 7x - 6x^2, \ y(0) = 1$$

in the interval 0 to 2 by dividing it into ten equal segments. The function $f(x)$ is graphed in Figure 9–15.

SOLUTION Solving a differential equation numerically in an interval is equivalent to finding the values of its solution at a sufficient number of points in that interval. If we divide the specified interval into ten equal parts, then we will have a step size of $(b - a)/N = (2 - 0)/10 = 0.2$. Thus, we have $x_0 = 0$, $x_1 = 0.2, \ldots, x_{10} = 2$. The function is shown in Figure 9–15. Note that its slope decreases rapidly for $x > 1.2$.

Using Equation 9–17 and the trapezoidal rule for the integration, the solution at $x_1 = 0.2$ is determined to be

$$y_1 = y_0 + \int_{x_0}^{x_1} f(x)\,dx$$

$$\cong y_0 + (x_1 - x_0)\frac{f(x_1) + f(x_0)}{2}$$

$$= 1 + (0.2 - 0) \times \frac{(7 \times 0.2 - 6 \times 0.2^2) + (7 \times 0 - 6 \times 0^2)}{2} = 1.116$$

since $f(x) = 7x - 6x^2$. This result differs from the exact value of 1.124 by 0.71%.

The solution at $x = 0.4$ can be determined similarly to be

$$y_2 = y_1 + \int_{x_1}^{x_2} f(x)\,dx$$

$$\cong y_1 + (x_2 - x_1)\frac{f(x_1) + f(x_2)}{2}$$

$$= 1.116 + (0.4 - 0.2) \times \frac{(7 \times 0.4 - 6 \times 0.4^2) + (7 \times 0.2 - 6 \times 0.2^2)}{2}$$

$$= 1.416$$

which differs from the exact value of 1.432 by 1.12%

Continuing in this manner, the solution at the remaining eight points is determined and tabulated in Table 9–3. The exact values obtained from the analytical solution

$$y(x) = 1 + 3.5x^2 - 2x^3$$

are also listed for comparison. We can improve the accuracy by dividing the interval into smaller segments or by using a more accurate numerical integration technique such as Simpson's rule.

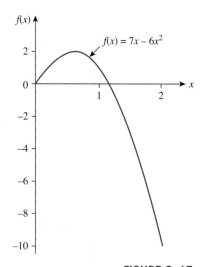

FIGURE 9–15

The function $f(x, y)$ used in Example 9–4.

TABLE 9–3

Comparison of the Numerical Solution Obtained Using the Trapezoidal Rule with the Exact Solution for $y' = 7x - 6x^2$, $y(0) = 1$

x	Trapezoidal Rule	Exact Value	Relative Error
0.0	1.000	1.000	0.00%
0.2	1.116	1.124	0.71%
0.4	1.416	1.432	1.12%
0.6	1.804	1.828	1.31%
0.8	2.184	2.216	1.44%
1.0	2.460	2.500	1.60%
1.2	2.536	2.584	1.86%
1.4	2.316	2.372	2.36%
1.6	1.704	1.768	3.62%
1.8	0.606	1.676	10.65%
2.0	−1.080	−1.000	8.00%

Case 2: $f = f(x, y)$

When the function f depends on both x and y, the numerical integration techniques presented earlier will not work, and we need to use a different approach. We observe that the function $f(x, y)$ in the differential equation

$$\frac{dy}{dx} = f(x, y) = \text{slope} \qquad (9\text{–}19)$$

represents the slope of the solution function y at any point (x, y). The numerical methods we are about to discuss are based on assuming this slope to remain constant at some value for each step (Figure 9–16). Then the solution at any point x_{n+1} can be expressed in terms of the solution at the previous point x_n as (see Equation 9–16)

New value = old value + slope × step size

or

$$y_{n+1} = y_n + s_n h \qquad (9\text{–}20)$$

where the step size is $h = x_{n+1} - x_n$. Numerical methods differ primarily in the way the slope s_n is estimated. The **Euler method**, which is named after L. Euler (1707–1783), is the simplest numerical method for solving differential equations; this slope is taken to be the value of the function $f(x, y)$ at the beginning of each step. In the **improved Euler method**, it is taken to be the arithmetic average of the values of $f(x, y)$ at the end points of the step. In higher-order *Runge–Kutta methods*, the slope is determined with greater accuracy using a more complex procedure. In the following sections, we will discuss these methods and demonstrate their use.

All of the methods just mentioned use the solution at only one point to determine the solution at the next point and are called **single-step** or **starting methods**. In contrast, the methods that use the solution at two or more previous points to determine the solution at the next point are called

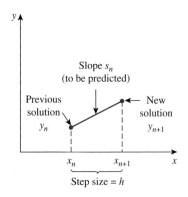

FIGURE 9–16

Numerical methods for the solution of differential equations are based on predicting the average slope of the solution function during each step and then using it to determine the solution at the end of that step.

multistep or **continuing methods**. Actually, multistep methods are hybrid methods, since they depend on a starting method to provide them with the minimum number of solutions they need to get started.

It always should be remembered that the results obtained by any numerical method are approximations to the true solution values, and care should be exercised in their interpretation. The error in numerical methods is caused by two effects. One is the **truncation** or **discretization error**, which is due to the approximations made during numerical formulation of the problem. The other is due to **round-off error**, which is due to retaining a limited number of digits during calculations. Both effects are discussed in detail in Section 9–4.

Throughout the discussions in this chapter, we will use the initial-value problem

$$\frac{dy}{dx} = 5y - 25x^2 + 2, \quad y(0) = 2 \tag{9-21}$$

to illustrate the use of different numerical methods and to compare their accuracy. This is a linear first-order initial-value problem, and its exact analytical solution easily can be determined to be

$$y(x) = 2e^{5x} + 5x^2 + 2x \tag{9-22}$$

The exact value of the solution y at any point x can be obtained by substituting that x value into the analytic solution. The solution values obtained this way are exact, and they will be used as a basis for comparison. The relative (percent) error in the numerical results can be determined from

$$\text{Relative error} = \left| \frac{y_{\text{exact}} - y_{\text{numeric}}}{y_{\text{exact}}} \right| \times 100(\%) \tag{9-23}$$

where y_{numeric} is the approximate value obtained from the numerical solution and y_{exact} is the exact value obtained from the analytic solution.

Section Review

9–4C   When discussing the numerical solution of differential equations, why did we focus on the first-order equations?

9–5C   Can we solve a differential equation numerically if no initial condition is specified?

9–6   Using a calculator, determine the numerical solution of the following initial-value problem after (a) one step and (b) two steps using a step size of $h = 0.2$. Use the indicated methods for numerical integration. Also, solve the initial-value problem analytically, and determine the relative error of the numerical results.

$y' = x - 1, y(0) = 1$ Rectangular strip method, Trapezoidal rule

(*Answer:* The exact solution is $y(x) = 0.5x^2 - x + 1$. For both methods, the relative error is 0% for both one and two steps.)

9–3 ▪ THE EULER METHOD

Consider the first-order initial-value problem

$$y' = f(x, y), \quad y(x_0) = y_0 \tag{9-24}$$

whose solution is to be determined numerically on the interval from $x = a$ to $x = b$ using a constant step size (equal increments in x). If the number of steps to be used is N, then the step size h for this problem becomes $h = (b - a)/N$. The x values at any two consecutive values are related to each other by

$$x_{n+1} = x_n + h, \quad n = 0, 1, 2, \ldots, N - 1 \tag{9-25}$$

Our goal is, as usual, to determine the approximate solutions $y_1, y_2, \ldots, y_N$ at the points $x_1, x_2, \ldots, x_N$ using the solution y_0 at x_0 as the starting point. Again the main question is how to determine the solution y_{n+1} at the point x_{n+1} when the solution y_n at the point x_n is available.

The Euler method is based on the fact that the function $f(x, y)$ represents the slope of y (the rate of change of y with respect to x) at the point (x, y) and assumes that for small changes in x this slope remains constant at its initial value for each step. For example, the value of the slope at the initial point (x_0, y_0) is $f(x_0, y_0)$. Now y is assumed to change at this constant rate as x increases from x_0 to $x_1 = x_0 + h$. Then the change in y is (Figure 9–17)

$$\begin{aligned} \Delta y &= \text{slope} \times \Delta x \\ &= f(x_0, y_0)(x_1 - x_0) \\ &= f(x_0, y_0)h \end{aligned}$$

Therefore, the value of the function at $x_1 = x_0 + h$ under this assumption becomes

$$y_1 = y_0 + hf(x_0, y_0) \tag{9-26}$$

which is the approximate solution at x_1. The slope of the solution function at this point is $f(x_1, y_1)$, which is again assumed to remain constant from x_1 to $x_2 = x_1 + h$. The approximate solution at x_2 is determined in a similar manner to be

$$y_2 = y_1 + hf(x_1, y_1) \tag{9-27}$$

Generalizing, the approximate solution at any point x_{n+1} is (Figure 9–17)

$$y_{n+1} = y_n + hf(x_n, y_n), n = 0,1,2,3, \ldots \tag{9-28}$$

which is the general formula of the Euler method.

A graphical interpretation of the Euler method is given in Figure 9–18. Note that the term $hf(x_n, y_n)$ corresponds to the area of the shaded rectangle on the $y' - x$ diagram, and it is intended to approximate the entire area under the curve between x_n and x_{n+1}. The difference between the two areas is the error involved in the Euler method during that step. Obviously, the smaller the step size, the smaller the error.

For $f = f(x)$, the Euler method becomes analogous to the strip method for numerical integration, except that the average value of the function for a step here is taken as the value of the function at the starting point instead of the midpoint. Obviously, we can increase accuracy significantly if we use

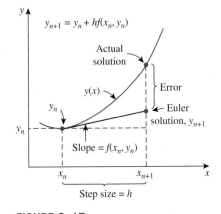

FIGURE 9–17

Graphical representation of the Euler method on the $y - x$ diagram.

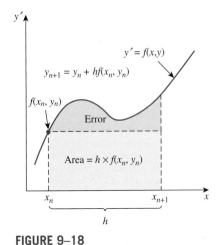

FIGURE 9–18

Graphical representation of the Euler method on the $y' - x$ diagram.

the value of the function f at the midpoint instead of the first point of each step. This is the basic idea in the modified Euler method, which is discussed later in this chapter.

The Euler method is simple and very easy to use, but it is not a very accurate method. Often it is necessary to use a very small step size h to obtain acceptable accuracy. However, this is not practical for problems that involve numerous such calculations since very small step sizes may cause the round-off error introduced at each step to accumulate (round-off error is discussed later in this chapter). The computation time also increases with the number of steps, but this is often not an issue any more because of the high speed of most computers. However, if the program must run on a slow microprocessor, such as those used in embedded microcontrollers, the computation time could be an issue.

Nevertheless, the Euler method can be used to obtain rough preliminary results with minimal effort, since it is very easy to program. Then a more accurate method can be used to refine the results if warranted. The use of the Euler method is now illustrated with an example.

EXAMPLE 9–5   The Euler Method

Using the Euler method with a step size of $h = 0.1$, determine the solution of the initial-value problem

$$y' = 5y - 25x^2 + 2, \quad y(0) = 2$$

in the interval $0 \le x \le 1$. Compare the results to exact solution values.

SOLUTION   We have $f(x, y) = 5y - 25x^2 + 2$, $x_0 = 0$, $y_0 = 2$, and $h = 0.1$. Then the solutions at the points $x_1 = 0.1, x_2 = 0.2, \ldots, x_{10} = 1$ are obtained by repeatedly applying the Euler formula (Equation 9–28)

$$y_{n+1} = y_n + hf(x_n, y_n)$$

For $n = 0$,

$$y_1 = y_0 + hf(x_0, y_0)$$
$$= 2 + 0.1f(0, 2)$$
$$= 2 + 0.1 \times (5 \times 2 - 25 \times 0^2 + 2)$$
$$= 3.2$$

Thus, the Euler method predicts the solution at $x_1 = 0.1$ to be $y_1 = 3.2$. The exact solution at this point is determined from Equation 9–22 to be 3.54744. Therefore, the value obtained with the Euler method is in error by $100 \times (3.54744 - 3.2)/3.54744 = 9.79\%$. It is important to realize that this erroneous value, not the exact one, will be used as the starting point for the next step, and the error will keep propagating as the number of steps increases. Therefore, in general, the percent error gets larger at later steps.

Repeating the calculation for $n = 1$ gives

$$y_2 = y_1 + hf(x_1, y_1)$$
$$= 3.2 + 0.1f(0.1, 3.2)$$
$$= 3.2 + 0.1 \times (5 \times 3.2 - 25 \times 0.1^2 + 2)$$
$$= 4.975$$

which differs from the exact value of 6.03656 by 17.59%.

```
h = 0.1; nstep = 10;
f = @(x,y) (5*y-25*x^2+2);
x = 0; y = 2;
for n = 1:nstep
        y = y + h*f(x,y);
        x = n*h
        y

        exact = 2*exp(5*x)+5*x^2+2*x
        error = 100*abs(y-exact)/exact
end
```

FIGURE 9–19

A MATLAB program for the
Euler method.

The calculations for $n = 2, 3, \ldots, 9$ are performed in the same manner using the simple MATLAB program shown in Figure 9–19, and the results are listed in Table 9–4 together with the exact results for comparison. Note that the error reaches 61.60%.

Table 9–4 also presents results obtained using different step sizes at intervals of 0.1. Note that the Euler solution approaches the exact solution as the step size decreases, but the number of calculations increases with decreasing step sizes. For example, obtaining the results for $h = 0.01$ required ten times the computer time needed to obtain the results for $h = 0.1$. Therefore, any improvement in accuracy with decreasing step sizes must be weighed against the increase in round-off error and computation time.

TABLE 9–4

Comparison of Results Obtained Using the Euler Method with Five Different Step Sizes with the Exact Results for $y' = 5y - 25x^2 + 2$, $y(0) = 2$

x	$h = 0.1$	$h = 0.05$	$h = 0.01$	$h = 0.001$	$h = 0.0001$	Exact
0.0	2.00000	2.00000	2.00000	2.00000	2.00000	2.00000
0.1	3.20000	3.34688	3.50150	3.54269	3.54696	3.54744
0.2	4.97500	5.41074	5.89006	6.02132	6.03503	6.03656
0.3	7.56250	8.53866	9.66066	9.97647	10.00966	10.01138
0.4	11.31875	13.27291	15.61958	16.29829	16.37008	16.37810
0.5	16.77813	20.46079	25.08012	26.45257	26.59862	26.61499
0.6	24.74219	31.42623	40.18158	42.85298	43.13902	43.17107
0.7	36.41328	48.23786	64.40859	69.47398	70.01976	70.08091
0.8	53.59492	74.12791	103.4373	112.8603	113.8818	113.9963
0.9	78.99239	114.1467	166.5134	183.7888	185.6730	185.8842
1.0	116.6636	176.1855	268.6975	300.0054	303.4409	303.8263

Section Review

9–7C Why is the Euler method not used widely in practice despite its simplicity?

9–8 Using a calculator, determine the numerical solution of the following initial-value problem after (a) one step and (b) two steps with a step size of $h = 0.2$ using the Euler method. Also, solve the initial-value problem analytically, and determine the relative error of the numerical results.

$$y' = x + y, \quad y(0) = 0$$

(*Answer:* The exact solution is $y(x) = e^x - x - 1$. The Euler method has a relative error of 100% after one step and 56.4% after two steps.)

9–4 · ERRORS IN NUMERICAL METHODS

A comparison of the numerical results in Table 9–4 with the exact results listed in the last column confirms what we have been saying all along, that the results obtained by a numerical method are approximate, and they may or may not be sufficiently close to the exact (true) solution values. The difference between a numerical solution and the exact solution is the *error* involved in the numerical solution, and it is primarily due to two sources:

1. The **discretization error** (also called the *truncation* or *formulation error*) is caused by the approximations used in the formulation of the numerical method.
2. The **round-off error** is caused by the computer representing a number using a limited number of significant digits and continuously rounding (or chopping) off the digits it cannot retain.

Discretization Error

The discretization error involved in the Euler method is due to replacing the actual solution function in each step by a straight line segment. The slope of this line segment for any step is assumed to be the value of the slope at the beginning of that step, as illustrated in Figure 9–20.

Note that both solutions coincide at the beginning of the step, but the numerical solution deviates from the exact solution as x increases. The difference between the two solutions is due to the approximation at this step only and is called the **local discretization error**. One would expect the situation to get worse with each step, since the second step uses the erroneous result of the first step as its starting point and adds a second local discretization error on top of it, as shown in Figure 9–21. The accumulation of the local discretization errors continues with increasing step numbers, and the total discretization error at any step is called the **global** or **accumulated discretization error**. Note that the local and global discretization errors are identical for the first step. The global discretization error usually increases with increasing number of steps, as was the case in Example 9–5. However, the opposite may occur when the function $f(x, y)$ frequently changes direction, giving rise to local discretization errors of opposite signs that tend to cancel each other.

To have an idea about the magnitude of the local discretization error, consider the Taylor series expansion of the solution function about the point x_n,

$$y(x_{n+1}) = y(x_n) + hy'(x_n) + \frac{h^2}{2!}y''(x_n) + \frac{h^3}{3!}y'''(x_n) + \cdots$$

$$+ \frac{h^n}{n!}y^{(n)}(x_n) + \cdots \qquad \textbf{(9–29)}$$

where $y(x_n)$ is the actual (exact) solution at x_n. The Euler solution at the point x_{n+1} was expressed as (see Equation 9–28)

$$y_{n+1} = y_n + hf(x_n, y_n)$$

This relation resembles the Taylor series expansion terminated after the first two terms and with the approximate solutions y_{n+1} and y_n replacing the

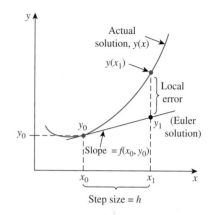

FIGURE 9–20

The local discretization error of the Euler method at step 1.

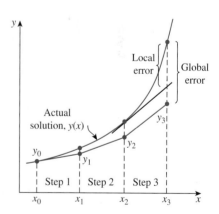

FIGURE 9–21

The local and global discretization errors of the Euler method at step 3.

exact values $y(x_{n+1})$ and $y(x_n)$. In general, the numerical solution y_n and the exact solution $y(x_n)$ will not be the same. However, we will take these two solutions to be identical so that we can estimate the discretization error that occurs during one step only. Noting that $f(x_n, y_n) = y_n'$ and subtracting the Euler formula from the Taylor series expansion (Equation 9–29) gives us the following important relation for the local discretization error:

$$\text{Error} = y(x_{n+1}) - y_{n+1}$$

$$= \frac{h^2}{2!}y''(x_n) + \frac{h^3}{3!}y'''(x_n) + \cdots + \frac{h^n}{n!}y^{(n)}(x_n) + \cdots \qquad \text{(9–30)}$$

For a sufficiently small step size h, the terms decay rapidly as n increases, and their contributions become smaller and smaller. Therefore, the first term in Equation 9–30 is the most significant, and it represents the error fairly closely. Therefore,

$$\text{Local error} \cong h^2\frac{y''(x_n)}{2} \le h^2 K \qquad \text{(9–31)}$$

where K is a constant whose value is half the absolute maximum value of the second derivative of the solution function in the interval of interest.

It seems like we can determine the error at each step using Equation 9–31, but it is not practical to do so. This is because it is not easy to determine the value of the constant K. However, K is independent of the step size h, and thus, we conclude that *the local discretization error in the Euler method is proportional to the square of the step size*. Therefore, halving the step size from h to $h/2$ will reduce the local discretization error to a quarter of what it was before.

The local discretization error is the formulation error associated with a single step and gives an idea about the accuracy of the method used. However the solution results obtained at every step except the first one involve the *accumulated* error up to that point, and the local error alone does not have much significance. What we really need to know is the *global* discretization error.

To obtain an estimate of the global error, consider an initial-value problem that is to be solved in the interval $a \le x \le b$ by dividing it into N steps of step size $h = (b - a)/N$. In the worst case, the local discretization errors all will be positive (or all negative) at the maximum value of Kh^2. In this case, the maximum accumulated error will be $2Kh^2$ after the second step, $3Kh^2$ after the third step, and NKh^2 after the Nth step. Noting that $h = (b - a)/N$ and $N = (b - a)/h$, the global discretization error can be expressed as

$$\text{Global error} \le NKh^2 = \frac{b - a}{h}Kh^2 = (b - a)Kh \qquad \text{(9–32)}$$

where $b - a$ (and thus $(b - a)K$) is a constant whose value is independent of the step size h. Therefore, we conclude that *the global discretization error of the Euler method is proportional to step size*. In other words, it is proportional to the first power of h, and thus, the Euler method is said to be a *first-order* approximation. Therefore, we can reduce the maximum global error to half of what it was by simply halving the step size. In other words, we can double the accuracy of the results obtained by the Euler method by halving the step size. Likewise, reducing the step size by a factor of 10 will cut the maximum error to one-tenth of what it was before (Figure 9–22).

The line of reasoning just used to relate the global error to the local error is applicable to any numerical method and can be expressed as follows.

If the local discretization error in a numerical method is proportional to h^k, then the global or accumulated discretization error is proportional to h^{k-1}.

It is clear from these discussions that the discretization error can be reduced by using a more accurate algorithm or by decreasing the step size. The decrease in error with decreasing step size is illustrated in Table 9–5 by comparing the Euler solution of the problem in Example 9–4 at $x = 1$ with the exact solution at that point. Note that even for this small interval of 0 to 1, a very large number of steps are needed to obtain sufficiently accurate results.

Round-Off Error

If we had a computer that could retain an infinite number of digits for all numbers, the difference between the exact solution and the approximate (numerical) solution at any point would entirely be due to discretization error. However, we know that every computer (or calculator) represents numbers using a finite number of significant digits. The number of significant digits used depends on the computer and on the program. Use of seven digits is referred to as *single precision*. However, the user may perform the calculations using 15 significant digits for the numbers, if he wishes, and this is called *double precision*. Of course, performing calculations in double precision will require more computer memory and a longer execution time.

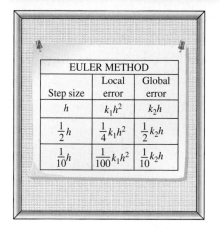

EULER METHOD		
Step size	Local error	Global error
h	$k_1 h^2$	$k_2 h$
$\frac{1}{2}h$	$\frac{1}{4}k_1 h^2$	$\frac{1}{2}k_2 h$
$\frac{1}{10}h$	$\frac{1}{100}k_1 h^2$	$\frac{1}{10}k_2 h$

FIGURE 9–22

The local and global discretization error of the Euler method are proportional to h^2 and h, for several different step sizes.

TABLE 9–5

Comparison of the Euler Solution at $x = 1$ with the Exact Solution for $y' = 5y - 25x^2 + 2$, $y(0) = 2$, for Several Different Step Sizes

Number of Steps N	Step Size $h = 1/N$	Euler Solution at $x = 1$	Relative Error
1	1.0	14.000	95.39%
2	0.5	25.8750	91.48%
5	0.2	64.8000	78.67%
10	0.1	116.6636	61.60%
20	0.05	176.1855	42.01%
50	0.02	239.4539	21.19%
100	0.01	268.6975	11.56%
200	0.005	285.4348	6.05%
1000	0.001	300.0054	1.26%
10,000	0.0001	303.4409	0.13%
100,000	0.00001	303.7873	0.01%

Exact Solution: 303.8263

Given:
$$a = 7777777$$
$$b = 7777776$$
$$c = 0.4444432$$

Find:
$$D = a - b + c$$
$$E = a + c - b$$

Solution:
$$D = 7777777 - 7777776 + 0.4444432$$
$$= 1 + 0.4444432$$
$$= 1.444443 \text{ (Correct result)}$$

$$E = 7777777 + 0.4444432 - 7777776$$
$$= 7777777 - 7777776$$
$$= 1.000000 \text{ (In error by 30.8\%)}$$

FIGURE 9–23

A simple arithmetic operation performed with a computer in single precision (seven significant digits), which results in 30.8% error when the order of operation is changed.

In single-precision mode with seven significant digits, a computer will register the number 44444.666666 as 44444.67 or 44444.66, depending on the method of rounding the computer uses. In the first case, the excess digits are said to be rounded to the closest integer, whereas in the second case, they are said to be chopped off. Therefore, the numbers $a = 44444.12345$ and $b = 44444.12032$ are equivalent for a computer that performs calculations using seven significant digits. Such a computer would give $a - b = 0$ instead of the true value of 0.00313.

The error that is due to retaining a limited number of digits during calculations is called the **round-off error**. This error is random in nature, and there is no easy and systematic way of predicting it. It depends on the number of calculations, the method of rounding off, the type of the computer, and even the sequence of calculations.

In algebra, you learned that $a + b + c = a + c + b$, which seems quite reasonable. However, this not necessarily true for calculations performed with a computer, as demonstrated in Figure 9–23. Note that changing the sequence of calculations results in an error of 30.08% in just two operations. Considering that any significant problem involves thousands or even millions of such operations performed in sequence, we realize that the accumulated round-off error has the potential to cause serious error without giving any warning signs. Experienced programmers are very much aware of this danger, and they structure their programs to prevent any build up of the round-off error. For example, it is much safer to multiply a number by 10 than to add it ten times. Also, it is much safer to start any addition process with the smallest numbers and continue with larger numbers. This rule is particularly important when evaluating series with a large number of terms with alternating signs.

The round-off error is proportional to the number of computations performed during the solution. In the Euler method, the number of calculations increases as the step size h decreases. Halving the step size, for example, will double the number of calculations and thus the accumulated round-off error.

Controlling the Error

The total error in any result obtained by a numerical method is the sum of the discretization error, which decreases with decreasing step size h, and the round-off error, which increases with decreasing step size, as shown in Figure 9–24. Therefore, decreasing the step size too much in order to get more accurate results may actually backfire and give less accurate results because of a faster increase in the round-off error. We should be careful not to let round-off error to get out of control by avoiding a large number of computations with very small numbers.

In practice, we will not know the exact solution of the problem, and thus, we will not be able to determine the magnitude of the error involved in the numerical method. Knowing that the global discretization error is equal to a constant times the step size is not much help either, since there is no easy way of determining the value of that constant. Besides, the global discretization error alone is meaningless without a true estimate of the round-off error. Therefore, we recommend the following workable procedures to assess the accuracy of the results obtained by a numerical method.

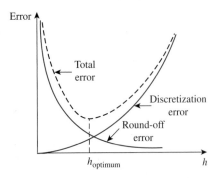

FIGURE 9–24

As the step size decreases, the discretization error decreases, but the round-off error increases.

Step 1. Start the calculations with a reasonable step size h based on experience. Then repeat the calculations using a step size of $h/2$. If the results obtained by halving the step size do not differ significantly from the results obtained with the full step size, we conclude that the discretization error is at an acceptable level. However, if the difference is larger than we can accept, then we have to repeat the calculations using a step size $h/4$ or smaller. We continue in this manner until halving the step size does not cause any appreciable change in the results, which indicates that the discretization error is reduced to an acceptable level.

Step 2. Repeat the calculations using double precision, holding the step size h constant. If the changes are not significant, we conclude that the round-off error is at an acceptable level. However, if the changes are too large to accept, we may try reducing the total number of calculations by increasing the step size. If this gives unacceptable discretization errors, we may have no choice but to switch to a more accurate method that gives acceptable results with fewer calculations.

These discussions on the error associated with the numerical solutions were presented using the Euler method as an example, but they are equally applicable to other numerical methods to be discussed.

Finally, it always should be kept in mind that the results obtained by any numerical methods may not reflect any trouble spots in certain initial-value problems. The results that seem quite reasonable may actually be grossly in error. Consider, for example, the initial-value problem

$$(x - 0.79)y' + y = 1, \quad y(0) = 2, \tag{9-33}$$

The solution of this initial-value problem obtained by the Euler method using a step size of $h = 0.1$ looks quite reasonable (Table 9–6) and gives no clues that there are any pitfalls. When we repeat the calculation with $h = 0.05$, we see some unusual change around the point $x = 0.8$, which

---

TABLE 9–6

Comparison of the Euler Solution $(x - 0.79)y' + y = 1$, $y(0) = 2$ with Different Step Sizes to the Exact Solution (the numerical method may jump over the discontinuities in the solution function without giving any warnings)

x	$h = 0.1$	$h = 0.05$	$h = 0.01$	Exact
0.0	2.000	2.000	2.000	2.000
0.1	2.127	2.135	2.143	2.145
0.2	2.290	2.313	2.333	2.339
0.3	2.508	2.556	2.600	2.612
0.4	2.816	2.909	3.000	3.026
0.5	3.282	3.471	3.667	3.724
0.6	4.069	4.500	5.000	5.158
0.7	5.684	7.000	9.000	9.778
0.8	10.889	22.000	1.3×10^7	80.000
0.9	−88.000	−13.000	−8.200	8.182
1.0	−7.091	−4.250	−3.600	4.762

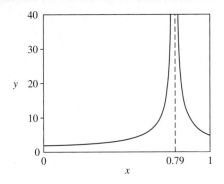

FIGURE 9–25

The plot of the actual solution of
$(x - 0.79)y' + y = 1, y(0) = 2$.

makes us suspicious. Finally, the solution blows up in that neighborhood when we use an even smaller step size. This is not surprising, since the exact solution of this problem is

$$y = \frac{0.79}{|x - 0.79|} + 1 \tag{9–34}$$

which has a singularity at $x = 0.79$. That is, the solution becomes infinity at this point, as shown in Figure 9–25. In this case, we could predict that there will be trouble at $x = 0.79$ by looking at the differential equation since the function $y' = f(x, y) = (1 - y)/(x - 0.79)$ has a discontinuity at that point. However, the appearance of some differential equations is very deceiving and gives no indication that there is trouble ahead. This is another good reason for always repeating the calculations at least twice with different step sizes before accepting them as the solution of the problem.

Note that the solution given by Equation 9–34 is unique in the interval $0 \le x < 0.79$, but not necessarily so for $x > 0.79$. The values given in Table 9–6 for $x > 0.79$ correspond to an initial condition $y(0) > 0.79$.

Section Review

9–9C Why do the results obtained using a numerical method differ from the exact results obtained analytically? What are the causes of this difference?

9–10 Using a calculator, determine the local and the global discretization error in the numerical solution of the following initial-value problems after (a) one step and (b) two steps with a step size of $h = 0.2$ using the Euler method.

$$y' = 1 - 2x - 3y, \quad y(0) = 0$$

(*Answer:* The exact solution is $y(x) = -(5/9)e^{-3x} - (2/3)x + 5/9$. After one step, both errors are identical and equal to -70.46%. After two steps, the local error is -37% and the global error is -64%.)

9–5 ▪ THE IMPROVED EULER METHOD

Reconsider the first-order initial-value problem

$$y' = f(x, y), \quad y(x_0) = y_0 \tag{9–35}$$

which we solved earlier with the Euler method using a step size of h. The Euler method is easy to understand and simple to program, but it requires the use of very small step sizes for accurate results. Therefore, it is not used in practice very often, especially for problems that are to be solved over a large interval.

Decreasing the step size is certainly one way of increasing the accuracy of a numerical method, but the preferred way is to use a better approximation. Numerical methods with more accurate formulations require more calculations at each step, but they give very accurate results—even with relatively large step sizes and thus fewer total number of calculations.

All single-step methods are based on the same general formula:

$$y_{n+1} = y_n + h \times \text{slope} \tag{9–36}$$

These methods differ only in the way the slope is evaluated. The Euler method assumes the value of the slope at the left end point of each interval applied across the entire interval. This immediately suggests that the accuracy of the results can be improved considerably if we evaluate the slope at both end points of the interval and use their average as the average slope for that interval. The method that is based on this principle is called the **improved Euler method** or **Heun method**, and is expressed as (Figure 9–26)

$$y_{n+1} = y_n + h\frac{f(x_n, y_n) + f(x_{n+1}, \tilde{y}_{n+1})}{2} \tag{9–37 a}$$

where

$$\tilde{y}_{n+1} = y_n + hf(x_n, y_n) \tag{9–37 b}$$

Note that we cannot determine the exact value of the function $f(x, y)$ at the point x_{n+1}, since we do not know the solution y_{n+1} at that point. Therefore, we first use the Euler method to predict the value of y_{n+1} approximately and then denote this value by $\tilde{y}_{n+1}$ in the improved Euler formula to obtain a better value for y_{n+1}. Therefore, each step of the improved Euler method involves the evaluations of the functions $f(x, y)$ twice.

The improved Euler method is clearly superior to the Euler method, because it represents the average slope in each interval by the average of the slopes at the end points of the interval instead of the value of the slope at the left end point. In fact, the local and global discretization errors of the improved Euler method are proportional to h^3 and h^2, respectively. Therefore, halving the step size reduces the global error to a quarter and the local error to one eighth of what they were before.

The improved Euler method belongs to a class of numerical techniques called the *predictor–corrector methods*: Equation 9–37b first *predicts* the value of y_{n+1}, which is then corrected by Equation 9–37a (Figure 9–27). Note that the predictor equation is simply the Euler formula in this case, and thus, $\tilde{y}_{n+1}$ is the solution we would get using the Euler method. In the improved Euler method, this result is treated as an intermediate value and is refined using the corrector equation.

It is also worth noting that the y_{n+1} value obtained from the corrector equation can be used in the same equation in place of $\tilde{y}_{n+1}$ to obtain a more accurate value of y_{n+1}. That is, the corrector equation can be used as the predictor after the first iteration. This process can be repeated to improve the value of y_{n+1} even further. The converged y_{n+1} value obtained in this manner usually involves a much smaller error, but it is not necessarily the exact solution value. Reducing the step size is a more direct and simpler alternative to improve the accuracy of the results, and thus, we will not discuss the iteration of the corrector equation any further.

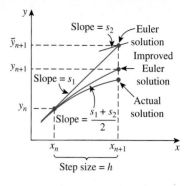

FIGURE 9–26

Graphical representation of the improved Euler method.

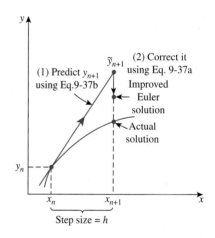

FIGURE 9–27

A schematic of the improved Euler method.

EXAMPLE 9–6   **The Improved Euler Method**

Using the improved Euler method with a step size of $h = 0.1$, determine the solution of the initial-value problem

$$y' = 5y - 25x^2 + 2, \quad y(0) = 2$$

in the interval $0 \le x \le 1$. Compare the results to the exact solution values.

SOLUTION We have $f(x, y) = 5y - 25x^2 + 2$, $x_0 = 0$, $y_0 = 2$, and $h = 0.1$. Then the solutions at the points $x_1 = 0.1$, $x_2 = 0.2, \ldots, x_{10} = 1$ are obtained by repeatedly applying the improved Euler formula (Equations 9–37):

$$y_{n+1} = y_n + h \frac{f(x_n, y_n) + f(x_{n+1}, \widetilde{y}_{n+1})}{2}$$

where

$$\widetilde{y}_{n+1} = y_n + hf(x_n, y_n)$$

For $n = 0$,

$$\widetilde{y}_1 = y_0 + hf(x_0, y_0)$$
$$= 2 + 0.1f(0.2)$$
$$= 2 + 0.1 \times (5 \times 2 - 25 \times 0^2 + 2)$$
$$= 3.2$$

and

$$y_1 = y_0 + h \frac{f(x_0, y_0) + f(x_1, \widetilde{y}_1)}{2}$$
$$= 2 + 0.1 \frac{f(0, 2) + f(0.1, 3.2)}{2}$$
$$= 2 + 0.1 \times \frac{12 + 17.75}{2}$$
$$= 3.4875$$

Thus, the improved Euler method predicts the solution at $x_1 = 0.1$ to be $y_1 = 3.4875$. The exact solution at this point is determined from Equation (9–22) to be 3.54744. Therefore, the value obtained with the improved Euler method is in error by $100 \times (3.54744 - 3.4875)/3.54744 = 1.69\%$. Repeating the calculations for $n = 1$ gives

$$\widetilde{y}_2 = y_1 + hf(x_1, y_1)$$
$$= 3.4875 + 0.1f(0.1, 3.4875)$$
$$= 3.4875 + 0.1 \times (5 \times 3.4875 - 25 \times 0.1^2 + 2)$$
$$= 5.40625$$

and

$$y_2 = y_1 + h \frac{f(x_1, y_1) + f(x_2, \widetilde{y}_2)}{2}$$
$$= 3.4875 + 0.1 \frac{f(0.1, 3.4875) + f(0.2, 5.40625)}{2}$$
$$= 3.4875 + 0.1 \frac{19.1875 + 28.03125}{2}$$
$$= 5.8484375$$

which differs from the exact value of 6.03656 by 3.12%.

The calculations for $n = 2, 3, \ldots, 9$ are performed in the same manner using the simple MATLAB program shown in Figure 9–28, and the results are given in Table 9–7 together with the exact results for comparison. Note that the error reaches 14.02% at $x = 1$.

Table 9–7 also presents results obtained using the step sizes $h = 0.01$ and $h = 0.001$ as well as results obtained by the Euler method for comparison. Note that for $h = 0.001$, the improved Euler solution is practically identical to the exact solution.

It is also worth noting that the improved Euler results with $h = 0.1$ are very close to the Euler results with $h = 0.01$. This is very significant because the results obtained with the Euler method requires roughly five times more calculations. This is because the function $f(x, y)$ is evaluated a total of 20 times in the improved Euler method, since it is evaluated twice at each step but 100 times in the Euler method. Therefore, the improved Euler method gives more accurate results with fewer calculations, which more than justifies the slight increase in complexity.

```
x = 0; y = 2;
h = 0.1;
nstep = 10;
f = @(x,y)(5*y-25*x^2+2);
for n = 1:nstep
  y1 = y + h*f(x,y);
  y = y + h*(f(x,y)+f(x+h,y1))/2
  x = n*h
  exact = 2*exp(5*x)+5*x.^2+2*x
  error = 100*abs(y-exact)/exact
end
```

FIGURE 9–28

A MATLAB program for the improved Euler method.

TABLE 9–7

Comparision of the Improved Euler Method with the Euler Method and the Exact Results for $y' = 5y - 25x^2 + 2$, $y(0) = 2$

	Euler	Method	Improved	Euler	Method	
x	$h = 0.1$	$h = 0.01$	$h = 0.1$	$h = 0.01$	$h = 0.001$	Exact
0.0	2.00000	2.00000	2.00000	2.00000	2.00000	2.00000
0.1	3.20000	3.50150	3.48750	3.54662	3.54743	3.54744
0.2	4.97500	5.89006	5.84844	6.03396	6.03654	6.03656
0.3	7.56250	9.66066	9.56621	10.00713	10.01331	10.01338
0.4	11.31875	15.61958	15.42634	16.36470	16.37797	16.37810
0.5	16.77813	25.08012	24.70531	26.58783	26.61472	26.61499
0.6	24.74219	40.18158	39.47738	43.11809	43.17054	43.17107
0.7	36.41328	64.40859	63.11324	69.98012	70.07990	70.08091
0.8	53.59492	103.4373	101.0903	113.8081	113.9944	113.9963
0.9	18.99239	166.5134	162.3092	185.5377	185.8809	185.8842
1.0	116.6636	268.6975	261.2337	303.1954	303.8200	303.8263

A variation of the improved Euler method involves the evaluation of the slope at the midpoint of the interval and treating it as the average slope for that interval. The method that is based on this principle is called the *modified Euler method* or the polygon method. Its accuracy is comparable to that of the improved Euler method.

Special Case: $f = f(x)$

When the function $f(x, y)$ depends on x only, the improved Euler method reduces to the trapezoidal rule (Figure 9–29), and the modified Euler method reduces to the trapezoidal rule. Recall from Section 9–1 that these two numerical integration numerical integration techniques are of comparable accuracy.

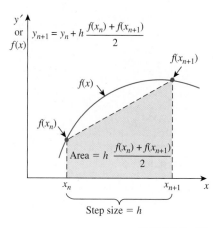

FIGURE 9–29

When the function $f(x, y)$ depends on x only, the improved Euler method reduces to the trapezoidal rule.

Section Review

9–11C What is the improved Euler method based on? How does it differ from the Euler method?

9–12 Using a calculator, determine the numerical solution of the following initial-value problem after (a) one step and (b) two steps with a step size of $h = 0.2$ using the improved Euler method. Also, solve the initial-value problem analytically, and determine the relative error in the numerical results.

$$y' = x + y, \; y(0) = 0$$

(*Answer:* The exact solution is $y(x) = e^x - x - 1$. After one step, the relative error is 6.5%. After two steps, the relative error is 3.7%.)

9–6 · THE TAYLOR SERIES METHODS

As an alternative to purely numerical methods, we can find an approximate analytical expression for the solution of the first-order initial-value problem

$$y' = f(x, y), \quad y(x_0) = y_0 \tag{9–38}$$

by expressing the solution function $y(x)$ as an infinite power series.

You will recall from Section 9–4 that the Euler formula $y_{n+1} = y_n + hf(x_n, y_n)$ can be obtained from the Taylor series expansion of $y(x)$ about the point x_n:

$$y(x_{n+1}) = y(x_n) + hy'(x_n) + \frac{h^2}{2} y''(x_n) + \frac{h^3}{3!} y'''(x_n)$$

$$+ \cdots + \frac{h^n}{n!} y^{(n)}(x_n) + \cdots \tag{9–39}$$

by retaining the first two terms and replacing the exact solution values $y(x_{n+1})$ and $y(x_n)$ by the approximate ones y_{n+1} and y_n (Figure 9–30). This suggests that more accuracy can be obtained by retaining more terms in the approximation. Retaining three terms, for example gives

$$y(x_{n+1}) \approx y(x_n) + hy'(x_n) + \frac{h^2}{2} y''(x_n) \tag{9–40}$$

which is called the three-term (or second-order) Taylor series method (the Euler method is equivalent to the two-term or first-order Taylor series method). The first derivative is available from the differential equation, $y' = f(x, y)$. The second derivative is obtained by differentiating the given differential equation and applying the chain rule,

$$y''(x) = \frac{df}{dx} = \frac{\partial f}{\partial x} + \frac{\partial f}{\partial y}\frac{dy}{dx} = f_x(x, y) + f_y(x, y)f(x, y) \tag{9–41}$$

where f_x and f_y are partial derivatives of $f(x,y)$ with respect to x and y, respectively. Using the approximations $y(x_{n+1}) \cong y_{n+1}$ and substituting the relations for $y'(x)$ at point $y''(x)$ into Equation 9–40 gives

$$y_{n+1} = y_n + f(x_n, y_n) + \frac{h^2}{2}[f_x(x_n, y_n) + f_y(x_n, y_n)f(x_n, y_n)] \tag{9–42}$$

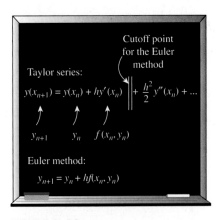

FIGURE 9–30

Obtaining the Euler (or two-term Taylor series) method from the Taylor series expansion of $y(x)$.

which is known as the three-term (or second-order) Taylor series formula. Note that the Taylor series method requires the evaluation of the partial derivatives of the function $f(x, y)$, which may or may not be easy to do.

The local and global (accumulated) discretization errors of the second-order Taylor series method are proportional to h^3 and h^2, respectively. This is not surprising, since the first term we truncated out in the Taylor series involves h^3. Note that the accuracy of the second-order Taylor series method is comparable to the accuracy of the improved Euler method. If the function $f(x, y)$ is sufficiently simple and has higher-order continuous derivatives to facilitate easy differentiation, then it may be worthwhile to retain more terms in the approximation. The approximation obtained by retaining $k + 1$ terms is called the kth-order (or $k + 1$ term) Taylor series method. Note that the first term truncated out in the kth-order Taylor series method is h^{k+1}, and thus, its local and global (accumulated) discretization errors are proportional to h^{k+1} and h^k, respectively.

The higher-order Taylor series methods give very accurate results, but they are awkward to use in practice since they require the evaluation of the higher-order derivatives of the function $f(x, y)$, as shown in Figure 9–31. The real value of the Taylor series method is that it serves as a basis of comparison for other higher-order numerical solution methods.

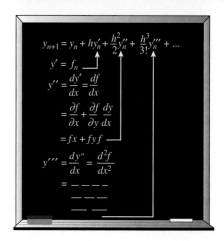

FIGURE 9–31

Higher-order Taylor series methods are awkward to use, because they require the evaluation of the higher-order derivatives of the function $f(x, y)$.

EXAMPLE 9–7 The Taylor Series Method

Using the three-term Taylor series method with a step size of $h = 0.1$, determine the solution of the initial-value problem

$$y' = 5y - 25x^2 + 2, \quad y(0) = 2$$

in the interval $0 \le x \le 1$. Compare these results to the exact solution values.

SOLUTION We have $f(x, y) = 5y - 25x^2 + 2$, $x_0 = 0$, $y_0 = 2$, and $h = 0.1$. The partial derivatives of the function $f(x, y)$ are

$$f_x(x, y) = -50x$$
$$f_y(x, y) = 5$$

Substituting these into Equation 9–42, the three-term Taylor series formula becomes

$$y_{n+1} = y_n + hf(x_n, y_n) + \frac{h^2}{2}[f_x(x_n, y_n) + f_y(x_n, y_n)f(x_n, y_n)]$$

$$= y_n + hf(x_n, y_n) + \frac{h^2}{2}[-50x_n + 5f(x_n, y_n)]$$

Then solutions at the points $x_1 = 0.1$, $x_2 = 0.2, \ldots, x_{10} = 1$ are obtained by repeatedly applying this formula. For $n = 0$,

$$y_1 = y_0 + hf(x_0, y_0) + \frac{h^2}{2}[-50x_0 + 5f(x_0, y_0)]$$

$$= 2 + 0.1 \times f(0, 2) + \frac{0.1^2}{2}[-50 \times 0 + 5f(0, 2)]$$

$$= 3.5$$

Thus, the three-term Taylor series method predicts the solution at $x_1 = 0.1$ to be $y_1 = 3.5$. The exact solution at this point is determined from Equation 9–22 to be 3.54744. Therefore, the value obtained with the Taylor series method is in error by $100 \times (3.54744 - 3.5)/3.54744 = 1.34\%$.

Repeating the calculations for $n = 1$ gives

$$y_2 = y_1 + hf(x_1, y_1) + \frac{h^2}{2}[-50x_1 + 5f(x_1, y_1)]$$

$$= 3.5 + 0.1 \times f(0.1, 3.5) + \frac{0.1^2}{2}[-50 \times 0.1 + 5f(0.1, 3.5)]$$

$$= 5.88125$$

which differs from the exact value of 6.03656 by 2.57%.

The calculations for $n = 2, 3, \ldots, 9$ are performed in the same manner using the MATLAB program in Figure 9–32, and the results are given in Table 9–8 together with the exact results and improved Euler results for comparison. Note that the improved Euler results and the three-term Taylor series results are very close. This is not surprising, since both methods are second-order approximations (their global error is proportional to h^2).

FIGURE 9–32

A MATLAB program for the three-term Taylor series method.

```
x = 0;
y = 2;
h = 0.1;
nstep = 10;
% Enter f and its derivatives here.
f = @(x,y)(5*y-25*x^2+2);
fx = @(x,y)-50*x;
fy = @(x,y)5;
for n = 1:nstep
    y = y + h*f(x,y) + h^2*(fx(x,y)+fy(x,y)*f(x,y))/2
    x = n*h
    exact = 2*exp(5*x)+5*x.^2+2*x
    error = 100*abs(y-exact)/exact
end
```

TABLE 9–8

Comparison of the Three-Term Taylor Series Results for Solution of $y' = 5y - 25x^2 + 2$, $y(0) = 2$ with the Improved Euler and Exact Results

x	Three-term Taylor $h = 0.1$	Improved Euler $h = 0.1$	Exact
0.0	2.00000	2.00000	2.00000
0.1	3.50000	3.48750	3.54744
0.2	5.88125	5.84844	6.03656
0.3	9.63203	9.56621	10.01338
0.4	15.54580	15.42634	16.37810
0.5	24.91193	24.70531	26.61499
0.6	39.82563	39.47738	43.17107
0.7	63.69165	63.11324	70.08091
0.8	102.0427	101.0903	113.9963
0.9	163.8693	162.3092	185.8842
1.0	263.7814	261.2337	303.8263

Section Review

9–13C Why are the Taylor series methods not popular in practice for solving differential equations?

9–14 Using a calculator, determine the numerical solution of the following initial-value problem after (a) one step and (b) two steps with a step size of $h = 0.2$ using the three-term Taylor series method. Also, solve the initial-value problem analytically, and determine the relative error in the numerical results.

$$y' = x + y, \quad y(0) = 0$$

(*Answer:* The exact solution is $y(x) = e^x - x - 1$. After one step, the relative error is 6.5%. After two steps, the relative error is 3.7%.)

9–7 ▪ THE RUNGE–KUTTA METHOD

Reconsider the first order initial-value problem

$$y' = f(x, y), \quad y(x_0) = y_0 \qquad \textbf{(9–43)}$$

which we solved earlier with the Euler and improved Euler methods using a constant step size of h. These two methods are special cases of a general single-step technique called the **Runge–Kutta method** named after the German mathematicians C. D. Runge (1856–1927) and M. W. Kutta (1867–1944).

We have seen in the previous section that very accurate results can be obtained using higher-order Taylor series methods. Unfortunately, such methods require the evaluation of the higher-order derivatives of the function $f(x, y)$, which is quite tedious and often results in rather lengthy expressions. Therefore, higher-order Taylor series methods are not practical despite their potential for great accuracy.

The beauty of the Runge–Kutta methods is that they offer the same accuracy of the Taylor series methods without requiring the evaluation of any derivatives. The formal derivations of the Runge–Kutta formulas are rather involved and are not given here. They can be found in most books on numerical methods.

Like the Taylor series methods, the Runge–Kutta methods have different orders, and each order has different versions. The higher the order, the better the accuracy of the method. Some versions of the Runge–Kutta method are more popular than others, and there is no standard Runge–Kutta method. The first-order Runge–Kutta method is equivalent to the Euler method and to the two-term (first-order) Taylor series method. The second-order Runge–Kutta method is essentially equivalent to the improved Euler method and the three-term (second-order) Taylor series method (Figure 9–33).

The most popular Runge–Kutta methods are of the fourth-order, which has several versions. Of those, the best known and the most widely used is the **classical fourth-order Runge–Kutta method**, which is expressed as

$$y_{n+1} = y_n + \frac{h}{6}(k_1 + 2k_2 + 2k_3 + k_4) \qquad \textbf{(9–44a)}$$

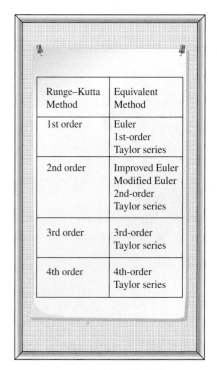

Runge–Kutta Method	Equivalent Method
1st order	Euler 1st-order Taylor series
2nd order	Improved Euler Modified Euler 2nd-order Taylor series
3rd order	3rd-order Taylor series
4th order	4th-order Taylor series

FIGURE 9–33

The numerical methods considered so far to solve differential equations are special cases of the Runge–Kutta methods.

where

$$k_1 = f(x_n, y_n) \tag{9-44b}$$

$$k_2 = f\left(x_n + \frac{1}{2}h, y_n + \frac{1}{2}hk_1\right) \tag{9-44c}$$

$$k_3 = f\left(x_n + \frac{1}{2}h, y_n + \frac{1}{2}hk_2\right) \tag{9-44d}$$

$$k_4 = f(x_n + h, y_n + hk_3) \tag{9-44e}$$

Note that, in this method, the average slope of the function $f(x, y)$ in the interval between x_n and x_{n+1} is represented by $(k_1 + 2k_2 + 2k_3 + k_4)/6$. Also note that k_1 appears in the equation for k_2, which appears in the equation for k_3, which appears in the equation for k_4. Such nesting is typical of Runge–Kutta methods and makes them very suitable for computer applications.

The local and global (accumulated) discretization errors of the fourth-order Runge–Kutta methods are proportional to h^5 and h^4 respectively. This is not surprising, since the order of a method indicates the degree of the step size to which the global error is proportional. Halving the step size h reduces the local error by a factor of 1/32 and the global error by a factor of 1/16. Therefore, halving the step size once in the fourth-order Runge–Kutta methods to increase accuracy is as effective as halving it successively four times in the Euler method.

The remarkable accuracy and simplicity of the classical Runge–Kutta method has made it one of the most widely used single-step methods for the numerical solution of ordinary differential equations. The Runge–Kutta formula appears to be more complicated than the Euler and improved Euler formulas. However, its high accuracy and ease of use often makes it the method of choice. The computer program in MATLAB for the classical Runge–Kutta method to solve the problem in Example 9–8 is given in Figure 9–34. This program is sufficiently general, and it easily can be modified for other problems by changing the initial condition on y in the second line, the step size h and the number of steps in `nstep` in lines three and four, and the definition of the function in the sixth line.

```
x = 0;
y = 2;
h = 0.1;
nstep = 10;
% Enter f here.
f = @(x,y)(5*y-25*x^2+2);
for n = 1:nstep
    k1 = f(x,y);
    k2 = f(x+h/2,y+h*k1/2);
    k3 = f(x+h/2,y+h*k2/2);
    k4 = f(x+h,y+h*k3);
    y = y + h*(k1+2*k2+2*k3+k4)/6
    x = n*h
    exact = 2*exp(5*x)+5*x.^2+2*x
    error = 100*abs(y-exact)/exact
end
```

FIGURE 9–34

A MATLAB program for the classical fourth-order Runge–Kutta method.

EXAMPLE 9–8   The Runge–Kutta Method

Using the classical fourth-order Runge–Kutta method with a step size of $h = 0.5$, determine the solution of the initial-value problem

$$y' = 5y - 25x^2 + 2, \quad y(0) = 2$$

in the interval $0 \le x \le 1$. Compare the results to the exact solution values.

SOLUTION   We have $f(x, y) = 5y - 25x^2 + 2$, $x_0 = 0$, $y_0 = 2$, and $h = 0.5$. Solutions at points $x_1 = 0.5$ and $x_2 = 1$ are obtained by applying the Runge–Kutta formulas (Equations 9–44) twice. For $n = 0$,

$$k_1 = f(x_0, y_0) = f(0, 2) = 12$$

$$k_2 = f\left(x_0 + \frac{1}{2}h, y_0 + \frac{1}{2}hk_1\right) = f\left(0 + \frac{1}{2} \times 0.50, 2 + \frac{1}{2} \times 0.5 \times 12\right)$$

$$= f(0.25, 5) = 25.4375$$

$$k_3 = f\left(x_0 + \frac{1}{2}h, y_0 + \frac{1}{2}hk_1\right) = f\left(0 + \frac{1}{2} \times 0.50, 2 + \frac{1}{2} \times 0.5 \times 25.4375\right)$$

$$= f(0.25, 8.359375) = 42.234375$$

$$k_4 = f(x_0 + h, y_0 + hk_3) = f(0 + 0.50, 2 + 0.5 \times 42.234375)$$

$$= f(0.50, 23.1171875) = 111.3359375$$

Thus,

$$y_1 = y_0 + \frac{h}{6}(k_1 + 2k_2 + 2k_3 + k_4)$$

$$= 2 + \frac{0.5}{6}(12 + 2 \times 25.4375 + 2 \times 42.234375 + 111.3359375)$$

$$= 23.55664$$

Therefore, the Runge–Kutta method predicts the solution at $x_1 = 0.5$ to be $y_1 = 23.55664$. The exact solution at this point is determined from Equation 9–22 to be 26.61499. Therefore, the value obtained with Runge–Kutta method is in error by $100 \times (26.61499 - 23.55664)/26.61499 = 11.49\%$.

Repeating the calculations for $n = 1$ gives

$$k_1 = f(x_1, y_1) = f(0.5, 23.55664) = 113.5332$$

$$k_2 = f\left(x_1 + \frac{1}{2}h, y_1 + \frac{1}{2}hk_1\right) = f\left(0.5 + \frac{1}{2} \times 0.50, 23.55664\right.$$

$$\left. + \frac{1}{2} \times 0.5 \times 113.5332\right)$$

$$= f(0.75, 51.93994) = 247.6372$$

$$k_3 = f\left(x_1 + \frac{1}{2}h, y_1 + \frac{1}{2}hk_2\right) = f\left(0.5 + \frac{1}{2} \times 0.50, 23.55664\right.$$

$$\left. + \frac{1}{2} \times 0.5 \times 247.6372\right)$$

$$= f(0.75, 85.46594) = 415.2672$$

$$k_4 = f(x_1 + h, y_1 + hk_3) = f(0.5 + 0.50, 23.55664 + 0.5 \times 415.2672)$$

$$= f(1, 231.19024) = 1132.9512$$

and thus,

$$y_2 = y_1 + \frac{h}{6}(k_1 + 2k_2 + 2k_3 + k_4)$$

$$= 23.55664 + \frac{0.5}{6}(113.5332 + 2 \times 247.6372$$

$$+ 2 \times 415.2672 + 1132.9512)$$

$$= 237.9144$$

which differs from the exact value of 303.8263 by 21.69%. These errors are large because of the large step size.

Using a smaller step size gives good results. The calculations for $h = 0.1$ and $h = 0.01$ were performed in the same manner using the MATLAB program shown in Figure 9–34. The results are given in Table 9–9 together with the exact results and the results obtained using the Euler method with $h = 0.01$ and the improved Euler method with $h = 0.1$ for comparison. Note that even for $h = 0.1$, the Runge–Kutta results are practically identical to the exact results.

It is also worth noting that the Runge–Kutta results obtained with two steps ($h = 0.5$) are almost as accurate as the improved Euler results with 10 steps ($h = 0.1$) and the Euler results with 100 steps ($h = 0.01$). This is very significant, because the results obtained with the improved Euler and Euler methods require roughly 2.5 and 12.5 times more calculations, respectively. Therefore, the Runge–Kutta method, in general, gives the most accurate results for the same number of calculations.

TABLE 9–9

Comparison of Results Obtained Using a Fourth-Order Runge–Kutta Method with the Euler, Improved Euler, and Exact Results for $y' = 5y - 25x^2 + 2$, $y(0) = 2$

x	Euler	Improved Euler	Runge–Kutta Method			Exact
	$h = 0.01$	$h = 0.1$	$h = 0.5$	$h = 0.1$	$h = 0.01$	
0.0	2.00000	2.00000	2.00000	2.00000	2.00000	2.00000
0.1	3.50150	3.48750		3.54675	3.54744	3.54744
0.2	5.89006	5.84844		6.03435	6.03656	6.03656
0.3	9.66066	9.56621		10.00805	10.01338	10.01338
0.4	15.61958	15.42634		16.36666	16.37811	16.37810
0.5	25.08012	24.70531	23.55664	26.59178	26.61498	26.61499
0.6	40.18158	39.47738		43.12578	43.17106	43.17107
0.7	64.40859	63.11324		69.99471	70.08087	70.08091
0.8	103.4373	101.0903		113.8353	113.9962	113.9963
0.9	166.5134	162.3092		185.5877	185.8841	185.8842
1.0	268.6975	261.2337	237.9144	303.2863	303.8461	303.8263

Special Case: $f = f(x)$

When the function $f(x, y)$ depends on x only, we have $k_2 = k_3$, and the classical fourth-order Runge–Kutta method formula reduces to

$$y_{n+1} = y_n + \frac{h}{6}\left[f(x_n) + 4f\left(x_n + \frac{1}{2}h \right) + f(x_n + h) \right] \tag{9–45}$$

which is Simpson's rule (Equation 9–12) for numerical integration. There-fore, the local and global (accumulated) discretization errors of Simpson's rule are also proportional to h^5 and h^4, respectively, making it one of the most accurate yet simple numerical integration techniques.

Runge–Kutta Fehlberg

An alternative approach to halving the step size to obtain an error estimate is to repeat the calculations with two Runge–Kutta methods of different order and taking their difference. This approach has the obvious drawback of greatly increasing the number of computations. For example, if we repeat the calculations using a fifth-order Runge–Kutta method, we will need to evaluate the function $f(x,y)$ six additional times, which will bring the total number of function evaluations to ten for the classical Runge–Kutta method. A clever technique called the **Runge–Kutta Fehlberg method** accomplishes this objective by requiring the evaluations of $f(x,y)$ a total of six times only. The details of this technique can be found in standard numerical methods books.

Finally, all of the single-step methods, including the classical Runge–Kutta method, allow for the variation of the step size during calculations. This flexibility enables programmers to optimize the number of computations and obtain sufficiently accurate results in less time. This is accomplished by automatically increasing the step size when the slope of the function $f(x, y)$ changes mildly and decreasing it when the slope changes rapidly.

Section Review

9–15C Why is the classical fourth-order Runge–Kutta method very popular?

9–16 Using a calculator, determine the numerical solution of the following initial-value problem after (a) one step and (b) two step with a step size of $h = 0.2$ using the classical fourth-order Runge–Kutta method. Also, solve the initial-value problem analytically, and find the relative error in the numerical result.

$$y' = x + y, \quad y(0) = 0$$

(*Answer*: The exact solution is $y(x) = e^x - x - 1$. After one step, the relative error is 0.00%. After two steps, the relative error is 0.00%.)

9–8 ▪ MULTISTEP AND PREDICTOR–CORRECTOR METHODS

All of the numerical methods discussed so far to solve the initial-value problem

$$y' = f(x, y), \quad y(x_0) = y_0 \tag{9-46}$$

use the solution at a single point x_n to predict the solution y_{n+1} at the next point x_{n+1} and are properly called single-step methods. After applying any of these methods several times, we will have the solution of the problem at several points. It is natural to wonder if we can use the information at these several preceding points instead of the information just at the last point x_n to predict the solution y_{n+1} at the next point x_{n+1}. The methods that are based on using the solution at two or more preceding points to predict the solution at the next point are called the **multistep methods** (Figure 9–35).

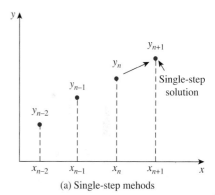
(a) Single-step methods

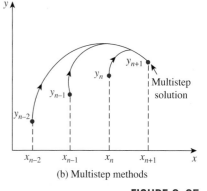
(b) Multistep methods

FIGURE 9–35

Geometrical representation of the (a) single-step and (b) multistep methods.

Consider a multistep method that uses the information at the previous four points when predicting the solution at the next point. The initial condition provides the information at the first point x_0, but we need to know the solution at three more points x_1, x_2, and x_3 before we can apply the multistep method. These solutions can be determined by a single-step method only. Therefore, a multistep method cannot solve the entire problem by itself, and it must rely on a single-step method for the solution at the first few points. For this reason, the single-step methods are called *starting methods*, and the multistep methods are called *continuing methods*.

Any starting method can be used to obtain the solution at the first few points. However, keep in mind that a solution procedure is as accurate as its weakest link, and thus, the starting method selected must be at least as accurate as the multistep method. For example, if the local discretization error of the multistep method is proportional to h^5, then we should use a fourth-order Runge–Kutta method as the starting method, since its local error is of the same order of magnitude.

Multistep formulas are obtained by integrating the given differential equation numerically after approximating $f(x, y)$ with a suitable function. Integrating $y' = f(x, y)$ from x_n to x_{n+1} gives

$$y_{n+1} = y_n + \int_{x_n}^{x_{n+1}} f[x, y(x)]dx \qquad (9\text{–}47)$$

Normally, we cannot perform this integration, because we do not know the solution function $y(x)$ that appears in the integrand. So we need an approximation.

We now approximate the function $f(x, y(x))$ by a polynomial, called the **interpolating polynomial**, which passes through some specified points. We chose a polynomial for the interpolating function, because polynomials are continuous functions, and they are easy to integrate. If the multistep method is to incorporate the solution at $m + 1$ preceding points, a polynomial of degree m is used as the interpolating polynomial. Note that a polynomial of degree m that passes through $m + 1$ points is unique. For example, one and only one straight line (a polynomial of degree one) passes through two specified points. Likewise, fixing four points uniquely specifies a third-degree polynomial that passes through them. The details of the determination of the interpolating polynomial can be found in numerical methods books. Once it is determined, we can integrate it from x_n (or another point) to x_{n+1} and substitute into Equation 9–47. The result is a multistep formula. Note that the greater the number of points used in the multistep method, the higher the order of the interpolating polynomial.

One of the best known multistep methods is the fourth-order **Adams–Bashforth method** named after J. C. Adams (1819–1892) and F. Bashforth (1819–1912). This method makes use of the solution at the preceding four points x_n, x_{n-1}, x_{n-2}, and x_{n-3}. It utilizes a third-degree polynomial as the interpolating polynomial that passes through the points (x_n, f_n), (x_{n-1}, f_{n-1}), (x_{n-2}, f_{n-2}), and (x_{n-3}, f_{n-3}), where we used the following notation.

$$f_k = f[x_k, y(x_k)] = y'(x_k) \qquad (9\text{–}48)$$

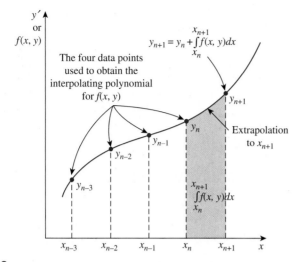

FIGURE 9–36

The development of the fourth-order Adams–Bashforth formula.

for any integer k. Substituting the interpolating polynomial obtained into Equation 9–47 and evaluating the integral (Figure 9–36) gives the multistep formula

$$y_{n+1} = y_n + \frac{h}{24}(55f_n - 59f_{n-1} + 37f_{n-2} - 9f_{n-3}) \qquad \textbf{(9–49)}$$

which is known as the fourth-order **Adams–Bashforth formula**. It has a local discretization error proportional to h^5. That is, it is a fourth-order formula, as the name implies. Note that this formula involves only one new evaluation of the function $f(x, y)$ at each step. The values of this function at the other three points are available from the previous steps.

Different multistep formulas can be obtained with the same interpolating polynomial by integrating the differential equation between different points. For example, if we change the lower limit of integration from x_n to x_{n-3}, integration of the third-degree interpolating polynomial just obtained would give

$$y_{n+1} = y_{n-3} + \frac{4h}{3}(2f_n - f_{n-1} + 2f_{n-2}) \qquad \textbf{(9–50)}$$

which is known as the **Milne's predictor formula**. This formula has a local discretization error proportional to h^5, and thus, it is also a fourth-order method. However, its constant of proportionality is much smaller than that of the Adams–Bashforth formula, and thus, Milne's formula usually gives more accurate results. Furthermore, it involves fewer calculations to achieve this high accuracy.

The Adams–Bashforth and Milne formulas are the most widely used explicit multistep formulas (their right side does not involve the unknown y_{n+1}).

However, they are usually used as the predictor equations in conjunction with the two popular predictor–corrector methods to be discussed. Even by themselves, they are as accurate as the fourth-order Runge–Kutta method, but they are not quite competitive, since they must rely on a fourth-order starting method (such as the Runge–Kutta method) for the solution values at the first three points. Usually, it is not practical to write two programs when one will do. This is especially the case for small problems where the computation time is not of much concern.

Predictor-Corrector Methods

We obtained the Adams–Bashforth and Milne formulas by utilizing a third-degree interpolating polynomial that passes through the four points (x_n, f_n), (x_{n-1}, f_{n-1}), (x_{n-2}, f_{n-2}), and (x_{n-3}, f_{n-3}). The solutions at all of these points are available, and thus, the resulting interpolating polynomial did not involve any unknown functions. As a result, we obtained explicit expressions for y_{n+1} when we performed the integration in Equation 9–47.

We now would like to advance one step further and involve the future point (x_{n+1}, f_{n+1}) in the determination of the interpolating polynomial. In other words, we force the third-degree polynomial to pass through the four points (x_{n+1}, f_{n+1}), (x_n, f_n), (x_{n-1}, f_{n-1}), and (x_{n-2}, f_{n-2}). As you would expect, the interpolating polynomial this time will involve f_{n+1}, which is not known. Substituting this new interpolating polynomial into Equation 9–47 and evaluating the integral (Figure 9–37) gives the **Adams–Moulton corrector formula**

$$y_{n+1} = y_n + \frac{h}{24}(9f_{n+1} + 19f_n - 5f_{n-1} + f_{n-2}) \qquad \text{(9–51)}$$

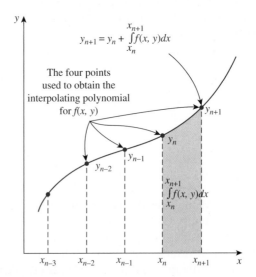

FIGURE 9–37

The development of the fourth-order Adams–Moulton predictor formula.

which also has a local discretization error proportional to h^5. This algorithm is named after Adams and F. R. Moulton (1872–1952). However, its constant of proportionality is about 1/13 that of the Adams–Bashforth formula, and thus, it can be used to improve the results obtained by the Adams–Bashforth formula.

The Adams–Bashforth and Adams–Moulton formulas make a natural pair, since the Adams–Moulton formula can give more accurate results. But it needs a fairly good initial estimate for f_{n+1} (and thus the solution y_{n+1}), because it is an implicit formula. This estimate is provided by the Adams–Bashforth formula. In other words, the solution value y_{n+1} predicted by the Adams–Bashforth formula is consequently corrected by the Adams–Moulton formula. The methods that are based on this principle are called **predictor–corrector methods**. In this case, the Adams–Bashforth formula is the predictor, and the Adams–Moulton formula is the corrector. Thus, we can express the Adams–Moulton predictor corrector method as

$$\text{Predictor: } y_{n+1} = y_n + \frac{h}{24}(55f_n - 59f_{n-1} + 37f_{n-2} - 9f_{n-3}) \qquad \textbf{(9-49)}$$

$$\text{Corrector: } y_{n+1} = y_n + \frac{h}{24}(9f_{n+1} + 19f_n - 5f_{n-1} + f_{n-2}) \qquad \textbf{(9-51)}$$

Once the solutions y_{n-3}, y_{n-2}, y_{n-1}, and y_n at the point x_{n-3}, x_{n-2}, x_{n-1}, and x_n are available, we can calculate f_{n-3}, f_{n-2}, f_{n-1} and f_n, using the function $f(x, y)$ in the given differential equation. Then we use the predictor formula to obtain an accurate first prediction of the solution y_{n+1} and substitute this value into the $f(x, y)$ relation to obtain the value of f_{n+1} for use in the corrector formula. The improved y_{n+1} value obtained from the corrector formula is usually very accurate, but it can be improved even further by treating it as the predicted value and applying the corrector equation one more time. This process is called *internal iteration*. As a general rule, it is better to reduce the step size if it takes more than two internal iterations to meet the specified error criteria. The solution procedure just described is applicable to any predictor–corrector method.

EXAMPLE 9–9   The Adams–Moulton Predictor–Corrector Method

Using the Adams–Moulton predictor–corrector method with a step size of $h = 0.1$, determine the solution of the initial–value problem

$$y' = 5y - 25x^2 + 2, \quad y(0) = 2$$

in the interval $0 \leq x \leq 1$. Compare these results to the exact solution values.

SOLUTION We have $f(x, y) = 5y - 25x^2 + 2$, $x_0 = 0$, $y_0 = 2$, and $h = 0.1$. The initial condition provides us with the solution at one point, but the Adams–Moulton method requires the solution at four points before it can be applied. Therefore, we need to determine the solutions at $x_1 = 0.1$, $x_2 = 0.2$, and $x_3 = 0.3$ using a starting method (such as the Runge–Kutta method). These results are available in this case from Example 9–8, and they are

$$y_1 = 3.54675$$

$$y_2 = 6.03435$$

$$y_3 = 10.00805$$

The solution at other points is obtained by applying first the predictor and then the corrector formulas (Equations 9–49 and 9–51). For $n = 3$, they yield

$$y_4 = y_3 + \frac{h}{24}(55f_3 - 59f_2 + 37f_1 - 9f_0)$$

$$= y_3 + \frac{h}{24}[55f(x_3, y_3) - 59f(x_2, y_2) + 37f(x_1, y_1) - 9f(x_0, y_0)]$$

$$= 10.00805 + \frac{0.1}{24}[55f(0.3, 10.00805) - 59f(0.2, 6.03435)$$

$$+37f(0.1, 3.54675) - 9f(0, 2)]$$

$$= 10.00805 + \frac{0.1}{24}[55 \times 49.79025 - 59 \times 31.17175$$

$$+ 37 \times 19.48375 - 9 \times 12]$$

$$= 16.309010$$

and

$$y_4 = y_3 + \frac{h}{24}(9f_4 + 19f_3 - 5f_2 + f_1)$$

$$= y_3 + \frac{h}{24}[9f(x_4, y_4) + 19f(x_3, y_3) - 5f(x_2, y_2) + f(x_1, y_1)]$$

$$= 10.00805 + \frac{0.1}{24}[9f(0.4, 16.309005) + 19f(0.3, 10.00805)$$

$$-5f(0.2, 6.03435) + f(0.1, 3.54675)]$$

$$= 10.00805 + \frac{0.1}{24}[9 \times 79.545050 + 19 \times 49.79025$$

$$- 5 \times 31.17175 + 19.48375]$$

$$= 16.364490$$

Thus, the Adams–Moulton method predicts the solution at $x_4 = 0.4$ to be $y_4 = 16.364490$. The exact solution at this point is determined from

Equation 9–22 to be 16.37810. Therefore, the value obtained with the Adams–Moulton method is in error by $100 \times (16.37810 - 16.364490)/16.37810 = 0.08\%$.

Repeating the calculations for $n = 4$ gives

$$y_5 = y_4 + \frac{h}{24}(55f_4 - 59f_3 + 37f_2 - 9f_1)$$

$$= y_4 + \frac{h}{24}[55f(x_4, y_4) - 59f(x_3, y_3) + 37f(x_2, y_2) - 9f(x_1, y_1)]$$

$$= 16.364490 + \frac{0.1}{24}[55f(0.4, 16.364490) - 59f(0.3, 10.00805)$$
$$+ 37f(0.2, 6.03435) - 9f(0.1, 3.54675)]$$

$$= 16.364490 + \frac{0.1}{24}[55 \times 79.822450 - 59 \times 49.79025$$
$$+ 37 \times 31.17175 - 9 \times 19.48375] = 26.492029$$

and

$$y_5 = y_4 + \frac{h}{24}(9f_5 + 19f_4 - 5f_3 + f_2)$$

$$= y_4 + \frac{h}{24}[9f(x_5, y_5) + 19f(x_4, y_4) - 5f(x_3, y_3) + f(x_2, y_2)]$$

$$= 16.364490 + \frac{0.1}{24}[9f(0.5, 26.492029) + 19f(0.4, 16.364490)$$
$$- 5f(0.3, 10.00805) + f(0.2, 6.03435)]$$

$$= 16.364490 + \frac{0.1}{24}[9 \times 128.2102 + 19 \times 79.822450 - 5 \times 49.79025$$
$$+ 31.17175] = 26.584240$$

which differs from the exact value of 26.614980 by 0.11%.

The calculations for $n = 5, 6, \ldots, 9$ were performed in the same manner using the simple MATLAB program shown in Figure 9–38. The results are given in Table 9–10 together with the exact and Runge–Kutta results for comparison. Note that both methods give very accurate results, but the Runge–Kutta method results are slightly better than those of the Adams–Moulton method in this case. However, the Adams–Moulton method requires fewer calculations. Also note that using the corrector formula one more time improves the results considerably, making them more accurate than the Runge–Kutta results. To use the program given in Figure 9–38 to solve other equations, simply change the first five lines, and delete the third-to-last and second-to-last lines.

```
h = 0.1;
nstep = 10;
x = 0;
y = 2;
fnc = @(x,y)(5*y-25*x^2+2);
f(1) = fnc(x,y);
for n = 1:3
    k1 = fnc(x,y);
    k2 = fnc(x+h/2,y+h*k1/2);
    k3 = fnc(x+h/2,y+h*k2/2);
    k4 = fnc(x+h,y+h*k3);
    y = y + h*(k1+2*k2+2*k3+k4)/6;
    x = n*h;
    f(n+1) = fnc(x,y);
end
for n = 3:nstep-1
    x = (n+1)*h;
    y1 = y+h*(55*f(n+1)-59*f(n)+37*f(n-1)-9*f(n-2))/24;
    f(n+2) = fnc(x,y1);
    y = y + h*(9*f(n+2)+19*f(n+1)-5*f(n)+f(n-1))/24
    exact = 2*exp(5*x)+5*x.^2+2*x
    error = 100*abs(y-exact)/exact;
end
```

FIGURE 9–38

A MATLAB program for the fourth-order Adams–Moulton predictor–corrector method.

TABLE 9–10

Comparison of Results Obtained Using the Adams–Moulton Predictor-Corrector Formulas with Those Obtained Using the Fourth-Order Runge–Kutta Formulas and Exact Results for $y' = 5y - 25x^2 + 2$, $y(0) = 2$

		Adams–Moulton		
x	Runge–Kutta $h = 0.1$	No Iteration $h = 0.1$	One Iteration $h = 0.1$	Exact
0.0	2.00000	2.00000	2.00000	2.00000
0.1	3.54675	3.54675	3.54675	3.54675
0.2	6.03435	6.03435	6.03435	6.03435
0.3	10.00805	10.00805	10.00805	10.00805
0.4	16.36666	16.36449	16.37489	16.37810
0.5	26.59178	26.55036	26.61424	26.61499
0.6	43.12578	42.99005	43.17822	43.17107
0.7	69.99471	69.67645	70.10674	70.08091
0.8	113.8353	113.1554	114.0617	113.9963
0.9	185.5877	184.1990	186.0297	185.8842
0.10	303.2863	300.5559	304.1282	303.8263

If the third-order interpolating polynomial used in the Adams–Moulton method was integrated from x_{n-1} to x_{n+1}, we would obtain the **Milne corrector formula**, which is identical to Simpson's rule. Therefore, the Milne predictor–corrector method can be expressed as

$$\text{Predictor: } y_{n+1} = y_{n-3} + \frac{4h}{3}(2f_n - f_{n-1} + 2f_{n-2}) \tag{9–50}$$

$$\text{Corrector: } y_{n+1} = y_{n-1} + \frac{h}{3}(f_{n+1} + 4f_n + f_{n-1}) \tag{9–52}$$

The predictor equation is of the fourth-order, and thus, its local discretization error is proportional to h^5. The corrector formula is of the second order, but its constant of proportionality is 1/8 that of the predictor formula. Thus, it is very effective in improving the results obtained by the predictor formula.

Of the two predictor–corrector methods presented, the Milne method gives more accurate results, and it does it with fewer calculations. This may lead someone to conclude that the Milne method is superior to the Adams–Moulton method. However, the Milne method has an inherent weakness: Sometimes it exhibits an unstable behavior. That is, the solution oscillates about the true solution with an exponentially growing error, as shown in Figure 9–39. Because of this possibility, the Adams–Moulton method is usually preferred.

The instability of the Milne method originates in its corrector and can be suppressed by modifying the corrector equation. A commonly used modification is due to Hamming, and is called **Hamming's method**, after R. W. Hamming (1915–1998). It uses the Milne predictor with the modified corrector

$$y_{n+1} = \frac{1}{8}(9y_n - y_{n-2}) + \frac{3h}{8}(f_{n+1} + 2f_n - f_{n-1}) \qquad \text{(9–53)}$$

which is stable, of the third-order, and has a local discretization error proportional to h^4.

There are other predictor–corrector methods available in the literature. The improved Euler method discussed earlier is a second-order predictor–corrector method, and the interpolating polynomial of the corrector formula is a first-degree polynomial. That is, it is the straight line that passes through the points (x_n, f_n) and (x_{n+1}, f_{n+1}). The integration of this interpolating polynomial is equivalent to the trapezoidal rule. The main drawback of multistep methods is that they are not self-starting. In the two methods discussed, for example, we must have the values of the function $f(x, y)$ at the first four equally spaced points, which must be obtained by an independent method. You may be wondering then why we are bothering with the cumbersome multistep formulas since the single-step Runge–Kutta methods are just as accurate and definitely much simpler. The reason is computational efficiency. The classical Runge–Kutta method requires the evaluation of the function $f(x, y)$ at four points during each step, whereas the Adams–Bashforth method requires the evaluation of that function at just one point for each step. Thus, the Adams–Moulton predictor–corrector method would require the evaluation of $f(x, y)$ twice during each step. For small problems with simple functions $f(x, y)$, the difference may not even be noticeable. However, for complicated functions $f(x, y)$, the difference in computation time can be very significant.

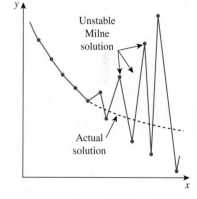

FIGURE 9–39

The instability of the Milne's method, which occurs during the solution of some differential equations with certain step sizes.

Section Review

9–17C How do multistep methods differ from the single-step methods?

9–18 Using a calculator, determine the numerical solution of the following initial-value problem after (a) one step and (b) two steps with a step size of $h = 0.2$

using the Adams–Moulton predictor–corrector method. Also, solve the initial-value problem analytically, and determine the relative error in the numerical results.

$$y' = x + y, \quad y(0) = 0$$

(*Answer*: The exact solution is $y(x) = e^x - x - 1$. After one step, the relative error is 0.00%. After two steps, the relative error is 0.00%.)

9–9 ▪ SYSTEMS OF FIRST-ORDER EQUATIONS

So far, we have considered the numerical solution of single first-order initial-value problems. However, most problems encountered in science and engineering involve second- or higher-order differential equations or systems of first-order equations instead of just a single equation, and it is often necessary to solve such equations numerically.

In this section, we will consider systems of first-order equations only, because an nth-order differential equation always can be expressed as a system of first-order equations. For example, the second-order initial-value problem

$$y'' = f(x, y, y'), \tag{9–54}$$

$$y(x_0) = y_0, \quad y'(x_0) = y_0'$$

can be expressed as a system of two first-order initial-value problems by defining a new variable as $z = y'$. Then $y'' = z'$ and $y'(x_0) = z(x_0) = z_0'$, and thus

$$y' = z, \quad y(x_0) = y_0 \tag{9–55a}$$

$$z' = f(x, y, z), \quad z(x_0) = z_0 \tag{9–55b}$$

Here x is the independent variable, and y and z are the two dependent variables. Primes denote differentiation with respect to x. This process can be extended to higher-order equations. Figure 9–40 gives an example involving a third-order equation.

Most commercial differential equation solvers also use this approach when solving higher-order differential equations. Note that n initial conditions must be specified to accompany an nth-order differential equation.

All of the solution methods discussed so far for single first-order equations are also applicable to a system of first-order equations. However, in this case, the method is applied to every equation during each step before we start the next step (Figure 9–41). That is, we should sweep through the equations one by one at each step.

Some significant engineering problems can involve hundreds of simultaneous first-order equations. However, for simplicity, we will consider a system of two first-order equations with specified initial conditions:

$$y' = f(x, y, z), \quad y(x_0) = y_0 \tag{9–56a}$$

$$z' = g(x, y, z), \quad z(x_0) = z_0 \tag{9–56b}$$

We will assume that the functions f and g and their first derivatives are continuous in the interval of interest that contains the point x_0 so that a unique solution exists in that interval. The procedure to be explained for a system

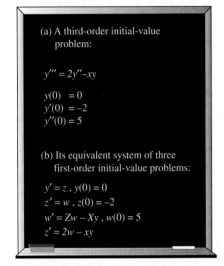

(a) A third-order initial-value problem:

$$y''' = 2y'' - xy$$

$$y(0) = 0$$
$$y'(0) = -2$$
$$y''(0) = 5$$

(b) Its equivalent system of three first-order initial-value problems:

$$y' = z, \, y(0) = 0$$
$$z' = w, \, z(0) = -2$$
$$w' = 2w - xy, \, w(0) = 5$$
$$z' = 2w - xy$$

FIGURE 9–40

An nth-order initial-value problem can be expressed as a system of n first-order initial-value problems.

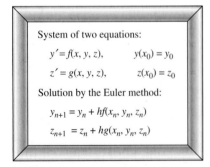

System of two equations:

$$y' = f(x, y, z), \quad y(x_0) = y_0$$
$$z' = g(x, y, z), \quad z(x_0) = z_0$$

Solution by the Euler method:

$$y_{n+1} = y_n + hf(x_n, y_n, z_n)$$
$$z_{n+1} = z_n + hg(x_n, y_n, z_n)$$

FIGURE 9–41

Systems of first-order differential equations are solved by any numerical method by applying it to every equation during each step.

of two equations easily can be extended to a system of three or more first-order equations.

Euler Method

Applying the Euler method to Equations 9–56 with a step size h gives the solution at $x_1 = x_0 + h$ to be

$$y_1 = y_0 + hf(x_0, y_0, z_0) \qquad \text{(9–57a)}$$

$$z_1 = z_0 + hg(x_0, y_0, z_0) \qquad \text{(9–57b)}$$

This solution then can be used to obtain the solution at the next point $x_2 = x_1 + h$.

Generalizing (Figure 9–41), we have

$$y_{n+1} = y_n + hf(x_n, y_n, z_n) \qquad \text{(9–58a)}$$

$$z_{n+1} = z_n + hg(x_n, y_n, z_n) \qquad \text{(9–58b)}$$

Classical Runge–Kutta Method

The solution of the system of two first-order equations (Equations 9–56) using the Runge–Kutta method can be expressed as

$$y_{n+1} = y_n + \frac{h}{6}(k_1 + 2k_2 + 2k_3 + k_4) \qquad \text{(9–59a)}$$

$$z_{n+1} = z_n + \frac{h}{6}(l_1 + 2l_2 + 2l_3 + l_4) \qquad \text{(9–59b)}$$

where

$$k_1 = f(x_n, y_n, z_n)$$

$$l_1 = g(x_n, y_n, z_n)$$

$$k_2 = f\left(x_n + \frac{1}{2}h, y_n + \frac{1}{2}hk_1, z_n + \frac{1}{2}hl_1\right)$$

$$l_2 = g\left(x_n + \frac{1}{2}h, y_n + \frac{1}{2}hk_1, z_n + \frac{1}{2}hl_1\right)$$

$$k_3 = f\left(x_n + \frac{1}{2}h, y_n + \frac{1}{2}hk_2, z_n + \frac{1}{2}hl_2\right)$$

$$l_3 = g\left(x_n + \frac{1}{2}h, y_n + \frac{1}{2}hk_2, z_n + \frac{1}{2}hl_2\right)$$

$$k_4 = f(x_n + h, y_n + hk_3, z_n + hl_3)$$

$$l_4 = g(x_n + h, y_n + hk_3, z_n + hl_3)$$

Note that the calculations must be performed in the order given during each step. For example, k_1 and l_1 must be determined before k_2.

Adams–Moulton Predictor–Corrector Method

The solution of the system of two first-order equations (Equations 9–56) using the Adams–Moulton predictor–corrector method can be expressed as

Predictors:

$$y_{n+1} = y_n + \frac{h}{24}(55f_n - 59f_{n-1} + 37f_{n-2} - 9f_{n-3}) \qquad \textbf{(9–60a)}$$

$$z_{n+1} = z_n + \frac{h}{24}(55g_n - 59g_{n-1} + 37g_{n-2} - 9g_{n-3}) \qquad \textbf{(9–60b)}$$

Correctors:

$$y_{n+1} = y_n + \frac{h}{24}(9f_{n+1} + 19f_n - 5f_{n-1} + f_{n-2}) \qquad \textbf{(9–61a)}$$

$$z_{n+1} = z_n + \frac{h}{24}(9g_{n+1} + 19g_n - 5g_{n-1} + g_{n-2}) \qquad \textbf{(9–61b)}$$

These equations can be extended to a system of three or more equations in the same manner.

EXAMPLE 9–10   **System of Two Equations**

Using (a) the Euler method and (b) the Runge–Kutta method with a step size of $h = 0.1$, determine the solution of the initial-value problem

$$y' = -y + 9z - 9, \quad y(0) = 6$$
$$z' = y - z + 1, \qquad z(0) = 1$$

in the interval $0 \le x \le 1$. Compare these results to the exact solution values obtained from

$$y = 3(e^{2x} + e^{-4x}) \quad \text{and} \quad z = e^{2x} - e^{-4x} + 1$$

SOLUTION   (a) In this case, we have $x_0 = 0$, $y_0 = 6$, $z_0 = 1$, and $h = 0.1$. Also,

$$f(x, y, z) = -y + 9z - 9$$
$$g(x, y, z) = y - z + 1$$

Then the solutions at the points $x_1 = 0.1$, $x_2 = 0.2, \ldots, x_{10} = 1$ are obtained by repeatedly applying the Euler formulas (Equations 9–58). For $n = 0$, we have

$$y_1 = y_0 + hf(x_0, y_0, z_0)$$
$$= 6 + 0.1f(0, 6, 1) = 6 + 0.1 \times (-6)$$
$$= 5.4$$
$$z_1 = z_0 + hg(x_0, y_0, z_0)$$
$$= 1 + 0.1g(0, 6, 1) = 1 + 0.1 \times 6$$
$$= 1.6$$

Thus, the Euler method predicts the solutions at $x_1 = 0.1$ to be $y_1 = 5.4$ and $z_1 = 1.6$. The exact solutions at this point are 5.675 and 1.551, respectively.

The solutions at other points are obtained in the same manner using the MATLAB program given in Figure 9–42, and are listed in Table 9–11.

(b) The Runge–Kutta solutions of the system of these two first-order equations are obtained by repeatedly applying the Runge–Kutta formulas (Equations 9–59). For $n = 0$, we have

$$y_1 = y_0 + \frac{h}{6}(k_1 + 2k_2 + 2k_3 + k_4)$$

$$z_1 = z_0 + \frac{h}{6}(l_1 + 2l_2 + 2l_3 + l_4)$$

where

$$k_1 = f(x_0, y_0, z_0) = f(0, 6, 1) = -6$$

$$l_1 = g(x_0, y_0, z_0) = g(0, 6, 1) = 6$$

$$k_2 = f\left(x_0 + \frac{1}{2}h, y_0 + \frac{1}{2}hk_1, z_0 + \frac{1}{2}hl_1\right)$$

$$= f\left(0 + \frac{1}{2} \times 0.1, 6 + \frac{1}{2} \times 0.1 \times (-6), 1 + \frac{1}{2} \times 0.1 \times 6\right)$$

$$= f(0.05, 5.7, 1.3) = -3$$

$$l_2 = g\left(x_0 + \frac{1}{2}h, y_0 + \frac{1}{2}hk_1, z_0 + \frac{1}{2}hl_1\right)$$

$$= g\left(0 + \frac{1}{2} \times 0.1, 6 + \frac{1}{2} \times 0.1 \times (-6), 1 + \frac{1}{2} \times 0.1 \times 6\right)$$

$$= g(0.05, 5.7, 1.3) = 5.4$$

$$k_3 = f\left(x_0 + \frac{1}{2}h, y_0 + \frac{1}{2}hk_2, z_0 + \frac{1}{2}hl_2\right)$$

$$= f\left(0 + \frac{1}{2} \times 0.1, 6 + \frac{1}{2} \times 0.1 \times (-3), 1 + \frac{1}{2} \times 0.1 \times 5.4\right)$$

$$= f(0.05, 5.85, 1.27) = -3.42$$

$$l_3 = g\left(x_0 + \frac{1}{2}h, y_0 + \frac{1}{2}hk_2, z_0 + \frac{1}{2}hl_2\right)$$

$$= g\left(0 + \frac{1}{2} \times 0.1, 6 + \frac{1}{2} \times 0.1 \times (-3), 1 + \frac{1}{2} \times 0.1 \times 5.4\right)$$

$$= g(0.05, 5.85, 1.27) = 5.58$$

$$k_4 = f(x_0 + h, y_0 + hk_3, z_0 + hl_3)$$

$$= f(0 + 0.1, 6 + 0.1 \times (-3.42), 1 + 0.1 \times 5.58)$$

$$= f(0.1, 5.658, 1.558) = -0.636$$

$$l_4 = g(x_n + h, y_n + hk_3, z_n + hl_3)$$

$$= g(0 + 0.1, 6 + 0.1 \times (-3.42), 1 + 0.1 \times 5.58)$$

$$= g(0.1, 5.658, 1.558) = 5.1$$

```
x = 0;
y = 6;
z = 1;
h = 0.1;
nstep = 10;
fnf = @(x,y,z)(-y+9*z-9);
fng = @(x,y,z)(y-z+1);
for n = 1:nstep
    y_previous = y;
    y = y + h*fnf(x,y,z)
    z = z + h*fng(x,y_previous,z)
    x = n*h
    y_exact = 3*exp(2*x)+3*exp(-4*x)
    z_exact = exp(2*x)-exp(-4*x)+1
end
```

FIGURE 9–42

A MATLAB program for solving a system of two first-order differential equations using the Euler method.

FIGURE 9–43

A MATLAB program for solving a system of two first-order differential equations using the classical fourth-order Runge–Kutta method.

```
x = 0;
y = 6;
z = 1;
h = 0.1;
nstep = 10;
fnf = @(x, y, z)(-y+9*z-9);
fng = @(x, y, z)(y-z+1);
for n = 1:nstep
        K1 = fnf(x, y, z);
        L1 = fng(x, y, z);
        K2 = fnf(x+h/2, y+h*K1/2, z+h*L1/2);
        L2 = fng(x+h/2, y+h*K1/2, z+h*L1/2);
        K3 = fnf(x+h/2, y+h*K2/2, z+h*L2/2);
        L3 = fng(x+h/2, y+h*K2/2, z+h*L2/2);
        K4 = fnf(x+h, y+h*K3, z+h*L3);
        L4 = fng(x+h, y+h*K3, z+h*L3);
        y = y + h*(K1+2*K2+2*K3+K4)/6
        z = z + h*(L1+2*L2+2*L3+L4)/6
        x = n*h
        y_exact = 3*exp(2*x) + 3*exp(-4*x)
        z_exact = exp(2*x)-exp(-4*x)+1
end
```

Substituting, we obtain

$$y_1 = 6 + \frac{0.1}{6}(-6 + 2(-3) + 2(-3.42) - 0 \cdot 636) = 5.6754$$

$$z_1 = 1 + \frac{0.1}{6}(5.4 + 2 \times 5.4 + 2 \times 5.58 + 5.1) = 1.551$$

The calculations for $n = 1, 2, 3, \ldots, 9$ are performed in the same manner using the MATLAB program given in Figure 9–43. The results are listed in Table 9–11 together with the exact results for comparison. Note that the Runge–Kutta results are much closer to the exact results, as expected.

TABLE 9–11

Comparison of the Results Obtained Using the Euler and the Fourth-Order Runge–Kutta Method with Exact Results for a System of First-Order Initial-Value Problems $y' = -y + 9z - 9$, $y(0) = 6$ and $z' = y - z + 1$, $z(0) = 1$

x	Euler Method $h = 0.1$		Runge–Kutta Method $h = 0.1$		Exact Solution	
	y	z	y	z	y	z
0.0	6.00000	1.00000	6.00000	1.00000	6.00000	1.00000
0.1	5.40000	1.60000	5.67540	1.55100	5.67517	1.55108
0.2	5.40000	2.08000	5.82376	2.04238	5.82346	2.04250
0.3	5.83200	2.51200	6.37023	2.52081	6.36994	2.52098
0.4	6.60960	2.94400	7.28254	3.02353	7.28231	3.02365
0.5	7.69824	3.41056	8.56100	3.58284	8.56085	3.58295
0.6	9.09792	3.93933	10.23256	4.22929	10.23251	4.22940
0.7	10.83352	4.55519	12.34799	4.99428	12.34803	4.99439
0.8	12.94984	5.28302	14.98123	5.91214	14.98138	5.91227
0.9	15.50958	6.14970	18.23063	7.02217	18.23091	7.02232
1.0	18.59335	7.18569	22.22168	8.37055	22.22212	8.37074

Section Review

9–19C What is the procedure for reducing an *n*th-order initial-value problem to a system of *n* first-order initial-value problems?

9–20 Using a calculator, determine the numerical solution of the following initial-value problems after (a) one step and (b) two steps with a step size of $h = 0.2$ using the Euler method.

$$y' = 2y - 3z, \quad y(0) = 2$$
$$z' = 4y - 5z, \quad z(0) = 3$$

(*Answer*: After one step, $y(0.2) = 1$ and $z(0.2) = 1.6$. After two steps, $y(0.4) = 0.44$ and $z(0.4) = 0.8$.)

9–10 ▪ NUMERICAL SOLUTIONS WITH COMMERCIAL PACKAGES

When using a numerical method to solve an equation for which no analytic solution is available, there are several ways to check the correctness of the numerical solution. Some of these, such as decreasing the step size to see if the solution changes, already have been discussed. First, you should try the numerical method on an analytically solvable equation that is similar to the equation under study. One way of doing this is to linearize a nonlinear equation. Another way is to use our physical insight to guard against grossly incorrect results. We can also check the equation for singularities that might affect the numerical procedure.

These approaches can be used with any program, but we now illustrate them using the MATLAB numerical solvers. A summary of the appropriate Maple, Mathematica, and MuPad functions are given at the end of the section.

MATLAB ODE Solvers

In addition to the many variations of the predictor–corrector and Runge–Kutta algorithms that have been developed, there are more advanced algorithms that use a variable step size. These "adaptive" algorithms use larger step sizes when the solution is changing more slowly. MATLAB provides several functions, called *solvers*, that implement the Runge–Kutta and other methods with variable step size. Two of these are the ode45 and ode15s functions. The ode45 function uses a combination of fourth- and fifth-order Runge–Kutta methods. It is a general-purpose solver, whereas ode15s is suitable for more difficult equations called "stiff" equations. These solvers are more than sufficient to solve the problems in this text. It is recommended that you try ode45 first. If the equation proves difficult to solve (as indicated by a lengthy solution time or by a warning or error message), then use ode15s. We will use ode45 in our examples; the syntax for ode15s and the other MATLAB solvers is the same.

When used to solve the equation $y' = f(x, y)$, the basic syntax is (using ode45 as the example)

```
[x,y] = ode45(@ydot, xspan, y0)
```

where @ydot is the handle of the function file whose inputs must be x and y and whose output must be a column vector representing dy/dx; that is, $f(x, y)$. The number of *rows* in this column vector must equal the *order* of the equation. The vector xspan contains the starting and ending values of the independent variable x and optionally any intermediate values of x where the solution is desired.

For example, if no intermediate values are specified, xspan is [x0, xfinal], where x0 and xfinal are the desired starting and ending values of the independent parameter x. As another example, using xspan = [0, 5, 10] tells MATLAB to find the solution at $x = 5$ and at $x = 10$.

The parameter y0 is the initial value $y(0)$. The function file must have its first two input arguments as x and y in that order, even for equations where $f(x, y)$ is not a function of x. You need not use array operations in the function file, because the ODE solvers call the file with scalar values for the arguments.

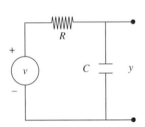

FIGURE 9–44

An *RC* circuit.

EXAMPLE 9–11   Response of an *RC* Circuit

The model of the *RC* circuit shown in Figure 9–44 can be found from Kirchhoff's voltage law and conservation of charge. It is $RCy' + y = v(x)$, where x denotes time. Suppose the value of RC is 0.1 s. Use a numerical method to find the free response for the case where the applied voltage is zero and the initial capacitor voltage is $y(0) = 2$ V. Compare the results with the analytical solution, which is $y(x) = 2e^{-10x}$.

SOLUTION   The equation for the circuit becomes $0.1y' + y = 0$ if we are solving only for the free response. First, solve this for y' to obtain $y' = -10y$. Next, define the right-hand side as a function. You can do this by defining it as an anonymous function or by defining it in a function file, which is the most general method. The former method works only for simple functions, so we now illustrate the file method.

Create and save the following function file. Note that the order of the input arguments must be x and y even though x does not appear on the right-hand side of the equation.

```
function yprime = RC_circuit(x,y)
yprime = -10*y;
```

The initial time is $x = 0$, so set x0 to be zero. Here we know from the analytical solution that $y(x)$ will be close to 0 for $t \geq 0.5$ s, so we choose xfinal to be 0.5. In other problems, we generally do not have a good guess for xfinal, so we must try several increasing values of xfinal until we see enough of the response on the plot.

The function ode45 is called as follows, and the solutions plotted along with the analytical solution y_true.

```
[x,y] = ode45(@RC_circuit,[0,0.5],2);
y_true = 2*exp(-10*x);
plot(x,y,'o',x,y_true),xlabel('Time(s)'),...
    ylabel('Capacitor Voltage')
```

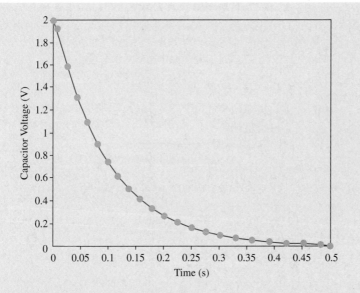

FIGURE 9–45

Free response of an *RC* circuit.

Note that we need not generate the array `x` to evaluate `y_true`, because `x` is generated by the `ode45` function. The plot is shown in Figure 9–45. The numerical solution is marked by the circles, and the analytical solution is indicated by the solid line. Clearly, the numerical solution gives an accurate answer. Note that we need not specify the step size, because it has been automatically selected by the `ode45` function.

EXAMPLE 9–12   **Round-Off Error and Unstable Equations**

Consider the following equation.

$$y' = y - 2e^{-x} \tag{9–62}$$

Its analytical solution is

$$y = e^{-x} + [1 - y(0)]e^{x} \tag{9–63}$$

Suppose that $y(0) = 1$. Obtain the solution numerically.

SOLUTION   For $y(0) = 1$, the analytical solution becomes $y = e^{-x}$. Ignoring the fact that we have the exact solution, suppose we solve the equation numerically for $0 \le x \le 12$. Using the following MATLAB program, we obtain the exact and numerical solutions plotted in Figure 9–46. Note that, in this program, we have used an anonymous function to define the right-hand side of the differential equation.

FIGURE 9–46

Exact and numerical solution of the
equation $y' = y - 2e^{-x}$ for $y(0) = 1$.

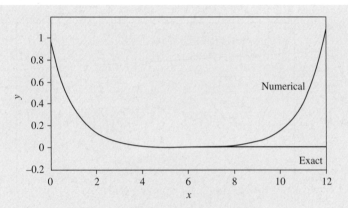

```
% Exact solution
x = [0:0.01:12]; yexact = exp(-x);
% Runge-Kutta solution
f = @(x,y)(y - 2*exp(-x));
[x1,y1] = ode45(f,[0,12],1);
plot(x,yexact,x1,y1),xlabel('x'),ylabel('y')
```

Clearly, the numerical solution has an error that increases greatly after a certain point. What has gone wrong, and how could we have detected the error
if we did not have the analytical solution?

If we examine Equation 9–62 we see that the term e^{-x} disappears for
$x > 4$ approximately, and the differential equation becomes approximately
$y' = y$, whose solution has the form $y = Ce^x$. So the solution will approach
$+\infty$ or $-\infty$ unless $C = 0$, in which case the solution approaches zero as
$x \to \infty$. It turns out that $C = 0$ only if $y(0) = 1$.

From the general solution given by Equation 9–63 we see that if $y(0) = 1$
the term e^x does not appear in the solution. However, the e^x term does
appear in the solution for *any* initial condition not equal to 1. The e^x term
corresponds to the unstable characteristic root $\lambda = 1$. This illustrates the differential equation's sensitivity to changes on the initial condition.

What does this say about our numerical solution? Suppose we were to
solve Equation 9–62 for $x \ge x_1$ with the condition $y(x_1) = y_1$. The solution is

$$y = e^{-x} + \left[e^{-x_1} y(x_1) - e^{-2x_1}\right] e^x \qquad (9\text{–}64)$$

Think of this as the solution generated by a numerical method starting at
x_1 with the value $y(x_1)$. The difference between this solution and the true
solution for $y(0) = 1$ is

$$\Delta(x) = e^{-x} + \left[e^{-x_1} y(x_1) - e^{-2x_1}\right] e^x - e^{-x} = \left[e^{-x_1} y(x_1) - e^{-2x_1}\right] e^x = De^x$$

Now if the numerical solution $y(x_1)$ does not equal the true solution for
$y(0) = 1$, then $y(x_1) \ne e^{-x_1}$, and $D \ne 0$. So, the error $\Delta(x)$ increases exponentially with x.

The reason the numerical solution $y(x_1)$ will not equal the true solution is
due to round-off error. The effect of round-off error is illustrated in Figure 9–47.
Suppose that because of round-off error, the solution at $x = 1$ deviates from

the exact solution e^{-1} by a small amount, say 0.001. The exact solution of Equation 9–62 with the starting condition $y(1) = e^{-1} + 0.001$ is $y = 0.001e^{-1}e^{-x} + e^x$. This gives the top curve in Figure 9–47. Note how it rapidly deviates from the solution for $y(0) = 1$—even though the initial difference is only 0.001.

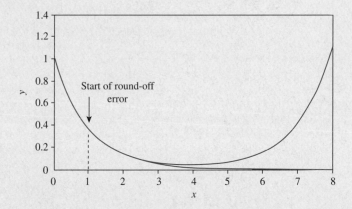

FIGURE 9–47

Sensitivity to round-off error. Plots of the exact solutions of $y' = y - 2e^{-x}$ for $y(0) = 1$ (bottom curve, e^{-x}), and for $y(1) = e^{-1} + 0.001$ (top curve).

Why does the effect of round-off error continue to grow? The reason is due to the fact that Equation 9–62 is an *unstable* equation. One characteristic of unstable equations is that their solutions are very sensitive to the initial conditions. For example, the solutions to Equation 9–62 all grow exponentially for any initial condition other than $y(0) = 1$. This is illustrated in Figure 9–48, which shows the exact solution for three slightly different initial conditions.

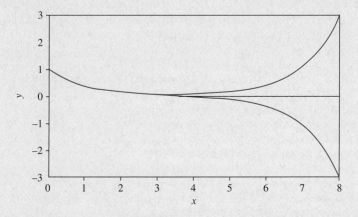

FIGURE 9–48

Sensitivity of an unstable equation to slight changes in initial condition. Plots of the exact solutions of $y' = y - 2e^{-x}$ for $y(0) = 1$ (middle curve), $y(0) = 1.001$ (top curve), and $y(0) = 0.999$ (bottom curve).

We conclude this example by noting that we have solved the differential equation in the absence of any information about its intended application; that is, its physical or engineering context. Such information may have told us that we needed the solution only over a shorter interval, say $0 \leq x \leq 2$. In such a case, the round-off error would not be as great, and the numerical solver would not need to be as accurate.

It was noted earlier that one way of checking a numerical solution is to decrease the step size and check to see if the solution changes. However, it is not possible to do this with adaptive methods, because the step size changes. It is also not possible to do this with commercial programs whose code is not accessible. The following example illustrates how to check the accuracy of a numerical solution when using MATLAB. Similar methods are available for the other popular computer packages.

EXAMPLE 9–13 **Reducing the Effects of Round-Off Error**

Discuss how to check the accuracy of a numerical solution in MATLAB when the step size cannot be changed. Use the following equation and initial condition.

$$y' = y - 2e^{-x}, \quad y(0) = 1 \tag{9–65}$$

SOLUTION We saw earlier in Example 9–12 and in Figure 9–46 that the basic form of the ode45 solver gave a large error for $x > 7$ approximately. We can reduce this error by using an optional argument in the ode45 solver that controls the relative error tolerance used by the solver. This is a scalar that is used to test the accuracy of the solution. It defaults to 10^{-3} in all of the solvers when the optional argument is not specified. This corresponds to 0.1% accuracy.

A different value of the relative error tolerance can be specified with the odeset command, which must precede the ode45 command. The following code shows how this is done to decrease the tolerance to 10^{-5}.

```
% Exact solution
x = [0:0.01:12]; yexact = exp(-x);
f = @(x,y)(y - 2*exp(-x));
% Runge-Kutta solution using default value of the
% relative error tolerance(0.001)
[x1,y1] = ode45(@f,[0,12],1);
% Runge-Kutta solution using a smaller
% relative error tolerance of 0.00001
options = odeset('RelTol',1e-5);
[x2,y2] = ode45(@f,[0,12],1,options);
plot(x,yexact,x1,y1,x2,y2),xlabel('x'),ylabel('y')
```

The result is shown in Figure 9–49. The lowest visible curve was generated using the smaller error tolerance and is visibly identical to the exact value for $x < 9$. The solution obtained with the default tolerance value (the upper curve) deviates greatly from the exact solution for $x > 8$.

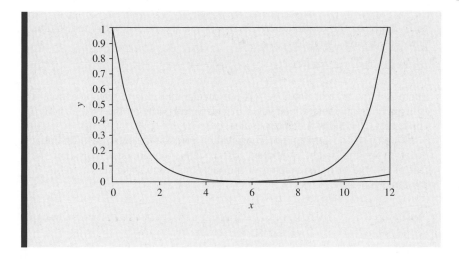

FIGURE 9–49

The effects of error tolerance. Plots of the solutions of $y' = y - 2e^{-x}$ for $y(0) = 1$: one using a relative error tolerance of 10^{-3} (top curve), and one using a relative error tolerance of 10^{-5} (bottom curve).

We conclude that when using a commercial program whose step size cannot be changed, one way of checking the accuracy is to change whatever parameters the program uses to specify the error tolerance. The common commercially available programs let you do this. Do not assume that the default values are acceptable unless you have other reasons for not doubting the accuracy of the numerical solution.

When the differential equation is nonlinear, we often have no analytical solution to use for checking our numerical results. In such cases, we can use our physical insight to guard against grossly incorrect results. We can also check the equation for singularities that might affect the numerical procedure. Finally, we can sometimes use an approximation to replace the nonlinear equation with a linear one that can be solved analytically. Although the linear approximation does not give the exact answer, it can be used to see if our numerical answer is "in the ballpark." The following example illustrates this approach.

EXAMPLE 9–14   Liquid Height in a Spherical Tank

Figure 9–50 shows a spherical tank for storing water. The tank is filled through a hole in the top and drained through a hole in the bottom. If the tank's radius is r, you can use integration to show that the volume of water in the tank as a function of its height h is given by

$$V(h) = \pi r h^2 - \pi \frac{h^3}{3} \qquad (9\text{–}66)$$

Torricelli's principle states that the liquid flow rate through the hole is proportional to the square root of the height h. Further studies in fluid mechanics

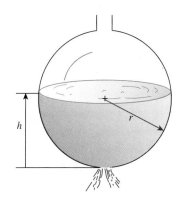

FIGURE 9–50

Draining of a spherical tank.

have identified the relation more precisely, and the result is that the volume flow rate through the hole is given by

$$q = C_d A \sqrt{2gh} \qquad (9\text{–}67)$$

where A is the area of the hole, g is the acceleration due to gravity, and C_d is an experimentally determined value that depends partly on the type of liquid. For water, $C_d = 0.6$ is a common value.

We can use the principle of conservation of mass to obtain a differential equation for the height h. Applied to this tank, the principle says that the rate of change of liquid volume in the tank must equal the flow rate out of the tank; that is,

$$\frac{dV}{dt} = -q \qquad (9\text{–}68)$$

From Equation 9–66, we have

$$\frac{dV}{dt} = 2\pi rh - \pi h^2 \frac{dh}{dt} = \pi h(2r - h)\frac{dh}{dt}$$

Substituting this and Equation 9–67 into Equation 9–68 gives the required equation for h.

$$\pi h(2r - h)\frac{dh}{dt} = -C_d A \sqrt{2gh} \qquad (9\text{–}69)$$

Use MATLAB to solve this equation to determine how long it will take for the tank to empty if the initial height is 9 ft. The tank has a radius of $r = 5$ ft and has a 1-in. diameter hole in the bottom. Use $C_d = 0.6$ and $g = 32.2$ ft/s^2. Discuss how to check the solution.

SOLUTION With $r = 5$, $g = 32.2$, and $A = \pi(1/24)^2$, Equation 9–69 becomes

$$\frac{dh}{dt} = -\frac{0.0334\sqrt{h}}{10h - h^2} \qquad (9\text{–}70)$$

We can first check this expression for dh/dt for singularities. The denominator does not become zero unless $h = 0$ or $h = 10$, which correspond to a completely empty and a completely full tank. So we will avoid singularities if $0 < h < 10$.

We can use the following approximation to estimate the time to empty. Replace h on the right side of Equation 9–70 with its average value, namely, $(9 - 0)/2 = 4.5$ ft. This gives $dh/dt = -0.00286$, whose solution is $h(t) = h(0) - 0.00286t = 9 - 0.00286t$. According to this equation, the tank will be empty at $t = 9/0.00286 = 3147$ s, or 52 min. We will use this value as a "reality check" on our answer.

The function file based on Equation 9–70 is

```
function hdot = height(t,h)
hdot = -(0.0334*sqrt(h))/(10*h-h^2);
```

The file is called as follows, using the ode45 solver:

```
[t, h] = ode45(@height,[0, 2475],9);
plot(t,h),xlabel('Time(sec)'),ylabel('Height(ft)')
```

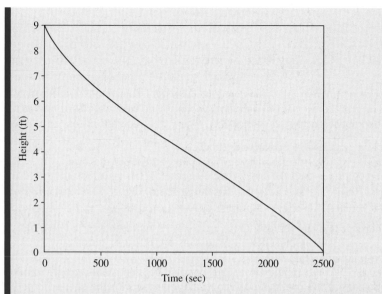

FIGURE 9–51

Plot of water height in a spherical tank.

The resulting plot is shown in Figure 9–51. Note how the height changes more rapidly when the tank is nearly full or nearly empty. This is to be expected, because of the effects of the tank's curvature. The tank empties in 2475 s, or 41 min. This value is not grossly different from our rough estimate of 52 min, so we should feel comfortable accepting the numerical results. We could also decrease the relative error tolerance and run the program again. The value of the final time of 2475 s was found by running the program with increasing values of the final time until the plot showed that the height became 0.

Higher-Order Differential Equations

To use the ODE solvers to solve an equation higher than an order of one, you must first write the equation as a set of first-order equations.

EXAMPLE 9–15   Solution of a Second-Order Equation

Consider the second-order equation:

$$5y'' + 7y' + 4y = f(x) \tag{9–71}$$

Solve it numerically for the case where for $0 \le x \le 6$ with the initial conditions $y(0) = 3$, $y'(0) = 9$, and $f(x) = \sin x$.

SOLUTION   First solve Equation 9–71 for the highest derivative:

$$y'' = \frac{1}{5}f(x) - \frac{4}{5}y - \frac{7}{5}y' \tag{9–72}$$

Define two new variables z_1 and z_2 to be $z_1 = y$ and $z_2 = y'$. Thus,

$$z_1' = z_2$$

and

$$z_2' = \frac{1}{5}f - \frac{4}{5}z_1 - \frac{7}{5}z_2$$

Now write a function file that computes the right-hand side of these two equations and stores them in a *column* vector. To do this, we must first have a function specified for $f(x)$. Since $f(x) = \sin x$, the required file is

```
function zprime = example_1(x,z)
% Computes the derivatives of two equations
zprime(1) = z(2);
zprime(2) = (1/5)*(sin(x)-4*z(1)-7*z(2));
zprime = [zprime(1); zprime(2)];
```

Note that `zprime(1)` represents z_1', `zprime(2)` represents z_2', `z(1)` represents z_1, and `z(2)` represents z_2. Note that the returned output, `zprime`, must be a *column* vector.

Once you become familiar with the notation for the state-variable form, you will see that the previous code could be replaced with the shorter form:

```
function zprime = example_1(x,z)
zprime = [z(2); (1/5)*(sin(x)-4*z(1)-7*z(2))];
```

We want to solve Equation 9–72 for $0 \le x \le 6$ with the initial conditions $y(0) = z_1(0) = 3$, $y'(0) = z_2(0) = 9$. Then the initial condition for the *vector z* is [3, 9]. To use ode45, you type

```
[x,z] = ode45(@example_1,[0, 6],[3; 9]);
plot(x,z),xlabel('x'),gtext('z_1'),gtext('z_2')
```

The resulting plot is shown in Figure 9–52. Each row in the vector z corresponds to a time returned in the column vector x. If you type `plot(x,z)`, you will obtain a plot of both z_1 and z_2 versus x. Note that z is a matrix with two columns. The first column contains the values of z_1 at the various times generated by the solver; the second column contains the values of z_2. Thus, to plot only z_1, type `plot(x,z(:,1))`. To plot only z_2, type `plot(x,z(:,2))`.

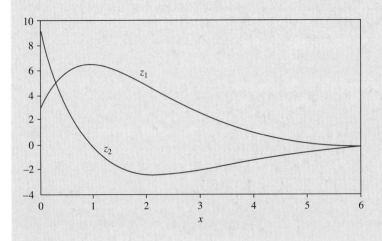

FIGURE 9–52

Plot of the solution of Equation 9–71, where $z_1 = y$ and $z_2 = y'$.

When we are solving nonlinear equations, sometimes it is possible to check the numerical results by using an approximation that reduces the equation to a linear one. The following example illustrates such an approach with a second-order equation.

EXAMPLE 9–16   A Nonlinear Pendulum Model

The pendulum shown in Figure 9–53 consists of a concentrated mass m attached to a rod whose mass is small compared to m. The rod's length is L. The equation of motion for this pendulum is

$$\frac{d^2\theta}{dt^2} + \frac{g}{L}\sin\theta = 0 \tag{9–73}$$

Suppose that $L = 1$ m and $g = 9.81$ m/s^2. Use MATLAB to solve this equation for $\theta(t)$ for two cases: $\theta(0) = 0.5$ rad and $\theta(0) = 0.8$ rad. In both cases, the initial velocity is zero. Discuss how to check the accuracy of the results.

SOLUTION   Note that the independent variable is now t. If we use the small-angle approximation $\sin\theta \approx \theta$, the equation becomes

$$\frac{d^2\theta}{dt^2} + \frac{g}{L}\theta = 0 \tag{9–74}$$

which is linear and has the solution $\theta(t) = \theta(0)\cos\sqrt{g/L}\,t$ if the initial velocity is zero. Thus the amplitude of oscillation is $\theta(0)$, and the period is $P = 2\pi\sqrt{L/g}$. We can use this information to select a final time and to check our numerical results.

First rewrite the pendulum Equation (9–74) as two first-order equations. To do this, let $x_1 = \theta$ and $x_2 = d\theta/dt$. Thus

$$\frac{dx_1}{dt} = \frac{d\theta}{dt} = x_2$$

$$\frac{dx_2}{dt} = \frac{d^2\theta}{dt^2} = -\frac{g}{L}\sin x_1$$

The following function file is based on the last two equations. Remember that the output xdot must be a *column* vector.

```
function dxdt = pendulum(t,x)
g = 9.81; L = 1;
dxdt = [x(2); -(g/L)*sin(x(1))];
```

This file is called as follows. The vectors ta and xa contain the results for the case where $\theta(0) = 0.5$. The vectors tb and xb contain the results for $\theta(0) = 0.8\pi$. In both cases, the initial velocity is zero.

```
[ta, xa] = ode45(@pendulum,[0,5],[0.5;0]);
[tb, xb] = ode45(@pendulum,[0,5],[0.8*pi;0]);
plot(ta,xa(:,1),tb,xb(:,1)),xlabel('Time (s)'), . . .
    ylabel('Angle(rad)'),gtext('Case 1'),gtext('Case 2')
```

The results are shown in Figure 9–54. For the case where $\theta(0) = 0.5$, the amplitude remains constant, as predicted by the small-angle analysis. The

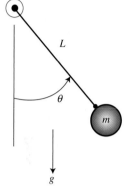

FIGURE 9–53

A pendulum.

period is a little larger than 2 s, which is the value predicted by the small-angle analysis. So we can place some confidence in the numerical procedure.

For the case where $\theta(0) = 0.8\pi$, the period of the numerical solution is about 3.3 s. This illustrates an important property of nonlinear differential equations. The free response of a linear equation has the same period for any initial conditions; however, the form (and therefore the period) of the free response of a nonlinear equation often depend on the particular values of the initial conditions.

In this example, the values of g and L were encoded in the function `pendulum(t,x)`. Now suppose you want to obtain the pendulum response for different lengths L or different gravitational accelerations g. You could use the `global` command to declare g and L as global variables, or you could pass parameter values through an argument list in the `ode45` function, but starting with MATLAB 7, the preferred method is to use a *nested function*. The following program shows how this is done for two different values of g and L. The final time was set to show approximately three periods of oscillation using the period formula from the small-angle analysis.

```
function pendula
g = 9.81; L = 0.75; % First case.
% Set the final time tF to approximately 3 periods.
tF = 6*pi*sqrt(L/g);
[t1, x1] = ode45(@pendulum,[0,tF],[0.4; 0];
%
g = 1.63; L = 2.5; % Second case.
% Set the final time tF to approximately 3 periods.
tF = 6*pi*sqrt(L/g);
[t2, x2] = ode45(@pendulum,[0,tF],[0.2; 0];
plot(t1,x1(:,1),t2,x2(:,1)), . . . .
    xlabel('Time(s)'),ylabel('Angle(rad)')
% Nested function.
    function xdot = pendulum(t,x)
    xdot = [x(2);-(g/L)*sin(x(1))];
end
end
```

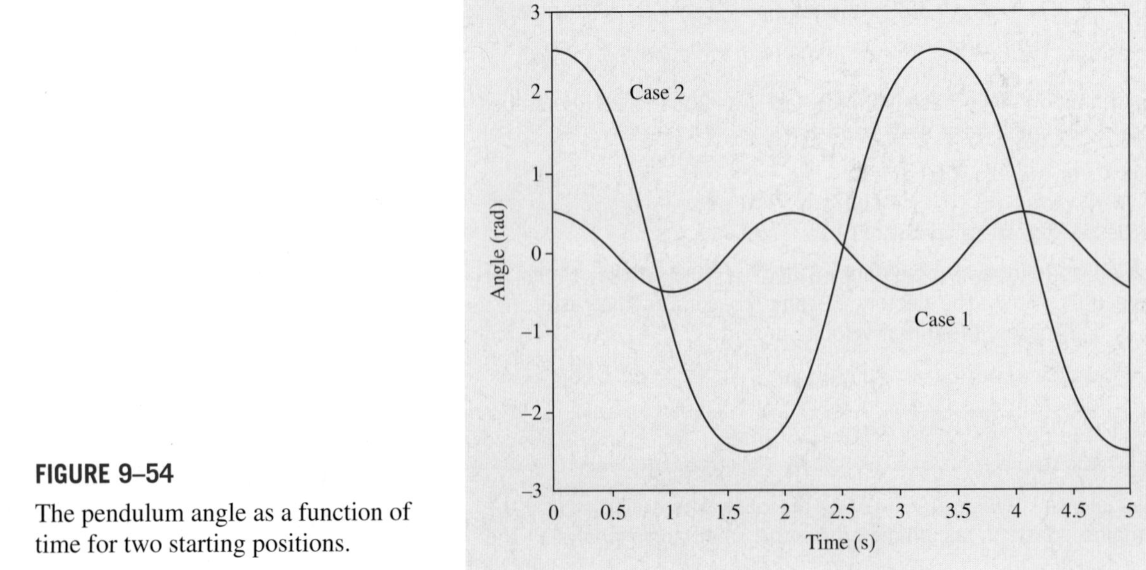

FIGURE 9–54

The pendulum angle as a function of time for two starting positions.

Numerical Solutions with Maple

To solve the initial-value problem

$$y' = y - 2e^{-x}, \quad y(0) = 1$$

with Maple over the interval $0 \le t \le 12$, you type

```
with(plots):
s:=dsolve({D(y)(x)=y(x)-2*exp(-x),y(0)=1},type=numeric,range=0..12):
odeplot(s)
```

For the pendulum equations with $g = 9.81, L = 1, x_1(0) = 0.5$, and $x_2(0) = 0$, we have

$$\frac{dx_1}{dt} = \frac{d\theta}{dt} = x_2$$

and

$$\frac{dx_2}{dt} = \frac{d^2\theta}{dt^2} = -\frac{g}{L}\sin x_1$$

To plot the solution for $x_1(t)$ over the interval $0 \le t \le 5$, you type

```
sys:={diff(x1(t),t)=x2(t),diff(x2(t),t)= -(9.81/1)*sin(x1(t)),x1(0)=0.5,x2(0)=0}:
s:=dsolve(sys,type=numeric,range=0..5):
odeplot(s)
```

The Maple numerical solvers for initial-value problems control the discretization error by means of the options `abserr`, `relerr`, `minstep`, `maxstep`, and `initstep`. The parameter `abserr` is an absolute error tolerance and `relerr` is a relative error tolerance. The exact meaning of these tolerances is dependent upon the particular solver.

Numerical Solutions with Mathematica

To solve the initial value problem

$$y' = y - 2e^{-x}, \quad y(0) = 1$$

with Mathematica over the interval $0 \le t \le 12$, you type

```
s=NDSolve[{y'[x]==y[x]-2*Exp[-x],y[0]==1},y,{x,0,12}];
Plot[Evaluate[y[x]/.s],{x,0,12},PlotRange->All]
```

For the pendulum equations with $g = 9.81$, $L = 1$, $x_1(0) = 0.5$, and $x_2(0) = 0$, we have

$$\frac{dx_1}{dt} = \frac{d\theta}{dt} = x_2$$

and

$$\frac{dx_2}{dt} = \frac{d^2\theta}{dt^2} = -\frac{g}{L}\sin x_1$$

To plot the solution for $x_1(t)$ over the interval $0 \leq t \leq 5$, you type

```
s=NDSolve[{x1'[t]==x2[t],x2'[t]==(9.81/1)*Sin[x1[t]],x1[0]==0.5,x2[0]==0},{x1,x2},{t,0,5}];
Plot[Evaluate[x1[t]/.s],{t,0,5},PlotStyle->Automatic]
```

The solver automatically detects and handles stiff equations. You can specify a method if you wish, say Runge–Kutta, by including `Method-> "ExplicitRungeKutta"` in the arguments of `NDSolve`. The parameter `AccuracyGoal` is an option for various numerical operations that specifies how many effective digits of accuracy should be sought in the final result. To decrease the relative error, include `AccuracyGoal->`∞ in the arguments of `NDSolve`.

Numerical Solutions with MuPad

MuPAD provides two functions for obtaining numerical solutions of initial value problems. The function `numeric::odesolve` returns a numeric approximation of the solution at a particular point. Typing `numeric:: odesolve2` returns a function representing a numeric approximation of the solution. This is useful for plotting the solution. To apply `numeric:: odesolve2` use the following steps:

1. Define your initial value problem as a list or a set.
2. Define a set of fields over which you want to get a solution.
3. Convert the initial value problem and the fields into a procedure acceptable by `numeric::odesolve2`. The function `numeric:: ode2vectorfield` generates the required procedure.
4. Call `numeric::odesolve2` to approximate the solution.
5. Use `plotfunc2d` to plot the solution.

For example, to solve the initial-value problem

$$y' = y - 2e^{-x}, \qquad y(0) = 1$$

with MuPAD over the interval $0 \leq t \leq 12$, you type

```
IVP := {y'(x) = y(x)-2*exp(-2*x),y(0) = 1}:
fields := [y(x)]:
ODE := numeric::ode2vectorfield(IVP, fields):
numApprox := numeric::odesolve2(ODE):
plotfunc2d(numApprox(x)[1], x = 0..12)
```

For the pendulum equations with $g = 9.81$, $L = 1$, $x_1(0) = 0.5$, and $x_2(0) = 0$, we have

$$\frac{dx_1}{dt} = \frac{d\theta}{dt} = x_2$$

and

$$\frac{dx_2}{dt} = \frac{d^2\theta}{dt^2} = -\frac{g}{L}\sin x_1$$

To plot the solution for $x_1(t)$ over the interval $0 \leq t \leq 5$, you type

```
IVP:={x1'(t)=x2(t),x2'(t)=-(9.81/1)*sin(x1(t)),x1(0)=0.5,x2(0)=0}:
fields:=[x1(t),x2(t)]:
ODE:=numeric::ode2vectorfield(IVP, fields):
numApprox:=numeric::odesolve2(ODE):
plotfunc2d(numApprox(t)[1],t=0..5)
```

Numerical precision is controlled by the variable DIGITS. Adaptive control of the step size keeps local relative discretization errors smaller than rtol = $10^{-\text{DIGITS}}$, unless a different tolerance is specified wih the option RelativeError = rtol. For small values of the solution vector, the absolute discretization error can be bounded by the threshold atol specified via the option AbsoluteError = atol. If AbsoluteError is not specified, only relative discretization errors are controlled and kept below rtol. The error control may be switched off by specifying a fixed Stepsize = h. Note that only local errors are controlled by the adaptive mechanism. No control of the global error is provided.

9–11 ▪ SUMMARY

Numerical methods are frequently used in practice to obtain approximate solutions to differential equations. Numerical methods give the solutions of differential equations at specified points rather than as a continuous function over an interval. Any higher-order differential equation can be expressed as a system of first-order differential equations, and thus, the emphasis in this chapter has been on the first-order initial-value problems of the form

$$\frac{dy}{dx} = f(x, y), y(x_0) = y_0$$

Solving Differential Equations for $f(x, y) = f(x)$ When the function f in the differential equation depends on x only, the solution of the first-order initial-value problem can be determined in a marching manner from

$$y_{n+1} = y_n + \int_{x_n}^{x_{n+1}} f(x)\,dx = y_n + I_n \qquad (9\text{–}18)$$

for $n = 0, 1, 2, \ldots$ using any numerical integration formula. In this case, the solution can be determined by numerical integration using any of the standard numerical integration techniques.

If the specified integration interval is divided into N segments of equal width h, the value of the integral can be determined by finding the area of these segments and adding them up. In the *rectangular strip method*, the average height of a segment is taken to be the value of the function $f(x)$ at the midpoint. In the *trapezoidal rule*, it is taken to be the arithmetic average of the values of the function at the end points. In *Simpson's rule*, it is determined in a more precise but complex manner. Using these methods, the area of a general segment between the points x_n and x_{n+1} can be determined. With one of the following three methods.

Rectangular strip method:

$$I_n \cong (x_{n+1} - x_n)f\left(\frac{x_{n+1} + x_n}{2}\right) \qquad (9\text{–}4)$$

Trapezoidal rule:

$$I_n \cong (x_{n+1} - x_n)\frac{f(x_{n+1}) + f(x_n)}{2} \qquad (9\text{–}9)$$

Simpson's rule:

$$I_n \cong \frac{x_{n+1} - x_n}{6}\left[f(x_n) + 4f\left(\frac{x_{n+1} + x_n}{2}\right) + f(x_{n+1})\right] \qquad (9\text{–}12)$$

Simpson's rule is a better approximation than the other two and gives much more accurate results. Here $h = x_{n+1} - x_n$ is called the *step size*.

Relative Error In general, the value obtained by a numerical method will differ from the exact value, and this difference is called the *error*. The error is usually expressed in terms of the *relative* or *percent error* defined as

$$\text{Relative error} = \left|\frac{\text{exact value} - \text{approximate value}}{\text{exact value}}\right| \times 100\,(\%)$$

$$(9\text{–}7)$$

Solving Differential Equations for $f(x, y) = f(x, y)$ When the function f depends on both x and y, the numerical solution procedure is based on the fact that the function $f(x, y)$ represents the slope of the solution function y at any point (x, y) and treats this slope as a constant for each step. The solution is then expressed as

$$\text{New value} = \text{old value} + \text{slope} \times \text{step size}$$

or

$$y_{n+1} = y_n + s_n h \qquad (9\text{–}20)$$

Numerical methods differ from each other primarily in the way the slope s_n is estimated.

The Euler Method In the Euler method, which is the simplest numerical method for solving differential equations, this slope is taken to be the value of the function $f(x, y)$ at the beginning of each step. Then the Euler method is expressed as

$$y_{n+1} = y_n + hf(x_n, y_n), n = 0, 1, 2, 3, \ldots \quad \textbf{(9–28)}$$

Thus, if the solution at the point x_n is known, the value of the function $f(x, y)$ at that point and the solution at the next point x_{n+1} can be determined from Equation 9–28.

The Improved Euler Method In the improved Euler method, the slope is taken to be the arithmetic average of the values of $f(x, y)$ at the end points of the step, and the method is expressed as

$$y_{n+1} = y_n + h\frac{f(x_n, y_n) + f(x_{n+1}, \widetilde{y}_{n+1})}{2} \quad \textbf{(9–37a)}$$

where

$$\widetilde{y}_{n+1} = y_n + hf(x_n, y_n) \quad \textbf{(9–37b)}$$

The improved Euler method belongs to a class of numerical techniques called the predictor–corrector methods. Equation 9–37b first predicts the value of y_{n+1}, and then Equation 9–37a corrects it. Note that the predictor equation is simply the Euler formula in this case, and thus, y_{n+1} is the solution we would get using the Euler method. In the improved Euler method, the result obtained by the Euler method is treated as an intermediate value and is refined using the corrector equation. When the function $f(x, y)$ depends on x only, the improved Euler method reduces to the trapezoidal rule.

Taylor Series Methods The three-term or second-order Taylor series method is based on expressing the solution function $y(x)$ as a Taylor series, which is an infinite power series, and then retaining only the first three terms of the series to approximate the solution function. After some manipulations it becomes

$$\begin{aligned} y_{n+1} = y_n + hf(x_n, y_n) + \frac{h^2}{2}[f_x(x_n, y_n) \\ + f_y(x_n, y_n)f(x_n, y_n)] \end{aligned} \quad \textbf{(9–42)}$$

where f_x and f_y are partial derivatives of $f(x, y)$ with respect to x and y, respectively. The Taylor series method requires the evaluation of the partial derivatives of the function $f(x, y)$, which in general is not easy to do. The higher-order Taylor series methods give very accurate results, but they are awkward to use in practice, since they require the evaluation of the higher-order derivatives of the function $f(x, y)$.

Runge–Kutta Methods The Runge–Kutta methods offer the accuracy of the Taylor series methods without requiring the evaluation of any derivatives. Like the Taylor series methods, the Runge–Kutta methods have different orders, and each order

has different versions. The higher the order, the higher the accuracy of the method. The first-order Runge–Kutta method is equivalent to the Euler method and to the two-term (first-order) Taylor series method. The second-order Runge–Kutta method is essentially equivalent to the improved Euler method and the three-term (second-order) Taylor series method.

The most popular Runge–Kutta methods are of the fourth-order, which has several versions. Of those, the best known and the most widely used is the classical fourth-order Runge–Kutta method, which is expressed as

$$y_{n+1} = y_n + \frac{h}{6}(k_1 + 2k_2 + 2k_3 + k_4) \quad \textbf{(9–44a)}$$

where

$$k_1 = f(x_n, y_n) \quad \textbf{(9–44b)}$$

$$k_2 = f\left(x_n + \frac{1}{2}h, y_n + \frac{1}{2}hk_1\right) \quad \textbf{(9–44c)}$$

$$k_3 = f\left(x_n + \frac{1}{2}h, y_n + \frac{1}{2}hk_2\right) \quad \textbf{(9–44d)}$$

$$k_4 = f(x_n + h, y_n + hk_3) \quad \textbf{(9–44e)}$$

When the function $f(x, y)$ depends on x only, we have $k_2 = k_3$, and the classical fourth-order Runge–Kutta method formula reduces to Simpson's rule of numerical integration. The remarkable accuracy and simplicity of the classical Runge–Kutta method has made it one of the most widely used single-step method for the numerical solution of ordinary differential equations.

Multistep Methods All of the numerical methods discussed so far use the solution at a single point x_n to predict the solution y_{n+1} at the next point x_{n+1}, and are properly called single-step methods. There are also methods that are based on using the solution at two or more preceding points to predict the solution at the next point. Such methods are called the multistep methods. The multistep formulas are obtained by finding a polynomial that passes through the solutions at several points, and then integrating this polynomial between two suitable points. The best known multistep methods are the predictor–corrector methods that involve two formulas: The first one predicts the value of the solution at the next point, and the second one refines and corrects it. One of the most popular predictor–corrector methods is the Adams–Moulton method expressed as

$$\text{Predictor: } y_{n+1} = y_n + \frac{h}{24}(55f_n - 59f_{n-1} + 37f_{n-2} - 9f_{n-3}) \quad \textbf{(9–49)}$$

$$\text{Corrector: } y_{n+1} = y_n + \frac{h}{24}(9f_{n+1} + 19f_n - 5f_{n-1} + f_{n-2}) \quad \textbf{(9–51)}$$

Another popular predictor–corrector method is the Milne's method, which is expressed as

$$\text{Predictor: } y_{n+1} = y_{n-3} + \frac{4h}{3}(2f_n - f_{n-1} + 2f_{n-2}) \quad \textbf{(9-50)}$$

$$\text{Corrector: } y_{n+1} = y_{n-1} + \frac{h}{3}(f_{n+1} + 4f_n + f_{n-1}) \quad \textbf{(9-52)}$$

The Milne's method, in general, gives more accurate results than the Adams–Moulton method. However, the Milne's method sometimes exhibits an unstable behavior. Therefore, the Adams–Moulton method is usually preferred.

Solving Systems of Equations All of the solution methods for single first-order equations are also applicable to a system of first-order equations. However, in this case, the method is applied to every equation during each step before starting the next step. For example, the solution of the system of two first-order equations with specified initial conditions given as

$$y' = f(x, y, z), \qquad y(x_0) = y_0 \quad \textbf{(9-56a)}$$

$$z' = g(x, y, z), \qquad z(x_0) = z_0 \quad \textbf{(9-56b)}$$

can be expressed using the Euler method as

$$y_{n+1} = y_n + hf(x_n, y_n, z_n) \quad \textbf{(9-58a)}$$

$$z_{n+1} = z_n + hg(x_n, y_n, z_n) \quad \textbf{(9-58b)}$$

Other methods can be applied to a system of two or more equations in the same manner.

Discretization and Round-Off Error The results obtained by any numerical method are approximations to the true solution values, and care should be exercised in their interpretation. The error in numerical methods is caused by two effects. One is the *truncation* or *discretization error,* which is due to the approximations made during numerical formulation of the problem. The other is the *round-off error,* which is due to retaining a limited number of digits to represent the numbers during calculations.

The discretization error that occurs during a single step is called the *local discretization error.* The local discretization error accumulates with increasing step numbers, and the total discretization error at any step is called the *global* or *accumulated discretization error.*

The discretization error increases as the step size h increases. If the local discretization error in a numerical method is proportional to h^k, then the global or accumulated discretization error is proportional to h^{k-1}. The local discretization error is proportional to h^2 in the Euler method, to h^3 in the improved Euler and the three-term Taylor series methods, and to h^5 in the fourth-order Runge–Kutta, Adams–Moulton, and Milne's methods. Therefore, halving the step size reduces the local error by a factor of 1/4 in the Euler method, by a factor of 1/8 in the improved Euler and three-term Taylor series methods, and by a factor of 1/32 in the fourth-order Runge–Kutta, Adams–Moulton, and Milne's methods.

Modern commercially available computer packages contain highly developed implementations and extensions of the methods described in this chapter. They are easy to use and powerful enough to handle equations of the type found in this text. We have illustrated how to use these tools and how to check their results for accuracy.

HISTORICAL NOTES

John Couch Adams (1819–1892) British mathematician and astronomer. He predicted the existence and position of Neptune from the motions of other planets, using only mathematics. The Adams–Bashforth methods were developed by Adams to solve a differential equation model of capillary action proposed by Bashforth.

Francis Bashforth (1819–1912) English mathematician. He conducted a series of systematic ballistic experiments and invented a chronograph to measure projectile speed. He also conducted research in bridge construction and with the effects of surface tension on the form of liquid drops.

Leonhard Euler (1707–1783) Swiss mathematician and physicist. He made important discoveries in infinitesimal calculus and graph theory, and contributed to mechanics, fluid dynamics, optics, and astronomy.

Richard Wesley Hamming (1915–1998) American mathematician. His research led to the invention of the Hamming error-correcting codes and to developments in computer science, signal processing, and telecommunications.

Martin Wilhelm Kutta (1867–1944) German mathematician and aerodynamicist. In addition to co-developing the Runge–Kutta method, he also developed the Zhukovsky–Kutta aerofoil, the Kutta–Zhukovsky theorem, and the Kutta condition in aerodynamics.

Forest Ray Moulton (1872–1952) American astronomer. He, along with Thomas Chamberlin, proposed what is now known as the Chamberlin–Moulton planetesimal hypothesis that the planets coalesced from smaller bodies that they termed planetesimals.

Carl David Runge (1867–1927) German mathematician, physicist, and spectroscopist. In addition to his work in numerical analysis, he conducted experiments involving spectral lines of various elements with applications to astronomical spectroscopy.

PROBLEMS

9–1 Numerical Integration

9–21C What is the value of numerical integration in the solution of differential equations?

9–22C What is numerical integration based on? When will numerical integration be equivalent to analytical integration?

9–23C In what ways do the numerical integration techniques differ from each other?

9–24C What is the basis of the grid method of integration?

9–25C How does the trapezoidal rule differ from the rectangular strip method of numerical integration? Which one of them is a more accurate method?

9–26C Consider a linear function $f(x)$ that is to be integrated numerically in a specified interval using the rectangular strip method and the trapezoidal rule by dividing the interval into two equal segments. What would your answer be if the interval is divided into four equal segments?

9–27C Consider a second-degree polynomial $f(x)$ that is to be integrated numerically in a specified interval using the trapezoidal rule by dividing the integration interval into 10 equal segments. Now the integration is repeated by dividing the interval into 20 equal segments. How do you think the results obtained in both cases would change? What would your response be if Simpson's rule were used for numerical integration in both cases?

Hand Calculations

Evaluate the following integrals using a calculator by dividing the integration interval into (a) one and (b) two segments using the indicated methods. Also, perform the integration analytically, and determine the relative error of the results obtained by numerical integration.

9–28 $\int_{-5}^{5}(x + 8)\,dx$, Rectangular strip method, Trapezoidal rule

9–29 $\int_{0}^{1}xe^{2x}dx$, Rectangular strip method, Trapezoidal rule

9–30 $\int_{0}^{\pi}xe^{2x}dx$, Trapezoidal rule, Simpson's rule

9–31 $\int_{0}^{\pi}e^{x}(\sin x - 1)\,dx$, Trapezoidal rule, Simpson's rule

9–32 $\int_{2}^{6}\dfrac{x}{x^2 - 1}\,dx$, Rectangular strip method, Simpson's rule

9–33 $\int_{0}^{2}(2x^2 + 1)\,dx$, Rectangular strip method, Simpson's rule

9–34 $\int_{1}^{3}(x^3 - 1)e^{2x}dx$, Rectangular strip method, Trapezoidal rule, Simpson's rule

9–35 $\int_{0}^{4}xe^{-x^2}dx$, Rectangular strip method, Trapezoidal rule, Simpson's rule

9–36 $\int_{0}^{1}\dfrac{1}{1 + e^x}\,dx$, Rectangular strip method, Trapezoidal rule, Simpson's rule

Computer Applications

Evaluate the following integrals by writing a computer program and dividing the integration interval into (a) 10 and (b) 100 segments using the indicated methods. Also, perform the integration analytically, and determine the relative error of the results obtained by numerical integration.

9–37 $\int_{0}^{2}(x - 1)\,dx$, Rectangular strip method, Trapezoidal rule

9–38 $\int_{-5}^{5}(x + 8)\,dx$, Rectangular strip method, Trapezoidal rule

9–39 $\int_{0}^{1}xe^{2x}dx$, Rectangular strip method, Trapezoidal rule

9–40 $\int_{0}^{\pi}x\cos x\,dx$, Trapezoidal rule, Simpson's rule

9–41 $\int_{0}^{\pi}e^{2x}\sin x\,dx$, Trapezoidal rule, Simpson's rule, Rectangular strip method, Simpson's rule

9–42 $\int_{2}^{6}\dfrac{x}{x^2 - 1}\,dx$, Rectangular strip method, Simpson's rule

9–43 $\int_{0}^{2}(2x^2 + 1)\,dx$, Rectangular strip method, Simpson's rule

9–44 $\int_{1}^{3}(x^3 - 1)e^{2x}dx$, Rectangular strip method, Trapezoidal rule, Simpson's rule

9–45 $\int_{0}^{4}xe^{-x^2}dx$, Rectangular strip method, Trapezoidal rule, Simpson's rule

9–46 $\int_{0}^{1}\dfrac{1}{1 + e^x}\,dx$, Rectangular strip method, Trapezoidal rule, Simpson's rule

9–2 Numerical Solution of Differential Equations

9–47 What is the basis of the numerical methods used to solve first-order initial-value problems?

9–48 Why is the differential equation $y' = f(x, y)$ easier to solve numerically when the function f depends on x only?

9–49 When can the numerical integration techniques be used to solve first-order initial-value problems numerically?

9–50 How do multistep numerical methods differ from the single-step methods?

9–51 How is the relative error associated with the numerical solution of differential equation defined?

Hand Calculations

Using a calculator, determine the numerical solution of the following initial-value problems after (a) one step and (b) two steps using a step size of $h = 0.2$. Use the indicated methods for numerical integration. Also solve the initial-value problems analytically, and determine the relative error of the numerical results.

9–52 $y' = x^2 + 1$, $y(0) = 2$, Rectangular strip method, Trapezoidal rule

9–53 $y' = (x - 1)e^x$, $y(1) = 3$, Trapezoidal rule, Simpson's rule

9–54 $y' = x\cos 2x$, $y(0) = 1$, Trapezoidal rule, Simpson's rule

9–55 $y' = \dfrac{x}{x^2 + 1}$, $y(2) = -1$, Rectangular strip method, Simpson's rule

9–56 $y' = \dfrac{1}{x^{0.2}}$, $y(1) = 4$, Rectangular strip method, Simpson's rule

9–57 $y' = \dfrac{1}{\sqrt{x + 1}}$, $y(0) = 1$, Rectangular strip method, Trapezoidal rule, Simpson's rule

9–58 $y' = 2xe^{-x^2}$, $y(0) = 2$, Rectangular strip method, Trapezoidal rule, Simpson's rule

Computer Applications

Writing a computer program, determine the numerical solution of the following initial-value problems after (a) 10 steps with a step size of $h = 0.2$ and (b) 20 steps with a step size of $h = 0.1$. Use the indicated methods for numerical integration. Also, solve the initial-value problems analytically, and determine the relative error of the numerical results.

9–59 $y' = x - 1$, $y(0) = 1$, Rectangular strip method, Trapezoidal rule

9–60 $y' = x^2 + 1$, $y(0) = 2$, Rectangular strip method, Trapezoidal rule

9–61 $y' = (x - 1)e^x$, $y(1) = 3$, Trapezoidal rule, Simpson's rule

9–62 $y' = x\cos 2x$, $y(0) = 1$, Trapezoidal rule, Simpson's rule

9–63 $y' = \dfrac{x}{x^2 + 1}$, $y(2) = -1$, Rectangular strip method, Simpson's rule

9–64 $y' = \dfrac{1}{x^{0.2}}$, $y(1) = 4$, Rectangular strip method, Simpson's rule

9–65 $y' = \dfrac{1}{\sqrt{x + 1}}$, $y(0) = 1$, Rectangular strip method, Trapezoidal rule, Simpson's rule

9–66 $y' = 2xe^{-x^2}$, $y(0) = 2$, Rectangular strip method, Trapezoidal rule, Simpson's rule

9–3 The Euler Method

9–67 What is the Euler method based on? How is it used to solve the initial-value problem $y' = f(x, y)$ with $y(x_0) = y_0$?

9–68 On a y–x diagram, explain how the solution of a first order initial-value problem at x_1 is obtained by the Euler method using an initial condition at x_0.

9–69 In the Euler method, why are we using the value of the function $f(x, y)$ at the left end point instead of at the midpoint of an interval when solving the differential equation $y' = f(x, y)$?

Hand Calculations

Using a calculator, determine the numerical solution of the following initial-value problems after (a) one step and (b) two steps using a step size of $h = 0.2$ using the Euler method. Also, solve the initial-value problems analytically, and determine the relative error of the numerical results.

9–70 $y' = x^2y - x + 2$, $y(0) = 5$

9–71 $y' = 5y$, $y(0) = 1$

9–72 $y' = y^2 + 1$, $y(0) = 2$

9–73 $y' = x^2y^3$, $y(0) = 3$

9–74 $y' = 4xy$, $y(1) = 0$,

9–75 $y' = x(y^2 - 1)$, $y(1) = 1$

9–76 $y' = \dfrac{x^2}{y^2}$, $y(1) = -2$

9–77 $y' = \dfrac{x^2}{y^2 + 1}$, $y(1) = 4$

9–78 $y' = \sqrt{x} - 1$, $y(1) = 2$

Computer Applications

Writing a computer program, determine the numerical solution of the following initial-value problems after (a) 10 steps with a step size of $h = 0.2$ and (b) 20 steps with a step size of $h = 0.1$ using the Euler method. Also, solve the initial-value

problems analytically, and determine the relative error in the numerical results.

9–79 $y' = x^2 + 2y, y(0) = 0$

9–80 $y' = y x^2, y(1) = 1$

9–81 $y' = e^{xy} - 3e^x, y(0) = -2$

9–82 $y' = 2y - 3x + 4, y(2) = 4$

9–83 $y' = y, y(1) = 1$

9–84 $y' = y - x, y(0) = 3$

9–85 $y' = 2xy, y(0) = 0$

9–86 $y' = x^3 y - e^x + 1, y(0) = 1$

9–87 $y' = xe^y, y(0) = 1$

9–88 $y' = x^2 - y, y(0) = 1$

9–89 $y' = e^{-y}, y(0) = 0$

9–90 $y' = x + y + 3, y(1) = 4$

9–91 $y' = \dfrac{4xy}{y^2 + 1}, y(1) = 2$

9–92 $y' = y^2, y(0) = 1$

9–93 $y' = x\sqrt{y - 1}, y(1) = 5$

9–4 The Error in Numerical Methods

9–94 What is the cause of the discretization error? How does the global discretization error differ from the local discretization error?

9–95 Can the global (accumulated) discretization error be less than the local error during a step? Explain.

9–96 How is the Euler formula related to the Taylor series expansion of the solution function?

9–97 Explain why the local discretization error of the Euler method is proportional to h^2.

9–98 Explain why the global discretization error of the Euler method is proportional to the step size h.

9–99 What causes the round-off error? What kind of calculations are most susceptible to round-off error?

9–100 What happens to the discretization and the round-off errors as the step size is decreased?

9–101 Suggest some practical ways to reduce the round-off error.

9–102 What is a practical way of checking if the round-off error has been significant in calculations?

9–103 What is a practical way of checking if the discretization error has been significant in calculations?

Hand Calculations

Using a calculator, determine the local and the global discretization error in the numerical solution of the following

initial-value problems after (a) one step and (b) two steps using a step size of h = 0.2 using the Euler method.

9–104 $y' = x\sqrt{y}, y(0) = 5$

9–105 $y' = x^2 \ln y, y(2) = 5$

9–106 $y' = 2x(y - 1), y(2) = 2$

9–107 $y' = x^3 - y, y(0) = 0$

9–108 $y' = e^x + 2y, y(1) = 0$

Computer Applications

Write a computer program to determine the local and the global discretization errors in the numerical solution of the following initial-value problems after (a) 10 steps with a step size of h = 0.2 and (b) 20 steps with a step size of h = 0.1 using the Euler method. List the results after each step.

9–109 $y' = 1 - 2x - 3y, y(0) = 0$

9–110 $y' = x\sqrt{y}, y(0) = 5$

9–111 $y' = x^2 \ln y, y(2) = 5$

9–112 $y' = 2x(y - 1), y(2) = 2$

9–113 $y' = x^3 - y, y(0) = 0$

9–114 $y' = e^x + 2y, y(1) = 0$

Write a computer program to determine the largest step size for use with the Euler method that will guarantee that the numerical result at x = 1 rounded to three significant digits is identical to the exact solution. (Hint: start with the step size h = 0.1, and keep halving the step size until the first three digits of the results no longer change.)

9–115 $y' = x + 2y, y(0) = 2$

9–116 $y' = 3x^2 y, y(0) = 1$

9–117 $y' = 2y, y(0) = 5$

9–118 $y' = 2e^{xy}, y(0) = 2$

9–119 $y' = x^3(y + 2), y(0) = 3$

9–120 $y' = e^x - y, y(0) = 0$

9–5 The Improved Euler Method

9–121 Why is the improved Euler method classified as a predictor-corrector method? Why does the improved Euler formula need a predictor formula?

9–122 How does the modified Euler method differ from improved Euler method?

9–123 Under what conditions will solving the initial-value problem $y' = f(x, y)$ with $y(x_0) = y_0$ by the improved Euler method be identical to solving it by numerical integration using the trapezoidal rule?

9–124 Develop the formulation of the modified Euler method, and give its geometrical interpretation on a y–x diagram.

Hand Calculations

Using a calculator, determine the numerical solution of the following initial-value problems after (a) one step and (b) two steps using a step size of h = 0.2 using the improved Euler method. Also, solve the initial-value problems analytically, and determine the relative error in the numerical results.

9–125 $y' = \dfrac{y - 4}{x^2 - 1}, y(0) = 5$

9–126 $y' = 5y, y(0) = 1$

9–127 $y' = y^2 + 1, y(0) = 1$

9–128 $y' = x^2 y^3, y(0) = 3$

9–129 $y' = 4xy, y(1) = 10$

9–130 $y' = x(y^2 - 1), y(1) = 1$

9–131 $y' = \dfrac{x^2}{y^2}, y(1) = -2$

9–132 $y' = \dfrac{x^2}{y^2 + 1}, y(1) = 4$

9–133 $y' = \sqrt{x} - 1, y(1) = 2$

Computer Applications

Write a computer program to determine the numerical solution of the following initial-value problems after (a) 10 steps with a step size of h = 0.2 and (b) 20 steps with a step size of h = 0.1 using the improved Euler method. Also solve the initial-value problems analytically, and determine the relative error in the numerical results.

9–134 $y' = x^2 + 2y, y(0) = 0$

9–135 $y' = yx^2, y(1) = 1$

9–136 $y' = 3ye^x, y(0) = -2$

9–137 $y' = 2y - 3x + 4, y(2) = 4$

9–138 $y' = y, y(1) = 1$

9–139 $y' = y - x, y(0) = 3$

9–140 $y' = 2xy, y(0) = 0$

9–141 $y' = x^2\sqrt{y}, y(0) = 1$

9–142 $y' = -xe^y, y(0) = 1$

9–143 $y' = x^2 - y, y(0) = 1$

9–144 $y' = e^{-y}, y(0) = 0$

9–145 $y' = x + y + 3, y(1) = 4$

9–146 $y' = \dfrac{4xy}{x^2 + y^2}, y(1) = 2$

9–147 $y' = -y^2, y(0) = 1$

9–148 $y' = x\sqrt{y} - 1, y(1) = 5$

9–6 The Taylor Series Method

9–149 Why is the three-term Taylor series method a second-order method?

9–150 If the three-term Taylor series method gives the exact solution of $y' = f(x, y)$ with $y(x_0) = y_0$, determine the general form of the function $f(x, y)$.

9–151 What can you say about the magnitude of the local discretization error associated with the six-term Taylor series method?

9–152 Develop the formulation of the four-term Taylor series method for the solution of the initial-value problem $y' = f(x, y)$ with $y(x_0) = y_0$.

Hand Calculations

Using a calculator, determine the numerical solution of the following initial-value problems after (a) one step and (b) two steps using a step size of h = 0.2 using the three-term Taylor series method. Also, solve the initial-value problems analytically, and determine the relative error in the numerical results.

9–153 $y' = \dfrac{y - 4}{x^2 - 1}, y(0) = 5$

9–154 $y' = 5y, y(0) = 1$

9–155 $y' = y^2 + 1, y(0) = 1$

9–156 $y' = x^2 y^3, y(0) = 3$

9–157 $y' = 4xy, y(1) = 10$

Computer Applications

Write a computer program to determine the numerical solution of the following initial-value problems after (a) 10 steps with a step size of h = 0.2 and (b) 20 steps with a step size of h = 0.1 using the three-term Taylor series method. Also, solve the initial-value problems analytically, and determine the relative error in the numerical result.

9–158 $y' = x^2 + 2y, y(0) = 1$

9–159 $y' = yx^2, y(1) = 1$

9–160 $y' = 3ye^x, y(0) = -2$

9–161 $y' = 2y - 3x + 4, y(2) = 4$

9–162 $y' = y, y(1) = 1$

9–163 $y' = y - x, y(0) = 3$

9–164 $y' = 2xy, y(0) = 0$

9–165 $y' = x^2\sqrt{y}, y(0) = 1$

9–7 The Runge–Kutta Method

9–166 When solving the initial-value problem $y' = f(x, y)$ with $y(x_0) = y_0$ with classical Runge–Kutta method, at which values of x is the function $f(x, y)$ evaluated during the step between x_n and x_{n-1}?

9–167 How can you modify the MATLAB program in Figure 9–34 for the classical Runge–Kutta method to solve the initial-value problem $y' = x^2 + y^2$ with $y(0) = 2$ from $x = 0$ to 1 using a step size of $h = 0.1$? (*Hint*: You need to modify only one line.)

9–168 Which numerical method will meet a specified error criteria with the fewest number of calculations: Euler, improved Euler, or the classical Runge–Kutta method?

9–169 How are the classical Runge–Kutta method and Simpson's rule related to each other?

9–170 Can we change the step size h during calculations in the classical Runge–Kutta method?

Hand Calculations

Using a calculator, determine the numerical solution of the following initial-value problems after (a) one step and (b) two steps using a step size of $h = 0.2$ using the classical fourth-order Runge–Kutta method. Also, solve the initial-value problems analytically and the relative error in the numerical result.

9–171 $y' = \dfrac{y - 4}{x^2 - 1}, y(0) = 5$

9–172 $y' = 5y, y(0) = 1$

9–173 $y' = y^2 + 1, y(0) = 1$

9–174 $y' = x^2 y^3, y(0) = 3$

9–175 $y' = 4xy, y(1) = 10$

9–176 $y' = x(y^2 - 1), y(1) = 1$

9–177 $y' = \dfrac{x^2}{y^2}, y(1) = -2$

9–178 $y' = \dfrac{x^2}{y^2 + 1}, y(1) = 4$

9–179 $y' = \sqrt{x} - 1, y(1) = 2$

Computer Applications

Write a computer program to determine the numerical solution of the following initial-value problems after (a) 10 steps with a step size of $h = 0.2$ and (b) 20 steps with a step size of $h = 0.1$ using the classical fourth-order Runge–Kutta method. Also, solve the initial-value problems analytically, and determine the relative error in the numerical results.

9–180 $y' = x^2 + 2y, y(0) = 0$

9–181 $y' = yx^2, y(1) = 1$

9–182 $y' = 3ye^x, y(0) = -2$

9–183 $y' = 2y - 3x + 4, y(2) = 4$

9–184 $y' = y, y(1) = 1$

9–185 $y' = y - x, y(0) = 3$

9–186 $y' = 2xy, y(0) = 0$

9–187 $y' = x^2\sqrt{y}, y(0) = 1$

9–188 $y' = -xe^y, y(0) = 1$

9–189 $y' = x^2 - y, y(0) = 1$

9–190 $y' = e^{-y}, y(0) = 0$

9–191 $y' = x + y + 3, y(1) = 4$

9–192 $y' = \dfrac{4xy}{x^2 + y^2}, y(1) = 2$

9–193 $y' = -y^2, y(0) = 1$

9–194 $y' = x\sqrt{y - 1}, y(1) = 5$

9–8 ■ Multistep and Predictor–Corrector Methods

9–195 Can we change the step size h during calculations when using a multistep method?

9–196 What are the advantages and disadvantages of multistep methods?

9–197 Is the improved Euler method a multistep method? Is it a predictor–corrector method?

9–198 What is an interpolating polynomial?

9–199 Why are the single-step methods also called starting methods?

9–200 Explain how the third-order multistep predictor formulas are obtained. Also, explain how the third-order corrector formulas are obtained.

9–201 The Milne predictor–corrector method, in general, gives more accurate results than the Adams-Moulton method. Why is it then the Adams–Moulton formulas usually preferred to the Milne formulas?

9–202 How would you recognize instability in a numerical solution?

9–203 When you are given the two formulas of a predictor–corrector method, how can you tell which formula is the predictor and which one is the corrector?

9–204 How does internal iteration improve the accuracy of a predictor–corrector method?

Hand Calculations

Using a calculator, determine the numerical solution of the following initial-value problem after (a) one step and (b) two steps using a step size of $h = 0.2$ using the Adams–Moulton predictor–corrector method. Also, solve the initial-value problems analytically, and determine the relative error in the numerical results.

9–205 $y' = \dfrac{10x + 1}{y + 4}, y(0) = 5$

9–206 $y' = 5y, y(0) = -1$

9–207 $y' = y^2 + 1, y(0) = -2$

9–208 $y' = x^2 y^3, y(0) = -1$

9–209 $y' = 4xy - x, y(1) = 0$

Using a calculator, determine the numerical solution of the following initial-value problems after (a) one step and (b) two steps using a step size of h = 0.2 using the Milne predictor–corrector method. Also, solve the initial-value problems analytically, and determine the relative error in the numerical results.

9–210 $y' = x(y^2 - 1), y(1) = 0$

9–211 $y' = \dfrac{x^2}{y^2}, y(1) = -2$

9–212 $y' = \dfrac{x^2}{y^2 + 1}, y(1) = 4$

9–213 $y' = \sqrt{x} - 1, y(1) = 2$

Computer Applications

Write a computer program to determine the numerical solution of the following initial-value problems after (a) 10 steps with a step size of h = 0.2 and (b) 20 steps with a step size of h = 0.1 using the Adams–Moulton predictor–corrector method. Also, solve the initial-value problems analytically, and determine the relative error in the numerical results.

9–214 $y' = x^2 + 2y, y(0) = 0$

9–215 $y' = yx^2, y(1) = 1$

9–216 $y' = 3ye^x, y(0) = -2$

9–217 $y' = 2y - 3x + 4, y(2) = 4$

9–218 $y' = y, y(1) = 1$

9–219 $y' = y - x, y(0) = 3$

9–220 $y' = 2xy, y(0) = 0$

9–221 $y' = x^2\sqrt{y}, y(0) = 1$

Write a computer program to determine the numerical solution of the following initial-value problems after (a) 10 steps with a step size of h = 0.2 and (b) 20 steps with step size of h = 0.1 using the Milne predictor-corrector method. Also, solve the initial-value problems analytically, and determine the relative error in the numerical results.

9–222 $y' = -xe^y, y(0) = 1$

9–223 $y' = x^2 - y, y(0) = 1$

9–224 $y' = e^{-y}, y(0) = 0$

9–225 $y' = x + y + 3, y(1) = 4$

9–226 $y' = \dfrac{4xy}{x^2 + y^2}, y(1) = 2$

9–227 $y' = -y^2, y(0) = 1$

9–9 Systems of First-Order Equations

9–228 Discuss how you would use a numerical method to solve an nth-order boundary-value problem where some of the variables are specified at x_0 and the remaining variables are specified at x_1.

9–229 Explain how you would apply the improved Euler method to a system of three first-order initial-value problems, and write down the formulation.

Hand Calculations

Using a calculator, determine the numerical solution of the following initial-value problems after (a) one step and (b) two steps using a step size of h = 0.2 using the Euler method.

9–230 $y' = z, \quad y(0) = 0$
$z' = x + y + z, \quad z(0) = 1$

9–231 $y' = z - y - e^{-x}, \quad y(0) = 1$
$z' = z + y + 2e^{-x}, \quad z(0) = 0$

9–232 $y'' - 4y = 0, \quad y(0) = 1, \quad y'(0) = 0$

9–233 $y'' + 2y' + y = 5, \quad y(0) = 0, \quad y'(0) = 1$

Using a calculator, determine the numerical solution of the following initial-value problems after (a) one step and (b) two steps with a step size of h = 0.2 using the classical Runge–Kutta method.

9–234 $y' = y - 4z, \quad y(0) = 2$
$z' = y + z - 2, \quad z(0) = 1$

9–235 $y' = y + z, \quad y(0) = 0$
$z' = y - z - 1, \quad z(0) = 2$

9–236 $y' = 2z + 3y, \quad y(0) = 2$
$z' = 3z - 2y, \quad z(0) = 0$

9–237 $y'' + y' + y = 5, \quad y(0) = 0, \quad y'(0) = 1$

9–238 $y''' + 3y'' + 3y' + y = 1 + e^{2x}, y(0) = 0,$
$y'(0) = 0, y''(0) = 0$

Computer Applications

Write a computer program to determine the numerical solution of the following initial-value problems after (a) 10 steps with a step size of h = 0.2 and (b) 20 steps with a step size of h = 0.1 using the Euler method.

9–239 $y' = 2y - 3z, \quad y(0) = 2$
$z' = 4y - 5z, \quad z(0) = 3$

9–240 $y' = z, \quad y(0) = 0$
$z' = x + y + z, \quad z(0) = 1$

9–241 $y' = z - y - e^{-x}, \quad y(0) = 1$
$z' = z + y + 2e^{-x}, \quad z(0) = 0$

9–242 $y'' - 4y = 0, \quad y(0) = 1, \quad y'(0) = 0$

9–243 $y'' + 2y' + y = 5, \quad y(0) = 0, \quad y'(0) = 1$

Write a computer program to determine the numerical solution of the following initial-value problems after (a) 10 steps with a step size of $h = 0.2$ and (b) 20 steps with a step size of $h = 0.1$ using the classical Runge–Kutta method.

9–244 $y' = y - 4z$, $y(0) = 2$
$z' = y + z - 2$, $z(0) = 1$

9–245 $y' = y + z$, $y(0) = 0$
$z' = y - z - 1$, $z(0) = 2$

9–246 $y' = 2z + 3y$, $y(0) = 2$
$z' = 3z - 2y$, $z(0) = 0$

9–247 $y'' + y' + y = 5$, $y(0) = 0$, $y'(0) = 1$

9–248 $y''' + 3y'' + 3y' + y = 1 + e^{2x}$, $y(0) = 0$,
$y'(0) = 0$, $y''(0) = 0$

9–10 Numerical Solutions with Commercial Programs

Use a commercial program to plot the solution of the following initial-value problems. Discuss how to select an upper value for x and how to check the accuracy of the solution.

9–249 $y' = x^2 + 1$, $y(0) = 2$,

9–250 $y' = (x - 1)e^x$, $y(1) = 3$,

9–251 $y' = x \cos 2x$, $y(0) = 1$,

9–252 $y' = \dfrac{x}{x^2 + 1}$, $y(2) = -1$,

9–253 $y' = \dfrac{1}{\sqrt{x + 1}}$, $y(0) = 1$,

9–254 $y' = 2xe^{-x^2}$, $y(0) = 2$,

9–255 $y' = x^2 + 2y$, $y(0) = 0$

9–256 $y' = y x^2$, $y(1) = 1$

9–257 $y' = e^{xy} - 3e^x$, $y(0) = -2$

9–258 $y' = 2y - 3x + 4$, $y(2) = 4$

9–259 $y' = y - x$, $y(0) = 3$

9–260 $y' = x^3 y - e^x + 1$, $y(0) = 1$

9–261 $y' = xe^y$, $y(0) = 1$

9–262 $y' = x^2 - y$, $y(0) = 1$

9–263 $y' = e^{-y}$, $y(0) = 0$

9–264 $y' = x + y + 3$, $y(1) = 4$

9–265 $y' = \dfrac{4xy}{y^2 + 1}$, $y(1) = 2$

9–266 $y' = y^2$, $y(0) = 1$

9–267 $y' = x\sqrt{y - 1}$, $y(1) = 5$

9–268 $y' = 1 - 2x - 3y$, $y(0) = 0$

9–269 $y' = x\sqrt{y}$, $y(0) = 5$

9–270 $y' = x^2 \ln y$, $y(2) = 5$

9–271 $y' = 2x(y - 1)$, $y(2) = 2$

9–272 $y' = x^3 - y$, $y(0) = 0$

9–273 $y' = e^x + 2y$, $y(1) = 0$

9–274 $y' = x + 2y$, $y(0) = 2$

9–275 $y' = 2e^{xy}$, $y(0) = 2$

9–276 $y' = x^3(y + 2)$, $y(0) = 3$

9–277 $y' = e^x - y$, $y(0) = 0$

9–278 $y' = yx^{2x}$, $y(1) = 1$

9–279 $y' = 2y - 3z$, $y(0) = 2$
$z' = 4y - 5z$, $z(0) = 3$

9–280 $y' = z$, $y(0) = 0$
$z' = x + y + z$, $z(0) = 1$

9–281 $y' = z - y - e^{-x}$, $y(0) = 1$
$z' = z + y + 2e^{-x}$, $z(0) = 0$

9–282 $y' = y - 4z$, $y(0) = 2$
$z' = y + z - 2$, $z(0) = 1$

9–283 $y' = y + z$, $y(0) = 0$
$z' = y - z - 1$, $z(0) = 2$

9–284 $y' = 2z + 3y$, $y(0) = 2$
$z' = 3z - 2y$, $z(0) = 0$

9–285 $y''' + 3y'' + 3y' + y = 1 + e^{2x}$, $y(0) = 0$,
$y'(0) = 0$, $y'''(0) = 0$

9–286 Even though an equation is linear, it may be difficult to solve if the forcing function is a complicated function. The equation for the voltage y across the capacitor of an RC circuit is

$$RC \frac{dy}{dt} + y = v(t)$$

where $v(t)$ is the applied voltage. Suppose that $RC = 0.2$ s and that the capacitor voltage is initially 2 V. Suppose also that the applied voltage is $v(t) = 10[2 - e^{-t} \sin(5\pi t)]$ V. Plot the voltage $y(t)$ for $0 \le t \le 5$ s.

9–287 The equation describing the water height h in a spherical tank with a drain at the bottom is

$$\pi h(2r - h)\frac{dh}{dt} = -C_d A \sqrt{2gh}$$

Suppose the tank's radius is $r = 3$ m and the circular drain hole has a radius of 2 cm. Assume that $C_d = 0.5$ and that the initial water height is $h(0) = 5$ m. Use $g = 9.81$ m/s^2.

(a) Use an approximation to estimate how long it takes for the tank to empty.

(b) Plot the water height as a function of time until $h(t) \approx 0$.

9–288 A certain jet-powered ground vehicle is subjected to a nonlinear drag force. Its equation of motion, in British units, is

$$50\frac{dv}{dt} = f - (20v + 0.05\,v^2)$$

Use a numerical method to plot the vehicle's speed as a function of time if the jet's force is constant at 8000 lb and the vehicle starts from rest.

9–289 The following model describes a mass supported by a nonlinear, hardening spring. The units are SI. Use $g = 9.81$ m/s^2.

$$y'' = 5g - (900y + 1700y^3)$$

Suppose that $y'(0) = 0$. Use a numerical method to plot the solution for two different initial conditions.
(a) $y(0) = 0.06$ (b) $y(0) = 0.1$

9–290 Van der Pol's equation has been used to describe many oscillatory processes. It is

$$y'' + \mu(1 - y^2)y' + y = 0$$

where $y' = dy/dt$. Plot $y(t)$ for $\mu = 1$ and $0 \le t \le 20$, using the initial conditions $y(0) = 5$, $y'(0) = 0$.

9–291 The equation of motion for a pendulum whose base is accelerating horizontally with an acceleration $a(t)$ is

$$L\frac{d^2\theta}{dt^2} + g\theta = a(t)\cos\theta$$

Suppose that $g = 9.81$ m/s^2, $L = 1$ m, and $\theta'(0) = 0$. Plot $\theta(t)$ for $0 \le t \le 10$ s for the following cases.

(a) The acceleration is constant: $a = 5$ m/s^2, and $\theta(0) = 0.5$ rad.

(b) The acceleration is constant: $a = 5$ m/s^2, and $\theta(0) = 3$ rad.

(c) The acceleration is linear with time: $a = 0.5t$ m/s^2 and $\theta(0) = 3$ rad.

9–292 Van der Pol's equation is

$$y'' + \mu(1 - y^2)y' + y = 0$$

where $y' = dy/dt$. This equation is stiff for large values of the parameter μ. Compare the performance of your chosen program's basic numerical solver with that of its stiff equation solver (if you are using MATLAB, these are ode45 and ode15s). Use $\mu = 1000$ and $0 \le t \le 3000$, with the initial conditions $y(0) = 2$, $y'(0) = 0$. Plot $y(t)$ versus t.

9–293 Even though a set of equations is linear, they may be difficult to solve if the forcing function is a complicated function. The equations for an armature-controlled dc motor are the following. The motor's current is i, and its rotational velocity is ω.

$$L\frac{di}{dt} = -Ri - K_b\omega + v(t)$$

$$I\frac{d\omega}{dt} = K_Ti - c\omega$$

where L, R, and I are the motor's inductance, resistance, and inertia; K_T and K_b are the torque constant and back emf constant; c is a viscous damping constant; and $v(t)$ is the applied voltage. Use the values $R = 0.8\,\Omega$, $L = 0.003$ H, $K_T = 0.05$ N $\cdot$ m/A, $K_b = 0.05$ V $\cdot$ s/rad, $c = 0$, and $I = 8 \times 10^{-5}$ kg $\cdot$ m^2.

(a) Suppose the applied voltage is 20 V. Plot the motor's speed and current versus time. Choose a final time large enough to show the motor's speed becoming constant.

(b) Suppose the applied voltage is trapezoidal:

$$v(t) = \begin{cases} 400t & 0 \le t < 0.05 \\ 20 & 0.05 \le t \le 2 \\ -400(t - 0.2) + 20 & 0.2 < t \le 0.25 \\ 0 & t > 0.25 \end{cases}$$

Plot the motor's speed versus time for $0 \le t \le 0.3$ s. Also, plot the applied voltage versus time. How well does the motor speed follow a trapezoidal profile?

9–294 The term *chaotic behavior* refers to the behavior of a set of equations that is very sensitive to the initial conditions. Some nonlinear equations display chaotic behavior; one example is the *three-body problem*, which is a set of equations that describes the motion of three objects due to their mutual gravitational attraction. A simpler set of equations displaying chaotic behavior is the *Lorenz system*. For a particular set of coefficients, these equations are

$$\frac{dx}{dt} = 10(y - x)$$

$$\frac{dy}{dt} = 28x - y - xz$$

$$\frac{dz}{dt} = -\frac{8}{3}z + xy$$

(a) Plot the solution for $x(t)$ using the initial conditions $x(0) = 3$, $y(0) = 4$, and $z(0) = 5$. Then increase the initial condition for $z(0)$ by a small amount ε until you find a value of ε for which the $x(t)$ solutions begin to differ significantly. Note the time at which they start to differ.

(b) Repeat part (a) using a smaller error tolerance for your solver, and note the time at which the solutions start to differ. Compare this time with the value found in part (a). Is the result what you would expect?

Basic Properties of the Laplace Transform

1. $L\{C_1 f_1(t) + C_2 f_2(t)\} = C_1 L\{f_1(t)\} + C_2 L\{f_2(t)\}$

2. $L\{e^{kt} f(t)\} = F(s - k)$

3. $L\{t^k f(t)\} = (-1)^n \dfrac{d^n F(s)}{ds^n}$

4. $L\left\{\dfrac{1}{t} f(t)\right\} = \displaystyle\int_s^\infty F(s)\,ds$

5. $L\left\{\displaystyle\int_0^t f(t)\,dt\right\} = \dfrac{1}{s} F(s)$

6. $L\{f(kt)\} = \dfrac{1}{k} F\left(\dfrac{s}{k}\right)$

Laplace Transforms of Common Functions

$f(t)$	$F(s) = L\{f(t)\}$
$C_1 f(t) + C_2 g(t)$	$C_1 F(s) + C_2 G(s)$
$e^{kt} f(t)$	$F(s - k)$
$f(kt)$	$\dfrac{1}{k} F\left(\dfrac{s}{k}\right)$
$t f(t)$	$-\dfrac{dF(s)}{ds}$
$t^n f(t)$	$(-1)^n \dfrac{d^n F(s)}{ds^n}$
$\dfrac{1}{t} f(t)$	$\displaystyle\int_s^\infty F(s)\,ds$
$\displaystyle\int_0^t f(t)\,dt$	$\dfrac{1}{s} F(s)$
1	$\dfrac{1}{s}$
$t^a,\ a > -1$	$\dfrac{\Gamma(a + 1)}{s^{a+1}}$
$t^{-1/2}$	$\sqrt{\dfrac{\pi}{s}}$
t	$\dfrac{1}{s^2}$
t^2	$\dfrac{2}{s^3}$
$t^n,\ n = 1,2,3,\ldots$	$\dfrac{n!}{s^{n+1}}$
e^{at}	$\dfrac{1}{s - a}$
$t^n e^{at},\ n = 1,2,3,\ldots$	$\dfrac{n!}{(s - k)^{n+1}}$

Basic Properties of the Laplace Transform

1. $L\{C_1f_1(t) + C_2f_2(t)\} = C_1L\{f_1(t)\} + C_2L\{f_2(t)\}$

2. $L\{e^{kt}f(t)\} = F(s - k)$

3. $L\{t^kf(t)\} = (-1)^n\dfrac{d^nF(s)}{ds^n}$

4. $L\left\{\dfrac{1}{t}f(t)\right\} = \displaystyle\int_s^\infty F(s)\,ds$

5. $L\left\{\displaystyle\int_0^t f(t)\,dt\right\} = \dfrac{1}{s}F(s)$

6. $L\{f(kt)\} = \dfrac{1}{k}F\left(\dfrac{s}{k}\right)$

Laplace Transforms of Common Functions

$f(t)$	$F(s) = L\{f(t)\}$
$C_1f(t) + C_2g(t)$	$C_1F(s) + C_2G(s)$
$e^{kt}f(t)$	$F(s - k)$
$f(kt)$	$\dfrac{1}{k}F\left(\dfrac{s}{k}\right)$
$tf(t)$	$-\dfrac{dF(s)}{ds}$
$t^nf(t)$	$(-1)^n\dfrac{d^nF(s)}{ds^n}$
$\dfrac{1}{t}f(t)$	$\displaystyle\int_s^\infty F(s)\,ds$
$\displaystyle\int_0^t f(t)\,dt$	$\dfrac{1}{s}F(s)$
1	$\dfrac{1}{s}$
$t^a,\, a > -1$	$\dfrac{\Gamma(a + 1)}{s^{a+1}}$
$t^{-1/2}$	$\sqrt{\dfrac{\pi}{s}}$
t	$\dfrac{1}{s^2}$
t^2	$\dfrac{2}{s^3}$
$t^n,\, n = 1,2,3,\ldots$	$\dfrac{n!}{s^{n+1}}$
e^{at}	$\dfrac{1}{s - a}$
$t^ne^{at},\, n = 1,2,3,\ldots$	$\dfrac{n!}{(s - k)^{n+1}}$